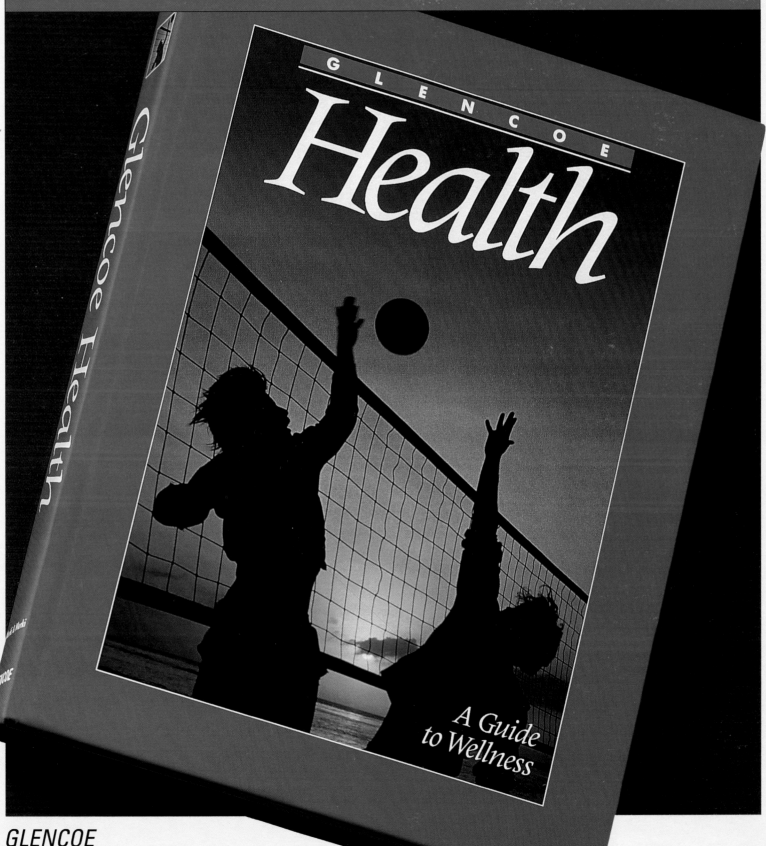

The health program with the most options — for you and your students

• Violence • AIDS • Drugs • Responsible Sexuality Special Supplements & Videos

GLENCOE

Health

GLENCOE

A Guide to Wellness

Glencoe Health

GLENCOE

Keep your students today's most up-to

Glencoe Health is the most comprehensive health program available for your students.

It thoroughly covers traditional health topics such as *body systems* and *social health* in a high-interest manner, while also facing today's toughest health issues head on. With supplements for violence, AIDS, drugs, and responsible sexuality, this program takes a realistic look at life and speaks directly to your students in a language they can understand.

With *Glencoe Health*, your students will get the straight answers they need to lead an informed, healthy lifestyle.

Lesson Openers

divide each chapter into short, easy-to-manage lessons. They make learning more manageable for your students, and topic selection easier for you.

Conflict Resolutions

allow students to think about real-life situations and how they would resolve them.

CONFLICT RESOLUTION

Andrew has tried repeatedly to get his parents' permission to go to a tanning salon. He's not convinced by their claim that the radiation is harmful. Andrew has heard that the new tanning beds mostly use UV-A radiation, which causes the skin to burn more slowly than UV-B rays.

As Andrew's friend, what comments would you make to him about this topic?

Health Update

challenges students to examine and form their own opinions on specific health issues and health-related technology — from medical ethics and weapons in schools, to arthroscopic surgery and lasers.

HEALTH UPDATE

LOOKING AT THE ISSUES

Violence on Television

Televised violence has been shown to have harmful effects on behavior, relationships, and physical and mental health. One recent report to the American Psychiatric Association suggests that eliminating violence from TV and films could result in 10,000 fewer murders, 70,000 fewer rapes, 1 million fewer car thefts, and 2.5 million fewer burglaries.

Despite these facts, there is heated disagreement in our society about how much violence should be allowed to be shown on television—particularly during prime time when children or young teens might be watching.

Analyzing Different Viewpoints

ONE VIEW. Some people claim that freedom of speech and freedom of the press should ensure people's right to see what they want. Censorship, they claim, denies these rights.

A SECOND VIEW. Others claim that children should not be exposed to television violence, but that it is the responsibility of parents, not the networks, to control their viewing.

A THIRD VIEW. Many parents and organizations feel children should not be exposed to violence in any form, and the best way to ensure this is to keep violence in TV programming to a minimum.

Exploring Your Views

1. Do you think all violence should be banned from television? Why?
2. Do you think TV violence should be allowed if parents control their children's viewing? Until what age?
3. Do you think all TV violence is bad for children, including cartoons where characters are flattened but then get up unharmed and walk away? Why or why not?

informed with
date health program

Self-Inventory and Decision-Making

Self-Inventory and Decision-Making activities for each chapter help students apply concepts they've learned, while helping you evaluate the attitudes, behavior, knowledge, and skills of each student. **Self-Inventories** help students improve their own health by rating their current behavior and setting new goals for themselves. **Building Decision-Making Skills** enables students to practice decision-making as they read case studies through identifying the situation, considering various choices, determining possible consequences, and evaluating the outcome.

Overcoming the Odds

is a feature in each chapter that uses actual interviews to examine how real people have faced and overcome some very challenging situations. These stories show students that self-esteem, persistence, and determination can help them to succeed.

Culturally Speaking

Culturally Speaking provides students with interesting multi-cultural information that relates to concepts presented in the text.

Cross-cultural Cancer

Researchers from China, Canada, and the United States have been studying why Chinese-Americans have four to seven times more colon and rectal cancer than Chinese who live in China. In fact, the colon cancer risks increase the longer a Chinese immigrant lives in North America.

The study concludes that saturated fats in the western diet may be the single greatest factor in the high colo-rectal cancer rates here. Also cited as a cause for higher cancer rates is the sedentary life-style of many Americans—particularly the amount of time they spend sitting.

Additional Features:

Each chapter presents several other high-interest health features that students can apply to their lives each day.

• **Keeping Fit** offers tips, suggestions, and activities for maintaining fitness and health

• **Did You Know** gives students a glimpse at little known, but fascinating, health-related facts

• **Finding Help** lists resources such as health associations and organizations, along with addresses and telephone numbers

• **Help Wanted** discusses various health-related careers and lists sources to contact for more information

Information and teach effectively

To design an effective lesson plan takes hours of research and preparation. And that's exactly what *Glencoe Health* has done for you. *Glencoe Health* takes the work out of developing lesson plans.

Each page provides answers to the tough questions students are asking today. We've also included well thought-out activities and, most importantly, ideas for teaching strategies, developing skills, and meeting the ability level of every student you teach.

Lesson Plans follow the 4-step teaching model: *Focus, Teach, Assess, and Close.* This system allows you to plan your class quickly and easily.

Performance Assessment strategies are activities that allow for opportunities to assess student learning in realistic situations. These are optional, and are in addition to traditional assessment tools.

videodisc series, *Understanding Ourselves,* is correlated to the *Glencoe Health* program in the Teacher's Wraparound Edition. This series can be ordered from:

Optical Data Corporation
30 Technology Drive
Warren, NJ 07059
(800) 524-2481

ideas to help you

English-Spanish Glossary is included.

Self-Esteem • • •
strategies give students
opportunities to gain
confidence in themselves.

All answers to Lesson
Reviews and Chapter
Reviews are provided, allowing
you more teaching time.

• • • **Across the
Curriculum** provides
ideas for health-related activities
that encompass other areas of
your curriculum such as language
arts, science, and math.

Glencoe Health — It's
Complete Program

To help you mold this course to fit your own personal teaching style, *Glencoe Health* includes a comprehensive, one-of-a-kind package of supplementary material.

The books, software, and videos are filled with learning activities, tests and quizzes, transparencies, and more. You'll spend less time searching for materials and still have all the resources you need to make your teaching effective.

Special Issue Materials —
Supplements that take a closer look at today's prevailing issues.

The Reality of Violence
is an all-new supplement that takes an in-depth look at the effects of violence in our society and how it affects the health of individuals and the larger community. Five major goals of this book include helping students:
- explore acts of violence and the impact they have on society
- become alert to the harmful effects of violent behavior
- reflect on the risks and results of violent activities
- develop an awareness of the laws related to violent crimes
- become advocates of violence prevention

A corresponding *Teacher's Annotated Edition* is provided.

The Reality Of Drugs
is a new supplement to this program that takes a hard look at drug use and the effects it has on students. A corresponding *Teacher's Annotated Edition* is provided.

Education in Sexuality
allows you to incorporate current developments and information into your expanded human sexuality program. A corresponding *Teacher's Annotated Edition* is provided.

AIDS and Society
is a full-color supplement that gives you all the current facts that are essential in covering the AIDS crisis effectively. It covers the topics and kinds of questions your students need to know in today's world. A corresponding *Teacher's Annotated Edition* is also provided.

Activities —
All the activities your students will need to help reinforce what you're teaching.

Performance Assessment
strategies are in addition to traditional assessment tools and allow you to assess your students' learning in realistic situations.

the Most Available

Tapes & Software –
Multimedia options to help you in the classroom.

VHS Videos
include videos on health-related issues, providing you with a high-impact teaching tool that compliments the student text and reaches out to your students. Topics include **Violence, AIDS, Drugs, and Responsible Sexuality.**

Testmaker Software
lets you choose from over 1,500 questions — or you can add your own questions. Available in IBM, Apple, or Macintosh.

Laser Videodiscs
with barcode correlations in the Teacher's Wraparound Edition provide multimedia teaching options. Titles include Glencoe's **Human Biology** and the ABC News InterActive series **Understanding Ourselves**, which includes these titles: **Tobacco, Teenage Sexuality, AIDS, Alcohol, Drugs and Substance Abuse** and **Food and Nutrition.** The ABC News InterActive discs may be ordered from:

Optical Data Corporation

Optical Data Corporation
30 Technology Drive
Warren, NJ 07059
(800) 524-2481

Body Awareness Resource Network (BARN) Software
gives students the opportunity to study health issues on an in-depth and independent basis.

Spanish Resources –
Special resources for Spanish-speaking students.

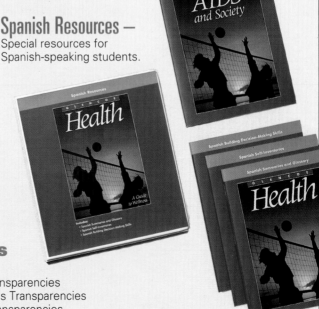

Teacher Resources –
Materials that help you reinforce key points to your students.

60 Full-Color Teaching Transparencies Include:
- Health Awareness Transparencies
- Life Management Skills Transparencies
- Conflict Resolution Transparencies
- Body Systems Transparencies
- Teaching Transparencies: Strategies and Activities Booklet

Glencoe Health. The Most Complete Program Available

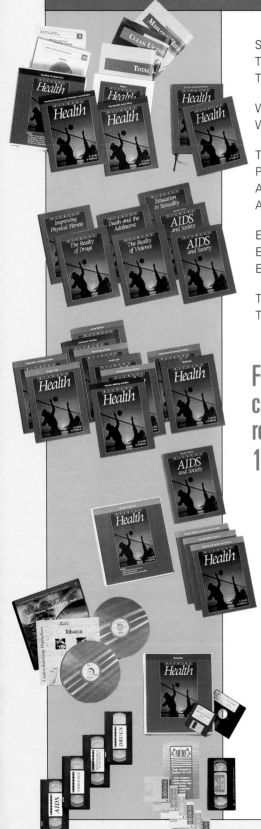

Student Edition	0-02-652600-X
Teacher's Wraparound Edition	0-02-652602-6
Teacher's Classroom Resources	0-02-652643-3
Workbook	0-02-652622-0
Workbook, Teacher's Annotated Edition	0-02-652623-9
Teaching Transparencies	0-02-652615-8
Posters	0-02-652617-4
AIDS and Society	0-02-652624-7
AIDS and Society, Teacher's Annotated Edition	0-02-652625-5
El Sida y la Sociedad	0-02-652626-3
Education in Sexuality	0-02-652628-X
Education in Sexuality, Teacher's Annotated Edition	0-02-652629-8
The Reality of Drugs	0-02-652619-0
The Reality of Drugs, Teacher's Annotated Edition	0-02-652621-2

The Reality of Violence	0-02-652645-X
The Reality of Violence, Teacher's Annotated Edition	0-02-652646-8
Death and the Adolescent	0-02-652642-5
Spanish Resources	0-02-652641-7
VHS Videos	0-02-652633-6
Testmaker, IBM	0-02-652631-X
Testmaker, Apple	0-02-652630-1
Testmaker, Macintosh	0-02-652632-8
Body Awareness Resource Network (BARN)	
BARN: Apple 3 1/2" Software Package	GG 400 A3 SP
BARN: Apple 5 1/4" Software Package	GG 400 A5 SP
BARN: IBM 3 1/2" Software Package	GG 400 I3 SP
BARN: IBM 5 1/4" Software Package	GG 400 I5 SP
Macintosh	GG 400 M3 SU

For more information, contact your nearest regional office or call 1-800-334-7344.

GLENCOE
McGraw-Hill

1. Northeast Region
GLENCOE
17 Riverside Drive
Nashua, NH 03062
603-880-4701
800-424-3451

2. Mid-Atlantic Region
GLENCOE
5 Terri Lane, Suite 5
Burlington, NJ 08016
609-386-7353
800-553-7515

3. Atlantic-Southeast Region
GLENCOE
Brookside Park
One Harbison Way, Suite 101
Columbia, SC 29212
803-732-2365

4. Southeast Region
GLENCOE
6510 Jimmy Carter Boulevard
Norcross, GA 30071
404-446-7493
800-982-3992

5. Mid-America Region
GLENCOE
4635 Hilton Corporate Drive
Columbus, OH 43232
614-759-6600
800-848-1567

6. Mid-Continent Region
GLENCOE
846 East Algonquin Road
Schaumburg, IL 60173
708-397-8448
800-762-4876

7. Southwest Region
GLENCOE
320 Westway Place, Suite 550
Arlington, TX 76018
817-784-2100
800-828-5096

8. Texas Region
GLENCOE
320 Westway Place, Suite 550
Arlington, TX 76018
817-784-2100
800-828-5096

9. Western Region
GLENCOE
610 East 42nd Street, #102
Boise, ID 83714
208-378-4002
800-452-6126
Includes Alaska

10. California Region
GLENCOE
15319 Chatsworth Street
P. O. Box 9609
Mission Hills, CA 91346
818-898-1391
800-423-9534
Includes Hawaii

Glencoe Catholic School Region
GLENCOE
25 Crescent Street, 1st Floor
Stamford, CT 06906
203-964-9109
800-551-8766

Canada
Maxwell Macmillan Canada
1200 Eglinton Avenue, East
Suite 200
Don Mills, Ontario M3C 3N1
Telephone: 416-449-6030
Telefax: 416-449-0068

Overseas
Macmillan/McGraw-Hill
International
10 Union Square East
New York, NY 10003
Telephone: 212-353-5700
Telefax: 212-353-5894

 Printed on Recycled Paper

2/94   HL 90944-9

GLENCOE

Health

A Guide to Wellness

FOURTH EDITION

Teacher's Wraparound Edition

Mary Bronson Merki, Ph.D.

Don Merki, Ph.D.

Contributing Authors

Eddye Eubanks, Ph.D.
Gale Cornelia Flynn
Charlotte Sorrel

GLENCOE
Macmillan/McGraw-Hill

New York, New York   Columbus, Ohio   Mission Hills, California   Peoria, Illinois

Meet the Authors

Mary Bronson Merki has taught health education in grades K-12, as well as health education methods classes at the undergraduate and graduate levels. As Health Education Specialist for the Dallas School District, Dr. Merki developed and implemented a district-wide health education program, *Skills for Living,* which was used as a model by the state education agency. She also helped develop and implement the district's Human Growth, Development and Sexuality program, which won the National PTA's Excellence in Education Award and earned her an honorary lifetime membership in the state PTA. Dr. Merki has assisted school districts throughout the country in developing local health education programs. In 1988, Dr. Merki was named the Texas Health Educator of the Year by the Texas Association for Health, Physical Education, Recreation, and Dance. Dr. Merki is also the author of Glencoe's *Teen Health,* a junior high textbook adopted in school districts throughout the country. She currently teaches in a Texas public school where she was recently honored as Teacher of the Year.

Don Merki has spent virtually his entire professional life of over 35 years in some aspect of health education. As a teacher, he has taught at every level from elementary to graduate school. He has worked for corporations and state health departments as well as for the World Health Organization where he served as a consultant in India and Sri Lanka. Dr. Merki was instrumental in getting Health required as a curriculum in Texas secondary schools and in the separate certification of health teachers in that state. Currently, he teaches part-time for Lovelace Health Services and the Santa Fe Public Schools and is a consultant with the University of New Mexico, School of Family Medicine.

Eddye F. Eubanks has served as educator, author, supervisor, and state education consultant for over 25 years. She has taught grades 9 to 12 as well as undergraduate and graduate courses at the university level. Twice she received the Mortar Board award, "Outstanding Faculty Member." Dr. Eubanks has authored textbooks and educational supplements in the areas of health, personal development, and comprehensive home economics. These publications are widely adopted in school districts throughout the country. Dr. Eubanks has provided on-site technical assistance to public school teachers and administrators in educational planning and program evaluation. In addition, she has conducted many local, regional, and statewide conferences for students and school personnel.

Gale Cornelia Flynn is a widely published freelance writer whose work has appeared in many well-known textbooks for junior high and senior high school students. She has also authored a variety of magazine articles for teens on subjects ranging from values, self-esteem, and blended families to peer pressure, chemical dependency, and codependency. Flynn taught for many years at both junior high and senior high school levels. An educational and creative consultant to both publishers and schools, she now conducts in-service programs in a variety of schools in Delaware, where she lives. She speaks to students at all levels on subjects ranging from alcoholism to creativity, and runs workshops for parents and teachers on related subjects. She is also considered an expert in creative teaching strategies.

Charlotte Sorrel has been in the health education field for 17 years as a teacher, curriculum writer, and state consultant. In addition to teaching health education in the Richardson Independent School District, Richardson, Texas, she also conducted inservice training, organized peer education programs related to alcohol and drug use for students, and served as a crisis intervention specialist. As a state consultant for the Texas Education Agency, she developed health curriculum, conducted workshops for teachers and administrators, and was the liaison to other agencies and health organizations. She has served on writing committees for numerous publications in health education and was chosen the Texas Health Educator of the Year by the Texas Association for Health, Physical Education, Recreation, and Dance.

The ABC News InterActive series, <u>Understanding Ourselves,</u> referenced in the *Glencoe Health* Teacher's Wraparound Edition, may be ordered from Optical Data Corporation, 30 Technology Drive, Warren, NJ 07059, 1(800) 524-2481.

Send all inquiries to:
Glencoe Division, Macmillan/McGraw-Hill
936 Eastwind Drive
Westerville, Ohio 43081
ISBN: 0-02-652602-6 (Teacher's Wraparound Edition)
ISBN: 0-02-652600-X (Student Text)

Printed in the United States of America

2 3 4 5 6 7 8 9 A-KP 99 98 97 96 95 94

Contents
Teacher's Wraparound Edition

Contents: Student Edition T4

Philosophy...T6
About the Program T6

Course Presentation Charts...T7

Program Supplements..T8
AIDS and Society T8
Education in Sexuality T8
The Reality of Drugs T8
The Reality of Violence T9
Improving Physical Fitness T9
Death and the Adolescent: Teacher's Professional Resource T9

Program Supplements..T10
Enrichment Activities T10
Guided Reading Activities T10
Reteaching Activities..T10
Lesson Quizzes..T11
Chapter Tests..T11
Decision-Making Activities...T12
Health Labs...T12
Cooperative Learning Activities..T12
Workbook..T13
Performance Assessment Activities T13
Spanish Resources Binder T14
AIDS and Society (Spanish Edition)...T14
Reproducible Lesson Plans..T15
Posters...T15
Teaching Transparencies T15

Media Resources T16
VHS Videos T16
Testmakers T16
BARN Software..T16
Science and Technology Video Disc..T16

Creating a Positive Learning Environment for all Students T17
Teaching Students with Varying Ability Levels and Learning Styles.......T17
Teaching Students with Special Needs...T17
Teaching Students with Learning Disabilities (LD)...............................T17
Teaching Students with Limited English Proficiency (LEP)....................T18
Teaching Students from Various Cultural and Ethnic Backgrounds.........T18
Reinforcing Reading Skills T18
Teaching Critical Thinking...T19
Teaching Decision Making in the Health Classroom.............................T20

Performance Assessment...T21

Performance Assessment Strategies T23

ABC News InterActive™ Charts T26

Resources...T29
Resources by Units T29

Student Edition...i

Contents
Student Edition

Unit 1 You and Your Health

Chapter 1 Your Health 2

Unit 2 Mental Health

Chapter 2 Mental Health 26

Chapter 3 Mental Disorders and Mental Health 48

Chapter 4 Stress In Your Life 64

Unit 3 Family and Social Health

Chapter 5 You and Your Family 82

Chapter 6 Your Relationships With Others 100

Chapter 7 Marriage and Parenthood 118

Unit 4 The Life Cycle

Chapter 8 The Beginning of the Life Cycle......................................136

Chapter 9 Adolescence..158

Chapter 10 Continuing Through the Life Cycle................................174

Unit 5 Body Systems

Chapter 11 Integumentary, Skeletal, and Muscular Systems..............196

Chapter 12 The Nervous and Endocrine Systems 220

Chapter 13 Cardiovascular, Lymphatic, and Respiratory Systems 248

Chapter 14 Digestive and Urinary Systems.....................................274

Chapter 15 The Reproductive Systems...296

Unit 6 Personal Health and Physical Fitness

Chapter 16 Personal Health 314

Chapter 17 Fitness and Your Health...336

Chapter 18 Getting Fit and Staying Fit...352

Unit 7 Nutrition

Chapter 19 Making Responsible Food Choices...370

Chapter 20 Avoiding Problems with Foods 402

Unit 8 Medicines and Drugs

Chapter 21 Understanding Medicines 424

Chapter 22 Tobacco 440

Chapter 23 Alcohol 458

Chapter 24 Illegal Drugs...478

Chapter 25 Recovering From Addiction and Codependency 496

Unit 9 Diseases and Disorders

Chapter 26 Communicable Diseases 516

Chapter 27 Sexually Transmitted Diseases..536

Chapter 28 AIDS 554

Chapter 29 Noncommunicable Diseases..568

Unit 10 Community and Environmental Health

Chapter 30 Global Environmental Issues...596

Chapter 31 Protecting Your Environment..614

Unit 11 Consumer Health

Chapter 32 You, the Health Consumer...632

Chapter 33 Health Services and Health Care...652

Unit 12 Safety and Emergency Care

Chapter 34 Your Safety and Well-Being 670

Chapter 35 First Aid..692

Chapter 36 Handling Emergencies...714

Diseases that result from unhealthy life-style choices threaten many people's lives today. Leading causes of death for Americans over age 40 are heart disease, cerebrovascular disease, and lung cancer. Life-style choices affect each one of these causes of death.

Health problems and diseases affect not only the individuals involved but also others in the larger community. Consider the impact of HIV infection and AIDS. Consider the concerns of health-care costs. Undoubtedly, lives can be saved and be of higher quality if behaviors that promote health are chosen.

The health of adolescents is a special concern. Decisions teenagers make at this time in their life are known to have long-lasting effects. Motor vehicle crashes (frequently related to the use of alcohol and other drugs), homicide, and suicide are the leading causes of death of teenagers. The highest rate of increase in sexually transmitted diseases occurs in this population. The incidence of HIV infection and AIDS also continues to increase in this age group.

The importance of health education has never been greater. Knowledge gained in health education affects attitudes and, consequently, behavior. *Glencoe Health: A Guide to Wellness* coincides with this philosophy by providing factual, current content. This text focuses on the relationship that exists among physical, mental, and social health. Students learn that their decisions affect all of these areas of health. They discover that the decisions they make can promote their health and their enjoyment of life now and in the future. Healthy decisions not only help prevent disease but also help students feel good physically and enable them to energetically do those tasks they choose. Healthy decisions help students feel good about themselves, feel comfortable with others, and cope with the challenges of life. Healthy decisions help students choose and build positive relationships.

Throughout the *Glencoe Health* program, students are provided many opportunities to apply their understanding of health knowledge. By incorporating decision-making skills, they learn and practice ways to make healthy choices. They learn how taking responsibility for their own health has positive effects not only for themselves but also for others around them.

About the Program

Glencoe Health: A Guide to Wellness consists of the following Program Supplements and Teacher's Classroom Resources.
Student Text
Teacher's Wraparound Edition

Program Supplements
AIDS and Society
AIDS and Society Teacher's Annotated Edition
Education in Sexuality
Education in Sexuality Teacher's Annotated Edition
The Reality of Drugs
The Reality of Drugs Teacher's Annotated Edition
The Reality of Violence
The Reality of Violence Teacher's Annotated Edition
Improving Physical Fitness
Death and the Adolescent: Teacher's Professional Resource

Media Resources
VHS Videos
Testmakers
BARN Software
Human Biology Videodisc

Teacher's Classroom Resources
Enrichment Activities
Guided Reading Activities
Reteaching Activities
Lesson Quizzes
Chapter Tests
Decision-Making Activities
Health Labs
Cooperative Learning Activities
Workbook
Workbook Teacher's Annotated Edition
Performance Assessment Activities
Spanish Summaries and Glossary
Spanish Self-Inventories
Spanish Building Decision-Making Skills
AIDS and Society (Spanish Edition)
Reproducible Lesson Plans
Teaching Transparencies
Posters

Glencoe Health: A Guide to Wellness is a comprehensive health text with 100 lessons. The study of this text may extend over the course of one year. This text also is suitable for a semester or nine-week survey course. Consider the following possible outlines as course work alternatives.

OUTLINE 1
One-year course (36 chapters)

Unit 1   You and Your Health
         Chapter 1
Unit 2   Mental Health
         Chapters 2, 3, 4
Unit 3   Family and Social Health
         Chapters 5, 6, 7
Unit 4   The Life Cycle
         Chapters 8, 9, 10
Unit 5   Body Systems
         Chapters 11, 12, 13, 14, 15
Unit 6   Personal Health and Physical Fitness
         Chapters 16, 17, 18
Unit 7   Nutrition
         Chapters 19, 20
Unit 8   Medicines and Drugs
         Chapters 21, 22, 23, 24, 25
Unit 9   Diseases and Disorders
         Chapters 26, 27, 28, 29
Unit 10 Community and Environmental Health
         Chapters 30, 31
Unit 11 Consumer Health
         Chapters 32, 33
Unit 12 Safety and Emergency Care
         Chapters 34, 35, 36

OUTLINE 2
One-semester survey course (24 chapters)

Unit 1   You and Your Health
         Chapter 1
Unit 2   Mental Health
         Chapters 2, 4
Unit 3   Family and Social Health
         Chapter 6
Unit 4   The Life Cycle
         Chapters 9, 10
Unit 5   Body Systems
         Chapter 15
Unit 6   Personal Health and Physical Fitness
         Chapters 17, 18
Unit 7   Nutrition
         Chapters 19, 20
Unit 8   Medicines and Drugs
         Chapters 22, 23, 24, 25
Unit 9   Diseases and Disorders
         Chapters 26, 27, 28, 29
Unit 10 Community and Environmental Health
         Chapter 31
Unit 11 Consumer Health
         Chapter 33
Unit 12 Safety and Emergency Care
         Chapters 34, 35, 36

OUTLINE 3
One-semester course-Physical Health (24 chapters)

Unit 1   You and Your Health
         Chapter 1
Unit 5   Body Systems
         Chapters 11, 12, 13, 14, 15
Unit 6   Personal Health and Physical Fitness
         Chapters 16, 17, 18
Unit 7   Nutrition
         Chapters 19, 20
Unit 8   Medicines and Drugs
         Chapters 21, 22, 23, 24, 25
Unit 9   Diseases and Disorders
         Chapters 26, 27, 28, 29
Unit 11 Consumer Health
         Chapter 33
Unit 12 Safety and Emergency Care
         Chapters 34, 35, 36

OUTLINE 4
One-semester course-Mental and Social Health (21 chapters)

Unit 1   You and Your Health
         Chapter 1
Unit 2   Mental Health
         Chapters 2, 3, 4
Unit 3   Family and Social Health
         Chapters 5, 6, 7
Unit 4   The Life Cycle
         Chapters 8, 9, 10
Unit 5   Body Systems
         Chapter 15
Unit 7   Nutrition
         Chapter 20
Unit 8   Medicines and Drugs
         Chapters 22, 23, 24, 25
Unit 9   Diseases and Disorders
         Chapters 26, 27, 28
Unit 10 Community and Environmental Health
         Chapters 30, 31

OUTLINE 5
Nine-week survey course (13 chapters)

Unit 1   You and Your Health
         Chapter 1
Unit 2   Mental Health
         Chapter 4
Unit 5   Body Systems
         Chapter 15
Unit 6   Personal Health and Physical Fitness
         Chapter 18
Unit 8   Medicines and Drugs
         Chapters 22, 23, 24
Unit 9   Diseases and Disorders
         Chapters 27, 28, 29
Unit 10 Community and Environmental Health
         Chapter 31
Unit 11 Consumer Health
         Chapter 33
Unit 12 Safety and Emergency Care
         Chapter 36

OUTLINE 6
Six-week survey course (10 chapters)

Unit 1   You and Your Health
         Chapter 1
Unit 2   Mental Health
         Chapter 4
Unit 6   Personal Health and Physical Fitness
         Chapter 18
Unit 7   Nutrition
         Chapter 20
Unit 8   Medicines and Drugs
         Chapters 22, 23, 24
Unit 9   Diseases and Disorders
         Chapters 27, 28
Unit 10 Community and Environmental Health
         Chapter 31

Program Supplements

AIDS and Society, Education in Sexuality, and The Reality of Drugs

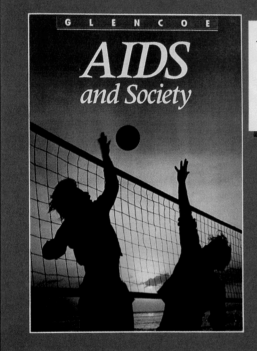

AIDS and Society is a full-color text that provides current information on HIV infection and AIDS. A Teacher's Annotated Edition is available. A Spanish edition of **AIDS and Society** student edition is also available.

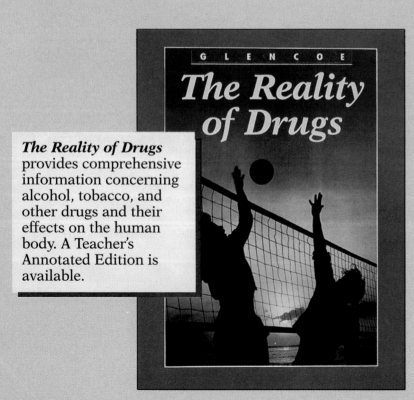

The Reality of Drugs provides comprehensive information concerning alcohol, tobacco, and other drugs and their effects on the human body. A Teacher's Annotated Edition is available.

Education in Sexuality is a full-color text that may be used as a primary text for a human sexuality course or as an extension of *Glencoe Health*. A Teacher's Annotated Edition is available.

The Reality of Violence, Improving Physical Fitness, and Death and the Adolescent: Teacher's Professional Resource

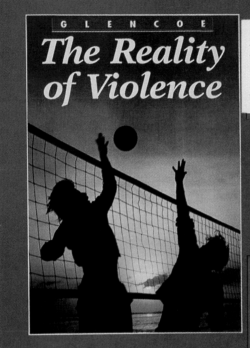

The Reality of Violence is an in-depth look at the effects of violence in our society and how it affects the health of individuals and the larger community. A Teacher's Annotated Edition is available.

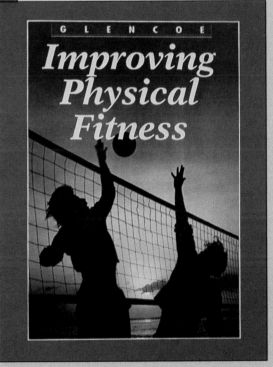

Improving Physical Fitness provides information for teens about starting and maintaining a specific exercise program.

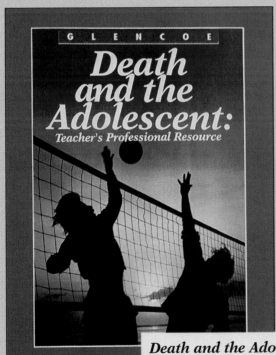

Death and the Adolescent: Teacher's Professional Resource is designed to provide teachers with background information and strategies for dealing with death.

Teacher's Classroom Resources

Enrichment Activities, Guided Reading Activities, and Reteaching Activities

---

NAME _____ DATE _____ CLASS _____

CHAPTER 18 SPORTS MEDICINE
ENRICHMENT ACTIVITY

DIRECTIONS: After reading this material, answer the questions that follow.

A 15-year-old high school student hopes to become a gymnast. She works out as often as she can. After a while, however, she begins to experience back pain. She ignores the pain until she is forced to see a doctor. The doctor places the girl in traction. Her dream of becoming a great gymnast is shattered.

A 32-year-old reporter takes up tennis. She plays three or four times a week with friends and finds she likes playing competitively. One day during a tight doubles match she ruptures an Achilles tendon in her heel. She now hobbles to work with a cane.

A 48-year-old business professional decides to take up jogging to help lose weight and condition his body. On a particularly hot and humid day, he suffers a heart attack while jogging near his home.

These three people, and thousands more like them, have experienced serious injury because they placed undue stress on a body that was not properly conditioned. A great many part-time athletes, as well as full-time ones, could prevent such injuries if they followed the guidelines and recommendations of experts involved in a fairly new field known as sports medicine.

Why Sports Medicine Developed

Millions of Americans participate in some type of sport or physical activity each day. It is estimated that more than 100 million people in the United States swim and about 50 million people ride bicycles. Millions more run, lift weights, and participate in sports such as softball or baseball, basketball, football, hockey, tennis, and golf. Many engage in even riskier activities such as hang gliding, rock climbing, and parachuting.

In the past 10 years, the number of people who regularly engage in physical activity has increased dramatically. With that increase has come an equally dramatic increase in injuries. Experts estimate that over 15 million Americans are injured in recreational and sports activities each year. These injuries range from minor sprains to permanent disability, and even to death in some cases. It is in response to these alarming statistics that sports medicine has developed.

The Scope of Sports Medicine

Until a little over a decade ago, a patient's regular doctor would treat sports-related injuries with rest, prescription painkillers, and sometimes surgery. Since then, sports medicine has become a medical field unto itself. In the early 1980s, it was dominated by orthopedic surgeons—surgeons who specialize in treating injuries to the bones, joints, and muscles. Today, however, the field of sports medicine includes a variety of specialists, including psychiatrists, sociologists, physical therapists, athletic trainers, exercise physiologists, and certified exercise program directors. It also includes specialists in kinesiology—the study of human motion—and biomechanics—the study of how body parts move. These specialists try to find ways of improving an athlete's proficiency in a particular sport.

Sports medicine has expanded its focus in other ways as well. In its early years, it served mainly professional athletes. Now, however, because of an increasing interest in physical fitness, its focus has expanded to include everyone who engages in physical activity. Moreover, doctors are no longer interested in just treating injuries. They are also trying to prevent them through research and counseling on nutrition and proper training. By helping people learn more about their capabilities and their limits, experts

Copyright © by the Glencoe Division of Macmillan/McGraw-Hill School Publishing Company   GLENCOE HEALTH **35**

Enrichment Activities allow students the opportunity to explore concepts further. There is one activity for each chapter of *Glencoe Health*. Answers for the teacher are provided at the back of the booklet.

NAME _____ DATE _____ CLASS _____

CHAPTER 28 GUIDED READING ACTIVITY 77

DIRECTIONS: Briefly answer the following questions in the space provided.

1. For whom is HIV testing required? For whom is it recommended?

2. What is ELISA? _____

3. What steps are taken after a positive ELISA result?

4. Why is it important for an outwardly healthy HIV-infected person to practice safe behaviors?

5. How long can a person be infected with HIV before showing signs of the infection?

6. Name five symptoms of HIV infection.

7. What factors are used in making a diagnosis of AIDS?

Copyright © by the Glencoe Division of Macmillan/McGraw-Hill

Guided Reading Activities are provided for each lesson in *Glencoe Health*. The format of the activities varies. Activities are designed to assess a student's comprehension of the lesson content. Answers for the teacher are provided at the back of the booklet.

NAME _____ DATE _____ CLASS _____

CHAPTER 14 RETEACHING ACTIVITY 37

DIRECTIONS: In the space provided, briefly summarize the role each organ plays in digestion.

Teeth

↓

Salivary Glands
Secrete saliva, which softens and moistens food, cleanses teeth, and neutralizes acids in mouth

↓

Esophagus

↓

Sphincters

↓

Stomach
Stores food until ready to be used; mixes food with gastric juice to form a substance called chyme; controls rate at which food enters small intestine

↓

Small intestine, Large intestine

↓

Liver

↓

Gallbladder

↓

Pancreas
Produces alkaline juices that flow into the small intestine and stop the action of the gastric juices once food has passed through

Copyright © by the Glencoe Division of Macmillan/McGraw-Hill School Publishing Company   CHAPTER 14 RETEACHING ACTIVITY 37 **37**

Reteaching Activities allow students who are having difficulty with mastering the major concepts of a lesson to review the concepts from a different perspective. Answers for the teacher are provided at the back of the booklet.

Lesson Quizzes and *Chapter Tests*

NAME   DATE   CLASS

CHAPTER
10 LESSON 1 QUIZ

DIRECTIONS: In the space at the left, write the letter of the choice that best completes the statement or answers the question.

_____ 1. Accomplishments that must be mastered at each stage of life are
    a. task masters   **c.** chores
    b. life accomplishments   **d.** developmental tasks

_____ 2. The study of the life cycle is
    a. not very important   **c.** done only in the United States
    b. relatively new   **d.** easy using computers

_____ 3. Self-actualization is
    a. developing abilities to the fullest   **c.** reality training
    b. accomplished at an early age   **d.** unavailable for teens

_____ 4. Which of the following is NOT an example of how adults might show an interest in society?
    a. volunteer work   **c.** neighborhood recycling programs
    b. hiking alone   **d.** coaching local sports team

_____ 5. Development
    a. ends at adolescence   **c.** continues throughout life
    c. is greatest in adulthood   **d.** ends at age 40

_____ 6. Failure with developmental tasks may lead to
    a. personal dissatisfaction   **c.** mental retardation
    b. a decrease in income   **d.** a split personality

_____ 7. Many of life's early developmental tasks result from
    a. practice   **c.** personal desire
    b. physical maturation   **d.** personal intelligence

_____ 8. Which of the following is NOT a developmental task for adults?
    a. developing relationships   **c.** acquiring an image
    b. developing identity   **d.** determining an occupational role

_____ 9. In what way do young adults begin to achieve self-actualization?
    a. they leave home
    b. they change their names
    c. they leave behind their friends from high school
    d. they start calling their parents by their first names

_____ 10. One of the most difficult developmental tasks is
    a. establishing societal ties   **c.** accepting aging and death
    b. career development   **d.** establishing adult relationships

GLENCOE HEALTH, CHAPTER 10   Copyright © by the Glencoe Division of Macmillan/McGraw-Hill School Publishing Company   23

Lesson Quizzes provide a one-page quiz for each lesson in *Glencoe Health*. The quizzes may also be used as a pretest. Answers for the teacher are provided at the back of the booklet.

Chapter Tests provide two forms of tests, A and B. Either or both forms may be used as alternative or make-up tests. Answers for the teacher are provided at the back of the booklet.

NAME   DATE   CLASS

CHAPTER
30 TEST

FORM B

DIRECTIONS: In the space at the left, write the letter of the choice that best completes the statement or answers the question. (3 points each)

_____ 1. The condition that occurs when a nuclear reactor melts is called
    a. radiation countdown   **c.** nuclear fusion
    b. a meltdown   **d.** an atomic bomb

_____ 2. Microscopic organisms such as green algae are
    a. phytoplankton   **c.** micro cells
    b. jellyfish   **d.** parasites

_____ 3. When a substance is known to be carcinogenic, it
    a. causes cancer   **c.** pollutes the air
    b. pollutes the water   **d.** causes erosion

_____ 4. The number of people in the world who die each year from starvation and malnutrition-related problems is
    a. less than 500,000   **c.** 1 to 5 million
    b. 500,000 to 1 million   **d.** more than 5 million

_____ 5. The energy created by radioactive materials is
    a. conservation   **c.** nuclear energy
    b. hydroelectric energy   **d.** thermal energy

_____ 6. The percent of the earth's water that is salt water is
    a. 20 percent   **c.** 80 percent
    b. 50 percent   **d.** more than 95 percent

_____ 7. In 1986, several people died and others were permanently injured as a result of what type of environmental disaster at Chernobyl?
    a. nuclear meltdown   **c.** flood
    b. oil spill   **d.** war

_____ 8. The greenhouse effect is caused by
    a. a greater number of trees   **c.** increased nitrogen levels
    b. increased ozone levels   **d.** increased carbon dioxide levels

_____ 9. Skin cancer has been linked to
    a. exposure to carbon dioxide
    b. the earth's cooler temperatures
    c. a thinning ozone layer
    d. the use of central heating

_____ 10. People with a "throw away mentality"
    a. waste resources   **c.** cannot remember where they put things
    b. recycle   **d.** are environmentalists

GLENCOE HEALTH, CHAPTER 30 TEST, FORM B   Copyright © by the Glencoe Division of Macmillan/McGraw-Hill School Publishing Company   119

Decision-Making Activities, Health Labs, and Cooperative Learning Activities

Decision-Making Activities give students an opportunity to practice the decision-making process as they consider a variety of hypothetical situations.

Health Labs give students experience with making observations and hypotheses, collecting and recording data, and forming conclusions based on analysis and interpretations of experimental results. There is one Health Lab for each chapter in the text. Teacher pages provide helps and answers to questions.

Cooperative Learning Activities give students opportunities to learn working relationship skills, such as how to listen, respond, agree, disagree, clarify, encourage and evaluate. Teacher notes are included for each activity.

Workbook and *Performance Assessment Activities*

The **Workbook** contains a Vocabulary Activity for each lesson and an Application Activity for each chapter. The Application Activities vary in format and involve conflict resolution, decision making, and life management skills. A Teacher's Annotated Edition is available.

NAME   DATE   CLASS

CHAPTER
10 VOCABULARY ACTIVITY 25

DIRECTIONS: Before reading Lesson 3, write beneath each term in Column A two ideas that you think relate to the term's meaning. After reading the lesson, correct in Column B any inaccurate information you wrote in Column A. Then write a clear definition of the term in Column C.

Column A   Column B   Column C

1. chronological age

2. biological age

3. social age

4. age norms

Copyright © by the Glencoe Division of Macmillan/McGraw-Hill School Publishing Company

---

NAME   DATE   CLASS

CHAPTER
1 APPLICATION ACTIVITY
DECISION MAKING

DIRECTIONS: At the beginning of this chapter, you were asked to imagine yourself writing a video about the story of your health. Here's another chance to write a video. Assume you've been asked by a Hollywood producer to write a portion of a video script about the life of an American teen. The main character is a 17-year-old named Joe.

Your job is to write the next scene in a story about Joe's life-style and its consequences for his health. The scene before yours portrays Joe's current health choices. You should assess those choices, come up with healthier alternatives, and then write a script for the next scene, in which you, as Joe's best friend, convince him that making better health choices will help him lead a longer, healthier, happier life. Base the alternatives you provide for Joe on the life-style factors you read about in this chapter. Use your own imagination to come up with ways to convince Joe to make wiser decisions about his health.

Scene: When Joe finally forced his eyes open and looked at the alarm clock he panicked—it was already 9 A.M. Then he remembered that it was Saturday and he didn't have to go to school. Joe was exhausted from staying up until 3 A.M.–partying with his friends and hung over from drinking at least a dozen beers. As soon as Joe sat up in bed, he started coughing, just like every other morning after he'd smoked heavily the night before. In fact, Joe really wanted a cigarette right then, but his parents didn't let him smoke in the house. He'd have to wait until he threw on some clothes and slipped outside to the garage.

Joe tried squeezing into an old pair of jeans, but they wouldn't button. He'd been forcing him to realize that he was getting a "beer belly." Of course, he'd love to have the trim, muscular physique of one of the guys on the basketball team he managed, but Joe just wasn't into the jock routine. Sitting on the sidelines was more his style.

Joe finally slipped into an old sweatsuit and headed for the garage for his first cigarette of the day. As he passed by the kitchen he grabbed a soft drink from the fridge. His mom was cooking oatmeal, and just smelling it made Joe queasy. He hoped his stomach would settle down after the soft drink and a smoke. Then he'd make himself a real breakfast–bacon, eggs, and toast loaded with butter.

Your Scene:

Copyright © by the Glencoe Division of Macmillan/McGraw-Hill School Publishing Company

GLENCOE HEALTH WORKBOOK   5

NAME   DATE   CLASS

CHAPTER
32 BUMPER STICKER
PERFORMANCE ASSESSMENT ACTIVITY

THE TASK: You are an advertising company and you have been asked to submit a design for an original bumper sticker with a wellness message on it. Bumper stickers that are great will be selected for display in area auto dealerships.

THE AUDIENCE FOR THE TASK: The original bumper stickers are to be designed to be interesting and appealing to adults who go to auto dealerships to look at new cars.

THE PURPOSE OF THE TASK: The purpose of your work is to get the attention of adults and put a memorable idea about health and wellness in their heads.

INDIVIDUAL OR COOPERATIVE GROUP TASK: If this is an individual task, you will complete it by yourself. If this is a group task, each person in the group must make his or her own bumper sticker. The group will decide on one area of health and wellness as a theme, and each person in the group will make a bumper sticker that will support that theme.

PROCEDURE:

1. Review the list of criteria that will be used to judge the quality of bumper stickers.

2. Brainstorm ideas for your original bumper sticker. If you are working alone, you may brainstorm with other people. If you are working in cooperative groups, do the brainstorming in your group. Keep a list of all your brainstormed ideas. This list will be submitted along with the final version of your bumper sticker.

3. If you are working in cooperative groups, select a theme for all the bumper stickers in your group. As soon as you have selected a theme, tell your teacher. All groups must have different themes. If another group has already selected your theme, you must select another theme.

4. Make a first draft of your original bumper sticker. Use the criteria for judging the quality of bumper stickers to assess your first draft. If you are working in cooperative groups, use the criteria to assess each other's work.

5. Make a final draft of your original bumper sticker.

6. Write one paragraph that states why the message on your original bumper sticker is important.

7. Turn in your brainstorming list, the first and final drafts of your original bumper sticker, and your paragraph.

Copyright © by the Glencoe Division of Macmillan/McGraw-Hill School Publishing Company

GLENCOE HEALTH WORKBOOK   **185**

Performance Assessment Activities assess learning in ways that require a student to manipulate information in flexible and creative ways. Assessment activities are a learning tool for the student and use a variety of strategies to assess student learning.

Spanish Resources: Spanish Summaries and Glossary, Self-Inventories, Building Decision-Making Skills and AIDS and Society (student text)

A **Spanish Resources** Binder includes three booklets: **Spanish Summaries and Glossary, Self-Inventories,** and **Building Decision-Making Skills.** A Spanish edition of **AIDS and Society** student text is also available.

The **Self-Inventories** and **Building Decision-Making Skills** are full-page activities in the student edition of *Glencoe Health.* They are reproduced in Spanish for inclusion in the *Spanish Resources* Binder.

The **Spanish Summaries** are brief summaries of each of the 36 chapters of *Glencoe Health.* The summaries are followed by brief questions and/or statements that help the student grasp the chapter content. Answers for the teacher are provided at the back of the booklet.

Reproducible Lesson Plans, Posters, and Teaching Transparencies

Eleven full-color posters are designed to be used in the classroom to enhance and reinforce important health concepts.

TOTAL HEALTH

Physical

LESSON PLAN Chapter 33, Lesson 1 (pages 65...

Date ___

Date(s) ___

Teacher's Name ___

Class(es) ___

TWE: Teacher's Wraparound Edition   **TCR:** Teache...

Local Objectives

OBJECTIVES

Recognize different health care facilities and type...
...e variety of health resources available for...

Reproducible Lesson Plans are provided for each lesson in *Glencoe Health*. The lesson plans follow the teaching cycle — FOCUS, TEACH, ASSESS, and CLOSE— that is developed in the Teacher's Wraparound Edition of *Glencoe Health*. The lesson plans include references to all resources available with *Glencoe Health*.

TWE p. 653
...E p. 654

...54-656
...ds, TWE p...
...WE p. 666

Over...
Self-Inventor...WE p...
Building Decision-Making...

• **Independent Practice**

The *Teaching Transparencies* Binder includes 60 transparencies plus an activity booklet complete with teaching strategies for use with the transparencies.

58

BODY SYSTEMS TRANSPARENCY

TEETH

IS YOUR H...

Media Resources

Four VHS Videos include up-to-date information on the "hot" topics — *AIDS, Drugs, Violence,* and *Responsible Sexuality.*

The computer software Testmaker is available for Apple II, IBM, and Macintosh computers. Each of the testmakers allows you to add questions of your own.

Body Awareness Resource Network (BARN) is an interactive software program for the Apple II family of computers with 128k and IBM compatible computers with 256k. Disks are available in 3.5-inch and 5.25-inch sizes. *BARN* reinforces key concepts, helps students examine their attitudes and behavior, and answers student questions in a confidential, nonjudgmental setting. Students using *BARN* have been shown to be more aware of the consequences of their risk-taking and more likely to support each other in avoiding or coping with risks.

The *"Human Biology"* videodisc that is a part of the *Science and Technology Videodisc Series* contains 43 videoreports, each about 90 seconds in length. The subjects of the reports fall into three categories: Human Physiology, Medical Technology, and Health. In addition to adding to student understanding, the videoreports also introduce career opportunities to your students.

Creating a Positive Learning Enviroment for all Students

Teaching Students with Varying Ability Levels and Learning Styles

This Teacher's Wraparound Edition provides many types of activities to support the concepts in the text. Select those that are most appropriate to the needs, abilities, interests and maturity levels of your students. To assist you, the codes for each level of activity appear on the first page of every chapter in the Teacher's Wraparound Edition.

Teaching Students with Special Needs

Students with special needs are often mainstreamed in health classes. These students are learning the same information and skills and competing for the same grades. It is important to provide equal opportunities for students. If an activity requires students to write on the chalkboard, these students should be required to do so also—as long as they are physically and/or mentally capable. Students in wheelchairs may require a lowered chalkboard or the use of an overhead transparency. For the visually impaired, an oral response is appropriate. The following suggestions can help you structure your classroom or adapt your teaching methods to create a positive learning environment for all students.

For Physically Challenged Students

- Adjust the room arrangement to fit students' needs.
- Encourage verbal activities and small group participation.
- Encourage students to participate in physical activities within their capabilities.

For Visually Impaired Students

- Seat students in good light near the front of the classroom.
- Whenever possible, provide hands-on experiences.
- Assign another student to assist the visually impaired student.
- Allow students to record assignments or complete them verbally.
- Tape-record each chapter of the textbook.
- Encourage verbal participation.
- Administer tests orally.
- Allow students to move about freely so they can get close to charts or displays.

For Hearing Impaired Students

- Seat students near the front of the classroom.
- Use the chalkboard to highlight key terms.
- Guide students to the appropriate text page during discussions.
- Ask a responsible student to make copies of his or her notes for the hearing impaired students.
- Give written tests.
- Look directly at hearing impaired students when speaking. Talk normally.
- Learn sign language.
- Write directions for activities on the chalkboard.
- Encourage as much verbal interaction as possible.
- Encourage small group participation.
- Encourage students to express themselves verbally.
- Be very clear in the directions you provide.
- Provide easy-to-read, short handouts.
- Make sure expectations are clear and realistic.
- Provide positive feedback whenever possible.
- Modify assignments to ensure success.

For Limited English Proficiency Students

- Provide familiar and practical examples during class discussions.
- Provide a variety of media experiences to exemplify and reinforce concepts.
- Utilize teaching strategies that require students to demonstrate their understanding, such as by creating collages, role-playing, and so on.

Teaching Students with Learning Disabilities (LD)

A disability may be a subtle one. Sometimes, it may seem as if these students should be able to handle classroom work if they were only more diligent. However, they often have difficulty with reading and language skills, in sorting important information, in writing effectively, and in keeping up with the workload because of their own particular. Once LD students become frustrated with their work, behavior problems may result. Try to make certain allowances that will enable students to grasp the essentials of the lessons without being overwhelmed by specific details.

Because you must consider each LD student on an individual basis, we recommend a preliminary meeting with the special education teacher or child study team to assess the student's needs. The following suggestions will allow you to use *Glencoe Health* more efficiently with LD students:

- LD students should be able to grasp main ideas, but should not be held accountable for specifics.

- LD students should not be required to answer all questions in the Lesson Reviews. Choose the most important and have them complete those.

- Providing a basic skeletal outline of each chapter with blanks for the students to fill in could be used as effective study guides, as most LD students lack organization and note-taking skills.

- Provide numbered diagrams to follow when doing a complex lesson, such as fetal development.

- Most LD students do not read on grade level and have a great deal of difficulty with independent reading assignments. Try to provide a peer tutor or ask the special education teacher if help is available. Feel free to allow LD students to skip some of the more complex reading sections. Many LD students who are poor readers use illustrations as a main source of information concerning concepts.

- The chapter tests will probably be too difficult. A convenient way to modify the test is to asterisk certain questions for the LD students to answer and encourage them to complete the whole test. (Possibly give extra credit for those questions without asterisks that are answered correctly.)

- If research is assigned, you may need to provide support, since most LD students lack good time management skills, are not self-starters, and have difficulty managing multi-step projects. Perhaps provide an alternate project or narrow the topic and reduce the number of required sources.

Remember the goal of mainstreaming LD students is that they get a basic foundation in health. Realistically, this will not be as comprehensive a foundation as your other students receive. However, modifications you make will enhance their learning experience.

Teaching Students with Limited English Proficiency (LEP)

Students with limited English proficiency may not have trouble mastering the content. Their difficulty may be only with the language. With these students, it is important to remember that requiring tasks before a student is ready for them can slow the learning process.

Accept mistakes and praise students' efforts. Remember that students can often understand more than they can express. Students may be able to use simple, direct English sentences but have trouble with figures of speech, idioms, and words with multiple meanings.

As students begin to develop writing skills, they may mix English with their native language. Accept these language mixtures. At this stage, confidence and enjoyment of writing are the most important goals. Students who feel comfortable with English will be more motivated to write in English.

Provide peer learning by grouping English proficient students with students with a limited proficiency. Encourage students to work in pairs or small groups.

Teaching Students from Various Cultural and Ethnic Backgrounds

Health and health information is one area that is influenced by culture, ethnicity, and socioeconomic background. It is important that teachers be sensitive to these differences. It is important not to say a student's culture is wrong, but rather reinforce what is presently known as factual health information. If students are willing to share practices and beliefs unique to their culture, it may help other students better understand the culture and its influence on a person's health.

Reinforcing Reading Skills

Can your students read the textbook? By focusing on simple reading and studying techniques, you can help your students learn more effectively.

Vocabulary Development
It is important that students do more than just look up vocabulary words in the dictionary and write definitions. Vocabulary is developed in seven ways in *Glencoe Health.*

- **In the Chapter Lessons.** Major terms are printed in bold and defined.

- **In the Lesson Reviews.** Vocabulary terms are reinforced as students define and apply health terms.

- **In the Chapter Review.** Terms are reinforced as students pair the correct terms with definitions.

- **In the Text Glossary.** Major terms are cross-referenced to the chapter in which they are first introduced and subsequently used in important ways.

- **In the Teacher's Wraparound Lesson Plans.** Teaching strategies are provided to reinforce and build vocabulary skills.

- **In the Lesson Quizzes and Chapter Tests.** One part of each Lesson Quiz and each Chapter Test is a review of vocabulary.

- **In the Workbook.** A Vocabulary Activity is provided for each of the 100 lessons in the text.

Reading Comprehension.
Reading comprehension can be divided into three levels: literal, inferential, and applicative. Literal comprehension involves the understanding of what the author said and meant. Inferential comprehension entails understanding what is implied or inferred. Applicative comprehension involves applying what is learned in the reading to situations outside the text.

Improving Literal Comprehension. An effective way to assure that students read the assigned text material is to provide them with a worksheet on which you have listed several statements, some of which are directly from the text. Other statements included should have no connection with the literal content of the reading. It is important that these unrelated statements not be so far astray that students can identify them without completing the reading. Ask students to indicate which statements represent what the author said.

Improving Inferential Comprehension. A teacher-developed reading guide can help students read at a higher level of comprehension. On the guide, list at least ten statements that interpret either correctly or incorrectly what the author said. Also list several statements that do not relate to the reading. After each statement, note the page numbers where the content on which the statements were based is provided. Ask students to read the entire assignment first; then have students return to the pages following each inferential statement to judge if the statement has been interpreted incorrectly (I), has been interpreted correctly (C), or is unrelated to the content of this reading (U).

Improving Applicative Comprehension. Before students can master this level of reading they must first master reading for literal comprehension and reading for inferential comprehension. Even though a student reads rapidly, it should not be assumed that he or she has achieved a high level of thinking. Reading for application means that a student will be able to understand what he or she has read, interpret the complete meaning, and be able to use this information in another situation. Develop a reading guide that lists solutions to problems or situations in the reading. Then list a number of problems or conditions to which the solutions can be applied. List more problems or conditions than solutions. Ask students to match the solutions to the problems.

Teaching Critical Thinking

Helping students think should be a primary goal of all education. Learning only easily testable facts is inadequate preparation for living in the 21st century.

Definitions of Thinking
Critical thinking can be defined simply as the process of reasonably or logically deciding what to do or believe. It is a process that is made up of many considerations. The learner needs to (1) understand his or her own and others' meanings and views; (2) look for relationships, causes, inferences, theories, patterns; (3) look for alternatives; and (4) make judgments, choices, or decisions based on the information.

Creative thinking requires the ability to identify and formulate problems, and the ability to generate alternative solutions. Fluency (quantity of ideas), flexibility (variety of ideas), originality (unusual or unique ideas), and elaboration (details for implementating ideas) are necessary components of creative thinking.

Assumptions for Teaching Thinking
These assumptions underlie the teaching of thinking:

- All students are capable of higher-level thinking.

- Thinking skills can be taught and learned.

- Thinking can be effectively taught within any content area.

- Appropriate expectations for logical thinking are based on physiological maturation, social experiences, and the knowledge level of the students.

- Learners can be taught to transfer thinking skills from a specific content area to an internalized process applicable to a variety of new learnings.

Actions for Teaching Thinking
All learning requires thinking. Benjamin Bloom's Taxonomy of the Cognitive Domain is probably the most widely recognized schema for levels of thinking. Questions, statements, and activities can be designed based on the taxonomy that will elicit the complexity of thinking congruent with the lesson's objective(s).

- **Knowledge:** define, recognize, recall, identify, label, understand, examine, show, collect

- **Comprehension:** translate, interpret, explain, describe, summarize, extrapolate

- **Application:** apply, solve, experiment, show, predict

- **Analysis:** connect, relate, differentiate, classify, arrange, check, group, distinguish, organize, categorize, detect, compare, infer

- **Synthesis:** produce, propose, design, plan, combine, formulate, compose, hypothesize, construct

- **Evaluation:** appraise, judge, criticize, decide

To use Bloom's Taxonomy successfully, consider the following:

- The levels of the taxonomy build, one on the other. Students cannot be expected to operate at a higher level of thinking without the necessary foundation. For example, a student cannot plan a campaign for a drug-free school without understanding drugs and the effects of drugs on the human body.

- The level of complexity (from knowledge to evaluation) is not equal to the level of difficulty. For example, labeling all bones of the human body is a difficult task, but it remains a task at the lowest level of the taxonomy, knowledge.

- All students at any age and any ability level can experience thinking at each of the levels of taxonomy. For example, very young students can be asked to evaluate which foods are healthy foods, which are "junk" foods and to give supporting reasons.

Questions and Activities
Examples of questions that promote thinking at various levels are shown below.

Knowledge—the identification and recall of information:
- Who, what, when, where, how...?
- Describe...

T19

Comprehension—the organization and selection of facts and ideas:
- Retell in your own words...
- What is the main idea of...?

Application—the use of facts, rules, principles:
- How is...an example of...?
- How is...related to...?

Analysis—the separation of a whole into component parts:
- What are the parts or features of...?
- Classify...according to...
- How does...compare/contrast with...?

Synthesis—the combination of ideas to form a new whole:
- What would you predict/infer from...?
- What might happen if you combined...with...?

Evaluation—the development of opinions, judgments, or decisions:
- What do you think about...?
- Prioritize...

Not all questions or interactions need to move from teacher to student. Dialogue among peers is an effective technique to use when teaching thinking. When students discuss, explain, debate, decide, or solve problems together they increase their thinking and learning. Asking students to generate their own questions and activities is another strategy that encourages student thinking.

Responses

Responses to student interaction can be crucial. Dialogue and thinking can be readily turned off by both criticism or praise. It is easy to recognize that such responses as "Wrong," "Who has the right answer?" or "Oh no!" are obvious turn-offs. But so are responses that praise: "That's right!" "Exactly," or "What a great answer." By using silence (wait time) you demonstrate that you expect answers and have faith in the students' ability to provide those answers. Given sufficient time, students will respond with more complete thoughts, show evidence of more creative thinking, and exhibit an increased speculativeness in their thinking. Accepting responses can provide a psychologically safe climate in which students can take risks and time to explore their own thinking. When using passive types of responses, you simply receive the student's input with such phrases as "I see," "That's one idea," or "Umhmm." More active kinds of responses allow you to rephrase, translate, or summarize the input: "You say that...," "Your point then is that...,"

Emphatic acceptance lets you show feeling as well as understanding: "I can see why you would violently disagree...,"

Critical Thinking in *Glencoe Health*

While all material in this text promotes critical thinking at some level, the Lesson and Chapter Review merit particular attention.

- *Reviewing Facts and Vocabulary* in each Lesson Review checks knowledge and comprehension.

- *Recalling the Facts* in each Chapter Review similarly questions students on chapter content.

- *Thinking Critically and Applying Health Knowledge* in each Lesson Review and Chapter Review challenge students to operate within the higher levels of Bloom's cognitive categories and requires application of knowledge.

Teaching Decision Making in the Health Classroom

Consider adolescents and the issues around which they make decisions. Many are emotionally charged. Their decisions are often made in the midst of peer pressure. You can help students improve their decision-making skills. Refer to pages 18-21 in *Glencoe Health* to use the five basic steps in the decision-making process.

Practicing the decision-making process in the classroom with real-life situations helps students develop the ability to examine options and evaluate consequences in an unemotional, unpressured setting. Later, when students are faced with decisions, they are much more likely to use this process if they have such practice.

The skill of goal-setting is a critical part of helping students make responsible decisions. Students who have set realistic short- and long-range goals can weigh their choices for any given situation with reference to those goals. Having goals also gives people some sense of personal control over their own lives. Students should realize they can make decisions that help or hinder them in achieving their goals.

Decision-making skills will be used for a lifetime. Encourage your students to master the process so that it becomes automatic for them when they make decisions.

Performance assessment strategies are activities that are used to assess learning in ways that require the student to use and manipulate information learned. Students must decide which information and concepts to use to craft a product such as an informative poster, a booklet for younger children, a public service video, a handbook, consumer decision-making and letters to manufacturers. Such tasks require the student to both know concepts and information, and be able to communicate them to specific audiences that are not limited to the teacher and students in the Health class but include younger and older students and individuals or groups in the community. Performance tasks assess students' research, writing, drawing, and oral presentation skills and attitudes such as persistence, dependability, and concern for quality. The more varied the strategies to assess student learning, the more flexible and creative the student has become in displaying his or her grasp of the subject matter. The diversity enables students with different strengths to experience success when they might not have done so before. The processes and products are authentic in that they are the same or similar to what is found in the larger world outside the classroom.

Cooperative learning is often a part of a performance task. Being able to work on a team and contribute a specific service and product to the team's overall effort is a very authentic skill. Group work is sometimes used to begin the task, then the individuals continue on their own. It can also be used for peer sharing and editing.

As with any other skill, the criteria for quality group work must be set in advance so that the student and his or her peers and teachers can assess group work more objectively. A video of an effective group from another class or previous year could be used as a model for what excellent group work looks and sounds like.

Performance assessment activities include an engaging task; clear criteria or guidelines for assessing the quality of the student's process and the product; and, when possible, models of excellent student work to guide the students towards the targets of quality. Students are shown these lists of criteria and models of excellence at the beginning of the task so that they are clear as to what is expected of them. During the project and at its completion, students learn how to use the lists of criteria and models to assess their own work.

Assessment of how competent a student is becoming should be judged in a variety of ways. Vocabulary quizzes, multiple-choice tests, short-answer exams, and performance assessment tasks can all work together to help the student and the teacher understand the quality of the learning going on. Because performance assessment tasks take much longer than other forms of assessment, teachers should begin slowly and try relatively short, engaging tasks first. Having examples of excellent work on similar assignments done by your previous students helps your current students know what is expected of them.

Rubrics and Classroom Lists

A rubric is a set of instructions of the quality of a process and/or a product. The set of descriptions includes a continuum of quality from excellent to poor. There are many varieties of rubrics. The one used here is a six-level rubric called a "Two-Decision Rubric." A rubric and a classroom list for an oral presentation will be used here as examples. Level S of the rubric for oral presentation describes an eloquent and unusually superb presentation "for that grade level." Level T describes an excellent presentation "for that grade level." Level U describes a presentation that is mostly excellent except for one or two important components that were not excellent. In other words, level U describes "mostly excellent" presentation. Level W describes an evenly poor presentation while level V describes a presentation that is mostly poor except for one or two important elements that were better than poor. Level X describes a very poor presentation.

Rubric for Oral Presentation

S: The presentation is eloquent. The speaker shows a flair for communicating with the audience. Humor and creativity are clearly present. The speaker seems confident and at ease.

T: The presenter speaks in a clear voice that can be heard by all. The speaker shows interest and enthusiasm. The rate of speech is appropriate. The speaker makes eye contact with everyone in the class. The speaker has no nervous habits which distract the listeners. The speaker is appropriately dressed and has excellent grooming and posture. Body movements add to the presentation. The presentation is organized with a beginning, a body of information, and a conclusion. There is a strong organizing theme to the presentation. There are clear main ideas with transitions between them. The details and examples used make the main ideas meaningful to the audience. Information is complete and accurate. It is clear that the student understands the core curriculum related to this project. Visual aids are used to make the presentation more interesting and meaningful. The visual aids are well done and can be seen by everyone in the class. The speaker allows time for the audience to think. The speaker involves the audience in some active way in the presentation. The presentation is the appropriate length.

U: The presentation is generally as good as one receiving a rating of T. There are one or two elements of the presentation that are less polished.

V: The presentation is generally similar to one receiving a rating of W, but there are one or two elements that are relatively well done.

W: The presenter is difficult to hear. The rate of speaking is too fast or too slow. The speaker does not show much interest and/or enthusiasm in the topic. It may sound like the speaker is reading the presentation. Eye contact is made with only some of the audience. The speaker may have nervous habits which distract from the presentation. The speaker is not presentable. The presentation itself shows little organization. The presentation rambles or it may seem like a list of facts. Details and examples are lacking or not well chosen for the topic and audience. Some information may be incomplete or inaccurate. It is not clear that the student understands the core curriculum related to the project. Visual aids are not well done and can not be seen by everyone in the class. The speaker does not involve the audience actively in the presentation. The presentation is not of the appropriate length.

X: The presentation is poorly done.

To use the rubric, the assessor observes the presentation and makes the first of two choices. The assessor decides if the presentation was more like a T (excellent) or more like a W (poor). If the first decision was that the presentation was more like a T, then the second and final decision is made. Was the presentation one of those unusually eloquent and superb ones (S), was it evenly excellent (T), or was it unevenly excellent (U)? If the first decision was that the presentation was more like a W, then the second and final decision is made. Was the presentation evenly poor (W), mostly poor but with one or two better elements (V), or was it very poor (X)? In only two decisions, the student's oral performance is placed on a six-point scale.

For this rubric, letters were used instead of numerals. If numbers were used, someone will be tempted to use them incorrectly. If a student were to make a two on a presentation, and a four on another, someone would be tempted to add two and four and divide by two and say that the student made an average of three on oral presentations. To stay away from the temptation to manipulate the numbers incorrectly, letters have been used. It is perfectly correct to describe a student's long-term performance by saying that he or she made three Ts, three Us, and a V. Another observation may have been that the rating of T became most common during the later part of the course which showed that the student improved with time and practice.

The rubric is designed to lay out a continuum of quality from very excellent to very poor. It is a tool that puts this continuum into words and a tool that can be used to place students on the continuum of quality. Once a rubric has been created, it can be used unchanged by many teachers. But, the rubric may not be the best tool to give students. A simpler list of guidelines would probably be more useful to the students. Each teacher who uses the rubric makes his or her own classroom list. That classroom list uses terms the students can easily understand. While the rubric remains unchanged from teacher to teacher, the classroom lists will likely differ from teacher to teacher. The teacher decides how best to translate the rubric into a useful list of guidelines for a particular class of students. It should be noted that after a few experiences using classroom lists, the students, working either alone or in cooperative groups, can make their own list of guidelines; thus, further engaging them in active learning.

The list of criteria is the basis for the assessment, and it can also be used to give the student a grade. The criteria highlight each important aspect of the process and the product and final assessment provides the student with feedback as to how he or she did on the elements of the task. Each item in the list can also be worth points, and a grade can be given based on the percentage of the total possible points the student earned.

A classroom list for use with the rubric for oral presentations follows. For further information and other rubrics, refer to the *Performance Assessment Activities* booklet that is a component of the *Glencoe Health* program.

A Classroom List for Oral Presentation

1. The speaker can be heard by everyone in the audience.
2. The speaker shows interest and enthusiasm.
3. The rate of speaking is appropriate.
4. The speaker makes eye contact with individuals throughout the audience.
5. Body movements add to the presentation.
6. The speaker is dressed appropriately, has excellent grooming, and excellent posture.
7. The presentation is organized with a beginning, body of information, and conclusion.
8. There is a clear focus to the presentation and the focus is not lost.
9. The main ideas support the focus and there are clear transitions between main ideas.
10. Appropriate support and elaboration are given to the main ideas.
11. It is clear that the speaker knows his/her subject.
12. Visual aids are well done, can be seen by all, and add to the presentation.
13. The speaker allows time for the audience to think.
14. The speaker actively involves his/her audience.
15. The presentation is the appropriate length.
16. The presentation communicates effectively with the intended audience.
17. The presentation is creative and interesting.

Performance Assessment Strategies

Chapter 1/Lesson 1
Create a poster that uses the concept of the Health Triangle. The purpose of your poster is to teach other people what the Health Triangle means. Humor and creativity are highly valued. Write a one paragraph explanation of what information you are trying to communicate in your poster.

Chapter 2/Lesson 2
Find articles in magazines or newspapers, or listen to information on TV about people who have mental health needs that are not being met. Combine students' articles into one big classroom display. Make titles and statements that describe what the pictures show. This display could be exhibited in the school. Write a one paragraph statement about what you have learned from all these articles.

Chapter 3/Lesson 1
Write a short pamphlet for teenagers about how a teenager should react when he or she has a friend who is talking about suicide. Excellent pamphlets will be given to the school's guidance department.

Chapter 4/Lesson 1
Make a videotape, public service radio announcement, pamphlet, or poster about the effects of stress on health. Excellent work can be published.

Chapter 5/Lesson 1
Make up a skit about different types of families. These skits should be humorous and not planned to "put people down." In each skit, characters need to relate how members of the family accomplish the two functions of the family:

A. The family is the primary support system to which individuals turn in order to have their basic needs met.

B. It is also the essential mechanism by which a child develops the capability to survive and to function independently in the world.

The skits can be videotaped for the use of other classes.

Chapter 6/Lesson 2
Make a poster depicting the consequences of peer pressure. Make the poster for younger students. The poster should show a situation where peer pressure is being exerted. The poster will now show what happens next. The younger students who view the poster will predict what would probably have happened next.

Chapter 7/Lesson 1
Work with a partner on this task.
Pretend that the two of you have decided to live on your own. You will earn your own money and pay your own bills. Decide on how much money it would cost to live each month. Categorize your list into Very Essential, Less Essential, and Non-Essential but Desirable. When the other students have completed their lists, review them. Revise your work if necessary. Make a graph that shows your living expenses for an average month.

Chapter 8/Lesson 1
Design a poster that warns of the dangers of using tobacco, drinking alcohol, or using illegal drugs during pregnancy.

Chapter 9/Lesson 2
Make a book cover of your personal Coat of Arms. This Coat of Arms has symbols of the kind of person you want to be. Use the book cover on one of your books. Write an explanation for what each symbol says about you.

Chapter 10/Lesson 3
Make a chart that shows the pluses and minuses of getting old. You may interview older people to get their opinions. Review the posters made by the other students in the class. Write a one-paragraph statement of the most interesting thing you learned from this activity.

Chapter 11/Lesson 3
Your class is writing a booklet on how to strengthen your muscles. Your teacher will assign you one set of opposing muscles. Your job is to make a poster showing where these muscles are. You are also to draw a person doing the appropriate exercise to keep that pair of opposing muscles strong. The finished booklet will be given to the Physical Education Department.

Chapter 12/Lesson 1
Select a behavior such as standing to applaud at a concert, reaching out to hold the door open for another person, or sticking an injured finger in your mouth. You may select a behavior that is humorous. In a very clear sequence of statements, describe how the sense organs, the nervous system, and the muscles work together to perform this behavior. You may use drawings. Excellent work will be given to the Science Department.

Chapter 13/Lesson 1
Make up a cartoon character who is a "drop of blood" in your body. Draw a cartoon that shows an adventure that this "drop of blood" has. The purpose of this cartoon is to both entertain younger children and to teach them about the structures such as the heart, lungs, arteries, veins, and capillaries through which the "drop of blood" travels. Excellent work will be sent to an elementary school.

Chapter 14/Lesson 1
Select a Super Hero. Enlarge the Super Hero to fill a

larger piece of paper or a poster board. Draw in the digestive system of this Super Hero. Label each important part. Use the correct name for each part. You may add a "super" adjective to each name to make your drawing interesting. For example, stomach may become Stupendous Stomach.

Share your labeled drawings with your class. Quiz them on what each part of the digestive system does.

Invent a super snack for your Super Hero. Describe what happens to this snack as it goes through the super digestive system. State the events in order. Be specific.

Chapter 15, Lesson 2
Do a survey of the pluses and minuses of being a girl in your school. Create a visual display of what you learned. Write one paragraph that tells one important thing you learned from your study.
Excellent work will be displayed in the school.

Chapter 16/Lesson 2
Your job is to make a poster that describes disease, injury, or disorder to one of the following:
    Eye, Ear, Teeth and Mouth
Your poster will also describe how to prevent and treat the problem. You may interview doctors and dentists. Excellent work will be sent to doctors and dentists for display.

Chapter 17/Lesson 1
Keep a log of the exercise you get during one week. Physical education classes should be included. After one week, review your log and plan one way to improve your exercise. Keep the log for one more week. Did you follow your plan? Write one paragraph that describes how you feel about the quality and quantity of your exercise.

Chapter 18/Lesson 1
Write a reasonable fitness goal for yourself. Write an action plan for how you will accomplish your goal. What evidence will you use to see if you have accomplished your goal after six weeks? Keep a log for six weeks that shows how you follow your action plan. At the end of six weeks, what is the evidence that you have reached your fitness goal? Write one paragraph that describes the degree to which you have reached your fitness goal.

Chapter 19/Lesson 2
You have been hired to be the advertising agent for a "nutrient." (You may select the important nutrient.) Design a poster which honestly advertised the value of this nutrient. Write a one paragraph explanation of why this nutrient is so important. Excellent work will be sent to local supermarkets.

Chapter 20/Lesson 1
You are a team of restaurant developers. You want to make a restaurant that is popular with teenagers and also serves nutritionally balanced menus. Create the following for the restaurant:
    Its name and logo.
    Its floor plan.
    Its menu.
Defend your menu. Describe how it will be both popular with teenagers and also nutritionally balanced. Excellent work will be sent to local fast-food restaurants.

Chapter 21/Lesson 2
Make a poster that shows a medicine that is advertised in newspapers and magazines. Explain what the medicine is used for. Explain how a person with that problem could prevent and/or solve the problem without taking that medicine. Excellent work will be sent to the school nurse.

Chapter 22/Lesson 1
You are planning an advertising campaign to persuade people to stop smoking. Tobacco companies spend millions of dollars planning advertising campaigns that persuade people to smoke. Take one of the tobacco company's ads and change it to make that ad be against smoking. Excellent work will be displayed.

Chapter 23/Lesson 1
Make a comic strip for younger students that will help convince them of the dangers of alcohol.
Excellent work will be sent to an elementary school.

Chapter 24/Lesson 1
Plan a skit for younger students that will help convince them of the dangers of taking drugs. Excellent work can be videotaped or put on "live" for elementary students.

Chapter 25/Lesson 1
Select one illegal drug. What are the "costs" of all types associated with this drug? The quality of your work will be measured, in part, by how thoughtfully you consider all the costs associated with this drug. Excellent work will be sent to the public libraries.

Chapter 26/Lesson 2
Make a humorous poster that teaches people good health habits so that they will not spread colds or the flu to other people. Excellent work will be displayed.

Chapter 27/Lesson 3
Brainstorm a list of laws that should be used to control the spread of sexually transmitted diseases (STDs.) Select the one law that you think would be the most important. Explain why you think it would be the most important. Excellent work will be sent to the local state representative.

Chapter 28/Lesson 1
Make a poster showing the following about HIV and AIDS:
    how HIV enters the body, or
    how HIV can be prevented from entering the body, or
    the action of HIV on the immune system.
    (Teacher Note: If information about condoms and their failure rates has been presented, student posters should reflect it.)

Chapter 29/Lesson 1

How would your home change if everyone in it decided to behave in ways to prevent cardiovascular disease? Describe your home before and after such a change occurred. Which of these changes do you think is the most important? Select the most important change. Can you get the people in your home to make this change? Write one paragraph that describes how you would go about getting the people in your home to make that change.

Chapter 30/Lesson 1

Make a poster that shows what you think the most serious global environmental problem is. Write one paragraph that states why you selected that problem. Make a list of several actions which should be taken to solve the problem. What is the most important action that should be taken? State that one action and describe why you think it is so important.

Excellent work will be displayed in the public libraries.

Chapter 31/Lesson 1

Conserving and safeguarding water, using less energy, and reducing waste and garbage are three examples of actions to take to protect our environment. Make a poster that describes one important action that could really be done in your school to protect the environment.

Excellent work will be displayed.

Chapter 32/Lesson 1

You and your family buy many, many products that are advertised in print and on TV. All of these ads make claims. Some claims are made directly and other claims are made very subtly. Select some ads that may not be entirely honest in their messages.

Explain why you choose that ad and why you think it is not being entirely honest.

Chapter 33/Lesson 2

Many opportunities such as CPR and first-aid courses, health or job fairs, courses in managing money are available. What kind of self-help or self-improvement activities are available to you as a citizen of your community? What workshops, training sessions, continuing education courses, and other opportunities are available to you? Which one is most appealing to you? Write a paragraph describing the opportunity and why it appeals to you.

Chapter 34/Lesson 1

Draw a floor plan of your house. Show where the smoke alarms are located. Show where the exits are.

List the rules for dealing with a fire in your house.

Show how you would escape from your house from any room if there were a fire.

Take a floor plan home and have all members of your family study it and sign it.

Try a practice emergency escape drill.

Chapter 35/Lesson 3

Pass a practical test on treating an injury such as a sprain, burn, or fracture.

Chapter 36/Lesson 2

Get a CPR certificate.

ABC News InterActive Understanding Ourselves Health Series
Videodisc Correlation to *Glencoe Health*

Videodisc Chapter	Teenage Sexuality	Tobacco	Drugs and Substance Abuse	AIDS	Teenage Sexuality	Tobacco	Drugs and Substance Abuse	AIDS
		Videodisc SIDE 1				Videodisc SIDE 2		
3	9:1, 15:1-2*	22:1	19:3, 20:2, 21:2	28:1	1:2, 2:1-2	1:3, 6:2, 22:1, 32:1	24:1, 25:2, 33:1	28:1-2
4	15:2	13:4, 22:1	8:1, 13:4, 22:1-2, 23:1, 29:1, 3	13:3, 26:2, 28:1	6:1, 9:1	1:3, 6:1, 3, 22:2	5:2, 23:3, 25:1, 3-4	28:1-2
5	15:1	13:4, 22:1, 29:1, 3	8:1, 23:1-3, 25:1-2	9:2, 24:3, 26:2, 27:1, 28:1	6:1, 9:1	1:2-3, 6:1, 3, 22:2	8:1, 23:3, 25:2, 33:1	28:1-2
6	8:1, 15:1-2	22:1, 29:3	24:1, 3	28:1	5:2	22:1-2, 32:1	1:1-3, 6:2, 24:1	28:1-2
7	8:1, 15:2	22:1, 29:3	24:1-2, 28:1	27:1, 3, 28:1	5:2, 9:2	22:1-2, 24:1	1:1-2, 24:1, 3	1:1, 28:1-2
8	8:1	22:1, 29:3	18:2, 24:1, 3, 28:1	28:1	5:2, 9:2	13:4, 22:1-2, 29:1, 3	22:1, 23:2-3, 32:1	5:2, 6:1, 28:1-2
9	6:1, 10:1-2	13:4, 22:1-2, 29:1, 3	24:1, 3	28:1	6:2, 9:2	1:3, 5:2, 6:3, 22:2, 24:1	22:2, 24:3	2:3, 28:1-2
10	6:1, 9:1, 10:1-2	22:1-2, 32:1	24:1-2, 28:1	24:3, 28:1	1:3, 6:3, 27:1, 3, 28:1	13:4, 22:1, 24:1, 29:1, 3	24:3	28:1-2
11	28:2	22:1-2, 32:1	24:1-2	8:1, 28:1	6:3, 27:1, 3, 28:1	1:1-3, 6:2-3, 13:2, 22:1-2, 29:2-3	6:1-3, 22:2, 23:2, 24:3	9:2, 27:1, 28:1-2
12	7:2	22:1-2, 32:1	24:1-2	13:2, 28:1	34:4	6:1, 22:1-2	22:2, 23:2, 24:1	2:3, 28:1-2
13	27:3, 28:1	22:1, 29:3	24:1, 3	28:1	6:1	1:2-3, 6:2-3, 22:2	4:1-2, 22:2, 24:1	10:4, 28:2
14	7:1-2, 8:1, 9:2	1:3, 22:2, 31:2	24:1-2	9:2, 26:2, 27:1, 28:1	1:3, 9:2, 27:1, 3, 28:1	1:2-3, 6:3, 22:2	1:2, 6:1, 3, 22:2, 23:2, 24:1, 3	9:1, 10:4, 28:2
15	8:1-2	22:1, 32:1	24:1, 25:1-4	26:2-3, 28:1	1:3, 8:1, 9:2, 27:1, 3, 28:1	1:2-3, 6:3, 22:1-2	1:2, 22:2, 23:2, 24:3	28:1-2
16	7:1-2, 8:1, 9:2	22:1, 32:1-2		28:1-2	1:3, 6:2	1:2-3, 6:3, 22:2	1:2, 22:2, 23:2, 24:3	27:1, 28:1
17	7:1-2, 9:2			28:1-2	7:1-2, 8:1	1:2-3, 6:3, 22:1-2	1:1-2, 22:2, 23:2, 24:3	27:1, 28:1
18	7:1-2, 9:2			28:1-2	15:1-2, 33:2	1:2-3, 6:3, 22:2	1:1-2, 22:2, 23:2, 24:3	6:1, 28:1
19	5:1, 7:2			28:2	7:1-2, 8:1, 15:1-2, 27:3, 28:1	1:2, 2:1, 3, 4:2, 22:2		
20	5:1, 7:2, 8:1, 9:2			28:1	7:1-2, 8:1, 27:3, 28:1	1:1, 22:2		
21				28:1				
22				28:2, 32:3, 33:1				
23				28:2				

*Correlated by chapter and lesson.

ABC News InterActive Teenage Sexuality

Videodisc Correlation to
Glencoe Health, Education in Sexuality, and *AIDS and Society*

Videodisc Chapter	Glencoe Health	Education in Sexuality	AIDS and Society	Glencoe Health	Education in Sexuality	AIDS and Society
		Videodisc SIDE 1			**Videodisc SIDE 2**	
3	9:1, 15:1-2*	2:2, 3:1-2		1:2, 2:1-2	1:1	
4	15:2	3:2		6:1, 9:1	1:1, 4:1-2	
5	15:1	3:1		6:1, 9:1	1:1, 4:1-2	
6	8:1, 15:1-2	3:1-2, 6:1		5:2	4:1	
7	8:1, 15:2	3:2, 6:1-2		5:2, 9:2	4:1	
8	8:1	6:2		5:2, 9:2	4:1	
9	6:1, 10:1-2	1:1, 4:1-2		6:2, 9:2	1:1, 4:2, 5:2, 7:1	
10	6:1, 9:1, 10:1-2	2:1, 4:1		1:3, 6:3, 27:1, 3, 28:1	1:1, 4:2, 5:2, 7:1, 8:1-2, 9:1	2:1-2, 3:1-2
11	28:2	1:1, 4:1-2		6:3, 27:1, 3, 28:1	4:2, 7:1, 8:1-2, 9:1	3:1
12	7:2	7:3		34:4	4:2	
13	27:3, 28:1	4:2, 8:1-2, 9:1	2:1-2, 3:1-2, 4:1-2, 5:1-2	6:1	4:1	
14	7:1-2, 8:1, 9:2	5:2, 7:1-3		1:3, 9:2, 27:1, 3, 28:1	1:1, 4:2, 5:2, 7:1, 8:1-2, 9:1	3:1
15	8:1-2	6:1-2		1:3, 8:1, 9:2, 27:1, 3, 28:1	4:2, 5:2, 7:1, 8:1-2, 9:1	2:1-2, 3:1-2
16	7:1-2, 8:1, 9:2	5:1-2, 7:1		1:3, 6:2	1:1, 4:2, 7:1, 8:1-2, 9:1	3:1
17	7:1-2, 9:2	5:1-2, 7:1		7:1-2, 8:1	7:1-2, 8:1-2, 9:1	3:1-2
18	7:1-2, 9:2	5:2, 7:1-2		15:1-2, 33:2	6:1-2, 7:1-2	4:1, 5:1
19	5:1, 7:2	5:1-2		7:1-2, 8:1, 27:3, 28:1	3:1-2, 7:1-2	3:1-2
20	5:1, 7:2, 8:1, 9:2	5:2, 7:3		7:1-2, 8:1, 27:3, 28:1	7:1-2	3:1-2

*Correlated by chapter and lesson.

**Videodiscs available from Optical Data.
See page T26 for ordering information.**

ABC News InterActive AIDS

Videodisc Correlation to

Glencoe Health, Education in Sexuality, and AIDS and Society

Videodisc Chapter	Glencoe Health	Education in Sexuality	AIDS and Society	Glencoe Health	Education in Sexuality	AIDS and Society
	Videodisc SIDE 1			Videodisc SIDE 2		
3	28:1*	9:1-2	1:1-2	28:1-2	9:1-2	2:2, 4:2, 5:1
4	13:3, 26:2, 28:1	9:1	1:1-2	28:1-2	9:1-2	2:2, 4:2, 5:1
5	9:2, 24:3, 26:2, 27:1, 28:1	9:1	2:1-2	28:1-2	9:1-2	2:2, 4:2, 5:1
6	28:1	9:1	2:2	28:1-2	9:1-2	2:2, 4:2, 5:1
7	27:1, 3, 28:1	4:2, 7:1-3, 8:1-2, 9:1	3:1-2	1:1, 28:1-2	9:1-2	4:2, 5:1
8	28:1	7:2, 8:1, 9:1	3:2	5:2, 6:1, 28:1-2	4:1, 9:1-2	4:2, 5:1
9	28:1	7:3, 8:1, 9:1	2:2, 3:2	2:3, 28:1-2	9:1-2	4:2, 5:1
10	24:3, 28:1	9:1	2:2	28:1-2	9:1-2	2:2, 4:2, 5:1
11	8:1, 28:1	8:1, 9:1	2:2	9:2, 27:1, 28:1-2	4:2, 7:1-3, 8:1-2, 9:1	3:1-2, 4:2, 5:1
12	13:2, 28:1	9:1	2:2	2:3, 28:1-2	9:1-2	2:2, 4:2, 5:1
13	28:1	9:1	2:2	10:4, 28:2	9:1-2	4:2, 5:1-2
14	9:2, 26:2, 27:1, 28:1	8:1, 9:1	2:2	9:1, 10:4, 28:2	9:1-2	4:2, 5:1-2
15	26:2-3, 28:1	9:1-2	4:2, 5:1	28:1-2	4:2, 7:1, 8:1-2, 9:1	5:1-2
16	28:1-2	9:1-2	4:1, 5:1-2	27:1, 28:1	7:2, 9:1	3:2
17	28:1-2	9:1-2	2:2, 4:1-2	27:1, 28:1	1:1, 4:1-2, 7:1-2, 9:1	3:1-2
18	28:1-2	9:1-2	2:2, 4:1-2	6:1, 28:1	4:1-2, 7:3, 9:1	3:1
19	28:2	9:1-2	2:1, 4:1-2			
20	28:1	9:1-2	2:2, 4:1			
21	28:1	9:1	2:2			
22	28:2, 32:3, 33:1	9:2	5:1-2			
23	28:2	9:1-2	5:1			

* Correlated by chapter and lesson.

**Videodiscs available from Optical Data.
See page T26 for ordering information.**

A variety of health organizations and agencies can serve as resources for your health education classes. Many organizations provide speakers on various health topics or offer resource materials, such as pamphlets, posters, videos, and software.

Students can enhance oral and written communication skills by participating in community activities sponsored by health organizations and agencies. Students may correspond with these organizations to request information and literature. Consider encouraging your district to require community involvement as a high school graduation requirement.

Unit 1 You and Your Health

ERIC-Clearinghouse on Teacher Education-Health Education
One Dupont Circle, N.W.
Washington, DC 20036

National Health Council
622 Third Avenue
New York, NY 10017

World Health Organization
Avenue Appia CH-1211
Geneva 27, Switzerland

Unit 2 Mental Health

Mental Health Materials Center
P.O. Box 304
Bronxville, NY 10708

National Association for Mental Health
1790 Broadway
New York, NY 10010

National Clearinghouse for Mental Health Information
5600 Fishers Lane
Rockville, MD 20857

National Mental Health Association
1021 Prince Street
Alexandria, VA 22314

Unit 3 Family and Social Health

American Institute on Family Relations
5287 Sunset Blvd.
Los Angeles, CA 90027

Parents Anonymous
7120 Franklin Avenue
Los Angeles, CA 90046

Parents' Magazine
685 Third Avenue
New York, NY 10017

Unit 4 The Life Cycle

Cystic Fibrosis Foundation
6931 Arlington Road
Bethesda, MD 20814

March of Dimes Birth Defects Foundation
1275 Mamaroneck Avenue
White Plains, NY 10605

National Center for Education in Maternal and Child Health
38th and R Streets, N.W.
Washington, DC 20057

National Council on the Aging
600 Maryland Avenue, S.W.
Suite 100
Washington, DC 20024

National Easter Seal Society
70 East Lake Street
Chicago, IL 60601

National Genetics Foundation
180 West 58th Street
New York, NY 10019

Unit 5 Body Systems

Alzheimer's Disease and Related Disorders Association
70 E. Lake Street, Suite 600
Chicago, IL 60601

American Lung Association
1740 Broadway
New York, NY 10019

The Association for Retarded Citizens of the United States
2501 Avenue L
Arlington, Texas 76006

Asthma and Allergy Foundation of America
1717 Massachusetts Avenue,
Suite 305
Washington, DC 20036

Epilepsy Foundation of America
4351 Garden City Drive
Landover, MD 20785

The Muscular Dystrophy Association, Inc.
810 Seventh Avenue
New York, NY 10019

National Digestive Diseases Information Clearinghouse
Box NDDIC
Bethesda, MD 20892

National Hemophilia Foundation
110 Green Street, Room 406
New York, NY 10012

National Kidney Foundation
Two Park Avenue
New York, NY 10016

National Multiple Sclerosis Society
205 East 42nd Street
New York, NY 10017

United Cerebral Palsy Associations
66 East 34th Street
New York, NY 10016

Unit 6 Personal Health and Physical Fitness

American Dental Association
211 East Chicago Avenue
Chicago, IL 60611

American Foundation for the Blind
15 West 16th Street
New York, NY 10011

American Optometric Association
243 North Lindbergh
St. Louis, MO 63141

American Physical Fitness Research Institute
824 Moraga Drive
Los Angeles, CA 90049

Amputee Sports Association
11705 Mercy Boulevard
Savannah, Ga 31406

National Handicapped Sports and Recreation Association
Capitol Hill Station
P.O. Box 18664
Denver, CO 80218

National Society to Prevent Blindness
500 East Remington Road
Schaumburg, IL 60173

National Wheelchair Athletic Association
2107 Templeton Gap Road
Suite C
Colorado Springs, CO 80907

President's Council on Physical Fitness and Sports
450 5th Street, N.W.
Suite 7103
Washington, DC 20001

Unit 7 Nutrition

American Anorexia/Bulimia Association
418 E. 76th Street
New York, NY 10021

American Dietetic Association
216 W. Jackson Blvd., Suite 800
Chicago, IL 60606

American Institute of Nutrition
9650 Rockville Pike
Bethesda, MD 20814

Food and Nutrition Information and Education Resources Center
National Agricultural Library
U.S. Department of Agriculture
10301 Baltimore Blvd. Room 304
Beltsville, MD 20705

National Council on Obesity
P.O. Box 350306
Los Angeles, CA 90035

National Dairy Council
6300 North River Road
Rosemont, IL 60018

Nutrition Education Association
P.O. Box 20301
3647 Glen Haven
Houston, TX 77225

U.S. Food and Drug Administration
Public Health Service
A-V Facility
60 Eighth Street, N.E.
Atlanta, GA 30309

Unit 8 Medicines and Drugs

Al-Anon Family Group Headquarters, Inc.
1372 Broadway
New York, NY 10018

Alcoholics Anonymous World Services
Box 459
Grand Central Station
New York, NY 10163

Food and Drug Administration
5600 Fishers Lane
Rockville, MD 20857

Mothers Against Drunk Driving
511 E. John Carpenter Freeway
Irving, TX 75062

Narcotics Education, Inc.
12501 Old Columbia Pike
Silver Spring, MD 20904

National Council on Alcoholism
12 West 21st Street
New York, NY 10010

National Federation of Parents for Drug-Free Youth
1423 N. Jefferson
Springfield, MO 65802

Parents' Resource Institute for Drug Education
100 Edgewood Avenue
Suite 1210
Atlanta, GA 30303

Students Against Driving Drunk
P.O. Box 800
Marlboro, MA 01752

Unit 9 Diseases and Disorders

American Cancer Society
90 Park Avenue
New York, NY 10016

American Diabetes Association
P.O. Box 25757
1660 Duke Street
Alexandria, VA 22313

American Foundation for AIDS Research
40 W. 57th Street
New York, NY 10019

American Heart Association
7320 Greenville Avenue
Dallas, TX 75231

American Social Health Association
260 Sheridan Avenue, Suite 307
Palo Alto, CA 94306

Arthritis Foundation
1314 Spring Street, N.W.
Atlanta, GA 30309

Arthritis Information Clearinghouse
P.O. Box 9782
Arlington, VA 22009

Leukemia Society of America
733 Third Avenue
New York, NY 10017

National Cancer Institute
National Cancer Information Center
Bloch Building, No. 82
Bethesda, MD 20892

National Diabetes Information Clearinghouse
Box NDIC
Bethesda, MD 20892

National Institute of Allergy and Infectious Diseases
Information Office Room 7A-32
Building 31
Bethesda, MD 20014

Unit 10 Community and Environmental Health

Atomic Energy Commission
P.O. Box 62
Oak Ridge, TN 37830

Council on Environmental Quality
722 Jackson Place, N.W.
Washington, DC 20006

National Wildlife Federation
1412 16th Street, N.W.
Washington, DC 20006

Nuclear Regulatory Commission
1717 H Street, N.W.
Washington, DC 10555

Public Health Service, Environmental Health Service, U.S. Department of Health and Human Services
Rockville, MD 20857

Sierra Club
703 Polk Street
San Francisco, CA 94109

Unit 11 Consumer Health

American Insurance Association
Engineering and Safety Service
85 John Street
New York, NY 10038

American Medical Association
535 North Dearborn Street
Chicago, IL 60610

Consumer Information Center
P.O. Box 100
Pueblo, CO 81002

Consumer Product Safety Commission
5401 Westbard Avenue
Washington, DC 20207

Household Finance Corporation
625 North Michigan Avenue
Chicago, IL 60611

Public Inquiries Branch
Office of Information
U.S. Public Health Services
Washington, DC 20201

Unit 12 Safety and Emergency Care

American Red Cross
17th and D Streets, S.W.
Washington, DC 20006

National Center for Missing and Exploited Children
1835 K Street, N.W.
Suite 700
Washington, DC 20006

National Fire Protection Association
Batterymarch Park
Quincy, MA 02269

National Safety Council
444 North Michigan Avenue
Chicago, IL 60611

GLENCOE

Health

A Guide to Wellness

FOURTH EDITION

Mary Bronson Merki, Ph.D.

Don Merki, Ph.D.

Contributing Authors
Eddye Eubanks, Ph.D.
Gale Cornelia Flynn
Charlotte Sorrel

GLENCOE
Macmillan/McGraw-Hill

New York, New York   Columbus, Ohio   Mission Hills, California   Peoria, Illinois

CONFLICT RESOLUTION

Jean M. Brainard, Ph.D.
Consulting Medical Anthropologist
Fredericktown, Ohio

CULTURALLY SPEAKING

Karen Muir, Ph.D.
Instructor
Columbus State Community College
Columbus, Ohio

HELP WANTED

Rich Smith, M.S.
Director of Guidance
Westerville North High School
Westerville, Ohio

PERFORMANCE ASSESSMENT

K. Michael Hibbard, Ph.D.
Assistant Superintendent
Pomperaug Regional School District 15
Middlebury, Connecticut

Susan E. Kurtain
Thinking Skills Teacher
Bleyl Junior High School
Houston, Texas

Send all inquiries to:
Glencoe Division, Macmillan/McGraw-Hill
936 Eastwind Drive
Westerville, Ohio 43081

ISBN: 0-02-652600-X (Student Text)
ISBN: 0-02-652602-6 (Teacher's Wraparound Edition)
Printed in the United States of America

3 4 5 6 7 8 9 VH 99 98 97 96 95 94

MENTAL HEALTH

Rodney Page
Health Teacher
McNeil High School
Austin, Texas

Roger F. Puza
Health Educator
Central High School
LaCrosse, Wisconsin

FAMILY AND SOCIAL HEALTH

Gayle S. Jenkins
Health Education Program Specialist
Wake County Public School System
Raleigh, North Carolina

George E. Serednesky, Ph.D.
Psychologist
Child and Adult Guidance Center
Columbus, Ohio

THE LIFE CYCLE

Charles Balling
Superintendent of Leisure Services
Elmhurst Park District
Elmhurst, Illinois

Michael E. Childers, Ph.D.
Health and Physical Education Teacher
Clifton Middle School
Houston, Texas

BODY SYSTEMS

Bernadette L. Norris
Health and Physical Education Teacher
Lake View High School
Chicago, Illinois

PERSONAL HEALTH and PHYSICAL FITNESS

Doug Monaghen
Coordinator of Health Education
Alief Independent School District
Alief, Texas

Tinker D. Murray, Ph.D.
Associate Professor
Department of Health, Physical Education,
and Recreation
Southwest Texas State University
San Marcos, Texas

Don Rainey
Department Head, Physical Education and Health
Edward Marcus High School
Flower Mound, Texas

Rudiger K. Zimmerman
Health and Physical Education Department Chair
Gar-Field High School
Woodbridge, Virginia

NUTRITION

Roberta Duyff
Nutrition Education Consultant
Duyff Associates
St. Louis, Missouri

MEDICINES and DRUGS

John R. Lauritsen, Ph.D.
Community Relations Representative
Parkside Lodge of Columbus
Columbus, Ohio

Michael D. McNeer, M.D.
Associate Medical Director
Parkside Lodge of Columbus
Columbus, Ohio

Sandy Moreland
*Drug Education, Health and
Physical Education Teacher*
Arsenal Technical High School
Indianapolis, Indiana

Richard C. Rapp
Project Director
Substance Abuse Intervention Programs
Wright State University School of Medicine
Dayton, Ohio

Dolores Salazar
Health Educator
Homer Hanna High School
Brownsville, Texas

DISEASES and DISORDERS

Nita Auer
Health Educator
North Side High School
Fort Wayne, Indiana

Susan A. Tilgner
Epidemiologist
Columbus Health Department
Columbus, Ohio

COMMUNITY and ENVIRONMENTAL HEALTH

Charles Balling
Superintendent of Leisure Services
Elmhurst Park District
Elmhurst, Illinois

CONSUMER HEALTH

Robert D. Barrett
Administrative Resident
Prison Health Services
Xavier University
New Castle, Delaware

SAFETY and EMERGENCY CARE

Denise J.K. Abbott
Teacher, Registered Nurse
Timpriew High School
Provo, Utah

Lynn Gustafson Haley
Health Teacher
Mackenzie Junior High
Lubbock, Texas

Debra McMillan
Health and Physical Education Teacher
Douglas Byrd Junior High School
Fayetteville, North Carolina

MULTICULTURAL EDUCATION

Addie E. Pettaway
Education Consultant
Madison, Wisconsin

C O N T E N T S

UNIT 1: YOU AND YOUR HEALTH

CHAPTER 1: YOUR HEALTH 2

Lesson 1 Your Health, Your Responsibility 3

Lesson 2 Self-Esteem and Your Health 10

Overcoming The Odds 11

Lesson 3 Decision Making and Health 16

Self-Inventory 22

Building Decision-Making Skills 23

Chapter Review 24

UNIT 2: MENTAL HEALTH

CHAPTER 2: MENTAL HEALTH 26

Lesson 1 What Is Mental Health?......... 27

Overcoming The Odds...................... 29

Lesson 2 Understanding Your Needs, Understanding Personality 32

Lesson 3 Understanding Emotions........37

Self-Inventory 44

Building Decision-Making Skills 45

Chapter Review 46

CHAPTER 3: MENTAL DISORDERS AND MENTAL HEALTH 48

Lesson 1 What Are Mental Disorders? 49

Lesson 2 Knowing When Someone Needs Help 55

Overcoming The Odds 57

Self-Inventory 60

Building Decision-Making Skills 61

Chapter Review 62

CHAPTER 4: STRESS IN YOUR LIFE 64

Lesson 1 What Is Stress?......................65

Overcoming The Odds 68

Lesson 2 Coping With Stress 72

Self-Inventory 78

Building Decision-Making Skills...........79

Chapter Review 80

C O N T E N T S

UNIT 3: FAMILY AND SOCIAL HEALTH

CHAPTER 5: YOU AND YOUR FAMILY 82

Lesson 1 Looking at Today's Families 83

Lesson 2 Looking at the Health of the Family 89

Overcoming The Odds 94

Self-Inventory 96

Building Decision-Making Skills 97

Chapter Review 98

CHAPTER 6: YOUR RELATIONSHIPS WITH OTHERS 100

Lesson 1 The Need for Others..............101

Overcoming The Odds.........................104

Lesson 2 The Effects of Violence........106

Lesson 3 Building Healthy Relationships.......................111

Self-Inventory......................................114

Building Decision-Making Skills 115

Chapter Review 116

CHAPTER 7: MARRIAGE AND PARENTHOOD 118

Lesson 1 Marriage 119

Lesson 2 Parenthood............................125

Overcoming The Odds.........................130

Self-Inventory......................................132

Building Decision-Making Skills 133

Chapter Review 134

C O N T E N T S

UNIT 4: THE LIFE CYCLE

CHAPTER 8: THE BEGINNING OF THE LIFE CYCLE 136

Lesson 1 Before Birth..........................137

Lesson 2 Heredity and Genetics 144

Overcoming The Odds........................149

Lesson 3 Birth to Late Childhood 151

Self-Inventory.....................................154

Building Decision-Making Skills 155

Chapter Review..................................156

CHAPTER 9: ADOLESCENCE 158

Lesson 1 A Time of Growth and Change..................................159

Overcoming The Odds........................162

Lesson 2 A Time for Understanding Yourself..................................164

Self-Inventory.....................................170

Building Decision-Making Skills 171

Chapter Review..................................172

CHAPTER 10: CONTINUING THROUGH THE LIFE CYCLE 174

Lesson 1 Growth for a Lifetime...........175

Lesson 2 Young and Middle Adulthood 178

Lesson 3 Late Adulthood and Aging...182

Overcoming The Odds........................184

Lesson 4 Death—Part of the Life Cycle 187

Self-Inventory.....................................192

Building Decision-Making Skills 193

Chapter Review..................................194

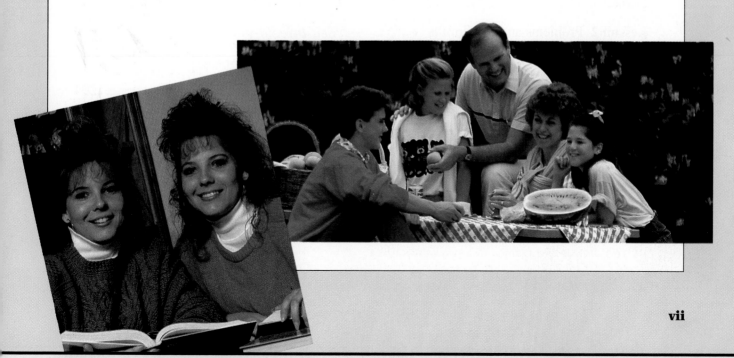

CONTENTS

UNIT 5: BODY SYSTEMS

CHAPTER 11: INTEGUMENTARY, SKELETAL, AND MUSCULAR SYSTEMS......196

Lesson 1 The Integumentary System...197

Lesson 2 The Skeletal System 204

Lesson 3 The Muscular System...........210

Overcoming The Odds 214

Self-Inventory 216

Building Decision-Making Skills 217

Chapter Review 218

CHAPTER 12: THE NERVOUS AND ENDOCRINE SYSTEMS 220

Lesson 1 The Nervous System 221

Overcoming The Odds 227

Lesson 2 Problems and Care of the Nervous System....................231

Lesson 3 The Endocrine System 238

Self-Inventory 244

Building Decision-Making Skills 245

Chapter Review 246

CHAPTER 13: CARDIOVASCULAR, LYMPHATIC, AND RESPIRATORY SYSTEMS 248

Lesson 1 The Cardiovascular System 249

Overcoming The Odds 253

Lesson 2 Problems and Care of the Cardiovascular System 256

Lesson 3 The Lymphatic System.........262

Lesson 4 The Respiratory System.......265

Self-Inventory 270

Building Decision-Making Skills 271

Chapter Review 272

CHAPTER 14: DIGESTIVE AND URINARY SYSTEMS 274

Lesson 1 The Digestive System...........275

Lesson 2 Problems and Care of the Digestive System..................282

Overcoming The Odds 284

Lesson 3 The Urinary System 288

Self-Inventory 292

Building Decision-Making Skills 293

Chapter Review 294

CHAPTER 15: THE REPRODUCTIVE SYSTEMS 296

Lesson 1 The Male Reproductive System 297

Lesson 2 The Female Reproductive System 302

Overcoming The Odds 307

Self-Inventory 310

Building Decision-Making Skills 311

Chapter Review 312

C O N T E N T S

UNIT 6: PERSONAL HEALTH AND PHYSICAL FITNESS

CHAPTER 16: PERSONAL HEALTH 314

Lesson 1 Teeth and Mouth..................315

Lesson 2 Eyes 319

Overcoming The Odds.....................323

Lesson 3 Ears................................326

Self-Inventory...............................332

Building Decision-Making Skills 333

Chapter Review.............................334

CHAPTER 17: FITNESS AND YOUR HEALTH 336

Lesson 1 The Benefits of Fitness.........337

Overcoming The Odds.........................339

Lesson 2 Exercise and Physical
Fitness 342

Self-Inventory...............................348

Building Decision-Making Skills 349

Chapter Review.............................350

CHAPTER 18: GETTING FIT AND STAYING FIT 352

Lesson 1 Beginning an Exercise
Program..............................353

Lesson 2 Avoiding Injury 360

Overcoming The Odds.........................364

Self-Inventory...............................366

Building Decision-Making Skills 367

Chapter Review.............................368

C O N T E N T S

UNIT 7: NUTRITION

CHAPTER 19: MAKING RESPONSIBLE FOOD CHOICES **370**

Lesson 1 Your Need for Food..............371

Overcoming The Odds........................374

Lesson 2 Your Body's Need for
Nutrients.............................376

Lesson 3 Choosing a Healthy Diet 385

Lesson 4 Being a Wise Food
Consumer 393

Self-Inventory....................................398

Building Decision-Making Skills 399

Chapter Review..................................400

CHAPTER 20: AVOIDING PROBLEMS WITH FOODS **402**

Lesson 1 Weight Control 403

Lesson 2 Eating Disorders and Sports
Nutrition..............................411

Overcoming The Odds........................414

Lesson 3 Food and Your Safety 416

Self-Inventory....................................420

Building Decision-Making Skills........421

Chapter Review 422

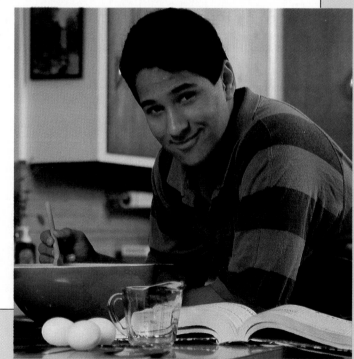

CONTENTS

UNIT 8: MEDICINES AND DRUGS

CHAPTER 21: UNDERSTANDING MEDICINES 424

Lesson 1 How Medicines Help............425

Lesson 2 Medicines and the
Consumer 430

Overcoming The Odds........................434

Self-Inventory......................................436

Building Decision-Making Skills 437

Chapter Review..................................438

CHAPTER 22: TOBACCO 440

Lesson 1 Problems for the Tobacco
User 441

Overcoming The Odds........................445

Lesson 2 Choosing Not to Smoke 448

Self-Inventory......................................454

Building Decision-Making Skills 455

Chapter Review..................................456

CHAPTER 23: ALCOHOL 458

Lesson 1 Alcohol: A Physical
Problem.................................459

Lesson 2 Alcohol: A Mental and
Social Problem......................463

Overcoming The Odds........................466

Lesson 3 Alcohol: A Serious
Problem 468

Self-Inventory......................................474

Building Decision-Making Skills 475

Chapter Review..................................476

CHAPTER 24: ILLEGAL DRUGS 478

Lesson 1 Costs and Problems of
Drug Use 479

Overcoming The Odds........................480

Lesson 2 Psychoactive Drugs 483

Lesson 3 Other Dangerous Drugs........488

Self-Inventory......................................492

Building Decision-Making Skills 493

Chapter Review..................................494

CHAPTER 25:RECOVERING FROM ADDICTION AND CODEPENDENCY 496

Lesson 1 Addiction: What Is It? 497

Overcoming The Odds........................499

Lesson 2 Recovering from Addiction 501

Lesson 3 Codependency: What Is It? 506

Lesson 4 Recovering from
Codependency 509

Self-Inventory......................................512

Building Decision-Making Skills 513

Chapter Review..................................514

C O N T E N T S

UNIT 9: DISEASES AND DISORDERS

CHAPTER 26: COMMUNICABLE DISEASES **516**

Lesson 1 Causes of Communicable Diseases 517

Overcoming The Odds 520

Lesson 2 Body Defenses Against Communicable Diseases 522

Lesson 3 Preventing Communicable Diseases 527

Self-Inventory 532

Building Decision-Making Skills 533

Chapter Review 534

CHAPTER 27: SEXUALLY TRANSMITTED DISEASES **536**

Lesson 1 Gonorrhea 537

Lesson 2 Syphilis 540

Lesson 3 Other Common STDs 544

Overcoming The Odds 548

Self-Inventory 550

Building Decision-Making Skills 551

Chapter Review 552

CHAPTER 28: AIDS **554**

Lesson 1 A Deadly Disease 555

Overcoming The Odds 557

Lesson 2 Testing for HIV Infection 560

Self-Inventory 564

Building Decision-Making Skills 565

Chapter Review 566

CHAPTER 29: NONCOMMUNICABLE DISEASES **568**

Lesson 1 Cardiovascular Diseases 569

Lesson 2 Treating and Preventing Heart Disease 575

Lesson 3 Cancer 579

Overcoming The Odds 584

Lesson 4 Diabetes 586

Lesson 5 Arthritis 589

Self-Inventory 592

Building Decision-Making Skills 593

Chapter Review 594

UNIT 10: COMMUNITY AND ENVIRONMENTAL HEALTH

CHAPTER 30: GLOBAL ENVIRONMENTAL ISSUES 596

Lesson 1 Air and Water 597

Self-Inventory 610

Lesson 2 Land....................................604

Building Decision-Making Skills 611

Overcoming The Odds......................608

Chapter Review..................................612

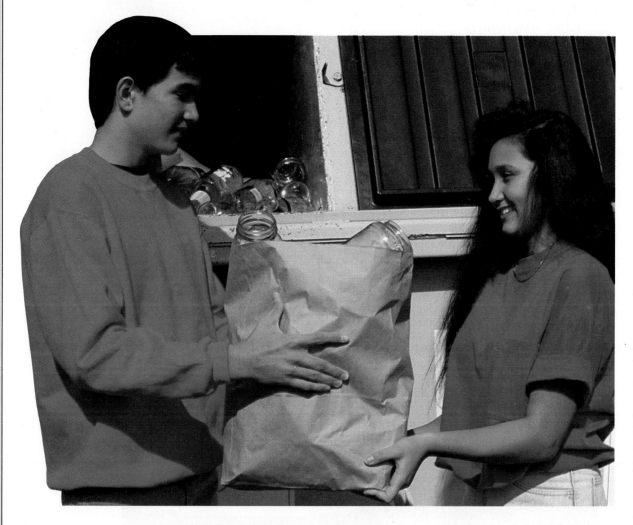

CHAPTER 31: PROTECTING YOUR ENVIRONMENT 614

Lesson 1 Reducing Waste....................615

Overcoming The Odds 623

Lesson 2 Being Informed and Involved..............................622

Self-Inventory 628

Building Decision-Making Skills 629

Chapter Review 630

C O N T E N T S

UNIT 11: CONSUMER HEALTH

CHAPTER 32: YOU, THE HEALTH CONSUMER 632

Lesson 1 What Is Consumer Health?...633

Overcoming The Odds........................636

Lesson 2 Fraud in the Marketplace......638

Lesson 3 Handling Consumer
Problems..............................641

Self-Inventory....................................648

Building Decision-Making Skills.........649

Chapter Review..................................650

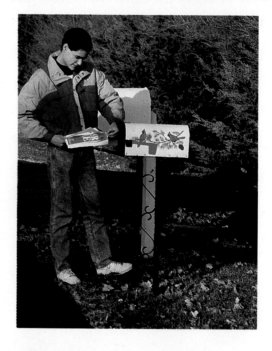

CHAPTER 33: HEALTH SERVICES AND HEALTH CARE 652

Lesson 1 What Are Health Services? 653

Overcoming The Odds........................657

Lesson 2 Seeking Health Care.............659

Self-Inventory....................................666

Building Decision-Making Skills 667

Chapter Review..................................668

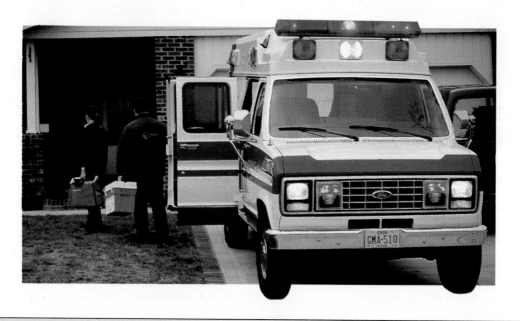

C O N T E N T S

UNIT 12: SAFETY AND EMERGENCY CARE

CHAPTER 34: YOUR SAFETY AND WELL-BEING 670

Lesson 1 Safety at Home 671

Lesson 2 Safety Away from Home 676

Overcoming The Odds 678

Lesson 3 Safety on Wheels.................680

Lesson 4 Personal Safety....................683

Self-Inventory 688

Building Decision-Making Skills 689

Chapter Review 690

CHAPTER 35: FIRST AID 692

Lesson 1 Administering First Aid........693

Overcoming The Odds 696

Lesson 2 First Aid for Poisoning.........698

Lesson 3 First Aid for Other Injuries   703

Self-Inventory 710

Building Decision-Making Skills 711

Chapter Review 712

CHAPTER 36: HANDLING EMERGENCIES 714

Lesson 1 Acting in an Emergency 715

Overcoming The Odds 719

Lesson 2 Cardiopulmonary
Resuscitation........................721

Self-Inventory 726

Building Decision-Making Skills 727

Chapter Review 728

GLOSSARY 730

SPANISH GLOSSARY 743

INDEX 759

SPECIAL FEATURES

CONFLICT RESOLUTION

Self-Esteem 13
Homeless 41
Schizophrenia 52
Riots 70
Family Separation 85
Arguments with Relatives 113
Changing Family Roles 126
Down Syndrome 148
Discussing a Problem 167
Dealing with the Death of a Parent 188
Tanning 202
Epilepsy 235
Heart Disease 261
Living With a Family Member
  With a Disability 290
Breast Cancer 309
Impaired Hearing 330
Exercise 343
Cool Down 354
Right-to-Know Law 395
Fat Self-Image 412
Encouraging Companies to
  Find Treatments 431
Passive Smoke 442
Alcohol in Advertising 467
Drug Dealer 490
Child of an Alcoholic 510
Protecting Others from Pathogens 526
Syphilis 543
HIV Infection 556
Having Cancer 581
Lead Paint 598
Effects of Pollution 624
Consumer Problem 646
Being Sick when Alone 664
Camping Safety 679
Dressing for the Cold 707
CPR 720

Overcoming The Odds

Living in a Shelter 11
Former Runaway 29
Reformed Juvenile Delinquent 57
Suicide Attempt Survivor 68
Incest Survivor 94
Former Gang Member 104
Living in a Stepfamily 130
A Family's Experience with
  Leigh's Disease 149
Being a Successful Teenager 162
92-year-old Marathon Runner 184
Living with Muscular Dystrophy 214
Surviving a Motorcycle Accident 227
A Family Recovers from a Mother's
  Heart Attack 253
Living with Diabetes 284
Coping with Miscarriages 307
Succeeding with Blindness 323
Balancing Time Commitments 339
Dealing with a Sports Injury 364
Daily Life with Celiac Sprue Disease ... 374
Struggling with Bulimia 414
A Family Copes with ALD 434
Quitting Smoking 445
Choosing not to Drink Alcohol 466
Helping a Friend who is
  Using Steroids 480
A Family Struggles with Alcoholism ... 499
Living with the Effects of Polio 520
Living with Genital Herpes 548
Having AIDS 557
Surviving Leukemia 584
Discipline Leads to Environmental
  Interest 608
Kids Against Pollution 623
Trying to Obtain Health Insurance 636
Balancing Family Practice with
  Family Life 657

Dealing with the Effects of a
   Broken Neck 678
Surviving Electrocution 696
Gaining Confidence in Using
   Safety Skills 719

Self-Inventory

What Is Your Level of Wellness?.............22
Rate Your Mental Health 44
Coping with Mental Disorders................60
Stress—The Danger Signals 78
You and Your Family 96
Are You a Good Listener?.....................114
Will You Be an Effective Parent? 132
Development During the Early Years:
   Are You in Touch? 154
Developmental Tasks 170
Are You Up-to-Date About
   the Elderly? 192
Care of Your Integumentary, Skeletal,
   and Muscular Systems 216
Care of the Nervous System 244
Care of the Cardiovascular and
   Respiratory Systems............................270
Care of the Digestive and
   Urinary Systems...................................292
Care of the Reproductive System 310
Your Personal Health 332
Figuring Out Your Fitness.....................348
Aerobic Alternatives 366
Making Healthy Food Choices 398
How Do You Manage Your Weight? 420
Using Medicines Carefully 436
Are You Passive About
   Passive Smoke?...................................454
Are You in Trouble with Alcohol?........474
What Is Your Attitude About
   Drug Use? 492

How Codependent Are You? 512
Your Disease-Prevention Efforts...........532
STDs: Where Do You Stand? 550
Are You at Risk? 564
Risky Business!......................................592
Environmental Alert Checklist 610
Are You Involved in Protecting
   the Environment?................................628
Are You a Wise Consumer?..................648
Are You an Advocate for Your
   Own Health? 666
Staying Safe 688
Emergency Behaviors and Attitudes.....710
Are You a Lifesaver? 726

HEALTH UPDATE

Health-Risk Appraisal...............................5
Emotions and the Brain...........................35
Who Has the Right to Prescribe?............54
Biofeedback 77
Should Adoptions Be Open
   or Closed? 87
Violence on Television..........................110
Should People Have Prenuptial
   Agreements? 120
Fetal Surgery: Surgery Before Birth 140
What Should Be Done About
   Weapons in Schools? 168
Medical Ethics 190
Arthroscopic Surgery 208
New Hope and Better Care 232
Some Heartening News
   About Hearts 260
How to Get Enough Organs for
   Transplants 290
Laparoscopy 308
Lasers: New Light on the Subject.........317
Biomechanics: Sports on a Screen........346

Magnetic Resonance Imaging...............358
How Much Meat Should We Eat?.........391
The Calorimeter 409
Generic Versus Brand-Name
　Medicines...428
The Debate Over the Sale of Tobacco
　to Minors...452
Alcohol, Advertising, and
　Adolescents...472
Drug Testing..490
Health Threats to Unborn Babies..........504
Should Animals Be Used for
　Medical Research?...............................525
Dangerous Liaisons: STDs
　and Lawsuits 541
Testing for HIV 562
Do Electromagnetic Fields
　Cause Cancer?.....................................582
The Ozone Layer....................................603
Jason, the Sludge-Detecting Robot.......621
Health Insurance 646
What's Coming In Health Care?...........664
DNA Banks: Genetic Information
　on File 686
Skin Banks: New Hope for
　Burn Patients.......................................708
Computerized Cardiac Defibrillators....723

Not Older, But Better 183
Skin Color and Vitamin D.....................198
Acupuncture...224
Hemoglobin, Malaria, and Sickle-
　Cell Anemia 259
Fiber from Many Cultures 277
Cross-cultural Cancer............................286
Sharing Pregnancy 303
Mixed Signals 324
Association Football 340
High Altitude Exercise..........................356
Foods on the World's Table...................375
Ice Cream Anyone?................................409
Dietary Cures 426
Toward a Smoke-free World 451
A Nonalcoholic Drink, Please...............464
Illegal Transport 486
Busted 503
Spreading Diseases 525
"Shadow" Disease 542
Attacking AIDS 561
Salt and Hypertension 570
Drip Irrigation 607
Reforestation Efforts.............................625
Foreign Language 635
Fighting Tuberculosis 658
Personal Space 685
Sandbox Trees..699
SIDS and Co-Sleeping 717

Culturally Speaking

So What Is Culture?.................................7
Knowing Your Heritage 31
Culture Shock...58
Working and Playing Worldwide............75
Multigenerational Families 84
One World, Many Tongues 105
What Does a Baby Need? 128
What's in a Name?................................138
Rites of Passage 160

HELP WANTED

Health Teacher 5
Social Worker...36
Psychiatrist...54
Guidance Counselor...............................76
Veterinarian..87
Coach 112

SPECIAL FEATURES

Childcare Assistant 127

Obstetrician 140

Teacher 168

Gerontologist......................................185

Prosthetics Technician 207

EEG Technician 234

Cardiology Technician........................260

Radiologic Technologist 279

Dialysis Technician.............................289

Gynecologist 304

Dental Hygienist 318

Optometric Technician........................320

Audiologist..327

Athletic Trainer...................................346

Physical Therapist Assistant 355

Exercise Physiologist..........................363

Dietician 390

Dietetic Technician 410

Pharmaceutical Sales Representative....435

Respiratory Therapist 447

Rehabilitation Counselor 471

Drug Enforcement Officer 491

Occupational Therapist........................504

Medical Laboratory Technician 518

Medical Illustrator...............................539

Epidemiologist 563

Surgeon 576

Marine Biologist 600

Environmentalist..................................626

Ombudsman 643

Surgical Technologist..........................661

Hospital Administrator.........................663

Licensed Practical Nurse......................672

Registered Nurse 694

Emergency Medical Technician
   (EMT) 723

FINDING HELP

Mental Health.......................................28

Mental Illness......................................53

Alcohol and Drug Use 74

Domestic Violence 92

Dwarfism..147

Healthy Skin.......................................200

Arthritis..209

Muscular Dystrophy............................212

Cerebral Palsy 222

Disorders of the Nervous System 233

Heart Disease 255

Breast Self-Exam 305

Closed-Captioned Programming...........328

Overeaters Anonymous........................415

Information About Medicines...............432

STAT 453

Alcohol...461

Chemical Dependence Coverage 489

Sierra Club 619

Tel-Med Tape Library 637

Resolving a Consumer Problem............644

CHAPTER 1

Overview

Lesson Summaries

LESSON 1. Health is the state of total well-being. While heredity and environment are health factors, your personal health is greatly influenced by the choices and decisions you make. To achieve a high level of health, you must balance physical, mental, and social aspects of your health.

LESSON 2. Self-esteem, one of the most important factors in your overall sense of well-being, is developed through both internal and external messages. High self-esteem results in a feeling of competence and healthy relationships. Low self-esteem allows others to influence you in negative ways. While everyone's level of self-esteem varies often, you can take steps to improve your perception of self.

LESSON 3. Each time you make a major decision, you exert power over how healthy, happy, and productive you may be for the rest of your life. That's why decision-making skills are so essential. A decision-making model can help you work through conflicts. It can help you recognize reasonable risks, consider the consequences of your choices, and make knowledgeable decisions.

Introducing the Chapter

Have students list the choices they have made in the last few days that have affected their health. Ask them to identify each choice as contributing to their physical, mental, or social well-being. Ask a few volunteers to share their lists with the class. Point out that the physical, mental, and social choices they make affect their overall level of health.

Performance Assessment ✓

Refer to pages T 23 to T 25 for a Performance Assessment strategy for this chapter. See the *Performance Assessment Activities* booklet for additional suggestions.

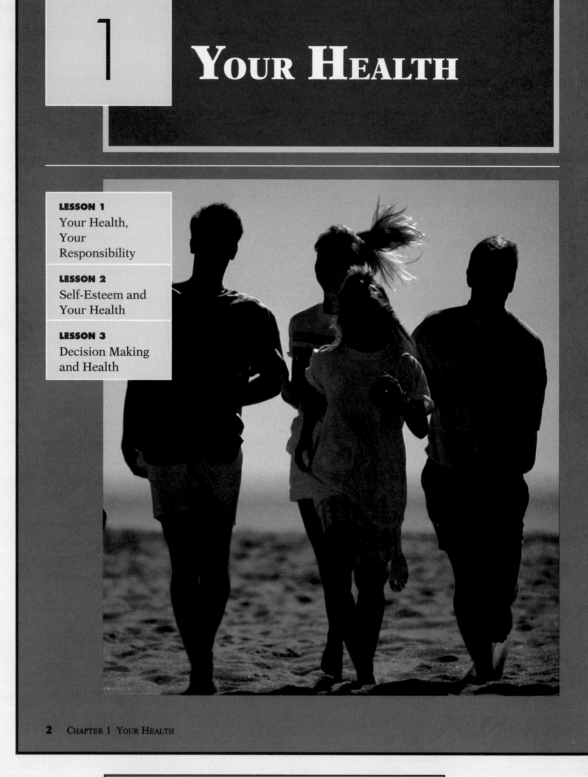

CHAPTER

1

YOUR HEALTH

LESSON 1
Your Health,
Your
Responsibility

LESSON 2
Self-Esteem and
Your Health

LESSON 3
Decision Making
and Health

Key to Ability Levels

Teaching strategies have been coded for varying learning styles and abilities.

L1 Level 1 activities are basic activities and should be within the ability range of all students.

L2 Level 2 activities are average activities and should be within the ability range of the average to above-average student.

L3 Level 3 activities are challenging activities designed for the ability range of above-average students.

LD LD activities should be within the ability range of learning-disabled students.

LEP LEP activities should be within the ability range of Limited English Proficiency students.

YOUR HEALTH, YOUR RESPONSIBILITY

Lesson Objectives

After studying this lesson, students should be able to:
- define health
- describe the importance of health education
- relate wellness to total health
- explain life-style factors

How do you feel this minute? Are you awake and alert? Do you have energy? Are you ready to face the day's challenges and stresses? Is your outlook generally upbeat? Are you happy to be alive?

What about yesterday? Did you eat well, exercise hard, get a good night's sleep? Did you spend time with people who make you feel good about yourself? Did you have a specific, positive goal that you worked at or achieved? Did you also find some time to relax, smile, and laugh?

Your answers to all of these questions may be a tip-off about your general level of health. Of course, you may be having an "off day." Everyone does sometimes. However, the health decisions you made yesterday or this morning may have more to do with how you feel this very minute than you suspect.

Taking Responsibility for Your Health

Imagine that the story of your health were made into a video. The video would portray your health from the day you were born until today. This video would show how well you felt and functioned at each stage of your life and how the health decisions you made along the way or that others made for you have affected your overall well-being.

Now imagine that you can keep adding to the video day after day, showing how the decisions you make today will affect your health tomorrow or how the decisions you make this year may affect the rest of your life. Do you like the way the story of your health is progressing?

The fact is that the remainder of the video—the story of your personal health for the rest of your life—is, for the most part, in your hands. True, there may be some factors influencing your health that are out of your control; but most of the choices and decisions affecting your health are yours to make. You, nobody else, are this video's director. So sit down in the director's chair, and get ready to take responsibility for your health—and your life.

The Many Definitions of Health

There are many ways to talk about health. The word *health* comes from an Old English word meaning "to make sound, whole, or well." Not surprisingly, it derives, or comes, from the same root as the word *heal.*

In the past the word *health* was defined as the absence of disease. Many people still think that if they are not sick, they are healthy. Others think that if they are physically fit or if they look good on the outside, they are healthy. Still others think they are healthy because they have never broken a bone, had stitches, or spent the night in the hospital. These definitions, however, are limited and inaccurate.

LESSON 1 FOCUS

TERMS TO USE
- Health
- Health education
- Wellness
- Holistic
- Life-style factors
- Quality of life
- Prevention

CONCEPTS TO LEARN
- Your health is your responsibility.
- Health education provides information to apply in all areas of your life.
- Your health is influenced by your life-style.

ATTITUDES AND BEHAVIORS TO EVALUATE
- Self-Inventory, page 22.
- Building Decision-Making Skills, page 23.

Bellringer

Write the following on the chalkboard for students to work on while attendance is being taken: *Write two choices you made in the last week that you think may have affected your health. Did the choices affect your health in a positive way or a negative way?*

Introducing the Lesson

Have volunteers share their responses for the Bellringer. As they read choices they have made in the past week, list their responses on the chalkboard. Go down the list an item at a time, and discuss with the class whether they agree that the choice could be a factor in a person's health. Ask students to explain their opinions.

Building Vocabulary

- Have students write a one- or two-line definition for health. Ask a few volunteers to share their definitions. Introduce the concept of wellness and have students point out similarities and differences between the two terms. Point out the historical perspective of health as definitions are discussed.
- Ask students to complete *Workbook Vocabulary Activity 1.*

YOUR HEALTH, YOUR RESPONSIBILITY **3**

Resources for Lesson 1

- **Transparencies** 1 and 2
- **Guided Reading** Activity 1
- **Workbook** Vocabulary Activity 1
- **Reteaching** Activity 1
- **Lesson 1 Quiz**
- **Posters** 1 and 2
- **Performance Assessment** Activity 1

DID YOU KNOW?

- "Sleeping like a log" implies total immobility. While many people say they don't move when sleeping, research has proved that all people toss and turn during the night. It's a good thing they do, because total immobility would result in circulatory problems.

Guided Practice

L1 DISCUSSION. Ask students to complete the following statement on a sheet of paper: *When you have good health you have . . . .* Have volunteers share their answers with the class.

L1 DISCUSSION. Ask students to explain why it is difficult to develop good health behaviors. Have students list the behaviors that are the most difficult to change. Then ask them to list the barriers involved in changing unhealthy behaviors. Ask students to discuss alternatives.

L2 DISCUSSION. Ask students to complete the following statements: *Good health depends on . . . ; A physically healthy person is . . . ; A mentally healthy person is . . . ; A socially healthy person is . . . .* Have students discuss their answers with the class.

L2 CLASS ACTIVITY. Draw a large health triangle on the chalkboard. Label the three sides. Ask students to list the life-style factors and/or activities that affect health. Have a volunteer write the factors and/or activities on the board as they are given. Ask each student to draw his or her own health triangle on a sheet of paper. Have students put those factors that relate to behaviors in their lives beside each component on the triangle. Ask students to determine if their triangles are balanced. Ask them to list behaviors that could be adopted to balance the health triangle.

L3 CLASS ACTIVITY. Have students design another symbol to show the balance of physical, mental, and social health without using the traditional triangle.

L1 USING HEALTH AWARENESS TRANSPARENCIES 1 AND 2. Refer to the Teaching Transparencies Binder.

L2 COOPERATIVE LEARNING. Have students form groups of three to four. Provide posterboard and magazines. Have each group draw a large health triangle on a posterboard and label each side. Have half the groups make collages of healthy behaviors, while the other groups make collages of unhealthy behaviors for each side

The three elements of your health—physical health, mental health, and social health—are related to each other and contribute to your total health. The more they are in balance, the better your health will be.

These days the definition of health has returned to the broader idea of wholeness. In its fullest sense, **health** is the state of total physical, mental, and social well-being, not just freedom from sickness or ailments. Someone who is totally healthy has a healthy body and mind as well as a positive attitude about life. Someone who is totally healthy has many relationships that enrich his or her life.

Your personal level of health affects everything about you. It affects how you look, how you feel, even how you act. It affects your attitudes and performance in school, work, and recreation. It affects how you feel about yourself and how successful you are in your relationships. It may even determine some of your goals and your ability to accomplish them.

Even though heredity and environment play a part in your one-of-a-kind health story, what you do to keep yourself healthy or to make yourself healthier is probably the greatest factor in your overall well-being.

The Importance of Health Education

Since health is so critical to the quality of your life, learning how to get and stay healthy should be a priority. That is why health education is so important. **Health education** is the providing of health information in such a way that it influences people to change attitudes so that they take positive action about their health. Its goal is to help people live long, zestful, and productive lives.

Health education is about gaining the tools to achieve and maintain total well-being. It is not just about teaching health facts. Its goal is to get students—and that includes you—to put these facts to use in all areas of their lives.

The Three Elements of Your Health

Notice that people ask, "How are you?" not "Do you have any diseases?" or "Are all your systems functioning properly?" That is because how you are doing involves much more than the absence of physical disease or the proper functioning of your body's many processes. It also includes how you are doing mentally and socially. To obtain a complete picture of your health, you must take into consideration all of these elements.

K E E P I N G F I T

Improving Your Social Health

Are you often lonely? Do you sometimes feel like there's nowhere that you fit in? Be creative and improve your social health at the same time.

For example, consider Handicap Introductions, a New Jersey-based social dating service that matches people with disabilities from all over the world.

What creative techniques might you try?
■ Join a club with people who have a similar interest or talent.

Or start one.
■ Get a part-time job where you expand your contacts to new people.
■ Have a party where everyone brings someone no one else knows.

Overcoming Misconceptions

The Physically Challenged. The following statement was provided by a social scientist blinded in World War II: "Getting around independently means to me the realization of that which has been said very frequently by others, that life is movement and involvement and that one needs to be able to move about, in and out, and for me at least, to be self-directing in that movement—to go where I want to go, when I want to go, how I want to go." Individuals with handicaps usually become quite independent and are capable of achieving a high level of wellness. They accept challenges and, with their successes, establish self-confidence, pride, and quality of life.

LOOKING AT TECHNOLOGY

Health-Risk Appraisal

Health-risk appraisal is a method used to evaluate health behaviors and to determine health risks. First, a person answers numerous questions about his or her life-style and family history. This information and the results of medical tests are then fed into a computer and combined with the latest statistics about disease and death. Taking into account age, race, and sex, the computer ranks the person's chances of developing various diseases and rates these risks in relation to others. The final health-risk appraisal printout may also make specific recommendations for disease prevention or changes in life-style. Hundreds of large corporations now rely on computerized health-risk appraisals as part of their health promotion programs.

You may not have access to a health-risk appraisal, but you can still begin to develop awareness about your health risks.

Physical Health

Physical health means that all parts and systems of the body work well together. It means that your body has the ability to withstand the stresses of normal daily life. It means having strength and energy to pursue physical, mental, emotional, and social challenges and changes.

To gain or maintain physical health, you need to have proper nutrition, adequate exercise, and enough rest and sleep. You also need to develop healthy skills, practice cleanliness in order to prevent disease, and get medical and dental checkups and care when needed.

Mental Health

Mental health includes how you like, accept, and feel about yourself; how well you relate to others; and how you meet the demands of daily life. A person with good mental health is in touch with his or her emotions and expresses them in acceptable, healthful ways. Such an individual can usually deal with the problems and frustrations of life without being overwhelmed by them.

Mental health also calls for a person to use his or her mind to develop thinking skills. People with good mental health enjoy learning and know that striving for information and understanding can be an exciting, lifelong process.

Social Health

Social health involves the way you get along with others. It includes your ability to make and keep friends and to work and play in cooperative ways, seeking and lending support when necessary. It involves communicating well and sharing your feelings with others.

HELP WANTED

Health Teacher

Discover the fountain of youth! It's been said that people who work with young people stay young themselves. What better position is there for working with youth than the teacher's, and what more relevant field to teach than health? The need for teachers will increase significantly in the early part of the twenty-first century. However, a teacher must be willing to relocate. If you relate to a wide variety of people, can communicate health knowledge, and can motivate others effectively, this is the job for you. Interest in working with extracurricular activities is a big plus.

For more information contact:
National Education Association
1201 16th Street NW
Washington, DC 20036

of the triangle. Have groups assign individuals to select pictures, cut, and paste the pictures on the poster. Have one student present the work of each group to the class. Display the posters in the classroom.

L2 CLASS ACTIVITY. Ask students to list their five favorite activities. Next to each, have them write one statement for each side of the health triangle describing how their levels of mental, physical, and social health influence the performance of that activity.

L1 CLASS ACTIVITY. Ask each student to create an example of an individual who has an unbalanced health triangle and to write a description of this person. Have students exchange descriptions and suggest specific ways to help the person balance his or her level of health.

L2 DISCUSSION. Ask students to answer the following question: *Is it true that if you are not sick you are healthy?*

L1 CLASS ACTIVITY. Ask students to compile a list of the major factors that influence their understanding of the concept of health in their lives. Discuss the influence of the entertainment industry, their friends, and society on their interpretation of a healthy person. Have students evaluate the choices that they need to make to achieve total health without the influence of others.

L2 CLASS ACTIVITY. Explain the health continuum in the textbook. Follow up with a discussion of the following question: *Is it possible to be physically, mentally, or emotionally challenged and still show a high level of overall wellness?* Ask students if they have ever been handicapped in any way. Explain that they are all to become physically challenged or handicapped for 15 to 30 minutes. Provide a wheelchair, crutches, arm slings, splints, earplugs, and blindfolds. Have students participate for half the class period as physically challenged individuals. You may want them to have partners and switch roles. Ask students to share their experiences with the class.

Additional Information

Doctors and Disease. The focus of medical practice in the U.S. today is on disease—not health. Doctors are educated primarily in the molecular basis of disease and how to cure it using prescription drugs and surgery. Illness is defined essentially as the outcome of disease, and it is assessed almost solely by deviations from norms for measurable biological variables.

By contrast, the social and psychological dimensions of illness are given little attention in medical schools and doctors' offices. The concept of wellness is neglected, and educating patients to practice preventive health measures is still the exception, not the norm.

When you neglect one area of your health, the other areas are affected. If you do not exercise regularly, for example, you will not be as alert in class, or able to enjoy certain activities with your friends.

Your Health Triangle

Have you ever been very tired or hungry? How did that feeling affect the way you acted toward others? Did it affect your work? If it went on too long, did it affect your physical well-being? A direct relationship exists among physical, mental, and social health. To be truly healthy, you must work hard in each of these areas.

An equilateral triangle illustrates these connections and the need for a balanced approach to health. To achieve and maintain a high level of health, you must develop all three sides—physical, mental, and social. Conversely, your health triangle can become lopsided and unbalanced if you do not work to develop any one of the sides, or if you spend too much time in one area.

The Health Continuum

Wellness means an overall state of well-being, or total health. It comes from a way of living each day that includes making decisions and choosing behaviors that are based on sound health knowledge and healthful attitudes. It implies a threefold commitment to physical health, mental health, and social health. This approach to health is called a holistic approach. **Holistic** means "whole," and the holistic approach considers physical, mental, and social influences on the whole person and his or her health.

A continuum is a chart, spectrum, or sliding scale showing the progress of an activity, movement, or cycle. The Health Continuum below shows the wide range of wellness and illness within which people may live and through which they may move back and forth over time.

As you study the Health Continuum, keep in mind that it is always changing. You experience different levels of total health, from day to day and from year to year. In any of the areas that affect health, there can be sudden change. Conversely, a person may slide from one side of the continuum to the other so gradually that he or she is not even fully aware of the change.

The sad fact is that too many people settle for functioning below their health midpoint—the place where they are not exactly sick but neither are they fully happy or functioning at their best. They make health choices that keep them from enjoying and living their lives to the fullest.

This continuum has opposite states of health and wellness at the ends with varying degrees in between. The choices you make will influence your level of wellness. Accept the responsibility of maintaining a high level of wellness for yourself.

Health Continuum

| Premature Death | Loss of Health and Wellness | | Improved Health and Wellness | High Level of Health |

Chronic disorders — Lack of energy, inattention, minor aches and pains — Free from aches and pains — Moderate level of energy — Optimal level of energy, feeling of well-being

People on this side of the continuum usually do not take responsibility for maintaining their own health.

Most people function below the wellness midpoint.

People on this side of the continuum usually exhibit a high degree of responsibility, discipline, and positive direction in life. They accept responsibility for maintaining their own health.

Across the Curriculum

Social Studies. Health education was practiced centuries ago. In ancient Greece, boys were sent to education centers known as "gymnasiums" where total health and learning were encouraged. There they engaged in physical activities such as wrestling and running. They also received military and philosophical training. Later, in ancient Rome, physical fitness was taught not so much to promote wellness as to develop superior soldiers who could win in battle. Ask students to research the health practices of one of these or other past cultures.

Promoting Your Health

Recent discoveries in medicine have helped wipe out many of the diseases that killed people 100, 50, even 30 years ago. Yet the way we live today poses new threats to our health and our lives. Millions of people get sick, become disabled, or die each year because of the decisions they make and the way they live. Their decision-making skills and personal behavior are directly related to their deaths. Many of these deaths could be prevented if people practiced a few simple health habits.

Life-Style Factors

After years of studying many groups of people, experts have identified seven habits that make a difference in people's overall health, happiness, and longevity—or how long they live. People who regularly practice these seven important habits tend to be healthier and live longer. These habits are called life-style factors. **Life-style factors** are repeated behaviors related to the way a person lives, which help determine his or her level of health. The following are important life-style factors:

- Get between 7 and 8 hours of sleep per night.
- Eat three meals a day at regular times.
- Refrain from smoking.
- Eat breakfast daily.
- Participate in aerobic exercise at least 20 to 30 minutes 3 to 4 times a week.
- Do not use alcohol.
- Maintain your recommended weight.

How many of these basic health habits do you practice regularly? If you do not practice them regularly, what are the reasons? What changes in habits can you make? Keep in mind that not following these guidelines can prove hazardous to your health and take years off your life.

Life Expectancy: Quantity of Life

Life expectancy is the average number of years a group of people is expected to live. It is dependent on many factors, including gender, heredity, environment, culture, access to medical care and, most importantly, basic health habits.

Culturally Speaking

So What Is Culture?

Culture is a whole way of life. It includes people's ideas, beliefs, and customs. It influences their arts, language, traditions, laws or rules, diet, and technology.

Understanding culture can help us understand and get along with others. We can see what all people have in common as we look at the variety of ways that people try to solve the same basic human problems. Knowing your own culture gives you a sense of identity as you take your place in a multicultural world.

K E E P I N G   F I T

An Attitude of Gratitude

Sometimes it's difficult to concentrate on what we have to be grateful for, particularly when things seem to be falling apart. However, with practice, you can learn to create an attitude of gratitude—reminding yourself to be grateful for what you have. Try one or more of these attitude boosters, and elevate your mood and overall health in the process.

- Learn to separate your wants from your needs.
- Identify what you can and can't change. Concentrate on the former. Let go of the latter.
- Be grateful just to be alive. This is the only life you've got!
- Use your humor. Laugh.

Independent Practice

L3 WRITING. Ask students to write a brief essay on the changes in health education over the last century, including the transition from an emphasis on disease prevention to the concept of promoting total health. Have them explain why the concept has changed from prevention to total health and include the medical pioneers that have made an impact on disease prevention influencing this change.

L2 RESEARCH. Explain to the class that life expectancy varies in different countries partly because of differences in standards of living and health-care facilities. Ask students to research a country that has a standard of living and health-care facilities that differ from those in the United States. Ask students to report to the class the results of their research.

L1 COMMUNITY INVOLVEMENT. Ask students to interview three senior citizens and to determine the quality of life for each one. Ask them to include age, physical activities, and status of health in a short written report.

L3 RESEARCH. Ask students to refer to *Healthy People 2000* (available from U.S. Department of Health and Human Services) to evaluate the changes in the health problems in the 1900s to the concerns for the year 2000. Ask students to present the results of their research to the class on a poster or chart, making a graph of any statistical data they have to share.

L2 PARENTAL INVOLVEMENT. Ask students to share the health goals for the year 2000 with their parents. Have students ask their parents to compare these goals with the health goals or problems they experienced when they were teenagers.

L2 COMMUNITY INVOLVEMENT. Explain to students that many companies have established wellness programs for their employees. Ask students to contact a company in their community that has established a health program for employees. Ask students to describe the type of program the company has implemented and the rationale for providing this program.

Life expectancy in the United States is almost twice as long as it was at the beginning of the twentieth century. In 1900 the average expected life span was 49 years, while in 1989 it was 75. Life expectancy has increased 9 years for women and 8 for men just since 1950.

At the turn of the century, the leading causes of death were pneumonia, flu, and tuberculosis—all communicable diseases spread from person to person. In contrast, the four leading causes of death today are not communicable. They are due to life-style factors. The leading causes of death in the United States today are heart disease, cancer, stroke, and accidents. The leading causes of death for 15- to 24-year-olds are injuries, murders, suicide, and cancer.

Life expectancy varies from country to country. For example, a person born in the United States in 1989 has an overall life expectancy of 75 years, while a person born in Ethiopia has a life expectancy of only 41 years. This is because of differences in availability and access to health care services, health education, immunizations, and medications, as well as to differences in nutrition, sanitation, and standards of living.

Life Enjoyment: Quality of Life

Just living a long time is not enough. Quality of life is as important as quantity of life. **Quality of life** means the level of health and satisfaction that a person has in being alive. Being able to function physically, mentally, and socially at a high level adds to the enjoyment and productivity of a person's life regardless of age. Practicing sound decision-making skills and health habits now can contribute to a good quality of life not only today but also in the future.

Your Attitudes, Your Health

Practicing good health habits involves much more than just knowing what to do. Your attitudes also affect how well you take care of yourself. For example, in order to practice good health habits, you must believe that there is some benefit for you, and believe that by not practicing good health habits, problems will develop.

You also need to become aware of your overall attitude, or outlook, on life since this can play a major role in both your quality of life and your health.

Studies have shown that optimists, people who tend to see the positives in situations, are less likely to suffer illnesses and die young than are pessimists, those who look for and see the negative in situations. Other studies have concluded that it is not what happens to a person but the person's attitude about what happens that determines how well that person will cope and how happy he or she will be with his or her quality of life.

Even if you live in a very difficult situation, it can be helpful to try to find something positive about your situation and try to build on that. By gradually improving your outlook on life, you can get to a point where you can really believe that you can make a difference in your health and your life.

The quality of your life will be enhanced as you explore new ideas and learn from others.

Across the Curriculum

Math. Ask students to do a scientific survey of the school population on students' thoughts about the saying, "You can never be too rich or too thin." Ask each student to survey 10 males and 10 females and then pool class data on the board. The survey should ask students to rate on a scale of 0 to 5 the above statement in terms of how important it is to them. Five is very important; 0 is not important. After the data is pooled, ask students to make a bar graph of the information, dividing it into male and female bars. The scale from one to five should be on the horizontal axis and the number of students on the vertical axis. Discuss with students the implications for the health of people who believe strongly in the survey statement.

Toward a Healthy 2000

In 1991 Dr. Louis Sullivan, Secretary of the U.S. Department of Health and Human Services, made public 300 new health goals for the United States. These were aimed at making America healthier and stronger as the year 2000 approaches. Among the many health goals he recommended were reducing infant mortality rates, reducing the cancer rate, limiting the number of AIDS cases, and getting people to be more responsible for their own health by doing the following:

- giving up smoking
- becoming physically active daily
- limiting dietary fat intake
- learning to deal with stress in positive ways
- never drinking and driving
- always wearing seat belts
- seeking current and reliable health information
- getting early prenatal care when pregnant
- immunizing children against communicable diseases
- teaching how to make safe decisions about health-risk behaviors such as smoking, drinking, using drugs, or having sex

According to Dr. Sullivan, Americans tend to use the health care system to patch themselves up rather than to prevent the very health problems that later need patching. Instead, **prevention,** or practicing healthy habits to keep a person well and free from disease and other ailments, should be the focus of everyone's personal health goals.

You, like many others, may think only in terms of today. You may not relate your present actions to how they will affect you in the future. Keep in mind, however, that the habits you practice now are setting the stage for how healthy or unhealthy you will be in your adult life.

Having regular checkups is a good preventive habit. You can learn about your health status and ask questions about maintaining or improving your health.

LESSON 1 REVIEW

Reviewing Facts and Vocabulary

1. In a paragraph define the terms *health*, *health education*, and *wellness*, and explain how these terms are related to one another.
2. What are the three elements of health?
3. What is the Health Continuum?

Thinking Critically

4. **Analysis.** Analyze some of the reasons that even health-informed teens do not always practice basic health habits.
5. **Synthesis.** From all the factors you have studied in Lesson 1, identify the most important influences on your health and life expectancy.

6. **Analysis.** What are some behaviors that might lead to the top three causes of death for teens? Do you or any of your friends engage in these behaviors? How might these top three categories of death be prevented? Which, if any, of these prevention techniques might you need to apply to your own life?

Applying Health Knowledge

7. Draw your own health triangle. Are its three sides equal? If not, how are they lopsided? What steps can you take to make them more equal?

YOUR HEALTH, YOUR RESPONSIBILITY   **9**

- Assign and discuss the lesson review. For LD students, have them define only the terms in question 1. Rephrase questions 4 to 6 and allow them to choose two of the three to answer.

Evaluate

- Administer, grade, and discuss the *Lesson 1 Quiz.*

Reteach

- Have students clip five articles on health from newspapers or magazines. Ask students to make a chart separating physical, mental, and social health. Have students summarize each article and indicate on the chart the frequency of topics related to each area of health.
- Ask students to complete *Reteaching Activity 1.*

Enrich

- Ask each student to design a health-behavior contract. Have them include a signature, date of commitment, name or topic of the health area, a specific goal, a plan with a time period, a way of recording progress, and a statement of how the behavior will improve their lifestyles.

Close

Ask students to state the most important concepts in the lesson. Have students list the healthful behaviors they will adopt to improve their quality of life.

Answers to Lesson 1 Review

1. Paragraphs will vary. See pages 4 and 6 for definitions.
2. Physical, mental, and social health.
3. A chart that indicates levels of health.
4. Answers will vary. Possible answers: the benefits of good health are not always obvious; some settle for a low level of wellness; requires effort.
5. Answers will vary.
6. Answers will vary. Possible answers: making unwise choices and associating with peers who engage in risk behaviors. By nurturing one's social, physical, and mental health.
7. Answers will vary.

DID YOU KNOW?

- According to Tom Parker, author of *In One Day*, on any given day in the United States, Americans collectively eat 815 billion calories of food, an estimated 200 billion more than they need.

Focus

Lesson Objectives

After studying this lesson, students should be able to:

- explain the relationship of self-esteem to health
- identify ways to improve self-esteem
- relate goal-setting to self-esteem

Bellringer

Write the following on the chalkboard for the students to work on while attendance is being taken: *Write a one- or two-line definition of self-esteem.* Ask a few volunteers to share their definitions with the class.

Introducing the Lesson

Refer to the Bellringer. Have students explain how self-esteem can influence behavior. Ask students to list as many factors as they can think of that influence self-esteem. Ask volunteers to share their lists with the class.

Building Vocabulary

- Have students discuss the difference between realistic and unrealistic goals and describe how setting goals affects self-esteem.
- Ask students to complete *Workbook Vocabulary Activity 2.*

DID YOU KNOW?

- One study indicates that the lower a young person's self-esteem when he or she enters the teen years, the greater the chance that that teen will become estranged, or increasingly distant, from his or her parents.
- Studies show that boys and girls as young as two respond differently to failure. When boys perform certain simple tasks, they show more pride in their achievements than their female counterparts. When girls fail at simple tasks, they show much more shame than their male counterparts do.

* Refer to pages T 26 to T 28 for a complete correlation.

SELF-ESTEEM AND YOUR HEALTH

LESSON 2 FOCUS

TERMS TO USE
- Self-esteem
- Goal

CONCEPTS TO LEARN
- Your self-esteem is related to your health.
- Certain skills can improve self-esteem.
- Setting and achieving goals is important to your self-esteem.

ATTITUDES AND BEHAVIORS TO EVALUATE
- Self-Inventory, page 22.
- Building Decision-Making Skills, page 23.

Think of five adjectives that describe you. How many of them are positive descriptions? How many are based on how others see you? How many are based on how you see yourself? Now close your eyes. Imagine looking in the mirror. What do you see? How do you feel about what you see? Now imagine that there was a mirror that would let you see your mind, your creative abilities, and various qualities of your personality. What would you see? How would you feel about what was reflected back at you?

Self-Esteem

Self-esteem is the confidence and worth that you feel about yourself. Your self-esteem influences everything you do, think, feel, and are. It is, in fact, one of the most important factors in your overall sense of well-being. How well you feel physically, mentally, and socially can affect your self-esteem. In turn, your level of self-esteem can directly affect your physical, mental, and social health.

Some of the messages about who you are and how likable you are come from outside yourself. They are called external messages. Others come from inside yourself. They are called internal messages.

Did you ever get a compliment that you were unable to accept? Negative internal messages can get in the way of and erase even the most positive of external messages. That is why working on those internal messages you give yourself is so important.

Many people base their self-esteem on external factors—on how they look, what they have, how they perform, how others see them, or with whom they are friends. In reality, however, self-esteem comes from knowing, accepting, and liking not what you have, whom you know, or what you do, but who you are.

Some Signs of High Self-Esteem

Your level of self-esteem varies from day to day—even from hour to hour. However, your basic level of self-esteem probably falls most often within one portion of a high-to-low self-esteem continuum.

If you have a high level of self-esteem, you can accept yourself, including any weaknesses, illnesses, or handicaps you may have. You can admit mistakes and take responsibility for your actions. You may have self-doubt sometimes—everyone does—but most days you basically like yourself. Besides that, you know you can always make changes when you realize there are things about yourself that you do not like.

If you have high self-esteem, you probably feel competent in some areas and are willing to learn and try new things in other areas. You are willing to take chances and even to fail sometimes. You see mistakes as part of the learning process. You use your abilities and talents and take

Resources for Lesson 2

- **Transparencies** 11 and 19
- **Guided Reading** Activity 2
- **Workbook** Voc Act 2
- **Reteaching** Activity 2
- **Lesson 2 Quiz**

Science and Technology Videodisc
Human Biology, Side 2
Ch 13 Bulimia

ABC News InterActive Videodiscs
Drugs and Substance Abuse, Side 2
Ch 16 Building Self-Esteem

Overcoming The Odds

Virginia Vasquez is 17. She works hard at her studies, has a part-time job in a snack bar, and is even taking flying lessons. Now she is making plans to go to college.

This is a good time in Virginia's life, but it has not always been that way. In fact, she has overcome great obstacles to get where she is today.

For much of Virginia's life, her mother, Maria Leyva, was a migrant farm worker, moving from place to place throughout the Southwest to find work harvesting onions. Virginia says, "The longest we lived in one place was in an apartment for three years. My sister and I didn't have fun in the summers back then. We had to wake up at 4 o'clock in the morning and go with my mom to her work in the fields. We had to go because we didn't have a baby-sitter, and we'd sleep in the back of the truck. It was cold. I first went to work in the fields myself picking onions when I was about 12 or 13.

"I now have a room of my own," she continues, "and it's big." The room Virginia refers to is her own bedroom at a center for homeless people in California. She lives there with her mother, stepfather, and younger half-brothers and sis-

ter. Her mother now works in the thrift store at the shelter and her stepdad works selling furnishings. Her sister, Lupe, who also lived at the center, attends college but comes "home" to visit. The family is

living at the shelter while they wait for affordable housing. They have been on a government waiting list for over two years.

"We came to the center about three years ago," she says. "Things have gotten a lot better since then. We eat better, we're more comfortable, and there's even a basketball team here. I played basketball until I hurt my knees. We have a doctor who comes here every week from the county. My knee ligaments are messed

up, and I have to wear two braces. The doctors are now helping me with this.

"There are also people who care here at the center like Dr. Judy." Dr. Judy, who has a Ph.D. in psychology, works at the center, counsels Virginia, and provides her with encouragement and advice. He even asks to see her report card on a regular basis, and she sometimes works in his office.

Virginia also has other role models. "I also use my sister Lupe (who is a junior at Stanford University) as an example, too. Dr. Judy tells me if my sister can do it, I can do it, too. He always advises me not to give up.

"As for my plans," she says, "well, I'm going to graduate from high school. Then I want to study psychology."

And how does Virginia feel about herself? "I feel pretty good about myself," she says.

1. How do we do people a disservice when we assume they can't achieve goals just because they are from a particular race, socioeconomic level, age, or for any other reason?
2. What effects might such attitudes have on their self-esteem? On our self-esteem?

Guided Practice

L1 DISCUSSION. How do we learn to look at ourselves? (Judging from how we are treated by others, we develop a picture of ourselves.) Discuss the things that other people say and do to you that affect how you look at yourself.

L1 USING LIFE MANAGEMENT SKILLS TRANSPARENCY 11. Refer to the Teaching Transparencies Binder.

Using Overcoming the Odds

■ **Discussion.** What changes in Virginia's life are likely to have improved her self-esteem? (Earning her own money, achieving short-term goals, getting encouragement from respected elders, and planning for long-term career goals.)

■ **Explanation.** Explain the importance of setting goals, such as Virginia's goal of being a successful counselor, in having a healthy, satisfying life. (Reinforce sense of control over your own life and health, without which self-esteem suffers and ill health may result.)

■ **Class Activity.** Review the process of setting and achieving goals by working through an example with the class that is drawn from Virginia's story. (One goal for Virginia would be to find sources of financial aid. To achieve this goal, she could talk to school personnel who can help her make a list of potential sources of loans and scholarships.)

■ **Answers**
1. By depriving them of a fair chance to prove their self-worth.
2. Lower their self-esteem and make us feel better about ourselves by comparison.

Meeting Students' Needs

Teen Esteem. Tell students that if they were working in a store, they might be asked to take inventory on a regular basis—that is, to tally up lists of what goods there are in stock to be used at any time. In a similar way, to assess your self-esteem, you might periodically make "inventory" lists of the following qualities or assets that YOU have "in stock":

■ your personality qualities
■ your skills
■ your natural talents
■ your friendships
■ your value to your family
■ your goals
■ your values
■ your achievements

L2 **CLASS ACTIVITY.** Ask each student to find a partner. Have one student pretend to be an advice columnist who answers inquiries from teens about ways to handle negative comments. The other student will provide negative comments he or she has heard from other people. The advice columnist will provide ways to handle the negative comments. Partners may change roles. Have students role-play some of their comments and responses in front of the class.

L1 **DISCUSSION.** Have students identify and discuss persons whose opinions they value. Ask students why these people are significant to them and how often they ask these people for feedback.

L2 **DEMONSTRATION.** Tell students that we are a blend of three selves. Our self-esteem has an influence on our private self, public self, and ideal self. The blend of these three selves is key in accepting and liking yourself and having successful relationships with others. Draw three sets of circles on the chalkboard. The first set should not intersect at all. Explain that the person these circles represent does not have a high level of self-esteem because his or her ideal, public, and private selves are not the same. Draw the next set so that the circles slightly overlap. This person feels better about him- or herself because the ideal, public, and private aspects of self blend. Draw all three circles overlapping each other entirely. Use three colors of chalk to distinguish the circles. This person has a high level of self-esteem because the three selves are in harmony. This person is happiest with him- or herself and does not confuse others by acting differently. Ask students to demonstrate situations where they act differently when associating with certain friends or family members. Discuss why most people are different in public than they are in private.

> **DID YOU KNOW?**
>
> - In 1981, multimillionaire Eugene Lang made a promise to a group of sixth graders in East Harlem, New York, that he would pay for their education if they stayed in school. Since then, his idea has become a program called the I Have A Dream Foundation (IHAD), serving more than 9,000 American young people in 36 different cities. Benefactors, people who put up money, become involved in all aspects of these preteens' and teens' lives, showing them that caring as well as money helps.

part in activities whether or not you are good at them. You believe that you are worthwhile as a human being and that you do not have to over-achieve to prove your worth. You have healthful habits and do not engage in self-destructive behaviors.

People with high self-esteem usually have healthful relationships. They seek out people who respect them. In turn, they respect others. They show respect for people of all races, religions, cultural backgrounds, and ages. They reach out to help people and to know them.

Some Signs of Low Self-Esteem

People with low self-esteem tend to let others influence them in negative ways. They may engage in people-pleasing and approval-seeking behaviors. They may get their identity from external rather than internal sources, and they may trust others' reactions more than their own. In short, they may worry too much about what others think of them. In addition, their self-esteem goes up and down like a thermometer, often depending on how others react toward them.

To seem cooler, tougher, or more confident than they feel on the inside, they may engage in unhealthy behaviors to try to gain recognition or to escape their insecurities. They may engage in activities that jeopardize their or others' health. For example, teens with low self-esteem are more likely to have sex early, get pregnant, drop out of school, engage in violent behavior, commit crimes and acts of prejudice, even commit suicide. They may use food, alcohol, tobacco, other drugs, and engage in unhealthful behaviors as ways of temporarily relieving the constant pain of not liking and accepting who they are.

Rather than using their time and energy to enjoy their lives, people with low self-esteem spend time and energy defending themselves, avoiding new challenges, trying to pump up their fragile egos, or putting down others in attempts to feel better.

People with low self-esteem often have few satisfying relationships. They may boast too much, bully too much, or even threaten others they see as weaker than themselves. They may go to great, even very dangerous, lengths to prove how smart, rich, tough, attractive, right, or talented they are. However, these attempts usually backfire when their behavior turns off or frightens away other people.

People with low self-esteem may get caught in a vicious cycle. They may think that they cannot succeed, so they do not try. In not trying, they may feel even worse about themselves. Living with low self-esteem can be a terribly painful way of life, but it does not have to stay that way.

K E E P I N G F I T

Goals

Most teens would probably agree that what they want is to be loved, to be healthy, and to get a job they really enjoy.

Take time to ask yourself, "What do *I* really want more than anything else?" Then set goals that will help you work toward getting what you want.

Try these suggestions:
- List short- and long-range goals.
- Break major goals into smaller ones.
- Stay flexible. If one method of

achieving your goal doesn't pan out, try others. Be creative in your approaches.
- Start small. Set one small goal today that you wish to achieve by tomorrow.

Meeting Students' Needs

Goal Attainment. Visualizations are deliberate attempts to conjure up particular mental images. Olympians have used this technique for years to improve performance. Bruce Jenner, winner of an Olympic decathlon gold medal, pictured every detail of every event several times a day before his winning performance.

There is some scientific evidence, as well, that programming the mind can help to program the body. Researcher Eric Jacobson demonstrated that people who visualize shooting baskets actually tense up the correct muscles. Visualization, then, may be a useful tool to use in setting and achieving goals.

Skills for Improving Your Self-Esteem

There are many positive steps that you can take to begin to improve your self-esteem. Doing so will not only increase your self-esteem, it may also improve your relationships and your overall level of health. Here are some simple ways that you can begin to make these changes:

- Assist others when appropriate.
- Find something that you can enjoy doing and that gives you a feeling of success. Make time to do that activity regularly.
- Stop making life a contest. Recognize that there will always be people both more and less able than you are in all areas of life.
- Aim for improvement, not perfection.
- Build a network of supportive relationships.
- Surround yourself with people who respect, approve, and accept you as an individual.
- Accept mistakes and errors as learning tools rather than as signs of your failure.
- Reject any negative feedback from others that is intended to put you down.
- Practice visualizing situations in which you are successful.
- Whenever you look at your weaknesses, spend equal time considering your strengths.
- Give yourself credit for all accomplishments or improvements, even the smallest ones.
- Practice basic health habits, giving attention to your physical, mental, and social health.
- Stay in school.
- Improve your mind—read a book, write a story.
- Use your creative talents on a regular basis.
- Get some training in an area of interest.
- Make lists of your qualities, skills, and talents. Read them often.
- Avoid engaging in self-destructive behaviors to escape your shyness or lack of social success. Doing so will just make matters worse.
- Do something nice for someone else. Do something nice for yourself.
- Set some realistic, achievable goals, and work at them.

CONFLICT RESOLUTION

Isabel is a freshman at the same school where her older sister Rosa is a junior. Both are good students, but they have very different personalities. Rosa is full of life and outgoing, while Isabel is quiet and reserved. Recent comments about how different Isabel is from Rosa have left Isabel feeling inadequate. Isabel has always envied her older sister's outgoing nature and busy social life. She's tried to be more outgoing in class, but doing so only makes her feel uncomfortable.

How do you think Isabel can improve her self-esteem and resolve the conflict she feels?

Try new activities. Volunteer to help in order to learn new skills and to discover new areas of interest.

Additional Information

Health Goals. Ask students if they have ever made a New Year's Resolution. Did they ever break that resolution? Why?

Surveys indicate some 70 percent of the resolutions adults make involve their health. Yet, only 19 percent of these resolutions are kept for two or more years. So why do people break these promises to themselves?

Experts cite two major reasons. The first is emotional distress; the second, social pressure. For example, if someone has given up smoking but goes through a stressful time, he or she is more likely to light up again. Or, if everyone around him or her smokes, that person may also resume smoking.

LEP **DISCUSSION.** Have students select books or magazines about teens who have a high level of self-esteem. Also, have students choose a hero or star who exhibits positive signs of self-esteem. Discuss these individuals with the class, asking students to give examples that show that these individuals feel comfortable with themselves, feel right about other people, and are able to meet the demands of life.

L2 **SELF-ESTEEM.** Divide the class into two groups. Have one group develop a list of things persons might hear as they grow up that would enhance their self-esteem. Have the other group develop a list that would inhibit the development of a good self-esteem. Compare the lists. Discuss the impact of negative statements on self-esteem.

LEP **CLASS ACTIVITY.** Ask students to make a collage with pictures that show examples of ways to improve self-esteem. Display the work in the room.

L1 **CLASS ACTIVITY.** Have the class think of all the ways the word *goal* is used and list them on the chalkboard. (Examples: field goal, goalie, basketball goal.) Ask students what the words in their list have in common. Write the following on the board: *If you don't know where you're going, you'll probably end up somewhere else.* Discuss this statement in relation to goals. (Goals give us direction. Imagine a basketball game without goals.) Ask students to list why goals are important to achieve wellness and share their lists with the class.

L1 **DISCUSSION.** Explain to students that it is important to have goals to have a meaningful life. Some goals are easier to attain than others. The difficulty of attaining a goal is not as important as setting one. Individuals differ in the types of goals that they attempt to achieve. Discuss the variables that could exist to determine the type of goals an individual may set. Relate goal setting to self-esteem for all individuals.

L1 **USING LIFE MANAGEMENT SKILLS TRANSPARENCY 19.** Refer to the Teaching Transparencies Binder.

14 CHAPTER 1 YOUR HEALTH

L1 SPEAKER. Invite someone who has overcome an impairment to give a personal view on the importance of having a high level of self-esteem in dealing with the challenges of everyday life. Have the speaker share how he or she improved his or her level of self-esteem even though impaired and how positive support from others and how negative responses can affect self-esteem. Have the speaker explain how he or she overcame personal feelings of negativism, and how students might improve their self-esteem and be supportive of others.

Independent Practice

L2 PERSONAL INVOLVEMENT. Assign students to keep a tally of negative comments they hear or make in the course of a day. Their challenge is to turn at least two negative statements around, making them positive. Have them report back to the class reactions they receive.

L3 WRITING. Ask students to develop, on the computer, models for setting and attaining goals. They should include criteria from the model in the text and add other criteria that would benefit teens in setting and attaining goals. Have students copy and share their models with the class.

L2 PARENTAL INVOLVEMENT. Have students determine five long-term goals they would like to achieve. Have them ask their parents to help them use the goal-setting model in planning to achieve these goals. Ask how their parents could help them achieve their goals.

L1 PERSONAL INVOLVEMENT. Ask each student to determine two goals he or she wishes to reach this week. Have them use the goal-setting model to plan how they will reach one. Ask them to assess their progress every morning. If they find they are working toward a goal, but need more time to reach it, have them adjust their plans.

L1 USING THE LESSON RESOURCES. For additional student activities, refer to the lesson resources on page 10.

Choose a schedule of classes that will help you qualify for a future goal. You want to be ready to prepare for the career that interests you.

The Importance of Goals

Do you view your life as a series of events that simply happen to you? Do you see it as a work of art that you are constantly shaping and creating? How you view your life can have major effects on your health and your self-esteem.

Having and setting goals is one way to help shape your life in positive directions and enhance your self-esteem. A **goal** is something you aim for that takes planning and work. People who identify and work at achieving goals feel more satisfaction with themselves and with their lives.

If you do not have many personal goals, think about why not. Are you afraid of failure? Of success? Of standing out apart from your friends? Are you afraid of being made fun of? Are your standards of perfection so high that you would rather not even try?

If you do not have positive goals, the first question you must ask yourself is why? The second question is, How can I remove the roadblocks that stand in the way of my having positive goals?

Goal-setting is a skill. It involves a process that gives you direction, a framework within which to work, and a timetable for completing that work. Practicing the following steps will help you improve your goal-setting skills and, in turn, your self-esteem:

DID YOU KNOW?

■ Among the famous people who have overcome handicaps are fairy tale teller Hans Christian Andersen, King Karl XI of Sweden, athlete Jim Abbott, President Woodrow Wilson, TV writer-producer Stephen J. Cannell, poet Amy Lowell, general George Patton, and famous physicist and genius Albert Einstein. In fact, Einstein did not learn to read until he was 9.

K E E P I N G   F I T

Take a Stroll Down Memory Lane

The memories you hold of yourself in the past can affect your present feelings of self-esteem.

For a few minutes, close your eyes, and remember times when you felt loved, cared for, or valued by others. Think, too, of times when you did something nice for somebody else, helping them feel loved, cared for, or valued. Experience the feelings that come with each of these esteem-building positive memories.

Open your eyes. Think of someone you know now who gives you positive feedback. Then think of someone in your life now to whom you can give some positive feedback. Reaching out to others is one good way to boost your own self-esteem.

14 CHAPTER 1 YOUR HEALTH

Meeting Special Needs

The Physically Challenged. Society is finally recognizing the capabilities of the handicapped and impaired. These individuals are having the opportunity to set realistic goals and achieve them. Special facilities are required now to help an individual with a handicap achieve these goals easier than in the past. Job opportunities, recreational activities, and changes in attitudes toward the handicapped are finally becoming a reality. Ask someone in the community who works with Special Olympics to speak to the class. Ask students to relate achievements in the Special Olympics to self-esteem.

Practice is involved in reaching some goals. A coach can help you set realistic short-term goals in order to be ready to meet your long-term goal.

1. Select one goal to work toward.
2. List what you will do to reach this goal.
3. Identify others who can help you and support your efforts.
4. Give yourself an identified period of time to reach your goal.
5. Build in several checkpoints to evaluate how you are doing.
6. Give yourself a reward once you have achieved your goal.

When setting a goal, keep these additional guidelines in mind:

- Make certain your goal will not harm your health or anyone else's.
- Be sure that your goal shows respect both for you and for everyone else affected by it.
- Ask yourself, Whose goal is this? Make sure the goal is what you want and what is good for you rather than what you think someone else wants for you.
- Set a goal because it will help you grow, not because you want to outdo someone else or win someone else's attention.
- Avoid setting unachievable, unreasonable goals.
- Break down long-term goals into achievable short-term goals.
- If you fail to reach your goal, use what you learn from the failure to set a new goal.

LESSON 2 REVIEW

Reviewing Facts and Vocabulary

1. Use the term *self-esteem* in a paragraph.
2. Identify some of the steps a person can take to improve his or her self-esteem.
3. Identify at least three important steps to follow in goal attainment.

Thinking Critically

4. **Analysis.** Write one sentence that describes your general level of self-esteem. Then ana-

lyze what factors might be at least in part responsible for the way you view yourself.

5. **Synthesis.** Write a song, poem, story, or skit in which there are two characters—one with high self-esteem, one with low self-esteem. Have them interact.

Applying Health Knowledge

6. Write a one-page paper about how your level of self-esteem has affected one important relationship in your life.

SELF-ESTEEM AND YOUR HEALTH **15**

Answers to Lesson 2 Review

1. Paragraphs will vary but should reflect the meaning of self-esteem.
2. Answers will vary. Accept any of the bulleted items from page 13.
3. Answers will vary. Accept any of the numbered items on page 15.
4. Answers will vary. Respect student's right to privacy if discussing answers.
5. Answers will vary. Interaction between characters should reflect how one character can influence the other character's self-esteem, either positively or negatively.
6. Answers will vary. Respect student's right to privacy if discussing answers.

Focus

Lesson Objectives

After studying this lesson, students should be able to:

- give examples of decisions that affect a person's health
- explain the difference between reasonable and unreasonable risks
- identify the steps in the decision-making model
- explain why it is important to practice decision making

Bellringer

Write the following on the chalkboard for students to work on while attendance is being taken: *Write a list of all the decisions you made today from the time you woke up until now.* Ask a few volunteers to share their lists.

Introducing the Lesson

Refer to the Bellringer. Ask students to take one of the decisions they made this morning and describe how they went about making the decision. Focus on the process. Tell students they will learn more about problem solving and decision making as they study this section.

Building Vocabulary

- Repeat the following for students: You have probably heard someone say, "You must act responsibly or deal with the consequences." Ask students what this statement means.
- Ask students to complete *Workbook Vocabulary Activity 3.*

DID YOU KNOW?

- Studies show that between 80 and 90 percent of adult smokers began smoking when they were teenagers.

DECISION MAKING AND HEALTH

LESSON 3 FOCUS

TERMS TO USE

- Decision
- Risk
- Precaution
- Consequence

CONCEPTS TO LEARN

- Health and well-being are affected by one's decisions.
- Decisions involve some degree of risk.
- Practicing decision making can help prepare you for real-life situations.

ATTITUDES AND BEHAVIORS TO EVALUATE

- Self-Inventory, page 22.
- Building Decision-Making Skills, page 23.

Do you ever feel as if you have no power? Does it seem that one minute people expect a lot of you but the next minute they treat you like a child? Most teens feel that way at least some of the time. The truth is, you have more power than you ever suspected. You have personal power. Each time you make a major decision, you are exerting enormous power—power over how healthy, happy, and productive you may be for the rest of your life. That is why learning decision-making skills is so important. Some of the decisions you make may not only make or break your day; they could make or break your whole life.

Big Decisions, Little Decisions

What is a decision? A **decision** is the act of making a choice or coming to a solution. You make hundreds of decisions every day. Many of these are not very important in the overall scheme of things. Should you have ice cream or frozen yogurt? Which shoes should you wear? Should you go to the movies or to the mall? Other decisions, however, are very important because they may affect

- your health and well-being,
- someone else's health or well-being,
- your future,
- someone else's future.

Imagine that you find three beautifully wrapped boxes at your front door along with a note that states, "Whichever box you choose will determine how your life proceeds." At first they all seem identical. Then you notice that on each box is a card. One says, "Decisions that will keep you healthy." One says, "Decisions that will make you unhealthy." One says, "Decisions that will kill you." Which box would you choose?

The answer seems clear-cut, right? Yet when you make actual decisions in your everyday life, do you stop to think which one of these outcomes you might be choosing?

Some of the big decisions that teens face include:

- Should I drink?
- Should I try drugs?
- Should I have sex?
- Should I be a passenger in the car of a driver who has been drinking?
- Should I stay in school?
- Should I get married?
- Should I further my education?
- Should I get some help with a particular problem?
- Should I smoke?
- Should I tell someone I am being abused?
- Should I get a job?

Resources for Lesson 3

- **Transparency** 18
- **Guided Reading** Activity 3
- **Decision-Making** Activity 1
- **Workbook** Voc Act 3, Appl Act 1
- **Reteaching** Activity 3
- **Enrichment** Activity 1
- **Health Labs** Activity 1
- **Cooperative Learning** Activity 1

- **Lesson 3 Quiz, Chapter 1 Test**
- **Poster** 3

ABC News InterActive Videodiscs
Teenage Sexuality, Side 2
Ch 10 Deciding Not to Have Sex

Making decisions about major life issues like these must be done carefully and deliberately. These are the kinds of decisions for which you must stop and really think about which of the three boxes you are choosing.

Sometimes there are conflicts in your life between what might appear to be a good choice at the moment and what ultimately may be best for you. These conflicts are very real, so it helps to know and use an effective decision-making model to ease you through such conflicts safely with your health and self-esteem intact.

Reasonable and Unreasonable Risks

Many activities involve risk. A **risk** is a behavior with an element of danger that may cause injury or harm. If you take a risk, you expose yourself to these possible dangers.

Some risks are unavoidable. You take a risk in getting hurt when you cross the street or ride a bike. Reasonable risks are those in which the likelihood of damaging your or someone else's safety or health is low. Trying out for the school play may be scary but can bring you great enjoyment and heightened self-esteem.

Unreasonable risks are ones in which the likelihood that someone may get hurt now or in the future is high. Many unreasonable risks are taken by people trying to make up for low self-esteem. Remember, however, that there are healthy ways to boost self-esteem without putting life and limb at risk.

You can cut down on the risks in a situation when you plan ahead and take precautions. A **precaution** is a planned, preventive action taken before an event to increase the chances of a safe outcome. Learning to ski, for example, though risky, is less risky if you receive proper instruction and use safe equipment. Some activities have dangers involved, but you have to do them anyway. For example, riding in a car is risky business, but taking a precaution like wearing a seat belt can decrease the chances you will get hurt, even if things go wrong.

Most accidents involve high-risk behaviors and making high-risk decisions. Before making any big decision, it is important to consider what the risks involved will be. Then ask yourself these questions:

- Are they necessary risks?
- Are they reasonable risks?

In any sport, there are many precautions you can take to reduce the chances of getting hurt. Can you identify the risks that are lessened by each piece of equipment shown?

Guided Practice

L1 EXPLANATION. Tell students that while all decisions are not problems, most problems usually require making a decision. Ask students to list some common problems during the teen years that require decisions on the part of teens, their parents, or their teachers.

L1 USING LIFE MANAGEMENT SKILLS TRANSPARENCY 18. Refer to the Teaching Transparencies Binder.

L2 CLASS ACTIVITY. This activity can be used to help relate behaviors that pose risks to students' own health continuum. Ask students to draw a horizontal line across a sheet of paper. Ask them to put a dot at each end of the line. At the beginning of the line, put a 0 representing time of birth. Put dots at ten-year increments from birth till death. At the end of the line, have them put the number of years they wish to live or believe they will live.

Listed below are habits or conditions that may cause a person to die prematurely. Review the list with your students. The years following the habits or conditions are hypothetical.

- smoking 2 packs of cigarettes a day (−8 years)
- drinking alcohol 3 or more ounces a week (−10 years)
- overeating (more than 2500 calories per day) (−5 years)
- eating excess fat in your diet (more than 20 percent of fats such as beef, pork, and cheese) (−5 years)
- eating lots of sugar (pastry, cookies, candy) (−8 years)
- not exercising at least three times a week (−10 years)
- being overweight or obese (−10 years)
- having lots of stress in your life (−7 years)

K E E P I N G   F I T

Get Up and Go

Resisting exercise? Consider the following benefits that can be yours if you simply get up and go. Exercise

- strengthens your cardiovascular system,
- helps you control weight,

- burns off unnecessary fat,
- improves your appearance,
- improves your sleep,
- improves your breathing,
- reduces stress,
- improves your mood and outlook,

- decreases your appetite,
- gives you more energy and decreases fatigue,
- uses time productively,
- reduces boredom,
- provides social opportunities,
- boosts your self-esteem!

Overcoming Misconceptions

Myth. Teenagers often feel they are invincible. **Fact.** The Centers for Disease Control report that among persons aged 1 to 24 years, approximately 68 percent of all deaths are due to 4 causes: motor vehicle crashes (33 percent), other unintentional injuries (15 percent), homicide (10 percent), and suicide (10 percent).

Behaviors contributing to these causes of death include: carrying a weapon; physical fighting; attempting suicide; drinking or using drugs while driving a motor vehicle; not wearing a seat belt while riding in a motor vehicle; not using a helmet while operating a motorcycle; and participating in unsafe water recreation.

- often handling firearms (−3 years)
- often working with or handling toxic chemicals (−3 years)
- often being depressed or unhappy (−5 years)
- driving or riding in a car without seat belts (−3 years)

Have students list on their papers any of these behaviors that they engage in. Ask them to add the total number of years for these behaviors and subtract the total from their projected age at death on their life line. Have them change the number of years expected to live to reflect the lost years. Explain that this could be their premature age of death due to unhealthy habits.

Have them put another dot on their life lines at their present age. Ask students to write five goals they would like to achieve and indicate the age by which they plan to achieve these goals on their life line. Ask them how many of their goals will be affected due to the lost years. Ask students if there are other unhealthy behaviors not on this list that would affect their life line. Have them begin a log to chart daily behavioral changes to improve their life expectancy.

L2 **CLASS ACTIVITY.** Ask students to write an example of one situation they were involved in during the past week that involved a risk behavior. Have volunteers share their experiences with the class. Allow students to role-play how they would handle each situation.

LD **CLASS ACTIVITY.** Have LD students come up with a dilemma and work through the five steps of the decision-making model together. Then, assign one to do on an individual basis for reinforcement.

L1 **EXPLANATION.** Explain to students that there are times when we do not have time to use the decision-making model in making all of our decisions. Ask students to give examples of some decisions that must be made quickly. Explain what to do in these situations. Allow the students to practice decision-making skills so they will be prepared for these situations.

- If they are reasonable and you plan to take them, what precautions can you take to increase your chances of a safe outcome?
- If they are to show off or to get recognition, what more healthful alternative actions can you take to increase your self-esteem?

The Decision-Making Model

The decision-making model is effective to use when you are faced with a situation that requires a major decision. It is designed to help you make decisions that will protect your rights, health, and self-esteem while also respecting the rights, health, and self-esteem of others.

Think of approaching a busy intersection in the road as the driver of a car. You would not continue at a high rate of speed. You would slow down and look for approaching cars, then proceed with caution. Failing to use caution puts your health and life at risk.

Now think of approaching a big life decision in the same way. How well you come through to the other side of the decision will depend in great part on how prepared you are when you enter the decision-making process, how carefully you look and proceed, and which road you finally choose to take. All of these factors can have major effects on your health and life. There are five basic steps that you need to take when faced with making a major decision.

1. State the situation that requires a decision.
2. List the possible choices.
3. Consider the consequences and your values—personal, family, religious, spiritual, moral, and legal.
4. Make a decision based on everything you know, and act on it.
5. Evaluate your decision.

State the Situation

It is important that you clearly identify the problem or situation. It is sometimes helpful to ask questions such as these:

- Why is there a decision to make?
- Why am I in this situation?
- Who is involved?
- How much time do I have to decide?

Use the decision-making model when faced with a major decision.

Family Health History. Help students recognize the health tendencies, strengths, and risks they may have inherited. Encourage them to hold a family Health-history Meeting, inviting grandparents, aunts, uncles, cousins, etc. Have them make a chart that lists all family members and ancestors and the following information about each: birth date and death date; genetic or inherited diseases; other major or chronic illnesses; known risk factors such as smoking, drinking habits, obesity, etc. At the bottom of the chart, have students list life-style changes family members can take to reduce those particular health risks present in their families.

List the Possible Choices

Ask yourself, What are all the possible choices that I could make? Write them down if this will help. Remember to include "not act at all" if such an option is appropriate.

Consider the Consequences

A **consequence** is the result of an action. You need to consider both positive and negative results of each choice as well as the possible short-term and long-term consequences. You need to think about how risky each of the alternatives may be. At this point in the decision-making process, you need to consider the many possible costs to you or others of making a particular decision. Some of the obvious costs of a decision might be time or money. Among the other questions you might ask yourself are these:

- Is it safe? Is it a reasonable risk?
- Am I comfortable with this possible outcome?
- How will it affect my health triangle?
- How will it affect my self-esteem?
- How will it affect others?
- How will my family feel about this decision?
- Is my decision something I will feel proud of?
- Is it legal?
- How might this decision affect my life goals?
- How might this decision affect other decisions I have made?

You may also decide that you need more time to gather some up-to-date health data, consider others' opinions, analyze alternatives, and weigh the possible consequences. You may also decide at this point that you want to consult various resource people, such as a doctor, teacher, parent, or counselor. Bouncing decision-making thoughts off someone knowledgeable and understanding can be a terrific help in guiding you in healthful directions.

Make a Decision and Act

Use everything you know at this point to make a decision. Remember, you are not perfect. There are no guarantees about results. However, as you move ahead, you can feel good that you have prepared so carefully.

KEEPING FIT

Twelve Attitudes that Can Hurt Your Health

Could your attitude be getting in the way of your total health? Are you stuck in any of these attitudes too much of the time?

- That could never happen to me.
- I'm too young.
- I don't know anyone who ever got in trouble doing that.
- What I do won't matter.
- I'll show him (or her)!
- I'll get around to a checkup when I'm older.
- I'll start tomorrow.
- But everybody's doing it.
- We're all going to die someday anyway.
- I've never been sick.
- Nobody else cares about me, so why should I?
- I'm in control. I can stop any time I want.

Across the Curriculum

Computer Science. Ask a computer teacher to help the students design a risk appraisal for their class on a computer. Students should decide which behaviors are considered to be the most common ones that teenagers engage in now. They should also determine an effective way to evaluate the risk behaviors. Have students print copies of the risk appraisal for each member of the class. Have students participate in answering the questions on the risk appraisal on a volunteer basis. Help students design a bar graph listing all the behaviors in the risk appraisal. Compare the results with the national statistics on the Youth Risk Behavior Survey at the Centers for Disease Control.

L1 RESEARCH. Ask students to watch television programs that involve people making decisions. List the decisions that were made and whether they were successful.

L2 WRITING. Ask students to collect cartoons featuring decision making. Have them write new captions based on information in this lesson. Have them share their cartoons with the class.

L3 WRITING. Designate students to develop a board game using behaviors teens engage in. Include the opportunity for students to make choices that will be responsible decisions or ones that will cause some risk. Have them provide results for the students to determine whether or not their choices were correct.

L2 PARENTAL INVOLVEMENT. Ask students how their problems compare with the problems their parents faced when they were teens. Ask if problems are more difficult to deal with today. Have students ask their parents about the types of problems they had as teens relating to school, friends, and family and to find out what methods they used to solve their problems. Ask the students to share some of their problems with parents and to seek their parents' help in solving these problems. Have students share the decision-making model with their parents and use it to solve a problem. Discuss with the class any similarities between problems parents experienced as teens and the ones teens have today.

L2 COMMUNITY INVOLVEMENT. Have students contact the Centers for Disease Control to determine the percentages of teen accidents and deaths related to engaging in risk behaviors in the United States.

L1 USING THE LESSON RESOURCES. For additional student activities, refer to the lesson resources on page 16.

If you get some last-minute information that changes the situation, you may want to go back to the first step and start the process over again.

Once you have made the decision, you need to take action. Timing can be important. You may need to set a deadline for yourself. Be sure you are ready to take action. If you have strong doubts, do not proceed.

Evaluate

After you have made the decision and taken the necessary action, reflect on what happened. Ask yourself these questions:

- What was the outcome?
- Was it what I expected?
- How did it affect each element of my health triangle?
- How did it affect my self-esteem?
- What was the effect of my decision on others?
- Would I make the same decision again? Why or why not?
- What can I take from this experience that I can apply in healthful ways to my next major decision-making experience?

One Big Decision: A Walk-Through

Consider the following situation and how one teen uses the model for decision making to make an important life decision:

Steve is 15. He will not get his driver's license for another 6 months. His friend Ben, who is 16, has driven him to a party.

When it is time to go home, Steve realizes that Ben has had a lot to drink. He is nervous about riding with him. He cannot offer to drive because he does not have a license. He cannot walk home because it is too far. There is no one else he knows well enough to ask for a ride home.

If Steve were to use the decision-making model, his thinking might go something like this:

1. **State the Situation.** I have to get home from this party, but I do not want to ride with a driver who has been drinking. What should I do?
2. **List the Choices.**
   a. I can ride home with Ben.
   b. I can ask someone here I do not know for a ride.
   c. I can borrow money and take a taxi or bus home.
   d. I can ask to spend the night and call Dad when he gets home.
3. **Consider the Consequences of Each Choice.** Steve might reason that if he rides home with Ben, there could be two possible positive consequences: Ben would not be mad at him, and they might get home without incident. Then Steve considers the many negative consequences of this possible choice: Ben could be arrested for drunk driving or cause a crash. Now Steve would think of the pros and cons for the other possible choices he has listed, thinking about the risks involved and the short-term and long-term effects of each.
4. **Make a Decision and Act.** Steve does not know if Ben is legally drunk, but he knows he is not in full control, so he decides that riding home with Ben is not an acceptable choice. He also discounts

After considering the consequences of his choices, Steve chose a safe ride home.

20 CHAPTER 1 YOUR HEALTH

Drama. Divide the class into groups. Have groups write and perform a skit.

Base the script on the following scenario: John is having a party at his house. He is inviting anyone who would like to attend. He explains that his parents will be out of town. He asks you to chip in for the kegs of beer and other refreshments. Ask students to act out a scene at the party and include examples of skills to deal with the possible risk behaviors that could occur at the party. After each group has performed, ask students to list all the possible consequences of attending this party.

riding with someone he does not know, since other people have been drinking. He calls his dad, who says he has to work a double shift, and after consulting with him, Steve decides to borrow the money from the host of the party and take the long bus ride home. Though it is hard for him to do, Steve tells Ben why he is not riding home with him and borrows the money from the host. He asks Ben to come with him on the bus, but Ben declines. Then Steve heads for the bus stop.

5. **Evaluate.** The next day Steve reflects on the situation. He thinks he made the right decision. He realizes that next time he should bring a few dollars with him in case that situation arises again. He also knows that from now on he will try to ride to parties with drivers who do not drink. He knows, too, that the next time he is faced with a friend who is drinking and who wants to drive, he will try to get the car keys away from the person.

The Benefits of Practice

Obviously, in situations like these, you may not feel comfortable sitting down and writing out all the options or walking through the decision-making model step-by-step with a friend. That is why practicing this model and walking yourself through the many kinds of situations and problems you are likely to face should be done ahead of time as a precaution. Doing so can make you prepared for those times when real-life risky situations occur, the same way practicing fire drills can prepare you for real fires.

Caring for your health is primarily your responsibility. The benefits gained from choosing healthy habits and making healthy decisions will be mostly yours to enjoy. Who would deliberately pass up opportunities for improved physical, mental, and social health; for higher self-esteem; or for a better quality of life? So go for it! Start today. Aim for total health!

DID YOU KNOW?

- According to a poll of 1,237 delegates to the National Association of Student Councils Convention in 1991, the three top problems facing American high schools are alcohol, apathy (having an attitude of not caring), and drug use.
- People in the 15-to-19 age group have the greatest risk of getting STDs, or sexually transmitted diseases. The greatest factor in this risk is ignorance of the facts.

LESSON 3 REVIEW

Reviewing Facts and Vocabulary

1. Define and use the terms *decision, risk, precaution,* and *consequence* in a paragraph, describing how they relate to one another.
2. What are the five steps in the decision-making model?
3. Why are the questions about consequences so important when using the decision-making model?

Thinking Critically

4. **Analysis.** Analyze some of the reasons a teen might take an unreasonable risk.

5. **Synthesis.** Write an interior monologue (the thoughts of one person written from the "I" point of view) in which a teen uses the decision-making model to decide whether or not to smoke a cigarette.

Applying Health Knowledge

6. Think about an important decision you have made. Analyze how you made the decision. Now rethink it, using the decision-making model.

DECISION MAKING AND HEALTH **21**

Answers to Lesson 3 Review

1. Paragraphs will vary. See pages 16, 17, and 19 for definitions.
2. State the situation. List the choices. Consider consequences. Make and act on a decision. Evaluate.
3. Doing so can prepare one for potentially risky situations, when the risk may not be apparent.
4. Answers will vary. Possible answers: having low self-esteem, feeling invincible, not considering consequences.
5. Answers will vary but should reflect steps explained on pages 20 and 21.
6. Answers will vary.

Check for Understanding

- Assign and discuss the lesson review.
- Assign and discuss the chapter review.

Evaluate

- Administer, grade, and discuss the *Lesson 3 Quiz.*
- Administer, grade, and discuss the *Chapter 1 Test.*
- Refer to the Performance Assessment strategy for this chapter. See pages T 23 to T 25.

Reteach

- Have students think of a decision they have made in the last year. Ask them to evaluate how they arrived at the decision and to compare their process with the steps given in this lesson. Which of these five steps did they use? Not use? How might the outcome have been different if they had used all five steps suggested?
- Ask students to complete *Reteaching Activity 3.*

Enrich

- Decision making must be learned and practiced to be developed. Ask students to develop a method of problem solving or decision making that can be used in making quick decisions.
- Ask students to complete *Enrichment Activity 1.*

Close

Ask students to state the most important concept in the chapter. Ask the students to list the behaviors that they would like to change in order to improve self-esteem and total health.

Helping Students Improve Their Health

Reinforcing Vocabulary

- **Passive smoke.** Smoke in the air coming from the burning end of a cigarette.
- **Aerobic exercise.** Vigorous activity which increases the lungs' capacity to hold air.

Teaching Strategies

L1 EXPLANATION. Students will sometimes be ashamed or embarrassed about negative behavior; i.e., smoking and drug use. Try to stress that this inventory is for their own use in determining a baseline for wellness; therefore, it is important that they answer all the questions truthfully.

L1 EXPLANATION. Throughout the rest of the course, students will have the opportunity to learn ways to improve their health habits. Encourage students to retake this self-inventory at the end of the course.

L1 DISCUSSION. In class, come up with a definition of *hobby.* Using this definition, discuss the wide range of hobbies available to students to reduce stress.

L1 CLASS ACTIVITY. Have students track their life-styles for one week. Ask them to list three positive behaviors and three negative behaviors that they took part in each day. Along with this, have them list alternatives to the negative behaviors.

Self-Inventory

What Is Your Level of Wellness?

HOW DO YOU RATE?

Number a sheet of paper from 1 through 36. Read each item below and write *true* for each one that accurately describes you or your behavior. Total the number of *true* responses. Then proceed to the next section.

Physical Health

1. I get at least 8 hours of sleep each night.
2. I brush my teeth and use dental floss after each meal.
3. I do not use tobacco, and I try to avoid passive smoke.
4. I keep within 5 pounds of my ideal weight or within the normal weight range for people of my age, height, frame, and sex.
5. I use a seat belt and refuse to ride in cars with drivers who have been using alcohol or other drugs.
6. I do at least 20 minutes of aerobic exercise at least 3 times a week.
7. I eat a healthy breakfast every day.
8. I do not use alcohol or illegal drugs or misuse standard medicines.
9. I relax 10 minutes each day.
10. I eat a balanced diet.
11. I use sunscreen when necessary.
12. I get dental and medical checkups once each year.

Mental Health

13. I generally like and accept who I am.

14. I ask for help when I need it.
15. I can express my emotions in healthy ways.
16. I can enjoy being alone.
17. I can name 3 good qualities about myself.
18. I feel okay about crying.
19. I can accept constructive criticism.
20. I can be satisfied when I have done my best.
21. I express my thoughts and feelings to others.
22. I have at least 1 hobby that I enjoy.
23. I deal with stresses as they happen and don't let them build up.
24. Sometimes I feel afraid, angry, sad, or jealous, but I am not overwhelmed by these emotions.

Social Health

25. I am generally satisfied with my relationships with others.
26. I meet people easily and am usually comfortable entering into conversations.
27. I can be myself when I'm with people I know well.
28. I can still participate in an activity even though I don't get my way.
29. I have at least 1 or 2 close friends.
30. I do not abuse others or allow them to abuse me.
31. When working in a group, I can accept other people's ideas and suggestions.
32. I can say *no* to my friends

and peers, especially when they ask me to do things that might damage my or someone else's health, safety, or self-esteem.
33. I can accept the differences in people.
34. If I have a problem with someone, I try to work it out.
35. I avoid gossiping about people.
36. I make important life decisions carefully.

HOW DID YOU SCORE?

Give yourself 1 point for each *true* response. A score of 10–12 in any of the 3 areas indicates a *very good* level of health in that area; 7–9 is *good;* 4–6 is *fair;* below 4 is *poor.* Then score your total health. 30–36 is *very good;* 21–29 is *good;* 12–20 is *fair;* below 12 is *poor.*

WHAT ARE YOUR GOALS?

Look over your scores and choose an area in which you scored low. Choose one item on which you need to work and use the goal-setting process below to begin making a change.

1. The behavior I would like to change or improve is ____.
2. If this behavior were completely changed, the benefits I would receive are ____.
3. The steps involved in making this change are ____.
4. The people I will ask for support and assistance are ____.
5. My reward for achieving this goal will be ____.

Meeting Students' Needs

For students who score *Very Good.* Suggest possible advanced readings in the areas that the students didn't score as well in to increase knowledge and understanding of a wellness life-style.

For students who score *Good.* Have students anonymously list methods they use for self-motivation.

For students who score *Fair.* Have students make a list of behaviors they would like to change and how to bring about change.

For students who score *Poor.* Have students review their risk behaviors and set written goals to change those behaviors to fit into a wellness life-style.

Building Decision-Making Skills

S tacy is a freshman whose brother is a junior basketball star. Dewayne, a friend and teammate of her brother, has begun to notice that Stacy has "grown up," and Stacy considers his attention very flattering since Dewayne is very good-looking and popular. Unfortunately his attention has progressed from casual comments to suggestive remarks.

Today he stopped by the apartment while Stacy's brother and parents were gone and acted in ways that made her very uncomfortable. Luckily her brother returned before Dewayne forced himself on Stacy any further. What should Stacy do? Some choices include the following:

A. Tell her brother, knowing he might harm Dewayne.

B. Tell her brother everything is OK at the time, but later confide in him and ask him to talk with Dewayne but not to harm him.

C. Don't tell anyone else, but tell Dewayne she doesn't want trouble and she doesn't want him touching her.

D. Tell Dewayne she likes him, but not his behavior.

WHAT DO YOU THINK?

1. **Choices.** What other options does Stacy have?

2. **Consequences.** How will everyone involved react to each of these options? How will her actions affect her relationship with Dewayne, other kids in school, her parents, and others?

3. **Consequences.** How would the different parts of Stacy's health triangle be affected by each possible action?

4. **Consequences.** What might happen if Stacy doesn't tell anyone?

5. **Decision.** What do you think Stacy should do?

6. **Decision.** Would the decision be different if the person were not her brother's friend?

7. **Evaluation.** Do you believe that there are certain ages when self-esteem and social maturity are strong enough that people are able to handle such situations? If you do, how can you prevent being in such situations before then? How have you handled such situations?

8. **Evaluation.** In similar situations what has been the best way for you to let the other person know how you differentiate between appropriate and inappropriate activity?

9. **Evaluation.** What have you found to be the best way to let others know your limits?

C arla is a senior in high school who is working part-time. Her grades are slightly below average. She plays on the basketball team and is on student council. After working at Yogurt Palace for six months, Carla has been asked to manage the evening

shift. With this promotion comes a 20 percent raise—and the satisfaction of knowing she'll be the youngest manager the store has ever had. She will have to increase her work hours from 16 to 24 hours a week. Should she accept this promotion?

WHAT DO YOU THINK?

10. **Choices.** What are Carla's choices?

11. **Consequences.** What are the advantages of each choice?

12. **Consequences.** What are the disadvantages of each choice?

13. **Consequences.** How might Carla's goals affect this decision?

14. **Consequences.** How might Carla's parents be affected by this decision?

15. **Consequences.** How might Carla's health triangle be affected by this decision?

16. **Consequences.** How might her friends be affected by this decision?

17. **Consequences.** What risks are involved in this decision?

18. **Decision.** What do you think Carla should do? Explain your answer.

Helping Students Improve Their Health

Building Decision-Making Skills

Teaching Strategies

L1 CLASS ACTIVITY. Have students participate in a role-play situation in which Stacy confronts Dewayne about the suggestive remarks and the way they made her feel. Dewayne can be either combative or apologetic.

L1 CLASS ACTIVITY. Create another role-play where Stacy is talking to her friends about the situation. Have one of the friends be very supportive and the other try to get her to go along with Dewayne's approaches.

L1 CLASS ACTIVITY. Consider a role-play experience in which Carla is talking with her boyfriend about the situation. Have her boyfriend be more concerned with not seeing her as much.

L1 COOPERATIVE LEARNING. Divide the class into groups of five to six students. Have these groups research the different wellness programs or assistance programs that employers provide for their employees. What impact have these programs had on the employer, both positive and negative? On the employee?

L1 DISCUSSION. Inform the class that a good friend is using drugs. Ask if they should tell their friend's parents? Why? Why not?

Discussing the Answers

Situation 1. In your discussion, it might be important to mention that neither Stacy nor anyone should give in to any situation or person that makes them feel uncomfortable. Emphasize the importance of having someone to talk to; i.e., clergy, teacher, or friend.

Situation 2. Stress the importance of both short- and long-range goals. For example, is college one of Carla's long-range goals? If so, how will the increase in hours affect her grades?

Answers to Chapter 1 Review

Using Health Terms

1. Life expectancy
2. Quality of life
3. Prevention
4. Self-esteem
5. Goal
6. Consequence

Building Academic Skills

7. Answers will vary but should be organized in a logical way, giving an accurate picture of the student's health history.
8. Mike has decided to improve his self-esteem by trying out for the wrestling team, asking Sandy to the dance on Friday, and studying three extra hours a week.
9. A branch or division.

Recalling the Facts

10. You are.
11. Nutrition, exercise, rest and sleep, hygiene, medical and dental checkups.
12. Answers should include two of the following: expressing emotions in acceptable ways; relating well to others; using one's mind to develop thinking skills.
13. A health triangle represents the relationship among one's physical, mental, and social health.
14. Answers should include four of the following: getting eight to nine hours of sleep a night; eating three meals a day at regular times; not smoking; eating breakfast daily; doing aerobic exercise regularly; avoiding alcoholic beverages; maintaining recommended weight.
15. Answers should include three of the following: gender, heredity, environment, culture, access to medical care, basic health habits.
16. Heart disease, cancer, stroke, accidents.
17. Availability and access to health care services, health education, immunizations and medications; and differences in nutrition, sani-

REVIEW

Using Health Terms

On a separate sheet of paper, write the term that best matches the definitions given below.

LESSON 1

1. The average number of years a group of people is expected to live.
2. The level of health and satisfaction that a person has in being alive.
3. Practicing healthful habits to keep one well and free from disease.

LESSON 2

4. The confidence and worth that you feel about yourself.
5. Something to aim for that takes planning and work.

LESSON 3

6. The result of an action.

Building Academic Skills

LESSON 1

7. **Writing.** Write an outline for a personal health video of your life. Divide your life into segments. Describe your health during each period, and tell what you or other family members did to promote your health. For each period, include information about your diet, exercise, diseases and injuries, relationships, and other activities that contributed to your overall health.

LESSON 2

8. **Writing.** Rewrite the following sentences using appropriate spelling, capitalization, and punctuation:
   Mike has decided to improve his Self-Esteem by trying out for the wressling team asking Sandy to the dance on friday and Studying three extra hours a week.

LESSON 3

9. **Reading.** In the following sentence, what is the meaning of *fork?* We came to a fork in the road.

Recalling the Facts

LESSON 1

10. Who is the most important person affecting your health?
11. What factors affect physical health?
12. Name two characteristics of a mentally healthy person.
13. What is meant by the health triangle?
14. List four life-style factors that promote good health.
15. List three factors on which a person's life expectancy is based.
16. What are the four leading causes of death in the United States today?
17. What causes differences in life expectancy from one country to another?
18. Why is health education important?

LESSON 2

19. List three factors that can affect your self-esteem.
20. Explain the difference between external and internal messages related to self-esteem.
21. What are two characteristics of people with high self-esteem?
22. What are two characteristics of people with low self-esteem?
23. List three ways in which you can improve your goal-setting skills.

LESSON 3

24. What are the factors that make a decision important?
25. Name two activities that involve risk. Describe the risks involved and tell how they can be reduced.
26. What is the purpose of the decision-making model?
27. List five factors you should consider in assessing the consequences of a decision.
28. During the decision-making process, what people might you consult for help?
29. After you have made a decision, what is the next step?
30. List five things you might consider in evaluating a decision you have made.

tation, and standards of living.
18. Health education provides people with the information they need to take positive action about their health.
19. How well you feel physically, mentally, and socially.
20. External messages are those that come from out-

side yourself; internal messages are those that come from within yourself.
21. Answers should include two of the following: accept self; able to admit mistakes; take responsibility for actions; like self; willingness to change; willing to learn and try new things; take chances; believe in

own abilities and talents; believe in own worth; practice healthful habits; have healthful relationships; show respect for others.
22. Answers should include two of the following: negatively influenced by others; engage in people-pleasing and approval-seeking behaviors; get identity from

REVIEW

Thinking Critically

LESSON 1

31. Analysis. Consider the seven life-style factors. Decide whether each one applies to you always, sometimes, or never. What conclusions can you draw from this experience?

32. Analysis. Anita is the starting forward on the girls' basketball team. She also runs cross-country. She eats three nutritious meals a day and gets eight hours of sleep every night. On school days, Anita spends three hours studying in the evening. Anita has never attended a high school social function. Draw a health triangle for Anita. Which side is the shortest? What can Anita do to balance her health triangle?

LESSON 2

33. Evaluation. Evaluate your self-esteem. In what areas do you feel competent? In what areas are you willing to try new things?

34. Analysis. Make a list of your best physical, mental, and social accomplishments. Then list some of your failures. Decide what contributed to your successes and what caused your failures. Describe how you could have turned your failures into successes.

LESSON 3

35. Synthesis. What precautions could a person take to reduce the risks involved of being in a car accident?

Making the Connection

LESSON 1

36. Social Studies. From the bubonic plague in Europe in the 1300s to epidemics carried to Central America by Spanish explorers in the 1500s, public health problems have always influenced history. Research how health problems of the past compare with today's public health issues including AIDS, environmental pollution, and population growth. Report how current health problems might affect the future.

Applying Health Knowledge

LESSON 1

37. Would you describe yourself as an optimist or a pessimist? Does this description change from time to time? Explain your answer.

LESSON 2

38. Choose an area in which you would like to improve your self-esteem. Make a poster listing five things you could do to build self-esteem in this area. Hang the poster in your room, and read it every morning when you get up. Do two of the items on the list every day.

LESSON 3

39. For each question below, write *important* if the decision you make could affect your health or the rest of your life. Write *unimportant* if it could not. Write a sentence justifying your answer to each question.
- Should I go to college?
- Should I buy the brown or the black shoes?
- Should I ask Sandy to go to the dance?
- Should I quit school and get a job when I turn sixteen?
- Should I transfer to a vocational high school?
- Should I smoke cigarettes?

Beyond the Classroom

LESSON 1

40. Community Involvement. Survey five people of different ages. Ask them what good health means to them. Compare your findings with other members of your class.

LESSON 3

41. Parental Involvement. Ask a parent or other adult at home to tell you about an important decision he or she had to make as a teen. Find out how the decision was made and if he or she believes it was the right choice.

external sources; engage in unhealthy behaviors to gain recognition or escape insecurities; spend time and energy defending self; avoid new challenges; put others down; have few satisfying relationships.

23. Answers should include three of the following: select one thing to work on; list what you will do to reach this goal; identify others who can help you; set a deadline; evaluate your progress at several checkpoints; choose a reward for yourself for achieving your goal.

24. How it affects: your health and well-being, someone else's health and well-being, your future, someone else's future.

25. Crossing the street, riding a bike, trying out for the school play, learning to ski, or riding in a car. Taking precautions such as receiving instruction or using safety equipment can reduce risks.

26. To help one make decisions that protect one's rights, health, and self-esteem as well as the rights, health, and self-esteem of others.

27. Answers should include five of the following: possible positive and negative results; costs to you and others; safety; effect on one's health triangle; effect on one's self-esteem; effect on others; family reaction; pride in decision; legality; effect on life goals; effect on other decisions.

28. Parent, teacher, counselor, minister, friend.

29. Take action; set a deadline.

30. Answers should include five of the following: outcome; meet expectation; effect on health triangle; effect on self-esteem; effect on others; willingness to make same decision again; growth acquired from this experience, and implications on future decisions.

34. Answers will vary. Respect student's right to privacy if discussing answers.

35. Answers will vary. Possible answers: drive only when alert and unimpaired by alcohol or medicines, follow all rules and road signs, accept rides only from people whose driving judgment you trust.

Making the Connection

36. Answers will vary.

Applying Health Knowledge

37. Answers will vary.

38. Answers will vary. Items to improve self-esteem should reflect skills listed on page 13.

39. Answers will vary. All items except the second one may be considered important. Accept answers with reasonable justifications that reflect students' life goals.

Beyond the Classroom

40. Answers will vary.

41. Answers will vary.

Thinking Critically

31. Answers will vary but should build on life-style factors found on page 7.

32. The social side. Anita needs to become involved in social functions and activities.

33. Answers will vary. Respect student's right to privacy if discussing answers.

Lesson Summaries

LESSON 1. Being able to feel and deal with a variety of emotions and situations is key to good mental health. Though it is difficult to identify specific standards for evaluating a person's mental health, some general characteristics of good mental health exist.

LESSON 2. Maslow's hierarchy of needs ranks things human beings must have to survive and thrive. As individuals progress through their hierarchy of needs, they move toward reaching their full potential, and in the process, develop a richer quality of life.

LESSON 3. Your emotions influence everything you do, affecting your thinking, behavior, and relationships. Patterns of negative emotions can greatly affect your physical health. Learning to recognize emotions and deal with them in healthy ways are two skills important to good mental health.

Introducing the Chapter

William Glasser provides a model on the psychology of strength versus weakness. He discovered that the most effective way to develop strength, happiness, and positive emotional health is to consistently apply the following pathways: a) giving and receiving love, b) becoming self-disciplined, c) gaining worth and recognition, and d) having fun. Have students brainstorm ways that they accomplish each pathway at home and at school.

Performance Assessment ✓

Refer to pages T 23 to T 25 for a Performance Assessment strategy for this chapter. See the *Performance Assessment Activities* booklet for additional suggestions.

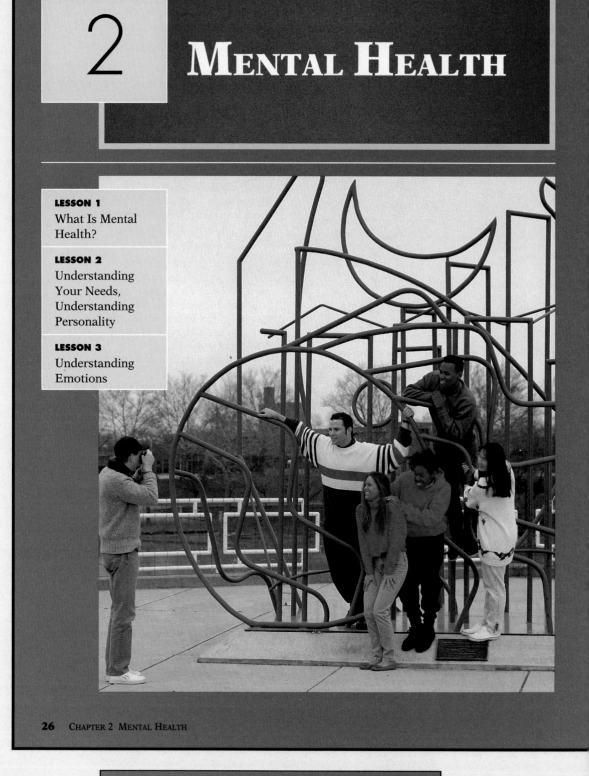

CHAPTER

2

MENTAL HEALTH

LESSON 1
What Is Mental Health?

LESSON 2
Understanding Your Needs, Understanding Personality

LESSON 3
Understanding Emotions

Key to Ability Levels

Teaching strategies have been coded for varying learning styles and abilities.

L1 Level 1 activities are basic activities and should be within the ability range of all students.

L2 Level 2 activities are average activities and should be within the ability range of the average to above-average student.

L3 Level 3 activities are challenging activities designed for the ability range of above-average students.

LD LD activities should be within the ability range of learning-disabled students.

LEP LEP activities should be within the ability range of Limited English Proficiency students.

WHAT IS MENTAL HEALTH?

L ike a collage made up of many different materials and shapes, the definition of mental health has many parts and can take many different forms. **Mental health** means generally accepting and liking oneself and adapting to and coping with the emotions, challenges, and changes that are part of every human being's life.

Mental health, like physical health, cannot be taken for granted. Working to achieve and maintain a high level of mental health should be a specific goal in each person's plan for achieving total health.

Everyone has varying levels of mental health at different times. Mental health does not mean feeling happy all the time. It does not mean always being in control. It does not mean never falling apart or never feeling angry, afraid, or insecure. In fact, being able to feel and deal with a variety of emotions and situations are key components of a person's "mental health collage." Being down, identifying why, doing something about it, and bouncing back can give a person a true sense of accomplishment and worth—and strengthen his or her mental health in the process.

A GREAT NATURAL FEELING

Did you know you can improve your feelings of well-being with strenuous exercise? When you engage in high intensity exercise, your body, specifically your brain, produces hormonelike substances called endorphins. These are released into your blood during intense exercise. Endorphins target your nervous system and can affect your sleep, eating behavior, body temperature, memory, ability to learn, and can reduce your response to pain. Besides feeling good, another benefit of exercise is that you will discover that success at exercise gives you good feelings about yourself.

Your Mental Health

It is difficult to identify specific standards for evaluating a person's mental health. However, some general characteristics of good mental health do exist. By looking at these characteristics, you can get an idea of what it means to be mentally healthy. You can also begin to determine your personal level of mental health. Keep in mind, however, that no one has every one of the characteristics described below all of the time. Still, knowing what the basic components of mental health are can help you define and work toward your own mental health goals.

A person with good mental health is described as one who

- feels good about herself or himself,
- feels comfortable with other people,
- is able to meet the demands of life.

WHAT IS MENTAL HEALTH? **27**

LESSON 1 FOCUS

TERMS TO USE
- Mental health
- Feedback

CONCEPTS TO LEARN
- Mental health means much more than not being mentally ill.
- There are varying levels of mental health.
- Self-esteem is directly related to your general level of wellness.

ATTITUDES AND BEHAVIORS TO EVALUATE
- Self-Inventory, page 44.
- Building Decision-Making Skills, page 45.

Focus

Lesson Objectives
After studying this lesson, students should be able to:
- explain how mental health means much more than not being mentally ill
- discuss the varying levels of mental health
- describe how self-esteem is directly related to an individual's general level of wellness

Bellringer
Write the following on the chalkboard for students to work on while attendance is being taken: *Write as many words as you can think of that describe a person with good mental health.*

Introducing the Lesson
Have students share their responses for the Bellringer. (Words may include *happy, carefree, smiling.*) Ask students whether they think good mental health is something that some people are simply lucky to be born with or whether they think it can be achieved. (They may provide a mixed response.) Assure students that good mental health is attainable, and tell them that in this lesson they will learn some ways of achieving it.

Building Vocabulary
- Have students write statements that use the vocabulary words in correct context. Their statements should be relevant to their own lives and be expressed in their own manner. Ask volunteers to share their responses.
- Ask students to complete *Workbook Vocabulary Activity 4.*

DID YOU KNOW?

- Laughing increases blood flow to the brain and stimulates the release of endorphins, helping you to feel better.

Resources for Lesson 1

- **Guided Reading** Activity 4
- **Workbook** Vocabulary Activity 4
- **Reteaching** Activity 4
- **Lesson 1 Quiz**
- **Performance Assessment** Activity 2

ABC News InterActive Videodiscs

Teenage Sexuality, Side 2
Ch 3 Self-Esteem and Sexuality

Drugs and Substance Abuse, Side 2
Ch 16 Building Self-Esteem

Guided Practice

L1 EXPLANATION. Tell students that being or pretending to be happy all the time is not necessarily mentally healthy. The array of emotions is a healthy part of everyone as long as one emotion does not dominate the others or is not expressed inappropriately.

L1 DISCUSSION. Ask students how they can express anger in a way that does not hurt themselves or others.

L1 COOPERATIVE LEARNING. Divide the class into three groups with the following assignments. Group One: List five ways to get out of a relationship with someone who has been your friend but now does not meet your standards of behavior. Group Two: List five ways to cope with the fact that you didn't get the job you badly wanted, which means you won't have money for a spring-break trip. Group Three: List five ways to deal with the fact that your friends can stay out all night on prom night and your parents won't let you. Ask representatives from each group to share their responses. Discuss alternatives with the class. Ask students to identify the positive and negative solutions. Which will promote mental health best?

L3 CLASS ACTIVITY. Have students create their own list of behaviors that indicate mental wellness and those that may indicate a need for help. The list should be as specific as possible.

LEP DISCUSSION. Making friends when you cannot speak the language is difficult at best. Have students share ways to let someone else know they are open to being friends. These could include body language, such as smiling or moving closer to a group in a classroom setting, or asking a peer for help with an assignment. Ask students to consider how it might feel to be in a school where they didn't understand the language. How would they want others to treat them? What might students do to help LEP students feel welcome? How might they help LEP students learn English?

FINDING HELP

For mental health information or to locate help, you can call your local Mental Health Association or contact:

- The National Mental Health Association
1021 Prince Street
Alexandria, VA 22314

Feeling Good about Yourself

When you feel good about yourself, you have self-respect. You take care of yourself. For the most part, you accept who you are and do not overestimate or underestimate your abilities. You recognize your value as a human being and do not consider yourself more or less important than other people. You try to make decisions that will add to your physical and emotional well-being. When you feel good about yourself, you are not overwhelmed by emotions for long periods of time, and when you do feel strong emotions, you find ways to express them that do not hurt you or others. You take pleasure in everyday things. You enjoy your own company. You are not too hard on yourself when you make a mistake, and you do not try to do things perfectly. Sometimes, you can even laugh at yourself.

Feeling Comfortable with Other People

Feeling comfortable with other people means allowing others to get close to you and allowing yourself to get close to them. It means feeling free to be who you really are. It does not mean that you are never shy or never feel uncomfortable or angry with others. It does suggest that you generally like and trust people and respect the differences in their appearance, race, religion, interests, and abilities. When you are comfortable with others, you make friends and find these friendships satisfying. You nurture friendships that are important to you and maintain at least some of them over time. You recognize when a relationship is hurting you and work to change or end relationships that are damaging to your physical or mental health. You consider the needs and rights of others but not at the expense of your own safety or self-respect.

Meeting the Demands of Life

Meeting life's demands means facing problems when they arise. It means being able to deal with the minor crises of daily life, and when the big problems come along, being able to reach out and ask for help. Meeting life's demands means not staying paralyzed when problems are big, but working to try to solve them instead. It means making positive changes when you can and letting go when you cannot. It means developing decision-making and coping skills and putting them to use. You become willing to learn from mistakes and disappointments. You plan

KEEPING FIT

Knowing When To Get Help

How do you tell the difference between normal ups and downs of daily life and more serious mental problems?

Consider getting help when
- you feel unhappy, sad, or numb for weeks at a time;

- your efforts to solve a major problem continue to fail;
- most of your energy goes into keeping it together instead of into enjoying daily life;
- you feel yourself withdrawing from others;

- you feel so insecure that you are sure people are watching you;
- you are living with or affected by someone else's illegal drug use, mental illness, or abusive behavior.

Meeting Special Needs

The Physically Challenged. Ask for volunteers to write a skit, poem, or song about their personal experiences with a physical impairment. Have them share their viewpoints on dealing with life's challenges. Ask them to portray how positive support from others helps, and negative responses hinder, when dealing with personal feelings of negativism or depression.

Lead the entire class in brainstorming ways students might be supportive of others.

The Mental or Emotional Connection. Ask for volunteers to share their personal experiences in dealing with traumatic experiences and losses. Have them discuss how they felt during times of crisis and what kind of help, if any, they received in coping with anxiety, fear, and stress.

Overcoming The Odds

Daryl is 15, and things in his family and in his neighborhood have been tough for a long time. As he puts it, "I was always the guy who stood out. I was real skinny and real tall. Friends used to call me names like Stick and Jav, for javelin, when I was younger. It hurt. Then I turned it around and became the best basketball player in the neighborhood. I showed them all. I put all my height and time and hope into it, you know, but I never figured my knees would give out. All of a sudden the one thing that made me feel like I was somebody was taken away. There I was again, with no hope and no way out.

"Things at home weren't any better. Since my mom split, I was doing a lot of the care for my two brothers and sister. We had money troubles. My dad had to work all the time. Sometimes I thought I would go out of my mind. I felt like there was this giant scream building up inside me and nowhere to go with it—not even to the basketball court.

"One night my dad slapped me around. He said I wasn't doing my part. I know now he was just totally stressed out, too, but it really hurt. I figured, what good am I? I can't do anything right. So I just took off.

"I went downtown and roamed around for a few days. I was lonely, scared, and confused. I had only a few bucks. I was hungry. All I knew was that I wanted to get as far away from home as possible.

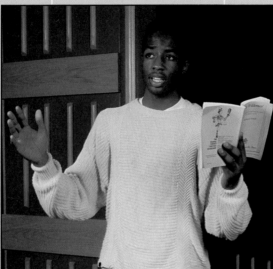

But if things at home were bad, things on the street were even worse. I'll spare you the details.

"The third night out this man gave me a card. He had a stack of them. It was for a runaway hotline. He told me to call them so at least they could let my father know I was okay. He said they wouldn't rat on me either. Then he showed me that on the back of the card was the address of a temporary shelter. He gave me money for the bus and wished me well. I had my doubts about him and that the place was what he said it was, but it was legit. I stayed there for three weeks.

"I'm back home now and things still aren't great. But this Youth at Risk group the shelter hooked me up with is helping me to learn that everything wrong in my life isn't my fault, that I have value, that I matter. I don't feel alone or crazy any more. Leon, the group leader, keeps telling us to remind ourselves that we've done really well considering all we've had to deal with. He also keeps telling us to tell ourselves when the tough stuff happens, 'This, too, shall pass.'

"I can't play ball, but I'm taking acting classes now at the High School of Performing Arts, and they're telling me I've got what it takes. And you know what? I'm starting to believe them."

1. What factors do you think were influencing Daryl's self-esteem when he ran away? Are any of these factors negatively affecting your self-esteem? If they are, what steps can you take to get help?
2. What factors or people helped him begin to recognize his own worth? Explain.

■ **Discussion.** What negative feedback did Daryl get throughout his life? What positive feedback did he get? What is the role of positive and negative feedback in how we feel about ourselves? (Daryl's negative feedback included being mocked by friends for his height and abused by his father. His positive feedback included earning recognition for his skills at basketball and acting. Negative feedback lowers self-esteem; positive feedback raises it.)

■ **Class Activity.** Have students review the skills for improving self-esteem in Chapter 1. From this list, ask the students to select a few steps Daryl might take to improve his self-esteem.

■ **Answers**
1. No longer being able to play basketball, money troubles, abandonment by his mother, too much responsibility at home, and abuse from his father; help could come from a teacher, counselor, or support group.
2. The support group showed him he was not alone; feedback in acting classes convinced him that he could do something well.

L1 **COOPERATIVE LEARNING.** Divide the class into four groups that are composed of students with differing ability levels. Select a scribe for each group and a task master to keep the group on the topic assigned. Have two groups develop a list of things a person might hear as he or she grows up that would enhance self-esteem. Have the other two groups develop a list that would inhibit or lower self-esteem. Give the groups 10 minutes to complete the initial exercise. Next have the groups with like assignments meet together to combine lists. There must be consensus on each item listed, not just a majority supporting the concept. Ask representatives to share results.

Meeting Students' Needs

Counseling. Students will seek support and counseling from their peers as their first step in getting help with problems. Often, teens don't know when they can provide real support and when they need to get their friend to a trained adult. Young people may feel that it isn't serious enough to bother someone or that adults would not understand. It's important to empower students with knowledge about mental illness and to know the difference between just being "blue" and being depressed. Let students know who is available to talk with in the school counseling department and in the community. Don't forget to include the students' parents.

Independent Practice

L1 PERSONAL INVOLVEMENT.
Tell students that sometimes people feel down for no reason and can't figure out why. For example, some people find that they feel really bad after eating certain foods, overeating, not eating anything, after getting too much sleep or after sleep that is always interrupted, after not getting any exercise, just before their menstrual periods, etc.

Tell students they can make a mood map to determine a pattern of these episodes by getting a blank calendar and writing down what their basic moods are each day and what their eating, drinking, sleeping, exercising, and other habits are that may account for how they feel. At the end of the month, see if they can establish both a pattern and a cause for their mood shifts. If their bad feelings continue, increase in severity, or are really incapacitating, however, they should get help.

L2 COMMUNITY INVOLVE-MENT. Suggest that students volunteer to participate in the "Big Brother, Big Sister Program" at their school or in their community.

L3 RESEARCH. Many schools have established peer-to-peer helpers. These student volunteers are trained by a counselor and work with students who express a need to "talk." The peer counselors learn how to assist their friends in problem-solving 10 common issues. Have students find out how to start peer helper groups in your school.

L2 SELF-ESTEEM. Create a "warm fuzzy" board. This is an area where students can leave secret messages for other students in the class. Give each class member the name of one person in class for whom they should provide a special treat or encouraging message each day for the duration of the mental health section. Tell students that they may give warm fuzzy messages to others in class as well. Tell them all messages should make the receivers feel better about themselves.

L1 USING THE LESSON RESOURCES. For additional student activities, refer to the lesson resources on page 27.

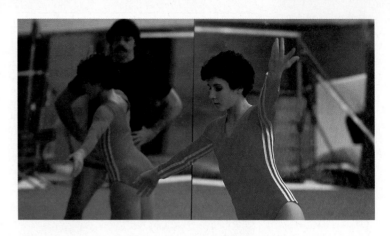

Positive feedback plays an important role in building self-esteem.

ahead for the future, welcoming new people, ideas, challenges, and experiences along the way. With good mental health, you work to put your talents and abilities to good use.

Self-Esteem and Your Mental Health

Self-esteem is directly related to your general level of wellness. How you feel mentally and physically, as well as how you take care of yourself—your health habits—are all affected by what you think of yourself. Having high self-esteem promotes good mental health.

The Role of Positive and Negative Feedback

How is self-esteem formed? Over the years you have received **feedback**—messages from others that tell you how they feel about you. You have received positive and negative feedback from many sources—from the adults who first took care of you, your brothers and sisters, extended family, neighbors, teachers, coaches, friends, and your peers.

From the moment you were born, you began to receive, process, and store these messages. Some messages were nonverbal ones. People hugged you, patted you, and smiled at you. Perhaps they frowned at you or ignored you. All of these actions made deep impressions on you. These first caretakers gave you verbal messages, too, like "Oh, what a

---

DID YOU KNOW?

- Nearly half of all teens have jobs. Working outside of school can add to your self-esteem. But working too much can be hazardous to your mental health. According to one recent study, teens who work more than 15 to 20 hours a week spend less time with their parents, more time daydreaming in class, and are more likely to drink, smoke, use marijuana, and have behavioral problems than teens who do not work as much.

K E E P I N G   F I T

Giving the Other Person a Break

One of the keys to good mental health is to realize that you have no real control over how others feel and act; you have control only over how you act.

The next time you feel someone has not lived up to your expectations, try to remember that
- everyone makes mistakes;
- everyone has value, even if they do not behave as you would like;
- most people who do and say awful things are themselves hurting;
- having compassion will help the other person feel better about his or her mistake;
- people are not in this world to make you happy.

Across the Curriculum

English. Have students write a story about someone they know well and admire greatly. Have them include the qualities this person has that they find so admirable. Ask them to explain the influence this person has had on their lives and why. Ask how this person has contributed to their self-perception or self-esteem.

Social Studies. Ask students to do a study of TV, radio, and music messages that repeatedly tell American society "Don't worry, be happy." Draw conclusions about the impact of these messages and why they may lead to a personal sense of failure or unhappiness.

Music. Have students write lyrics to a song or rap about how to feel positive about themselves.

cute baby!" or "Bad boy!" With all of these verbal and nonverbal messages that you took in, you began to develop your self-esteem.

By the time you reached school age, other factors started to play a part in how you viewed yourself. Now, in addition to how your family responded to you, your feelings about yourself were influenced by how friends, teachers, and coaches reacted to you and by how well you could perform in the classroom and on the playing field. More importantly, you often set the stage for how others would respond to you by how you felt about yourself.

So what does self-esteem have to do with overall mental health? A person who has received mostly positive feedback probably has higher self-esteem and better mental health than a person who has received mostly negative feedback. On the other hand, someone who has received lots of negative messages may be more likely to have low self-esteem and more fragile mental health. This person may also misinterpret the feedback he or she gets from others, sometimes assuming messages are negative even when they are not. It is never too late to begin improving your self-esteem and, in turn, your mental health. Spending time with people who give you positive feedback and choosing healthy activities and environments can be an important step in working to achieve full mental health.

WHEN CARING IS THERE

Many teens who come from troubled families or face other difficult situations growing up do turn out to be mentally healthy, productive young adults. They seem to bounce back more easily than others. Perhaps the strongest factor in their growing up successfully was not some inborn ability to cope with stress but the continual presence of a caring adult figure in that young person's life. This might have been someone inside or outside the family, such as a grandparent, a coach, or a neighbor. Whoever it was, though, the message is clear: the caring made the difference.

LESSON 1 REVIEW

Reviewing Facts and Vocabulary

1. Describe the characteristics of mental health.
2. Define *mental health*. Discuss in a paragraph how self-esteem is related to mental health.

Thinking Critically

3. **Analysis.** Make two lists—one of the positive feedback and one of the negative feedback that you received as a child. Describe how this feedback affected your self-esteem.

4. **Synthesis.** Using material in the chapter and your own experience, write a 10-step plan for improving mental health.

Applying Health Knowledge

5. Think of a caring adult who has been important in your life and who has given you positive feedback. Write a letter to this person, thanking him or her for caring and listing ways the positive feedback made an impact on your life.

Answers to Lesson 1 Review

1. Feeling good about oneself, feeling comfortable with others, and being able to meet life's demands.
2. Accepting and liking oneself and adapting to and coping with emotions, challenges, and changes that are part of every human being's life. Paragraphs will vary.
3. Answers will vary but may include encouraging words or hugs as positive feedback and critical words or being ignored as negative feedback.
4. Answers will vary. Possible answers: improve physical and mental health; make decisions that do not hurt self or others; enjoy life's simple pleasures; express feelings.
5. Answers will vary.

Focus

Focus

Lesson Objectives

After studying this lesson, students should be able to:

- recognize that all human beings have basic needs
- describe Abraham Maslow's hierarchy of needs pyramid
- state three main factors that influence the development of one's personality

Bellringer

Write the following on the chalkboard for students to work on while attendance is being taken: *List 25 needs you have and categorize them under the appropriate levels of Maslow's hierarchy of needs.*

Introducing the Lesson

Refer to the Bellringer. Have students identify the categories where most of their needs were listed. Ask why people tend to think in terms of physical needs rather than emotional or aesthetic needs. Ask students to assume all their physical needs were met and have them brainstorm emotional, aesthetic, and self-actualization needs of adolescents as a group. Explain that as people get older, their needs change.

DID YOU KNOW?

- *Sense of humor* originally referred to the Latin word for fluid, which is *humor*. The Greeks believed that health related to the balance of the body's basic component, or humors. Similarly, during the Middle Ages, people believed that physical and mental wellness came from the balance of four humors, which they thought flowed through the body. These were phlegm, black bile, yellow bile, and blood. Imbalances, they claimed, might result in emotional disturbances. They believed a cheerful person was full of warm blood, a person too easily angered had an excess of yellow bile, a lazy person had too much phlegm, and a depressed person had an overabundance of black bile.

UNDERSTANDING YOUR NEEDS, UNDERSTANDING PERSONALITY

All of us have basic needs. Getting these needs met is essential to a person's physical and mental health. Most human behavior reflects an attempt to get these needs met, and when they are not or cannot be met, the result is often physical illness, mental illness, or both.

A Hierarchy of Needs

Abraham Maslow, an American psychologist, presented human needs in the form of a pyramid. His idea is that we all have needs, but some are more basic than others. Consequently, there is a **hierarchy of needs**—that is, a ranked list of those things human beings must have to survive and thrive. The most basic needs come first. We must meet these before we even become aware of the other needs. For example, if the first level of physical needs is not satisfied, we have little awareness of our other needs. Our behavior is aimed entirely at satisfying our hunger or thirst. Once these needs are met, we move to the next level and begin to satisfy our needs for safety and security. It is not until these needs are met that we address our emotional needs, and so on.

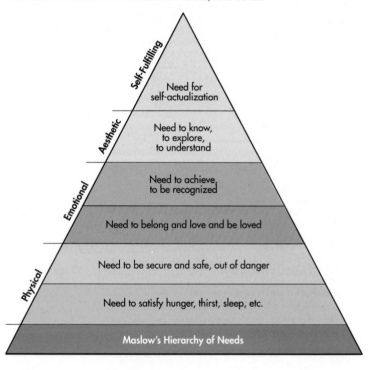

Self-Fulfilling — Need for self-actualization

Aesthetic — Need to know, to explore, to understand

Emotional — Need to achieve, to be recognized

Need to belong and love and be loved

Physical — Need to be secure and safe, out of danger

Need to satisfy hunger, thirst, sleep, etc.

Maslow's Hierarchy of Needs

Resources for Lesson 2

- **Transparencies** 3 and 4
- **Guided Reading** Activity 5
- **Workbook** Vocabulary Activity 5
- **Reteaching** Activity 5
- **Lesson 2 Quiz**
- **Poster** 4

Science and Technology Videodisc
Human Biology, Side 1
Ch 18 Detecting the Body's Magnetic Fields

ABC News InterActive Videodiscs
Teenage Sexuality, Side 2
Ch 3 Self-Esteem and Sexuality

Physical Needs

The most basic human needs (those on the bottom of the pyramid) are physical needs. These include the need to satisfy hunger, thirst, sleep, and so on. People who are denied food or water not only become physically weak, they become mentally weak as well. Food and water can preoccupy their thinking until these physical needs are met.

SLEEP AND MENTAL HEALTH

Our needs for sleep vary. At different ages and stages, we need different amounts of sleep. For example, a premature baby may sleep up to 20 hours a day. Adults need half the sleep they needed as young babies. Children spend more time than adults in the deepest stages of sleep—when the growth hormone is secreted. Children seem to tire out most quickly just before puberty. On average, teens need more sleep than they get.

So what happens when people do not get enough sleep? Effects of sleep deprivation include slowed reaction time, lack of concentration, increased sensitivity to pain, blurred vision, perceptual difficulties, and depression. Constant interruption of REM, or dream-state sleep, can result in disorientation and hallucinations. A good night's sleep, then, should be part of your mental health plan.

Emotional Needs

Meeting your emotional needs can have a great effect on your mental and physical health. The emotional needs—the need to love and be loved, the need to belong, and the need to feel worthwhile have an impact on your self-esteem. After we meet our physical needs, most of our behavior is an attempt to meet emotional needs.

The Need to Be Loved. Everyone needs to give love and to feel that he or she is loved in return. This is a basic need. Studies have shown that babies who are not picked up and talked to are stunted physically, emotionally, and mentally. They fail to thrive. Some even die.

The Need to Belong. Everyone has the need to belong. Human beings are social beings; that is, they need to be with and interact with people.

DID YOU KNOW?

- The amount of time parents devote to discussing emotions with their children may affect how sensitive these children will be to others' feelings when they become adults.
- Experts estimate that 90 percent of people feel shy in certain social situations, and 30 to 40 percent of the population is shy on a regular basis.

K E E P I N G   F I T

Stopping the Urge To Be Superhuman

Many people expect too much of themselves. Trying to be superhuman adds to your mental and physical stress and can lead to poor mental health.

To avoid these superhuman tendencies, try these suggestions:

- Don't try to be good at everything. It's okay not to win or not to be the best.
- Allow yourself to make mistakes.
- Take time to relax when busy times arise.

- Take a good hard look at why you stay so busy or so intent on being perfect. Remember, you deserve to be valued for who you are as much as for what you do.

Meeting Special Needs

The Emotionally Challenged. The Federation of Families for Children's Mental Health believes that young people with emotional, behavioral, or mental disorders

- have special needs that require individualized services,
- must be respected for their rights, likes and dislikes, values, strengths, and cultural and racial backgrounds,

- are entitled to full citizenship in their communities,
- must get what they need to achieve their full potential,
- belong with families and need ongoing relationships with adults,
- make contributions to their families,
- and must receive the help they need to stay at home with their families when possible.

34 CHAPTER 2 MENTAL HEALTH

L1 CLASS ACTIVITY. Divide students into groups of five or fewer. Provide each group with three sheets of different colored paper, using as many variations as possible. Ask the groups to write the emotions or feelings each color evokes from them on the corresponding color paper. Put the colored papers on the walls and have each group select a reporter who shares the group's responses with the class. Have students circle emotions that are the same but are responses to different colors. Discuss why similar reactions may come from different colors.

L3 CLASS ACTIVITY. Ask students to plan a color scheme for a children's hospital, home for the aging, psychiatric center, or hospice center. All rooms and areas of these facilities need to be considered in their plan. Have students develop the sequence of steps they will need to follow in order to plan the various color schemes.

L2 DISCUSSION. Write on the chalkboard the following statement. *You own your own behavior and should expect logical consequences as the result of your actions.* Give students time to think about the statement and then ask if they agree. You may need to explain the term *logical consequences* as it relates to behavior by giving an example, such as if you waste time in class, you'll need to spend an equal amount of time after school to complete your work. Ask students to write a list of negative and positive behaviors and logical consequences for those behaviors. Remind students that the word *consequences* does not always have a negative connotation.

Independent Practice

L2 WRITING. Ask students to visit an art exhibit at a local art museum or art gallery. There will usually be different types of art works displayed. If no exhibit is available, borrow a selection of paintings or artwork to bring into the classroom to make an exhibit. Ask students to describe in a brief written report which pieces of art they found pleasing and why.

Admiring art, in any form, can bring rhythm, order, and beauty into our lives.

Inherited traits help determine one's personality.

We need to feel like we belong to and are a valued member of a group. When we are mentally healthy, we meet these needs in positive ways that benefit ourselves and those to whom we are connected. When we are not mentally healthy, we may isolate ourselves from others or become overly attached to them.

The Need to Be Valued and Recognized. Another emotional need that all human beings have is feeling that they have personal value or worth. We have a need to achieve—to have ourselves and others recognize that we are competent at something and that we can make a positive contribution to the world. We must have something that we can do well, and we need recognition from others.

It is important to find healthy, positive ways to meet these needs for recognition. This is such a strong need that some people will seek negative attention just to be recognized.

Think of the child who is constantly being scolded for misbehaving. That child has probably learned that one sure way to get attention is to act up. How do you think this child might act as an adolescent or as an adult in order to meet the need to be recognized?

Aesthetic Needs

Maslow's hierarchy includes **aesthetic** needs. The word *aesthetic* means artistic; it means responding to or appreciating that which is beautiful. Aesthetic needs include our appreciation of beauty in its many forms. These needs also include the desire for order and balance in our lives. Our senses are constantly stimulated by the rhythms, forms, and colors around us, which can, in turn, affect our behavior and mental health.

Self-Fulfilling Needs

Finally, it is Maslow's theory that we each have a need to reach or strive for our full potential as a person. This striving to be the best that one can be is called **self-actualization.**

You can certainly survive with only the basic physical and emotional needs met. For a rich and full quality of life, however, you need to have goals and ideals that motivate and inspire you. Defining and meeting your self-fulfilling needs is a lifelong process, not something you simply achieve in one day. Each of us is continually striving to satisfy this need, and when the need is neither acknowledged nor met, depression, boredom, and other mental disorders can set in.

According to Maslow, in order to feel fulfilled, people need not only to do what they are capable of doing, but also to do it as well as they can. By challenging ourselves, Maslow theorized, we find a greater sense of fulfillment in life.

Personality and Mental Health

Everyone has a personality. Your **personality** is that complex set of characteristics that makes you unique and distinguishes you from everyone else. It encompasses all of your traits, attitudes, feelings, behaviors, and habits. It includes your strengths, weaknesses, likes, and dislikes. It

Across the Curriculum

Language Arts. Poetry expresses emotional, aesthetic, and self-fulfilling needs. Have students choose a poem by an American or an English poet and analyze the emotions expressed in its words and symbolism. "Lost" by Carl Sandburg is a good example. Have students express themselves by writing a short poem. Encourage them to use any of the following poet's tools: imagery, simile, metaphor, personification, onomatopoeia, alliteration, rhyme, symbols, rhythm, or free verse.

HEALTH UPDATE

LOOKING AT TECHNOLOGY

Emotions and the Brain

Among new technological findings about how emotions work are these:

- A tiny part of the brain called the amygdala in the temporal lobe is now thought to be the emotion switchboard—the central computer directing emotional responses.
- The right and left hemispheres, or halves, of the brain may have separate functions in registering and communicating emotions. Using electroencephalograms, or EEGs, which measure the electrical activ-

ity in the brain, researchers have detected less electrical activity in the left frontal lobes of people feeling sad and more electrical activity in that lobe when subjects are feeling happy. People who have suffered from clinical depression also show decreased left frontal lobe activity. When study subjects feel emotions like disgust, fear, and certain kinds of distress, instruments detect more electrical activity in the right frontal lobes of their brains.

includes how you see yourself and the way you respond to your friends, your family, and the world. All of these factors go together to make up the person that you are and the person that others see.

Three main factors influence the development of your personality: heredity, environment, and personal behavior. To some extent, these factors work to influence your personality throughout your life.

Personality and Heredity

Heredity is the first influence on your personality. You inherit some basic traits from your parents and relatives. The most obvious traits are physical ones such as the color of your hair and eyes, the shape of your nose and ears, and your body type and size. You also inherit basic intellectual abilities. What you do with these abilities determines how well they develop. There is increasing evidence that heredity also plays an important role in your emotions and perhaps even some of your behaviors.

DID YOU KNOW?

- People placed in unattractive or cluttered environments may have greater levels of stress than those living in ordered and pleasing environments.
- Painting cell walls pink has a positive, calming effect on inmates' behavior.
- People are less helpful in noisy environments.
- People may be less likely to express their emotions openly in cold or sparsely furnished rooms.

K E E P I N G F I T

Avoiding the "Tube Blues"

The average young person in this country watches 20 to 25 hours of TV per week. This is habit-forming and can be bad for one's mental health.

A 13-year study found that the longer a person sits in front of the television set, the more likely he or she is to feel sad, lonely, bored, or sleepy.

To find out how big a part TV plays in your life and your moods, turn the set off for a week. Keep a diary of your physical and emo-

tional reactions. Write down what activities you do to replace your tube time. Bake, play board games, read, play sports, listen to new music. Enjoy your newfound time and its positive effects on your total health.

UNDERSTANDING YOUR NEEDS, UNDERSTANDING PERSONALITY **35**

L1 **PERSONAL INVOLVEMENT.** Ask students to take a walk around a shopping mall and look at the window displays in different stores. Ask them to develop a rating sheet to evaluate five different window displays. The sheet should include display color, items on display, method of display, and why they like or dislike the window display.

L2 **WRITING.** Write the statement *Beauty is in the eyes of the beholder* on the chalkboard. Ask students to write a paragraph that either supports this statement or points out its weaknesses.

L1 **CLASS ACTIVITY.** Have each student print his or her name in a vertical line on a sheet of paper. Instruct students to list adjectives that start with each letter of their name and that closely describe their personality traits. Have each of them write a paragraph discussing how accurately their individual lists of adjectives reflect their personalities.

L3 **READING.** Have students locate and read magazine articles or newspaper clippings that discuss individuals whose basic needs are unmet for some reason, such as during wars, civil unrest, or due to social problems such as homelessness. Ask them to be prepared to discuss their readings in class.

L1 **WRITING.** Have students visit a store that sells greeting cards and read the messages on cards with friendship or caring themes. (Suggest that students seek out a store clerk if they need help locating such cards.)

Students should then compose an original greeting card that meets an emotional need of someone they care about. If they like, they may give it to the person.

L1 **USING THE LESSON RESOURCES.** For additional student activities, refer to the lesson resources on page 32.

Across the Curriculum

Math. Organize students into groups. Have students in each group brainstorm ideas for a "cheer-up list." Each group should come up with a list of crazy things to do to distract themselves from problems and depressing thoughts. Give as examples: Wearing a fur coat on the beach, and smiling widely all during class. Pool the best ideas and then survey students in other grades to see if they would see the items on the list as appropriate cheer-up material. Ask them to rate the items on a scale of 1-10, with 1 being low on the scale and 10 being high on the scale. Ask students to make a graph of their results and ask students to draw conclusions about whether age and being in different grades makes a difference in what people see as zany.

CHAPTER 2 MENTAL HEALTH **35**

Check for Understanding

- Assign and discuss the lesson review. For LD students, emphasize question 1.

Evaluate

- Administer, grade, and discuss the *Lesson 2 Quiz.*

Reteach

- Have students outline the lesson as they read it for a second time, using the lesson heads for Roman numeral entries. Ask them to list at least three facts from the lesson under each main entry.
- Ask students to complete *Reteaching Activity 5.*

Enrich

- Have students consider possible hereditary, environmental, and behavioral factors that they think have most influenced their personality development to this point. Ask them to identify any factors they could modify to enhance their mental health and further shape a personality that they desire.

Close

Have students give one positive example and one negative example of the role each of the following can play in the development of personality: heredity, environment, behavior.

Personality and Environment

The second factor influencing the development of your personality is your environment. Your environment includes all of your surroundings—your family, where you grew up, where you live now, and all of your experiences.

People who come from unhealthful environments may suffer from poor mental health as a result of exposure to rejection, physical or verbal abuse, hostility, or other negative behaviors.

People who live in healthful environments have support from others. These relationships help them feel good about themselves. Feeling good about themselves enables them to reach out and support others.

Personality and Personal Behavior

The third factor affecting your personality is the one you have the most control over—your behavior. The way you choose to act within your environment and with your inherited abilities has a very important impact on who you are.

Many factors affect how you act. You have already read how your basic human needs affect your behavior. Another very important factor in how you act is your values. **Values** are those principles that you find important and that guide the decisions you make and how you live. You develop your values primarily from your family, but values are also shaped and developed by your personal beliefs, religion, school, friends, the media, and society.

How do values affect your behavior and, in turn, affect your mental health? Your actions are reflections of what is important to you. For example, if you value good health—that is, good physical and mental health is important to you—you will practice good health habits. You will actively work to take care of yourself and will choose behaviors that promote health. It is unlikely that you will take risks that threaten your health or the health of others.

LESSON 2 REVIEW

Reviewing Facts and Vocabulary

1. In one paragraph, define *personality* and describe three factors that influence the development of a person's personality.
2. Over which of the three factors that influence a person's personality does a person have the most control? Why?

Thinking Critically

3. **Analysis.** Compare the environment in which you grew up with that of a friend's. How has your environment affected your personality?

4. **Synthesis.** Give an example of a situation in which a person would have two different levels of needs present but would make a choice to meet the more basic need.

Applying Health Knowledge

5. List five ideals that you value most, such as honesty or loyalty. Pick one of these. For a week record how your behavior reinforces or supports this value or ideal.

Answers to Lesson 2 Review

1. Personality is that complex set of characteristics that makes you unique and distinguishes you from everyone else. Paragraphs will vary but should include the terms *heredity, environment,* and *personal behaviors.*
2. Personal behavior, because one chooses how to act within the environment and with inherited abilities.
3. Answers will vary.
4. Answers will vary but should reflect the understanding of the hierarchy of needs with physical needs being met first, then emotional needs, then aesthetic needs and, finally, self-fulfilling needs.
5. Answers will vary.

UNDERSTANDING EMOTIONS

How do you feel right now? Are you in a good mood? Are you down or bored? Your feelings, or **emotions,** influence everything you do. They affect your thinking, your relationships with the people around you, your behavior, and even your success or failure at accomplishing a given task. Your emotions have an impact on your mental and physical health.

Having Mixed Emotions

Being a teen can be an especially emotional time. You want to be treated as an adult, but sometimes you still feel like a child. You get confusing signals both from inside and outside yourself. This pressure and turmoil can trigger all kinds of emotional responses. Sometimes these emotions may feel so strong that you want to act on them right away before you have had a chance to think them through.

You are experiencing what most young people do as they go through adolescence. This time of rapid growth and change is caused by body chemicals called **hormones.** Besides physical changes, hormones also cause emotional changes. It is important that you know that emotions are normal. Emotions themselves are neither healthy nor unhealthy. How you express your emotions, however, can be healthy or unhealthy.

Recognizing Your Emotions

Recognizing your emotions and handling them effectively are two of the most important skills a person can learn. Perhaps one of the most critical aspects of good mental health is learning to recognize and express feelings in a healthful manner. The key here is that this expression of emotions is learned.

LESSON 3 FOCUS

TERMS TO USE
- Emotions
- Hormones

CONCEPTS TO LEARN
- Your emotions influence everything you do.
- Chemicals called hormones cause growth and changes in the body.
- There are positive and negative ways to handle emotions.

ATTITUDES AND BEHAVIORS TO EVALUATE
- Self-Inventory, page 44.
- Building Decision-Making Skills, page 45.

THE RESPONSE

When you say that you are bored, what do you really mean?
- There's nothing to do that's fun.
- I'm feeling tired and can't get motivated.
- I'm lonesome.
- I'm not getting enough attention.
- No one asked me to go to the party.
- I have too much homework and don't know where to start.
- I'm depressed and don't really feel like doing anything.
- I'm totally stressed out.

If you focus on the real meaning behind your response, you will be in a better position to do something about it. What solution(s) would you give for each of the statements above?

UNDERSTANDING EMOTIONS **37**

Lesson Objectives

After studying this lesson, students should be able to:
- describe how emotions influence overall health
- give examples of positive and negative ways of handling emotions

Bellringer

Write the following on the chalkboard for students to work on while attendance is being taken: *Briefly describe in writing two situations when you experienced one of the following: fear, anger, hate, love, mixed emotions.*

Introducing the Lesson

List the emotions from the Bellringer on the chalkboard. Ask volunteers to share their situations. As the students share, place a check by the appropriate emotion. List the most common emotions recalled by students in order of frequency. Ask students if they would have placed the emotions in the same order of frequency based on their own experiences. Which emotions would they have ranked higher or lower? Why? Do this activity with each of your health classes and make a list that represents the larger sample of students. Share this with your classes the next day.

DID YOU KNOW?

- When you laugh, your body increases its production of endorphins, the body's natural painkillers. Your chest, abdomen, face, legs, and arms also get a workout. Laughter increases oxygen in the blood. A good laugh stimulates your heart and blood circulation as well as your immune responses. After hearty laughter, your body may stay relaxed for as long as 45 minutes.

Resources for Lesson 3

- **Transparency** 37
- **Decision-Making** Activity 2
- **Reteaching** Activity 6
- **Health Labs** Activity 2
- **Cooperative Learning** Activity 2
- **Lesson 3 Quiz, Chapter 2 Test**

Science and Technology Videodisc
Human Biology, Side 1
Ch 20 Panic Disorder and Brain Activity

ABC News InterActive Videodiscs
Tobacco, Side 2
Ch 19 Stress and Boredom

- Ask students to use the vocabulary words in three different sentences, leaving blanks where the vocabulary words would be. Collect the sentences and read some aloud, allowing students to fill in the blanks with the appropriate vocabulary words. Have students evaluate whether or not each statement appropriately used the vocabulary word.
- Ask students to complete *Workbook Vocabulary Activity 6.*

Teach

Guided Practice

L1 **DISCUSSION.** Introduce the term *hate.* Ask students to tell you what they hate. Make a list on the chalkboard. Ask students to rank-order the items listed to determine what evokes the most to least intense feelings. Ask students to give you other words that might better describe the feelings evoked by each situation. Discuss the use of the word *hate.* Explain how using expressions such as "I dislike, I'd rather not," or "That makes me angry" might at times be more appropriate and more clearly represent their feelings.

L2 **DISCUSSION.** Young people often feel they don't have charge of their lives. Some of this perception is reality, due to their age. Some is due to their perceptions of control. Ask students to discuss the perception of control in each of the following statements:

- I don't get a vote.
- I feel blame, shame, and regret.
- I say "yes" and mean "no".
- Please love me.
- I fear your disapproval if I do not do what you want me to.
- I wait for someone else to handle it.
- I wait for something else to happen.
- I have a good reason for every broken agreement.
- I "try" to get things done.

Have students come up with statements that reflect a person feeling "in control."

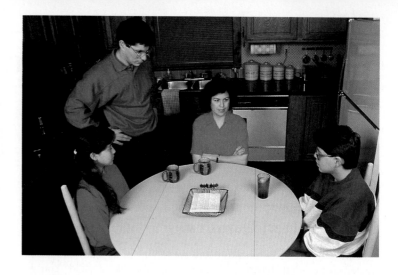

Learning healthy ways to express emotions is a key to good mental health.

In growing up, you have probably learned various ways of expressing your emotions. We learn from watching others, from our environment, and from our own experiences. Suppose that as a young child you were repeatedly told that crying is a sign of weakness. Do you think that now you would be likely to express an emotion of sadness by crying? How have you learned to express joy and excitement?

Handling Emotions in Healthy Ways

Emotions are neither positive nor negative. The way that a particular emotion is expressed differs from person to person and from time to time. The way emotions are expressed can be either healthful or unhealthful, positive or negative.

Learning to recognize emotions and deal with them in healthful ways are two of the most important skills leading to good mental health. Both kinds of skills can be developed with practice. If you learned unhealthful ways to express your emotions growing up, it is never too late to learn new, healthful ways.

Certainly the ways you express your emotions may have to do with your personality. You may be easily brought to tears or quick to fly off the handle. Many of the ways you express your feelings have been

K E E P I N G   F I T

Foods and Moods

Scientists have found that low-fat proteins tend to stimulate while carbohydrates tend to calm you down. Among the brain booster foods are low-fat milk, skinned chicken, and dried beans. Mood soother foods include bread, pasta, and cereals.

Need to stay awake to study? Don't load up on bagels. Need to get a good rest and calm down after a stressful day? Try a bowl of cereal or a piece of toast.

Do an experiment. Try to eat only low-fat proteins for a snack. Record your mood and mental alertness one, two, and three hours after you eat. The next day, repeat the experiment snacking only on carbohydrates. Compare your results.

38   CHAPTER 2 MENTAL HEALTH

Additional Information

Mental Health. Current research is underway to see if mental health problems can be prevented through education programs aimed at children. The types of programs currently being assessed include family-support programs, parent-infant education programs, early childhood education, school-based social competence promotion, and other social learning programs.

Some of the most important mental health problems requiring treatment in children and adolescents include autism, attention deficit disorder, hyperactivity, severe conduct disorders, depression, and alcohol and other drug abuse.

learned from observing others. Perhaps in your family, people have family meetings and talk about their feelings openly. Maybe they express themselves indirectly with looks or smiles or with behaviors like crying or slamming doors. Perhaps they do not talk much at all, and you learned from their example that emotions were something not to be shared. Even so, you can still learn healthful ways to express feelings. It takes practice.

As you read about the emotions described in the following sections, think about how you generally handle each of them. Think, too, about how, when, where, and from whom you probably learned these ways of expression. Evaluate whether or not the ways you express emotions are mentally healthy and add to the quality of your life. If you discover that there are more healthful ways to deal with your emotions, begin changing the way you respond to them.

Fear

Everyone has fears. If you did not have some fears, you probably would not have survived this long. Fear can be a safeguard, a protection from danger.

As with all emotions, fear produces a physical reaction in your body. When you experience fear, your sympathetic nervous system (see Chapter 12) responds by preparing your body for necessary action. Hormones cause your heart to beat faster and increase the force of each contraction. This sends an increased supply of blood to your heart and muscles, while blood vessels in other parts of your body constrict. Your breathing rate increases. These responses are ways your body prepares to protect itself from danger. When the situation causing fear is gone, your body returns to its normal state. Some people like the response the body gets during times of fear. You may know someone who enjoys going to scary movies or doing daring acts.

Psychologists believe that most fears are learned, except for possibly the fear of loud noises and the fear of falling. What are some fears you learned as a child? Before you were old enough to reason and to recognize potential danger, someone probably instilled some fears in you to help protect you. For example, fear of playing with matches or playing in the street probably helped keep you safe when you were young. As you grew older, you may have developed fear about being hurt in a car accident. This fear may have helped you decide to wear a seat belt every time you ride in a car.

Other fears are not helpful and can even be destructive. Unrealistic fears, fears that immobilize us, and fears that damage potentially healthy relationships are not healthy. They can, in fact, greatly affect a person's total health.

Healthful Ways to Deal with Fear. In dealing with fear, it is important to identify what your fears are and find someone you trust to share your fears with. Perhaps together you can think of ways to help lessen your fear. This person may give you a perspective you may not have thought of or suggestions on ways to deal with your fear. This person may know about other resources you can contact for help. Working to increase your confidence may also help you overcome your fear and/or give you alternatives in dealing with it.

UNDERSTANDING EMOTIONS **39**

DID YOU KNOW?

- Both males and females cry. Perhaps because of different levels of the hormone prolactin, when males cry they are more likely just to get watery eyes; when females cry, tears fall down their cheeks.
- On average, females cry 5 times more often than males.
- The average cry lasts 6 minutes.
- Peak times for crying are between 7 and 9 P.M.
- Though public speaking is the number one fear among Americans, at least 100,000 people a day make speeches in the United States. If they were all waiting in line for a turn to speak, the line would stretch out over 28 miles.

L2 **DISCUSSION.** Below is a list of 20 irrational statements. Have students discuss how each statement could affect one's mental health. Bring out in the discussion that everyone may experience these thoughts to some extent, but no one should allow such thoughts to be predominant.

- I must be punctual, courteous, orderly, and reliable all the time.
- I need to be first or win at all costs.
- I must control everything and everyone if I possibly can, including myself.
- I should not get angry, because everything can be solved by reason and intellect.
- I must be efficient at all costs.
- I must depend on intellect and logic and ignore my feelings.
- I should really not trust anyone.
- I deserve more respect.
- Being right is more important than anything else.
- I get along best with others when I can tell them things I know.
- I must be loved or approved of by everyone important to me.
- I am not worthwhile unless I am completely competent, adequate, and achieving.
- I am unable to control my own happiness.
- I am controlled by my history and by my important past experiences.
- I face disaster if I cannot find the perfect solution to my problems.
- I must always be prepared for the worst by constantly agonizing over it.
- I believe that wicked people should be blamed and punished.
- I face disaster if my life does not work out just as I plan.
- I am better off if I avoid difficulties and responsibilities rather than face them.
- I must become very disturbed over other people's problems.

L1 **DISCUSSION.** In what ways do teens' emotions affect their schoolwork? What impact do they have on relationships with friends and family members?

Across the Curriculum

Art. Many photographers specialize in capturing emotional moments. Ask an art teacher to talk about photography as an art form of capturing emotion and to share poignant works by famous photographers, such as Margaret Bourke-White.

Divide students into small groups. Using pictures from magazines (such as *Life*),

newspapers, and personal photos, have each group create a book showing the emotions of adolescence. To encourage students to study the photographs, have them write a caption for each picture. Students who enjoy doing their own photography might work together to record on film the emotions expressed by students in your school.

Ask groups of four to design a brochure for potential customers as if they were co-owners of a "rent-a-ghost" agency. These "ghosts" should be the apparitions of people's most common fears and nightmares. Students should design a brochure listing their available ghosts, describing their habits, appearances, special abilities, and hourly rental fees. Describe the kinds of occasions when people may want to rent a "ghost" and what can be accomplished by the rental. First ask them to brainstorm a list of possible "ghosts." Provide color markers and blank paper for students to fold into a three-part brochure.

L1 **DISCUSSION.** Have students identify a time they were truly frightened. What happened? How did they respond? Compare this to other fears they have but may not have experienced. Compile a list of childhood fears. How do these usually develop? (They are learned, usually from things children are told.)

L2 **DISCUSSION.** Ask students to list 10 things that make them angry. Ask if they always tell the person they are angry with what the problem is. Explain that we sometimes don't tell others we are angry for fear of hurting their feelings or believing they would not understand or probably just don't care. Instead we "bank" our anger in small deposits. After a while, the bank gets full and we cash in. We explode to vent our anger. The source of the anger may not even be relevant any more, but it all comes out and affects anyone around us. Ask students if they can relate to this description and if they have ever released anger in this way. Process other more successful ways to handle the emotions.

L1 **DISCUSSION.** Ask students to describe the difference between being angry and being violent. Ask why people sometimes become violent with the people they love most, such as their spouses, children, or grandparents.

L1 **USING CONFLICT RESOLUTION TRANSPARENCY 37.** Refer to the Teaching Transparencies Binder.

MAJOR FEARS

A team of researchers asked 3,000 Americans, "What are you most afraid of?" They received the following replies:

1.	Speaking before a group	41%
2.	Heights	32%
3.	Insects and bugs	22%
4.	Financial problems	22%
5.	Deep water	22%
6.	Sickness	19%
7.	Death	19%
8.	Flying	19%
9.	Loneliness	14%
10.	Dogs	11%
11.	Driving/riding in a car	9%
12.	Darkness	8%
13.	Elevators	8%
14.	Escalators	5%

According to a poll of 160,000 teens, the 3 greatest fears of 13- to 18-year-olds were losing their parents (58 percent), dying (28 percent), and not getting a good job or not being thought of as successful (21 percent).

DID YOU KNOW?

The word *phobia* comes from the Greek word *phobos*, which means "terror" or "flight." In Greek mythology, Phobos was the god who could inspire terror or panic, causing mortals to flee.

Among the phobias from which people suffer are:
- bibliophobia (fear of books),
- brontophobia (fear of thunder),
- claustrophobia (fear of closed spaces),
- murophobia (fear of mice),
- pyrophobia (fear of fire),
- aerophobia (fear of flying),
- zoophobia (fear of animals).

Anger

Anger is often thought of as a negative emotion. Perhaps this is because anger is often expressed in negative or violent ways. Keep in mind, however, that anger is a normal emotion that everyone experiences from time to time. Learning how to express anger in healthful ways is a sign of good mental health and emotional maturity. This can be difficult to learn, but it can be accomplished with practice.

Think of some ways you have seen anger expressed. Perhaps you have seen a child throw a temper tantrum or seen someone kick a wall or take a swing at someone else. Some people let their anger build up, without saying or doing anything, until they explode and strike out at anyone who happens to be around.

Healthful Ways to Express Anger. How can you express your anger in a constructive way? As in the case of other emotions, you must first recognize your feelings and, if possible, identify the source of your feelings. Sometimes there is nothing you can do about what is causing the anger,

KEEPING FIT

Some Tips to GROW By

GROW is a community mental health movement led by people in recovery from mental illness.

To handle an emotionally upsetting time, GROW suggests that you ask yourself these questions:

- What exactly am I troubled about?
- Is it certain, probable, or only possible that what I fear will, in fact, happen?
- How important is it?

- What shall I do about it?

The answers to these questions may help you see things more clearly and help you decide on the best course of action.

Additional Information

Fear. Here are some common and not-so-common phobias: hematophobia (fear of blood); ailurophobia (fear of cats); demophobia (fear of crowds); nyctophobia (fear of the dark); thanatophobia (fear of death); mysophobia (fear of dirt); batrachophobia (fear of frogs); belonephobia (fear of needles); agoraphobia (fear of open spaces); algophobia (fear of pain); ophidiophobia (fear of snakes); arachnophobia (fear of spiders); xenophobia (fear of strangers); phobophobia (fear of phobias); and panophobia (fear of everything).

but you can find ways to cope with the anger so that it does not build up. Letting your anger out in safe and nondestructive ways can help you reduce the risk that you might act on impulse and be sorry later.

Here are some suggestions:

- Channel your energies into productive work or recreational activity. Hammer, paint, build, play the drums, draw, or sew.
- Get away by yourself, or have a good cry. Often underneath the anger you will find sadness or hurt.
- Do hard physical exercise. Run, race-walk, swim, or play basketball.
- Punch a pillow or a punching bag.
- Count to 10 very slowly. Take a deep breath as you do, then slowly exhale to the count of 10. Repeat this breathing exercise several times to help you relax.
- Pick up the phone. Call a good friend and talk it out.
- Close your eyes and listen to good music. Let it take your mind off the situation.
- Write down exactly how you are feeling and why. Express yourself freely. No one needs to see what you write.

Learn to channel your anger in safe ways. Acting irrationally could prove dangerous to your or someone else's health.

What do you gain from trying to express feelings like anger? First, you have identified the emotion and expressed it. It is over, so you do not carry the feeling around with you, wasting energy by seething over it. Chances are you will feel better. The knot in the stomach that is usually present in emotions like anger subsides, or goes away.

The most important gain is that you are more likely to carry on healthful relationships with people you are close to. How is this so? Getting angry with someone is normal and likely if you spend much time with that person. You clear the air if you express the emotion. If you bury or ignore it, you will carry it around with you. Then it can begin to affect how you feel about the other person, which can be unhealthful for you and the relationship.

Talking with a friend is one way of channeling anger.

TALKING IT OVER

When you are angry with another person, follow these guidelines as you discuss the situation.
1. Tell what has happened and how you feel.
2. Start all your statements with the word *I*. Try not to use the word *you*. By using the word *I*, you are taking responsibility for how you feel rather than blaming someone else. When you use *I*, people have no need to be defensive and are more likely to talk out the problem with you because they do not feel attacked.
3. Tell the other person how your anger involves him or her.
4. Discuss what measures you think will reduce your anger and how the other person can help you. Offer to do your part.
    Following these steps does not ensure that you will solve the problem. The other person may choose not to talk about the problem. You have no control over how the other person responds or reacts. However, you have expressed your feelings in a healthful, constructive manner, and you will feel better for doing it.

CONFLICT RESOLUTION

Though many of the homeless people on America's streets can no longer afford housing, a large number are mentally ill individuals who have been discharged from mental hospitals without adequate follow-up care. They may refuse to stay in shelters for the homeless and may sometimes behave erratically. Their presence is being felt as a new "urban blight" by some of their more fortunate neighbors, who are disturbed by the presence of unwashed, homeless people in their nice neighborhoods. Imagine that such an individual has "camped out" in your neighborhood.

How would you feel?

How do you think your neighbors would react?

Additional Information

Adjustment Disorder. An adjustment disorder is a reaction to a source of stress that occurs up to three months after the event that caused the stress. The reaction may last as long as six months. In adults, the most common symptom of an adjustment disorder is depression. In children and adolescents, behavior and emotional problems are more likely to be symptoms. An example of an expression of an adolescent adjustment disorder might be temper outbursts and moodiness after an adolescent experiences failure in school. Therapists who treat this kind of disorder in adolescents usually involve other family members in order to get a complete picture of the situation that may have caused the adjustment disorder. A usual treatment for children and adolescents is supportive therapy, which involves reassuring and advising the patient, as well as teaching problem-solving skills.

L1 RESEARCH. Have students find out who the mental health helpers are in your school. Ask them to provide each person's name and title and to write a paragraph about what each person does to help young people. The list could include the school nurse, school psychologist, school counselors, and social workers affiliated with the school. To preclude having all students visit each of these individuals in their offices to acquire information about their jobs, you may want to invite the school's mental health helpers to class to speak briefly. Share the research with other classes.

L2 COMMUNITY INVOLVEMENT. Ask for volunteers to interview clergy—ministers, priests, or rabbis—about the kinds of counseling, if any, they provide to the people they serve. Have them find out what kinds of mental health problems are addressed. Request that students share their findings with the class.

L1 WRITING. Have students write paragraphs about how they feel when they are angry. Ask them to discuss any physical changes they notice.

LD WRITING. Have students rewrite, in their own words, the ways to improve mental health. Ask them to provide their own examples for each.

L1 USING THE LESSON RESOURCES. For additional student activities, refer to the lesson resources on page 37.

DID YOU KNOW?

- Having a bad temper is not a healthy trait for young adults. People who are hostile at age 19 are likely to have high cholesterol levels at age 40.

Strong emotions can produce tension. It is important for people to find healthy ways to express emotions. Taking a pill is not a healthy way to deal with emotions.

Understanding the Body-Mind Connection

Your physical and mental health are closely connected. Emotions can greatly affect your physical health. Strong emotions like anger cause physical changes to take place in your body. Your heart beats faster, you may perspire, your muscles tense, your stomach tightens. If you do not do something to deal with the emotions, the body does not relax. It stays in this state of tension. Over a period of time, fatigue can set in and physical illnesses may develop.

It is unhealthy to keep feelings inside, for you put an added strain on your body. In addition, you are not learning constructive ways to deal with emotions.

Consider these facts:

- People who hold emotions in and become highly stressed may experience an increased heart rate and rising blood pressure.
- Young people who have positive attitudes are likely to live longer than young people who have negative attitudes.
- Women with breast cancer who have positive attitudes are more likely to survive for longer periods of time than those who feel hopeless.
- Living with higher mental stress can lead to panic attacks and a lowered ability to handle pain.
- People who are frequently hostile have a higher rate of heart attacks.
- People under 30 tend to get sick more often from the daily hassles of life than do those in middle and later years. This may be because they feel emotions more deeply and do not yet have the perspective and the coping skills of older people. That is why learning these skills is so important to your overall health.

If negative patterns are developing, they may follow you throughout your adult life. The longer you practice them, the harder they are to change. Try some different ways of expressing your feelings. Learn new, healthful ways to deal with emotions. Try out some of the suggestions you have read about in this section.

DAILY EXPRESS

A new study suggests that writing and sharing your feelings in a journal can actually strengthen your body's immune responses—its ability to fight infections. In this study 25 adults kept a journal over a 5-day period, describing the most disturbing events that had happened in their lives and their emotional reactions to them. A control group of 25 people kept journals with insignificant details about their lives. When their immune systems were measured after 6 weeks and again after 6 months, the first group had an improved immune response, while the control group's immune response stayed the same.

Improving Your Mental Health

Throughout your life there will be periods when your emotions may seem to be stronger than usual. You may for a time feel overwhelmed, very frustrated, enraged, disappointed, or depressed. You also will have

---

Additional Information

Mental Aerobics. In France, there is a long history of doing mental exercises to stimulate the brain, memory, and imagination. Formal workshops, courses, and programs in clubs and clinics are now giving the middle-aged and elderly in France new formal and challenging mental puzzles and exercises to keep their minds working at top form well into old age. Among the

mental aerobics they routinely do: finding synonyms and antonyms for words and memorizing the names of people, train schedules, and poems.

Remind students that to keep their minds in top-notch form, both today and long into the future, they should give their brains a workout every day.

times when you feel really good about yourself. Regardless of how you feel, you know that there are steps you can take to feel better and keep improving your mental health.

Ways to Improve Your Mental Health

Emotions are like weather. You cannot accurately predict them. They are always there but are also always changing. They may come quickly from out of nowhere and pass just as quickly. Sometimes they bring sunshine, sometimes storms. In either case, you can choose healthful ways to deal with them by remembering these key points:

- Acknowledge that you are feeling an emotion strongly.
- Identify that emotion. Then identify the source of the emotion—what exactly you think triggered it.
- Express that emotion in a constructive way—one that will not damage you or anyone else.
- If possible, share your feelings with someone safe or neutral—someone not involved with the situation or person that has upset you.
- Remember that feelings are not facts. Do not feel guilty for feeling negative things. We all do. Do distinguish between the way you are feeling and the way you act about it. You may not have control over what you feel, but you do have control over how you act.
- Remember, too, that no matter how upsetting the emotion may be, it will pass—just like the weather.
- If a strong and disturbing emotion stays with you for too long and begins to affect your relationships or the quality of your life, get help. There are lots of people available to help you through a tough time. Remember that everyone needs help sometimes to deal with his or her emotions.

Many studies have concluded that it is not what happens to a person but rather that person's attitude toward what happens that makes a difference in his or her overall sense of happiness and mental health. So think positive. Be good to yourself. Be good to others. Take one thing at a time. Enjoy your life.

DID YOU KNOW?

- Pets can be good for your mental health. According to the Center for Interaction of Animals and Society at the School of Veterinary Medicine at the University of Pennsylvania, people with pets are approached more often for conversation.
- Some daily hassles that may make people angry are waiting for late people, being caught in traffic, waiting in line, waiting in the doctor's office, and getting slow restaurant service.

LESSON 3 REVIEW

Reviewing Facts and Vocabulary

1. What are some healthful ways to express anger?
2. How do emotions affect your overall level of health?

Thinking Critically

3. **Analysis.** What does the statement "emotions are neither positive nor negative" mean? Give examples to support the statement.

4. **Synthesis.** Write a dialogue in which a mind and a body talk to one another about the influence each has on the other's well-being.

Applying Health Knowledge

5. Keep track of positive and negative ways that you handle anger for one week. During the second week, stop yourself when using a negative approach and switch over to a positive one.

Check for Understanding

- Assign and discuss the lesson review. Have LD students focus on question 1, rephrasing the healthful ways to express anger.
- Assign and discuss the chapter review.

Evaluate

- Administer, grade, and discuss the *Lesson 3 Quiz*.
- Administer, grade, and discuss the *Chapter 2 Test*.
- Refer to the Performance Assessment strategy for this chapter. See pages T 23 to T 25.

Reteach

- Ask students to complete *Reteaching Activity 6*.

Enrich

- Ask students to use their imaginations to describe how they think emotions would "look" if they had color. Ask students to write an analogy for five emotions, such as "Anger looks like the color _____ because. . . ." Then have them paint five watercolors, one to express each of the emotions in their analogies.
- Ask students to complete *Enrichment Activity 2*.

Close

Divide the class into small groups. Ask each group to develop a radio announcement that focuses public attention on emotional health.

DID YOU KNOW?

- The ways of expressing emotions differ from culture to culture. Some cultures allow people to freely show fear, joy, sorrow. In other cultures, it is required that those emotions be hidden.

Answers to Lesson 3 Review

1. Channel energies into productive work or recreation; get away and cry; do hard physical exercise; punch a pillow or punching bag; breathe deeply and count to 10 slowly; call a friend; listen to music; write down your feelings.
2. Emotions affect one's thinking, relationships with others, behavior, and success or failure with a given task.

3. The ways one chooses to express one's emotions are either positive or negative, not the emotions themselves. Examples will vary.
4. Answers will vary but should reflect the interrelationship of mind and body.
5. Answers will vary.

Helping Students Improve Their Health

Using the Self-Inventory

Reinforcing Vocabulary

- **Optimism.** To anticipate the best possible outcome.
- **Consequence.** A result or effect.

Teaching Strategies

L1 **EXPLANATION.** Occasionally students will hide their true emotions. This inventory may be a starting point for students to being dealing with emotional problems, such as depression. Be aware of students who are inflexible and extremely high or low achievers. Often, students have a difficult time developing coping strategies that effectively deal with teenage pressures.

L1 **EXPLANATION.** Question 7 could be misinterpreted by parents and students. Some parents may not want limitations placed on their children. Explain that "limits" refers to what they are presently incapable of doing. Stress that they can often overcome those limits.

L1 **DISCUSSION.** Have students list behaviors that adolescents engage in to avoid problems. Discuss how they can change those behaviors.

L1 **DISCUSSION.** Discuss "life change" experiences and how they can affect an adolescent's life.

L1 **DISCUSSION.** Ask students if they can remember a time in their lives when something very good/bad caused them to experience stress. How did they cope with this situation?

L1 **DISCUSSION.** Ask students if they feel it is easier for boys or girls to express their feelings and emotions. Why do they feel this

L2 **CLASS ACTIVITY.** Have students brainstorm a list of mental health specialists. Then create a list of situations that might necessitate seeking help, and places students could go for appropriate help.

Self-Inventory

Rate Your Mental Health

HOW DO YOU RATE?

Number a sheet of paper from 1 to 10, 11 to 20, and 21 to 30. Leave a space between the three sections. Read each item below and write *yes* for each item that describes you all or most of the time. Total the number of *yes* responses in each part. Then proceed to the next section.

Part 1. Feeling Comfortable about Myself

1. I can express my thoughts and feelings.
2. I am not overcome by my emotions.
3. I can cope with both disappointment and success.
4. I recognize my own personal shortcomings.
5. I can laugh at myself.
6. I am generally optimistic and active.
7. I know my limits as well as my abilities.
8. I live by a set of values and know what is important.
9. I like and accept who I am.
10. I enjoy spending time alone.

Part 2. Feeling Comfortable with Others

11. I get along well with others.
12. I trust most people and want them to trust me.
13. I continue to participate when I do not get my way.
14. I do not try to dominate or control others.

15. I can accept differences in other people.
16. I feel I am part of a group.
17. I am interested in and enjoy being with others.
18. I have several satisfying personal relationships.
19. I do not feel consumed by fear, suspicion, or jealousy of others.
20. I am considerate of other people's needs and rights, but I respect my own needs and rights, too.

Part 3. Meeting the Demands of Life

21. I face my problems rather than avoid them.
22. I can ask for help when it is needed.
23. I do not make excuses for my actions.
24. I set realistic personal goals and have a plan for working toward them.
25. I can cope with change and see challenges and experiences as opportunities for growth.
26. I avoid trying to be perfect all the time.
27. I can relax and do nothing.
28. I know how to have fun and relax.
29. On important issues, I weigh the consequences before taking action.
30. I am generally happy to be alive.

HOW DID YOU SCORE?

Give yourself 1 point for each *yes* response. The highest possible score in each part is 10; the highest total score is 30. If you answered between 8 and 10 in any part, that suggests good mental health in that area. A score between 6 and 8 suggests acceptable mental health, though there is room for improvement. A score of 5 or less suggests that this is an area in which you need to set some specific goals for change and get some help. If your overall score is 25 to 30, that suggests good mental health; 20 to 25 suggests acceptable mental health; 16 to 20 suggests fair mental health. If your overall score is 15 or less, you should probably act now in seeking professional help.

WHAT ARE YOUR GOALS?

Write down one item from each of Parts 1, 2, and 3 in which you would like to improve. Under each of these three general goals, record three items for how you will go about improving that area of mental health. For example, under "I can express my thoughts and feelings" you might write: 1. Call one friend on the phone each day; 2. Read one book on communication skills. Include what resources you will use for making these changes and your timetable for achieving each goal. Record the progress you make with each of the three goals at the end of one, two, three, and four weeks.

Meeting Students' Needs

For students who score *Good*. Suggest becoming a peer pal to assist younger students in dealing with teen problems and challenges.

For students who score *Acceptable*. Suggest possible summer intern positions and careers in mental health that they could investigate.

For students who score *Fair*. Suggest that students consider reading a self-help book. Titles are available through your school media specialist.

For students who *Need Help*. (1) Do an "I Am Loveable and Capable" activity. (2) Suggest they do an extra-credit report on "positive coping behaviors."

Building Decision-Making Skills

A udrey is a senior at a suburban high school that sends a large percentage of its students to college. Much of the discussion in the school centers around the question, "Where are you going to college?" Audrey has given in to peer and parental pressure for three years and has taken college-prep courses. She has even passed up vocational opportunities that were appealing because of her perception of this pressure. However, as she enters her senior year, she doesn't want to take more college-prep courses. Instead she has chosen an interesting work-study program in marketing. She hopes to attend the local community college to obtain a two-year associate's degree. What should Audrey do? Here are some possible choices:

A. Tell her parents she feels this is an adult decision she must be allowed to make in accordance with her own life goals, and that she is prepared to pay her own way if necessary.

B. Using her counselor's and teacher's help, work with her parents to help them understand that this is the best alternative for her.

C. Play the game, so that she can get their financial help and go ahead to college and have a good time, then quit at some point and go to community college or to work.

D. Give her parents' plan an honest try.

WHAT DO YOU THINK?

1. **Situation.** Who will be affected by this decision? In what ways?

2. **Situation.** Where can Audrey get information about the differences between her plan and her parents' plan?

3. **Choices.** What other choices does Audrey have?

4. **Consequences.** What are the advantages of each choice?

5. **Consequences.** What are the disadvantages of each choice?

6. **Consequences.** Should parents or the student have the final say in this matter?

7. **Consequences.** How might Audrey's self-esteem be affected?

8. **Decision.** What do you think Audrey should do?

9. **Evaluation.** Have you been in situations in which you've chosen to ignore someone with more experience because you just knew your decision was right for you? Explain. How did you feel afterward? Would you handle the same situation in the same way now?

Discussing the Answers

Situation 1. While discussing the answers, be certain that the importance of Audrey having all the possible information regarding the work-study program and the community college, as well as college-prep classes and college is mentioned. From that information, Audrey and her parents could make an informed decision.

It is possible that the best resolve might include a compromise between Audrey and her parents. For example, if her parents are adamant about her going to college, she may have to agree to try college and switch to the community college if she is unhappy; or, she could attend the community college at her own expense.

Helping Students Improve Their Health

Building Decision-Making Skills

Teaching Strategies

L1 **CLASS ACTIVITY.** Have students participate in a role-playing situation in which Audrey talks to her parents about the decision she has to make. Have the parents take an opposing stance. To create more tension, have one parent for and one against the work-study and community college.

L1 **CLASS ACTIVITY.** Have students role-play Audrey discussing her dilemma with (a) her school counselor and (b) two friends. How might the two support systems differ in their suggestions? How would they be similar?

L1 **CLASS ACTIVITY.** Other possible role-plays pertaining to mental health include: (1) Your teachers and parents frequently compare you to your older brother/sister and want you to perform as well in sports and/or academics. (2) You are being pressured by peers to continue acting like the class clown, but this behavior has resulted in poor grades and disciplinary action by the teacher.

L2 **DISCUSSION.** Debate the value of advice columnists or the role of the school as the medium by which morals and values are being instilled in young people.

L2 **DISCUSSION.** Allow students to form two groups. Have one group support "pro-college curriculum" and the other "pro-skilled-labor curriculum."

DID YOU KNOW?

■ Workers with a high-school diploma average $967 per month. College graduates average $1,804, and those with master's degrees average $2,317.

Answers to Chapter 2 Review

Using Health Terms

1. Self-respect
2. Feedback
3. Emotional needs
4. Aesthetic
5. Self-actualization
6. Heredity
7. Environment
8. Values
9. Emotions
10. Hormones
11. Body-mind connection

Building Academic Skills

12. Meeting life's demands means facing problems and working to solve them.
13. Emotions are like weather. You can't always accurately predict them. They are always changing.

Recalling the Facts

14. Dealing successfully with a variety of emotions and situations. Feeling comfortable with others. Setting realistic goals.
15. Answers will vary. Accept any five statements from "Feeling Good about Yourself" on page 28.
16. Through feedback from others that illustrates how others feel about an individual.
17. Answers may include but are not limited to: significant caregivers from one's early childhood, siblings, extended family, neighbors, teachers, coaches, friends, peers.
18. Answers may include but are not limited to: hugging, patting, smiling, praising.
19. Answers may include but are not limited to: frowning, ignoring, criticizing, insulting.
20. By finding people, activities, and environments that provide positive feedback and avoiding those that provide negative feedback.
21. All humans have needs, but some are more basic than others. More basic needs must be met first.
22. Physical needs such as hunger, thirst, and sleep.

23. Slowed reaction time, lack of concentration, sensitivity to pain, blurred vision, perceptual difficulties, depression, and in extreme cases, disorientation and hallucinations.
24. Heredity, environment, and personal behavior.
25. By doing what one is capable of doing to the best of one's ability and by challenging oneself.
26. Depression, boredom, and other mental disorders.
27. Answers may include but are not limited to: looks, smiles, crying, slamming doors.
28. Emotions should not be shared.

Using Health Terms

On a separate sheet of paper, write the term that best matches each definition given below.

LESSON 1

1. When you feel good about yourself.
2. Messages from others that tell you how they feel about you.

LESSON 2

3. The need to love and be loved, to belong, and to feel worthwhile.
4. Artistic; responding to and appreciating what is beautiful.
5. Striving to be the best one can be.
6. Traits or characteristics that are inherited through parents.
7. Everything that makes up a person's surroundings.
8. Principles that are important to a person and that guide his or her decision making.

LESSON 3

9. Feelings.
10. Body chemicals that cause emotional changes.
11. The relationship between your physical and mental health.

Building Academic Skills

LESSON 1

12. **Reading.** What is the main idea of the following paragraph?

    Meeting life's demands means facing problems and working to solve them. It means using decision-making skills and learning from mistakes and disappointments. It means setting goals for the future and using your talents.

LESSON 3

13. **Writing.** Rewrite the following passage to eliminate sentence fragments and run-on sentences.

    Emotions are like weather you can't predict them. Always changing.

Recalling the Facts

LESSON 1

14. Identify each characteristic listed below that is a sign of good mental health.
    ■ Feeling happy all the time.
    ■ Lacking self-respect.
    ■ Dealing successfully with a variety of emotions and situations.
    ■ Feeling comfortable with others.
    ■ Setting realistic goals.
    ■ Being in control all the time.
15. List five characteristics of people who have self-respect.
16. How is self-esteem formed?
17. Who are some of the people that contribute to a person's self-esteem?
18. Give an example of positive feedback.
19. Give an example of negative feedback.
20. How can a person improve his or her self-esteem?

LESSON 2

21. What is the theory underlying Maslow's hierarchy of needs?
22. What are the most basic human needs in Maslow's hierarchy?
23. What are some effects of not getting enough sleep?
24. What three main factors influence the development of your personality?
25. How can people meet their need for self-actualization?
26. What are some effects of not fulfilling the need for self-actualization?

LESSON 3

27. Give an example of expressing emotions indirectly.
28. If parents do not talk about their feelings, what conclusions are the children in the family likely to draw?
29. Describe the body's physical reaction to fear.
30. What are two advantages of expressing anger in healthful ways?
31. List five guidelines for dealing with strong emotions in healthful ways.

REVIEW

Thinking Critically

LESSON 1

32. Evaluation. Make a list of ten events that took place during your day. How did each one affect your self-esteem?

33. Synthesis. Decide whether each statement below is likely to raise or lower the self-esteem of the person who receives it.
- "Thanks for cleaning the garage without being asked."
- "I see you cleaned up the kitchen, but why didn't you take out the garbage?"
- "Another *F!* Do you think you'll ever be able to pass an English test?"

LESSON 2

34. Analysis. Label each section below as a positive or negative way to fulfill the need for recognition.
- Getting a good grade on a test.
- Using offensive language.
- Stealing a car.
- Cleaning your room.
- Destroying someone else's property.
- Doing volunteer work in a hospital.

35. Analysis. Label each activity below as a healthy or unhealthy way to express anger.
- Breaking dishes.
- Running around the block.
- Punching a pillow.
- Counting to ten slowly.
- Talking to a friend about the anger.

36. Evaluation. Are there appropriate and inappropriate times and places in which to express emotions? Explain.

Making the Connection

LESSON 3

37. Art. A photographer is often able to capture emotional moments on film. Using pictures from magazines, newspapers, and personal photos, make a book that shows the emotions of teens. Study each photograph carefully and write a caption to go with each one.

Applying Health Knowledge

LESSON 1

38. How are relationships with others important to mental health?

39. Give five examples of how people with good mental health meet life's demands.

40. Describe a problem you have encountered at some time in your life. Tell how you coped with it.

41. Describe a relationship you've had that harmed your mental health in some way.

LESSON 2

42. What are some things parents can do to fulfill an infant's need to be loved?

43. Interview five people. Ask them to tell you three things they do well. Write a report summarizing their responses.

LESSON 3

44. Discuss one of your fears with a friend or classmate who has the same fear and another one who does not. Find out how each of them deals with situations in which this fear might arise.

Beyond the Classroom

LESSON 1

45. Community Involvement. Find out what kinds of mental health organizations exist in your community. Arrange to interview an employee of one of these organizations. Find out what the organization does to help people with mental health problems and how this person specifically helps others deal with their problems.

LESSON 3

46. Parental Involvement. Share with your parents and other family members the guidelines for discussing anger. Have all family members share one thing that makes them angry. Try to get everyone to follow the guidelines, but do not force any individual to participate. Be accepting of differences, even if you disagree.

29. The body prepares to take action; the heart beats faster and sends an increased supply of blood to the muscles.

30. The anger is let go; healthful relationships are fostered.

31. Answers will vary. Accept any five of the bulleted suggestions listed on page 43.

Thinking Critically

32. Answers will vary.

33. Raise. Lower. Lower.

34. Positive. Negative. Negative. Positive. Negative. Positive.

35. Unhealthy. Healthy. Healthy. Healthy. Healthy.

36. Answers will vary, but students should support their answers logically.

Making the Connection

37. Answers will vary.

Applying Health Knowledge

38. Answers will vary but should reflect the idea that relationships can affect one's self-esteem and ability to cope with the emotions, challenges, and changes of life.

39. Answers will vary but should include that such people work to solve their problems, use good decision-making skills, plan for the future, and put their talents and abilities to good use.

40. Answers will vary.

41. Answers will vary.

42. Answers will vary. Possible answers: hold, hug, kiss, smile at, and talk to their babies.

43. Answers will vary;

44. Answers will vary.

Beyond the Classroom

45. Answers will vary.

46. Answers will vary.

Overview

Lesson Summaries

LESSON 1. Mental illness affects the mind and prevents a person from leading a happy, healthy life. It results in an inability to cope in healthful ways with life's changes, traumatic experiences, and losses. Mental illness can be caused by a physical illness or injury that affects the brain or can occur as a result of psychological causes such as stress or poor coping skills. The four main categories of functional disorders are presented in this lesson.

LESSON 2. Being aware of and recognizing early warning signs of mental illness are the keys to getting help. Mental health care intervention is sometimes necessary. Such services are provided by psychiatrists, neurologists, and clinical psychologists. A host of counselors, social workers, and therapists often assist in the intervention process. The specific mental health counselor needed depends upon the nature of the illness and the type of treatment that is necessary.

Introducing the Chapter

Ask students to recall a particularly sad movie that they've seen that had a happy ending. Ask what events in the movie elicited their sad responses. What events occurred to turn the movie around and make it end happily? Tell students that sometimes people need help in dealing with the problems they face. Intervention often speeds recovery. In this chapter, students will study some of the resources available in the mental health field.

Performance Assessment ✓

Refer to pages T 23 to T 25 for a Performance Assessment strategy for this chapter. See the *Performance Assessment Activities* booklet for additional suggestions.

CHAPTER

3 MENTAL DISORDERS AND MENTAL HEALTH

LESSON 1
What Are Mental Disorders?

LESSON 2
Knowing When Someone Needs Help

Key to Ability Levels

Teaching strategies have been coded for varying learning styles and abilities.

L1 Level 1 activities are basic activities and should be within the ability range of all students.

L2 Level 2 activities are average activities and should be within the ability range of average to above-average students.

L3 Level 3 activities are challenging activities designed for the ability range of above-average students.

LD LD activities should be within the ability range of learning-disabled students.

LEP LEP activities should be within the ability range of Limited English Proficiency students.

WHAT ARE MENTAL DISORDERS?

Perhaps no area of health is less understood than that of mental illness. **Mental illness** is a medical disease or disorder that affects the mind and prevents a person from leading a happy, healthful life. People who suffer from some form of mental illness are often identified by their inability to cope in healthful ways with life's changes, traumatic experiences, and losses.

Mental illness carries a stigma in American society. A stigma means a mark of shame. People who have been treated for mental illness say that their biggest problem is their inability to be accepted by other people. Mental health professionals are working to help people better understand mental illness and thus lessen some of the negative attitudes that exist toward it.

Types of Mental Disorders

The term *mental disorders* is used to describe many different types of mental and emotional problems. Mental disorders are classified into one of two general categories: organic or functional.

When a disorder is caused by a physical illness or an injury that affects the brain, it is called an organic disorder. Brain tumors, alcoholism, infections such as syphilis and meningitis, and stroke are all possible causes of organic disorders.

Functional disorders occur as a result of psychological causes in which no brain damage is involved. These disorders result from conditions such as stress, emotional conflict, fear, or poor coping skills. The main categories of functional disorders are anxiety disorders, somatoform disorders, affective disorders, and personality disorders.

Anxiety Disorders

Most people experience some form of anxiety from time to time, but their fears do not affect their daily lives. Not so with people who have anxiety disorders. **Anxiety disorders** are disorders in which real or imagined fears prevent a person from enjoying life. People with anxiety disorders often arrange their lives so as to avoid that which makes them anxious or fearful. Four types of anxiety disorders are phobias, obsessive-compulsive disorders, general anxiety disorders, and post-traumatic stress disorders.

Phobia. When a person goes to extreme measures to avoid a fear and reacts in a way that limits normal functioning, it is called a **phobia.** A person with a phobia may be unable to carry out daily activities. Some mental health professionals believe that a phobia is related to some past experience that was upsetting to the individual. Although there is no longer a true threat or danger, the fear is still very real to the individual.

LESSON 1 FOCUS

TERMS TO USE

- Mental illness
- Anxiety disorders
- Phobia
- Hypochondria
- Manic-depressive disorder
- Schizophrenia

CONCEPTS TO LEARN

- Stigmas against the mentally ill take a variety of forms.
- Mental illness at any level poses special problems for the individual, the therapist, and society.
- Suicide affects the family, friends, and society.

ATTITUDES AND BEHAVIORS TO EVALUATE

- Self-Inventory, page 60.
- Building Decision-Making Skills, page 61.

Lesson Objectives

After studying this lesson, students should be able to:

- define organic and functional mental disorders
- define the four main categories of functional mental disorders
- describe signs of suicidal behavior and ways to help prevent suicide

Bellringer

Write the following on the chalkboard for students to work on while attendance is being taken: *Write as many words as you can think of when you hear the term mental illness.*

Introducing the Lesson

Collect students' responses to the Bellringer. On the chalkboard, list some of the students' words. Tell students that mental illness often is misunderstood, and that some individuals with a mental illness may not be accepted in the community. Others may be made fun of or may not get the help they need to lead satisfying, productive lives. Point out that mental illness can happen in any family and for this reason, it is important to understand mental and emotional disorders.

DID YOU KNOW?

- Each year about 6,000 students take their own lives and between 300,000 and 600,000 adolescents attempt suicide.
- According to a 1988 National Adolescent Student Health Questionnaire answered by 11,000 eighth and tenth graders, 18 percent of the girls and 11 percent of the boys said they had attempted suicide.

WHAT ARE MENTAL DISORDERS? **49**

Resources for Lesson 1

- **Transparencies** 17 and 38
- **Guided Reading** Activity 7
- **Workbook** Vocabulary Activity 7
- **Reteaching** Activity 7
- **Lesson 1 Quiz**
- **Performance Assessment** Activity 3

**Science and Technology Videodisc
Human Biology, Side 1**
Ch 19 PETT Scanner

- Have students divide a sheet of paper into three sections. At the top of the left section, ask them to define the term *anxiety disorders*. Below it, have them write descriptions of each type of anxiety disorder discussed in the lesson. At the top of the middle section, have them define the word *psychosis*. Underneath, have them write descriptions of three types of psychoses. At the top of the right section, ask students to define the term *personality disorder* and describe the three personality disorders identified in the lesson.
- Ask students to complete *Workbook Vocabulary Activity 7*.

Teach

Guided Practice

LD EXPLANATION. LD students may be able to learn the names and general symptoms of the disorders, but most will not be able to categorize them.

L1 DISCUSSION. Ask students to describe the difference between organic and functional disorders.

L2 CLASS ACTIVITY. Write the names of various phobias on slips of paper. Divide students into small groups, giving each group a separate slip of paper. Assign each group to locate the definition and characteristics of the phobia written on their slip of paper. Afterwards, bring the class together and have each group share the phobias they were assigned. (In addition to those phobias presented in Chapter 2, other examples include: astraphobia, a fear of thunder and lightning; bathophobia, a fear of depth; dromophobia, a fear of crossing streets; haptephobia, a fear of being touched; sistophobia, a fear of eating and food; taphephobia, a fear of being buried alive.)

L1 USING LIFE MANAGEMENT SKILLS TRANSPARENCY 17.
Refer to the Teaching Transparencies Binder.

L1 USING CONFLICT RESOLUTION TRANSPARENCY 38.
Refer to the Teaching Transparencies Binder.

Washing hands every few minutes for no particular reason would be an example of obsessive-compulsive behavior.

DID YOU KNOW?

- Each year in this country, more than 10 million adults are affected by serious depression.
- Studies suggest that women's depression tends to last longer than men's.
- After surveying 12,000 people in 105 different occupations, researchers concluded that lawyers are 3.6 times as likely to suffer from depression as other workers; school counselors 3 times as likely; and secretaries twice as likely as people in other fields. Among those with the lowest rate of depression: school teachers and doctors.

Claustrophobia, the fear of closed spaces, and arachnophobia, fear of spiders, are two examples of phobias.

Obsessive-Compulsive Disorder. A person who has an unreasonable need to think and act in a certain way has an obsessive-compulsive disorder. Obsessions are persistent thoughts or ideas that keep people from thinking about other things. Compulsions are urgent, repeated behaviors. For example, an individual with this disorder may feel the need to wash his or her hands 20 or 30 times a day, or to avoid stepping on cracks in the sidewalk. When these activities interfere with other daily functions and cause the person to overlook other commitments, such as time with family and friends, they are considered a problem.

General Anxiety Disorder. A person with a general anxiety disorder feels anxious, fearful, and upset most of the time, but for no specific reason. This constant state of anxiety may lead to a panic disorder, a sudden attack of fear and terror often characterized by trembling, difficulty breathing, and a feeling of loss of control. A person with a panic disorder can be anywhere when the attack begins, although the attack is usually connected with certain situations.

Post-Traumatic Stress Disorder. Post-traumatic stress disorder is a condition in which a person who has experienced a traumatic event feels severe and long-lasting aftereffects. This disorder is common among veterans of military combat, rape survivors, and survivors of a natural disaster, such as a flood, or an unnatural disaster, such as a plane crash. Typical symptoms include dreams about the event, insomnia, feelings of guilt, or an extreme reaction to an image or sound that reminds the person of the event. Symptoms may appear six months or even years after the event.

Somatoform Disorders

A somatoform disorder describes a condition in which a person complains of disease symptoms, but no physical cause can be found. **Hypochondria,** a preoccupation with the body and fear of presumed diseases, is an example of a somatoform disorder. A hypochondriac constantly feels aches and pains and worries about developing cancer, heart disease, or some other serious problem. Because hypochondriacs are convinced they are suffering from some imagined disease, they may refuse to believe doctors who tell them they are healthy.

Affective Disorders

Everyone has different moods. However, some mood swings are severe—from extreme happiness to extreme sadness—and last for a long period of time. When these mood swings interfere with everyday living, a person is said to be suffering from an affective disorder.

Clinical Depression. If feelings of sadness or hopelessness last for more than a few weeks and interfere with daily activities and interests, a person may be suffering from clinical depression. Clinical depression can

Across the Curriculum

Social Studies. Have students collect newspaper and magazine articles about wars, floods, earthquakes, tornadoes, hurricanes, and various other situations that might cause people in the United States and/or around the world to feel anxious, fearful, or upset. Discuss the articles, and ask students to share examples of situations in which they felt fear or anxiety.

History. Ask students to research mental disorders through history. In what way were mental disorders looked at differently during earlier times? What similarities still exist? Ask students to write their comparisons of mental disorders and the stigma attached to them.

occur over a single situation, or it can be about life in general. It can be a serious health problem that affects one's ability to concentrate, to sleep, to perform at school or work, or to handle everyday decisions and challenges.

Manic-Depressive Disorder. When a person's moods shift dramatically from one emotional extreme to another for no apparent reason, he or she may suffer from **manic-depressive disorder.** During manic periods, manic depressives may feel extremely happy or high. They may be overly talkative, often going rapidly from one topic of conversation to another. They may make lots of plans and take part in all sorts of activities. Manic depressives sometimes act impulsively or take unnecessary risks. Often this high period ends abruptly, and a period of depression sets in. Between episodes of extreme emotions, however, manic depressives may behave normally.

Although the exact causes of depression are unknown, depression tends to run in families. Any kind of emotional loss can cause depression. Unmet emotional needs and loneliness can also lead to feelings of depression. A healthy individual recognizes the feelings as a normal response to an event and looks for constructive ways to cope with feelings. It is when the person cannot cope with the feelings and is unable to get back into the swing of things that depression becomes a problem that could lead to thoughts of suicide.

Teenage Suicide. Suicide, the intended taking of one's own life, has become an increasing problem in the United States. Each year thousands of teenagers attempt suicide. In fact, suicide is now the second leading cause of death for people between the ages of 15 and 19. The rate of reported suicides among young people has nearly tripled in the last 30 years and continues to increase.

There are many possible causes of teen suicide. One explanation for suicide is that families are changing, and teenagers, like yourself, can have great difficulty coping with who they are, where they belong, and who cares about them. Teenagers also have many pressures to be responsible and to succeed. Failure in relationships, at school, or even at a job, can add to the depression. Pregnancy, alcohol and drug problems, having a sexually transmitted disease, or trouble with the law can be overwhelming to a teenager.

Sometimes feelings of failure or loss through death or divorce may be too much to bear. If you have experienced any of these situations and emotions, you know in a small way how bad a person can feel.

Manic-depressives often experience extreme shifts in their moods. These up and down feelings are often compared to a roller coaster ride. Can you explain the comparison?

K E E P I N G   F I T

Dealing With the Blues

If you are feeling down, or blue, here are some steps that you can take to help the blues pass. In addition to getting lots of sleep, healthful food, and exercise, you can try the following:
■ Make contact with family and

friends. Go to the movies, get a jogging buddy, or talk on the phone.
■ Spend some time with someone whom you consider to be positive, productive, and in a good state of mind.

■ Try writing down all of your feelings in a journal. If you're afraid somebody may read your journal, rip up and throw away your writings each day.
■ Be around people who are active. Spend less time alone.

Overcoming Misconceptions

Myth. The lives of people with mental disorders are completely different from those of most other people. **Fact.** Many people with mental illnesses go to school, get married, work, have families, do laundry, shop for groceries, etc.—like everyone else. **Myth.** Today, people are more knowledge-

able and accepting about the effects of a mental disorder. **Fact.** Unfortunately, a stigma still exists. The National Mental Health Association conducted a nationwide survey and reported that 43 percent of those surveyed considered depression to be an emotional or personal weakness.

L1 SPEAKER. Invite a speaker from a local crisis center or mental health center to talk to the class about types of mental disorders that affect teens and their families in the community.

LEP CLASS ACTIVITY. Have students draw pictures or make collages of newspaper and/or magazine illustrations to depict individuals experiencing mental disorders. Ask them to identify the disorder they are portraying.

L1 DISCUSSION. Have students brainstorm a list of words that stigmatize persons experiencing mental illness. Discuss the impact of these words on the victim and his or her family and friends.

L3 DISCUSSION. Have students discuss an antisocial personality. Are hermits a good example? Talk about the book *Walden* by Thoreau. Does it present a good example of an antisocial personality? Why or why not? Consider other examples in classical literature.

L1 COOPERATIVE LEARNING. Have small groups of students develop skits about a friend who is depressed or possibly considering suicide. Skits should focus on conveying the feelings of both the helper and the person being helped. They also should focus on ways to provide help and support.

L2 DISCUSSION. Ask students to list reasons for suicide attempts (e.g., unhappiness at home, disappointment in love, failure to achieve, etc.). Then divide them into three groups, and give each group one or two of the reasons. Have each group develop healthy ways to cope with its problem. Have them share their ideas with the class.

L1 DISCUSSION. Ask for volunteers to complete the following sentences: I feel that mental illness is. . . ; People with mental illness are. . . ; Someone with a phobia is. . . ; The hardest thing about having a mental disorder is. . . ; If I had a friend who was thinking about suicide, I would. . . ; When I'm feeling stressed or anxious, I. . . ; Some of the people I would ask for help if I couldn't handle a difficult situation are. . . .

Discuss students' responses to the sentence completions and reasons for some of the differences among them.

Independent Practice

L2 COMMUNITY INVOLVE-MENT. Ask for volunteers to develop a questionnaire surveying mental health workers in the community. Have them include questions about the types of mental disorders experienced by the population, as well as the age and sex of clientele.

L2 WRITING. Assign students to write a poem, song, or an essay about the stigma of mental illness and the sadness often surrounding it.

L1 PERSONAL INVOLVEMENT. Ask students to keep a personal journal of their daily experiences with stress, anxiety, fear, and depression. Have them write about how they dealt with their feelings. Tell them that their journals are personal and that they will not have to share them with anyone.

L3 COMMUNITY INVOLVE-MENT. Ask for students who are willing to attend and complete classes for crisis or hotline volunteers. Volunteers must be willing to serve a period of time after training.

L3 RESEARCH. Arrange for a small group of students to interview a suicide counselor or a person who answers a crisis hot line. What special training does the person have? What are the main objectives in talking with a person experiencing a crisis? What problems are most commonly heard?

L2 WRITING. Ask students to write letters to imaginary friends who confided that they are thinking about suicide. Have them include in their letters suggestions for handling potential suicides. Request volunteers to share their letters with the class.

LEP RESEARCH. Have students find examples of cartoons or other illustrations that stigmatize persons with mental disorders. Ask them to prepare an exhibit of their findings. Title the exhibit, "Can You Spot the Stigmas?"

L2 PARENTAL INVOLVEMENT. Ask for volunteers to enlist their parents' help in volunteering for a community mental health activity, such as a fundraiser, walkathon, fair, etc.

Teenagers who attempt suicide may be looking for some way to relieve the pain of a life that seems intolerable. Oftentimes suicide is accidental, a result of alcohol or drug abuse or misuse of firearms.

The vast majority of those who attempt suicide do not want to die. They are suffering and are making a plea for help. The lists below identify signs of potential suicides and suggest ways to help.

Warning signs of suicide can be verbal. Listen for

- direct statements, like "I want to die," "I don't want to live anymore," or "I wish I were dead";
- indirect statements, like "I want to go to sleep and never wake up," "They'll be sorry when I'm gone," "Soon this pain will be over," or "I can't take it anymore."

Warning signs of suicide can be reflected in a person's behavior. Look for

- depression, lack of energy;
- a change in sleeping patterns;
- an increase or decrease in appetite;
- withdrawal from usual social activities;
- loss of interest in hobbies, sports, job, or school;
- a good student's drop in grades or a poor student's new concern about grades;
- the giving away of possessions;
- increased risk-taking and other aggressive activity, such as driving a car recklessly;
- frequent accidents;
- personality changes—withdrawal, apathy, moodiness;
- previous suicide attempts (many of those who commit suicide have attempted suicide before).

Thoughts of suicide can also stem from certain situations. Look for warning signs if someone is

- experiencing a loss (death, divorce, breakup of a relationship);
- having difficulties with parents;
- encountering problems with school or employment;

CONFLICT RESOLUTION

Joyce is 15. She used to be a happy, popular student—that is, until her older brother Tim was diagnosed with schizophrenia two years ago. Now, her classmates often make remarks about how "crazy" Tim is and imply that Joyce might be "crazy" too. Joyce knows her mental health is fine and that, with good treatment, Tim may make a full recovery some day, but the cruel remarks have left her feeling bitter. Even though she loves her brother, she has started feeling resentful toward him. She thinks that if her classmates understood the illness better, especially the fact that, in Tim's case, it has a genetic cause, they would be less judgmental.

How can Joyce help her classmates understand Tim's condition?

HEARING SOMEONE'S CRY FOR HELP

Here are some suggestions for handling potential suicides:
- If a person threatens suicide, take him or her seriously.
- Ask whether the person has a specific plan and means to follow through with it.
- Be direct; talk openly and freely.
- Allow the person to express his or her feelings.
- Do not give advice. Express what you think, but do not be judgmental.
- Do not dare or challenge the person.
- Do not allow yourself to be sworn to secrecy.
- Be willing to listen. This affirms a person's feelings.
- Suggest to the person that he or she call a suicide center or crisis intervention center, or talk with a trusted teacher, counselor, doctor, member of the clergy, or other adult. If your friend refuses, talk to one of these people and your parents for advice on handling the situation.

Across the Curriculum

Art. Assign students to create sketches, posters, murals, or other forms of art to represent signs of mental health problems such as sadness, hopelessness, fear, and anger.

History. Many famous artists and composers have used their creative abilities as a defense mechanism to cope with stress.

For some, such as Dutch painter Vincent van Gogh and German composer Robert Schumann, mental illness has been part of their creative genius. Have students research the personal backgrounds of other talented people. How might their work have been different if they had not suffered from some form of mental illness?

- abusing drugs or alcohol;
- getting into trouble with the law;
- going through a time when there is no significant other person in his or her life (this is a critical factor, for a person who feels no one is interested in him or her has little reason to keep on trying);
- experiencing low self-esteem because of failure.

Personality Disorders

A variety of conditions are described as personality disorders. Unlike anxiety disorders, personality disorders have no apparent, distinct signs or symptoms. The individual continues to function, often effectively, in his or her environment. A person who has a personality disorder may respond inappropriately in certain situations or may interfere with others' interactions.

Antisocial Personality Disorder. One common personality disorder is termed the antisocial personality, characterized by a person's constant conflict with society. The antisocial individual may display behavior that is cruel, uncaring, irresponsible, and impulsive. Although he or she can distinguish right from wrong, the antisocial personality often does not care and therefore is usually in trouble with the law.

Passive-Aggressive Personality Disorder. People with passive-aggressive personality disorder are often uncooperative with others. They resent being told what to do, but they show their anger indirectly. For example, a passive-aggressive person who does not want to take part in a school activity may either forget to show up or may arrive late and leave early. He or she has not openly refused to participate, but the resentment is obvious by the failure to be reliable.

Schizophrenia. A mental disorder meaning *split mind*, **schizophrenia** disorder affects about 1 to 2 percent of the population and appears most frequently among people between the ages of 15 and 35. Schizophrenics are severely disturbed. They exhibit abnormal emotional responses or, in some cases, no emotional response at all. They may respond inappropriately in some situations. Some schizophrenics withdraw, often losing a sense of time and space. Others talk to themselves, act in an odd manner, or neglect to care for themselves. People with paranoid

FINDING HELP

Don't be in the dark about mental health and mental illness. The organizations listed below can provide helpful information.

- National Mental Health Association 1021 Prince Street Alexandria, VA 22314
- Mental Health Materials Center P.O. Box 304 Bronxville, NY 10708
- National Institute of Mental Health 5600 Fishers Lane Rockville, MD 20857

KEEPING FIT

Six Things to Remember When You're Down

1. Everyone has bad times and feels depressed now and then.
2. Remind yourself that you are not alone. There are many others who feel just as you do.
3. Be certain to take care of the basics when you're feeling down. Get enough sleep, eat regular and healthful meals, and get lots of exercise. Believe it or not, all of these efforts will improve your state of mind.
4. Avoid alcohol and other drugs, even caffeine. They will only add to the problem.
5. You, more than anyone else, control the way you feel.
6. It isn't what happens to you that counts as much as how you view what happens to you!

WHAT ARE MENTAL DISORDERS? **53**

Overcoming Misconceptions

Myth. Suicide is related to the weather. **Fact.** Attempted suicides or suicides have no connection to weather situation. **Myth.** Suicidal persons show signs of depression. **Fact.** Not all suicidal persons experience depression. Other emotional factors can be involved. **Myth.** A person can inherit tendencies toward suicide. **Fact.** There is no genetic connection to suicide. **Myth.** Depression is a sign of weakness. **Fact.** It is a sign of built-up emotional stress and/or chemical imbalance. **Myth.** If a person is suicidal, he or she will remain that way. **Fact.** Most people who are suicidal only remain that way for a limited time.

L2 WRITING. Have students write essays about imaginary experiences with depression. Each paper should come to some kind of conclusion regarding what was done about the depression. Have one or two volunteers share their papers with the rest of the class. Discuss each of the papers read. Talk about when help may be needed.

L3 WRITING. Assign students to design and write a "care manual" for friends and family members of a teen who has considered suicide. Have them include in the manual warning signs of potential suicide and suggestions for dealing with an individual who shows signs of sadness and hopelessness.

L3 READING. Have students look up skits or plays that deal with mental health, phobias, depression, post-traumatic stress disorder, suicide, or schizophrenia. Assign them to review the plays for accuracy, using information from the text.

L2 WRITING. Ask students to write thank-you notes to an imaginary individual who helped a friend who was considering suicide. Have them include in the letters some of the warning signs of suicide that the person noticed, as well as some of the steps he or she took to handle the potential suicide.

L2 RESEARCH. Assign students to research the lives (and in some cases, the deaths) of celebrities who experienced mental illness. Have them share their findings with the class.

L2 WRITING. Invite a school counselor, psychologist, or school nurse to speak to the class about being alert to the warning signs of depression and suicide. Afterwards, have students write a short paper, summarizing the presentation.

L1 USING THE LESSON RESOURCES. For additional student activities, refer to the lesson resources on page 49.

Assess

Check for Understanding

- Assign and discuss the lesson review. Allow LD students to prepare only a poster for question 6 or make the presentation a group project.

Evaluate

- Administer, grade, and discuss the *Lesson 1 Quiz*.

Reteach

- Have students write an article for the school newspaper presenting the warning signs for a potential suicide. Ask students to include verbal, behavioral, and situational warning signs.
- Ask students to complete *Reteaching Activity 7*.

Enrich

- Tell students they have a talk show on a local radio station. A caller claims that he or she has had trouble sleeping, concentrating, and handling everyday decisions for several months. What conclusion would students draw about this caller? What would they say to the caller?

Close

Write the lesson's major concepts on separate numbered slips of paper. Place slips in a box and let each student draw one. Next, going in numerical order, have students define and summarize the concept written on the slip of paper they have selected.

HELP WANTED

Psychiatrist

Are you fascinated by the human mind? Do you welcome the challenge of figuring out the most complex and abstract of all puzzles? If you do and you also like people and getting involved in their lives in a positive way, you might be the person we are looking for. You must be emotionally stable, a good communicator, and willing to make decisions and stand by them. Your extensive training, including your medical degree and additional years of study, will be a benefit to us and the people we try to help.

For more information contact:

American Medical Association
535 N. Dearborn Street
Chicago, IL 60610

HEALTH UPDATE

LOOKING AT THE ISSUES

Who Has the Right to Prescribe?

Only psychiatrists—medical doctors who specialize in mental disorders—can prescribe medicines for people who suffer from mental disorders. Now there is a plan to allow psychologists—professionals trained in mental disorders, but not in medical school—to prescribe medicines.

Analyzing Different Viewpoints

ONE VIEW. Many psychiatrists state that only those with medical training understand the impact of medicines on the mind and body.

A SECOND VIEW. Some psychologists argue that most medicines prescribed for mental disorders are described and adequately explained in sources like the *Physician's Desk Reference*, a standard medical resource book.

A THIRD VIEW. Still others claim that there is such a shortage of professionals available to help the vast numbers of people with mental disorders that the expanded right to prescribe would only help the plight of the mentally ill.

Exploring Your Views

1. If you were being treated for a mental disorder would you also be comfortable getting your prescription from a pharmacist, physician's assistant, or nurse practitioner who had specific training regarding medicines? Why or why not?

---

schizophrenic disorder mistrust others and are often suspicious. They may believe that they are being followed and that others mean to harm them.

Much research is being carried out to better understand schizophrenia. Some doctors believe its causes stem from a physical disorder. Others think it is genetic in nature. The disorder may come and go throughout life. Professional help is always recommended.

LESSON 1 REVIEW

Reviewing Facts and Vocabulary

1. Define the term *mental illness*.
2. Define and give the cause of an organic disorder and a functional disorder.
3. Describe a person who suffers from a phobia.

Thinking Critically

4. **Evaluation.** Why do you think there is a stigma attached to mental illness?

5. **Synthesis.** What might happen if someone suffering from some type of mental disorder fails to get professional help?

Applying Health Knowledge

6. Prepare a presentation for a group of classmates that discusses methods of preventing teen suicide. Include posters that list the warning signs of suicide.

Answers to Lesson 1 Review

1. A medical disease or disorder that affects the mind and prevents a person from leading a happy, healthful life.
2. Organic disorder—caused by a physical illness or an injury that affects the brain. Functional disorder—a result of psychological causes.
3. Avoids that which he or she fears, often preventing him or her from carrying out daily activities.
4. Answers will vary. Possible answers: Fear, ignorance, unfair stereotyping.
5. Answers will vary. Possible answers: The problem may get worse, the person may fail to get along with others, may be unable to complete daily activities, may harm self or others.
6. Answers will vary.

KNOWING WHEN SOMEONE NEEDS HELP

As you have read in this chapter, there are many different types of mental disorders. Within those types, the severity of the problems varies greatly. Unlike the symptoms of a cold or measles, specific symptoms of mental disorders are much more difficult to identify.

Signs of Mental Health Problems

Being aware of and recognizing early warning signs of mental disorders are the keys to getting help. Any of the following feelings or behaviors that persist over a period of days or weeks, and begin to interfere with other aspects of daily living, could be a sign that something is wrong:

- sadness over a specific event or for no reason
- hopelessness—the sense that one's life is out of control
- violent or erratic mood shifts
- inability to concentrate or to make decisions about daily life
- fear and anger at the world
- trouble getting along with others
- severe sleep disturbances—nightmares, insomnia
- compulsive self-destructive behavior—overeating, drinking, drug abuse
- frequent physical ailments, for which no medical cause can be found

Of course, no one symptom means a person has a mental disorder. However, any one of them may be an indication that stress in your life is building up and is something you need to look at closely, before more serious problems develop.

Health-Care Services for Mental Health

Often it is difficult to look in the mirror and do your own mental health checkup. Sometimes others are needed to help. Many times a friend may offer emotional first aid, that is, support and a listening ear, which may prevent more serious damage from taking place. However, this emotional first aid does not take the place of the aid that a mental-health professional can give.

The principal health-care providers for mental health are psychiatrists, psychiatric social workers, clinical psychologists, neurologists, and occupational therapists. These individuals may work in or outside a hospital setting.

Outside the hospital setting, help is available through marriage and family counselors, rehabilitation counselors, and pastoral counselors. In addition, there are various types of community services that deal specifically with rape, suicide, and family violence.

KNOWING WHEN SOMEONE NEEDS HELP **55**

LESSON 2 FOCUS

TERMS TO USE
- Psychiatrist
- Therapy
- Neurologist
- Clinical psychologist

CONCEPTS TO LEARN
- Serious mental problems require the assistance of a mental health professional.
- Mental health professionals work to help individuals improve their perception of self and the outside world.

ATTITUDES AND BEHAVIORS TO EVALUATE
- Self-Inventory, page 60.
- Building Decision-Making Skills, page 61.

Focus

Lesson Objectives

After studying this lesson, students should be able to:
- identify signs of mental health problems
- contrast the various types of care providers for mental health
- describe various therapies that mental health professionals can practice

Bellringer

Write the following on the chalkboard for students to work on while attendance is being taken: *Look at the following list of feelings and behaviors: sadness, hopelessness, violent or erratic mood shifts, inability to concentrate, fear and anger at the world, insomnia, and self-destructive behavior. Imagine that you or a family member is suffering from one or more of these, and write a paragraph about where you (or they) might go for professional help to deal with the problem.*

Introducing the Lesson

Collect students' responses to the Bellringer. Ask students to share reasons for their selections of help. Tell them that there are a number of health-care services for mental health, and they will learn more about them as they study this lesson.

DID YOU KNOW?

- Hypnosis is the introducing of a trance-like state through suggestion. According to Greek legend, Hypnos lived inside a dark cave where the soothing sounds of the river Lethe, the river of forgetfulness, put him into a trance, and he fell asleep on a comfortable couch. The word *lethargy,* by the way, also derives from this legend. Meaning abnormal sleepiness or laziness, its root is the same as that of the river Lethe.

Resources for Lesson 2

- **Guided Reading** Act 8
- **Decision-Making** Act 3
- **Workbook** Voc Act 8, Application Activity 3
- **Reteaching** Activity 8
- **Enrichment** Activity 3
- **Health Labs** Activity 3
- **Cooperative Learning** Activity 3

- **Lesson 2 Quiz, Chapter 3 Test**

Science and Technology Videodisc

Human Biology, Side 1
Ch 19 PETT Scanner

Human Biology, Side 2
Ch 13 Bulimia

- Have students design and write a public-service brochure, listing and defining the principal health-care providers for mental health. Ask them to include the five types of therapies used by psychiatrists. Upon completion, have them exchange their brochures with each other to check the accuracy of each definition.
- Ask students to complete *Workbook Vocabulary Activity 8.*

Teach

Guided Practice

LD EXPLANATION. Most LD students have been examined by a neurologist. Stress that there are reasons other than mental illness for seeing a neurologist.

LEP DISCUSSION. Start with a brief discussion of the saying, *Laughter is the best medicine.* Have students search through newspapers and magazines for cartoons that help them laugh about themselves or about life. Develop a collage using these cartoons and pictures that are lighthearted or otherwise relaxing to students.

L2 SELF-ESTEEM. Divide the class into small groups. Have groups list ideas for overcoming momentary bouts of sadness. (They may mention phoning a cheery friend, thinking of a funny experience, talking out their problem with a family member, and so on.) Discuss how a person's level of self-esteem might help cope with sadness or disappointment.

L1 CLASS ACTIVITY Have students bring to class cassettes, CDs, and/or records that contain songs that describe human feelings and human relationships. Discuss the feelings depicted in the music. Do these songs portray an attitude of wellness and mental health? Remind them to pay attention to the tone of the music as well as to the words of the song.

L1 DISCUSSION. Talk about ways teens can offer support to a friend who is feeling alienated or lonely.

Psychiatrist

A **psychiatrist** deals with mental, emotional, and behavioral disorders of the mind. This person has completed four years of medical school and one year of internship and has passed a state licensing exam. Although this is all that is legally required, many psychiatrists have also spent several years as resident physicians in an institution that treats mental illness. Because psychiatrists are physicians, they can prescribe medicines.

The psychiatrist uses many **therapies,** or treatment techniques. Among them are the following:

- psychoanalysis—an analysis of a patient's past, particularly his or her early life, to determine the early roots of a mental problem
- psychotherapy—patient and psychiatrist discussions to understand the problem and find a solution
- medical therapy—the use of certain medications to reduce a mental disorder or to prepare for the above two treatments
- electroconvulsive therapy—electric shock given to a patient under anesthetic, usually on one side of the brain (a treatment that can sometimes help severely depressed patients)
- group therapy—meetings held with other people with similar problems, during which the participants pool their experiences and learn from one another, with the doctor as a guide

Neurologist

A **neurologist** is a physician who specializes in organic disorders of the brain and nervous system. This person has a degree in medicine, postgraduate training and experience in this field, certification as a specialist, and a state license permitting practice. Neurologists usually have received some training in psychiatry. Those who specialize in surgery are called neurosurgeons or neural surgeons. Consultation with and testing by a neurologist may be required for patients whose mental symptoms are suspected of being caused by an organic disease.

Clinical Psychologist

The **clinical psychologist** is a psychologist who diagnoses and treats emotional and behavioral disorders. The person may have any

---

K E E P I N G   F I T

When Does Depression Warrant Help?

According to the American Psychiatric Association, if you or someone you know has had four or more of the following symptoms for more than two weeks, help should be sought:
- change of appetite or weight
- change in sleeping patterns
- loss of interest in activities
- loss of energy or tiredness
- feelings of being worthless
- feelings of hopelessness
- feelings of inappropriate guilt
- problems with concentration, thinking, or decision making
- repeated thoughts of death
- overwhelming sadness
- disturbed thinking not based on reality
- physical symptoms such as stomachaches and headaches

Additional Information

Dance Therapy. Young people often cannot seem to be reached by words alone when they are emotionally distressed. Only when a person learns to express what's hurting him or her can the healing begin. Dance therapy gives people permission to have their emotions and feelings, whether they are good or bad, and confront them. Where traditional psychotherapy uses words, dance therapy works with movement and words to change feelings. Dance can be an especially intimate and powerful medium for therapy. An angry person can display and work through emotions in aggressive dance, which enables the release of pent-up emotions. A frightened child can become a strong giant, able to conquer all of the bad things in his or her world.

Overcoming The Odds

Today, Dr. Warren A. Rhodes, a child psychologist, professor, and author, is a model of success. But it wasn't always that way. In fact, as a teen, he was a juvenile delinquent.

Rhodes started out in Baltimore, Maryland, where he lived with his parents and two siblings. He says, "Things were going well for me until the fifth grade when my mother's brother died. Two of his boys came to live with us. They fought with knives, skipped school, and eventually got in trouble with the law. One Christmas I got a lot of tips for selling papers. I hid the money in my sock to protect it from the people in my house who might steal it. While I was asleep, somebody cut the money out of my sock, and when I woke up, everybody was laughing about how they were slick enough to get my money. That's when I said if you can't beat 'em, join 'em."

"Joining them" took Rhodes onto a track that included failing sixth grade, failing eighth grade, and finally getting kicked out of school.

"I started shooting dope at 16." New at shooting, he almost killed himself accidentally by injecting air into his veins, but his brother stopped him. While still a teen, Rhodes was arrested three times.

Finally, a fight over a girl took Rhodes to his turning point. He says, "When someone broke up the fight, I told them I'd be back. I got my brother and 15 of his friends to go after those dudes. They were waiting for us. A shot rang out. My brother was shot in the head near the temple. It grazed his head, but if his head had been turned differently, he could have died. That was the worst thing. I realized I had to change because, otherwise, I'd either be dead in a year or I'd kill somebody."

Rhodes signed up with the Job Corps where he stayed for eight months. "I got certificates for perfect attendance. Teachers saw something in me and kept encouraging me. Ultimately, I finished the pro-gram." He felt triumphant.

Rhodes then got a job and went to night school for three years to get his GED. He quit his job, determined that he'd go to college even if it took 20 years. "I didn't have great confidence. In fact, I thought I was dumb, but I would ask questions. To my surprise, I did very well."

He finally graduated from Morgan State College in Baltimore, got a fellowship to the University of Illinois that paid his way through graduate school, and went to the University of Mississippi Medical Center where he earned a postdoctoral degree in clinical child psychology.

These days, Rhodes is a professor at Delaware State College, where he focuses on kids who are in trouble with the juvenile justice system. He concludes, "We can never determine what's going to happen to a kid once he or she has become motivated." His advice to young people despite the tough odds they may have stacked against them: "Never give up. All things are possible."

1. At what point do you think Dr. Rhodes's self-esteem became positive?
2. How can turning one's pain into helping others increase a person's self-esteem?

Using Overcoming the Odds

■ **Discussion.** What behaviors of Dr. Rhodes as a teenager reflect an antisocial personality? What aspects of his childhood do you think influenced his antisocial behavior? (Getting into fights and trouble with the law. He was greatly influenced by his home environment, where his cousins' antisocial behavior was condoned.)

■ **Discussion.** If Dr. Rhodes had received professional help as a teen, how would counseling offered by a psychiatrist differ from that provided by a social worker? How might other mental health professionals (e.g., psychologist, lay counselors, etc.) have approached Dr. Rhodes's problems as a teen? (A psychiatrist or psychologist might use one-on-one discussions with the patient to find the root of the problem in the individual's early life experiences. A social worker would focus more on improving the current family context within which the problem occurred.)

■ **Answers**
1. When he did well in the Job Corps.
2. By showing them their own suffering and value.

L1 COOPERATIVE LEARNING. Ask students to list signs of mental health problems that teens, their friends, and/or their family members might experience. Record the list on the chalkboard. Assign students to small groups, and ask each group to select one of the signs of problems from the list on the board. Have them identify possible causes and various sources of health-care services that might be used to address the problem. Have them arrive at a consensus as to where someone might go to receive help. Ask each group to select a spokesperson to share the group's thinking with the class.

Overcoming Misconceptions

Myth. Children do not have mental illnesses. **Fact.** Millions of children from infancy to 18 years of age suffer disorders such as depression, learning disabilities, and developmental disorders. Children also inherit genetically based illnesses such as schizophrenia and manic-depressive illnesses. **Myth.** Ever since the beginning of time, there has been effective treatment for major mental illnesses. **Fact.** Successful therapies have come about only since about 1940. Since that time, clinical practice and research have advanced rapidly, and information about the structure and chemistry of the brain promises even more effective treatment of mental disorders.

Independent Practice

L2 **RESEARCH.** Ask students to watch TV shows that deal with mental health problems and/or services. Have them prepare a written synopsis of the program to share with the class. Be prepared to discuss the problem or service in detail as well as how the problem was solved or how the service was used in the program. (If the problem was not solved, explain why.) Does this episode of the program reinforce positive or negative thinking about mental health and mental disorders? Why?

L2 **COMMUNITY INVOLVEMENT.** Have students begin a "Yellow Pages Directory" of community sources of mental health help. Ask them to include telephone services, such as hot lines for suicide, child abuse, spousal abuse, and elderly abuse. The directory should include the name of each program, a brief description of the services, an address, and a phone number. Students probably will need to contact social workers, clergy, counselors, and public health agencies to gather this information. Have students add other health services to this directory throughout the course. Ask volunteers to computerize the information. Make printouts for the class.

DID YOU KNOW?

According to Dr. David Shaffer, of the New York State Psychiatric Institute . . .
■ cluster suicides account for about 1 in 10 suicides,
■ 2 out of 3 suicides involve alcohol or drugs,

one of several college degrees: master of arts, master of science, doctor of philosophy in psychology, doctor of psychology, or doctor of education.

State law usually governs the title *psychologist*. Requirements include a doctoral degree, at least two years of supervised experience at a psychiatric hospital or clinic, and the passing of an examination.

The clinical psychologist can practice psychotherapy, group therapy, and individual counseling, in addition to testing for many kinds of specific mental disorders.

Educational Counselor

An educational counselor or school counselor is a person who generally works with young people, helping them in personal or educational matters. Counselors usually have a master's degree in counseling. They generally have special training in psychological testing, as well as in counseling students in a school or college setting. Some counselors address themselves to students' personal problems; others confine themselves to dealing with learning problems or assisting students in educational and vocational choices.

Pastoral Counselor

Informally, the clergy—ministers, priests, and rabbis—have been mental health practitioners for hundreds of years. A pastoral counselor helps people within the context of mental and social problems.

The American Association of Pastoral Counselors is a professional organization that has set standards for training and certification of individuals and institutions in the field of pastoral counseling. Today many members of the clergy receive formal education in counseling as part of their training. Those who are particularly interested in this aspect of their ministry usually take additional training.

Many members of the clergy provide counseling for couples and families.

Overcoming Misconceptions

Myth. People with mental illnesses won't get better. **Fact.** The fact is that mental illness is often temporary. It is treatable. Many people can and do get better. **Myth.** People who are mentally ill are likely to be violent. **Fact.** They are no more likely to be violent than other members of society. In fact, according to one study, they are only more likely to be victims of violent crimes. **Myth.** People with mental illness are likely to "flip out" at any time. **Fact.** Most mental illness and relapses into it are gradual, not sudden. Besides that, people with mental illness are more likely to become withdrawn and quiet than explosive and out of control.

Social Worker

A social worker is a person who provides a link between the medical service center and the client and his or her family. The social worker has completed four years of college and two years of postgraduate study in a school of social work. A psychiatric or clinical social worker is one who has concentrated on psychiatric casework, doing fieldwork in a mental hospital, mental health clinic, or family service agency that provides guidance and treatment for clients with emotional problems.

A psychiatric social worker in a hospital maintains contact between patients and their families, serves as part of a treatment team (along with the psychiatrist, psychologist, nurses, and aides), helps the families understand and adjust to problems resulting from hospitalization, and supervises the rehabilitation of patients after they are released.

Occupational Therapist

The occupational therapist evaluates a person's abilities in light of his or her emotional or physical handicap. This person usually works in a psychiatric hospital or general hospital, conducting programs that involve work, recreation, and creative activities. An occupational therapist has completed a four-year college program with specialization in occupational therapy.

Behavioral Therapist

The behavioral therapist works with patients to help them change their habits. This technique is called behavioral therapy. This approach has become popular with people who want to give up smoking or drinking. The behavioral therapist also works with people who have phobias and other unreasonable fears. The behavioral therapist has completed a four-year college program, with further specialization in behavioral therapy.

LESSON 2 REVIEW

Reviewing Facts and Vocabulary

1. Select three mental health providers and create situations in which you would seek each for treatment or consultation.
2. Identify five signs of mental health problems.
3. Define the term *therapy*. List those therapies commonly used by a psychiatrist.

Thinking Critically

4. **Analysis.** Compare a psychiatrist with a neurologist.
5. **Synthesis.** Why might a psychologist refer a patient to a neurologist?

Applying Health Knowledge

6. After studying mental health disorders and different types of mental health professionals, create a Help Wanted ad that lists the personal qualities one would need to fill a position at a mental health clinic.
7. You have learned about support groups and how they can assist an individual. Develop an idea for a support group at your school. Identify the specific area of focus and why you think there is a need for this at your school.

KNOWING WHEN SOMEONE NEEDS HELP **59**

L2 **WRITING.** Write the types of professionals presented in the lesson on separate slips of paper. Place slips in a box, and let every student draw a slip. Have students design a brochure, explaining the training received and services offered by the type of professional written on their slip of paper.

L1 **USING THE LESSON RESOURCES.** For additional student activities, refer to the lesson resources on page 55.

Assess

Check for Understanding

- Assign and discuss the lesson review. For LD students, assign only questions 1, 2, and 3.
- Assign and discuss the chapter review.

Evaluate

- Administer, grade, and discuss the *Lesson 2 Quiz.*
- Administer, grade, and discuss the *Chapter 3 Test.*
- Refer to the Performance Assessment strategy for this chapter. See pages T 23 to T 25.

Reteach

- Have students use the information in the lesson to answer these questions: When should you get help with a mental health problem? Where can you go for help? Why is it important to get help?
- Ask students to complete *Reteaching Activity 8.*

Enrich

- Assign students to research the use of pet therapy for persons who are experiencing sadness, hopelessness, and/or loneliness.
- Ask students to complete *Enrichment Activity 3.*

Close

Summarize the major concepts by outlining the signs of mental health problems and listing the types of mental health professionals and the therapies they provide.

Answers to Lesson 2 Review

1. Selections of providers will vary. Situations will vary but should reflect each therapist's area of expertise.
2. Answers will vary. Accept five signs from bulleted items on page 55.
3. A treatment technique. Psychoanalysis, psychotherapy, medical therapy, electroconvulsive therapy, group therapy.
4. Both treat mental disorders. A psychiatrist treats functional disorders; a neurologist treats organic disorders.
5. If the psychologist believes the patient suffers from an organic mental disorder.
6. Answers will vary.
7. Answers will vary.

Helping Students Improve Their Health

Using the Self-Inventory

Reinforcing Vocabulary

- **Discrimination.** A prejudged outlook, action, or treatment of an individual based on fear, rather than fact.

Teaching Strategies

L1 DISCUSSION. Students may have preconceived ideas of mental illness that are based upon TV programs. Discuss the various roles that TV personalities have portrayed and compare these roles with reality.

L1 DISCUSSION. Have students list reasons why they may feel embarrassed to tell friends about a family member who is suffering from mental illness. Have students respond to each listed reason.

L2 CLASS ACTIVITY. Have students brainstorm a list of individuals who have suffered from mental illness and are accomplished members of society. Have students list the positive contributions of these individuals.

L2 CLASS ACTIVITY. Have students create a play in which a character struggles with mental illness and experiences discrimination in school or on the job. Demonstrate how this individual overcomes this situation.

DID YOU KNOW?

- In many non-Western societies, the great majority of people who display nonviolent abnormal behavior are permitted freedom in their communities, and their needs are met by family members. In many African communities, for example, even the severely psychotic are often accommodated as functioning members of the community if they can maintain themselves at some level of sufficiency.

Self-Inventory

Coping With Mental Disorders

HOW DO YOU RATE?

Number a sheet of paper from 1 through 20. Read each item below and respond by writing *agree* or *disagree* for each item. Then proceed to the next section.

1. Most people with mental disorders are not dangerous.
2. Most people with anxiety disorders should be hospitalized.
3. Most people who have been successfully treated for a mental disorder are usually able to hold down a job.
4. I would be embarrassed to tell my friends that someone in my family was suffering from a mental disorder.
5. Mental illness is sometimes incurable.
6. I feel that people with mental disorders are safer in clinics or institutions.
7. The media can help change people's negative views about mental disorders.
8. I have nothing in common with a person who has a mental disorder.
9. Mental illness is not the fault of the individual.
10. I would feel uncomfortable if a residence for people suffering from mental disorders was next door to my home.
11. I feel comfortable in the presence of someone with a mental disorder.
12. If I were an employer, I would not hire someone who had been treated for a mental disorder.
13. People with mental disorders have the same emotions as other people.
14. People who have recovered from a mental disorder are usually not interested in working.
15. People with mental disorders should not be discriminated against.
16. Anyone suffering from a mental disorder should not be out in public.
17. It is easy for me to see people with mental disorders as real people.
18. Those who have been treated for a mental disorder should live in a separate neighborhood.
19. Once a person suffers from a mental disorder, he or she can return to society and make many worthwhile contributions.
20. Mental illness is a problem only for those who have it.

HOW DID YOU SCORE?

Give yourself 1 point for each *agree* response to an odd-numbered item. Give yourself 1 point for each *disagree* response to an even-numbered item. Find your total to see how you scored. Then proceed to the next section.

18 to 20
Outstanding. You have a positive, healthful attitude about mental disorders.

12 to 17
Good. Although you have a good attitude about mental disorders, you could still make some improvements in your attitude toward mental illness.

Below 12
Needs Improvement. Your attitude toward those who have a mental disorder is an unhealthful one. It is time you know the facts about mental illness and consider a change in your attitude.

WHAT ARE YOUR GOALS?

If you received an *outstanding* or *good* score, complete the statements in Part A. If your score was rated *needs improvement*, complete Parts A and B.

Part A

1. I plan to learn more about mental disorders by ____.
2. My timetable for accomplishing this is ____.
3. I plan to share my information with others by ____.

Part B

4. The attitude or behavior toward those with a mental disorder that I would most like to change is ____.
5. The steps involved in making this change are ____.
6. The people or groups I will ask for support are ____.
7. My rewards for making this change will be ____.

Meeting Students' Needs

For students who score *Outstanding*. (1) Suggest working for an agency which helps fight for the rights of those who have suffered from mental illness and have experienced discrimination because of mental illness. (2) Suggest working as a summer intern at a local mental health agency as a volunteer.

For students who score *Good*. Suggest that students consider reading books that describe the lives of successful individuals who have experienced mental illness and have triumphed.

For students who *Need Improvement*. Discuss how one's perceptions of the mentally ill may be influenced by the media.

Building Decision-Making Skills

Your good friend Victoria—a junior in high school and a popular classmate—committed suicide last night. The principal of your school is holding an emergency meeting with the teachers to determine how the school will handle this situation—with the students, with her friends, with her family, and with the community. What advice would you give the principal and the teachers?

WHAT DO YOU THINK?

1. **Choices.** What are several ways to help the students cope with this situation?
2. **Choices.** List several ways the school might help Victoria's friends cope with their loss.
3. **Choices.** Does the school have any responsibility toward Victoria's family?
4. **Choices.** Should the school get involved with the community in regard to this situation? If so, in what way?
5. **Consequences.** What are the advantages of each choice you listed in number 1?
6. **Consequences.** What are the disadvantages of each choice you listed in number 1?
7. **Consequences.** What will probably happen if the school takes no action?
8. **Decision.** What do you think the school should do to help Victoria's friends cope?
9. **Decision.** Do you think a different action is appropriate for the student body at large? Explain your answer.
10. **Evaluation.** Have you ever known someone who committed suicide? How did you feel? What helped you most as you coped with this loss?

Emily had a bad year last year. She had been depressed and experienced severe mood swings. Her friends were worried about her. Over the summer, Emily was treated by a psychiatrist. She is now on medication for a chemical imbalance. She is feeling much better, though she is embarrassed by her actions last year. It is now time to go back to school. Emily, her family, and her doctor are deciding what to tell other people about her condition.

WHAT DO YOU THINK?

11. **Situation.** What decisions need to be made by Emily?
12. **Situation.** Why do you think it is important for Emily to consider carefully exactly what she is going to say about her illness?
13. **Consequences.** How do you think her friends will react when they hear about this?
14. **Consequences.** How might her friends' reactions affect her recovery?
15. **Consequences.** How will her friends' reactions affect her self-esteem?
16. **Decision.** Who do you think should be told about this situation?
17. **Decision.** What should Emily tell each of the people you listed in number 16?

Building Decision-Making Skills

Teaching Strategies

L1 **CLASS ACTIVITY.** Have students participate in a role-play situation in which a class deals with the empty chair in the classroom created by the suicidal death of Victoria.

L1 **CLASS ACTIVITY.** Have students role-play the dilemma of Victoria's death with (a) Victoria's younger brother or sister (b) Victoria's best friend or boyfriend. How would individuals' reactions differ? How would they be similar?

L1 **CLASS ACTIVITY.** Other possible role-plays pertaining to mental health include: (1) Your best friend has confided in you that he or she is seriously considering suicide. You have to promise that you will not tell anyone or he or she will kill him- or herself immediately. (2) While snooping through your older sister's purse, you find a note that she has recently written. The note is written to your parents and contains phrases such as, "I can't take it anymore" and "You'd be better off without me."

L1 **DISCUSSION.** Have students brainstorm the possible signs of depression and/or approaching suicide that Victoria may have demonstrated.

L2 **DISCUSSION.** Have students discuss the emotions that one experiences following the survival of a death of a loved one by suicide. How are anger and guilt important, normal, valid, and necessary emotions?

DID YOU KNOW?

- Suicide is the eighth leading cause of death in the U.S. and a serious potential outcome of mental illness. In 1987, 30,783 people died of suicide.
- For young males, antisocial personality disorder is frequently associated with suicidal behavior.

Discussing the Answers

Situation 1. While discussing the answers, be certain that "copy cat" suicidal occurrences are mentioned. Discuss how it is common for close friends and relatives to think about suicide themselves after they have survived the suicide of a loved one. Peer discussion groups that allow students to talk about their feelings in the presence of mental health workers should be considered. Support should be provided to the family.

Situation 2. Students should consider the value of sharing this information with others who may be suffering. Knowing someone who has suffered from mental illness and how the person coped with it could create greater awareness.

Answers to Chapter 3 Review

Using Health Terms

1. Anxiety disorders
2. Phobia
3. Obsessions
4. Compulsion
5. Post-traumatic stress disorder
6. Hypochondria
7. Organic disorder
8. Clinical depression
9. Psychiatrist
10. Neurologist

Building Academic Skills

11. Mistrust of others and often suspicious.
12. Ten to twenty.

Recalling the Facts

13. Anxiety disorders, somatoform disorders, affective disorders, personality disorders.
14. A habit is an activity performed on a regular and reasonable basis; a compulsion is an activity performed so frequently as to interfere with a person's normal functioning.
15. Feeling anxious, fearful, and upset.
16. A—dreams about the event; C—can't sleep; E—feels guilty.
17. A condition in which a person complains of disease symptoms but no physical cause can be found.
18. Moods.
19. A—not a good idea; B—good idea; C—good idea; D—good idea; E—not a good idea; F—good idea.
20. Antisocial personality disorder, passive-aggressive personality disorder, schizophrenia.
21. This therapy consists of electric shock given to a patient under anesthetic, usually on one side of the brain.
22. Doctor of medicine.
23. Psychiatrist and neurologist.

Thinking Critically

24. Answers will vary. Possible answer: Through education.
25. Organic disorders have an underlying physical condition which has damaged the brain. Functional disorders are the

Using Health Terms

On a separate sheet of paper, write the term that best matches each definition given below.

LESSON 1

1. Disorders in which real or imagined fears prevent a person from enjoying life.
2. An extreme fear that causes a person to react in ways that limit normal functioning.
3. Persistent thoughts or ideas that keep people from thinking about other things.
4. An urgent need to repeat certain behaviors.
5. A condition in which a person who has lived through a traumatic event experiences severe and long-lasting aftereffects.
6. A preoccupation with the body and fear of imagined disease.
7. A type of mental disorder that is caused by a physical illness or injury that affects the brain.
8. A mental disorder characterized by feelings of sadness or hopelessness that lasts for more than a few weeks and interferes with daily activities and interests.

LESSON 2

9. A medical doctor who treats people with mental, emotional, and behavioral disorders of the mind.
10. A medical doctor who specializes in the treatment of organic disorders of the brain and nervous system.

Building Academic Skills

LESSON 1

11. **Reading.** Use the context clues in the following sentence to define *paranoid*.
    People with paranoid schizophrenic disorder mistrust others and are often suspicious.
12. **Math.** If schizophrenia affects 1 to 2 percent of the population, among a group of 1,000 people between the ages of 15 and 35, how many individuals are likely to be affected by schizophrenia?

Recalling the Facts

LESSON 1

13. What are the four main categories of functional disorders?
14. How do habits and compulsions differ?
15. What are three characteristics of a person with a general anxiety disorder?
16. Which of the following symptoms are characteristic of persons suffering from post-traumatic stress disorder?
    a. dreams about the event
    b. overeats
    c. can't sleep
    d. loses weight
    e. feels guilty
17. What is a somatoform disorder?
18. On which one of the following does an affective disorder have the most extreme effect: heart rate, sleeping patterns, moods, eating habits?
19. Write *good idea* or *not a good idea* for each suggestion below for handling potential suicides.
    a. Joke about it; don't take it seriously.
    b. Be willing to listen, but don't promise to keep it secret.
    c. Try to get the person to seek help.
    d. Don't dare or challenge the person.
    e. Give strong advice; tell the person what he or she is planning is wrong.
    f. Allow the person to express his or her feelings.
20. Name three types of personality disorders.

LESSON 2

21. Describe electroconvulsive therapy.
22. Which one of the following degrees is a clinical psychologist unlikely to have: master of science, doctor of psychology, doctor of medicine?
23. Which of the following mental health professionals can legally prescribe drugs: psychiatrist, neurologist, psychologist, social worker, educational counselor, pastoral counselor, occupational therapist, behavioral therapist?

result of psychological causes in which no brain damage is involved.
26. Answers will vary. Accept any three of the following: phobia, obsessive-compulsive disorder, general anxiety disorder, post-traumatic stress disorder. Examples of each may come from text pages 49

and 50 or may be of the students' choosing.
27. One suffering from manic-depressive disorder will exhibit extreme mood swings for no apparent reason. Episodes of extreme happiness alternate with periods of depression. One suffering from clinical depression does not exhibit

REVIEW

Thinking Critically

LESSON 1

24. Evaluation. How do you think the stigma attached to mental illness could be eliminated?

25. Analysis. How are organic and functional disorders different?

26. Analysis. Compare three types of anxiety disorders and give an example of each.

27. Analysis. Compare the behavior of someone suffering from manic-depressive disorder with that of someone suffering from clinical depression.

28. Synthesis. Give an example of a passive-aggressive response on Joe's part to the following situation.

Joe is failing chemistry. So are four other students. Ms. Vronsky agrees to give them extra help every morning for an hour before school starts.

LESSON 2

29. Synthesis. After looking over the Self-Inventory on page 60, how would you describe the major challenges in coping with mental illness?

30. Synthesis. There are many types of mental health professionals. What common characteristics do they all share?

31. Evaluation. If you were to seek therapy from a psychiatrist, which of the therapies described in the text would you prefer? Which would you not want to consider?

32. Analysis. Compare and contrast the educational requirements and the responsibilities of an educational counselor, a pastoral counselor, and a social worker.

Making the Connection

LESSON 1

33. Language Arts. Read a synopsis of Shakespeare's *Romeo and Juliet* to explore the causes, futility, and tragedy of teenage suicide. Then write a less tragic ending.

Applying Health Knowledge

LESSON 1

34. Write *yes* for each statement below that might be a sign of an unhealthful mental attitude. Write *no* for each statement that indicates a healthful mental attitude.
  a. Jerry has asked me to the prom. This is the happiest day of my life.
  b. I don't think I did very well on the last biology quiz, but I'm going to study harder for the next one.
  c. I didn't get the job because I am female.

LESSON 2

35. If you want to be a psychiatrist, what is the minimum number of years of education and training you will need after you are graduated from high school?

36. A famous psychiatrist once said that the line between mental health and mental illness is a thin one that we cross over many times each day. How do you relate to that statement?

Beyond the Classroom

LESSON 1

37. Parental Involvement. Ask your parents if they know anyone who has suffered from any phobias during their lives. Ask them to tell you what they believe caused the phobia, how the individual conquered it or adjusted to it, and how it affected the individual's life.

38. Community Involvement. Investigate the resources in your community for suicide prevention. Find out what services are provided. Report your findings to the class.

39. Further Study. Read an article or watch a movie about the life of a person with multiple personalities. What caused this person's mental disorder? How did he or she cope with the disorder? What kind of professional help did he or she seek? Was it effective? What was the end result?

mood swings but is depressed for long periods of time.

28. Answers will vary. Possible answers: Joe fails to show up, Joe shows up late or unprepared.

29. Answers will vary. Possible answer: The major challenge is changing attitudes toward mental disorders and mental illness through education.

30. Answers will vary. Possible answer: All wish to help others, all must be intelligent and insightful, all must be committed to helping people attain happiness and fulfillment.

31. Answers will vary.

32. Answers will vary. Possible answer: All have specialized training. Educational counselors usually have a master's degree in counseling and training in psychological testing and work with young people on personal or educational matters. Pastoral counselors often have training in counseling; they assist people with mental and social problems. Social workers often have four years of college and two years of postgraduate study in social work, some have additional training in a mental hospital, mental health clinic, or family service agency; they provide a link between mental health facilities, patients, and their families; they provide guidance, counseling, and treatment for people with emotional problems.

Making the Connection

33. Answers will vary.

Applying Health Knowledge

34. A—no; B—no; C—yes.

35. Nine.

36. Answers will vary but may include the ideas of being familiar with mental health symptoms and knowing when to seek help.

Beyond the Classroom

37. Answers will vary.

38. Answers will vary.

39. Answers will vary.

Overview

Lesson Summaries

LESSON 1. Stress is the body's general response to any situation. Some stress is vital. It can even improve the way you function. Other stress has negative consequences. Learning to manage and cope with stress is an important part of staying healthy. The body's response to stress is involuntary, activated by the autonomic nervous system. Once a stressor has been dealt with, the body returns to normal. However, when a stressor is prolonged or the body is continually exposed to stressors, the body becomes exhausted. As a result the system breaks down, making the individual more susceptible to illness and accidents.

LESSON 2. Although some stress is good, even motivating, the body cannot distinguish between positive and negative sources of stress. The body's response is the same. As a result, your body depends on you to identify and manage stress in your life. Research shows that people who eat properly, get plenty of sleep, and exercise regularly are better able to cope with stress.

Introducing the Chapter

Many corporations hold seminars and classes to help their employees deal with stress. Ask students why they think companies take the time and spend the money to do this. Then ask students if they experience stress. On the chalkboard, list all of the events students consider stressful. Tell them that as they study this chapter, they will learn more about recognizing stress, how it affects them, both positively and negatively, and how to manage stress.

Performance Assessment ✓

Refer to pages T 23 to T 25 for a Performance Assessment strategy for this chapter. See the *Performance Assessment Activities* booklet for additional suggestions.

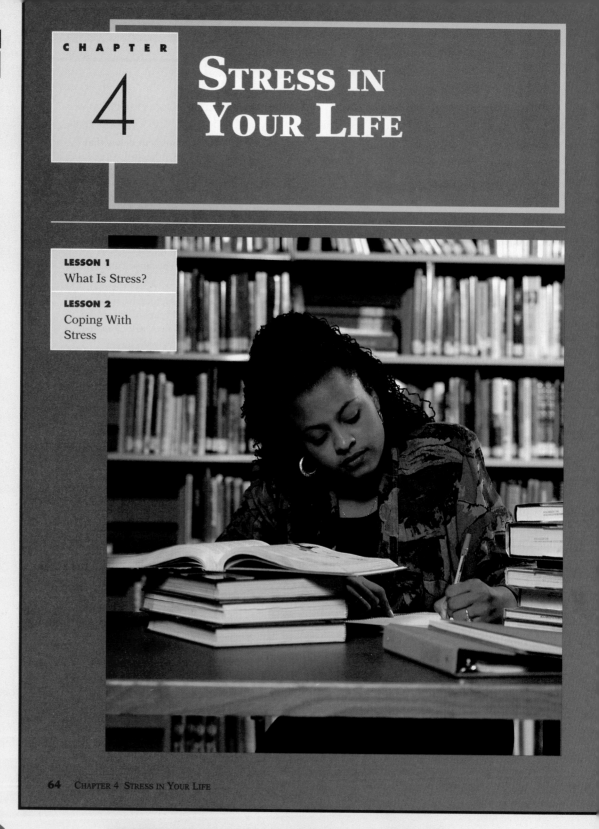

CHAPTER

4

STRESS IN YOUR LIFE

LESSON 1
What Is Stress?

LESSON 2
Coping With Stress

64   CHAPTER 4 STRESS IN YOUR LIFE

Key to Ability Levels

Teaching strategies have been coded for varying learning styles and abilities.

L1   Level 1 activities are basic activities and should be within the ability range of all students.

L2   Level 2 activities are average activities and should be within the ability range of average to above-average students.

L3   Level 3 activities are challenging activities designed for the ability range of above-average students.

LD   LD activities should be within the ability range of learning-disabled students.

LEP   LEP activities should be within the ability range of Limited English Proficiency students.

WHAT IS STRESS?

The word *stress* is used in many ways. To some people, it can mean an event that causes tension. It can mean a person's perception of an event or a response to a situation or demand on the body. Here, **stress** is defined as the body and mind's reactions to everyday demands. Stress requires the body to adjust so it can return to a normal state. The siren of an ambulance, the smell of fire, the hissing of a snake—all of these may cause the body to respond in a physical or psychological way. That response is different for each individual and may change for each situation.

Kinds of Stress

Stress is usually referred to in a negative sense. **Distress** is negative stress. Having too much stress, not knowing how to cope with stress, or experiencing a distressful situation causes distress. Having to play an away basketball game the night before a big test while a parent is ill at home can cause distress. Not all stress is bad. A certain amount of stress is necessary for life. As a matter of fact, experts say that moderate amounts of stress improve productivity. **Eustress** is positive stress. Eustress can help someone achieve his or her goals, such as studying for a test or working hard on a speech.

Factors Influencing Stress

Many reasons are given for the great variation in how well and how long people can hold up when feeling stress. Some people break down very quickly, while others endure for seemingly endless periods of time. What factors can you identify that might affect the way people respond to stressors? How might a person's life-style or attitude toward health affect his or her ability to endure stress?

The variation in the impact of a stressor on a person is related to the person's age, social status, income, state of health, diet, sleep habits, cultural background, and previous experience. Your response to a stressor also varies depending on how much control you think you have over a situation. If you feel you are helpless, the stress can be overwhelming.

What Is a Stressor?

Before looking at the problems related to stress, let us examine the relationship between stress and stressors. Imagine a bell sounding. Each time the bell sounds, you clench your fist. The sounding of the bell is known as a stressor. A **stressor** is any stimulus that produces a stress response. Stressors can be people, objects, places, or events. Think of some stressors you face during your day.

LESSON 1 FOCUS

TERMS TO USE
- Stress
- Distress
- Eustress
- Stressor
- Fatigue
- Chronic fatigue syndrome
- Psychosomatic (SY•KOH•SUH•MAT•IHK)

CONCEPTS TO LEARN
- A certain amount of stress is necessary for life.
- Stress can affect your mental, physical, and social health.

ATTITUDES AND BEHAVIORS TO EVALUATE
- Self-Inventory, page 78.
- Building Decision-Making Skills, page 79.

Focus

Lesson Objectives

After studying this lesson, students should be able to:
- distinguish between stress and distress
- identify stressors in daily life
- discuss how the body responds to stressors
- distinguish between physical, pathological, and psychological fatigue
- relate excessive stress to disease

Bellringer

Write the following on the chalkboard for students to work on while attendance is being taken: *Write, in your own words, a definition of* stress. *Then describe a stressful situation that you or someone you know had to deal with. Explain how the situation was handled. Do you think this situation was handled positively or negatively? How might it have been handled more positively?*

Introducing the Lesson

Refer to the Bellringer. Ask volunteers to share their definitions and descriptions of stressful situations. Lead the class in brainstorming a list of common stressors in an adolescent's life. Have them identify those that can be controlled or eliminated. Tell them that this lesson is about stress and how it affects the human body.

DID YOU KNOW?

- During exam time, teens are more likely to get colds than during non-stress times. That's because periods of high stress suppress disease-fighting immune-system cells.
- Psychoneuroimmunology (PNI) deals with the relationship between the mind and the body's immune system. PNI researchers have found that immune cells are better able to fight infection when a person's mood is good.

Resources for Lesson 1

- **Guided Reading** Activity 9
- **Workbook** Vocabulary Activity 9

- **Reteaching** Activity 9
- **Lesson 1 Quiz**

- **BARN Software,** Stress Management
- **Performance Assessment** Activity 4

Science and Technology Videodisc
Human Biology, Side 2
Ch 13 Bulimia

ABC News InterActive Videodiscs
Tobacco, Side 2
Ch 19 Stress and Boredom

■ Assign students to work in pairs to write a short paper using each of the vocabulary words. Afterwards, ask them to test each other's understanding of the words' definitions.

■ Ask students to complete the *Workbook Vocabulary Activity 9.*

Teach

Guided Practice

LD EXPLANATION. Provide a simple working definition of stress, providing examples from everyday experience.

L3 CLASS ACTIVITY. Assign selected students to locate and read current findings about the relationship of stress to physical illnesses such as heart disease, high blood pressure, asthma, ulcers, colitis, and migraine headaches. Ask them to share their findings with the class.

L1 DISCUSSION. Lead a discussion of the statement, *Change produces stress.* Talk about simple changes that students can make to lessen stress in their lives.

L1 SPEAKER. Invite the school counselor or a counselor or psychologist from the community to speak to the class about stress and distress and ways to deal with stressors. Afterwards, have students write papers summarizing the presentation.

L1 DISCUSSION. Talk about the role that the hypothalamus plays in responding to stress.

L1 DISCUSSION. Talk about why adrenaline is known as the emergency hormone. Ask students to give personal examples of the results of the production of adrenaline during a time of stress.

L1 SPEAKER. Invite a police officer, fire fighter, or emergency medical worker to speak to the class about stress they experience at work. Have them talk about the effect of adrenaline on their body during stressful events.

DID YOU KNOW?

■ It may not be a stressor you have in your life but whether or not you feel you can control it that affects your health. According to a study published in the *Journal of the American Medical Association*, men who found their jobs demanding but had little control over them were three times as likely to have high blood pressure as other men. On the other hand, men studied with demanding jobs but having control over them had no such increases in blood pressure.

The clenching of your fist each time the bell rings is stress, or your response to that stressor. In this case, the response is voluntary; that is, you have conscious control over it. You can notice the tension in your fist as you clench it.

The stress response that takes place inside your body is involuntary. Sometimes we are completely unaware of the changes that occur. Other reactions, however, we can notice.

Have you ever been unable to sleep the night before a big event? Have you ever had knots in your stomach before a big game or a speech? Has your throat ever become dry when you were being confronted with a problem? All of these reactions were involuntary.

How the body responds to a stressor depends largely on how the individual perceives the stressor. What is stressful for one person may be a source of relaxation for another.

The Body's Response to Stressors

Two major body systems are active in the body's response to stressors: the nervous system and the endocrine system. You will study the nervous system and the endocrine system in Chapter 12, but here is some information on how these systems influence reactions to stressors.

The physical changes that are a part of stress begin in the hypothalamus, a nerve center in the brain, and a part of the endocrine system. When the hypothalamus is excited by a stressor, a complex series of changes takes place in the body. The result is a change in the functioning of almost every part of the body.

Nerve centers in the hypothalamus regulate some functions of the autonomic nervous system, the system that controls involuntary actions. Some of the nerves activate the pituitary gland. The pituitary gland secretes a hormone that stimulates the adrenal glands. The adrenal glands produce and secrete a hormone, called adrenaline, which prepares a person for a "fight or flight" response. Adrenaline is known as the "emergency" hormone.

Because of adrenaline, the heart speeds up its activity, providing more blood for the brain and muscles. Breathing becomes faster and deeper, providing more oxygen to the body. Saliva and mucus dry up, increas-

Stress increases when you feel out of control.

Across the Curriculum

Physical Education. Have students do library research and also interview physical education teachers and athletic coaches about types of lifetime sports and other exercise that can help teens and their families cope with daily stressors. Follow up by having students share their findings and demonstrate some of the exercises to the class.

Science. Have students compare and contrast research on biofeedback and meditation in dealing with stress and anxiety. Also, have them interview mental-health professionals in the community who teach various types of relaxation techniques. Ask students to share their research with the class.

The Effects of Stress on the Body

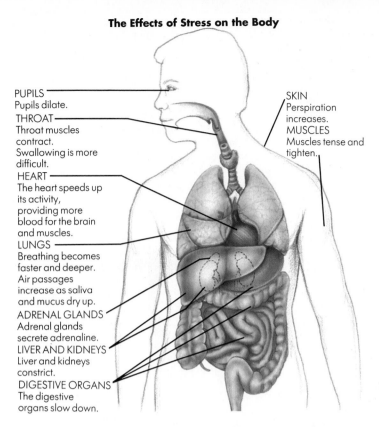

PUPILS
Pupils dilate.

THROAT
Throat muscles
contract.
Swallowing is more
difficult.

HEART
The heart speeds up
its activity,
providing more
blood for the brain
and muscles.

LUNGS
Breathing becomes
faster and deeper.
Air passages
increase as saliva
and mucus dry up.

ADRENAL GLANDS
Adrenal glands
secrete adrenaline.

LIVER AND KIDNEYS
Liver and kidneys
constrict.

DIGESTIVE ORGANS
The digestive
organs slow down.

SKIN
Perspiration
increases.

MUSCLES
Muscles tense and
tighten.

Many body organs respond to stressors.

DID YOU KNOW?

■ Laughing is an effective way to keep your body fit. When you laugh, your chest, thorax, and abdominal muscles, as well as your diaphragm, heart, lungs, and possibly your liver contract. A good belly laugh can make your blood pressure soar and can increase your heart rate. Laughing is a result of adrenaline production.

■ After a good laugh, all systems return to normal or even a little below normal. This results in less stress and lower blood pressure, as well as in an all-around good feeling.

ing the size of the air passages to the lungs. Throat muscles may contract, making swallowing difficult. Perspiration increases, helping to cool the body. Muscles tense and tighten to prepare the body for action. The pupils dilate. Other body functions, such as digestion, are suspended to conserve energy.

All of these changes take place when we are faced with something we perceive to be a stressor. Once the stressor has been dealt with, the body returns to normal. However, in cases where the stressor is prolonged or not dealt with, the body continues to work at the stimulated level. After a period of time, the body becomes exhausted. It becomes more susceptible to illness and accidents.

K E E P I N G   F I T

Avoiding the Perfectionist Trap

Perfectionists have many characteristics in common. These include wanting their work to be better than everyone else's, being competitive even in noncompetitive situations, always looking for mistakes and ways to improve, not being really satisfied by the praise they've worked for once they get it, going to any lengths to avoid mistakes, and feeling overly ashamed by even minor mistakes. Perfectionists may also procrastinate, be indecisive, play it safe, or do one part of a task over and over until it is perfect.

If any of these characteristics describe you, perhaps it's time to work on accepting that you are just human. Everyone makes mistakes.

WHAT IS STRESS?   **67**

Across the Curriculum

Science. Designate one or more students to prepare an in-depth written report on lactic acid and carbon dioxide and their roles in producing fatigue.

Language Arts. Have students write stories about a person who was the victim of a practical joke and how he or she responded. Read some of the completed stories to the class. Talk about how the experience relates to the lesson.

Home Economics. Select students to research the topic "Children and Stress." Have them identify stressors in today's world that affect children and some of their effects on children.

LEP **CLASS ACTIVITY.** Have students draw cartoons or present short skits depicting "adrenaline to the rescue" during a stressful event. Allow time for students to share their completed projects.

L1 **CLASS ACTIVITY.** Ask for volunteers to create radio or TV commercials for imaginary products designed to help someone cope with stress. Share the commercials with the entire class.

L1 **DISCUSSION.** Have students complete and discuss the following statements: When I am at the doctor's office, I feel. . .; Sitting in the dentist's chair makes me feel. . .; During a test, I feel. . .; When I am with people who are arguing, I feel. . .; Having an argument with a friend makes me feel. . . . Understanding things/events that upset them can help students deal with stress.

L1 **DISCUSSION.** Ask students why they think fatigue is a common complaint among many people. Talk about the differences between pathological, physical, and psychological fatigue.

L2 **CLASS ACTIVITY.** Select students to design a bulletin board, using the outline of a sports car and the title "Lower Your Idling Speed." Have them feature drawings or commercial illustrations showing healthy ways to reduce fatigue.

L1 **DISCUSSION.** Talk about why rest is the best solution to physical and pathological fatigue, but not to psychological fatigue.

L2 **CLASS ACTIVITY.** Have each student create a skit, poster, bulletin board, or short story to contrast pathological, physical, and psychological fatigue.

L1 **DISCUSSION.** Talk about some topics to discuss that might be of interest when teens are introduced to adult friends of their parents.

L1 **DISCUSSION.** Lead a discussion about ways that school can be a source of stress. Talk about ways in which classmates cope with stress.

■ **Discussion.** What are some of the stressors that led Marci to try to commit suicide? Using the Adolescent Life-Change Event Scale, calculate Marci's score based on the events you know of in her life. (Some of the most important stressors Marci had to deal with were: her parents' divorce and remarriage—86 points; the suicide of her cousin, who was like a brother to her—95 points; doing poorly in school—86 points; and breaking up with her boyfriend—74 points. Her total score is well over 300, putting her at great risk of ill health due to stress.)

■ **Answers**
1. For Paul, drugs and social isolation; for Marci, her parents' divorce and remarriage and the breakup with her boyfriend; Paul's suicide made her feel alone and hopeless.
2. For Paul, his artwork and withdrawal from society; for Marci, sleeping a lot and dropping out of school activities.
3. Suicide ends the pain—but also the joy; support from others helps you find other options for dealing with pain.

L2 DISCUSSION. Talk about what physical and emotional signs of stress students sometime see in themselves. How do these signs affect their ability to study? How do they affect friendships? What do they do to family relationships?

L1 DISCUSSION. Ask students to share their responses to these questions: What kind of problem would make you want to talk to someone about your stress? To whom would you talk? Why would you choose this person?

LEP CLASS ACTIVITY. Have students create cartoon strips based on a teen meeting a date's parents for the first time. Post the cartoons in the class. Talk about the kind of stress involved in the situation.

L1 DISCUSSION. Ask students to answer the following questions: During an average day, when do you feel the greatest need to relax? Why? What do you do to relax?

Overcoming The Odds

Marci is 17. A little over a year ago she tried to commit suicide. Since then, she has been in therapy and in a suicide survivor's group. These days she'd tell you she's grateful to be alive, but it hasn't been an easy journey. She says, "This is all really hard to talk about, but I guess I want to help anyone out there who may be facing the same kinds of stuff I faced. I guess you could say there have always been tensions in my family. I love them and all, but there was a lot of fighting along the way. Then my parents got divorced and my mom got remarried. When my dad remarried, it just felt like I didn't belong anywhere anymore. Even then, I didn't lose it in a big way until my cousin Paul. . . ."

Marci gets quiet. She is talking about Paul, her 18-year-old cousin, who committed suicide 2 years ago. "He was like a brother I never had. I knew he was in trouble, but I didn't know how badly. He was doing drugs. He painted and drew all kinds of weird pictures toward the end, and my aunt says he stayed in his room a lot, but I had no idea. One tip-off, looking back, is that he gave me our great-grandfather's stopwatch—this

beautiful watch we always joked about his getting because he was the oldest cousin and hardly ever on time. I guess I should have known. Anyway, one weekend when his parents were out, he committed suicide in his garage. My uncle found him in his car.

"After that I just couldn't hold it together," Marci says. "I felt completely alone, like I was falling into this deep hole without a bottom. It felt like my parents didn't understand, that no one could understand, and there was no sense to anything any more. I saw what the pain was doing to Paul's family, but I got beyond caring. I was sleeping a lot, dropped out of stuff at school,

and couldn't concentrate. All I can tell you is I felt incredibly bad, and then my boyfriend left me, and that did it. I took all these pills I'd been collecting. I don't even know if I cared if they found me or not, but they did, and now I'm grateful. I am incredibly grateful. I cry just thinking about it. I wish Paul had the same second chance."

For the last few months, Marci and her family have been getting professional help. "I guess we're getting a lot out in the open that needed to get out. I realize that those terrifying dark times do get better. I'm feeling better all the time. I don't feel so alone any more.

"I really want to say to any teen who's thinking about suicide, don't do it. Please. Things will get better. Trust me. They really will."

1. What factors led to Paul's suicide? To Marci's attempt? How did Paul's suicide affect her?
2. What signs of being in trouble did each display?
3. If you or someone you know has ever seriously thought about suicide, what lessons from Marci's story might you be able to apply? What message does her story give about getting help?

Overcoming Misconceptions

Myth. Any kind of stress is harmful. **Fact.** Stress is not necessarily bad. In order to function, the human body needs a certain amount of stress. Too much negative stress, or distress, can lead to fatigue and physical illness. Stress becomes unhealthy whenever the individual cannot control it, cope with it, or learn to manage it. **Myth.**

Stress is not an important factor in the workplace. **Fact.** Stress-related health disorders cause significant absenteeism at work, thus costing businesses millions of dollars each year. Because of this, many businesses hold seminars to help their employees deal with stress. Some also provide exercise facilities for their employees.

ADOLESCENT LIFE-CHANGE EVENT SCALE

The Social Readjustment Rating Scale

Life Events	Mean Value	Life Events	Mean Value
1. Getting married	101	23. Breaking up with boyfriend or girlfriend	53
2. Unwed pregnancy	92	24. Beginning to date	51
3. Death of parent	87	25. Suspension from school	50
4. Acquiring a visible deformity	81	26. Birth of a brother or sister	50
5. Divorce of parents	77	27. Increase in number of arguments with parents	47
6. Fathering an unwed pregnancy	77	28. Increase in number of arguments between parents	46
7. Becoming involved with drugs or alcohol	76	29. Loss of job by parent	46
8. Jail sentence of parent for one year or more	75	30. Outstanding personal achievement	46
9. Marital separation of parents	69	31. Change in parents' financial status	45
10. Death of a brother or sister	68	32. Being accepted at a college of your choice	43
11. Change in acceptance by peers	67	33. Beginning senior high school	42
12. Pregnancy of unwed sister	64	34. Serious illness requiring hospitalization of sibling	41
13. Discovery of being an adopted child	64	35. Change in father's or mother's occupation requiring increased absence from home	38
14. Marriage of parent to stepparent	63	36. Brother or sister leaving home	37
15. Death of a close friend	63	37. Death of a grandparent	36
16. Having a visible congenital deformity	62	38. Addition of third adult to family (i.e. grandparent)	34
17. Serious illness requiring hospitalization	58	39. Becoming a full fledged member of a church	31
18. Failure of a grade in school	56	40. Decrease in number of arguments between parents	27
19. Move to a new school district	56	41. Decrease in number of arguments with parents	26
20. Not making an extracurricular activity you wanted	55	42. Mother or father beginning to work	26
21. Serious illness requiring hospitalization of a parent	55		
22. Jail sentence of parent for 30 days or more	53		

Fatigue—It Is Not All Physical

Many illnesses and conditions have been linked to stress. One of the most common conditions is that of **fatigue**—a tired feeling that lowers your level of activity. Fatigue affects all levels of your health—physical, mental, and social. It interferes with work, school, relationships, and recreation. It affects your ability to successfully manage stress. It affects your general feeling of well-being.

Physical Fatigue

You have probably experienced one type of fatigue—physical fatigue, which is fatigue of the body in general. It occurs at the end of the day when the body signals a need for rest and sleep. It also occurs during exercise when the body produces waste products in the form of lactic acid from the muscles and carbon dioxide from all of the body's cells. A buildup of wastes in the muscles can produce soreness. When these wastes reach a certain level in the blood, the brain receives a message,

Scoring:

- If your total is below 150, you have a low stress level and your life has been stable in most areas.

- If your total is between 150 and 300, you have a moderate stress level and there has been a lot of change in your life.

- If your total is over 300, you have a high stress level and there have been major adjustments in your life.

WHAT IS STRESS? **69**

Across the Curriculum

Science. Invite a science teacher to talk to the class about adrenaline and the role it plays in the body.

Social Studies. Have students research life-styles in Japan where, in recent years, the incidence of stress-related illnesses has risen. Ask students to give reasons to explain this phenomenon.

Science. Select students to locate current information about two extremely powerful analgesics (endorphins and enkephalins) and their relationship to stress. Ask them to share what they learn with the class.

Art. Assign students to use various art media to illustrate the human body's response to stress.

L2 CLASS ACTIVITY. Ask for volunteers to act out skits about being anxious in one or more of the following situations: waiting to talk with a teacher about the results of a test; being at a party with people they hardly know; waiting for a blind date to arrive at the door; or applying for a job. Have students discuss the skits and ways to cope with similar situations.

L1 DISCUSSION. Lead students in a discussion of their reactions to the *Adolescent Life Change Event Scale*. Ask them to identify the events they can control and those they cannot control. Discuss how too many stressors over a period of time can result in physical illness.

L1 CLASS ACTIVITY. Set up a "Dear Abby" box in the classroom for students to submit short, anonymous letters about a problem they are experiencing. After screening the problems submitted, let the class identify some of the stressors in the letters. Talk about how much control over the situation the writer has.

L2 CLASS ACTIVITY. Have students write and perform a play in which the villains, "Stressor," "Physical Fatigue," "Pathological Fatigue," "Psychological Fatigue," and "Chronic Fatigue Syndrome," from the "Stress Family," try to rob health and energy from a teen and his or her family. Ask them to use actual information they learned from the lesson.

L1 SPEAKER. Invite a well-known athlete from the community to speak to the class about stress in sports. Ask him or her to talk about the effect of adrenaline on the body during sporting events.

L3 CLASS ACTIVITY. Select students to create a videotape, public service announcement, or brochure titled "Stress, Sanity, and Survival." The focus should be on the effects of stress on wellness.

L1 DEMONSTRATION. Invite a local practitioner of yoga to the classroom to demonstrate ways to relieve stress and distress.

Independent Practice

L1 **PERSONAL INVOLVEMENT.** Have students keep journals of their daily lives, including stressors that they experience and how they respond to each of them. Let students know that they will not have to share their journal entries with anyone.

L1 **RESEARCH.** Ask for volunteers to find examples of people experiencing stress on TV. Have them relate what they viewed with what they learned in the lesson.

L1 **SELF-ESTEEM.** Have students divide sheets of paper in half. Have them label one half "Things I Like About My Life" and the other half "Things I Don't Like About My Life." Ask students to list things they can change and things they cannot change. How did they feel about themselves? How did their level of self-esteem affect their list? Students need not share their lists.

L1 **PARENTAL INVOLVEMENT.** Ask for volunteers to talk to their parents about the kinds of stress that they (or other adults) face in today's world and ways they cope with the stress.

L2 **WRITING.** Assign students to write a short paper to submit to the school newspaper about some of the main ideas in the lesson.

L2 **RESEARCH.** Have students use classroom and library resources to locate current information on psychosomatic illnesses.

L3 **RESEARCH.** Have students interview two people in each of the following age groups: 13-18, 19-25, 26-35, 36-45, 46-55, and 56 and older. Ask students to find out what each person's greatest stressors are and what he or she does to manage stress. Have students make a chart to share with the class, comparing the stressors. Have them draw conclusions about how stress varies with age.

L1 **USING THE LESSON RESOURCES.** For additional student activities, refer to the lesson resources on page 65.

DID YOU KNOW?

- A survey of over 1,000 people indicates that 71 percent get headaches and most report that the reason is because they have too much to do and not enough time to do it.
- According to Dr. Paul Rosch, president of the American Institute of Stress in Yonkers, New York, more than 66 percent of all visits to primary-care doctors are for problems that are stress-related.

CONFLICT RESOLUTION

The poverty and racial discrimination experienced by many inner-city teens often produce conflicting feelings of anger and helplessness. This can result in stress. Why? Because the less control one has, the more stressed out a person tends to be. The 1992 Los Angeles riots were, in part, a response to such stress—some individuals acted out their anger and tried to take control through destructive acts. However, in the long run, the riots made a bad situation worse.

Can you think of more positive ways social change can occur rather than through violence and destruction?

---

and your activity level drops. Physical fatigue can build up to a point where the body cannot take any more effort.

The best solution for physical fatigue is rest. If getting regular periods of rest does not revive you, you might need to look for another cause of your fatigue.

Pathological Fatigue

A second kind of fatigue is pathological fatigue, which is fatigue brought on by the overworking of the body's defenses for fighting disease. When a disease does develop, your body becomes overworked trying to fight the disease and, at the same time, trying to keep you going. The result is fatigue.

The common cold, the flu, and anemia are all examples of illnesses brought on by pathological fatigue. Being overweight and having a poor diet are also causes of pathological fatigue. This type of fatigue is the body's way of warning you that it is not well and that you need to rest and care for yourself.

Psychological Fatigue

The third and most common type of fatigue is psychological fatigue, which is brought on by mental stress. Almost everyone experiences this type of fatigue. Depression, boredom, worry about schoolwork, home, dates, how you look, and being liked—all of these can cause fatigue. Trying to do too many activities and having conflicts also can cause it. Lack of exercise, which means that your body does not circulate oxygen fast enough, can also be a factor in psychological fatigue.

Unlike the answer to the other two types of fatigue, rest is not the answer to psychological fatigue; setting your priorities is. Choose activities such as exercise that promote your health. If fatigue continues, take a closer look at the source of it. Is there a problem you need to address? Perhaps you need to set a goal for changing a certain behavior. Perhaps you just need to talk to someone. Try to find out what is at the root of your fatigue. That is the first step toward eliminating it.

Remember, fatigue is your body's way of warning you that something is wrong. You risk further health problems by merely covering up the symptoms.

If you are not sure what kind of fatigue you are experiencing, examine what you were doing and how you were feeling before you got tired. Strong negative feelings can cause fatigue. So can worrying about something that is in your near future.

Chronic Fatigue Syndrome (CFS)

A new type of fatigue has been identified in the last few years. It is called **chronic fatigue syndrome (CFS).** The cause of this new disorder is unknown, and it is very difficult to diagnose.

The Centers for Disease Control and Prevention have identified these symptoms of the disease:

- persistent severe fatigue for at least six months
- mild fever and sore throat

70 CHAPTER 4 STRESS IN YOUR LIFE

Across the Curriculum

Physical Education. Invite a physical-education teacher to come to class to demonstrate physical exercises that may be helpful in reducing psychological fatigue. Afterward, ask for volunteers to sketch illustrations of the exercises, along with brief directions about each exercise (if needed). Make copies to share with each class member.

History. Ask for volunteers to compile a list of historical events during this century that could be considered stressful to the majority of Americans. Ask them to make a chart of the events and discuss their list with the class.

- headaches and joint pains
- muscle weakness and pain
- sleep problems
- difficulty in thinking clearly
- fatigue after light exercise

There are many unanswered questions about CFS and how to treat it. Any long-term fatigue is a good reason for a medical checkup.

The Effects of Stress on Health

It is easy to look at stress in purely physical terms because the body's physical response to a stressor can be felt and seen. In recent years, however, the stress response has been associated with situations involving mental health. Situations causing anxiety, frustration, or tension trigger the stress response and can lead to the development of physical ailments. The term **psychosomatic,** involving both the mind and the body, is used to describe such illnesses.

A number of diseases, including cardiovascular disease, hypertension, asthma, ulcers, colitis, and migraine headaches, are thought to be related in some way to stress. In some cases stress seems to be a contributing factor in all of these diseases. However, it is hard to identify stress as the major factor because so many other factors can be involved.

One point is certain. There is increasing evidence that emotions cause physical reactions, which, over time, may be damaging to the body.

Stress has more than just a physical effect on the body. People feeling stress may not think as clearly as usual. Stress has been linked to accidents and injuries. People under stress may take more risks and may be less careful with their health. Stress also can affect your social health. When a person feels stress, he or she may not feel like being with others or may be impatient with them. If the effects of stress continue over time, relationships may suffer.

If this student had studied harder for this test, he probably wouldn't be feeling so stressed.

LESSON 1 REVIEW

Reviewing Facts and Vocabulary

1. Define *stress.* Why is stress necessary for life?
2. Give an example of an involuntary response to a stressor.
3. Define *stressor.* Give an example of a person, situation, and thought that could serve as a stressor.

Thinking Critically

4. **Analysis.** How might a person's response to a stressor affect his or her health?

5. **Analysis.** How might stress affect an individual's mental health? Social health?
6. **Analysis.** Compare eustress and distress, giving examples of each.
7. **Analysis.** Explain what makes the stress response such an individualized one.

Applying Health Knowledge

8. Give examples of at least five positive and negative stressors in your life. Discuss how they may or may not affect your health.

WHAT IS STRESS? **71**

Answers to Lesson 1 Review

1. Stress—the body and mind's reactions to everyday demands. Stress is necessary for the body to function.
2. Examples will vary.
3. Stressor—any stimulus that produces a stress response. Examples will vary.
4. Answers will vary.
5. Answers will vary.
6. Eustress is positive stress. Distress is negative stress. Examples will vary.
7. A person's age, social status, diet, sleep habits, cultural background, and previous experience have an impact on one's stress response.
8. Answers will vary.

Check for Understanding

- Assign and discuss the lesson review. Encourage LD students to focus on question 4, as it encompasses the main idea.

Evaluate

- Administer, grade, and discuss the *Lesson 1 Quiz.*

Reteach

- Have students list stressors in their lives that they consider positive and stressors that they consider negative. Have them underline the negative stressors that cannot be changed; circle the negative stressors that can be changed, lessened, or overcome; and write out a plan for overcoming or lessening the circled stressors.
- Ask students to complete *Reteaching Activity 9.*

Enrich

- Ask students to read material by and about Dr. Hans Selye, a leading authority on stress. Have them contrast information in popular literature on stress with findings by Dr. Selye.

Close

Summarize the most important concepts in the lesson. Write the lesson's major concepts on separate, numbered slips of paper. Place slips in a box, and let each student draw one. Next, going in numerical order, have each student define and summarize the concept on his or her slip of paper.

Focus

Lesson Objectives

After studying this lesson, students should be able to:
- discuss the relationship between time management and stress management
- describe common defense mechanisms used to cope with stress
- discuss ways to manage stress

Bellringer

Write the following on the chalkboard for students to work on while attendance is being taken: *Explain the difference between a type A and a type B personality. Which type best describes you? What are the reasons for your choice?*

Introducing the Lesson

Ask students to share their responses to the Bellringer. Discuss type A and type B personality types and the importance of identifying and managing stress-producing behaviors and personal responses to stress. Tell students that they will learn more about personality types in this lesson. Next, inform them that the lesson also will focus on time management, defense mechanisms that people use to cope with stress, and six ways of managing stress effectively.

Building Vocabulary

- Have students use the terms *time-management skills* and *priorities* in a short paragraph. Ask for volunteers to read their paragraphs to the class.
- Ask students to complete *Workbook Vocabulary Activity 10.*

DID YOU KNOW?

- Being a "latchkey kid"—a young person whose parents are at work when he or she gets home from school—can be very stressful. According to one study of 5,000 California eighth graders published in *Pediatrics,* junior-high latchkey kids have much higher stress levels, take more dangerous risks, and have more conflicts with their parents than non-latchkey kids.

COPING WITH STRESS

LESSON 2 FOCUS

TERMS TO USE
- Time-management skills
- Defense mechanisms

CONCEPTS TO LEARN
- Practicing good health habits can help you cope with stress.
- Time is a major factor in stress management.
- Defense mechanisms are used to help deal with stressful situations in life.
- All of us manage stress, either successfully or unsuccessfully.

ATTITUDES AND BEHAVIORS TO EVALUATE
- Self-Inventory, page 78.
- Building Decision-Making Skills, page 79.

Although it is true that some stressors are good, even motivating, your body cannot distinguish between positive and negative sources of stress. The body's response is the same. You will need to identify the stressors in your life and learn to manage them. You can do this by following these guidelines:

- Identify your own sources of stress, and examine your methods of coping.
- Make conscious choices that help control the amount of stress you experience.
- Develop and use coping and relaxation techniques to diffuse the tension that builds up excess stress.
- Practice good health habits daily.

What is the relationship between health, fitness, and the ability to cope? Stress researchers believe that people who choose a healthful diet, get plenty of sleep, and exercise regularly are better able to cope with daily stress. When the unexpected does occur, a healthy body is better able to respond appropriately and efficiently.

Are you aware of your own needs, your anxieties, your motivations, and your goals? The better you know yourself, the better able you are to identify and manage stress-producing situations and your typical responses to stressors.

Personality Types

Several years ago two doctors developed a theory about personality types and their relationship to stress. You may have heard someone described as a type A or type B personality. Doctors Friedman and

Good health habits help you cope with stress.

Resources for Lesson 2

- **Transparency** 15
- **Guided Reading** Activity 10
- **Decision-Making** Activity 4
- **Workbook** Voc Act 10, Appl Act 4
- **Reteaching** Activity 10
- **Enrichment** Activity 4
- **Health Labs** Activity 4

- **Cooperative Learning** Activity 4
- **Lesson 2 Quiz, Chapter 4 Test**
- ABC News InterActive Videodiscs
- **Drugs and Substance Abuse, Side 2**
- Ch 13 Coping With Stress

Rosenman have described these two personality types primarily on the basis of behavioral patterns.

Type A personalities seem to be more competitive, rushed, and time-oriented. Type B personalities appear to be more flexible and less rushed. While not wholly accurate, the theory is still a useful model.

Most people have characteristics of both type A and type B personalities. Think about your personality patterns. In different situations you may take on different characteristics. When you have a deadline for a paper, you may take on characteristics of a type A personality. When your homework is finished, and you are relaxing with friends, you may show a type B personality. Neither type A nor B determines intelligence, ambition, or success. Nor is one better than the other.

By being aware of your personality type, you can help eliminate some of your stress. Knowing how you respond to certain stress-producing situations can motivate you to plan ahead.

Time Management

In any discussion of stress, we must consider time. Time is a major factor in relieving stress. People who manage their time well are better able to control stress in their lives. They look at time as an ally and not as an opponent. How do you look at time? What are your **time-management skills**—your effective ways of arranging your time? Check yourself on the following behaviors:

- Are you always rushing?
- Do you bounce back and forth between unpleasant alternatives?
- Do you have trouble finding things?
- Do you find yourself tired from hours of nonproductive activity?
- Do you find you do not have enough time for rest or for personal relationships in your life?
- Do you regularly miss deadlines?
- Are you overwhelmed by demands and details?
- Do you find yourself doing several tasks at a time?
- Do you have trouble deciding what to do next?

If you answered yes to six or more of these questions, you may need to work on managing your time better.

Some people have difficulty managing their lives because they do not have good time-management skills. Part of this problem occurs because of a person's inability to say *no* to others. Sometimes you may be afraid to say *no* because it might offend someone. Perhaps you are afraid of what the other person will do if you say *no*. Saying *yes* to virtually anything that is proposed to you says that you have not established your priorities. It may also show that you do not think you are important. When you do not want to do something or have much to do, know when to say no. Make choices that help you do the tasks you must do to achieve your goals. This shows you can manage your life.

Defense Mechanisms

At times everyone uses **defense mechanisms,** which are strategies to deal with stressful situations. Defense mechanisms contribute to emotional health by providing relief from anxiety and helping someone cope

Trying to do many things at one time is not a good way of managing time—or reducing stress.

DID YOU KNOW?

- A yawn doesn't always mean you're tired; a sigh doesn't always mean you're in love. Sometimes these phenomena simply mean that your body is relieving itself of stress.
- Most workers in Europe get four to six weeks of vacation.
- In Australia, workers get four weeks of vacation and also receive a salary bonus during those weeks.
- In the U.S. the standard vacation time is two weeks per year.

COPING WITH STRESS **73**

Teach

Guided Practice

L1 DISCUSSION. Have students list three examples that illustrate situations in which they let stress manage them. Talk about ways they might change each situation.

L2 CLASS ACTIVITY. Have volunteers design a poster or bulletin board about stressful situations or events that give them or other people "butterflies." (Examples might include taking a test, getting ready for a big game, giving an oral report, asking someone out on a date, etc.) Ask the class to share examples of other stressful events or situations.

L1 DISCUSSION. Talk about the ways that type A personalities are different from type B personalities.

L1 USING LIFE MANAGEMENT SKILLS TRANSPARENCY 15. Refer to the Teaching Transparencies Binder.

L1 CLASS ACTIVITY. Lead students in brainstorming a list of jobs at home and school that can be dovetailed, or combined.

L1 EXPLANATION. Tell students that the better they know themselves, the better able they will be to manage stress-producing behaviors and their responses to stress. Understanding priorities is one step in this process.

L1 CLASS ACTIVITY. Lead students in brainstorming some tactful ways to say *no* to others' demands when they are pressed for time.

L1 DISCUSSION. Talk about some tactful responses students can give when friends call while they are studying. Select some of the responses for students to practice in groups of two.

Across the Curriculum

Language Arts. Organize the class into groups of three to four. Ask each group to write a paragraph about a friend asking another for a favor that is an imposition. Next, have groups exchange their papers. Ask each group to write a second paragraph, describing a tactful and successful response. Afterward, ask them to share their paragraphs and responses with the class.

Driver Education. Invite a driver's education teacher to speak to the class about safe and effective ways for drivers to deal with stress.

L1 **CLASS ACTIVITY.** Have students check their time-management skills on page 73. Ask students who answered *yes* to six or more of the questions to list ways they can manage their time better.

LD **EXPLANATION.** Some of the terms for common defense mechanisms are quite similar. Perhaps narrow them down to *denial, escape, rationalization, repression,* and *displacement* for LD students to focus on.

L1 **DISCUSSION.** Lead students in a discussion of ways in which denial and escape are used to cope with stress. (Examples include refusing to talk about or to accept a difficult situation, daydreaming, sleeping excessively, choosing to be alone a great deal of the time, etc.)

L2 **DEMONSTRATION.** Assign students to demonstrate the use of rationalization to justify one's actions. Follow up with a discussion of why rationalization is not an effective way of managing stress.

L2 **CLASS ACTIVITY.** Have students find examples of projection in cartoons, TV programs, or movies. Ask them to discuss their examples with the class. Talk about ways to avoid projecting one's feelings or actions on others as a means to reduce stress.

L1 **DISCUSSION.** Ask students to give examples in which regression could bring about disastrous consequences. Discuss how regression actually can increase stress rather than reduce it.

L3 **CLASS ACTIVITY.** Assign several students to choreograph short dances to represent instances of displacement and regression. Have them present their dances to the class. Afterward, ask the class to define and explain the two concepts. Next, ask the dancers to describe the situations depicted in their dance.

FINDING HELP

Tempted to drink or use other drugs? Don't be afraid to get help and support from family, friends, a favorite teacher, school nurse or counselor, your spiritual leader, or local groups. For additional help or information, contact some of the following sources:

- Alcoholics Anonymous World Service, Inc. Grand Central Station P.O. Box 459 New York, NY 10163

- National Council on Alcoholism and Drug Dependence 12 West 21st Street New York, NY 10010

- National Clearinghouse for Alcohol and Drug Information P.O. Box 2345 Rockville, MD 20852

with problems. However, too much dependence on them can lead to avoidance in facing the problems of day-to-day life.

The following are common defense mechanisms:

- **Denial.** Refusal to accept reality. Carol's pet dog has died. She had had the dog since she was a small child. Carol refuses to accept the dog's death. She refuses to talk about it and continues to act as if her dog is alive.

- **Escape, or fantasy.** Running away from a problem through daydreams, books, and excessive sleep. Jim has failed to make the basketball team. He imagines that he is suffering from some hidden physical problem. When others find out about his problem, they will view his effort to make the basketball team as a success, rather than as a failure.

- **Rationalization.** An attempt to justify one's actions with an excuse rather than by admitting one's failure or mistake. Anne justifies flunking her math test because she was absent the day it was scheduled.

- **Projection.** An attempt to protect one's self-esteem by blaming unpleasant feelings or inappropriate actions on others. Getting poor grades and blaming it on the teacher's dislike for you is an example of evading personal responsibility.

- **Repression.** Blocking out thoughts about unpleasant things or experiences—forgetting on purpose. Repression is actually an unconscious method of escaping something unpleasant. You may have chores to do this weekend while your parents are away. You simply do not think about any of your responsibilities so that you can enjoy your weekend of fun with friends.

- **Identification.** Acting like or modeling one's behavior after a person one likes. Identification is a form of hero worship. However, it can take another form. People who have had a similar achievement or experience may identify with one another, sharing in something they all have in common.

- **Displacement.** Expressing feelings toward someone or something not associated with the source of the feelings. Suzanna is upset because she did not get picked for the team. When her sister greets her at home, Suzanna gives her a shove, says "Leave me alone," and slams the door to her room.

- **Regression.** Retreating to an earlier time that seems less threatening and requires less responsibility. Paul is having trouble adjusting to high school, with its challenges, greater number of students, and new atmosphere. He goes back and visits his former teachers and principal in junior high school, and entertains the idea that it would be nice to stay there.

- **Compensation.** An attempt to make up for something one did not have, or did not receive. Paul is not very good at basketball, but he is a first-rate swimmer.

- **Sublimation.** Transforming unacceptable behaviors into acceptable ones. Sublimation can involve redirecting specific behaviors. Jack is always fighting with people. He redirects this energy as a member of the wrestling team.

74 CHAPTER 4 STRESS IN YOUR LIFE

Overcoming Misconceptions

Myth. All defense mechanisms are psychologically unhealthy. **Fact.** There are times when defense mechanisms can contribute to emotional health by giving people relief from stress and helping them cope with problems. Difficulties occur when people depend on defense mechanisms to help them avoid facing daily problems. **Myth.** You can't do two things at once. **Fact.** "Dovetailing," or overlapping activities, can frequently be done with some tasks and activities. For example, you can do exercises and watch TV at the same time, or you can sew a button on your shirt while talking on the phone. Dovetailing is an important concept in time management.

Managing Stress

You may not be able to control some stressors. However, you can control the effect you allow them to have on you. Five major ways to manage stress are planning, laughing, rechanneling your energy, learning to relax, and calling on your support system.

Planning

Planning is a major key to managing stress effectively. People who handle stress plan well, yet they know that even with the best plans, other things can happen to change those plans. By recognizing that changes can and often do occur, especially when other people are involved, people are better able to deal with changes, disappointments, frustrations, delays, or whatever might take place.

You further manage stress by being realistic about your plans and your expectations. Learn to anticipate the unexpected. Sometimes this simply means thinking ahead. Rather than concentrating on and living from moment to moment, think ahead to know what you might expect.

Of course, as in the case of each of these strategies, great variation exists. Some people spend so much time planning and anticipating what might happen that they do not enjoy the actual activity. This can be as stressful a situation as not planning at all. You have to decide what works for you.

Laughing

Another effective way to deal with stress is to laugh. There is the story of the little boy on his bicycle who went over a bump on the sidewalk and took a tumble. He got up, brushed himself off, and then burst out laughing.

Laughing and relaxing help you relieve stress.

Working and Playing Worldwide

■ According to a German publication called *Der Arbeitgeber*, or *The Employer*, the average employee in France works 33.8 hours per week, while the average worker in Great Britain works 34.1 hours per week; in Switzerland, 36 hours per week, in the U.S., 36.3 hours, and in Japan, 36.8 hours.

■ In Japan, new attention is being paid to the importance of relaxation for better overall productivity and health. In fact, the National Recreation Association of Japan now offers training sessions for people to become leisure counselors, helping people to learn how and where to have fun and relax.

L2 DISCUSSION. Lead students in brainstorming various ways that people compensate to make up for something they do not have or did not receive. Ask them to explain how compensation is often used to cope with stress.

L2 CLASS ACTIVITY. Have students work in small groups to prepare and present a skit showing the relationship between planning and stress management.

LEP DISCUSSION. Begin by quietly playing a recording, CD, or record that most individuals would find relaxing. Ask students to close their eyes and imagine they are at a beautiful place, such as a beach, in the mountains, or in a forest. After a few minutes of music (and with it still playing in the background), talk about ways people can rechannel their energy (such as by listening to music, daydreaming, imagining a beautiful scene, etc.). Ask for volunteers to share ways that they rechannel their energy.

L2 CLASS ACTIVITY. Assign students to design posters showing a variety of relaxation techniques. Feature the posters in a display titled "Relax to the Max."

L2 COOPERATIVE LEARNING. With the help of a school counselor, have groups of students create and conduct a survey at school to find out (1) what events are most stressful to their peers and (2) what positive methods teens use to control or relieve stress. Using the results, have students share practical information from their survey with other students in the form of a brochure.

L1 DISCUSSION. Ask students to talk about ways they can be supportive of their friends and family.

L1 DISCUSSION. Have students name and describe some TV programs that feature supportive relationships. Talk about ways the characters help each other deal with stress.

L1 SPEAKER. Invite a school counselor, a local psychologist, or other mental-health worker to talk to the class about typical counseling procedures. Perhaps a mock demonstration could be arranged. Use the activity to make students more familiar with professional counseling and less stressful to those who might benefit from it.

Across the Curriculum

History. Supportive people have been extremely important throughout history. Have students locate instances in which family members, friends, teachers, fellow soldiers, etc. have offered support to others in times of stress. Ask students to share what they learn with the class.

Music. Ask for volunteers to interview adults for names of musical compositions that they feel are calming in times of stress. If possible, arrange for the class to listen to recordings of some of these compositions. Ask them to identify the characteristics of the music that may produce the described effect.

L1 PERSONAL INVOLVEMENT. Have students keep journals, recording their successes and failures at time management for several weeks. Have them write about how the use of their time affected their levels of stress. Afterward, ask them to analyze their journals, looking at ways they might be able to manage time more effectively, thus reducing stress. Ask volunteers to share some of their experiences.

L1 PERSONAL INVOLVEMENT. Have each student make and follow a "To Do List" for several days. Ask them to assign priorities to each of the items on their lists and to cross them off as they complete them. Afterward, discuss ways they can make their lists more effective.

L1 PERSONAL INVOLVEMENT. Have each student write a list of ways to reduce stress. Ask them to underline the two methods that work best for them. Afterward, have each student write on the chalkboard his or her two best. Keep a tally of the students' most common ways of reducing stress, and talk about reasons that they are used most frequently.

L1 READING. Have students collect comic strips and cartoons showing supportive friendships. Display some of these on the bulletin board.

L3 RESEARCH. Have volunteers research the studies done on self-help groups and how support systems have been shown to be an important factor in coping.

L1 PARENTAL INVOLVEMENT. Ask for volunteers to interview a parent, grandparent, or other adult in their lives about what it was like to be a teenager. Have them find answers to questions such as: When each adult was a teen, what were his or her feelings and concerns about appearance? physical changes? friends? dating? recreation? music? parents? school? What were his or her greatest fears? How were stressful events and situations handled? Afterward, ask students to write short reports on their interviews. Follow up with a class discussion of the experience.

L1 USING THE LESSON RESOURCES. For additional student activities, refer to the lesson resources on page 72.

HELP WANTED

Guidance Counselor

Helping students navigate the sometimes stormy sea known as high school can be a challenging, fascinating, frustrating, and very rewarding career. Your awareness of the world-of-work and educational opportunities are important. Your people skills (listening, feeling, and communicating orally and in writing), empathy, and creative problem-solving skills are equally valuable. Your certification, master's degree, and teaching experience are musts. Your interest in being involved in extra-curricular activities is a major plus.

For more information contact:
National Education Association
1201 16th Street NW
Washington, DC 20036

A man passing by, who saw no fun in the scraped knee and elbow, asked, "What's so funny? Why are you laughing?" The boy replied, "Mister, I'm laughing so I won't cry." Laughter can be a relief when things have gone wrong. By laughing, you accept the reality that you are human and realize that sometimes unfortunate things happen.

By laughing, you release the stress that builds up when things go wrong. This does not mean that you do not care about what happened. It simply means that you have chosen a healthful way to deal with the stress of that particular situation.

Rechanneling Your Energy

Transferring or rechanneling your energy is another way to manage stress. If you find that a situation is causing you to become tense, you might transfer your energy to some other activity—washing a car, taking a walk, cleaning your room, or just taking a break.

If you cannot physically get away from the situation, give your mind a break. Let it wander for a few minutes. Daydreaming can be an excellent stress reducer. Of course, be sure to know and use appropriate times to relax. Daydreaming when you are supposed to be taking notes or taking a test in class can be a source of added stress.

Learning to Relax

One effective way of relieving stress is physical exercise. It burns pent-up energy and clears the mind, allowing you to relax. Choose exercise you enjoy and do it in a peaceful environment. Choose a setting that prevents more stress from developing.

Calling on Your Support Group

A support group can help greatly in managing stress. What is a support group? *Support* means "to hold up." There are times when things get very difficult for you, and your energy and strength are worn down. On such occasions it is important for you to have a support system and to use it.

The supportive people in your life may include family, friends, a church leader, teachers, or employers. A strong support system might

---

KEEPING FIT

Avoid Getting "Testy" Over Tests

Studying for and taking tests can be very stressful. Consider these helpful hints:
- Use 2-hour blocks of time, then take a half-hour break, then return to work.
- Become aware of the messages

you give yourself about your ability to take tests.
- Before taking the test, take the time to physically and mentally relax.
- First answer all the questions you are sure of. Then go back

and answer the ones that are more difficult.
- Make an outline for any essay questions on a test.
- Remind yourself that tests are learning tools meant to help you improve.

Across the Curriculum

Home Economics. Good nutrition can play an important role in keeping the body healthy during stressful times. Have students develop menus for a week, following guidelines for good nutrition. Invite a home economics teacher to demonstrate the preparation of an easy-to-prepare meal that is high in fiber and low in fat.

Home Economics. There are many over-the-counter products in the marketplace that are advertised as being "stress-reducing." Choose students to visit a local drugstore and to make note of such products, their ingredients, their prices, and their claims. Ask them to share what they learn with the class.

LOOKING AT TECHNOLOGY

Biofeedback

When you are stressed out, your body reacts. Your pulse races, your muscles tighten, and your hands sweat. One device—the biofeedback machine—monitors these bodily changes and shows them to the person hooked up to the machine. The machine may read brain waves, changes in the electricity and temperature of the skin, or muscle tension. It then "feeds back" information about the person's level of tension or relaxation by moving a temperature indicator, by emitting a certain tone, or by flashing lights. By showing a person what happens when he or she is stressed or relaxed, the person develops a greater awareness of what each state feels like and what physical signs indicate each one. With practice and by learning various relaxation techniques, the person can then learn to "tune in" to a more relaxed state. Once the person has learned to stop the beeping tone or slow down the flashing lights with his or her own relaxation response, the machine will no longer be needed.

Assess

Check for Understanding

- Assign and discuss the lesson review. Questions 1 and 3 are most appropriate for LD students.
- Assign and discuss the chapter review.

Evaluate

- Administer, grade, and discuss the *Lesson 2 Quiz*.
- Administer, grade, and discuss the *Chapter 4 Test*.
- Refer to the Performance Assessment strategy for this chapter. See pages T 23 to T 25.

Reteach

- Have students imagine they are efficiency experts. Have them make a list of tips for time management they would use in advising clients. Ask them to underline those tips they currently use in their own lives. Then ask them to think of ways they might personally implement those tips they did not underline.
- Ask students to complete *Reteaching Activity 10*.

Enrich

- Ask students to complete *Enrichment Activity 4*.

---

include several of these people. This puts less pressure on any one person. It also reduces the problem of depending on only one person for some assistance and discovering that that person is not available at the time help is needed. Building a strong support system is perhaps one of the most important strategies for managing stress.

LESSON 2 REVIEW

Reviewing Facts and Vocabulary

1. Define the term *time-management skills*.
2. Which personality type—type A or type B—is more prone to stress? Explain.

Thinking Critically

3. **Synthesis.** How can setting priorities be an effective way of managing stress?
4. **Analysis.** Compare five defense mechanisms, giving an example of each.
5. **Evaluation.** Are there circumstances when being a type A personality is preferred over being a type B personality? Explain.

Applying Health Knowledge

6. Keep a journal of highly stressful situations at school, and record how you and others respond in those situations. Draw conclusions about the most effective ways to cope with stress.
7. On a sheet of paper list as many expressions as possible that include the word *time*. For example, "Time flies when you're having fun," "Time out," "Time is up." Choose one of these expressions and draw an illustration that shows a way you practice time management.

COPING WITH STRESS **77**

Close

Write the lesson's major concepts on numbered, separate slips of paper. Place slips in a box, and let each student draw one. Next, going in numerical order, have students define and summarize the concept written on the slip of paper they selected.

Answers to Lesson 2 Review

1. Effective ways of arranging one's time.
2. Type A. This type of personality tends to be more competitive and rushed.
3. It can help one effectively manage one's time by establishing what is important. It helps one determine when to say no.
4. Answers will vary but should reflect an understanding of the definitions given on page 74.
5. Answers will vary but should reflect an understanding of the two personality types and should be logically supported.
6. Answers will vary.
7. Answers will vary.

Helping Students Improve Their Health

Using the Self-Inventory

Teaching Strategies

L1 EXPLANATION. In some cases, due to social, familial, or environmental factors, students may not perceive some items as stressors. Try to identify these items after the students take the inventory, i.e., eating on the run, or trouble sleeping at night.

L1 EXPLANATION. Items 23 and 24 could cause misgivings on the part of some parents. Males, in our society, are told that it's not manly to cry or show emotions and to keep one's problems to oneself. Explain that in some cases crying is a healthy way to deal with stress. Also share that help can be found by sharing problems with some people.

L2 DISCUSSION. List some of the physical activities that adolescents are involved with. Then discuss how physical activity allows our bodies to return to homeostasis.

L2 DISCUSSION. Distribute an index card to each student. On the cards, have students relate anonymous situations they were involved with when stress caused them to lose control. Then discuss how the situation might have been handled in a more positive manner.

L2 DISCUSSION. On the board, make a list of stress-related illnesses. Then divide the class into groups of three to four students each. Have each group pick an illness and attempt to tell how the effects of stress on the body caused the illness.

L2 CLASS ACTIVITY. As a way to better understand defense mechanisms, divide the class into groups of three to four students. Assign a defense mechanism to each group and have them make up a skit portraying it. Have the class guess which defense mechanism is being used.

Self-Inventory

Stress—The Danger Signals

HOW DO YOU RATE?

Number a sheet of paper from 1 through 25. Read each item below and respond by writing *yes* or *no* for each item. Then proceed to the next section.

1. I am aware of when I am tense.
2. I try to be perfect at everything I do.
3. I like to work with others on projects.
4. I try to do everything right. If I cannot do something right, I do not do it at all.
5. I avoid eating on the run.
6. I have trouble expressing anger.
7. I offer help to others even when I get no personal gain from it.
8. I get angry with others easily.
9. I feel that my problems are no worse than anyone else's.
10. I am usually in a hurry.
11. I finish one thing before I start another.
12. I tend to do things the way I have always done them.
13. When I start making mistakes, I take a break from the task for a while.
14. It is hard for me to wait in lines.
15. It is easy for me to relax.
16. Things do not move fast enough for me.
17. When I have a problem, I like to share it with others.
18. I have trouble sleeping at night.
19. I use physical activity to help reduce my stress.
20. I can usually figure out what people are going to say before they say it.
21. I can laugh at myself when I make mistakes.
22. I find myself thinking about the next thing that I have to do while I am in the middle of something else.
23. I cry when I am hurt.
24. I keep my problems to myself.
25. I can enjoy what I am doing even before it is completely finished.

HOW DID YOU SCORE?

Give yourself 1 point for each *yes* response to an odd-numbered item. Give yourself 1 point for each *no* response to an even-numbered item. Find your total to see how you scored. Then proceed to the next section.

21 to 25
Excellent. You manage stress very well. Keep it up!

16 to 20
Very Good. You have a low-stress life-style.

11 to 15
Fair. You have low stress in some areas, but high stress in others. You need to make some changes in order to be a better stress manager.

Below 11
Needs Improvement. You do not handle stress well. This will have a negative impact on both your physical and mental health.

WHAT ARE YOUR GOALS?

If you received an *excellent* or *very good* score, complete the statements in Part A. If your score was *fair* or *needs improvement,* complete the statements in Parts A and B.

Part A

1. I plan to learn more about stress management by ____.
2. My timetable for accomplishing this is ____.
3. I plan to share my information with others by ____.

Part B

4. The behavior or attitude toward stress I would most like to change is ____.
5. The steps involved in making this change are ____.
6. My rewards for making this change will be ____.

Meeting Students' Needs

For students who score *Excellent*. Suggest students write essays on adolescent stress and coping techniques to share with other students.

For students who score *Very Good*. While these students have low-stress lifestyles, have them identify where they could improve their coping skills.

For students who score *Fair*. Have students list things that they perceive are causing stress and then describe ways to cope better.

For students who *Need Improvement*. Suggest students research the topics of stress identification and coping skills.

Building Decision-Making Skills

Marty is a 6'5", 275-pound lineman whose speed makes him one of the top recruits in his state as he heads into his senior year. Currently he has a 2.5 GPA (out of a possible 4.0) in his school's college-preparatory core curriculum. His GPA is above the required 2.0 for an athletic scholarship. Marty's second set of ACT scores arrived in today's mail. He is very upset and depressed because his composite score of 15 is not high enough to qualify him for the athletic scholarship he's been offered. Although Marty's grades have always been above average, he has never done very well with standardized tests. He just doesn't seem to be able to handle the anxiety of those testing situations. What should Marty do?

WHAT DO YOU THINK?

1. **Situation.** Where might Marty get accurate information on which to base this decision?

2. **Situation.** What do you think causes Marty's anxiety: heredity, not being prepared, or some other factor?

3. **Choices.** What choices does Marty have?

4. **Consequences.** List the advantages of each choice.

5. **Consequences.** What are the disadvantages of each choice?

6. **Consequences.** What are the financial implications of this situation?

7. **Consequences.** How will each of these choices affect Marty's self-esteem?

8. **Decision.** What do you think Marty should do?

9. **Decision.** How should Marty respond to those who ask about his scores—friends, coaches, and the media?

Juanita and Allison have been good friends since elementary school. They live in the same neighborhood, hang out with the same group of friends, and even take the same courses in school. Last Saturday they spent the day at the local mall looking for the "perfect outfit" for their school's holiday dance. Juanita found her outfit early on. Allison, however, continued to try on many things only to find that with each outfit something just wasn't right. Either the color didn't work or her size wasn't available. Finally, in the last store, Allison found just what she was looking for. Juanita, too, thought it was perfect, and she left the fitting room to browse while Allison was getting dressed. When Allison came out of the dressing room she was carrying a package, but not the outfit. Juanita said, "Hey, where's your outfit?" Allison replied, "Oh, I decided not to spend the money."

The following weekend was the holiday dance and Juanita and Allison were double-dating. When Juanita picked up Allison she came out of her house wearing the new outfit. When Juanita asked her if she'd gone back to the store to get it Allison whispered, "Oh, I'm just borrowing it. That store will never know." What should Juanita do?

WHAT DO YOU THINK?

10. **Situation.** What decision does Juanita need to make?

11. **Choices.** What are Juanita's choices?

12. **Consequences.** What are the advantages and disadvantages of each choice?

13. **Consequences.** How might this decision affect Juanita and Allison's friendship?

14. **Consequences.** If Juanita does nothing, how may her self-esteem be affected?

15. **Consequences.** If Juanita confronts Allison and gets her to see her error, what action might Juanita expect Allison to take?

16. **Decision.** How do you think Juanita should handle this situation?

17. **Decision.** If Juanita decides to confront Allison, how and where should the confrontation take place?

COPING WITH STRESS **79**

Discussing the Answers

Situation 1. During the discussion of this situation, try to see if there are any alternatives for Marty. If so, what are they? Also look into why Marty is going to college. Is it to play football or get an education? Could there be a compromise anywhere?

Situation 2. While discussing this situation, see if students can see any defense mechanism(s) being used, and if so, which one(s). Look into ways that Juanita could bring up the fact that she is uncomfortable with what has happened. Could there be a compromise here?

Answers to Chapter 4 Review

Using Health Terms

1. Stress
2. Hypothalamus
3. Adrenaline
4. Fatigue
5. Chronic fatigue syndrome
6. Psychosomatic
7. Type A personality
8. Type B personality
9. Priorities
10. Defense mechanisms

Building Academic Skills

11. Forty-two patients.
12. Paragraphs will vary but should reflect an understanding of type A and type B personalities and be supported logically.

Recalling the Facts

13. Some stress is necessary for life. Moderate stress can increase productivity, excite, stimulate, and challenge.
14. Answers will vary. Accept five of the following factors: age, social status, income, state of health, diet, sleep habits, cultural background, or previous experience.
15. One has conscious control over voluntary responses to stress but not over involuntary responses.
16. The nervous system and the endocrine system.
17. The pituitary gland.
18. Rest.
19. The common cold, flu, anemia.
20. Answers will vary. Accept three of the following: depression, boredom, worry about schoolwork/home/dates, how one looks, being liked.
21. Answers will vary. Accept three of the following: set priorities, engage in activities that promote one's health, set a goal for changing certain behavior, talk to someone, find out what is at the root of the fatigue.
22. Anxiety, frustration, tension.
23. It doesn't. The body's response is the same to positive or negative stress.

24. Answers will vary. Accept three of the following: identify sources of stress, examine methods of coping, make conscious choices that help control stress, develop and use coping and relaxation techniques, practice good health habits.

25. Answers will vary. Accept three of the following: denial, escape/fantasy, rationalization, projection, repression, identification, displacement, regression, compensation, sublimation.

Using Health Terms

On a separate sheet of paper, write the term that best matches each definition given below.

LESSON 1

1. The body's general reaction to everyday demands.
2. A nerve center in the brain that initiates physical changes associated with stress and is part of the endocrine system.
3. The "emergency" hormone.
4. A tired feeling that lowers a person's level of activity.
5. A type of fatigue that lasts for a long period of time and seems to have no identifiable cause.
6. A word used to describe physical ailments that seem to be triggered by the stress response.

LESSON 2

7. A personality type characterized by competitiveness and a desire to be active and busy.
8. A personality type characterized by a flexible and easygoing attitude toward life.
9. The things that are most important to an individual.
10. Strategies a person uses to deal with stressful situations.

Building Academic Skills

LESSON 1

11. **Math.** It is estimated that two-thirds of all office visits to family doctors are a result of stress-related symptoms. Using this figure, if a doctor sees 21 patients each day for 3 days, how many patients have stress-related symptoms?

LESSON 2

12. **Writing.** Write a paragraph explaining whether you think you are a type A or type B personality. Use details and examples to support your evaluation of your own personality type.

Recalling the Facts

LESSON 1

13. In what ways can stress be good?
14. List five factors that are related to the effect stressors have on a person's life.
15. How do voluntary stress responses differ from involuntary stress responses?
16. What two major body systems participate in the body's response to stressors?
17. What gland secretes a hormone that stimulates the adrenal gland to secrete adrenaline?
18. What is the best remedy for physical fatigue?
19. List three illnesses that can be brought on by pathological fatigue.
20. What are three causes of psychological fatigue?
21. List three ways to overcome psychological fatigue.
22. Name three conditions that can contribute to psychosomatic illnesses.

LESSON 2

23. How does the body distinguish between positive and negative stress?
24. List three strategies for managing stress and describe them.
25. What are three defense mechanisms people use to deal with stressful situations?
26. What theory regarding personality types was developed by Friedman and Rosenman? How does their theory relate to stress?
27. What does the phrase "Know when to say no" have to do with managing your time?
28. Explain how the management of time is related to a person's stress level.
29. What are some behaviors characteristic of a person who is using the defense mechanism of escape, or fantasy?
30. How might a person who is using the defense mechanism of projection behave if he or she gets a low grade on a test?
31. List five main ways to manage stress.
32. How can exercise help one manage stress?
33. What is a support system?

REVIEW

Thinking Critically

LESSON 1

34. Synthesis. Terri feels tired all the time. She has trouble sleeping at night. She cannot concentrate in school. She is having a lot of headaches, and her muscles and joints feel sore. Just walking up a flight of stairs exhausts her. She thinks she may have the flu. What might Terri's problem be, and what should she do?

LESSON 2

35. Evaluation. What are the limitations of trying to classify people according to personality types?

36. Synthesis. Which defense mechanism is each of the following people using?

- Bob has an aggressive personality. He is always getting into fights with the other boys in the neighborhood. He decides to try out for the football team.
- Rosita does not believe she can pass the algebra test on Monday. She spends the entire weekend reading novels instead of studying.
- Harold missed several easy shots during the basketball game on Tuesday night. He tells his friends that the coach has not let him play enough in previous games.
- Judy's best friend has begun taking ballet lessons. Although Judy has no interest in ballet, she has enrolled in a ballet class.
- Matt tried out for the lead in the school play. Jeff got the part. When Matt got home, he slammed the door to his room.

Making the Connection

LESSON 1

37. Music. Many contemporary songs express themes of alienation, frustration, loneliness, interpersonal conflict, and other stressful emotions. Listen to two or three songs of various styles with these themes. Include rhythm and blues, country and western, and rap. Compare and contrast each artist's interpretation of these themes.

Applying Health Knowledge

LESSON 1

38. You have probably given some thought to the kind of job you would like to have when you finish school. Name three jobs you think would be highly stressful and explain why. Name three jobs you think would have low stress levels and explain why.

LESSON 2

39. Make a pie graph illustrating the percentages of time you spend on daily activities. Think about the following activities and include the ones that apply to your life: sleeping; attending classes; eating; engaging in extracurricular activities; exercising; watching television; reading; talking on the phone; going to and from school; studying; working at a job; doing household chores; and any other activities that take up more than an hour of your day.

40. Keep a diary of your activities for a week. Label each activity *A,* for high priority; *B,* for medium priority; or *C,* for low priority. Compare your priority labels with the pie graph you made in item 39. Is there a logical relationship between your priority labels and the amount of time you spend on each activity? What adjustments might you need to make?

Beyond the Classroom

LESSON 1

41. Parental Involvement. Ask your parents about the stressors they experience in their lives. Make a list of the things they find stressful about their jobs, how these stressors affect their relationships and their health, and how they cope.

LESSON 2

42. Community Involvement. Find out what kinds of support groups exist in your community to help people deal with stress. Make a list of these.

---

26. Friedman and Rosenman identified two personality types based primarily on the basis of behavioral patterns. Type A personalities experience a more stressful life-style based on their behavior, while type B personalities do not.

27. Answers will vary but should reflect the idea that saying *no* to certain activities or demands shows that a person has established priorities and thinks well of himself or herself.

28. People who manage their time well are better able to control stress in their lives.

29. Daydreaming, reading novels, excessive sleep.

30. He or she may blame the poor grade on the teacher's dislike for him or her.

31. Planning, laughing, rechanneling one's energy, learning to relax, calling on support systems.

32. By rechanneling energy.

33. Individuals or groups a person can talk to about stress-related problems.

Thinking Critically

34. Answers will vary. Possible answer: She may be suffering from chronic fatigue syndrome. She should see a doctor.

35. Answers will vary. Possible answer: Most people exhibit traits from each of the personality types in different situations.

36. Bob—sublimation, Rosita—escape or fantasy, Harold—rationalization or projection, Judy—identification, Matt—displacement.

Making the Connection

37. Answers will vary.

Applying Health Knowledge

38. Answers will vary, but explanations should logically support student's choices.

39. Graphs will vary but should accurately reflect percentages of time.

40. Answers will vary.

Beyond the Classroom

41. Answers will vary.

42. Answers will vary.

Lesson Summaries

LESSON 1. The family is the basic unit of society. A family exerts a strong influence on the lives and personalities of its members, just as each member affects the physical, mental, and social levels of the total family's health. The many types of families and some of the changes that families have gone through during the last 50 years are discussed in this lesson.

LESSON 2. It's important for us to be aware of the threats to the health of our families, so that we can take steps to maintain a healthy family, and thus a strong society. A family system can break down for a variety of reasons, often ending in divorce and/or restructuring. In many cases, the troubled family remains intact and, depending on the problems and whether or not family members seek help, the health of individual members can be threatened.

Introducing the Chapter

Tell students that members of a family affect one another economically, socially, emotionally, and in some ways, physically. As the basic unit of society, the family plays a critical role in the healthy growth and development of the individual. Students will study this chapter from two reference points: as responsible contributing members of their current families; and as potential parents and heads of their own future families. Remind students that this material is not intended to delve into their private lives; rather, it is meant to create an awareness of the importance of the family unit and an understanding of what constitutes a healthy family.

Performance Assessment ✓

Refer to pages T 23 to T 25 for a Performance Assessment strategy for this chapter. See the *Performance Assessment Activities* booklet for additional suggestions.

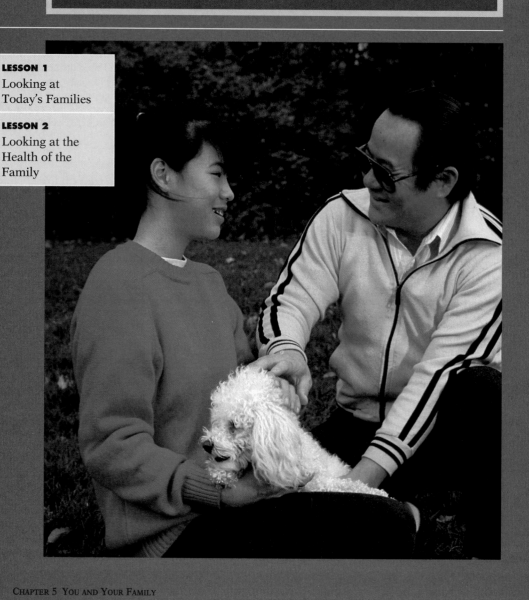

CHAPTER

5

YOU AND YOUR FAMILY

LESSON 1

Looking at Today's Families

LESSON 2

Looking at the Health of the Family

82 CHAPTER 5 YOU AND YOUR FAMILY

Key to Ability Levels

Teaching strategies have been coded for varying learning styles and abilities.

L1 Level 1 activities are basic activities and should be within the ability range of all students.

L2 Level 2 activities are average activities and should be within the ability range of average to above-average students.

L3 Level 3 activities are challenging activities designed for the ability range of above-average students.

LD LD activities should be within the ability range of learning-disabled students.

LEP LEP activities should be within the ability range of Limited English Proficiency students.

LOOKING AT TODAY'S FAMILIES

For many people the word *family* is often associated with warm feelings and pleasant scenes. Perhaps it reminds you of a holiday or vacation when all of the family, including aunts, uncles, cousins, and grandparents, got together for a celebration. Maybe the word brings to mind an older brother or sister who has moved away or a favorite aunt or uncle who comes for frequent visits. Although the word *family* means different things to different people, it often is defined as a group of people related by blood, marriage, or adoption. It is the group in which most people live their lives and in which people bring up children. The family is the basic unit of society.

The Family as a System

From the time you were born, your family exerted a strong influence on your life and personality. Families not only provide food, clothing, and shelter, but they also give family members a sense of security and a feeling of belonging. Families help children form their religious beliefs and values, and they pass on traditions and customs from one generation to the next.

Considering the family as a social system—knowing that what one person does affects every other person—can make you more aware of how your family works. A comparison can be made to the human body. For example, all parts of the body are interconnected to compose a whole being. Although separate elements can be identified, such as the heart or a specific muscle, no part exists in isolation. The body is in constant motion—taking in air, digesting food, healing itself—and it routinely deals with both the inner environment and the outside world. Just as your body functions because of the interrelationships of the different parts and the exchanges with the outside, so does your family.

As a system, the level of health—physical, mental, and social—of each family member affects the level of the total family's health. The reverse is also true. The health of the family system directly affects the health of its individual members. In addition, because the family is the basic social unit of society, society's health is directly related to the family's health. If we are to survive and maintain a healthy society, then everyone must work to promote healthy families.

Types of Families

There are many different types of families in today's world. Families vary in size, in relationships, and in the way in which they meet the needs of family members.

The Nuclear Family. The nuclear family unit is a common type of family. It consists of parents and one or more children sharing a household.

LOOKING AT TODAY'S FAMILIES **83**

LESSON 1 FOCUS

TERMS TO USE
- Mobile
- Blended family

CONCEPTS TO LEARN
- The family is the basic social unit of society.
- Many factors influence the health of the family.

ATTITUDES AND BEHAVIORS TO EVALUATE
- Self-Inventory, page 96.
- Building Decision-Making Skills, page 97.

Focus

Lesson Objectives
After studying this lesson, students should be able to:
- describe the family in terms of a system
- compare types of families
- explain two major functions of the family
- analyze three significant changes affecting today's families

Bellringer
Write the following on the chalkboard for students to work on while attendance is being taken: *Think of 10 families that you know. List the people (mother, father, children, and so on) that make up each family. Please do not use names.*

Introducing the Lesson
Refer to the Bellringer. Ask volunteers to share their lists of families. Discuss the differences and the similarities. Point out that the structure of the family refers to the types of people who belong to it. Ask them if any one structure is more common than others. Tell students they will learn about different types of families and ways in which today's families are changing. Explain that the lesson will focus on the family as a social system, much like all parts of the body are interconnected to compose a whole being.

DID YOU KNOW?

According to the 1990 Census:
- 64.2 percent of Americans own their own homes. This figure is down from 64.4 percent in 1980.
- 55 percent of homeowners are married, down 5 percent from 1980.
- the size of the average household in the U.S. fell from 2.75 persons per home in 1980 to 2.63 in 1990.

Resources for Lesson 1

- **Guided Reading** Activity 11
- **Workbook** Vocabulary Activity 11
- **Reteaching** Activity 11
- **Lesson 1 Quiz**
- **Performance Assessment** Activity 5

ABC News InterActive Videodiscs
Teenage Sexuality, Side 1
Ch 19 Single Parenting: Maureen and Regina

- Have students use the terms *family* and *mobile* in a sentence. Ask them to read their sentences to the class.
- Have students design crossword puzzles using the terms *family* and *mobile,* plus the names of each of the family types. Ask them to exchange their puzzles with partners. Provide time for completion.
- Ask students to complete *Workbook Vocabulary Activity 11.*

Teach

Guided Practice

L1 **DISCUSSION.** Lead students in brainstorming a list of words they think of when they hear the word *family.* Write the words on the chalkboard. Next, discuss ways in which families are similar to body systems.

L1 **DISCUSSION.** Ask students to find several definitions of *nuclear* and to write them on the chalkboard. Discuss how the definitions relate to the nuclear family.

L1 **SPEAKER.** Invite a social worker or other official to talk to the class about adoption and foster family requirements and procedures. You may wish to include one or more families who have adopted children or served as foster parents to discuss their experiences.

L1 **CLASS ACTIVITY.** Set up a panel of parents representing different types of families. Ask each person to describe his or her family and how the family works to stay healthy.

L2 **CLASS ACTIVITY.** Select students to create and present skits about different types of families. Follow up with a discussion of each skit and the type of family portrayed.

L2 **CLASS ACTIVITY.** Choose students to write and present positive public service announcements about types of families and the changing family system.

Love and care are two important characteristics of any healthy family structure.

Multigenerational Families

Many cultures live in multigenerational households. In China, a son traditionally brings his bride home to live in his parents' house. Each female will have her own kitchen area, but the house is shared. The Amish typically build a small living space onto the main house for when the parents wish to "retire" from farming. Several generations then live together on the farm. Some American fishing families on the east coast also maintain multigenerational family homes today.

Years ago, as employment in industry increased, many Americans left farm homesteads that housed several generations to live in nuclear families. Today, due to the increase in single-parent families and economic conditions, the multigenerational family is making a comeback.

The Single-Parent Family. Some families are single-parent families—that is, only one parent lives with the child or children. Most often the parent is the mother, especially in the case of a divorce, because she generally is awarded custody of the children. However, a growing number of fathers are now receiving custody of their children. Other types of single-parent families consist of a parent whose husband or wife has died or a single adult who has adopted one or more children.

The Extended Family. An extended family includes one or more relatives in addition to the nuclear family or single-parent family. Sometimes these relatives live in the same household as nuclear or single-parent families. This extended family may be composed of grandparents, aunts, uncles, and cousins who serve as an extra support system for the nuclear family.

Although newly married couples usually establish a separate home, family ties tend to remain intact with the extended family. However, as people become more and more **mobile,** or likely to move from place to place, there often is less direct involvement with the extended family. Transfers, job opportunities, and schooling can all mean moving away from the larger family unit. However, many people maintain contact in other ways—by letters, telephone calls, and visits. Mobile families also tend to establish other friends and relationships to maintain a support system that is important to a healthy family system.

The Blended Family. Many families, such as a blended family, reflect the effects of divorce and remarriage. A **blended family** is a type of nuclear family in which one or both people have been married before. Each may have a child or children from a previous marriage. *Stepparents, stepbrothers,* and *stepsisters* are terms frequently used to describe the various family members who are not related by birth.

The Adoptive Family. This type of family may be a nuclear, single-parent, or blended family. The children are not related by birth to the parents. Through a legal procedure, one or more children have become part of the family through adoption. The parent or parents are responsible for the children they have adopted as if they were their children by birth.

The Foster Family. A foster family can also be a nuclear, single-parent, or blended family. One or more of its children are not the birth children

Across the Curriculum

Language Arts. Have students write papers about the kind of family they would like to have when they become adults. Have them describe the place they want to live, the attributes of their family members, the careers of the adult family members, and activities they could share. Ask for volunteers to discuss their "family of the future."

Language Arts. Have students spend a day listening to the way others in their families communicate. Ask them to make notes on their observations. Ask if most of the interactions they observed were healthy. Why or why not? How could communication within the family be changed? How could improved communication benefit the family?

of the parent or parents. Through special arrangements with governmental agencies or foster parent and child organizations, the children are cared for by a particular family. Sometimes the children stay for extended periods of time. In some circumstances they are adopted later by the foster family.

Other Family Types.   Many groups do not consist of parents and children but are still considered families. An example is a married couple with no children. In other situations people who do not have families sometimes band together and take care of one another. These people function as a family because of the ways in which they meet one another's needs.

Functions of the Family

The family, as the basic social unit of society, serves two essential functions:

- It is the primary support system to which individuals turn in order to have their basic needs met.
- It is also the essential mechanism by which a child develops the capability to survive and to function independently in the world.

From the family come the first opportunities for physical well-being, learning, and loving. Some psychologists believe that a child's intelligence and personality are almost fully developed by age 4 or 5. The child's primary environment during those early years is in the family.

The Changing Family System

There have been major changes in family life-styles in the United States over the past 50 years. These changes directly affect the health of the family system. For example, in the mid-1900s, children may have spent a few hours a day interacting with various members of their immediate family. Today, many teenagers spend only minutes each day talking with their parents. Unfortunately, most of that time is often spent dealing with problems or family conflict. Families today also move more often due to parents' job changes. Thus, the extended family and neighborhood no longer have the significant role they used to have.

Through television, we are introduced to a variety of people and situations.

CONFLICT RESOLUTION

Hasso has a big problem—he feels totally responsible for his parents' recent breakup. Hasso and his dad were always fighting, and Hasso thinks that's why his father walked out six months ago. Hasso's mom refuses to discuss his dad—she just tries to act as if everything's normal. Yet Hasso is sure his mom blames him, and when she sometimes gets upset and cries about his dad, Hasso feels really guilty. At the same time, he can't help feeling relieved that his dad is out of the house and the fighting has stopped. Hasso's getting more confused about his conflicting feelings.

How has poor communication led to an unhappy situation for Hasso's family?

Additional Information

Healthy Families. According to psychiatrist David Palframan, family fun is essential for child development and family attitudes.

Healthy families take time to enjoy togetherness in daily activities—mealtime, household tasks, and bedtime. These offer time to talk, tease, and resolve issues in nonhostile ways.

Healthy families encourage individual recreation. They also respect personal pursuits.

Healthy families know the importance of relaxing together. They celebrate and vacation together. They cultivate recreation that everyone enjoys and, when necessary, compromise for individual preferences.

L1 **SELF-ESTEEM.** Divide the class into two groups. One group will list ways the family can affect an individual's level of self-esteem. The other group will list ways an individual's level of self-esteem can affect the family's level of health.

LEP **CLASS ACTIVITY.** Ask students to write a short paper describing how they think families have changed over the past fifty years. Ask volunteers to share their papers. Correct any misconceptions and encourage students to talk with their parents, grandparents, and other adult members about family life in the past.

L1 **CLASS ACTIVITY.** Set up a panel of stepparents to talk to the class about the pros and cons of being a stepparent. Have students prepare a list of questions to ask the panel members.

L1 **DISCUSSION.** Have students identify which of the three changes affecting the family system today they think is the most significant—smaller families, working wives and mothers, or single-parent heads of households. Ask them to discuss reasons for their choices.

L1 **DISCUSSION.** Lead students in talking about some of the reasons many of today's parents are deciding to have fewer children.

L1 **CLASS ACTIVITY.** On the chalkboard, list the names of some popular TV programs. Ask students to determine what the programs have in common. When they identify family as a common denominator, discuss the strengths portrayed in the TV families. Ask questions such as these: Why are these families successful (or unsuccessful)? Are the portrayals realistic? Are there any elderly people and/or two-income couples in these families? Conclude by saying that there are many kinds of families, and each one has strengths and weaknesses.

L1 **CLASS ACTIVITY.** Ask for volunteers to bring photographs of their grandparents' families as well as current photos of their own families. Display the photographs in an exhibit titled "Families: Then and Now."

Some American children between ages 6 and 11 watch about 23 hours
of television per week. Through television, young people are introduced
to a variety of different role models, as well as many varied value systems. The role models and values may or may not support what the
young person is being taught at home by the family.

Three significant changes are affecting the family system today:

- Family size tends to be smaller than in the past.
- More women are working outside the home.
- The number of single-parent heads of households is increasing.

Smaller Families

The decision of couples to have fewer or no children is often based on
costs, health, the economy, jobs, or beliefs. Choosing to have fewer children is seen by some as a positive sign, because it may enable parents to
better provide for the children they already have.

Working Wives and Mothers

The increase in the number of women entering the labor force stems
largely from the fact that many of today's households need two incomes
to support a family. The two-income family brings with it significant
changes in traditional family roles. The impact on the health of the family system depends on how each family adjusts to these changes.

Another major reason for the growing numbers of working wives and
mothers is the increasing divorce rate. Other women work outside the
home because they want to use their talents and training—and there are
more opportunities in the workplace now than in the past.

One of the greatest concerns that arises from the mother's working
outside of the home is that of quality day care. Almost one-third of the
women who are employed have preschool-aged children. Some studies
have shown that when children receive quality care, the effects of day
care are no different from those of care in the home.

Single-Parent Heads of Households

One of the greatest changes in the American family has been the
increase in single-parent households. Over 11 million children—more

---

K E E P I N G   F I T

Dealing with Sibling Rivalry

If you and your siblings always
seem to be at odds, here are some
tips that might help:
- Learn to talk out your differences rather than shouting or
  acting them out.
- When disagreeing, make an

effort to stay on the subject.
- Use "I" messages, telling the
  other person how you feel in
  reaction to his or her behavior.
- Plan an activity where you can
  do something together that you
  both enjoy. Agree beforehand

that you won't squabble.
- Try to figure out if the tension
  between you and your siblings
  is part of a larger family problem. If so, help your family to
  address that problem. This may
  take outside help.

Across the Curriculum

Home Economics. Ask students to interview each family member to determine his
or her preferences in food, music, TV programs, and sports. In class, have students
summarize their findings. Discuss how the
findings illustrate that each family member is a unique individual with his or her
own interests, preferences, feelings, and
needs. Ask if personal likes and habits differ according to the individual's age.

Home Economics. Ask each student to
bring his or her family's favorite recipe to
class. Discuss how each family has its own
preferences and ways of preparing foods,
even though all families share the need for
nourishment. Compile the recipes to create a class cookbook.

than 1 out of every 4 under the age of 18—live in a single-parent home, either with a mother or a father.

The number of households headed by women is largely the result of an increasing divorce rate. The first divorce recorded in the United States was in the early 1600s, soon after Plymouth Colony was settled. By 1804, 1 marriage in 100 ended in divorce; and by the end of the 1920s it was 1 in 6. Today about half of all marriages end in divorce.

The term *single-parent family* is not an accurate description in some cases. Some youngsters in single-parent families are children of divorced parents; thus they still have two parents. Because their parents live in separate households, a more accurate term is *single-parent house-*

HELP WANTED

Veterinarian

It's been said that a veterinarian must be even better than a doctor, because the patients can't say what's wrong. I'm looking for a person who subscribes to this opinion to buy my small-town practice. You will have to be able to treat a variety of animals and you will have to be able to relate well to people—not just the owner, but the entire family. An honest, hard-working and knowledgeable person will have a very satisfying career here.

For more information contact:
American Veterinary
Medical Association
1931 N. Meacham Road
Schaumburg, IL 60173

HEALTH UPDATE

LOOKING AT THE ISSUES

Should Adoptions Be Open or Closed?

Every year in the United States, about 100,000 children are adopted. Many of these adoptions are closed adoptions—adoptions in which records are sealed. This means that the names, addresses, and phone numbers of the birth parents remain unavailable to either the adoptive parents or the children.

Increasingly, however, there are open adoptions where information is made available to both sides in an adoption. Adoptive parents may meet birth parents or even be with the birth mother during the delivery.

Analyzing Different Viewpoints

ONE VIEW. Some people believe that records are sealed to protect the adoptive parents from unwanted contact by biological parents who have given up their children but may decide they want contact with them again.

A SECOND VIEW. Other people believe that laws that call for closed adoptions may also protect the biological parents from adoptive parents who want to find out more about

the family background, or even, in some cases, try to return babies with problems to them.

A THIRD VIEW. Others maintain that people have a need for accurate medical information from their families of origin as well as an emotional need to know their roots.

A FOURTH VIEW. Some people believe that records should remain closed to protect the rights of the adoptive parents, the adoptees, and/or the biological parents and to avoid confusing the person who has been adopted. They fear that sharing families can prove unhealthy and confusing for all parties.

Exploring Your Views

1. Do you think adoptions should be open or closed? Do you think it should depend on the situation? Explain.
2. What might be gained from being able to contact one's birth parents? What might be the risks be?
3. If you were an adoptive parent, would you support an adult adoptee's desire to find his or her natural parents? Explain.

Overcoming Misconceptions

Myth. Most families are nuclear families.
Fact. Traditionally, families were nuclear or extended. The nuclear family was composed of mother, father, and children. The father was the primary wage earner. Extended families had adult children and other relatives living at home. Many of today's families differ. Fewer than half of

U.S. families have a traditional nuclear structure, and many mothers are employed outside the home. About 20 percent are single-parent families, with divorce as the major reason. However, teenage pregnancy also contributes to this statistic. Most single-parent households are headed by women.

L2 PARENTAL INVOLVEMENT. Ask for volunteers to plan and carry out a family holiday or vacation activity. Afterwards, have them write a short paper about the family experience.

L1 PERSONAL INVOLVEMENT. Ask students to keep logs for one week of the number of hours they spend with each member of their family. Have them specify the activities in which they engage with each family member during these times. Then ask them to analyze their findings, and tell how they might improve the quality or the quantity of time spent with family members.

L2 WRITING. Have each student write a one-page paper titled "Maintaining a Healthy Family While Coping with a Changing World." Ask them to present ideas for positive ways that families can address the stresses of change facing them.

L1 PARENTAL INVOLVEMENT. Have students interview their grandparent(s) or an adult of their grandparents' generation. Ask them to focus on questions that reflect the older adult's type of family and its functions. Have volunteers share their findings. Discuss the changes in today's families and some of the reasons for the changes.

L2 COMMUNITY INVOLVEMENT. Choose students to interview adults who have adopted new roles that meet their needs, interests, and abilities. The new roles might be the result of a career change, the addition of a job to existing work requirements, or the addition of new family members due to birth, remarriage, adoption, etc.

L2 COMMUNITY INVOLVEMENT. Select students to interview local child-care directors and in-home day-care providers about their services. Have them prepare a chart, summarizing the types of programs offered, child-to-adult ratios, qualifications of personnel, rates, hours, facilities, equipment, ages of children served, discipline procedures, and snack and meal times. Ask them to compare the programs, and present their findings to the class.

L1 USING THE LESSON RESOURCES. For additional student activities, refer to the lesson resources on page 83.

Check for Understanding

- Assign and discuss the lesson review. Encourage LD students to focus on questions 1, 2, 5, and 6.

Evaluate

- Administer, grade, and discuss the *Lesson 1 Quiz.*

Reteach

- Have students write the phrase *types of families* at the top of a sheet of paper. Ask them to list seven family types, and define and/or describe each one.
- Ask students to complete *Reteaching Activity 11.*

Enrich

- Have students select two different cultures and compare and contrast their life patterns, family structure, behavior, and health practices. Ask them to write a comparative report on their findings.

Remove the label and top lid from seven large coffee cans. Write the name of one of the following types of families on each can: *nuclear, single-parent, extended, blended, adoptive, foster, other family types.* Divide the class into seven groups, and give each group one of the cans. Provide basic art supplies for each group to design a label describing their group's type of family. Afterwards, bring the class together, and ask each group to present and discuss its family type. Briefly discuss whether it accurately describes the family.

Single-parent families occur very frequently in our society.

hold. In spite of its inaccuracy, however, the term *single-parent family* has come to mean a family in which children live with one parent at a time.

In single-parent families everything may not be the same as when parents lived together, but the new arrangement can work. Single-parent families can be, and many times are, very healthy families. As in any family, it is necessary for all family members to work together to cope with changes and increased stress that may arise.

Each of these changes reflects the changing times in which we live. None of the changes are necessarily bad. And as individuals, we have little control over some of them. The important point is that they all influence the health of the family system. The healthy family copes with the changes while maintaining the family structure.

LESSON 1 REVIEW

Reviewing Facts and Vocabulary

1. Write a short paragraph describing nuclear, extended, and blended families.
2. Define the term *mobile,* and give an example of someone you know or have read about who is mobile.

Thinking Critically

3. **Evaluation.** Write a short skit or play, pointing out how trends toward smaller families, employed mothers, and increasing numbers of single-parent families have affected today's family unit.
4. **Analysis.** Read at least two magazines geared to teens. Write a short paper comparing how these magazines treat family issues. Discuss how the families and family issues reflected in these magazines compare with your family and its beliefs and values.

Applying Health Knowledge

5. Talk to an adult about his or her view of the ideal family. Write a brief report about the conversation.
6. Develop a list of questions to be used to interview an older individual, such as a family member, other relative, or adult friend, about the type of family in which he or she was reared. Ask this person to share his or her views about some of the changes affecting families today.

Answers to Lesson 1 Review

1. Paragraphs will vary but should reflect an understanding of definitions for nuclear, extended, and blended families as given on pages 83 and 84.
2. Mobile—likely to move from place to place. Examples will vary.
3. Answers will vary.
4. Answers will vary.
5. Answers will vary.
6. Answers will vary. Possible questions: Did both of your parents live in your home? How many siblings did you have? What type of employment did members of your family have? Who was responsible for household chores? What were the education levels of your family members? How old were your parents when they married?

LOOKING AT THE HEALTH OF THE FAMILY

As mentioned in Lesson 1, the health of society depends on the health of families. It is important for us to be aware of the threats to the health of our families so that we can take steps to maintain a healthy family and thus, a strong society.

Troubled Families

A family system can break down for a variety of reasons. This breakdown may end in divorce, in which case the family system is restructured. In many cases the family system, though troubled, remains intact. If family members do not seek help for serious problems, however, the health of individual members can be threatened.

Recognizing Physical and Mental Abuse

The rising incidence of abused children, battered spouses, and runaways is evidence of troubled family systems. Family members may act out their hurts, miseries, and frustrations in numerous ways.

Spousal and Elder Abuse.   Persons with spouses who physically or mentally abuse them have become the subject of national attention. They are usually women who are married to men who are very authoritarian, who have low self-esteem, who do not handle stress well, or who become violent when drinking alcohol or using other drugs.

In the past many wives felt trapped in their situation. They usually had no means of employment and were dependent upon the husband's financial support. Their friends and neighbors often ignored the problem or did not want to get involved.

Elderly family members may also be the object of violence. A family member may take out his or her frustration on elderly parents or aunts or uncles who cannot defend themselves.

The problem of battered spouses and elders occurs in all levels of society. However, agencies and centers now exist in many communities to help provide support and, sometimes, a temporary place of refuge from the violence.

Child Abuse.   No one knows for sure how many children are abused in families. The statistics represent only reported cases, and it is likely that there are many more unreported cases. **Child abuse** can be physical harm, including sexual abuse, as well as emotional harm. The emotionally abused child is perhaps the most difficult to identify, because there may be no physical evidence of mistreatment.

Abuse of children can occur among any socioeconomic group, culture, or religious affiliation. Generally, the abusers are parents or close

LOOKING AT THE HEALTH OF THE FAMILY   **89**

LESSON 2 FOCUS

TERMS TO USE
- Child abuse
- Exploited
- Communication
- Compromise
- Crisis

CONCEPTS TO LEARN
- Because the family is the basic social unit of society, it is critical that we learn ways to improve and maintain the health of the family.
- Family violence continues to be a major problem in our society.

ATTITUDES AND BEHAVIORS TO EVALUATE
- Self-Inventory, page 96.
- Building Decision-Making Skills, page 97.

Focus

Lesson Objectives

After studying this lesson, students should be able to:
- explain factors that may cause a family system to break down
- describe some of the signs of physical and mental abuse
- explain factors that lead to child abuse
- describe elements that healthy families have in common
- outline steps they can take to show they care and to strengthen their family
- identify sources of help for families in crisis

Bellringer

Write the following on the chalkboard for students to work on while attendance is being taken: *There are many threats to the health of today's families. List some specific things that you can do to help strengthen your family.*

Introducing the Lesson

Have students share their responses to the Bellringer. Tell the class that this lesson is about troubled families as well as healthy family systems. Students will learn more about doing their parts and where families can go for help in times of trouble.

DID YOU KNOW?

Hugging at home pays off. A 36-year study reported in the *Journal of Personality and Social Psychology* suggests that
- healthy physical affection and warmth from parents toward their children is a good predictor of the children's later ability to have close marriages, close friendships, better mental health, and success in the workplace, and
- children who got affection from both their mothers and their fathers tended to show the best long-term adjustments in all areas of life.

Resources for Lesson 2

- **Guided Reading** Activity 12
- **Decision-Making** Activity 5
- **Workbook** Voc Act 12, Appl Act 5
- **Reteaching** Activity 12
- **Enrichment** Activity 5
- **Health Labs** Activity 5
- **Cooperative Learning** Activity 5
- **Lesson 2 Quiz, Chapter 5 Test**

ABC News InterActive Videodiscs
Drugs and Substance Abuse, Side 2
Ch 4 Drugs and the Family

- Divide the class into two groups. Ask each student in the first group to use the terms *chronic, communication, compromise,* and *crisis* in a written paragraph. Have each student in the second group write a paragraph, using the terms *child abuse, exploited,* and *structure.* Ask for volunteers from each group to read their paragraphs to the class. Afterwards, ask them to test each other's understanding of the words' definitions.
- Ask students to complete *Workbook Vocabulary Activity 12.*

Teach

Guided Practice

L2 CLASS ACTIVITY. Select students to act out situations involving a friend who is a victim of abuse in the family. Have them practice encouraging their friend to seek help. Follow up by discussing sources of help available at the local level.

L2 CLASS ACTIVITY. Choose several students to call the national toll-free Domestic Violence Hotline (1-800-333-SAFE) to request information about recognizing and dealing with physical and mental abuse in the family. Have them share their findings with the class.

L1 DISCUSSION. Talk about some factors that make a person susceptible to abusing a child. Discuss what a parent could do in a moment of anger instead of hitting his or her child. Ask students why they think people often wait until the damage is done before seeking help.

L1 SPEAKER. Ask a social worker, representative from the Department of Public Welfare, or a representative from Parents Anonymous to speak to the class about troubled families, physical and mental abuse, and where to get help. Assign students to prepare a list of questions to ask the speaker.

A teen who feels alone needs help either from family, friends, or a professional.

relatives, and the incidents happen repeatedly. In many cases abusive parents and other relatives were themselves abused children.

Abusive parents generally are isolated. They may have no one to turn to for relief from everyday frustrations. In many cases parents lack information about child development. They do not know what a child can reasonably be expected to do or how a child may act at certain ages. The tendency to abuse children is increased by such problems as unemployment, low self-esteem, poor stress-management skills, marital conflicts, and drug and alcohol use.

Over 4,000 children die each year in the United States from physical abuse. Many of these deaths occur in children under the age of 2 years. Aside from the risks of death or physical injury, the abused child tends to be depressed, fearful, and withdrawn. The abused child may also exhibit destructive behaviors.

A large number of child abuse cases involve sexual abuse. Typically, the sexually abused child is between 6 and 8 years of age and is victimized by someone in his or her own home—a father, stepfather, uncle, or some other trusted authority figure.

Reports of sexually abused boys and young girls are becoming more and more common. Sexual abuse can last for years and may never be reported. The child may be threatened with severe punishment, embarrassment, ridicule, or even death if he or she tells anyone.

It is important that the victim in this situation know that he or she is not at fault. The child has done nothing wrong—it is the abuser's behavior that is wrong. Victims should talk to some adult whom they trust, so that the adult can get help for them. If help does not come with the first try, it is important that victims seek assistance from other appropriate adults to get the help they need.

Young Runaways. Some children and teens try to get out of an abusive home by running away. Unfortunately, because runaways usually have no money or job skills to help them survive, they often end up being **exploited,** or used for someone else's benefit. Runaway children are prime targets for people dealing in pornography and prostitution.

Running away is not the answer; help is available for the abused child or teenager. Before anyone can help an abused person, however, someone must report the abuse. All states now have laws requiring doctors and other health professionals to report suspected cases of child abuse. In many states, anyone who suspects or knows of an abuse situation is required to report it. Legally, children and teens can be removed from an abusive environment until it is corrected.

KEEPING FIT

Keeping Family Fights Fair

Consider these strategies when arguing:
- Don't draw the names of relatives or friends who agree with you into the argument.
- Don't dredge up the past.
- Don't attack the person or his or

her personality. Point to the behavior or situation that isn't working for you.
- Don't use labels or put-downs.
- Let the other person finish his or her sentences.
- Listen to the other person's

point of view.
- Don't storm out, mid-argument.
- Don't yell or use the "silent treatment."
- Don't get into an argument with someone who's under the influence of alcohol or other drugs.

90 CHAPTER 5 YOU AND YOUR FAMILY

Across the Curriculum

Language Arts. Assign students to look in magazines and newspapers for stories about troubled families. Ask them to select one family. Have them write a letter they would like to send to that family, suggesting ways to keep the family together and where to get help locally. Choose several letters (and their original stories) to read to the class.

History. Arrange class time for students to visit the library to research the cultural background of their families. Then have students write several paragraphs on how this background may have influenced their families' traditions, values, and life-styles.

Family Counseling. Counseling is available for both the child and the parents. Many communities now have crisis intervention hot lines. Parents who realize that they are losing control can get immediate help.

Parents Anonymous is a national organization that helps parents overcome their tendencies toward violence. In meetings, parents make up a support system for one another. Parents learn how to help themselves and one another as they talk about their feelings and problems.

Just as important as the rehabilitation of abusive parents is the long-range prevention of abuse in society as a whole. Parents and prospective parents need opportunities for learning about family life, child development, and parent-child relationships.

Strengthening Your Family

When you hear about troubled families, families in crisis situations, violent families, and families on the edge of survival, you may conclude that only a few families are strong and able to function in a healthy manner. On the contrary, most families do work through their problems and resolve their conflicts—usually without outside help.

Healthy Family Systems

What characteristics go into making a family healthy and strong? What can family members do to change a hurting family into a healthy family? Loving, caring families do not just happen. There is no magic formula for building a healthy family, but there are some elements that healthy families seem to have in common. The following elements are characteristics of healthy families:

- Family members care about each other. They stick together even when times are tough.
- Family members communicate with each other. They listen and work to understand each other. **Communication,** or openness among family members, includes showing tenderness, warmth, and humor. It also means being able to express negative feelings. In general, members of a healthy family communicate with one another and approach life from a positive viewpoint.
- Family members support each other. Each member is recognized as a unique individual. Family members express their thoughts and feelings, and they listen to each other.

Open communication helps everyone in the family contribute to its well-being.

L1 EXPLANATION. Tell students that abuse in a family is a very serious problem. Stress the availability of help for both the child and the parents. Explain that the child is not at fault in these situations and should not feel guilty.

L1 CLASS ACTIVITY. Have students locate newspaper and magazine articles about cases of spouse abuse, elder abuse, and child abuse. Discuss factors that apparently led up to the situation. Talk about ways the abuse might have been prevented.

L1 EXPLANATION. Point out the following facts to students: Child abuse is divided into three categories—physical abuse, sexual abuse, and emotional abuse. Physical abuse is inflicting physical injury on a person. Sexual abuse is forcing a person to engage in sexual activities. Emotional abuse is regularly, and over an extended period of time, demanding that a person do more than he or she is capable of handling and criticizing and humiliating him or her for not living up to the demand; or making such unclear requirements that the person simply cannot understand what he or she is supposed to do.

L1 SPEAKER. Invite a police officer, other community worker, or a school counselor to speak to the class about the problems of young runaways in today's society. Have the speaker talk about the reasons for running away, the ages of young runaways, the dangers they face on the street, where runaways can go for help, and the percentage who return to their original families.

L1 DISCUSSION. Ask students to identify situations in which a teenager may face the danger of physical or mental abuse. List students' responses on the chalkboard. Then have them discuss how some of the situations might be avoided.

LEP CLASS ACTIVITY. Ask each student to complete the following sentence: A healthy family is . . . followed by a specific detail. (An example might be: "A healthy family is my sister splitting the last slice of cake with me.")

Across the Curriculum

Home Economics. Ask for volunteers to visit a local supermarket and make a list of various food products designed for ease and quickness of preparation. If there are students who have tried these products, ask them to rate the foods in terms of ease of preparation, flavor, economy, etc. Talk about the pros and cons of prepared foods versus "from scratch" foods.

Language Arts. Have students locate different kinds of music, poems, and essays about healthy families and families in trouble. Have a second group locate examples of healthy families. Ask students to share their findings with the entire class.

We all need praise and encouragement to build up our self-esteem.

As you know, everyone has basic emotional needs. Individuals must meet these needs in order to feel good about themselves. The family can be the primary source of meeting these emotional needs. In supportive families, emotional needs are met in the following ways:

- Family members trust and respect each other. They do not gossip about family members; nor do they hide problems from one another —even serious ones such as addiction, abuse, and teen pregnancy. They are honest about their feelings toward all family members. They keep promises made to one another.
- Differences of opinion are allowed. Family members are able to disagree without attacking one another.
- Family members take time for one another and for the family as a whole. They share celebrations and traditions, and they find ways to have fun together.
- Everyone is included in important family decisions. Together, family members discuss issues that affect the entire family, such as finding a new place to live or deciding where to go on vacation.
- Everyone pitches in and shares responsibilities. Having each member do his or her share can go a long way.
- Family life has structure. People need structure—a certain rhythm in their lives and the realization of where they fit into society. Going to school, eating at certain times and at certain places, and playing on a team all give structure to your daily life. The family, too, needs structure. The members need to know their place in it and what their general functions are.
- Family members are willing to be flexible. Although there is structure in a healthy family, the leaders of the family, as well as the other members, need to be flexible and open to change when it is best for the family as a whole.

Doing Your Part

What can you do to help keep your family strong? What steps should you follow if your family is hurting? Here are some ways to show you care and to strengthen your family.

- Show appreciation for things done well. Saying "thank you" works at home, too.
- Encourage others, even your parents. Most people never get enough encouragement.
- Show concern when a family member has a problem. Offer to help or to get help.
- Stop criticizing. Be tactful and constructive. Avoid nagging.
- Show empathy by putting yourself in the other person's position. Try to see situations from his or her point of view.
- Listen to what other family members say. Listening is more than simply not talking. Avoid interrupting, daydreaming, jumping to conclusions, or just waiting for your turn to talk.
- Keep your promises. Do not make promises you cannot keep.
- Be dependable and on time. Your family must be able to depend on you. You owe family members your best.
- Be willing to compromise with family members. A **compromise** is a

FINDING HELP

Domestic violence is a crime that can result in serious physical injury and even death. If you know that a battering incident is occurring, call the police immediately. Contacting the police does not always mean the abuser will be put in jail. It is simply the most effective way to protect the victim and the children from immediate harm.

92 CHAPTER 5 YOU AND YOUR FAMILY

Additional Information

Divorce. Divorce can be a result of troubled families. About one in two marriages ends in divorce. When divorce involves children, it puts extreme emotional stress on family members. Children often are caught in a battle between parents. Many times they blame themselves. They may fear abandonment and loss of love. Children experience stages of grieving before they finally accept the finality of divorce. This may take years.

Divorce may also create a financial crisis. Without child support, it is difficult to rear children on one income. For the parent with custody, being a single parent can be both physically and emotionally exhausting, frustrating, and lonely.

way of solving a problem in which each person gives up something in order to find a solution that satisfies everyone. Being willing to give a little so that the other person will get something can result in a healthier relationship.

Getting Help

When people live together, conflicts are bound to occur. However, it is important to try to work out family problems as soon as they come up. If not resolved, minor concerns often become major problems.

Family problems range in size from small misunderstandings to major crises. A **crisis** is an extreme change in a person's life. There are many types of major crises. Five of the most common are financial problems, divorce, drug use, violence, and death. Help is available for coping with all of these crises.

Financial Problems. The causes of financial problems within the family vary greatly. Overdue bills, the loss of a job, serious illness, a natural disaster, or death could be the source of serious financial problems.

How your parents cope with financial loss directly affects you. You may notice a decrease in spending money if financial recovery takes a great deal of time. To resolve money problems, some single-parent families live together. Other families exchange help or share the expense of paying for services. Two or three parents might share a baby-sitter, for instance, and help each other with big jobs.

Some teens help with family money problems by learning how much such essentials as food and rent cost and doing their share to stay within the budget. They often try to get part-time jobs to pay for special clothes or entertainment. Most parents would view this type of assistance with pride and appreciation.

Divorce. To divorce is to end a marriage relationship, and it means a permanent separation. If your parents are divorcing, you might feel all alone, but you are not. In the United States, 12 million children under the age of 18 have divorced parents. Whether the mother or father leaves, it is important to remember that parents divorce each other—not their children. Although their feelings for each other have changed, their love for their children can stay the same. Parents who deliberately break the bond between parent and child may have deep, unsolved emotional problems of their own.

Most children of parents who are getting a divorce go through a difficult period of emotional adjustment. It is similar to the time of grief following the death of a loved one. They usually experience shock, disbelief, anger, sorrow, and finally, acceptance.

During the breakup of a marriage, children sometimes feel they are the cause of their parents' separation. However, divorce happens for many reasons, and children are seldom the cause.

Children of divorce must learn to cope with the lack of one parent's daily presence. This often leads to having less money and to a lower standard of living. Eventually, the children may find themselves faced with learning to accept a stepparent if one of their parents remarries.

If your parents are going through a divorce, share your feelings with them and try to understand their feelings. Find an older person with whom you can discuss your feelings.

LOOKING AT THE HEALTH OF THE FAMILY **93**

DID YOU KNOW?

- Estimates of the number of homeless in the U.S. are as high as 3 million.
- People are homeless for many different reasons. For example, in some areas, there are inadequate facilities provided for addicted or mentally ill persons. Many communities have limited funds to operate shelters. In other areas, there is a lack of affordable housing.
- It is estimated that about 40 percent of the homeless are heavy users of or addicted to alcohol and/or other drugs; 29 percent are mentally ill; and 18 percent have jobs.
- Many U.S. homeless are adolescents. Between 500,000 and 2 million teens run away from home each year. One in 20 stays away from home for more than 1 year.
- It is estimated that 1 in 4 homeless children regularly misses school and about 50 percent do not attend at all.

L1 DISCUSSION. Lead students in brainstorming a list of factors that might deter families from seeking outside support or help with problems. (Examples might include embarrassment, denial that a problem exists, fear of the unknown, lack of knowledge about what help is available, refusal to admit failure or inadequacy, cost of professional services, fear of a breach of confidentiality, etc.)

L1 EXPLANATION. Talk about the fact that children spend a considerable amount of time watching TV and that the role models and values seen on TV may not support what is taught at home. Also, explain that in the past, families were less mobile and more likely to stay in close proximity to each other. Stress that these changes make the task of rearing responsible people within the family system more difficult, but not impossible.

Independent Practice

L3 COMMUNITY INVOLVEMENT. Select students to interview representatives from the local chapter of the Alzheimer's Association. Ask students to request information about ways family members can deal with stress when caring for an Alzheimer's patient.

L2 COMMUNITY INVOLVEMENT. Ask students to interview someone they know about the person's family structure. Have them find answers to questions such as: How does the family divide household responsibilities? Who is the "head" of the household? Who is employed? Who cares for the children? What household responsibilities are shared by the children?

L2 READING. Have each student read a book or several articles about body language as a form of communication. Ask them to give reports on what they learned, demonstrating what various facial expressions, gestures, postures, and movements communicate.

Across the Curriculum

Home Economics. Give each student a section of the newspaper. Instruct them to locate articles about families. Ask them to circle information in the articles about the following: communication, being part of a family, family responsibilities, family crises, coping with crises, and sources of help for the family. Collect the articles, and share some of them with the class. Point out instances that spotlight good family communication, family members who share household responsibilities, family members who are coping with crises, and families that are receiving help in dealing with crises.

CHAPTER 5 YOU AND YOUR FAMILY **93**

Overcoming The Odds

She calls herself Leah. That's not her real name, but that doesn't matter. She's 19 years old and the victim of incest. She says, "I was sexually abused as a child from the time I was about 5 until I was about 13. The person who did it to me is my uncle. He is my mother's younger brother—younger by a lot—and for many years he lived with us. It started when he would babysit for my sister and me when my mom and dad had to work double shifts at their restaurant. He would come into my room. He would be real friendly and all, and then he would be . . . too friendly. I didn't really know what was going on, but I sensed, even as a young kid, that it wasn't right. He told me never to tell anyone or I would be in big trouble, and so I just kind of locked it all up inside.

"People say to me now, well, why didn't you tell anyone? I guess I was too afraid, and maybe I thought I somehow deserved it, like there was something wrong with me or this wouldn't be happening.

"Then, when my sister was about 23, she started to get some flashbacks of awful things happening to her when our uncle was around. So she joined some kind of group and started to talk about it all. The

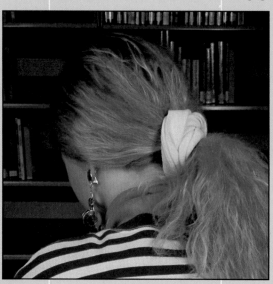

night she told my mom was an awful night. My mother said my sister must be crazy. My sister yelled and cried and stormed out. I stood in the kitchen just shaking. But after that, my sister and I started to really *talk*, and more and more about my uncle started to come back—for both of us.

"When I left home two years ago, I had lousy self-esteem. I felt like I couldn't trust anyone, like maybe I was crazy or making it up or it wasn't that bad after all. But with my sister's help and the help of an incest survivor's group I've joined, I'm coming to realize I didn't choose what happened to me as a child. It was done to me. Now I'm working on a letter to my uncle who lives on the other side of the country to

tell him how he hurt me, how he messed up my life, and that I hope he gets help before he does it to anyone else. I still have whole pockets of my childhood I can't remember," Leah says. "I still have some shame and a tendency to think that when things go wrong it's my fault. There's anger at my mom for not having realized what was going on. And I still have very bad days where I feel shaky about things. But I guess you'd have to say that knowing I'm not alone has helped. Knowing I'm not perverted or crazy helps, too. Just being able to say the word molested was a start. And my sister's support has been the greatest."

1. How did Leah's experience affect her self-esteem? Her ability to trust?
2. Why do you think the victims of incest often feel that it is somehow their fault or that they deserve it? How are these feelings unjustified? How do they get in the way of getting help?
3. If you or someone you know is the victim of incest or other sexual abuse, what safe steps can be taken to confront the situation?

Overcoming Misconceptions

Myth. Good communication skills are something you're born with. **Fact.** They can be learned—with both study and practice. For example, sometimes the words people choose encourage family members and friends to talk and listen; other words may hinder communication.

These phrases encourage communication within a family:

■ Please explain how. . . .
■ Let's talk about it.
■ Are you saying that. . . ?

These phrases hinder communication:
■ That's stupid (dumb)! I don't believe that . . . , I don't want to talk about it!
■ Nobody your age can understand what I'm going through.

Drug Use. Drug use within the family is almost always destructive. Parents—and others in the family—who are alcoholic or who use other drugs neglect their responsibilities, become very irritable, often lose their jobs, and may even abuse other family members.

When the health of the family is threatened by drug use, all of the members need help. By asking the right people for assistance, you can be the one who starts your family on its way back to a healthy life. The people most likely to help you are members of your extended family, a member of the clergy, a school counselor or trusted teacher, your school nurse, or a youth worker. Knowing how to get help is a way of caring for your family. These people can help you understand the problem and can help you get additional assistance.

Violence. Violent abuse is a real problem that happens in many families every year. Ignoring the problem never works; the code of silence does not help anyone. Family members in serious trouble may not be able to help themselves. Child welfare agencies, family doctors, school nurses, school counselors, religious leaders, or even the police are sources of help for a family experiencing violence.

Death. No family can escape death, and when there is a death in the family, there is grief. People go through grief in very different ways. Family members need to allow each other to mourn in their own ways.

Sometimes after a death it is difficult to determine what to do next. There are hundreds of details that a family must deal with when a member dies. Conflict among family members is common because of increased emotions during this time. Talking with each other—or with good friends or counselors—can be helpful in coping with this loss.

Enjoying recreational activities together is one way of keeping a family strong.

LESSON 2 REVIEW

Reviewing Facts and Vocabulary

1. Define the term *child abuse,* and summarize an article about a child abuse incident from a current newspaper or magazine.
2. Write a one- or two-minute public service announcement for families in trouble. Use the following terms in the announcement: *exploited, communication,* and *crisis*.

Thinking Critically

3. **Analysis.** Design a dance or pantomime contrasting the feelings of family members in troubled families with those in healthy family systems.
4. **Evaluation.** Do you think a child who complains of physical abuse should be returned to his or her family after a court hearing? Why or why not?

Applying Health Knowledge

5. Interview a school or family counselor, social worker, or other mental health professional about the occurrence of child, elder, and spousal abuse in the community. Make a list to share with the class of sources of available help.
6. Keep a log for one week of the number of hours you spend with each member of your family. Total these hours, illustrating them on a simple graph showing each 24-hour period. Write a brief summary of your feelings about the time spent with your family and how you might have improved the quality or the quantity of time spent with family members. Conclude by making a written plan for a special family activity for the following week.

Check for Understanding

- Assign and discuss the lesson review. Encourage LD students to focus on question 1 and work with a partner to accomplish question 2.
- Assign and discuss the chapter review.

Evaluate

- Administer, grade, and discuss the *Lesson 2 Quiz.*
- Administer, grade, and discuss the *Chapter 5 Test.*
- Refer to the Performance Assessment strategy for this chapter. See pages T 23 to T 25.

Reteach

- Ask students to describe how a family is a system, explaining the relationship between the health of the family and the health of the individual. Next, have students discuss their responsibility to contribute to their family's health.
- Ask students to complete *Reteaching Activity 12.*

Enrich

- Have students investigate the kidnapping of children by their parents. Ask them to find answers to questions such as: In what kinds of situations does this occur? How often does it happen? What effects do they think the experience might have on the children involved? What are the legal consequences for the kidnappers? Have students summarize their findings and speculations in writing.
- Ask students to complete *Enrichment Activity 5.*

Answers to Lesson 2 Review

1. Child abuse—physical harm, including sexual abuse, as well as emotional harm directed at a minor child. Summaries will vary.
2. Announcements will vary but should reflect an understanding of the following: exploited—used for someone else's benefit; communication—openness among family members; crisis—an extreme change in a person's life.
3. Dances/pantomimes will vary.
4. Answers will vary but should be supported logically.
5. Answers will vary.
6. Answers will vary. Respect student's right to privacy if discussing answers.

Close

Write the lesson's major concepts on numbered, separate slips of paper. Place the slips in a box, and let each student draw one. Next, going in numerical order, have students define and summarize the concept written on the slip of paper they selected.

Helping Students Improve Their Health

Teaching Strategies

L1 EXPLANATION. It is rare for a majority of students in today's society to come from a traditional family setting. Many families are single-parent families. Individuals from such families often feel isolated and different because they lack a two-parent household. It is important to validate these individuals and respect the special struggles that they experience.

L2 DISCUSSION. Have students compare the families of today with the images of the families of yesterday. Have students watch TV shows that focus on families from different time periods. Have students compare and contrast the similarities and differences between these families. Have students discuss how the family structure has changed over the years. Is the current trend in families more or less healthy? What can students do to ensure the best chance of success in their current families and their future families?

L1 CLASS ACTIVITY. Have students break into groups of four. Have students pick the top five items from the Self-Inventory that would best help an individual make an exceptional contribution as a family member. Have students create a behavior contract to be signed by the student and a family member. The goal of the contract is to have the student and family member focus on improving the top five areas selected by the students.

DID YOU KNOW?

■ Most teens don't give much thought to their parent's wishes—not because they're rebelling, but because they're preoccupied with their own problems.

Self-Inventory

You and Your Family

HOW DO YOU RATE?

Number a sheet of paper from 1 through 25. Read each item below, and rate yourself by writing *always*, *sometimes*, or *never* for each item. After you have rated yourself, ask a family member to use a separate sheet to rate you on each behavior. Total the number of *always*, *sometimes*, and *never* responses on each sheet. Then proceed to the next section.

1. Cares about others.
2. Communicates well.
3. Is trustworthy.
4. Respects differences of opinion.
5. Pitches in and helps when needed.
6. Shares responsibilities.
7. Is flexible when necessary.
8. Is appreciative.
9. Encourages others.
10. Shows concern for others.
11. Avoids criticizing others.
12. Tries to see others' point of view.
13. Listens well.
14. Avoids interrupting others.
15. Keeps promises.
16. Is dependable and punctual.
17. Is willing to compromise when necessary.
18. Cooperates with others.
19. Is cheerful.
20. Is enthusiastic.
21. Is hardworking.
22. Puts self in other's place.

23. Is loyal to other family members.
24. Is patient with others.
25. Works to solve conflicts in a positive way.

HOW DID YOU SCORE?

Give yourself 2 points for every *always* answer, 1 point for every *sometimes* answer, and 0 points for every *never* answer. Find your total from both sheets, and read below to see how you scored. Then proceed to the next section.

91 to 100
Excellent. You are making an exceptional contribution as a family member.

31 to 90
Good. You are a caring family member, but you could try harder.

Below 31
Poor. You need to improve your behavior toward family members. You are missing out on some terrific rewards that come from caring about others.

WHAT ARE YOUR GOALS?

If you received an *excellent* or *good* score, complete the statements in Part A. If your score was *poor*, complete the statements in Parts A and B.

Part A
1. I plan to learn more about healthy, caring behaviors by ____.
2. My timetable for accomplishing this is ____.
3. I plan to share my information with others by ____.

Part B
4. The behavior or attitude toward my family I would most like to change is ____.
5. The steps involved in making this change are ____.
6. My rewards for making this change will be ____.
7. My timetable for making this change is ____.
8. The people or groups I will ask for help are ____.

Meeting Students' Needs

For students who score *Excellent*. Have students volunteer to work for organizations who care for families in need, such as family services.

For students who score *Good*. Suggest that students arrange for a family meeting time in which all family members could discuss the items on the Self-Inventory and plan ways in which family members could

improve on the items in this inventory.

For students who score *Poor*. Suggest that students objectively view their own behaviors in their family. Have students determine one area of the Self-Inventory in which they will attempt to improve. Have students keep a written log, describing their strategies to improve their communication with family members.

Building Decision-Making Skills

Shelley babysits for two cute little neighbor children. Lately she has become very concerned because she has seen some signs of possible child abuse. One child has a black eye, and the other has a sprained arm. When she asked about the injuries, the children seemed afraid, and their mother answered nervously that they had fallen down the stairs. The mother seems very unhappy, and the father seems very stressed out over business matters. What should Shelley do?

WHAT DO YOU THINK?

1. **Choices.** What choices does Shelley have?
2. **Consequences.** What potential danger exists and for whom?
3. **Consequences.** What are the probable consequences of each choice?
4. **Consequences.** How might Shelley's health triangle be affected by her decision?
5. **Consequences.** What might happen if Shelley tries to talk to the children about this?
6. **Consequences.** What will be the effect on everyone concerned if Shelley reports the problem but is wrong?
7. **Consequences.** What might happen if Shelley doesn't report the problem?
8. **Decision.** What would you advise Shelley to do?

Ava and her sister, Deb, have shared a room at home for several years. Just recently has it become a problem. Ava keeps her part of the room very neat. Deb, on the other hand, has started to leave things wherever they fall. Usually there's a pile of clothes on the floor, and it is not at all unusual for Deb to borrow clothes from Ava when they get ready for school. Ava wouldn't mind, if Deb returned them—clean. Instead, they too get left in a pile. Ava is getting really annoyed. What should she do?

WHAT DO YOU THINK?

9. **Situation.** Why does a decision need to be made?
10. **Choices.** List five possible ways Ava might handle the situation.
11. **Consequences.** What might be the outcome for each choice?
12. **Consequences.** How might Ava's health triangle be affected by this decision?
13. **Consequences.** How might Deb's health triangle be affected by this decision?
14. **Consequences.** How might this decision affect the girls' parents?

Rob is a senior in high school and is busy making plans for college next year. He hopes to attend the state university and live on campus. Until recently he has been cooperative and helpful around the house. Now, however, he has developed the habit of leaving wet towels on the floor of his room. His sister, Becki, just found two of them when she went into his room to get the sweatshirt he had borrowed from her. It was under the wet towels! How should Becki handle this situation?

WHAT DO YOU THINK?

15. **Choices.** What choices does Becki have?
16. **Consequences.** What are the consequences of each choice?
17. **Decision.** What should Becki do? Explain the reasons for your answer.

Discussing the Answers

Situation 1. Perhaps the best thing for Shelley to do would be to discuss this situation with her parents. Shelley could call the child protection agency in her area and report the suspected abuse anonymously.

Situation 2. Ava can confront her sister Deb in a nonthreatening and uncriticizing manner. Ava has a right to keep her side of the room clean. Ava can choose to not lend her clothes to Deb if Deb will not care for the clothes better. Ava may not have the right to demand that Deb keep her side of the room clean. It is up to Ava's parents to require this from Deb.

Situation 3. If Becki is not pleased with the manner that Rob treats her sweatshirt when borrowing it, Becki has the right to refuse the next time he asks.

Helping Students Improve Their Health

Building Decision-Making Skills

Teaching Strategies

L1 CLASS ACTIVITY. Have students discuss the signs and symptoms of child abuse. Have students discuss the different options that Shelley has in dealing with this situation. Make sure that students understand that child abuse is serious and that there are local phone numbers available where someone can report suspected child abuse anonymously.

L1 CLASS ACTIVITY. Have students role-play the part of Ava as she confronts her sister, Deb, about her poor housekeeping skills. How can Ava discuss the situation with Deb without causing an argument?

L1 DISCUSSION. Have students weigh the advantages and disadvantages of Becki approaching a parent in this situation; of approaching Rob directly.

L1 CLASS ACTIVITY. Another possible role-play pertaining to the family is: Your eldest sister just recently graduated from college and has begun working her new job where she is a role model for children. Last night, you learned that your eldest, unmarried sister, whom you respect, is pregnant. She has no intentions of getting married or quitting her job.

L2 DISCUSSION. Have students debate whether or not it is better for the family to have two working parents who will provide more income for their family, or a single-income household where one parent stays home with the children. Have students compare and contrast the above situations with a single-parent household. What disadvantages does the single parent have when that parent must work and raise children by oneself?

L2 CLASS ACTIVITY. Suggest that students write a letter to the editor of their school newspaper in order to raise school interest in issues involving the family.

Using Health Terms

1. Family
2. Communication
3. Compromise
4. Crisis

Building Academic Skills

5. Seventy to 84 minutes per week. Five to 6.2 hours per month. Sixty hours and 50 minutes to 73 hours per year.
6. Thirty-six thousand hours. Forty-two thousand hours. Seventy thousand hours.
7. To solve a problem to the satisfaction of everyone involved.
8. Compositions will vary but may include ideas about caring, communicating, supporting, trusting, respecting, sharing, and showing appreciation, listening, and compromising.

Recalling the Facts

9. A sense of security and belonging. Families also provide religious beliefs, values, traditions, and customs from one generation to the next.
10. The behavior of each member of a family affects every other member of the family.
11. The family is the basic social unit of society, society's health is directly related to the family's health.
12. A single-parent family may be one in which the parents are divorced and only one of the parents lives with the children. It may consist of a single adult who has a child or children by birth or adoption. It may also be the result of the death of a parent.
13. The family is the primary support system for an individual and is the essential mechanism by which one develops the capability to survive and function independently in the world.
14. Four or five years of age.
15. Family size tends to be smaller than in the past. More women are working outside the home. The number of sin-

---

Using Health Terms

On a separate sheet of paper, write the term that best matches each definition given below.

LESSON 1

1. The basic unit of society; a group of people related by blood, marriage, or adoption.

LESSON 2

2. Talking about and expressing both positive and negative feelings.
3. A way of solving a problem in which each person gives up something in order to reach a solution that is satisfactory to everyone involved.
4. An extreme change in a person's life.

Building Academic Skills

LESSON 1

5. **Math.** If a family spends 10 to 12 minutes each day dealing with family conflict, how much total time is spent over a one-week period? Over a one-month period? In one year?
6. **Math.** Today by the time people reach the age of 18, they have spent an average of 18,000 hours watching television. Calculate the hours spent by a 36-year-old, a 42-year-old, and a 70-year-old.

LESSON 2

7. **Reading.** Use the context clues in the following sentence to define the word *compromise.*

   We were unable to agree on which restaurant to choose because no one was willing to compromise.
8. **Writing.** Write a composition of three to five paragraphs, beginning with the following words: "I can better contribute to and promote my family's health by. . . ." Before you begin writing, make an outline of the points you want to include. Use what you have learned in this chapter to generate ideas for your composition.

Recalling the Facts

LESSON 1

9. What do families provide besides food, clothing, and shelter?
10. Explain how the family is a system.
11. How does family health relate to the health of society as a whole?
12. List and describe two types of single-parent families.
13. What are the two essential functions of the family?
14. At what age do some psychologists believe that a child's intelligence and personality are almost fully developed?
15. What three significant changes are affecting the family system today?
16. Name three factors that may influence the decision of couples to have fewer children.
17. What are two reasons for the increase in the number of wives and mothers who work outside the home?
18. How can children be properly cared for if both parents work outside the home?

LESSON 2

19. How many children under the age of 2 die each year in the United States from physical abuse?
20. Why is it difficult for sexually abused children to seek help?
21. Describe several characteristics of a healthy family.
22. Describe the role of structure in family life.
23. List five things you can do to make your family healthy and strong.
24. What are the five most common types of crises in a person's life?
25. What emotions are children of divorced parents likely to feel? What adjustments might children of divorced parents have to make?
26. What are some ways children can cope with the divorce of their parents?
27. List three likely results of drug use in the family.

---

gle-parent heads of households is increasing.
16. Answers will vary. Accept three of the following: costs, health, the economy, jobs, beliefs.
17. Answers will vary.
18. Quality day-care facilities are needed.
19. More than one thousand.
20. The child may be threatened with severe punish-

ment, embarrassment, ridicule, or even death if he or she tells.
21. Family members care about each other, communicate with each other, and support each other.
22. Structure allows family members to know their place within the family and what their general functions are.

REVIEW

Thinking Critically

LESSON 1

28. Analysis. What is the difference between an extended family and a nuclear family?

29. Evaluation. How has television affected family life?

30. Synthesis. Keep a log of each family member's television viewing time for one week. Talk to family members about what programs they could give up in order to engage in family activities. Plan some family activities to take the place of watching television.

LESSON 2

31. Evaluation. Why do you think abused wives often stay in bad situations?

32. Evaluation. What do you think are three characteristics of a person who inflicts abuse on other family members?

33. Synthesis. What might you infer about a child in your neighborhood who tends to be depressed, fearful, and who sometimes exhibits destructive behaviors?

34. Synthesis. Summarize ways that healthy families can prevent abuse.

35. Synthesis. How could you help if your family experienced financial problems?

Making the Connection

LESSON 1

36. Social Studies. Television is a major part of many Americans' lives. How do you think television affects society? What impact is television having on your family? Is it a good or bad influence? Conduct a four-day study of your family's television viewing habits. Keep a log of what programs and the number of hours each member of your family watches television. What might your data suggest about the impact of television on your family? Make a list of healthful changes and alternatives to television viewing you can suggest to your family.

Applying Health Knowledge

LESSON 1

37. Label each type of family described below.
   a. Marisa and Miguel Esposito live in an apartment with their two children, Juan and Maria.
   b. Tom and Margaret Kenny have four children. Tom's sister, Anna, and her three children live with them.
   c. Alice Johnson is divorced. Her daughter, Sylvia, lives with her.
   d. Mary and Sam Gaines were not able to have children of their own. They adopted four Vietnamese children.

LESSON 2

38. Joyce and Judy are sisters who fight all the time. You are their best friend. What advice can you give them for getting along better?

39. Your cousin Angela's parents have recently separated. While they are trying to work out their problems, Angela is coming to live with your family. What can you do to help Angela get through this crisis in her life?

Beyond the Classroom

LESSON 1

40. Parental Involvement. Talk to your grandparents or two people you know who are over age 50. Ask them what they did in place of watching television when they were children. Evaluate their responses in relation to a healthy family life. Write a paragraph based on one of these people's early family life compared to your own. How does it compare?

LESSON 2

41. Community Involvement. The loss of a job and the death of a loved one are similar in many ways. Talk to at least two people who have experienced one or both of these crises. Find out what feelings they had after each event, how they dealt with the loss, whether they sought help and from whom.

Applying Health Knowledge

37. A—nuclear family; B—extended family; C—single-parent family; D—nuclear/adoptive family.

38. Answers will vary. Possible answers: Respect each other; stop criticizing each other; try to see situations from the other's point of view; listen to each other without interrupting; try to compromise.

39. Answers will vary. Possible answers: Listen to Angela's feelings and fears sympathetically; assure her that her parents' problems are not her fault; recommend a support group.

Beyond the Classroom

40. Answers will vary.
41. Answers will vary.

23. Answers will vary.
24. Financial problems, divorce, drug use, violence, and death.
25. Shock, disbelief, anger, sorrow, acceptance. They may have to adjust to a lower standard of living and, possibly, learning to live with a stepparent.
26. By sharing their feelings with their parents and trying to understand their parents' feelings and/or discussing their feelings with an older person.
27. Answers will vary. Accept three of the following: The drug user may neglect responsibilities; become irritable; lose his or her job; and/or abuse other family members.

Thinking Critically

28. Extended family is relatives beyond two parents and their children, such as grandparents, aunts, uncles, and so on.
29. Answers will vary. Possible answers: Time spent watching TV takes away from time spent with family. Some families watch TV together and so spend more time together than they might otherwise. TV role models and value systems sometimes conflict with those of the family's.
30. Answers will vary. Possible activities: playing games, engaging in family exercise programs, taking time to talk to each other.
31. Answers will vary. Possible answers: Low self-esteem; fear; may feel they cannot support themselves and any children.
32. Answers will vary. Possible answers: Low self-esteem; had been abused at some point in their lives; frustrated; angry; aggressive.
33. The child may be a victim of abuse.
34. Answers will vary. Possible answers: Develop support systems; become informed about parenting and child development; work on developing positive self-esteem; manage stress; avoid drugs and alcohol.
35. Answers will vary. Possible answers: Do without luxuries; recycle what you have; get a part-time job.

Making the Connection

36. Answers will vary.

Lesson Summaries

LESSON 1. Relationships allow us to meet our needs to be loved, safe, secure, valued, and recognized. The bond between individuals shapes more than the social aspects of health. It affects mental and physical health as well. People take on many roles in their relationships and often switch suddenly or change gradually over time. Friendships and dating provide teenagers opportunities to develop interpersonal skills and to become emotionally mature.

LESSON 2. Violence is now a major public health problem in the United States. Americans are constantly exposed to violence. Random violence is on the rise. More teens are committing violent crimes and also are increasingly the victims. Though the reasons violence has increased are complicated, many successful programs are being used to teach people ways to solve problems without violence.

LESSON 3. Building healthy relationships takes learning and using a variety of relationship skills. Among these are skills in verbal and nonverbal communication. To stand up to peer pressure, you must also learn refusal skills. The decisions you make and the manner in which you enforce them affects those around you, just as their decisions affect you.

Introducing the Chapter

Ask students to brainstorm qualities of a friend. Have them then consider which of the characteristics they personally display on a consistent basis. Tell the students that many attributes of a friend can be learned, as can other skills that contribute to healthy relationships.

Performance Assessment ✓

Refer to pages T 23 to T 25 for a Performance Assessment strategy for this chapter. See the *Performance Assessment Activities* booklet for additional suggestions.

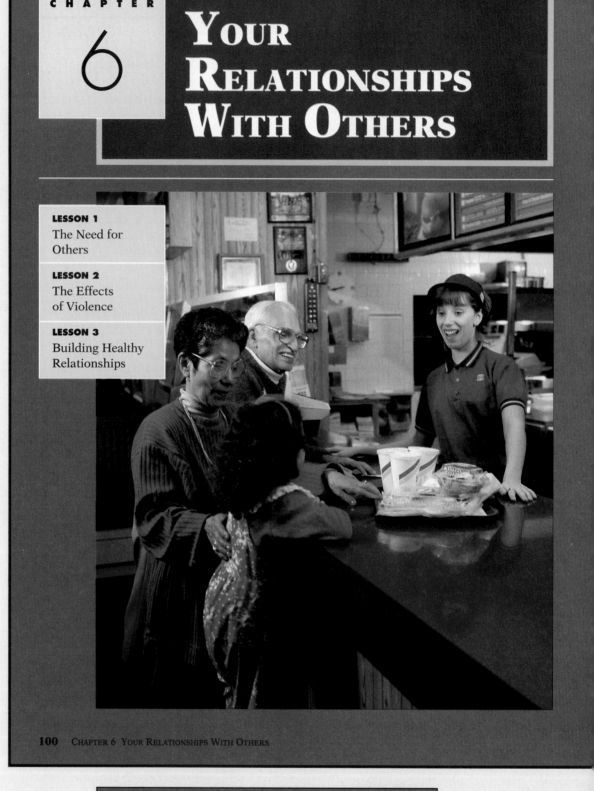

CHAPTER
6

YOUR RELATIONSHIPS WITH OTHERS

LESSON 1
The Need for Others

LESSON 2
The Effects of Violence

LESSON 3
Building Healthy Relationships

100   CHAPTER 6 YOUR RELATIONSHIPS WITH OTHERS

Key to Ability Levels

Teaching strategies have been coded for varying learning styles and abilities.

L1 Level 1 activities are basic activities and should be within the ability range of all students.

L2 Level 2 activities are average activities and should be within the ability range of average to above-average students.

L3 Level 3 activities are challenging activities designed for the ability range of above-average students.

LD LD activities should be within the ability range of learning-disabled students.

LEP LEP activities should be within the ability range of Limited English Proficiency students.

THE NEED FOR OTHERS

According to psychologist Abraham Maslow, everyone needs to be loved and to belong. Each of us also needs to feel safe, secure, valued, and recognized. By forming relationships, we are able to meet many of these basic human needs. A **relationship** is a bond or connection between people. Good relationships can affect a person's mental, social, and even physical health. You develop and learn from relationships throughout your life.

Who Matters to You?

Think of standing in one of those photo booths where you and a friend pull a curtain, drop four quarters into a slot, and get back four connected photos of the two of you. You are smiling or laughing, your faces side by side. Now imagine that you could have these four shots showing you with four different people with whom you have a significant connection—say, from your family; from your extended family, such as a grandparent or cousin; from your neighborhood; and from your school. Who would be with you in the four photos?

You have many relationships in your life, and all of them affect you. You are part of a network of people that includes your family, extended family, neighbors, friends, other peers, as well as people from social or religious organizations, sports teams, your town or city, your nation, and the world.

If you were suddenly plunked down on a desert island and removed from all of these relationships, you might like the peace and quiet for a short time, but chances are you would soon begin to get very lonely. Having relationships with others can, in fact, not only ward off loneliness; it can also have a direct effect on a person's total health.

Your Many Roles

You take on many roles in your relationships with others. A **role** is a part that you play, especially in a relationship. You may be a sister or brother, a daughter or son; a granddaughter or grandson; a member of the orchestra; a member of the volleyball team; a Scout; a student; an employee; a member of a synagogue, church, or mosque; and even someone's boyfriend or girlfriend—all at the same time.

Sometimes the roles you play are clear-cut. You know that when you mow the neighbor's lawn or wash his or her car, you are an employee and need to act as one. Sometimes, though, roles either switch suddenly or change gradually, depending on needs and situations. For example, some days you may be the caretaker for your disabled grandfather, but at other times he is a teacher and you are the student. Perhaps your lab partner becomes the person you are dating. Such changes in roles can be confusing. Sometimes you may not have a clue as to what your role is in a relationship. This can make it difficult for you to know how to act.

THE NEED FOR OTHERS **101**

Focus

Lesson Objectives

After studying this lesson, students should be able to:
- define the terms *relationship* and *role* and identify the needs relationships fulfill
- define *friendship* and distinguish among different types of friendships
- give examples of both positive and negative peer pressure and manipulation
- explain the relationship between prejudice and stereotype

Bellringer

Write the following on the chalkboard for students to work on while attendance is being taken: *Write a list of names of several different people with whom you interact regularly. Include family members, people from your neighborhood, and people from school.*

Introducing the Lesson

Refer to the Bellringer. Ask several students to share their lists. Tell students that the people they named are those with whom they have relationships—connections that satisfy basic emotional needs. Have volunteers describe their roles in the relationships listed. Use their examples to illustrate how roles vary from one relationship to another and change within the same relationship, depending on circumstances. Tell them that they will read about different kinds of relationships as well as how to avoid relationships that are damaging to their total health.

DID YOU KNOW?

- Researchers have found that there is a link between shyness and allergies beginning in childhood. People who are outgoing and those who are shy show differences in the area of the brain that regulates the sense of smell, mood, and immune-system responses. People who are shy are most prone to suffer from hay fever.

Building Vocabulary

- Ask students to explain how the following terms are related to one another and how they differ: *relationship, role, friend, date.*
- Have students volunteer examples from their own experience of both positive and negative peer pressure and manipulation. Then have them work as a class to define peer pressure and manipulation in their own words.
- Ask students to complete *Workbook Vocabulary Activity 13.*

Teach

Guided Practice

L1 CLASS ACTIVITY. Have students list all the roles they play during an average week. Ask a few volunteers to write their lists on the chalkboard. As a class, go through the lists and discuss the behavior that is expected in each role. Ask students to identify which roles are relatively clear-cut as guides to behavior and which are more ambiguous or situation-dependent. Explain that roles help relationships go more smoothly by helping guide our behavior and understand the behavior of others.

L1 CLASS ACTIVITY. Ask students to brainstorm the personal qualities they feel are important in friends. List these on the chalkboard as students call them out. Narrow down the list to about ten qualities that the class agrees are the most important. Why do they think these particular qualities are important to have in a friend?

L1 DISCUSSION. Ask students to volunteer ways they think that dating relationships differ from platonic relationships. Can platonic relationships turn into dating relationships, and vice versa? In their opinion, how does each type of relationship help prepare them for relationships in their adult lives?

L1 USING HEALTH AWARENESS TRANSPARENCY 5. Refer to the Teaching Transparencies Binder

- One large-scale survey on friendship suggests that, on average, people have between three and seven good friends.
- One way people hook up with friends is by telephone. There are 120 million telephone lines in the U.S. and 425 million lines in the world.
- One good way to find and make a new friend from a different culture is to get a pen pal. For more information, write to World Pen Pals 1690 Como Avenue St. Paul, MN 55108

Choosing Relationships

As a small child, you had a limited circle of relationships. Now, that you are older, you have a larger circle from which to choose your relationships. You may realize for the first time that there are people of all ages, races, religions, and backgrounds from which you can choose relationships. You can choose people who support and encourage your best qualities. You can change or back out of relationships that have a negative influence on your health, your safety, your self-esteem, or your values. No relationship can be healthy unless both parties feel valued and want the relationship.

Friendship

A **friendship** is a significant relationship between two people, based on caring, consideration, and trust. A friend is someone whose companionship you enjoy and who can be a source of help when you have a problem. A friend also may be someone with whom you share confidences, interests, hobbies, or other friends. Having friends can help you define, understand, and reinforce your values. There are many kinds of friendships. Friendships vary in importance and in how challenging and complicated they are. Maintaining friendships can be hard work, but they are usually worth the effort.

Close Friendships. Having one or more close friends is important to your total health. Sitting with a group at ball games or in the cafeteria can make you feel socially connected. These casual relationships, however, do not fill some of the deeper needs humans have. A close friend is more likely to share what he or she is really feeling and thinking and, in turn, make you feel comfortable doing the same. You may trust a close friend with your secrets or go to this person when you are hurting, confused, or in trouble. He or she might give you honest criticism and make you apologize or be accountable for your mistakes. Because you may care deeply, a real friend is also more likely to make you angry or hurt. Losing or having to share a close friend with someone else can be painful. It is important to remind yourself that no one owns anyone else—that people must be free to choose with whom they want to be and when. Friends try to work through conflicts. This helps friendships stay healthy and grow.

KEEPING FIT

Your Friends, Your Self-Esteem

The friends you have or want to have can have a major impact on your self-esteem. Think of someone you consider to be a good friend. Then ask yourself the following questions:
- What qualities does the person

have that you admire? What qualities bother you?
- How do you think this person feels about him- or herself?
- How does this person affect your health triangle?
- What positive peer pressure

does the person put on you? What negative peer pressure?
- What positive effects does this person have on your self-esteem? What negative effects?
- What changes would make this relationship healthier?

Across the Curriculum

Social Studies. Ask students to research dating behaviors of another culture. This might be done using media center materials or by interviewing persons from different cultural backgrounds. What similarities and differences exist? Findings might be written or presented orally. Oral presentations would allow for group discussions of the findings, which can help students

better understand other cultures.

Language Arts. Ask students to write an essay titled "Best Friends." Encourage each student to select two to three qualities that his or her best friend possesses and elaborate on the importance of these qualities in maintaining the friendship.

Platonic Relationships. Not all close friendships are made up of same-sex pairs. Sometimes a male and a female can become real buddies in what is a platonic relationship. A **platonic relationship** is one in which there is affection, but not romance. Such a relationship can be a wonderful way to grow to understand and feel comfortable with the opposite sex without feeling any of the pressures of dating. It can also help you begin to know that people of the opposite sex are human beings just like you, with the same kinds of fears, needs, and feelings.

Dating Relationships

Dating is part of the process of learning interpersonal skills. Dating provides an opportunity for you to get to know yourself better—to recognize your strengths and weaknesses. It also gives you an opportunity to interact with and feel comfortable with the opposite sex. By meeting and spending time with a variety of people, you learn what types of people you like and get along with best. In your dating experiences, you can practice your decision-making and communication skills and, in so doing, broaden your own development.

Dating often leads to an ongoing relationship with one person. There are some advantages to this type of relationship. However, teenagers who date only one person may be closing themselves off from meeting other people too early in their social development. Although this type of relationship may be convenient and ensures that you have a date, it may not be helpful in developing a healthy relationship.

It is important to remember that adolescence is a time of trying different relationships and roles. Breaking up, making up, and breaking up again can be painful, but this cycle is part of the process of emotional maturing. Staying in a relationship because you do not know how to get out of it gracefully or clinging to a relationship when the other person wants to call it off are two common but very painful situations. In both cases, honesty and open communication are essential. So is realizing that you have control over only your own actions and emotions. You cannot control the behaviors or feelings of others.

These days many teens go out in groups. Others do not date at all. The fact is, dating steadily, dating in groups, or waiting until later to date are all healthy ways of meeting your emotional and social needs.

Peer Pressure

Your peers are people your age or close to your age. They can have great influence over what you think, feel, say, and do. They may exert direct or indirect **peer pressure,** the control and influence people your age may have over you. Peer pressure can occur in many kinds of relationships. The way you handle peer pressure can have a great impact on the decisions you make and, in turn, on your total health.

Peer pressure can be positive or negative. Positive peer pressure may inspire you to pick up and recycle trash, volunteer your time to a worthy organization, exercise, or refrain from drinking or using other drugs. Negative peer pressure, however, may persuade you to take dangerous risks, use alcohol or other drugs, have sex, or cheat on an exam, just for the sake of being accepted by the crowd.

Dating provides an opportunity to feel comfortable with the opposite sex.

THE NEED FOR OTHERS **103**

Overcoming Misconceptions

Friendship. Being best friends does not necessarily mean being constant companions. Many times young persons are not secure enough in their relationships to accept the fact that friendships can be maintained even though physical companionship is not possible or necessary all the time.

Dating. Students need to recognize that not all persons desire to date at the same age or desire to date at all. Care must be taken so that persons who choose not to date for whatever reason are never made to feel inferior.

Using Overcoming the Odds

■ **Explanation.** Explain how the socioeconomic situation in which Chi grew up defined his options and led him to become a gang member. (Chi grew up in an environment where gang violence and drugs were the norm. Dying a violent death at a young age was a good possibility whether or not he joined a gang. His only apparent way to become admired and respected was to become a gang member—he had few if any role models or chances for success on any other terms.)

■ **Discussion.** Why do gangs, violence, and drugs always seem to go together? (In the subculture of inner-city poverty, gangs provide the social supports that are commonly lacking because of broken, dysfunctional families. Violence is one way of acting out frustrations and disappointments in a social situation of relative deprivation and poverty. Drugs are the quickest and easiest way of making money as well as an important source of emotional and physical solace in a painful world.)

■ **Answers**

1. His self-esteem was low; joining the gang appeared to be the only way to have respect, money, and power; instead, it led to drugs, depression, and prison.
2. Self-esteem and caring relationships with others are mutually reinforcing.
3. Answers will vary—the bottom line being that self-esteem comes from self-love, not from "proving" yourself to others.

L2 WRITING. Ask students to write a short essay titled "Peer Pressure—A Positive and Negative Influence on My Life."

L3 RESEARCH. Have students interview friends and family members to collect a list of stereotypical misconceptions based on physical attributes. Ask them to suggest ways in which specific stereotypes might lead to prejudicial treatment.

L1 USING THE LESSON RESOURCES. For additional student activities, refer to the lesson resources on page 101.

Chi is 16. He says, "I grew up in a tough place. More like a war zone. Lost more friends to gangs and guns than I can keep track of. Or want to. Anyway, where I grew up your choices were to join a gang and learn to defend yourself or learn to duck the bullets and fight for your life when the outside gangs moved in on you. Giving in just seemed easier. Figured we might not make it down the road anyway, so it was no big deal. It was sort of like, you know, when you get it, you get it.

"They got me started dealing dope when I was 11. Felt like it was the only way to have anything or be anything. It's like the OGs (original gang members) welcomed me and gave me power. At least, that's what I thought. By age 12 I was using pretty heavily and by 13, I didn't really care what happened to anybody else. We got into this rival gang thing then and I actually knifed a guy, or 'made my bones,' as the members would say. We trashed places, gave graffiti warnings, and stole for fun. Some of the members even did drive-by shootings—on a regular basis. For a while, it was a kind of high. I felt like somebody for a change. We even ate out in fancy restaurants. One time, I got my arm twisted and then

broken. I have scars on my back and face. I just figured that came with the turf. Besides, I was proud of my slices.

"When I was 14, I got into the corrections system. That didn't stop anything. I was really heading down a hole, deep into drugs, thinking about suicide or letting somebody else have it. Then they put me in this program with prisoners. First I thought it was stupid, almost cool. You know, some guys go out to the country for the weekend, I go to prison. Cracked me up. But then I saw what it was like. The conditions and everything. They paired me up with this guy who was there for life for killing a couple of people when he was in a gang and

doing drugs. I realized I didn't want to end up there like he did. He's a huge guy with big tattoos and a big smile. His name is Rajiv. He's in this program where he calls me every week, really talks to me about stuff, lets me know he cares. I go to visit him one Saturday a month. He's tough on me, too. And he tells me how it is when you go from the streets to the cells. He says I don't have to live out his ugly story, he's done it for me. He really listens. Let me put it to you this way: I never thought anybody was there for me. I was dead wrong. This beats being dead, which I almost was—more than once."

1. What kind of self-esteem do you think Chi had when he joined the gang? How did the gang appear to promise that they would make him feel better about himself? How did this promise backfire? Was it worth the cost?
2. What might Chi's story teach teens about self-esteem?
3. Have you ever done something dangerous because you didn't feel you measured up? How might you have boosted your self-esteem in healthier ways?

Across the Curriculum

Social Studies. Discuss prejudice in terms of the civil rights movement in the United States.

Expand students' thinking to include the prejudices that the handicapped have suffered throughout history in terms of job discrimination and accessibility. Discuss what has been done in your school and community to eliminate those prejudices. Invite a handicapped person to share with the class about the prejudicial barriers that they have had to overcome.

Language Arts. Have students write an essay titled "Prejudice—Is There a Place for It in Today's World?"

Manipulation

Manipulation is one way that people exert peer pressure over others. **Manipulation** is an indirect and often sneaky or dishonest means of trying to control another's attitudes or behavior. The person who manipulates another does so to get what he or she wants without respect for the well-being of the person being manipulated. Some means of manipulation include

- mocking or teasing the person in mean or hurtful ways;
- bargaining, or offering to make a deal to get what one wants;
- bribing, or promising money or favors if the person will do what another asks of him or her;
- using guilt trips to get desired results;
- making threats, or using words that show a person intends to use violence or some other negative means to get his or her way;
- using blackmail, or threatening to tell someone else some damaging information if the person does not conform;
- using flattery or undeserved praise to influence another person.

Prejudice

One of the more negative aspects of peer pressure that many high school students face is prejudice. **Prejudice** is a negative feeling toward someone or something that is based not on experience but, rather, on stereotypes. A **stereotype** is an exaggerated and oversimplified belief about an entire group, such as an ethnic group, a religious group, or a certain sex. Stereotypes may hold some truth but are in great part untrue. Prejudice, then, is a kind of ignorance. It denies each member of a group the right to be judged as an individual.

Prejudice prevents healthy relationships from forming. It is always a power relationship in which the victimizer wants to feel or appear superior to the person or group he or she is victimizing. In the process, the person exhibiting prejudice inflicts mental, social, and sometimes even physical damage. Discrimination is a form of prejudice in which people are singled out and often treated negatively as a result of one factor, such as age, sex, race, ethnicity, or even some physical trait.

Culturally Speaking

One World, Many Tongues

The word *language* comes from the Latin *lingua*, meaning "tongue." There are more than 3,000 languages spoken in the world today. This does not include the thousands of dialects, or local forms or variations of these languages.

There are over 100 languages spoken by a million people or more, but some of the most widely spoken languages in the world are: Arabic, Bengali, Chinese, English, French, German, Hindi, Italian, Japanese, Korean, Marathi, Portuguese, Punjabi, Russian, Spanish, Tamil, Telugu, and Urdu.

LESSON 1 REVIEW

Reviewing Facts and Vocabulary

1. Define the term *role*, and state some of the different roles a person may play.
2. Define the words *prejudice, stereotype,* and *discrimination* in a paragraph in which you discuss their relationship to one another.
3. List and explain at least five techniques some people use to manipulate others.

Thinking Critically

4. **Analysis.** Compare your roles as student, son or daughter, and best friend.

5. **Evaluation.** What do you think are some of the advantages and disadvantages of telling everything to your best friend?

Applying Health Knowledge

6. Tell about a friendship you have had or know about that has not worked. Explain why you think the friendship failed.

Check for Understanding

- Assign and discuss the lesson review.

Evaluate

- Administer, grade, and discuss the *Lesson 1 Quiz.*

Reteach

- Ask students to examine and write about a relationship they have with a relative or close friend. They should describe the various roles each of them plays to make the relationship work (e.g., helper, companion, adviser, etc.).
- Ask students to complete *Reteaching Activity 13.*

Enrich

- Through a series of interviews with parents, grandparents, and older friends, have students determine the changes that have taken place in dating behavior over the past several decades. Ask them to try to explain why the changes have taken place. They should share what they learn with the class through oral reports.

Close

Summarize the lesson by reviewing the following important concepts: relationships, roles, peer pressure, manipulation, prejudice.

DID YOU KNOW?

- A recent study found that women who had dogs for pets handled stress better with their pup present than with a good friend looking on. The reason? The pets were perceived as less judgmental.

Answers to Lesson 1 Review

1. Role—part one plays. Answers may include, but are not limited to, roles listed on pages 101 to 102.
2. Refer to page 105. Paragraphs will vary.
3. Answers will vary. Accept five of the techniques listed on page 105.
4. Answers will vary.

5. Answers will vary. Possible answers: An advantage might be having someone with whom you could talk about anything. A disadvantage might be that if your friendship ends you may wish you had not told that person so much.
6. Answers will vary.

Focus

Lesson Objectives

After studying this lesson, students should be able to:
- identify specific types of violence common in the United States today
- describe the increase in violence in the schools and on the streets and how it affects us
- explain why violence is increasing and what can be done to prevent it

Bellringer

Write the following on the chalkboard for students to work on while attendance is being taken: *Describe in a few sentences a situation that you witnessed or took part in, in which there was violence or the potential for violence.*

Introducing the Lesson

Refer to the Bellringer. Ask volunteers to share their responses. For each situation described, have students identify the victim and the perpetrator of the violence or near violence. Ask them to discuss why the situation turned violent. Were alcohol, drugs, gangs, or weapons involved? If actual violence did not occur, how was it avoided? If violence did occur, what might have been done to prevent it? Tell students that in this lesson they will learn why violence is on the increase in our society, particularly violence that involves teens, and what can be done to prevent it.

Building Vocabulary

- Ask students to describe real or hypothetical situations that illustrate each of the following types of violence: random violence, homicide, aggravated assault, battery, and carjacking.
- Ask students to complete *Workbook Vocabulary Activity 14.*

THE EFFECTS OF VIOLENCE

LESSON 2 FOCUS

TERMS TO USE
- Violence
- Random violence
- Homicide
- Aggravated assault
- Battery
- Carjacking

CONCEPTS TO LEARN
- Acts of violence are increasing in our society.
- Many measures are being taken to stop violence in schools.
- There are many complicated reasons for causes of violence.
- Many programs are being implemented to try to reduce violence.

ATTITUDES AND BEHAVIORS TO EVALUATE
- Self-Inventory, page 114.
- Building Decision-Making Skills, page 115.

Violence is the use of physical force to injure or abuse another person or persons. In addition to harming victims physically, acts of violence can leave victims with deep emotional scars. Violence is now a major public health problem in the United States.

Violence in Society

Americans are constantly exposed to violence. From television and music lyrics to so-called "slasher movies," images of violence influence lives and minds. We hear the words *murder, assault, battery,* and *mugging.* We read about increases in domestic abuse, child abuse, elder abuse, rape, and suicide. Now the new words in our "vocabulary of violence" are *drive-by shootings, carjackings,* and *hate crimes.* Many Americans no longer feel safe in their schools, on the streets, or even in their own homes.

Random Violence

In the past, most violent crimes were committed with specific intent—for a reason decided ahead of time and with a specific victim or property targeted. Today, violence has become more vicious and more random. **Random violence** is violence committed for no particular reason and/or against anyone who happens to be around at the time. Innocent people are the usual victims of random violence.

Teens and Violence

More teens than ever before are committing violent crimes and being arrested for serious crimes. They also are more likely to be tried as adults for these crimes and to be given stiffer "adult" sentences.

At the same time, more teens are also becoming the victims of violent crimes—often at the hands of their peers. Teens are three times more likely to be the victims of violent crime than adults.

Violence in Schools

There has been a dramatic increase in both the amount and the seriousness of violence in our schools. According to the United States Justice Department's National School Safety Center, as many as 3 million cases of assault, theft, robbery, and rape occur in United States schools every year. Stories of guns, knives, threats to both teachers and

---

Resources for Lesson 2

- **Guided Reading** Activity 14
- **Workbook** Vocabulary Activity 14
- **Reteaching** Activity 14
- **Lesson 2 Quiz**
- **The Reality of Violence**

Glencoe Health VHS Videos
Violence

ABC News InterActive Videodiscs
Drugs and Substance Abuse, Side 2
Ch 6 Drugs and the Community

students, hostage-taking, and even killings occur in the news. In such stressful environments, students may find it difficult to learn, and teachers find it hard to teach. Many students are afraid to go to school. This violence is occurring in schools across the nation—from rural to suburban to urban school districts. In addition, the seriousness of crimes in our schools continues to increase, and students are performing these violent acts at younger and younger ages.

Schools are taking steps to stop this violence and its effects. Some inner-city schools in the nation's major cities now use metal detectors to stop students from carrying guns and knives into school. Many schools now have security guards, some with gun-sniffing dogs. Some schools enforce more strict dress codes in an attempt to keep certain types of clothing or jewelry out of the schools to prevent thefts and fights. In addition to fire drills, some schools now have "drop drills" to teach students and teachers how to hit the floor when they hear gunfire. Other ways schools are trying to curb violence are presenting violence prevention programs more frequently and at earlier ages, teaching conflict resolution, working to help students build self-esteem, and teaching about the dangers of alcohol, other drugs, guns, and gangs.

Violence on the Streets

Our streets are no longer completely safe. The incidence of homicide, aggravated assault, battery, and rape continues to rise and take their toll on everyone—even law-abiding citizens. **Homicide** is the willful killing of one human being by another. **Aggravated assault** is unlawful attack, often with a weapon, and having the intent to hurt or kill. **Battery** is the use of physical force to control someone through the use of power. Battery often includes frightening and humiliating a person over time. In our society, battery is the most common form of injury among females. Males also can be victims. Battery is one technique used to pressure teenagers into drug use and/or gangs. Rape, or sexual intercourse by force or threat, is another crime of violence. It is one of the fastest-growing yet least reported crimes.

Guns

Firearms, or guns, claim the lives of about 3,000 young people a year in the United States. Many other teens are left permanently disabled. Along with automobile crashes, gunfire is a common cause of death among teens aged 15 to 19. Guns are readily available. Unfortunately when bought for self-protection by adults or teens, guns too often are used on impulse during arguments or are set off accidently. Many people who own guns keep them loaded, and many do not lock them up for safekeeping.

Gangs

Gangs were once found only in large cities; now they also are found in smaller cities. Because of gang activity, some cities can seem like war zones. Gang members come from all ethnic groups, both sexes, and all economic classes. Gangs have rules, dress codes, symbols, and mottos.

THE EFFECTS OF VIOLENCE **107**

DID YOU KNOW?

- Each day in the U.S. about 16,000 crimes take place on or near schools.
- According to U.S. Bureau of Justice statistics, in one recent year, 400,000 students between the ages of 12 and 19 were the victims of violent crimes.
- It is estimated that up to 90 percent of young people with guns get those guns from home.
- More than half of all homicide victims are killed by handguns.
- The Center to Prevent Handgun Violence reports that 1 percent of handgun violence in the schools occurs in pre-school, 24 percent in elementary school, 12 percent in junior high, and 63 percent in high school.

Guided Practice

L3 **DISCUSSION.** Initiate a discussion of the long-lasting emotional damage caused by violence by having students imagine themselves as victims of a violent act, such as a mugging. Ask them what emotions they think they would experience both during and after the attack. How do they think their self-confidence and self-esteem would be affected over the long run by the violent act?

L1 **CLASS ACTIVITY.** Have students name as many different types of violent crime as they can think of (e.g., murder, assault, rape, spousal abuse). Ask a volunteer to write the list on the chalkboard. Then have the class work together to select a criterion for deciding on the seriousness of violent crime, such as the degree of physical or emotional damage caused the victim. Then ask them to rank the crimes they listed in order of seriousness. They should justify their ranking.

L1 **EXPLANATION.** Explain the similarities and differences among murder, homicide, aggravated assault, battery, and rape.

L1 **COOPERATIVE LEARNING.** Have students work together in groups of four or five to make bulletin board displays titled: "Teens and Violence in the U.S. Today." They should collect clippings from newspapers and magazines that describe a wide variety of violent situations involving teens both as victims and as perpetrators of violent acts. Their objective should be to increase awareness of the risk of violence faced by today's youth.

L1 **SPEAKER.** Ask a member of the school's administration to speak to the class about the rise of violence in the school. You might suggest that the speaker address the following: the most common types of violence that occur on school grounds; causes of the violence; the role played by guns and other weapons; and measures employed or under consideration to prevent violence in school.

Across the Curriculum

History. Show students how relevant past events can be to today's problems by relating the following anecdote.

Right after the 1992 L.A. riots, ex-gang member Anthony Perry went through the collection of United Nations treaties at his local university library, finally selecting and copying the 10-page 1949 cease-fire accord between Egypt and Israel. The purpose? To use it as a model for a truce between two rival gangs, the Crips and the Bloods. Perry modified the diplomatic language of the agreement to reflect the rules of the street. The Mideast prohibition against land, sea, and air attacks, for example, became a ban on drive-by shootings and random slayings. A month later, gang-related homicides had dropped by over half.

Assign students to small groups. Ask each group to write a scene in which there is conflict between two or more teens. Instruct them to conclude the scene with a non-violent resolution of the conflict.

L1 SPEAKER. Ask a police officer or youth counselor who is knowledgeable about gang violence to speak to your class. Have the speaker address the following topics: avoiding gang recruitment techniques; behavior patterns of gang members; and ways schools can deter gangs.

L2 DISCUSSION. Elicit student views on the increasing popularity of gangs by asking them what they think gang membership has to offer to teens (e.g., sense of belonging, thrills, money, status). Who do they think is most vulnerable to gang recruitment pressures? Why?

L1 DISCUSSION. Initiate a discussion of the role of peer pressure in teen violence by giving the class examples, such as peer pressure may lead a teen to stand up to a bully to avoid being considered a coward.

L2 CLASS ACTIVITY. Divide the class into groups of two or three students. Assign each group a factor that is a possible cause for the increase in violence in our society. Factors might include the breakdown of the family or increases in alcohol abuse, availability of guns, racial prejudice, or poverty. Have a representative from each group explain to the class why the factor they were assigned is likely to cause an increase in violence. At the end of the presentations, have the class decide which factor or factors they think are the most significant and why.

L1 EXPLANATION. Explain why people who do not know healthy ways to vent their anger and deal with their emotions may be prone to violent behavior.

L1 SELF-ESTEEM. Have several groups of two or three students write and role-play scenarios in which a violent act occurs because the violent individual has low self-esteem. Ask the class to suggest alternative, nonviolent outcomes for the scenario, in which the previously violent individual shows improved self-esteem.

DID YOU KNOW?

- A cult is an exclusive group dedicated to a particular leader, figure, or system of beliefs.
- A cult holds its members by isolating them from others and by using techniques like brainwashing.
- Cults demand total dedication of a member's time, emotions, and even money.
- Relationships in cults are unhealthy because they often are dependent and one-sided. The needs of the individual members are sacrificed to meet the needs of the leader or organization.

Wearing certain colors tipping, one's hat a certain way, or spraying graffiti may all signal the presence of gang members. Gangs stake out their "turf" or territory, and rivalries between gangs over this territory are deadly. Often gangs compete for drug deals and drug money. Gang killings also occur.

Members of gangs are often desperate to belong somewhere and to "be somebody." They get a sense of power from the group and from committing crimes. Members look to the gang as a kind of extended family and as a place to get some control. They may seek short-term thrills—no matter how risky, brutal, or deadly. Persons in gangs may be attracted to the promise of large sums of money from drug deals, fancy cars, and/or gang position. Some teenagers may become part of a gang to stop the pressure and threats to join.

Gangs no longer use just knives for weapons. Gang arsenals include automatic weapons, like high-powered assault rifles and UZI submachine guns. Gang members usually "lose big" over time—first by living in fear and eventually by getting injured, killed, or sent to jail—even Death Row. Being in a gang is a no-win, dead-end situation.

Carjackings

Carjacking is the hijacking, or stealing, of a car by force with a weapon. This occurs when a motorist is stopped at a traffic sign or light or is forced to stop. Victims also may be rammed from behind. When they stop and get out to look at the damage, their cars are forcibly taken from them. Victims of this crime may be chosen because the criminal wants the particular make and model of the car. Stolen cars may be taken to "chop shops" where they are sold for parts or used as transportation to commit other crimes.

Some Causes of Violence

Why has violence increased? The many reasons are complicated including the breakdown of the family, high school dropout rates, drug and alcohol addiction and use, and the availability of guns and other weapons. Other reasons are violence in the media, cultural support for violent behavior, racial and gender discrimination, prejudice, low self-esteem, increases in child abuse and neglect, lack of love, few job opportunities, lack of skills, poverty, idle time, and loss of hope. Not knowing healthy ways to vent and deal with emotions is also a factor.

K E E P I N G   F I T

Fair Fighting

Fighting with fists or weapons is never fair. Fighting with words can also be unfair. To keep a fight fair, remember these tips:
- Stick to one issue at a time, not personalities.
- Avoid name-calling and other put-downs.
- Do not interrupt.
- Do not bring in the names of others who support your side of the argument.
- Do not bring up the past.
- Listen to the other person's point of view. Imagine what it is like for him or her.
- Consider working through the argument at another time.
- If things get abusive or scary, call a time-out. If your safety is in jeopardy, leave.

Overcoming Misconceptions

Gangs. Gangs are no longer only a problem of inner-city school systems. The problems have filtered out into even rural areas. Have students research the problem locally.

Cliques vs. Gangs. Typically we think there is a major difference between cliques and gangs; however, their dictionary definitions are very similar. Clarify the difference in your local schools.

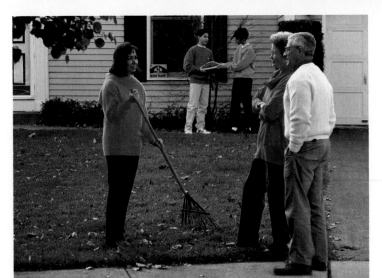
Many efforts are being made to reduce violence.

Stopping and Preventing Violence

It is not too late to do something to reduce violence. Many successful programs are being used to teach people ways to solve problems without violence. Conflict resolution and communication skills are being taught in schools. Family counseling, hotlines, shelters for battered and abused people, courses on effective parenting, and rehabilitation of the addicted, juvenile offenders, and former gang members are some of the available programs that exist to help prevent further violence. Prevention programs are now starting in schools with children as young as 6 or 7. Courses in personal safety are on the rise. Programs like Crime Watch, where neighbors look out for neighbors, are spreading. Many communities are now instituting curfews to ban youths under a certain age from city streets late at night. More "storefront" police stations in the middle of high-crime areas are opening. In addition, victims of violence are getting a chance to confront criminals through the legal system. Here victims can let criminals know the effects of their crimes.

What You Can Do

When it comes to violence, certain preventive steps are obvious, such as avoiding alcohol, drugs, guns, and gangs. A person also can learn to keep emotions from erupting into intense anger. Learning basic communication and conflict resolution skills and taking responsiblilty for one's actions are all important steps. A person also can work on building his or her self-esteem. People who feel good about themselves rarely need to lash out at others. Being a person with control doesn't have to mean using force. Reducing exposure to media that promotes and glamorizes violence, prejudice, and aggression can reduce fear and stress.

As individuals, families, schools, and a society, we must recognize that violence cannot be considered an acceptable way of dealing with anger and frustration. We must work together to replace growing fear and violence with growing safety and respect.

THE EFFECTS OF VIOLENCE   **109**

DID YOU KNOW?

- A recent study showed that 90 percent of the teens who experience violence either carry guns, have friends who carry guns, or deal drugs.
- One recent study of juveniles in jail indicated that 40 percent of them had been under the influence of illegal drugs and 33 percent under the influence of alcohol when they committed crimes.

Assess

Check for Understanding

- Assign and discuss the lesson review.

Evaluate

- Administer, grade, and discuss the *Lesson 2 Quiz*.

Reteach

- Have students prepare a detailed lesson outline using the following main headings: violence in society, violence in schools, violence on the streets, some causes of violence, and stopping and preventing violence. (You may provide the students with the outline headings or leave it to them to organize the material.)
- Ask students to complete *Reteaching Activity 14*.

Enrich

- Ask students to research and present orally the controversy over the legality of handguns. Have them present both sides of the issue and conclude with their own opinion.

Close

Sum up this lesson for students by reminding them that violence is on the rise in our society and teens are involved in much of the violence, including violence in schools. Empasize that it is important that they know what causes violence and how to prevent it.

DID YOU KNOW?

- Nearly half of all homicides in the U.S. are committed with handguns. On average, about 9,200 people are killed and 15,000 are wounded by handguns each year.

The impact of violence on television and its effect on society is being studied closely.

LESSON 2 REVIEW

Reviewing Facts and Vocabulary

1. Define *violence, random violence, homicide,* and *aggravated assault* and in a paragraph discuss their relationship to one another.
2. Explain some of the ways in which schools are trying to stop violence and its effects.

Thinking Critically

3. **Evaluation.** Why do you think the number of gangs in the United States has increased?

4. **Analysis.** Analyze this statement: "Violence breeds violence."

Applying Health Knowledge

5. Write a public service announcement about teens and guns. Include information about how to lessen your chances of becoming a shooting victim.
6. In small groups, come up with a plan to try to prevent or stop violence in and around your school. Present your ideas to the class.

110 CHAPTER 6 YOUR RELATIONSHIPS WITH OTHERS

Answers to Lesson 2 Review

1. Student paragraphs will vary.
2. Student answers may include the use of metal detectors and security guards, some with gun-sniffing dogs. In addition, some schools enforce more strict dress codes to prevent thefts and fights. Drop drills are used to help protect students and teachers from gunfire. Violence prevention programs are being presented to help students build self-esteem and teach about the dangers of alcohol, other drugs, guns, and gangs.
3. Student answers may include the need of gang members to belong somewhere and to "be somebody." Members look to the gang as a kind of extended family and as a place to get some control.
4-6. Student answers will vary.

BUILDING HEALTHY RELATIONSHIPS

T o be a good athlete, you must possess many skills. Skill development takes time and practice. In the same way, to build healthy relationships, you must practice and master a variety of skills, one at a time. Among these are skills in communicating and standing up to peer pressure.

Communication

Communication is a process through which we send messages to and receive messages from one another. With words, gestures, facial expressions, and behaviors, we communicate what we feel, what we need, and what we know. If you want a relationship to be healthy, you must identify and express your expectations—the rules or guidelines by which you are operating. By doing this, you open doors to communication. Then the other person in a relationship can respond or react and share his or her expectations. This type of give-and-take discussion is not easy. It takes practice and lots of energy, but it can be very helpful in preventing misunderstandings. When there is conflict in the relationship, you have already laid the groundwork for constructive communication.

Speaking Skills

When you are speaking, it is important to say what you mean. Do not assume that anyone else can read your mind or know your needs or expectations. It is your responsibility to make them clear. That is the first step to healthy communication.

The inflections, or changes in pitch or loudness, of your voice can also play a large role in how you communicate. Kind words delivered with a sarcastic tone, for example, may not be processed kindly. Talking too loudly can make you seem too bossy or arrogant, even if underneath it all you are actually shy. Saying no too softly may make it seem as if you do not mean what you are saying. So it is not just what you say that is important in communicating, it is also how you say it.

Listening Skills

Listening is an important skill associated with communication. Studies indicate that we may spend 80 percent of our waking hours communicating, with much of that time spent listening. Because listening takes up so much of our time, you would think that most people would be skilled at it—but the opposite is true. The average listener may correctly understand, properly evaluate, and retain only about 30 percent of what was said in a 10-minute presentation. Within 48 hours, memory of what was said dropped to an even lower percentage.

People like a good listener. Have you ever noticed that good listeners are often well-liked people? Everyone wants to feel that he or she is being heard and is not going to be judged, corrected, or interrupted.

BUILDING HEALTHY RELATIONSHIPS **111**

LESSON 3 FOCUS

TERMS TO USE
- Communication
- Refusal skills
- Passive
- Aggressive
- Assertive

CONCEPTS TO LEARN
- There are many ways to communicate with others.
- Refusal skills help you say no when faced with negative peer pressure.

ATTITUDES AND BEHAVIORS TO EVALUATE
- Self-Inventory, page 114.
- Building Decision-Making Skills, page 115.

Focus

Lesson Objectives
After studying this lesson, students should be able to:
- state several good listening rules
- give examples of nonverbal communication
- name several refusal-skill techniques

Bellringer
Write the following on the chalkboard for students to work on while attendance is being taken: *List ten things you communicated today and the communication methods you used.*

Introducing the Lesson
Ask several students to share their responses to the Bellringer. It is not unlikely that their lists contain only verbal communication. Pick out an example of verbal communication that probably had a great deal of inflection and body language when it was said, such as, "Mary, would you hurry up!" Ask a student to role-play the line, including actions, expressions, and inflections. Have another student just read the line. Compare and contrast reading the line and role-playing it. Ask the class to state the differences in the two, i.e., inflections, volume, words emphasized, facial expression, gestures, and posture.

Building Vocabulary
- Write each vocabulary word on a slip of paper. Have students draw slips from a box and then role-play situations to demonstrate the terms.
- Ask students to complete *Workbook Vocabulary Activity 15.*

Resources for Lesson 3

- **Transparencies** 12, 14
- **Guided Reading** Act 15
- **Decision-Making** Act 6
- **Reteaching** Act 15
- **Enrichment** Act 6
- **Workbook**
- **Health Labs** Act 6
- **Lesson 3 Quiz**
- **Chapter 6 Test**

ABC News InterActive Videodiscs
Drugs and Substance Abuse, Side 2
Ch 11 Ways to Say NO

Teenage Sexuality, Side 2
Ch 11 Saying "No"

Teach

Guided Practice

L1 **USING LIFE MANAGEMENT SKILLS TRANSPARENCIES 12 AND 14.** Refer to the Teaching Transparencies Binder.

L1 **DISCUSSION.** Discuss each of the "Good Listening Rules." Ask for volunteers to demonstrate each rule. If necessary, define phrases like *eye contact* and *closed responses*.

L2 **COOPERATIVE LEARNING.** Divide the class into groups of three—a speaker, an active listener, and an observer. Assign topics for the groups to talk about. Use time limits. Have the observer watch to see if good listening rules are being observed. After the speaker has spoken and the listener has paraphrased what has been said, have the observer tell them what he or she observed that was done well and where improvements could be made.

L2 **COOPERATIVE LEARNING.** Discuss judgmental or closed responses. Ask students to pair off and discuss situations that have happened in their own family relationships where closed responses were used. Ask them to role-play the situations using open responses that encourage communication and problem solving. Ask them to share their feelings about the two kinds of responses.

Independent Practice

L3 **RESEARCH.** Have students research body language and compile the information in a written or oral report to present to the class.

L2 **WRITING.** Have students write a paragraph explaining a situation in which being able to say no effectively is necessary to withstand negative peer pressure. Ask them to explain how it could be handled in a passive manner, an aggressive manner, and an assertive manner. Which would be the most effective and why?

HELP WANTED

Coach

A winner is determined by more than just the winning percentage. Obviously, we want people who believe you play to win, but we also want those who can keep winning and losing in perspective. If you can relate to a variety of young people, provide an excellent example of integrity, and can motivate, teach, and organize, you will be a success. We will consider those outside of education, but prefer those certified in areas in which we have openings.

For more information contact:
National Education Association
1201 16th Street NW
Washington, DC 20036

GOOD LISTENING RULES

- Give your full attention to the person speaking.
- Eliminate distractions, such as radio or TV.
- Make direct eye contact.
- Do not interrupt. Wait your turn.
- Try to get the general idea of what someone is saying rather than trying to remember every fact the speaker mentions.
- Listen to feelings and gestures as well as to words.
- Do not shift the attention from the other person's problem to your own.
- Indicate your interest. Lean toward the speaker; nod at or encourage the other person by quietly saying "Uh-huh" or "I understand" or "I see."
- Do not decide too early that the subject matter is too hard, too easy, or too upsetting. Give the speaker a chance.
- Ask questions only when it seems necessary.
- Avoid making judgmental or closed responses that might stop or hinder the conversation, such as, "That was dumb!"
- Do not spend so much time concentrating on what you will say next that you miss what the other person is saying.
- Remember what the speaker has said. To be sure you heard it correctly, repeat the idea back so that the person can correct you if necessary.
- When it is your turn to speak, recap the highlights of what the other person has said, using a phrase like, "As I hear it, you were saying. . . ."

Body Language Skills

Communicating without words is nonverbal communication. Expressions on your face and movements of your hands and body are examples. If your words and your face or body seem to be saying two different things, you may be misunderstood. People may get your nonverbal messages rather than your verbal ones. Consider these cues:

- People who are lying often nod their heads at the end of a lie, rub their bodies, rub their hands together, or stop moving altogether.
- Moving the hand to the nose or lips can be a way of showing shame.
- Putting the hands behind the head while talking may show an attitude of superiority.
- Standing with head or shoulders down may be communicating that the person is passive and will not stick up for him- or herself.
- Placing hands into pockets may indicate that the person is afraid.

KEEPING FIT

How to Say NO

Add these tips to your storehouse of refusal skills:

- Buy time. Say you'll get back to the person.
- State exactly how you feel. Be direct and honest.

- Don't apologize for your decisions or values.
- Use direct eye contact to show that you mean what you say.
- Use a firm and friendly tone of voice.
- Use the other person's name.

- Offer an alternative, healthier, more acceptable-to-you option.
- Avoid compromise if you feel strongly about something. Compromise can be a slow way of saying *yes* when you don't mean to.

112 CHAPTER 6 YOUR RELATIONSHIPS WITH OTHERS

Across the Curriculum

Drama. Ask the drama teacher for a pantomime suitable for beginners. Assign a group of volunteers the task of performing the pantomime for the class to view. Ask the performers their feelings while doing it. Ask the viewers what enabled them to follow what was being said.

Speech. Invite a professional actor/actress to speak about the techniques he or she uses to communicate on stage.

Refusal Skills

Refusal skills are those techniques and strategies that you can learn to help you say no effectively when faced with something that you do not want to do or is against your values.

Throughout your life people will make many requests of you. Some of these will call for you to respond with a yes, others with a firm and unapologetic no. How you respond can directly affect your mental, social, or physical health—or even your life.

Some styles of refusing are more effective than others. Those that are most effective generally show that you have respect both for yourself and for the other person. Find the way that is best for you to say no.

The Passive Way. Being **passive** means giving up, giving in, or backing down without standing up for your own rights and needs. People who are passive "go with the flow" and may find themselves in situations they do not want to be in, not knowing how to get out. They may think they are making friends by going along with peer pressure but, in fact, they may be viewed by their peers as pushovers, not worthy of much respect.

The Aggressive Way. Being **aggressive** means being overly forceful, pushy, hostile, or otherwise attacking in approach. The aggressive approach to saying no might involve punching, yelling, shouting insults, or displaying other kinds of physical or verbal force. The aggressive way violates the rights of others. Though aggressive people may think they will gain their own way and perhaps be seen as powerful and popular, their approach usually backfires. In the long run, people either stay away from aggressors or jump in and fight back. Either way can leave aggressive people hurting.

The Assertive Way. Being **assertive** means standing up for your own rights, in firm but positive ways. You state your position, acknowledge the rights of the other individual, then stand your ground. You do not bully or back away. You directly and honestly state your case and show that you mean what you say. Assertive people often become role models for other teens. Teens respect people who have the personal power to be true to who they really are.

CONFLICT RESOLUTION

A recent study found that most of our arguments are with relatives, and the negative results of fighting often exceed the benefits of pleasant encounters. Females, especially, tend to be unfavorably affected by family feuding, sometimes becoming depressed after quarrels. Researchers advise following a middle course when a relative makes you "see red"— don't hide your feelings, but if you do argue, try to resolve the conflict quickly and put it behind you.

Consider the most recent argument you had with a relative.
How would things have gone differently if you had followed this advice for conflict resolution?

LESSON 3 REVIEW

Reviewing Facts and Vocabulary

1. Define *verbal* and *nonverbal communication.*
2. List five skills needed for good listening.

Thinking Critically

3. **Evaluation.** Do you think there are situations that call for passive or aggressive behavior, instead of assertive behavior? Explain.

4. **Synthesis.** Write the script for a skit in which a person role-plays passive, aggressive, and assertive ways of saying no.

Applying Health Knowledge

5. Think of an issue, a project, or a person you care a lot about. How might you communicate your caring without using words?

BUILDING HEALTHY RELATIONSHIPS **113**

L1 **PARENTAL INVOLVEMENT.** To enhance good listening skills at home, have students ask their parents about the possibility of turning the TV off during mealtime so that family communication can take place in a setting with fewer distractions.

L1 **USING THE LESSON RESOURCES.** For additional student activities, refer to the lesson resources on page 111.

Assess

Check for Understanding

- Assign and discuss the lesson review.
- Assign and discuss the chapter review.

Evaluate

- Administer, grade, and discuss the *Lesson 3 Quiz.*
- Administer, grade, and discuss the *Chapter 6 Test.*
- Refer to the Performance Assessment Strategy for this chapter. See pages T 23 to T 25.

Reteach

- Divide the class into small groups. Hand each group a card with a situation written on it. Ask students to role-play the situations using passive, aggressive, and assertive refusals. Have the audience evaluate the effectiveness of each.
- Ask students to complete *Reteaching Activity 15.*

Enrich

- Ask students to watch a favorite family sitcom on TV. Discuss the types of refusal skills that were portrayed. Have students evaluate the effectiveness of each type.
- Ask students to complete *Enrichment Activity 6.*

Close

Ask students to state the most important concepts learned in the lesson.

Using the Self-Inventory

Reinforcing Vocabulary

■ **Eye contact.** A form of nonverbal communication; looking directly into the eyes of another individual while listening or talking.

Teaching Strategies

L1 EXPLANATION. Frequently students are unaware that there are several different types of listening. Students may confuse attentive listening with selective listening. Selective listening is used to hear only enough of what is spoken to allow the listener to argue or to support a previously held point of view. Attentive listening allows students to hear not only what is spoken, but the feelings that are also being communicated.

L1 EXPLANATION. Questions 6 and 8 could be misinterpreted by parents and students. Students who are diagnosed with attention deficit disorders find attentive listening extremely difficult. This condition cannot be voluntarily controlled by the individual. Adaptations in teaching methods allow these students to be successful in the classroom.

L1 DISCUSSION. Ask students to remember a time when they may have felt that someone was not listening to them. An example may include a parent, teacher, or a friend. Have students recall why they believed that the other person was not listening. Have students determine how body language may have indicated to them that listening was not taking place.

L1 CLASS ACTIVITY. Have students participate in a telephone game. See how communication changes from one person to the next.

L1 CLASS ACTIVITY. Have students pair off with classmates and practice attentive listening skills.

Self-Inventory

Are You a Good Listener?

HOW DO YOU RATE?

Number a sheet of paper from 1 through 10. Read each item below and indicate whether each statement describes you *most of the time, some of the time,* or *never.* Total the number of each type of response. Then proceed to the next section.

1. When listening, I assume I know what the other person is going to say.
2. I interrupt others when they are talking.
3. I find myself thinking about what I am going to say while the other person is talking.
4. I avoid eye contact when listening to the other person.
5. I do several things while I listen, such as doodle, watch TV, or play music.
6. I find that my mind is wandering while someone else is talking.
7. I make judgments on what is being said.
8. I have to ask for things to be repeated.
9. I carry on several conversations at one time.
10. I avoid asking questions if I am not sure I understand what was said.

HOW DID YOU SCORE?

Give yourself 4 points for every *most of the time* answer, 2 points for each *some of the time* answer, and 0 points for each *never* answer. Find your total and read to see how you scored. Then proceed to the next section.

0 to 4
Excellent. You have very good listening skills.

6 to 10
Good. You have some good listening skills but could develop your skills more.

12 or more
Needs Improvement. You have poor listening skills and need to improve them. Doing so may help improve your relationships.

WHAT ARE YOUR GOALS?

If you scored 11 or more, identify an area in which your score is low, and use the goal-setting process to begin making a change. If your listening skills are weak in several areas, set several specific goals for improving them, but do so one at a time.

1. The listening skill I most need to change or improve to better my communication is ____.
2. If this behavior were completely changed, the reaction I would probably find in the people trying to communicate with me would be ____.
3. The steps involved in making this change are ____.
4. My timetable for improving this listening skill is ____.
5. People I can ask for support, assistance, and gentle reminders in trying to develop this skill are ____.
6. The benefits I will receive are ____.
7. The benefits to my relationships will be ____.
8. My reward after identifying, working on, and improving each listening skill on which I need to concentrate will be ____.

Meeting Students' Needs

For students who score *Excellent.* Suggest that students consider working as a day camp counselor, child-care provider, or with physically and/or mentally challenged students where listening skills are a special asset.

For students who score *Good.* Suggest that students spend time observing individuals communicating and practice attentive listening skills.

For students who *Need Improvement.* Examine patterns of communication between family members. Analyze the effectiveness of the communication and set a goal of changing one specific behavior block to communication.

Building Decision-Making Skills

Drew works hard at school, is in a few school clubs, and works for neighbors some Saturdays. He knows the neighborhood he lives in is not considered the best, but it is home to him.

On Drew's way to and from school, he walks by an abandoned building. Some kids from school have kind of claimed this building as theirs. They seem to hang out there a lot, especially before and after school. This group considers itself a gang. They dress alike and have written graffiti on the building. On some occa-

sions, Drew has seen adults he didn't know talking to the kids there. Because of this, people at school think the gang does drugs.

Recently Drew's friend, Ron, has begun hanging out at the abandoned building. Ron has even showed Drew a small gun he said he was carrying for a gang member. Ron said he really likes being a part of the gang and wants Drew to be a part too. Ron told Drew that if he joined, he would always have protection in case he ever needed it. What should Drew do about Ron's invitation to join the gang?

A. Tell Ron he doesn't want to join the gang. Tell him he is not into that kind of thing.

B. Try going to the building a few times and see if it's fun. He will still have time to do his homework in the evening.

C. Ask Ron how he sees his friendship with the gang affecting his goals for the future.

WHAT DO YOU THINK?

1. **Choices.** What other choices does Drew have?

2. **Consequences.** What are the effects of each choice?

3. **Consequences.** How might Drew's self-esteem be affected by each choice?

4. **Consequences.** What might Drew's parents say about each choice?

5. **Consequences.** In what way might other people be affected by Drew's decision?

6. **Consequences.** What effect could going to the building have on Drew's total health?

7. **Decision.** What do you think Drew should do? Explain your answer.

8. **Evaluation.** Have you ever been asked to be a part of a gang or clique? For what reason(s) did or didn't you join? How did your decision affect your self-esteem?

Melanie is a very good student, and she has just completed a tough science assignment. Rob, her next-door neighbor and good friend, went away with his family

over the weekend to visit his uncle. Late Sunday night, Rob knocks on Melanie's door and asks if he can copy her answers to the science assignment.

WHAT DO YOU THINK?

9. **Choices.** Can you think of five or more choices that Melanie has?

10. **Choices.** Which of the above choices are positive and appropriate ones?

11. **Choices.** Which of the choices are inappropriate? Explain your answers.

12. **Consequences.** What are the advantages of each choice?

13. **Consequences.** What are the disadvantages of each choice?

14. **Consequences.** What risks are involved in this decision?

15. **Decision.** What do you think Melanie should do?

16. **Evaluation.** Have you ever faced a similar situation? If so, how did you handle it? How would you handle a situation like this now? Would it depend on the kind of relationship you had with the other person? Explain.

Discussing the Answers

Situation 1. Drew has worked hard in school and is involved in healthy activities at school and in his neighborhood. Drew realizes that by joining a gang, his efforts to reach his goals probably would be hindered. He also realizes that the activity at the abandoned building is not the best situation for his neighborhood.

Situation 2. It is possible that the best resolve would have Melanie politely refusing to assist Rob in cheating and graciously excusing herself. Friendships that are worth keeping do not involve dishonesty or asking a person to do something with which he or she is uncomfortable.

Answers to Chapter 6 Review

Using Health Terms

1. Relationship
2. Peer pressure
3. Manipulation
4. Bribery
5. Random violence
6. Battery
7. Communication
8. Refusal skills

Building Academic Skills

9. Answers will vary but should reflect the idea that people play different roles throughout their lives.
10. 7.68 hours a day.

Recalling the Facts

11. It can be a way to grow and to understand and feel comfortable with the opposite sex without the pressures of dating.
12. Answers may include but are not limited to: advantages—it is convenient and ensures one of having a date; disadvantages—it may prevent one from developing other relationships and cause pain if the relationship breaks up.
13. Answers may include but are not limited to: it might inspire one to participate in worthwhile community activities, to exercise, to say no to drugs.
14. Answers may include but are not limited to: it might cause one to take dangerous risks, to use drugs, to have sex, to cheat.
15. It shows no respect for the well-being of the person being manipulated.
16. Answers will vary. Accept any five of the following: mocking or teasing, bargaining, bribery, guilt trips, making threats, blackmail, flattery.
17. It is caused by ignorance and the desire of one person to feel superior to another person or group. Some effects are mental, social, and physical damage to the targeted person or group.
18. To feel valued, respected, and/or secure.

Using Health Terms

On a separate sheet of paper, write the term that best matches each definition given below.

LESSON 1

1. A bond or connection between people.
2. The control and influence people your own age may have over you.
3. An indirect and often dishonest means of trying to control another's attitudes or behavior.
4. A method of manipulation in which a person promises favors to another person in order to influence his or her behavior.

LESSON 2

5. Violence committed for no particular reason against anyone who happens to be around.
6. The use of physical force to control someone through the use of power.

LESSON 3

7. A process by which people receive and send messages.
8. Techniques that help a person say no when faced with negative peer pressure.

Building Academic Skills

LESSON 1

9. **Writing.** The following lines appear in Shakespeare's play *As You Like It:*
   All the world's a stage,
   And all the men and women merely players;
   They have their exits and their entrances;
   And one man in his time plays many parts.
   Write a paragraph giving your own interpretation of this quote.

LESSON 3

10. **Math.** Pilar gets 8 hours of sleep each night. If she spends 80 percent of her waking hours communicating and 60 percent of that time listening, how many hours a day does Pilar spend listening?

Recalling the Facts

LESSON 1

11. What are some advantages of platonic relationships with members of the opposite sex?
12. What are some advantages and disadvantages of dating one person exclusively?
13. Give two examples of possible results of positive peer pressure.
14. Give two examples of possible results of negative peer pressure.
15. Why is manipulation an unhealthy way for people to fulfill their needs?
16. List five methods of manipulation.
17. What is the cause of prejudice? What may often be its effect?

LESSON 2

18. Why do some teens join gangs?
19. What are some disadvantages of belonging to a gang?
20. Explain what can happen to stolen cars after a carjacking.
21. List several reasons violence has increased in our society.

LESSON 3

22. What can be an unwanted effect of speaking too loudly? Too softly?
23. How can you show your interest in what another person is saying?
24. What is a good way to verify that you have correctly understood a speaker?
25. What is body language?
26. List three examples of body language that might indicate that a person is lying.
27. Why is it important to learn refusal skills?

Thinking Critically

LESSON 1

28. **Analysis.** What is the difference between platonic and dating relationships?

LESSON 2

29. **Evaluation.** If you were the mayor of your town or city, what steps would you propose

19. Possible rejection by the group, becoming involved in situations which may threaten one's mental or physical health.
20. Stolen cars may be taken to "chop shops" where they are sold for parts or used as transportation to commit other crimes.
21. See page 108.
22. Speaking too loudly may make one seem too bossy or arrogant. Speaking too softly may make it seem like one does not mean what he or she is saying.
23. Lean toward the speaker; nod; use expressions such as "I see" or "I understand."

to stop violence in the community? Include ways you would carry out your plans.

30. **Evaluation.** Write a report for or against gun control. Support your position with current information.

LESSON 3

31. **Analysis.** Compare and contrast *passive*, *aggressive*, and *assertive* behavior.

32. **Synthesis.** Kim's father is criticizing her last performance on her grade card, which contained three *C*s and a *D*. Kim's father is threatening to cut off her allowance and ground her for two weeks. Kim put her head and shoulders down and shoved her hands into the pockets of her jeans. What emotions do you think Kim is probably feeling based on her body language?

33. **Analysis.** Classify each behavior as *passive*, *aggressive*, or *assertive*.
   - Every morning Elizabeth asks Sarah if she can copy her geometry homework. Sarah feels this is wrong, but she always gives Elizabeth her homework to copy.
   - Nick wants to take Anita to a party where beer will be served. Anita explains to Nick that although she would like to go out with him, she does not want be around people who may be drinking.
   - Anne is unkind to her sister Patti. She often yells at Patti when she forgets to clean up the room they share. Anne also loudly insults and embarrasses Patti at school. Anne does not have many friends.

Making the Connection

LESSON 2

34. **Language Arts.** Use the library to research the effect of television violence on child development. Is there a connection between what children watch on television and how they interact with others? After you have gathered information, write an editorial to your local newspaper to express your viewpoint.

Applying Health Knowledge

LESSON 1

35. Think about the relationship you have with your closest friend. What does each of you contribute to this relationship?

36. What types of prejudice, stereotyping, and discrimination are problems in your school? Why do you think the problems exist? What could students do to reduce the problems? What might teachers and administrators do to help the situation?

37. Is it possible to eliminate prejudice? Explain your answer.

LESSON 3

38. Review the rules for good listening. Divide a sheet of paper into two columns. Label one column "I usually do this"; label the other column "I need to work on this." Then write each rule in the column that applies to your listening skills. Concentrate on improving one skill every day.

Beyond the Classroom

LESSON 1

39. **Community Involvement.** Explore what opportunities there are in your community for people who live alone to make new friends.

LESSON 2

40. **Parental Involvement.** Ask your parents about violence that occurred when they were in high school. What did they see as the causes of this violence? What solutions, if any, were used?

LESSON 3

41. **Parental Involvement.** Ask your parents to give their opinion of what they think good communication skills are. Which skills do they feel they use in the course of their day?

24. Repeat the idea in your own words, giving the speaker a chance to correct you if necessary.

25. Messages conveyed by one's face, hands, and body movements.

26. Answers will vary. Possible answers: They may nod their heads at the end of the lie, rub their bodies, rub their hands together, or stop moving altogether.

27. To enable one to say no effectively when faced with something that one does not want to do or that goes against one's values.

Thinking Critically

28. Platonic relationships are those in which affection does not have romantic or sexual undertones. Dating relationships usually involve romantic or sexual feelings.

29. Answers will vary.

30. Answers will vary.

31. Answers will vary. Possible answer: All are ways of responding to situations. Passive and aggressive are unhealthy ways to respond. Assertive is a positive, healthy way to respond.

32. Shame.

33. Passive. Assertive. Aggressive.

Making the Connection

34. Answers will vary, depending on the research students choose to use.

Applying Health Knowledge

35. Answers will vary.

36. Answers will vary.

37. Answers will vary.

38. Answers will vary.

Beyond the Classroom

39. Answers will vary.

40. Answers will vary.

41. Answers will vary.

Lesson Summaries

LESSON 1. Marriage is a long-term, ongoing commitment. Legally, it is the joining of a male and a female by custom or law. In this lesson, marriage trends are presented, and factors affecting marital adjustment are discussed. Topics such as marriage and maturity, teen marriages, conflicts in marriage, divorce, and remarriage are also addressed.

LESSON 2. Parenting can be a wonderful experience. It can be rewarding to provide a nurturing environment for a child and watch that child grow and develop within it. But it is a huge, ongoing responsibility. This lesson presents the responsibilities of parenthood, trends in parenting, and a discussion of planned and unplanned pregnancies and adoption. Responsibilities of raising children are emphasized.

Introducing the Chapter

Give each student a chance to answer the following questions. Emphasize that there are no right or wrong answers. What do you look for in deciding whom to go out with? Whose responsibility is it to decide what to do on a date? What is the most important part of a relationship? How can someone show you that he or she loves you? In a marriage relationship, what is the role of the female? What is the role of the male? What do you consider the "right age" for marriage? What would you think is the hardest part of raising a child? What is the most difficult part of a lasting relationship? What is one thing you learned from the answers you heard?

Performance Assessment ✓

Refer to pages T 23 to T 25 for a Performance Assessment strategy for this chapter. See the *Performance Assessment Activities* booklet for additional suggestions.

CHAPTER 7
MARRIAGE AND PARENTHOOD

LESSON 1
Marriage

LESSON 2
Parenthood

118 CHAPTER 7 MARRIAGE AND PARENTHOOD

Key to Ability Levels

Teaching strategies have been coded for varying learning styles and abilities.

L1 Level 1 activities are basic activities and should be within the ability range of all students.

L2 Level 2 activities are average activities and should be within the ability range of average to above-average students.

L3 Level 3 activities are challenging activities designed for the ability range of above-average students.

LD LD activities should be within the ability range of learning-disabled students.

LEP LEP activities should be within the ability range of Limited English Proficiency students.

MARRIAGE

Getting married is deciding to spend the rest of your life with someone else. Marriage is a long-term, ongoing commitment. It is a very serious decision.

Marriage in the Past and Marriage Today

In ancient times a woman was often considered property belonging to her father. A prospective husband had to get permission from the father of his bride-to-be before a marriage could take place. Often there was an exchange of gifts or property in the marriage transaction. The union, which did not take into account the notion of romantic love, was both a business and a social contract. It represented the economic merging of two families.

Today in the United States few marriages are arranged. People choose their own mates. People meet and decide to marry for many reasons, including mutual attraction and affection. Romantic love is often the driving force behind a couple's decision to marry, but it is seldom the reason two people remain married.

Marriage and the Law

In the legal sense, marriage is the joining of a man and a woman according to custom or law. It is a legal agreement between two people to live together and share their lives.

Most states in the United States require a marriage license; some require that both parties have a blood test and undergo medical examinations. Most states also require a waiting period of 3 to 5 days during which either party can back out. Almost all states allow people to marry at age 18 without parental consent. More than half the states allow couples to marry with parental permission at 16.

Marriage Trends

Each year about 2.5 million couples are married in the United States. About 95 percent of all Americans marry by the age of 40. Yet there are many new trends in marrying practices today.

Marrying Later

According to the 1990 United States Census, Americans are marrying later now than at any other time during the past 100 years. In 1950 men married at an average age of 23; women, at 20. The average age for first marriages now, however, is 26 for men and 24 for women. Several social factors help explain this trend. High divorce rates may make

MARRIAGE **119**

LESSON 1 FOCUS

TERMS TO USE
- Marital adjustment
- Divorce

CONCEPTS TO LEARN
- There are many reasons people get married.
- Marriage is an arrangement between two people to face the realities of life as a couple.
- Teen marriages face many risks.

ATTITUDES AND BEHAVIORS TO EVALUATE
- Self-Inventory, page 132.
- Building Decision-Making Skills, page 133.

Focus

Lesson Objectives
After studying this lesson, students should be able to:
- describe changes in marriage patterns through time
- identify current marriage trends
- summarize factors that promote a successful marriage

Bellringer
Write the following on the chalkboard for students to work on while attendance is being taken: *Complete the following sentence with as many choices as apply:* The perfect spouse for me would be (have). . . . *Do you know anyone that has all the characteristics you want in a spouse? Which of your traits make you a good potential marriage partner?*

Introducing the Lesson
Refer to the Bellringer. Ask volunteers to share their responses. How many responses focus on superficial qualities, such as physical appearance or material possessions? Follow up on any responses that suggest a good marriage partner is one who shares many things with you, ranging from values and interests to affection and confidences.

Tell students that in this lesson they will learn about marriage and how it has changed through time. They will also learn the right reasons to marry, factors that promote a successful marriage, and how to prevent divorce.

DID YOU KNOW?

- The phrase *tying the knot*, which means getting married, began with an actual tying of knots during marriage ceremonies in Denmark. Couples actually joined and tied two ribbons or lengths of cord to symbolize their becoming one.
- In the U. S., rice has traditionally been thrown at the bride and groom. These days, however, many people throw bird seed instead, since the hard rice proved harmful to birds that often ingested it.

Resources for Lesson 1

- **Guided Reading** Activity 16
- **Workbook** Vocabulary Activity 16
- **Reteaching** Activity 16
- **Lesson 1 Quiz**
- **Performance Assessment** Activity 7
- **Education in Sexuality**

Glencoe Health VHS Videos
Responsible Sexuality

■ Ask students to find definitions for and describe in their own words the following different types of marriage: monogamy, bigamy, polygamy, polygyny, and polyandry. What do the diffferent word parts mean— that is, what do *mono-*, *bi-*, *poly-*, *-gamy*, *-gyny*, and *-andry* refer to?

■ Ask students to complete *Workbook Vocabulary Activity 16.*

Teach

Guided Practice

L1 **DISCUSSION.** What are the health implications of a happy marriage?

L1 **DISCUSSION.** How does marriage in the U.S. today differ from marriage in the past?

L1 **DISCUSSION.** What are the legal requirements for a couple to get married in the United States? (License, medical tests, age limits.) In general terms, how do these vary from state to state? Discuss the purpose behind each requirement.

L3 **CLASS ACTIVITY.** Ask students to share their feelings on how the AIDS epidemic will affect marriage and divorce for their generation. Overall, do they see it as a positive or negative influence?

L1 **EXPLANATION.** Explain why marriages today occur later, on average, than they did 40 years ago.

L2 **DISCUSSION.** Why are males typically at least a year or two older than the females they marry? How are men who marry much younger women perceived? How are women who marry much younger men perceived? Why is there this sex bias? Does it suggest that males and females marry for different reasons?

L2 **DISCUSSION.** What role do economic factors play in the age at which men and women marry today as opposed to several decades ago?

L1 **SPEAKER.** Invite a marriage counselor to class to talk about what makes marriages work and what leads to divorce.

some people marriage-shy. Young people with divorced parents may be wary about walking down the aisle.

These are also difficult economic times. Jobs are sometimes difficult to secure, and the cost of housing and raising families is high. Young people who want to finish their education or establish careers are also delaying marriage until they achieve their personal goals.

Two-Career Marriages

In 1940 only 15 percent of all married women worked outside the home. Today, about half of all married women in the United States have full-time or part-time jobs outside the home. Two-income households, particularly those without children, may have more money and more social contacts. For some couples, however, two partners working may add fatigue, stress, and competition to the marriage.

Many people today choose to delay marriage until they have completed their education and established careers.

HEALTH UPDATE

LOOKING AT THE ISSUES

Should People Have Prenuptial Agreements?

A prenuptial agreement is a contract signed by both partners before they marry. Usually, prenuptial agreements cover issues involving property—such as houses, inheritances, earnings, and real estate—and how they will be divided should the couple divorce.

Analyzing Different Viewpoints

ONE VIEW. People who favor prenuptial agreements state that working out the details beforehand can reduce conflicts and legal costs should the couple divorce. Such an agreement can also make things easier for a surviving spouse should one spouse die. The experts maintain that prenuptial agreements also benefit present and future children, since contracts can spell out details about who gets custody and who provides financial support. Some agreements even specify both parties' intentions about whether or not to have or adopt children.

A SECOND VIEW. People who oppose prenuptial agreements believe that a relationship built on trust does not need a legal document to solidify promises. They wonder how couples can sign such an agreement about potential divorce and then promise to love one another "until death do us part." They stress that marriage is not a business contract. Those who are against prenuptial agreements also say that people should not enter a marriage thinking they may divorce. Such negative thinking, they say, and having to negotiate things like division of property may actually cause unnecessary damage to a relationship.

Exploring Your Views

1. What do you think of prenuptial agreements? What do you see as the benefits and the drawbacks of such contracts?
2. If you marry, do you think you will have a prenuptial agreement? Why or why not?

Additional Information

Marriage. Marriage protects people from emotional isolation, which several studies have found to be detrimental to health.

In one study of 7,000 subjects, for example, those who were single, divorced, or widowed and who had few relatives or friends had death rates 2 to 5 times greater than those who were socially connected. In another study of 1,000 subjects, those identified as lonely and outwardly unemotional were 16 times as likely to die from cancer as those who were volatile and emotional. What explains these findings? People who are lonely have been found to have a low level of killer-cell activity, an important immune function in protection from illness.

Staying Single: The Other Option

Staying single has also become more popular. In 1990 there were fewer married couples in the United States in relation to the rest of the population than in previous years. Married couples, with or without children, presently make up 55 percent of the country's 92 million households. That is down from about 60 percent in 1980.

Reasons for Getting Married

Most people say they are marrying because they are "in love," and this may be true. Often, however, there are other motives hidden deep inside. People may decide to marry because they are lonely or they want to escape a bad situation at home. They also may marry because a pregnancy is involved or because they want financial security. Without close self-examination, couples may not even be aware of the motives driving them. If there are serious doubts or questions about reasons for marrying or about the intended spouse, the best time to face them and reconsider is before the marriage.

Factors Affecting Marital Adjustment

Sociologists have conducted extensive research to develop measures of **marital adjustment**—how well people adjust and adapt to marriage and to each other. Researchers have concluded that a well-adjusted marriage is one in which the husband and wife

- agree on critical issues in their relationship,
- share common interests and activities,
- demonstrate affection and shared confidences,
- have few complaints about the marriage,
- do not have feelings of loneliness or irritability.

Researchers have also identified some factors related to social background that were associated with successful marital adjustment. Some of the more significant factors they found included the following:

- similarity in family backgrounds
- domestic happiness of parents
- lack of conflict with parents
- educational achievement of both partners
- friends of both sexes
- participation in organizations
- close association prior to marriage
- security and stability of occupation

The more positive factors involved, the better the marital adjustment. In addition, the ability to be intimate, feel trust, give mutual respect, and be good friends have all been cited as important factors in healthy marriages. In a healthy marriage each partner needs to learn to accept the other person. That means not trying to change the person, not constantly judging him or her, and supporting the person in his or her pursuits. It means accepting that no relationship will ever be perfect.

This couple illustrates long-lasting marital happiness.

MARRIAGE **121**

Additional Information

Traditions in Marriage. Did you ever wonder why people follow certain traditions during wedding ceremonies? Many of these traditions began long ago.

The custom of exchanging rings, for example, dates back to the ancient Romans. The roundness of the rings represents eternity, and the presentation symbolizes that the two are united forever. Wearing the wedding rings on the ring finger of the left hand is done because people once believed that a vein or nerve ran directly from this finger to the heart. Throwing rice at the couple began as a wish for children and good fortune, because rice was once a symbol of fertility, happiness, and long life. The tossing of the bridal bouquet to the unmarried female guests probably began in France in the 1300s. According to the custom, the woman to catch the bouquet will be the next to marry.

L2 **CLASS ACTIVITY.** Have students work in small groups to compile a list of factors they think are conducive to a successful marriage. They should compare their lists with the maturity traits listed in the text. Is there any overlap in the lists? What factors other than maturity do the students think are important to a successful marriage? Why do they think these other factors are important?

L1 **DISCUSSION.** What are some of the reasons that people choose to remain single?

L3 **COOPERATIVE LEARNING.** Divide the class into four groups and assign to each group one of the descriptions of maturity given on page 122. Ask each group to present to the class a skit depicting its description of maturity. Follow up each skit with a discussion of what was portrayed.

L2 **DISCUSSION.** Refer to the developmental tasks of adolescence in Chapter 9. Have students discuss how marriage would affect a teenager successfully completing these tasks.

L1 **DISCUSSION.** What are the consequences of marriage and pregnancy on personal goals for teens?

L2 **DISCUSSION.** Write each of the following statements on the chalkboard and ask students to discuss their validity: Opposite personalities attract each other; He or she will change after we're married; People have to work at marriage to make it work; Marriage is more than love and sex; Love means never having to say you're sorry.

L1 **CLASS ACTIVITY.** Have students rank the list of factors that affect marital adjustment from most to least important. Compare rankings and discuss the differences in opinion. Have students give reasons for the order in which they placed the factors.

Independent Practice

L1 **RESEARCH.** Ask students to research the variations in types of marriages and marriage ceremonies in the United States and in other cultures.

L1 **RESEARCH.** Select students to research the number of couples who get married today because of pregnancy. What are the ages? What is the success rate for these marriages? How many out-of-wedlock pregnancies do not end in marriage?

Early marriage and parenthood presents many problems for teens.

Marriage and Maturity

Unfortunately, many young couples make a decision to get married based on only the romantic phase of their relationship. To be successful, however, a marriage requires emotional and social maturity. Maturity can be difficult to define, but it can be described in these ways:

- A mature person has the ability and skill to establish and maintain relationships.
- A mature person has the ability to give as well as receive.
- A mature person can perceive and process others' feelings.
- A mature person can compromise and accept not always getting his or her own way.
- A mature person can be flexible.
- A mature person accepts responsibility for his or her feelings and actions and does not blame them on someone else.
- A mature person is personally stable.
- A mature person has established values by which he or she lives. He or she has goals and plans for achieving those goals.
- A mature person is aware of his or her emotional needs and how to meet them in healthy ways. He or she does not expect the spouse or the marriage to meet all these needs.

Teen Marriages

Adolescence is a time to get to know oneself. This happens through participating in a variety of activities and relationships. During these interactions teens develop a sense of who they are and what they want out of life and a life partner. Unfortunately, teens who choose to marry or feel forced to marry because of unexpected pregnancies often choose their mates before they have any idea who they themselves are or what they want. The results can be disastrous. Consider these facts:

- Females between the ages of 14 and 17 who marry are twice as likely to divorce as females who wait until they are 18 or 19 and three times as likely to divorce as females in the 20-to-24 age group.
- About 80 percent of teenage couples who get married because of pregnancy are divorced within six years.
- Couples with low incomes and couples with little education are more likely to divorce than other groups. Teens who marry often fall into both categories.
- Couples in which neither spouse has a high school diploma are more likely to divorce than couples in which both have college degrees.

In other words, the odds for a successful teen marriage are not good. Teen marriages often deteriorate as the excitement wears off and the responsibilities increase.

Married teens often feel like social outcasts. They are not sure where they fit in. They are neither children nor adults. They are neither carefree teens nor settled married couples. Often they feel isolated from their peers, as if they are missing out on a normal social life. They may be jealous of social contacts outside the marriage. Not yet aware of effective ways to resolve conflicts, they may begin to blame each other for their unhappiness.

Additional Information

Marriage Arrangement. In many societies, marriage and the establishment of a family are considered far too important to be left to the young people. Many marriages are arranged for the economic and political advantage of the family.

Arranged marriages aren't commonplace in our society, but they do occur. Among ethnic minorities, they may serve to preserve traditional values that people fear might otherwise be lost if children married outside the ethnic group. Among families of wealth and power, marriages may be "arranged" by segregating the children in private schools and carefully steering them toward a "proper" marriage.

Conflicts in Marriage

Marriage takes work. Part of that work is learning to resolve conflicts fairly and without damaging one's own or one's partner's self-esteem. Among the issues that sometimes cause problems in marriages are differences in spending and saving habits, conflicting loyalties involving friends and families, intimacy or sexual problems, jealousy or infidelity, lack of attention, housework, decisions about having children, and child care. Unexpressed, ongoing anger over any of these issues can turn into rage. Unresolved rage can result in name-calling, belittling, ignoring, fighting, living separate emotional lives, or even attacking the partner physically. In some cases, a marriage that began with romantic visions of hope can deteriorate into a constant nightmare.

Developing skills in communication and resolving conflicts before they escalate or get out of hand are essential in dealing with the issues and conflicts in any marriage.

Divorce

A **divorce** is the legal dissolution, or ending, of the marriage contract. During the past two decades, the number of divorces in the United States tripled. The divorce rate for couples marrying today is about 50 percent. About 1 million couples in the United States divorce each year. Though the overall divorce rate has fallen in the last 3 years and is beginning to level off, the rate for teen divorces continues to increase.

The breakup of a marriage can be a highly charged emotional event. It can feel like a death. Dealing with the loss of a marriage may take time. Newly divorced people often display a wide range of physical and emotional reactions. They may suffer from hostility, guilt, rage, or jealousy. They may also suffer from symptoms like sleeplessness, headaches, or ulcers.

Divorce Prevention

During the 1970s and 1980s marriage counselors and other therapists often counseled couples in trouble to take an honest look at themselves and their spouses before deciding whether or not to split up or stay together. They still do. But these days some therapists are counseling people to try harder to stay together. New findings from a 10-year divorce prevention study funded by the National Institute of Mental Health show that couples in training for handling conflict have 50 per-

---

KEEPING FIT

If Your Parents Are Going Through a Divorce

Living in a home where parents are divorcing can be difficult. If you are in such a situation, keep these tips in mind:
■ Remind yourself that you did not cause the problem.
■ Ask your parents not to fight in front of you.
■ Ask your parents not to ask you to take sides.
■ Remember to take good care of your own health.
■ Find someone to talk to. It may be a friend, adult, or a teacher or counselor.
■ Consider joining a support group for children of divorce. Doing so will help you realize that you are not alone.

MARRIAGE **123**

Additional Information

Incest. No human society has ever been found to be without a rule, called the incest taboo, that prohibits marriages and sexual relations between certain close relatives. In all known societies, marriage and sexual intercourse are prohibited between parents and their children and (with a few exceptions) between siblings as well.

Many explanations have been given for the incest taboo. One of the most popular has been that it's just "human nature." However, because violations of the incest taboo are far from rare, this explanation isn't very convincing. In our American society, for example, an estimated 10 to 14 percent of children under 18 years of age have been victims of incest.

Check for Understanding

- Assign and discuss the lesson review. Encourage LD students to focus on questions 1, 2, and 3.

Evaluate

- Administer, grade, and discuss the *Lesson 1 Quiz*.

Reteach

- Have each student interview three different married couples to determine what they believe is the key to a successful marriage. What do they think are the most common problems married couples face? If the couples have children, students should ask how children affect the marriage. Ask students to summarize their findings and draw conclusions about skills necessary for a successful marriage.
- Ask students to complete *Reteaching Activity 16*.

Enrich

- Have students read about pre-marital counseling. Where is such counseling available, and what is its cost? What kinds of issues are addressed? What kinds of strategies, such as communication skills, are learned? How long does this form of counseling usually take? What are its advantages? Have students summarize their findings in writing.

Close

Tell students that in this lesson they learned that marriage is more than the happily-ever-after courtship. Instead, marriage is a partnership—and both members of the partnership may have to work hard at it if the marriage is to succeed.

DID YOU KNOW?

- When Richard Biddenstadt of Iowa pulled a strangely shaped beet from his garden, he noticed something doubly strange. Not only was the beet shaped like a figure eight, but there was a ring around its middle. On closer examination, Biddenstadt discovered it was the wedding ring his father had lost in the garden some 50 years before.
- The custom of having a best man and ushers at a wedding was probably first used to prevent bride-stealing, a common practice in earlier times. Attendants were chosen for their strength rather than for their friendship.

cent fewer divorces and one-third the verbal and physical abuse rates of married couples who do not undergo such training. Of course, sometimes staying in a marriage can be an unhealthy, even lethal decision—for example, where there is continual physical abuse. However, with help, destructive behaviors can be stopped and marriages can be made healthier than before.

Remarriage

Out of every 10 people who divorce for the first time, 4 remarry. About 50 percent of these do so within 3 years after the divorce is final. Women without children are more likely to remarry than women with children. Remarriages often occur between people more different in background, education, or age than those who marry for the first time. Some people view a second marriage as a solution to all their problems. However, too often, they repeat the same patterns in choosing a partner. They may also repeat the same patterns of emotional responses and actions as in their first marriages. In fact, of those divorced people who remarry, 44 percent divorce a second time.

Marriage and Health

At least half of all couples who marry do not divorce. Many married people who have matured together, weathered life's ups and downs as a team, and become deep friends say there is nothing like it. To have a life partner with whom to share one's goals, dreams, plans, home, children, and old age can be an enriching adventure.

Recent surveys show that many adults believe that being in a happy and intimate relationship is the most important thing in life. Other studies suggest a link between being married and having better health and living longer. Marriage is a major life decision that can affect both partners' physical, mental, and social health for many years.

LESSON 1 REVIEW

Reviewing Facts and Vocabulary

1. Name three factors that are important for good marital adjustment.
2. List two reasons Americans may have for marrying later.
3. What are some of the characteristics of maturity that are important for achieving a successful marriage?

Thinking Critically

4. **Analysis.** Analyze this statement, "Love may be enough to start a marriage, but it is not enough to keep it together."

5. **Synthesis.** Write a short story about a teen couple who marry and then divorce. Within the story dramatize some of the reasons for the failure of their relationship.

Applying Health Knowledge

6. Consider the characteristics of a mature person. Which of these characteristics describe you? Do you think you are ready for marriage? Why or why not?
7. Think of a couple you know who seem to have a successful marriage. What factors seem to play a part in their success?

Answers to Lesson 1 Review

1. Answers will vary. Possible answers: Similarity in backgrounds; domestic happiness of parents; lack of conflict with parents; educational achievement of both partners; friends of both sexes; participation in organizations; close association prior to marriage.
2. Answers will vary. Accept two of the following: fear of divorce; difficult economic times; choosing to finish education and establish careers first.
3. Answers will vary. See page 122.
4. Answers will vary. Possible answer: It should be based on friendship, mutual respect, trust, and intimacy.
5. Answers will vary.
6. Answers will vary.
7. Answers will vary.

PARENTHOOD

Having a child can be a wonderful experience. It can be thrilling to love someone so much and have someone love you in return. It can be rewarding to provide a nurturing environment for a child and watch that child grow and develop within it. However, parenting is a huge, ongoing responsibility. Like marriage, it is not something to be taken lightly.

Parenting in the Past and Parenting Now

In early America children were expected to work and contribute to the family's economic well-being by the time they were 6 or 7. Even in the 1800s most people were independent, working, and married by the time they were teens. But today childhood has been extended. Young people often do not reach economic independence until well into their 20s. In addition, in the past parents could often rely on an extended family to help with the raising and care of their children. Today, however, only an estimated 5 percent of families in the United States have an extra adult on whom they can rely in the raising or care of their children. Raising children in isolation and for longer periods of time has made childrearing today particularly demanding.

In the past when people got married, it was assumed they would have children. Today this is not always the case. Changing social attitudes, economics, the importance of education and careers, and new advances in reproductive medical technology have made it possible for parenthood to be a delayed or a deliberate choice.

Trends in Parenting

There are many current trends in parenting. Delayed parenthood, working mothers, father involvement in childrearing, and single parenthood are all more common these days than in the past.

Delayed Parenthood

At one end of the age scale, there are more teen pregnancies than in earlier times. At the other end, more couples are delaying childbearing until their 30s or 40s so that they can complete their education or establish careers before starting families. In fact, particularly among college-educated couples, delaying childbearing has increased in popularity.

More Working Mothers

There are more mothers working outside the home than ever before. According to government statistics, 53 percent of mothers of children

PARENTHOOD **125**

LESSON 2 FOCUS

TERM TO USE
- Adoption

CONCEPTS TO LEARN
- The costs of raising children are complex and demanding.
- Some of the responsibilities of parenthood are maintaining parent health, providing discipline, and giving love.

ATTITUDES AND BEHAVIORS TO EVALUATE
- Self-Inventory, page 132.
- Building Decision-Making Skills, page 133.

Resources for Lesson 2

- **Transparency** 39
- **Guided Reading** Act 17
- **Workbook** Voc Act 17

- **Reteaching** Act 17
- **Enrichment** Act 7
- **Health Labs** Act 7

- **Lesson 2** Quiz
- **Chapter 7** Test

ABC News InterActive Videodiscs

Teenage Sexuality, Side 1
Ch 16 Being a Teenage Mother: Lancy

Teenage Sexuality, Side 1
Ch 17 Being a Teenage Father: Billy

Building Vocabulary

- Ask students to write a paragraph explaining the differences between biological, social, and legal parenthood.
- Have students find out and explain in their own words how fosterage and adoption differ.
- Ask students to complete *Workbook Vocabulary Activity 17*.

Teach

Guided Practice

L1 DISCUSSION. What are the primary responsibilities of parenthood?

L2 DISCUSSION. What is unconditional love? Why is it such an important aspect of parenting?

L1 DISCUSSION. Why is it a bad idea to have a baby in order to save an ailing marriage?

L1 SPEAKER. Invite one or more couples to class who have recently become parents for the first time. Ask them to explain how having a child has affected their marriage. What has changed for them as a couple? How have they adapted?

L1 EXPLANATION. Explain how the economic value of children has changed over the past century in the United States.

L1 DISCUSSION. How has the trend from extended to nuclear families in the U.S. affected child-rearing and the decision to have children?

L1 EXPLANATION. Explain how parenthood differs today from parenthood in the past. (For example, delayed parenthood, more working mothers, greater paternal involvement.)

L2 DISCUSSION. What are some of the underlying socioeconomic and other reasons for the trends in parenting today?

L1 SPEAKER. Invite school personnel with young children to speak to the class about child-care problems when both parents work outside the home.

L1 USING CONFLICT RESOLUTION TRANSPARENCY 39. Refer to the Teaching Transparencies Binder.

CONFLICT RESOLUTION

Brooke is really proud of her mom. After having three kids, her mom went back to college, graduated from law school, and now works in one of the best law firms in the city. Brooke's dad worked hard for 16 years in a steel factory, financed his wife's education, and then retired when his wife started practicing law. Now he describes himself as a "domestic engineer," meaning he takes care of everything at home. Brooke loves her dad and knows he's happier now than when he worked in the factory, but she's embarrassed by her friends' comments about his "Mr. Mom" role. Brooke knows her dad is no different now than when he worked in the factory.

How can she convince her friends?

---

aged 5 and under now work outside the home, and about 66 percent of mothers of children 6 to 17 also have outside employment.

A report from the National Commission on Working Women states these facts:

- 75 percent of women return to their jobs within a year of giving birth.
- 75 percent of working mothers work full-time.
- 80 percent of divorced mothers work outside the home.
- 62 percent of married mothers work outside the home.

The report also points out that most mothers who work outside the home do not do so to buy luxuries, as is sometimes thought, but to help make ends meet. Making ends meet can be even more difficult when the cost of day care is high.

More Single Parents

According to the Census Bureau, some 50 percent of all children born now will spend some time in a one-parent household before the age of 18. Of the 10.6 million women who head households, two-thirds are single mothers. Most unmarried mothers in the United States now choose to keep their babies. Today an increasing number of fathers are also raising their children alone.

Many single parents do a good job of raising their children, but raising children alone is not easy. Single parents do not have partners with whom to share decisions, chores, disciplining, financial burdens, or even the joys of parenthood. With no one to relieve them, they often suffer from burnout or depression. Without relief, they may also be more likely to take out their frustrations on their children. They may find it difficult to find time for themselves and may feel they have no life besides their children and their jobs. Single parents with two or more children may also have a hard time finding a partner willing to take on the responsibility of several children.

Single parenthood may also prove stressful for children. One recent study showed that of children who were in trouble in school, more came from single-parent households than from households with two parents. New studies indicate that children from one-parent families are much more likely to live in poverty than children from two-parent households. Another study that followed the progress of 25,000 students for a year showed that children from single-parent families often perform less well in school than children from 2-parent families.

KEEPING FIT

Using Parenting "Warm Lines"

Hotlines, which offer free information and advice, are often for emergency or crisis situations. Recently, lower-key "warm lines" are being made available for parents or other caregivers who need information and support in some daily area of parenting. Right now about 40 agencies across the United States have set up warm lines to assist and support parents. Warm-line workers are either childcare or counseling professionals or have received training from such experts. They help to educate and support struggling parents about issues such as discipline. For more information about such a helpline in your area, consult a local counseling center or librarian.

126 CHAPTER 7 MARRIAGE AND PARENTHOOD

Additional Information

Family Responsibility. Role responsibilities are not the same in every family. In some families, responsibilities for decision making and doing chores are clearly defined. In others, these responsibilities depend upon who, at the time, is available to do them. For example, the mother may mow the lawn one week, and the father the next. During another week, the teenage daughter may have time to do this chore. Family roles depend on what works for the family and what each family decides to do. When family members are comfortable with their roles, the family can operate smoothly.

Because isolation and decreased time for socializing are common complaints of single parents, it is important for them to develop support systems. This may be done through relatives, friends, or organizations such as Parents Without Partners. In addition, providing positive role models of the opposite, absent sex is important for their children. Nearly every community has organizations that can offer advice and support for single parents.

More Father Involvement

Many fathers play a more active role in raising their children than they did in the past. New studies confirm the importance of fathers' roles in child rearing. One study showed that children whose fathers spent time alone caring for them were more capable of showing sympathy and compassion for others as adults. Father involvement also has been linked to children's higher self-esteem, greater sociability, and higher grades.

Some men become househusbands and stay home to take care of the house and children. The decision to do this may be based on many factors. Perhaps the mother's job pays more than the father's, and he stays home to care for his children to avoid day-care costs. Or the father's job may be flexible, allowing him to work from a home office. Regardless of need for income, some fathers choose to spend this time at home with their children.

Planned and Unplanned Pregnancy

The decision to have a child can be a very complex and private decision for a couple. It is often affected by religious, economic, career, emotional, cultural, and social considerations. Planned pregnancy is making a decision to get pregnant before the baby is conceived. Many couples deliberately decide when to conceive. They may wait until their marriages, careers, or finances are established. They may even put off having babies for years, waiting until they are in a financial and psychological position to parent. Though many babies who are unplanned, or conceived unexpectedly, become welcome additions to families, some of these unplanned children do not. Couples who are not ready to have children may resent new additions to the family. Shaky marriages may be further shaken by unwanted pregnancies. Marriages that take place because of pregnancy are more likely to fail than other marriages. A carefully planned pregnancy between two people ready to nurture and support a child to adulthood remains the route with the best chance of success for both the parents and the child.

Adoption

Some couples who are infertile (and some who are not) adopt children. **Adoption** is taking a child into one's family and legally assuming responsibility for that child, agreeing to raise him or her to adulthood. Adopted children are usually very much wanted and planned for as family additions. Adoptive parents often must go through a lengthy screening process and wait long periods before getting their adoptive children.

Currently there are about 2 million adopted children under age 18 in the United States, many of whom might otherwise be raised in institu-

Many fathers play an active role in their children's lives.

HELP WANTED

Child-Care Assistant
What could possibly be as good as a mother's care? Probably nothing, but care by a warm, hardworking, knowledgeable person in a modern, well-run, well-equipped facility with lots of other kids to play with can come close. We have the facility and the kids. We prefer those with certification but will consider your personal, work, and educational background carefully.

For more information contact:
National Childcare Association
920 Green Street NW
Washington, DC 20037

PARENTHOOD **127**

Additional Information

Parenthood. Having children can be a time of growth for parents. According to the Group for the Advancement of Psychiatry, several stages have been identified in this process for parents: anticipating what parenthood will be like; adjusting to new demands and learning to meet children's needs at every stage of their growth; and detaching from their role as children grow. Through children, parents can relive some of their childhood experiences and work on issues not resolved with their own parents. The personalities of children also are an influence on parents.

L1 **SPEAKER.** Invite someone from the local department of children's services or an adoption agency to speak to the class about the screening process involved in adopting a child.

L1 **DISCUSSION.** Why are there fewer babies available for adoption today than in the past?

L1 **DISCUSSION.** What do all children need to be physically healthy? What do they need to be mentally and emotionally healthy?

L3 **SELF-ESTEEM.** Ask selected students to act out a situation in which a child has all of his or her physical needs met, but few emotional or mental needs are met. How might the child's level of self-esteem be adversely affected as an adult as a consequence of such an upbringing?

L1 **DISCUSSION.** What is the role of parent wellness in raising children?

L1 **EXPLANATION.** Explain the importance of clearly defined rules for successful child development.

L1 **DISCUSSION.** What are some important guidelines to follow in disciplining children? (Act quickly, be consistent, etc.)

L1 **DISCUSSION.** Why is physical punishment never warranted? What are its consequences?

L1 **SPEAKER.** Invite a children's services staff person to discuss child abuse with the class. How is child abuse defined? Is abuse ever or often an attempt to discipline or is it done for other reasons? Who are child abusers? How many children are abused annually?

LEP **CLASS ACTIVITY.** Ask students to act out a skit in which a young child misbehaves and the parents discipline the child. Have the rest of the class rate the performance based on the disciplinary guidelines given in the text.

L2 **DISCUSSION.** What should the goal of discipline be?

L2 **DISCUSSION.** What is the role of distinguishing "bad" actions from the child performing them in the development of good self-esteem?

Culturally Speaking

What Does a Baby Need?

Ideas about infant care vary widely and reflect a person's culture. The Foré people of New Guinea emphasize group identity and flexibility. This cultural emphasis is reflected in infant care. The Foré keep constant physical contact with their babies in whatever they do. For example, they allow the babies to nurse when they wish, and encourage them to explore their surroundings.

Ideas about infant care are also reflected in some American group cultures. In groups that emphasize individuality, a child is frequently encouraged to sleep alone and may have his or her own room. Instead of interacting with people and exploring all of the time, the child may be put in a playpen to interact with objects by him- or herself.

tions or in foster care situations. About 150,000 children are adopted in the United States annually. Today there are also increasing numbers of adoptions of babies from other nations. Fewer babies are available in the United States than in the past, partly because of contraceptive practices and partly because more single mothers are keeping and raising their children. There are also campaigns to encourage people to adopt disabled, older, and other hard-to-place children. In the past children were usually placed with two parents that matched them in terms of physical characteristics, religion, race, and so on. Increasingly, however, the major requirements for placement of an adopted child are that he or she will be given a healthy, caring home where the child's physical and emotional needs will be met. Today some children are even adopted by single parents.

What Children Need to Be Healthy

According to the National Mental Health Association, to be physically healthy, children need nutritious food, shelter, clothing, sleep, exercise, immunizations, and a healthy and safe environment. To be mentally and emotionally healthy, children need loving and firm parenting. They need to feel loved and wanted. They need to feel there are people nearby who care what happens to them. They need to feel accepted and valued as human beings even if their parents or other caretakers do not approve of particular behaviors.

The Responsibilities of Parenthood

Parents must provide food, clothing, shelter, education, medical care, and protection from harm for their children. They are responsible not only for their children's physical care but also for the emotional, social, and intellectual upbringing of their offspring. Perhaps most important, they must provide unconditional love.

Caring for a child from infancy to young adulthood is expensive. Recent estimates say that to raise a baby born today through the age of 18 will cost between $150,000 and $180,000. Just the first year of a baby's life costs an average of $5,774. There are other costs that are not financial. Having a child requires a tremendous marital adjustment. The original couple now has a third party demanding time, attention, and resources that might have been used instead for only two people. If there were marital problems before the birth of a child, these problems are likely to increase with the birth of a baby.

In helping meet children's needs, parents play many roles. At different times in different situations, they act as teachers, disciplinarians, and counselors. Parents have many responsibilities in addition to the financial ones.

Maintaining Parental Health

Parents need to give their children lots of attention, but a parent should not neglect his or her basic health needs in the process of caring for children. Maintaining one's own health is part of the responsibility of parenting, since a parent cannot function well if he or she is tired,

128 CHAPTER 7 MARRIAGE AND PARENTHOOD

Additional Information

Childbearing. Demographers have developed economic models to explain why people have children. These usually involve some assessment of the costs relative to the benefits of reproduction.

Costs of reproduction include the extra food consumed during pregnancy and the work foregone by pregnant women, in addition to the cost of providing food, clothing, housing, medical care, and education for the children produced.

Benefits of reproduction include the contribution that children make to food production, to family income in general, and to the care and economic security of their parents. Children are also widely valued for their role in marital exchanges and intergroup alliances.

irritable, hungry, or always pressed for time. Parents also need to get away by themselves for short periods of time to relax and enjoy a day or an evening out. A parent must work to keep his or her mental and physical stamina at a high level and keep the relationship between the parents alive and healthy. Taking care of oneself means being a role model for children's future health habits. If children see physical, mental, and social health as parental priorities, they will be more likely to model such behavior in their own lives.

Setting Limits

Parents need to set limits and establish a clearly defined set of rules. Children need to learn restrictions and limitations on behavior. They need to learn to control their impulses. Children also need to learn the consequences of not following rules. When children learn these limits, they become self-directed. A self-directed child is one who can make correct decisions about behavior when adults are not there to enforce rules. Parents should follow these guidelines in disciplining their children:

- Parents should act quickly. Particularly with small children, it is important that misbehavior be dealt with soon after the fact. If children do not understand the link between their misbehavior and the consequences, they may feel they are being punished for no reason. As a result, children's self-esteem may suffer.
- Parents should be consistent. A consistent approach is different from random punishment. Children should come to expect that certain behaviors will result in certain consequences. Discipline should be structured. The children should know what the expectations are and they should know what will happen if they disobey. It can be helpful, especially as children get older, to explain reasons for limits or rules. This helps children develop an understanding of cause and effect. The goal of discipline should be to teach children appropriate behavior, not just to punish, shame, or get revenge. Physical abuse is never warranted; besides, it is not an effective teacher. It only teaches children to be angry and hurt.
- Parents should distinguish between the behavior and the child. Parents should try to make a distinction between actions (behaviors) and the person doing those behaviors. If parents do not make this distinction, children may develop low self-esteem and think of themselves as bad rather than as people who occasionally do bad things.
- Parents should try to ignore minor annoyances and save discipline for larger issues, such as those involving safety or respect.
- Parents need to praise positive behavior. Words of encouragement and pats on the back can do more to help children's self-esteem and promote good behavior than any disciplinary action.
- Parents should remain friendly, fair, and firm, even when disciplining. Parents should not jump into arguments and stoop to children's emotional levels. They should try not to act angry or out of control. They should remember who the adults are and who should be in control of the situation. They also should be unapologetic about exercising discipline but should do so in a positive manner.
- Parents should give children choices in some situations. Providing choices makes children feel they have some control in solving their problems. If parents give children two or more acceptable behavior

A parent acts as teacher, disciplinarian, and counselor.

DID YOU KNOW?

- There are 16 million children in the United States who live in households without fathers.
- It is estimated that 73 percent of mothers of school children work outside the home.
- About 25 percent of children under 18 live with a single parent.
- Only about 7 percent of children under 18 live with 2 parents, only 1 of whom works outside the home.
- It is estimated that 5 million children in the United States under the age of 6—about 25 percent of that age group—live below the poverty line.

PARENTHOOD **129**

Additional Information

Family Units. Nuclear families are composed of a set of parents and their children. Extended families add individuals from other generations, usually grandparents. Both types of families are characterized by particular advantages and disadvantages.

Nuclear families provide mobility, privacy, and independence. However, they put great

pressure on husband and wife to succeed on their own.

Extended families provide the benefits of economy through shared expenses, security, and companionship. They may be marred by lack of individual initiative, friction between parents and children and between siblings, domination by elders, and lack of privacy.

L1 CLASS ACTIVITY. Ask students to name several negative actions a young child might perform, ranging from spilling milk to hitting another child or running into the street. Ask students to rank the actions by order of seriousness. Have them justify their ranking. Based on their ranking, what would be an appropriate parental reaction to each action?

L1 EXPLANATION. Explain the role of choices in the development of cooperative behavior in a young child.

Independent Practice

L1 COMMUNITY INVOLVEMENT. Have students interview someone who is a parent. Find out what life is like as a parent, compared to life before having a child. Brainstorm the kinds of questions students might ask. Each student should have a list of four or five questions to ask. Have students prepare a short oral report on their findings and comment on how they feel they could adjust to such changes.

L1 RESEARCH. Have students research the costs of childbearing. How much does a typical pregnancy and birth cost?

L1 RESEARCH. Have students investigate and tally the cost of everything a baby needs for the first year—including diapers, clothes, bottles, formula and other special food, crib and other furniture, toys, medical care, etc.

L1 COMMUNITY INVOLVEMENT. Select a few students to interview several mothers they know who work outside the home. Do they work full-time or part-time? How many are single mothers? What conflicts between work and childbearing have the mothers experienced? How have they dealt with them? What is their single biggest problem in filling both roles (that of parent and that of worker)? Would they continue to work outside the home if they didn't need the income? Why or why not? Have the students summarize the results of their interviews for the rest of the class to discuss.

■ **Discussion.** In what ways was Gloria's mother's remarriage an act of good parenting? (By satisfying her own emotional needs, she was practicing good health maintenance; in remarrying, she apparently improved their financial situation.)

■ **Class Activity.** Ask for volunteers from the class who have stepsiblings to provide examples of some of the problems and rewards of living in a stepfamily.

■ **Answers**

1. Accepting her stepfather as a parent figure and sharing her time and space with stepsiblings.

2. The philosophy that her problems are relatively minor and can be overcome; playing softball and volunteering in a soup kitchen.

3. Answers will vary; see Chapter 4 for healthy ways to deal with stress.

L3 RESEARCH. Select students to research the concept of "maternal instinct." Is there such a thing? Is parenting different for males and females? Why or why not? Ask students to make a brief oral report of their findings to the class.

L1 COMMUNITY INVOLVEMENT. Ask for volunteers to take a survey of adults they know who have had at least one child. Why did they have children? Would they do it again? What about having children was unexpected? They should prepare a brief summary of their findings to share with the rest of the class.

L1 COMMUNITY INVOLVEMENT. Have students visit a well-baby clinic and interview an employee to determine the philosophy of the clinic. Are these clinics shown to be effective? How? Have students find out and make a list of routine well-baby visits that occur in the first year of life. When does each visit occur, and what takes place during each one?

L1 USING THE LESSON RESOURCES. For additional student activities, refer to the lesson resources on page 125.

Overcoming The Odds

Gloria Falanga is 15. She loves softball, drawing, and films. She's always wanted to be a filmmaker, she says, and she's always wanted to be part of a big family—until she got one. "The way I got a big family isn't the greatest," she says. "My father died and my mom went to work in a store in town about 25 miles from our house. It was really hard for her—and for me. We didn't have as much time together, and money was tight.

"When I was around 15, she started to see this man named Jack. He owned the store where she worked. He was divorced and he had three kids. After about six months, I could tell things were getting really serious for my mom, and I could tell she was beginning to prepare me for the news. Then the news hit: they decided to get married. I love my mom and wanted her to be happy and not alone, but I have to say I hated the idea. Nobody could ever take my dad's place. I felt like somehow she was betraying him or something—and me.

"So the next thing you know, they get married and we moved into Jack's house just outside of town. All of a sudden I'm

not the only 15-year-old in the house. There's Frank, who's my age, Angee, who's 16, and Kevin, who's 13.

"Jack came on too strong, too, at first, trying to take my dad's place. I finally told him he wasn't my dad and never would be and he backed off. But after a while—a long while—we all started to get adjusted. I think one of the things that helped the most was that this spring we all started playing on a family softball team in our town. We were good. We started really rooting for each other and getting better.

"We also got some family counseling. That helped. And then my mom and Jack decided that we should do something for other people as a family. We had a family meeting about it. So we started—all six of us—volunteering in a soup kitchen every other Friday night. And it has felt good. It also makes me realize that I don't have it so bad, that I'm lucky to have a home, and food, and a group of people who care—even if it's not a group I chose. I guess one of the ways I've learned to deal with it all is to accept what I can't change, then work like heck to make the best of the rest. And I'm even starting to feel closer to Jack."

1. What kinds of adjustments has Gloria had to make in her family life?

2. What philosophy has helped Gloria to adjust to her new stepfamily? What activities have helped family members adjust to one another?

3. Are there relationships in your family that cause you stress? What kinds of activities, outside help, or changes in attitude might you use to handle the situation with less stress?

130 MARRIAGE AND PARENTHOOD

Additional Information

Parenting. Parents around the world face the same basic tasks in raising their children. All teach their children the customs and beliefs of their own culture. In some cultures children are given a great deal of time to grow out of their infant behaviors. In others, there is a more accelerated timetable for children's journey into adulthood.

In societies where survival requires physical labor from all adults, parents often keep their children with them as they do their daily chores. Infants may be strapped to their mothers as the mothers plant or hoe. Later, these children mimic the adults by hoeing and planting small gardens of their own. Other responsibilities of adulthood, such as building houses, hunting, and cooking, are learned at an early age by observing adults and then mimicking adult behavior in childhood games.

options, the children are less likely to choose misbehavior as an option.

- Parents should set good behavior examples. What parents *do* is a more effective teacher than what they *say.*

Giving Love, Attention, and Guidance

Children can do without expensive toys or fancy clothes. What they cannot do without is love, attention, and guidance. Parents need to express their delight in their children and their existence whenever possible. They should praise their children for their efforts rather than the results of their efforts. They should give encouragement through words, letters, hugs, and facial expressions. They can show they care by giving their time. Such attention gives internal rewards to children. Children who are well-parented know they are loved not for what they do but for who they are.

Regardless of whether children are planned or unplanned, biological or adopted, or raised in one- or two-parent families, once they arrive, they all have certain basic needs that parents must work hard to meet. In addition to the basics of physical care and unconditional love, children need opportunities to learn and develop independence, responsibility, and competence while being protected and kept secure. They need to develop skills for getting along with others and handling problems. They need to learn how to make healthy decisions that demonstrate respect for themselves and others. They need to develop independence, responsibility, and capability in a variety of areas. They need to develop a sense of pride in their studies or work and recognize that they, more than anyone else, are responsible for their success or failure in life. As the old saying goes, parents must give a child "roots and wings"—a strong and secure family base and the right eventually to lead their own healthy, productive, and independent lives.

DID YOU KNOW?

- Raising children is costly. Just the cost of a college education can put families over the edge. According to The College Board, a child entering college in the year 2000 will need from $33,000 to $45,000 to complete 4 years at a state college and $120,000 to complete four years at a private institution.
- According to the Children's Defense Fund, yearly average costs of child care in New York City are $8,944; in Boston, $5,668; and in San Francisco, $4,264.

LESSON 2 REVIEW

Reviewing Facts and Vocabulary

1. Summarize some current trends in parenting.
2. What basic needs must be met by parents if children are to be healthy?
3. Write a paragraph about planned and unplanned pregnancy. Include the word *adoption* in the paragraph.

Thinking Critically

4. **Synthesis.** Summarize the major responsibilities that you will have to face as a parent.

5. **Synthesis.** Write a skit that illustrates three ways parents can use discipline both to punish and to teach.

Applying Health Knowledge

6. Find out about resources for children of divorce, pregnant teens, or teen parents. List books, articles, and local support groups. Post this information on a school bulletin board.

Answers to Lesson 2 Review

1. Summaries should reflect an understanding of descriptions of trends on pages 125 to 127.
2. Physical needs—nutritious food, shelter, clothing, sleep, exercise, immunizations, and unpolluted environment. Mental/emotional needs—loving and firm parenting.
3. Paragraphs will vary but should reflect an understanding of planned/unplanned pregnancy and adoption defined on pages 127 to 128.
4. Answers will vary but should reflect that parenthood involves financial, emotional, social, and intellectual responsibilities.
5. Skits will vary.
6. Answers will vary.

Assess

Check for Understanding

- Assign and discuss the lesson review. Encourage LD students to focus on question 2.
- Assign and discuss the chapter review.

Evaluate

- Administer, grade, and discuss the *Lesson 2 Quiz.*
- Administer, grade, and discuss the *Chapter 7 Test.*
- Refer to the Performance Assessment strategy for this chapter. See pages T 23 to T 25.

Reteach

- Have each student make a list of "Dos and Don'ts" for parents of young children. Ask students to check the lists with their own or some other experienced parents. Then, have them make a poster or bulletin board to convey the most important information in a succinct, eye-catching way.
- Ask students to complete *Reteaching Activity 17.*

Enrich

- Have students research the role of children in Western Europe at the time of the Industrial Revolution (between about 1750 and 1900). What role did children play in the family in both rural and urban settings? How early did children go to work? How did child-labor laws and mandatory education laws affect children? How did changes in the economy affect population growth?
- Ask students to complete *Enrichment Activity 7.*

Close

Tell students that in this lesson they learned that parenting is a huge responsibility—one that's best undertaken with advance planning and preparation. Children don't just need a roof over their heads and food on the table. They need lots of attention and unconditional love in a stable relationship with their parents and guardians.

Helping Students Improve Their Health

Using the Self-Inventory

Reinforcing Vocabulary

- **Communicate.** To be open with another person in order to allow information or emotion to be passed.
- **Physical needs.** Food, shelter, clothing, and medical care.
- **Guidance.** Advice based on experience.

Teaching Strategies

L1 EXPLANATION. Students may not understand the importance of distinguishing between the behavior of a person and the actual person. Question 6 may require some additional explanation.

L1 EXPLANATION. Question 7 could be misinterpreted by parents and students. Corporal punishment is currently viewed negatively by society; however, some parents may firmly support the use of physical punishment. Some individuals currently label corporal punishment as abuse; however, the term *abuse* is highly subjective. Question 7 reflects the current thinking of society. These attitudes have changed over the years and will probably continue to change.

L2 DISCUSSION. Have students compare disciplinary practices that were used in schools and the home forty years ago with practices used today. How has the term *abuse* changed over the years? How has this change in disciplinary practices affected the way that children are raised today? Is this change for the better?

L2 DISCUSSION. Have students debate the appropriateness of parents respecting their children's privacy. What are the boundaries of respecting children's privacy, and is there a healthful limit to this privacy?

Self-Inventory

Will You Be an Effective Parent?

HOW DO YOU RATE?

Studies show a relationship between the kind of parenting a person receives and the kind of parent he or she may become. Number a sheet of paper from 1 through 20. Read each statement below, and respond by writing *yes* or *no*. (If you were not raised by a parent, respond for your primary caregiver.) Total the number of *yes* responses. Then proceed to the next section.

1. My parent(s) give me love and affection.
2. My parent(s) give me lots of attention.
3. My parent(s) provide guidance.
4. My parent(s) often praise my efforts.
5. My parent(s) rarely yell at me.
6. My parent(s) distinguish between my misbehavior and me as a person.
7. My parent(s) never abuse me.
8. My parent(s) respect my privacy.
9. My parent(s) set rules and limits.
10. My parent(s) enforce rules and limits consistently.
11. My parent(s) communicate well with me.
12. My parent(s) try to meet my basic physical needs.
13. My parent(s) take good care of themselves and me.
14. My parent(s) make me feel valued.
15. My parent(s) accept me for myself and not for what I accomplish.

16. My parent(s) encourage me to make my own decisions.
17. My parent(s) teach me the value of money.
18. My parent(s) teach me to value and respect others.
19. My parent(s) teach me to take responsibility for my own health.
20. My parent(s) teach me to respect myself.

HOW DID YOU SCORE?

Give yourself 1 point for each *yes* answer and 0 points for each *no* answer. Find your total and read below to see how you scored. Then proceed to the next section.

14 to 20
Good. You are likely to be an effective and caring parent. You have experienced positive parenting.

6 to 13
Fair. You, too, have the potential to become an effective parent, but you may need to work a bit harder at developing positive parenting skills.

Below 5
Caution. You, too, have the potential to become an effective parent. However, you probably need to learn more about parenting before becoming a parent.

WHAT ARE YOUR GOALS?

Choose one or more statements to which your answer was *no*. Use the goal-setting process to start working to achieve improvement for the future.

1. The area related to parenting in which I would like to improve is ____.
2. One specific goal I would like to achieve is ____.
3. The steps involved in achieving this goal are ____.
4. My timetable for achieving this goal is ____.
5. The support materials, groups, and people I will rely on in trying to achieve this goal are ____.
6. My reward for achieving this goal will be ____.
7. I plan to share my information with others by ____.

Meeting Students' Needs

For students who score *Good*. Suggest that students work at a day-care center, tutor peers, or work with special-needs children.

For students who score *Fair*. Encourage students to organize and conduct peer-support groups for students who live in dysfunctional homes. Have students work cooperatively on skills to help break the cycle of ineffective parenting.

For students who score *Caution*. Help students to examine the manner in which parents learn how to parent. Explain to students that they may parent in the same manner that their parents parented unless they begin to work on skills that will allow them to become more effective parents. Have assistance from the guidance staff for students who have issues that need to be resolved.

Building Decision-Making Skills

E rin is committed to becoming a special education teacher, in part because of her love for her little brother, who is developmentally disabled. This summer she worked in a special school for such students, which strengthened her career interest. She has been disturbed, however, that some of the teachers do not encourage these students to prepare themselves for marriage and parent-hood. In fact, some even discourage it or promote the single life. They've explained that there is honest disagreement about this idea both within the profession and in society at large. Erin believes this is discriminatory. She believes that marriage and parenthood are the cornerstones of society for all people, and that marriage and parenthood should be encouraged for all. What should Erin do?

A. Recognize that there are problems of parenthood with which some developmentally disabled people may not be able to deal. Realize that discouraging parenthood is a realistic approach to promoting happiness.

B. Defer to more experienced people and accept their viewpoint.

C. Accept that some people believe one thing but that she is free to hold and promote her own beliefs.

D. Try to change people's minds.

E. Consider each case on its own merits, and encourage marriage and parenthood for some, but not for others.

F. Recognize that her opinion may be affected by personal feelings for her brother and that all people are not like he is.

WHAT DO YOU THINK?

1. **Situation.** Why does a decision need to be made?

2. **Choices.** What other solutions are there to Erin's dilemma?

3. **Consequences.** What are the pros and cons of each solution?

4. **Decision.** How should Erin proceed?

5. **Evaluation.** How do you handle a situation in which you disagree with someone who has more experience than you in dealing with an issue?

 elissa's 16-year-old friend has confided that she's pregnant. At least that's what her at-home pregnancy test showed. She's scared, and hasn't told anyone else yet.

WHAT DO YOU THINK?

6. **Situation.** What are the issues with which Melissa and her friend must deal?

7. **Situation.** Where might Melissa take her friend for information on the options available to her?

8. **Choices.** What are some of the solutions that Melissa can offer her friend?

9. **Choices.** Whom should the friend tell about her situation (parents, boyfriend, counselor, others)?

10. **Consequences.** What are the costs and benefits of each solution?

11. **Consequences.** Will the timing of when people are told (and in what order) affect the end result?

12. **Decision.** What advice do you think Melissa should give her friend?

13. **Evaluation.** Have you been in a situation similar to Melissa's in which you have had feelings of both happiness and sorrow for a friend? How did you handle the problem?

PARENTHOOD **133**

Discussing the Answers

Situation 1. Erin believes that discouraging developmentally disabled persons from becoming married and having children is discriminatory. Erin could research the success and failure rates of developmentally disabled individuals with regard to being married and raising children. Erin could compare these statistics with the total population. Do these couples fare better or worse? If Erin finds support for these conclusions, she could take these results to the management of this school.

Situation 2. Perhaps the best resolution to this situation would be to support Melissa in a decision to discuss with her parents her friend's suspected pregnancy.

Answers to Chapter 7 Review

Using Health Terms

1. Marriage
2. Two-career marriage
3. Single
4. Divorce
5. Single-parent family
6. Househusband
7. Delayed parenthood
8. Adoption
9. Discipline

Building Academic Skills

10. People with established careers have more time to devote to making a marriage work.
11. Compositions will vary.

Recalling the Facts

12. It is often the reason couples choose to marry, but it is seldom the reason two people remain married.
13. All aspects—physical, mental, and social.
14. Both partners agree on critical issues in their relationship, share common interests and activities, demonstrate affection and shared confidences, have few complaints about marriage, do not have feelings of loneliness or irritability.
15. It may cause sleeplessness, headaches, or ulcers.
16. Forty percent.
17. Advantages—more money, more social contacts. Disadvantages—may add fatigue, stress, and competition to the marriage.
18. 92 million households; 55 percent.
19. Answers will vary. Accept any six of the following significant factors discussed on page 121: similarity in family backgrounds; domestic happiness of parents; lack of conflict with parents; educational achievement of both partners; friends of both sexes; participation in organizations; close association prior to marriage; security and stability of occupation.

20. Teens often choose their mates before they have any idea who they themselves are or what they want.
21. To provide food, clothing, shelter, education, medical care, protection from harm, and unconditional love for their children.
22. Between $150,000 and $180,000.

23. It can put a strain on a marriage. If marital problems were present before the baby was born, they will likely increase with the birth of a baby.
24. A—yes. B—yes. C—yes. D—no. E—yes. F—no.
25. By developing support systems.
26. A parent cannot function

well if he or she is not attending to his or her physical needs. A parent provides a role model for children's future health habits.
27. Parents should: act quickly; be consistent; distinguish between the behavior and the child; try to ignore minor annoyances and

---

REVIEW

Using Health Terms

On a separate sheet of paper, write the term that best matches each definition given below.

LESSON 1

1. The joining of a man and a woman according to custom or law.
2. A marriage in which both spouses work outside the home.
3. A word used to describe a person who remains unmarried.
4. The legal ending of a marriage.

LESSON 2

5. A family with one or more children but only one parent.
6. A husband and father who stays home to care for the house and the children.
7. Waiting to have children until 30 to 40 years old.
8. Taking a child into one's family and legally assuming responsibility for that child.
9. The setting of restrictions on the behavior of children.

Building Academic Skills

LESSON 1

10. **Reading.** Read the following paragraph. Which of the details does not support the main idea?

    Several factors help explain the trend toward later marriages. High divorce rates make some people wary of early marriage. Many young people want to finish their education before marrying. People with established careers have more time to devote to making a marriage work.

LESSON 2

11. **Writing.** Assume that someday you will have a child. Write a three-to-five paragraph composition describing the goals you would have for your child and how you would help your child achieve those goals.

Recalling the Facts

LESSON 1

12. How big a factor is romantic love in the decision to marry and in the success of a marriage?
13. What aspects of a person's health triangle can marriage affect?
14. List five factors present in a well-adjusted marriage.
15. How can divorce affect a person's physical well-being?
16. What percent of divorced people remarry?
17. What are the advantages and disadvantages of two-career marriages?
18. According to 1990 Census figures, how many United States households are there and how many consist of married couples?
19. Name six characteristics related to social background that can have an effect on marital adjustment.
20. Why are teen marriages more likely to end in divorce than adult marriages?

LESSON 2

21. What are the basic responsibilities of parenthood?
22. What is the average estimated cost of raising a child from birth to age 18?
23. How can having a child affect the relationship in a marriage?
24. Write *yes* or *no* to indicate which of the following are problems faced by single parents:
    a. no help in disciplining children
    b. burnout or depression
    c. financial burdens
    d. plenty of free time for dating
    e. difficulty in finding another spouse
    f. fewer housekeeping responsibilities
25. How can single parents get help?
26. Why is it important for a parent to maintain his or her own physical health?
27. What are eight guidelines for disciplining children?
28. How can parents show love to their children?

REVIEW

Thinking Critically

LESSON 1

29. **Synthesis.** Create a test that you would administer to anyone considering marriage.

30. **Analysis.** What is behind the thinking in setting state laws that have minimum age requirements for marriage?

31. **Evaluation.** What is the purpose of requiring couples who want to marry to have blood tests and medical examinations?

32. **Evaluation.** Should an HIV test be required in order to obtain a marriage license?

33. **Evaluation.** Why is it important for married couples to develop skills in communication and resolving conflicts?

34. **Evaluation.** Do you think that "getting out of the house" is a valid reason for teens to get married? Explain your answer.

35. **Synthesis.** Outline a 5-minute presentation to junior high students on why teen marriage is "risky business."

36. **Analysis.** Analyze the factors contributing to the increasing number of mothers working outside the home.

37. **Evaluation.** What are your views on the topic of househusbands?

38. **Evaluation.** Why do you think parenthood is one of the most serious decisions a person makes?

Making the Connection

LESSON 1

39. **Music.** Choose a popular song about love. How do you think love depicted in the song compares with love in a marriage?

40. **Social Studies.** In ancient times marriages were arranged by the couple's parents. What might be some advantages and disadvantages of arranged marriages?

LESSON 2

41. **Language Arts.** Assume the role of a parent of a physically disabled child. Write a letter to a good friend describing the emotional burdens you carry as well as the special joys of parenthood you experience.

Applying Health Knowledge

LESSON 1

42. Two of your friends, Monica and Pedro, are thinking about marriage. At 18, what problems do they face that would not be problems if they wait 5 years to marry?

LESSON 2

43. Twenty years ago fewer than half of all married mothers worked outside the home. Today 62 percent do. Interview several mothers you know who work outside the home and several who do not. Find out why these women do or do not have outside employment. Categorize their responses and try to draw a conclusion based on their responses.

Beyond the Classroom

LESSON 1

44. **Community Involvement.** Survey the people living on your block or in your apartment building. Find out how many households are headed by a married couple and how many are headed by a single person. How do your neighborhood's statistics compare with national statistics?

45. **Parental Involvement.** Ask your parents what they have learned about each other since they got married. Find out what they have learned about marriage that they did not already know before their wedding.

46. **Further Study.** Investigate the laws regarding marriage in your state. Is a blood test or medical examination required? What are the age requirements with and without parental permission? Are certain persons not allowed to marry in your state?

LESSON 2

47. **Further Study.** Research and report the views of two child psychologists on the matter of spacing children. What do these doctors suggest as the best age for the first child to be before the next child is born? Do you agree or disagree?

save discipline for larger issues; praise positive behavior; remain friendly, fair, and firm, even when disciplining; give children choices in some situations; set good behavior examples.

28. By expressing their delight in their children; praising children's efforts; giving encouragement through words, letters, hugs, and facial expressions; giving of their time.

Thinking Critically

29. Answers will vary but should accurately reflect an understanding of the responsibilities and challenges of marriage.

30. To ensure that couples are mature and responsible enough to make the decision to marry, and if they are underage, to make their parents/guardians aware of the situation.

31. To make sure neither party has sexually transmitted diseases or hidden medical conditions.

32. Answers will vary but should be supported logically.

33. Answers will vary. Possible answer: Communication is essential to growth in a marriage.

34. Answers will vary but should be supported logically.

35. Answers will vary. See page 122.

36. Answers will vary. Possible answers: Difficult economic times, rising divorce rates, and an increasing number of single-parent families contribute to the increasing number of mothers working outside the home. Society's attitude of acceptance toward working mothers also makes it easier for a woman to choose to have a career and a family.

37. Answers will vary but should be supported logically.

38. Answers will vary but might include references to the fact that the responsibilities for another human life are very serious and it is a long-term commitment.

Making the Connection

39. Answers will vary.

40. Answers will vary. Possible answers: Advantages—no pressure of dating; the choice would be made by mature and wise people. Disadvantages—one may not love or even like the person to whom he or she is promised; the motivation behind the match may not be in the couple's best interest.

41. Answers will vary.

Applying Health Knowledge

42. Answers will vary. Possible answers: They lack the education needed to find well-paying jobs. They may not have experienced much independence or responsibility for another yet. They may not have a complete sense of self yet.

43. Answers will vary, but conclusions should be based on information gathered.

Beyond the Classroom

44. Answers will vary.
45. Answers will vary.
46. Answers will vary.
47. Answers will vary.

Lesson Summaries

LESSON 1. Life begins as a single microscopic cell. Over a 9-month period of time, the cell divides millions of times and develops the tissues, organs, and systems necessary for life. When an ovum is fertilized, it goes through numerous transitional stages as it is implanted in the uterus and goes through fetal development. Prenatal care is important because the female's health choices affect the health and well-being of the developing baby.

LESSON 2. Chromosomes within the nuclei of cells contain genes that control hereditary characteristics. The determination of sex is based on the father's sperm cell. In almost all other body cell development, the hereditary process involves complex chemical activity that results in dominant and recessive characteristics.

LESSON 3. Growth and development are affected by heredity, environment, and health choices. An individual's growth and development follows a predictable pattern, though the rate of these changes is unique to the individual.

Introducing the Chapter

Ask students to recall family reunions and some of the comments they heard from relatives they hadn't seen in a number of years. Follow their comments with the fact that physical changes are evident during early development, but that emotional, social, and intellectual growth and development are lifelong processes.

Performance Assessment ✓

Refer to pages T 23 to T 25 for a Performance Assessment strategy for this chapter. See the *Performance Assessment Activities* booklet for additional suggestions.

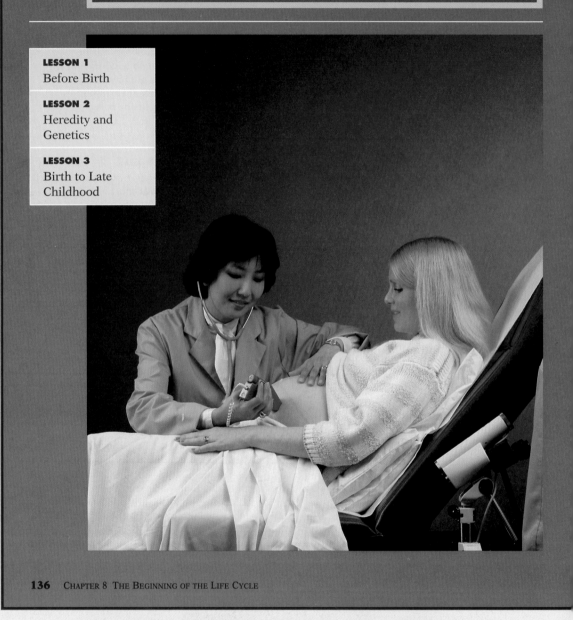

CHAPTER 8

THE BEGINNING OF THE LIFE CYCLE

LESSON 1
Before Birth

LESSON 2
Heredity and Genetics

LESSON 3
Birth to Late Childhood

136 CHAPTER 8 THE BEGINNING OF THE LIFE CYCLE

Key to Ability Levels

Teaching strategies have been coded for varying learning styles and abilities.

L1 **LEVEL 1** activities are basic activities and should be within the ability range of all students.

L2 **LEVEL 2** activities are average activities and should be within the ability range of average to above-average students.

L3 **LEVEL 3** activities are challenging activities designed for the ability range of above-average students.

LD **LD** activities should be within the ability range of learning-disabled students.

LEP **LEP** activities should be within the ability range of Limited English Proficiency students.

BEFORE BIRTH

E ach of us began as a single microscopic cell, much smaller than the tip of a pin. Over a nine-month period of time, this cell divided millions of times and developed the tissues, organs, and systems that make up our complex bodies.

Cells: The Basic Unit of Life

The **cell** is the basic unit of structure of all living things. Your body is made up of trillions of cells. With the exception of the cells that make up the nervous system, each cell has the ability to divide, reproduce, and repair itself.

Cells with similar structure and that do similar work make up a tissue. For example, muscle is a tissue, and blood is a tissue. Organs are two or more tissue types that perform a specific job. The heart, brain, liver, and lungs are examples of organs.

A group of organs that work together to perform a common function form a body system. Examples of body systems include the digestive system, cardiovascular system, and reproductive system. Your body systems work together and are dependent upon one another. You will learn more about the function and care of your body systems when you study Unit 5.

Fertilization

The entire complex human body begins as one cell that is formed by the union of an egg cell, or ovum, from a female and a sperm cell from a male. These two cells are microscopic in size. The union of these cells is called **fertilization** or conception. Fertilization usually occurs in the Fallopian tube. Refer to the illustration on page 138.

As soon as the ovum is fertilized, it is called a **zygote.** A protective membrane forms to surround the zygote and prevent any more sperm from entering the ovum. The zygote divides into two cells, then four cells, and so on, and begins to move through the Fallopian tube to the uterus. This takes about three days.

Implantation in the Uterus

By the time the zygote reaches the uterus, it has divided many times to form a cluster of cells that has a hollow space in the center. It is now called a **blastocyst.** As the cells divide, they begin to implant, or attach, to the lining of the uterus. This process is called implantation. The lining of the uterus is made up of layers of tissue that will protect and nourish the fertilized egg throughout pregnancy. Once implantation has occurred, the cluster of cells is called an **embryo.** At this time the embryo is about the size of the dot over this letter *i*.

BEFORE BIRTH **137**

LESSON 1 FOCUS

TERMS TO USE
- Cell
- Fertilization
- Zygote
- Blastocyst
- Embryo
- Placenta
- Umbilical cord
- Fetus

CONCEPTS TO LEARN
- A male and female both contribute significantly to the characteristics of the unborn.
- Growth before birth is a gradual process, much like growth after birth.

ATTITUDES AND BEHAVIORS TO EVALUATE
- Self-Inventory, page 154.
- Building Decision-Making Skills, page 155.

Focus

Lesson Objectives

After studying this lesson, students should be able to:
- outline the major events in the first 9 months of life, from fertilization through birth
- describe prenatal care and why it's important
- identify prenatal risks

Bellringer

Write the following on the chalkboard for students to work on while attendance is being taken: *List substances that pregnant females should avoid because they are harmful to the developing fetus.*

Introducing the Lesson

Refer to the Bellringer. Ask volunteers to share their responses. Point out that in addition to alcohol, tobacco, and illegal drugs, many medications and disease organisms may also harm the fetus. Tell students that in this lesson they will learn how a fetus develops and why such substances lead to problems in fetal development, including birth defects. They will also learn about the two end points of fetal development: event of fertilization and the process of birth.

DID YOU KNOW?

- Twenty-seven percent of 15-year-old girls have had sexual intercourse. This is an increase of 8 percent since 1982.
- Sixty-one percent of sexually active teenage girls have had multiple sex partners.
- Every day in the U.S., approximately 2,795 teens become pregnant.
- Only 1 in every 200 10- to 14-year-olds have given birth, but this is the only age group in which the birth rate is not going down.

Resources for Lesson 1

- **Transparency** 35
- **Guided Reading** Act 18
- **Workbook** Voc Act 18

- **Reteaching** Act 18
- **Lesson 1 Quiz**
- **Education in Sexuality**

- **Performance Assessment** Activity 8

Science and Technology Videodisc
Human Biology, Side 1
Ch 17 Brain Development

 Side 1, Ch 17

ABC News InterActive Videodiscs
Teenage Sexuality, Side 1
Ch 6 The Fertilization Process

Building Vocabulary

- Have students find illustrations of the vocabulary terms in biology books and draw diagrams to illustrate them. Ask volunteers to show and explain their illustrations to the class.
- Ask students to complete *Workbook Vocabulary Activity 18.*

Teach

Guided Practice

LD EXPLANATION. Due to the high-level vocabulary and complex subject matter of this chapter, LD students may depend upon class discussions for comprehension. Assignment of this lesson as independent reading is not recommended.

LEP DEMONSTRATION. Using a schematic drawing, show the hierarchial relationship between cells, tissues, and organs.

LEP CLASS ACTIVITY. Have students locate the female reproductive organs on a chart or model. Ask volunteers to explain the role of each organ in fertilization, pregnancy, and birth.

L1 EXPLANATION. Describe the process of fertilization and explain why so many sperm are required for fertilization to occur.

LEP DEMONSTRATION. Show how a zygote is formed, using illustrations on a transparency or drawing on the chalkboard.

L1 DISCUSSION. Ask students where fertilization usually occurs. Where does the zygote go after fertilization?

L1 EXPLANATION. Explain how and when the process of implantation occurs.

L1 DISCUSSION. What is a blastocyst? What does it look like?

L1 DISCUSSION. What is the difference between an embryo and a fetus?

L1 DISCUSSION. What is the placenta? What does it do?

As an ovum is released from an ovary, it moves through the Fallopian tube toward the uterus. If the ovum is fertilized by a sperm, it will attach to the lining of the uterus.

Fertilization

Site of fertilization · Ovum · Sperm · Fertilization · Fallopian tubes · Path of ovum · Ovum · Ovary · Site of implantation · Uterus · Path of sperm · Cervix · Vagina

Culturally Speaking

What's in a Name?
Naming a baby can be a big task. In many cultures, babies are named after relatives. Sometimes children are named for characteristics they have or qualities that their parents hope they will have, such as strength or beauty. In Indonesia, it is common to have only one name. In many Latin American cultures, a person may have several names, indicating the family name of their mother, their father, a patron saint, and, perhaps, even their place of birth.

Research your own name. What language does your name come from? Find out what your name means. Ask someone in your family why you were given your name.

Development of the Placenta and Umbilical Cord

The cells of the embryo continue to divide, forming three layers of tissue. One layer becomes the respiratory and digestive systems. Another layer develops into muscles, bones, blood vessels, and skin. The third layer becomes the nervous system, sense organs, and mouth.

At the same time, a thin membrane called the amniotic sac forms and surrounds the developing embryo. Fluid in this sac acts as a shock absorber that protects the embryo from jarring and bumping. It also helps insulate the embryo from temperature changes.

An outer layer of cells of the embryo with tissue from the mother develops into the **placenta.** The placenta is made of blood-rich tissue. The embryo is connected to the placenta by the **umbilical cord.** The cord contains blood vessels through which blood flows between the embryo and the placenta. The mother's blood vessels also extend into the placenta. Here nutrients and oxygen pass from the mother's blood into the embryo's blood. The nutrients and oxygen are carried by blood in blood vessels in the umbilical cord to the embryo.

Waste products from the embryo are carried through these same blood vessels to the placenta where they diffuse into the mother's blood. These wastes are then removed from the mother's body.

Fetal Development

During the first 6 weeks of pregnancy, the embryo grows rapidly in length and gains weight. At the start of the third week, it is about one-half to one inch long (2 to 2.5 cm), or 10,000 times the size of the original egg cell! At 8 weeks the embryo measures about an inch and one-half in length (3.5 to 4 cm). From the end of the eighth week until

138 CHAPTER 8 THE BEGINNING OF THE LIFE CYCLE

Overcoming Misconceptions

Myth. Many people believe that only drugs like alcohol, nicotine, and cocaine can be harmful to a developing fetus. **Fact.** The following list shows other harmful substances that can cross the "placental barrier" between mother and fetus:

- disease-causing organisms, such as the rubella virus that causes measles, HIV

that causes AIDS, and the herpes virus that causes oral and genital herpes;
- food additives, such as saccharin and caffeine;
- pharmaceuticals, including aspirin and many antibiotics;
- toxins, such as carbon monoxide and lead.

TEEN PREGNANCY

Over 1 million American teens become pregnant in the United States each year. Of these, about 500,000 give birth. This number is twice what it was just 25 years ago. That means that of every 100 teenage females, 10 will get pregnant and 6 will give birth to their babies before the age of 20. This rate for teenage pregnancy is twice that of European countries.

Pregnancy during adolescence has special risks. Before the age of 20, a young female is still growing. Her pelvis may not be large enough for the passage of a full-grown fetus. Her growing body may not be ready for the physical stress of pregnancy. Since her own nutritional needs are high, she may not consume enough nutrients for herself and her baby. Teenage mothers are more likely than other age groups to have low birth weight babies, who in turn, have a high mortality, or death, rate.

It has been estimated that five out of six of all teen pregnancies in this country are unplanned. They might happen because either the male or the female was unknowledgeable about how to get pregnant, was careless, or simply didn't consider that pregnancy could happen.

About one-sixth of these pregnancies, however, are planned. Teens who plan to get pregnant may not recognize how stressful the pregnancy might be. Combined with the normal anxieties of adolescence, the hormonal and physical changes of pregnancy can be difficult to cope with. Some teens assume that by having a child of their own, they will feel more fulfilled and have something all their own to love. What they don't take into consideration are the financial, emotional, social, and educational costs to themselves and their children, who will need care for the next 18 years of their lives.

Between 50 and 80 percent of teen mothers do not finish high school. A large percentage of the babies born to unmarried parents are born to teens, and many single-parent families where the mother is the head of household live in poverty. Females who have babies by the time they are 15 and 16 are highly likely to have a second child before the age of 20. Because of the poverty and other frustrations associated with teen parenting, many children of teen parents end up in foster care, or are abused or neglected.

Increasingly, there are programs within schools for pregnant teens or teens with young children. In fact, studies show that teen mothers who manage to stay in school after the birth of their babies are less likely to have more children while they are still teens.

a.

b.

c.

d.

A fertilized ovum divides rapidly to form a cluster: (a) an unfertilized ovum; (b) two-cell stage; (c) eight-cell stage; (d) a blastocyst, a mass of cells that form a hollow ball.

birth, the embryo is known as a **fetus.** The skin of the fetus is clear and hairless and covered with a waxy protective coating. The fetus contains millions of cells that will arrange themselves into tissues and organs.

The brain is one of the first organs to develop. The nervous system grows rapidly, and at 9 weeks the head develops. All the body systems are now present.

Growth of the fetus is rapid during the fourth month, but it slows down in the fifth month. During this time the mother can feel the fetus move. It may begin to suck its thumb. By the end of the sixth month, the fetus is about 14 inches (36 cm) long.

During the last 3 months of pregnancy, the weight of the fetus more than triples. The fetus moves freely within the amniotic sac. The eyes open during the seventh month. During the ninth month the fetus usually moves into a head-down position and is ready for birth. The fetus is now 18 to 20 inches (46 to 51 cm) long and weighs about 7 to 9 pounds (3 to 4 kg).

BEFORE BIRTH **139**

Additional Information

Cesarean Delivery. A cesarean delivery is the surgical removal of the fetus through the mother's abdominal wall. The most common reason for a cesarean delivery is that the baby is too large or the pelvis too small for a safe vaginal delivery. Fetal distress, detected by the baby's heart rate, is another common reason; in this case, the baby must be delivered quickly. Sometimes the fetus is in an abnormal position, making a vaginal delivery impossible. Recovery from a cesarean delivery is somewhat longer than from a vaginal delivery, though most females can resume their normal activities within six weeks.

Prenatal Care

As soon as a female confirms her pregnancy, she should begin prenatal care. This is important because the female's health choices affect the health and well-being of the developing baby. A pregnant female should have regular visits with an obstetrician, a doctor specializing in the care of a female and her developing baby.

The obstetrician gives the pregnant female a complete physical, including blood tests and a pelvic examination. Possible problems may be identified and corrected early. The doctor also helps educate the mother-to-be in important health behaviors. Her dietary choices, for example, are of special concern. She needs a well-balanced diet to ensure proper nourishment for herself and her developing child.

The doctor will monitor the female's weight during her pregnancy and discuss the importance of exercise. An exercise program will be recommended depending on the female's health and level of fitness. Prenatal care also gives the parents-to-be chances to ask questions about pregnancy and the birth process.

Medicines, Drugs, and Pregnancy

A pregnant female must be very careful about what substances she takes into her body. Any medicines should be taken only with her doctor's approval.

No illegal drugs should be taken. Illegal drugs present a very serious threat to the mother and her baby. Babies can be born physically dependent on the drugs their mothers used while pregnant. Use of certain drugs during pregnancy can cause serious birth defects, including mental retardation.

Alcohol and Pregnancy. Females who drink alcohol during pregnancy run the risk of giving birth to babies with birth defects. These babies may be physically, mentally, or behaviorally abnormal. This condition is called fetal alcohol syndrome (FAS).

Additional Information

Early Release From the Hospital. New mothers used to stay in the hospital for as long as 2 weeks after the birth of a baby. Now most return home in 24 to 48 hours after a birth. This early release is based for the most part on the high costs involved in hospital stays. The early release usually does not pose any risks to either the mother or the baby.

The parents, however, must be prepared to care for the baby upon its arrival. Parents can take advantage of prenatal childbirth education classes available at many hospitals and clinics. A first-time mother, especially, needs instruction in such areas as feeding and bathing the baby and choosing the right diet and exercises for herself.

Babies born with FAS are often shorter and weigh less than babies of mothers who did not drink alcohol. FAS babies may have a variety of problems, including impaired speech, a cleft palate, slow body growth, facial abnormalities, poor coordination, and heart defects. Mental retardation, poor attention span, nervousness, and hyperactivity are also common in these children.

When a pregnant female drinks alcohol, the alcohol in her blood flows through the vessels in the umbilical cord into the baby's bloodstream. Unfortunately, the developing baby's body cannot rid itself of the alcohol like an adult body can. A baby born to a female who drinks alcohol during her pregnancy can be born addicted to alcohol.

It is important to remember that fetal alcohol syndrome and all the problems associated with it are completely preventable. These problems do not occur in babies born to females who avoid the use of alcohol during pregnancy.

Tobacco and Pregnancy. A pregnant female also must avoid using tobacco. Babies born to females who use tobacco have a greater chance of being born prematurely with low birth weights. Babies born weighing 5½ pounds (2.5 kg) or less often develop serious health problems early in life. Low birth weight is a leading cause of death in a baby's first year of life.

Females who use tobacco during pregnancy are about two times more likely to have a miscarriage or stillbirth, the birth of a dead fetus, than females who do not use tobacco. As with FAS, the problems associated with tobacco use and pregnancy are preventable.

DID YOU KNOW?

- A female who is infected with HIV can pass the virus to her baby if she becomes pregnant. Most children infected with HIV got the virus from their infected mothers during pregnancy or at birth. During pregnancy, the virus can be transmitted to the unborn through the mother's blood system. At birth, the virus can be transmitted in the vagina. The virus also can be transmitted through breast-feeding.

K E E P I N G F I T

Babies as Intelligent Beings

When you see a baby, how do you react? Do you marvel at the way it responds to the world around it, or do you see it as an as-yet undeveloped person oblivious to its surroundings?

The fact is that babies are highly developed beings. They can see, hear, and even learn while still developing in the uterus.

The next time you see a baby, pay careful attention to its behav-ior. What information does it seem to be taking in? How aware does he or she seem of the surroundings? Spend some time with the baby, keeping in mind that babies are people, too.

BEFORE BIRTH **141**

Additional Information

Alcohol Warning Labels. As of November 1989, the United States Congress mandated that warnings appear on the labels of all alcoholic beverages. This warning reads in part, "According to the Surgeon General, women should not drink alcoholic beverages during pregnancy because of the risk of birth defects." In addition, the Alcoholic Beverage Labeling Act of 1988 mandated that the warnings be printed in a conspicuous part of the label and on a contrasting background.

Several social scientists have studied the impact of the warnings. Results suggest that the warning has not changed attitudes. Perhaps it is too early to tell. Perhaps the warning is too vague. Some suggest a shorter version: "Warning: Alcohol is a drug and may be addictive." A task force named by the Surgeon General is studying the need for labeling changes.

Independent Practice

L1 RESEARCH. Divide the class into nine groups and have each group research one month of fetal development. Ask students to summarize for the class the major events that occur during their assigned month. (Ask them also to identify maternal behaviors or substances that are particularly harmful to the fetus during their month. A good source for the latter is the March of Dimes.)

L2 RESEARCH. Have students locate newspaper and magazine articles about the role of exercise during pregnancy. Ask them to discuss their readings with the class.

L1 RESEARCH. Assign students to research and report to the class on how much weight is typically gained during pregnancy. How much weight gain is considered too little, and how much is too much? What are some of the negative health impacts on mother and fetus of too little and too much weight gain?

L2 RESEARCH. Ask students to research the number of calories and the amounts of protein, calcium, and iron that are needed by a typical female during pregnancy, relative to the nonpregnant female. Have them identify good food sources for these nutrients.

L1 COMMUNITY INVOLVEMENT. Arrange to have students visit an obstetrical practice or clinic. If possible, have the staff review what happens during a typical prenatal visit. What tests and procedures are routinely performed, and what is the purpose of each?

L2 RESEARCH. Select students to research the typical costs of pregnancy and delivery, including both vaginal and cesarean methods. Ask them to prepare a chart showing their findings.

L1 RESEARCH. Ask students to research positions of the fetus that would require cesarean delivery. Their report to the class might include textbook illustrations of the positions.

DID YOU KNOW?

- In our part of the world, twins are born at a rate of 1 pair in each 90 births. Triplets are born at a rate of 1 trio in every 8,000 births.
- In some cases, after one egg cell has been fertilized, it divides and two embryos develop. These embryos have the same genetic information, and therefore, are usually identical twins.

DEVELOPMENT IN THE UTERUS BEFORE BIRTH

End of First Month
- About one-quarter inch (6 mm) long
- Heart, brain, and lungs forming
- Heart starts beating on about the twenty-fifth day

End of Second Month
- About 1½ inches (4 cm) long
- Muscles and skin developing
- Arms, hands, and fingers forming
- Legs beginning to form, along with knees, ankles, and toes
- Every vital organ starting to develop

End of Third Month
- About 3 inches (8 cm) long
- Weighs about 1 ounce (28 g)
- Can open and close mouth and swallow

End of Fourth Month
- 8 to 10 inches (20 to 25 cm) long
- Weighs 6 ounces (170 g)
- Movement can be felt

End of Fifth Month
- About 12 inches (30 cm) long
- Weighs 1 pound (454 g)
- Eyelashes appear
- Nails begin to grow
- Heartbeat can be heard

End of Sixth Month
- Can kick and cry
- Can hear sounds
- Might even hiccup
- Has fingernails

End of Seventh Month
- Weighs 2 to 2½ pounds (910 to 1100 g)
- Can move arms and legs freely
- Eyes are now open

End of Eighth Month
- About 16½ inches (42 cm) long
- Weighs about 4 pounds (1800 g)
- Hair grows
- Skin gets smoother as a layer of fat develops under it

End of Ninth Month
- 18 to 20 inches (46 to 51 cm) long
- Weighs 7 to 9 pounds (3 to 4 kg)
- Organs have developed enough to function on their own

Six weeks

Five to six months

Four months

K E E P I N G   F I T

Being Prepared

Babysitting can have serious consequences if you are not prepared. When you babysit for young children, you should have the following phone numbers:
- where the parent(s) can be reached

- police and fire departments, ambulance, pediatrician, and Poison Control Center
- the nearest neighbor(s)

Do not allow children under 4 to eat foods that they might choke on, such as hard candies.

Do not allow them to put small objects in their mouths.

Keep the children within your sight at all times until they are safely asleep. Then be sure that you can hear them if they should awaken.

Across the Curriculum

Math. The infant mortality rate is relatively high in the U.S. as compared with most Western European countries. This is because many economically disadvantaged Americans do not have healthy diets or access to good prenatal care. This is especially true of members of racial and ethnic minorities. In these groups, the infant mortality rate may be as high as that in countries that are economically disadvantaged. The infant mortality rate for middle-class U.S. whites, by contrast, is as high as in any European country.

To reinforce basic math skills, have students demonstrate how an average rate calculated for an entire group can be influenced by a high rate in some of its component groups.

The Three Stages of Birth

Babies usually are born headfirst. In the last few weeks of pregnancy, the baby's head moves to the lower part of the uterus. During the birth process the baby is pushed out of the uterus and passes out of the mother's body. There are 3 stages in the birth process. The first stage is dilation, the stretching of the cervix. The cervix is the round, muscular neck, or bottom part, of the uterus. During the 9 months of pregnancy, it remained tightly closed, keeping the fetus inside the uterus. Now it opens to a diameter of about 4 inches (10 cm). This is about the width of your hand. Dilation begins with mild contractions of the muscles of the uterus. These contractions, called labor, shorten the uterus and pull the cervix open. The dilation stage is the longest, most difficult part of the birth process.

When the cervix is fully dilated, the muscles of the uterus continue to contract, moving the baby through the cervix and birth canal. This is the second phase of the birth process. The umbilical cord continues to connect the baby to the placenta during the birth process. Once the baby is born, the umbilical cord is clamped and cut near the baby's abdomen. Any part of the cord that is left will dry up and fall off.

After the baby is born, the contractions of the uterus continue for another 10 to 15 minutes. These contractions push the placenta, now called afterbirth, out of the mother's body. This is the third and final stage of birth.

The Apgar Test

Almost all American hospitals administer a routine test to determine an infant's physical condition at birth. It is named after the late Dr. Virginia Apgar. The Apgar test measures the baby's condition in five significant areas: appearance or coloring, pulse, grimace or reflex irritability, activity, and respiration. Any significant differences from the normal response in each of these areas may require further testing and observation.

LESSON 1 REVIEW

Reviewing Facts and Vocabulary

1. Use the following terms in a paragraph to demonstrate your understanding of their meanings: *embryo, fetus, zygote, blastocyst.*
2. List the main events of pregnancy in the order that they occur, beginning with fertilization and ending with birth.
3. Why is prenatal care important?
4. What are the risks involved in drug use during pregnancy?

Thinking Critically

5. **Analysis.** How is proper nutrition an example of good prenatal care?
6. **Analysis.** Compare and contrast an embryo and a fetus.

Applying Health Knowledge

7. Design a poster that warns of the dangers of using tobacco, drinking alcohol, or using illegal drugs during pregnancy.

BEFORE BIRTH **143**

Assess

Check for Understanding

- Assign and discuss the lesson review. For LD students, modify question 1 so that they define the terms; assign questions 3, 4, and 5.

Evaluate

- Administer, grade, and discuss the *Lesson 1 Quiz.*

Reteach

- Have students prepare a time-line that summarizes physical development in the uterus throughout pregnancy.
- Ask students to complete *Reteaching Activity 18.*

Enrich

- Have students do a study of midwifery—the use of midwives in childbirth. What is it? How often are midwives used in the United States? What percentage of these are women? How often are midwives used in other parts of the world? What kind of training is required? In what kinds of settings do midwives usually practice? What might be the benefits and drawbacks of using a midwife during childbirth? If possible, invite a midwife to class to address these topics.

Close

Tell students that in this lesson we have seen the importance of the environment of the womb in the normal development of the fetus. If the fetus is exposed to drugs or other harmful substances, the result may be lifelong disease or disability.

However, fetal development and the newborn's traits are not just the results of environmental influences during pregnancy. Much of what we are by the time we are born is due to the genes our parents pass on to us. How we get our genes and how they affect us are explained in the next lesson, which is about heredity.

Answers to Lesson 1 Review

1. For definitions, see pages 137 and 139 or Glossary. Paragraphs will vary.
2. Fertilization, implantation, development of the placenta and umbilical cord, fetal development, birth.
3. The pregnant female's health choices affect her health and that of the developing baby.
4. Babies can be born dependent on drugs or suffer from serious birth defects.
5. The pregnant female's diet provides nourishment for herself and the fetus.
6. Embryo—vital organs begin developing; appendages start to form; heart starts beating. Fetus—moves; nails/hair/eyelashes form; eyes open; organs develop; can live on its own at end of pregnancy.
7. Posters will vary.

Focus

Lesson Objectives

After studying this lesson, students should be able to:
- summarize the process of heredity
- identify and explain genetic disorders

Bellringer

Write the following on the chalkboard for students to work on while attendance is being taken: *Sit in your seat with your hands resting on the desk in front of you, fingers intertwined. Make note of which thumb is on top. Then change the position of your hands so that the other thumb is on top. How does that feel?*

Introducing the Lesson

Refer to the Bellringer. Ask how many of the students had the right thumb on top and how many had the left thumb on top when they first put their hands together. Ask volunteers to comment on how it feels to hold their hands in the position that didn't "come naturally." Explain that the tendency to hold the hands in one position or the other is genetically controlled; putting the hands in the other position usually feels strange and awkward. Tell students that in this lesson they will learn how traits such as this are passed from parents to their children. Add that they will also learn what happens when the process of heredity goes awry.

DID YOU KNOW?

- Many genetic disorders are caused by abnormalities in the X chromosome. According to the March of Dimes, male children have a 50 percent chance of inheriting an X-linked genetic disorder while female children have a 50 percent chance of being a carrier—or the person who passes on the genetic disorder to the next generation.

HEREDITY AND GENETICS

LESSON 2 FOCUS

TERMS TO USE
- Heredity
- Chromosomes
- Genes
- Fraternal twins
- Identical twins

CONCEPTS TO LEARN
- Heredity is a complex process.
- There are many types of genetic disorders.
- Scientists are continuing to explore the causes of many genetic disorders.

ATTITUDES AND BEHAVIORS TO EVALUATE
- Self-Inventory, page 154.
- Building Decision-Making Skills, page 155.

P erhaps no other area of health and the human body is as fascinating as heredity. **Heredity** is the passing of characteristics from parents to offspring. It is heredity that determines what makes you *you*.

Chromosomes and Genes

The process of heredity begins in complex structures called chromosomes. **Chromosomes** are tiny structures within the nuclei of cells. Chromosomes are found in all body cells, except mature red blood cells, which have no nuclei.

Genes are small sections of chromosomes that control hereditary characteristics. Through the genes, characteristics of the mother and father are passed to the offspring. For example, your genes determine your resemblance to your mother or father, the color of your hair, and the color of your eyes. This happens because genetic information merges when an ovum and sperm unite.

Structure of the Chromosomes

Every living organism has a certain number of chromosomes. Human body cells, with the exception of sperm and ova, contain 46 chromosomes. Ova and sperm have half that amount—23 chromosomes each. After fertilization the zygote has 46 chromosomes (23 from each parent), and the hereditary traits of the mother and the father are passed on to another generation.

As you know, the zygote divides, eventually producing trillions of cells that make up the human body. In between each cell division, each chromosome in the cell nucleus duplicates itself. As the cell divides, the two sets of 46 chromosomes separate and each new cell contains 46 chromosomes, identical to those in the first cell. This process continues throughout life.

Girl or Boy? Will the baby be a girl or a boy? Of the 46 chromosomes in a zygote, 2 are specialized sex chromosomes. In females, these two chromosomes look exactly alike and are called X chromosomes. In males, one chromosome is shorter and does not match the other. This smaller one is the Y chromosome. The larger one is the X chromosome.

Remember that sperm and ova contain only half the number of chromosomes as other cells. This means that these cells contain only one sex chromosome, not two. Sperm may contain either an X or a Y chromosome. The ovum can have only an X chromosome. If an ovum is fertilized by a sperm carrying an X chromosome, the baby is a girl because, as the chromosomes pair, the combination is XX. If the sperm is carrying a Y chromosome, the pairing forms an XY combination, resulting in a boy. So the determination of the sex of a child is based on the father's sperm.

144 CHAPTER 8 THE BEGINNING OF THE LIFE CYCLE

Resources for Lesson 2

- **Workbook** Vocabulary Activity 19
- **Reteaching** Activity 19
- **Lesson 2 Quiz**

Science and Technology Videodisc
Human Biology, Side 2
Ch 17 Detecting Cystic Fibrosis

 Side 2, Ch 17

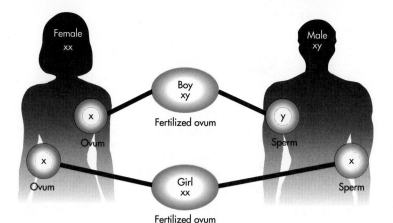

A female produces egg cells that all have the X chromosome. A male produces sperm that have either an X chromosome or a Y chromosome. Whichever sperm fertilizes the egg cell determines the sex of the offspring.

The Genetic Code

As in the case of almost all other body cell activities, the process of heredity involves complex chemical activity. The special chemical compound necessary for the process of heredity is deoxyribonucleic acid (DNA). The DNA code is also called the genetic code.

Each gene consists of a part of a DNA molecule. The DNA molecule resembles a twisted ladder, the rungs being made up of chemical compounds called *bases*. There are four kinds of bases that can be paired in only certain combinations according to their size, much like a jigsaw puzzle.

You have thousands of genes in every cell, and they all contain the same four bases. The variation among genes is a result of the arrangement of these bases along the DNA molecule. Since several hundred pairs of bases are in each gene, a countless number of arrangements is possible.

Cells will make proteins when they interpret the order of these bases, or DNA code. Proteins help build and maintain body tissues. Cells make different proteins when they interpret different orders of bases. Different kinds of proteins will result in individual traits.

Dominant and Recessive Genes

As you can see, the process of heredity is extremely complicated. What determines whether you have blue eyes or brown eyes, straight hair or curly hair? Every person inherits two genes for every trait—one from the mother and one from the father. As the chromosomes divide and separate, the two genes for a particular trait line up next to each other.

Let us take the trait of eye color as an example. The gene for brown eyes (B) is dominant over the gene for blue eyes (b). The gene for blue eyes is recessive.

In the case of many traits, one gene is dominant and the other recessive. This simply means that when the pair of genes lines up, the dominant gene overpowers the recessive one and determines that particular trait.

DID YOU KNOW?

■ One in every 2,000 infants is born with cystic fibrosis. The disease, which makes breathing and digestion difficult, is caused by two abnormal genes, one coming from each parent. There are about 8 million Americans who carry this gene, and many are not aware of the fact. If both parents are carriers, their offspring have a 25 percent chance of having the disease.

Teach

Guided Practice

LD EXPLANATION. Do not expect LD students to learn the specifics of chromosomes. They should be able to describe their function.

LEP DEMONSTRATION. Show the class pictures of individuals that reveal the diversity of humans with regard to a few of the obvious physical traits mentioned in the text, such as eye color, nose shape, and body size.

L1 DISCUSSION. What traits, other than obvious physical features, are genetically influenced to some degree? (For example, abilities such as artistic talent, mental disorders such as schizophrenia, destructive behaviors such as alcoholism, and personality traits such as shyness.)

L1 CLASS ACTIVITY. To help students make sense of and better appreciate the extent of human diversity, work with them to create categories of traits that vary. Consider the following: skin color, eye color, and hair color are all related traits of pigmentation; ABO blood type and Rh type are both blood-chemistry traits; height and weight are traits of body size and shape.

L1 EXPLANATION. Explain that many traits that are controlled by one or more genes are also influenced by environmental factors (e.g., body weight and skin color).

L1 DISCUSSION. Why do we not resemble our parents completely? What is the role of the environment in shaping how our genetic makeup is expressed?

Overcoming Misconceptions

Heredity. Contrary to popular belief, most traits aren't simply controlled by one gene, but instead are influenced by many genes and the environment in a complex, interactive way. Such traits are called polygenic. The genes controlling a given polygenic trait may or may not be located on the same chromosome, and tremendous numbers of genetic and environmental combinations can be produced. The result is a bewildering degree of diversity across the species.

Good examples of polygenic traits are: skin color (controlled by some half-dozen genes and exposure to sunlight), weight, height (controlled by many genes, diet, and exercise).

L1 DISCUSSION. Are identical twins really identical in every way? (Two genetically identical individuals could never have identical environments, allowing for differences in growth and development.) How might "identical" twins differ? (Height, weight, skin color.)

L1 DISCUSSION. Where in the cell do you find the chromosomes? Are they found in all of the cells of the body?

LEP DEMONSTRATION. Explain the relationship of genes to chromosomes by showing students a slide, transparency, or three-dimensional model of the DNA molecule.

L1 DISCUSSION. Why do sperm and ova have only half as many chromosomes as other cells in the body?

L1 EXPLANATION. Explain that the 46 chromosomes making up normal human cells actually consist of 23 pairs of chromosomes. (This is how ova and sperm, which have only one of each type of chromosome, can still carry a gene for each human trait.)

L1 CLASS ACTIVITY. Show how genes are passed from a set of parents to their children by drawing a diagram on the chalkboard. Use a capital and lower-case letter to represent dominant and recessive expressions of a single trait (e.g., D for dimples, d for no dimples). Ask student volunteers to write in all the possible combinations of the two genes in the children and how each type of child would appear.

L1 DISCUSSION. How is it that the father alone determines the sex of the child, even though each child receives half of his or her genes from each parent?

L2 DISCUSSION. If a person has the same genes in every cell, why do cells differ so greatly from each other (e.g., blood cells versus skin cells)?

L2 DISCUSSION. Why do some families have all or mostly boys and others all or mostly girls, even though any given child has an equal chance of being a boy or girl?

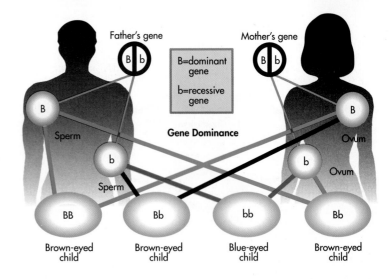

If each parent has one dominant gene and one recessive gene for eye color, their children will have a 75 percent chance to be brown-eyed and a 25 precent chance to be blue-eyed.

Consider, however, the possible combinations. If both parents have one dominant gene and one recessive gene for eye color, they both have brown eyes. Since both parents have a dominant gene for brown eyes, there is a one in four chance that they will have a blue-eyed child. There are three chances in four that they will have a brown-eyed child.

Genetic Disorders

When you consider the countless number of divisions and processes that must take place to form a fully developed baby, it truly is amazing that most babies are born healthy and normal. However, it is estimated that as many as 250,000 children may be born in the United States every year with major hereditary conditions and disorders that will seriously impair their health.

According to the National Institute of Health, 15 million Americans have some kind of genetic condition or birth defect. At least 40 percent of all infant mortality is the result of genetic factors. Millions of Americans are healthy themselves, but are carriers of defective genetic information. Many do not know it until they have a child born with a birth defect.

DID YOU KNOW?

■ Scientists have recently located the gene that causes Fragile X syndrome, the most common form of mental retardation that is inherited. The Fragile X syndrome occurs at a rate of 1 in 1,000 females and 1 in every 1,500 males. Its symptoms include various degrees of retardation as well as behavioral problems. Some people who inherit the gene may be normal but may be carriers—able to pass it on to future generations.

DOMINANT AND RECESSIVE TRAITS

Dominant	Recessive
curly hair	straight hair
black or brown hair	blonde or red hair
full lips	thin lips
dimples	smooth cheeks
straight nose	turned-up nose
brown eyes	blue eyes
long, full eyelashes	short, thin eyelashes
freckles	no freckles

146 CHAPTER 8 THE BEGINNING OF THE LIFE CYCLE

Additional Information

Function of Genes. Almost everyone knows that genes control heredity, but most people are unaware that genes also control the reproduction and daily functioning of all cells. It's largely through the activity of regulatory and operator genes that different types of cells differ from each other in structure and function. Operator genes excite nearby genes into activity unless they are repressed by a repressor substance secreted by regulatory genes.

Scientists are learning more and more about the role of genes through the Human Genome Project, a nationally funded, multi-faceted research project whose aim is to determine the function of the entire human "genome" (the total genetic makeup of the species).

THE MYSTERY OF TWINS

In most cases of twins, a female's ovaries release two mature ova instead of one. If a separate sperm fertilizes each ovum, two embryos develop. The two embryos, called **fraternal twins,** have different genetic makeup and therefore do not look any more alike than brothers and sisters normally do. Fraternal twins can be the same sex or different sex.

In about one-third of the cases of twins, identical twins result. In this situation, a single ovum that has been fertilized divides and two embryos develop. These embryos have the same genetic information. These twins will be the same sex and look almost exactly the same. They are **identical twins.**

Research on twins has been expanding greatly. Researchers now use twins to study a variety of physical health problems, as well as questions about psychological development and adjustment.

Twins and Genetic Research

Researchers are currently using twins to study

- genetic influence on temperament;
- genetic and environmental influence on fears and phobias, language development, and intelligence;
- genetic influence on antisocial behavior;
- the onset of alcoholism and affective emotional disorders;
- the causes of cancer and multiple sclerosis;
- the genetic components of coronary heart disease.

Researchers got an unexpected boost from the discovery of identical twins who had been separated from each other at birth. Neither twin nor his adoptive family knew about the other until the twins were reunited at age 39. The similarities in Jim Lewis and Jim Springer were startling. Researchers will try to determine how much was coincidental and how much was the result of being identical twins. What do you think?

- In school they both liked math and disliked spelling.
- Their first wives were both named Linda.
- They had both divorced and remarried, and their second wives were both named Betty.
- Both had a son named James Allen (one spelled Alan), and a dog named Tag.
- Both had gained weight at the same time, and had had the same kind of surgery.
- Both had a white seat around a tree in his yard.

Identical twins have the same genetic makeup. They are always the same sex.

Types of Genetic Disorders

There are more than 4,000 known types of genetic conditions and birth defects. In the broadest definition, any quality an individual inherits is a genetic condition. As used here, however, *genetic condition* refers to genetic diseases and disorders, illnesses, or other conditions of malfunction with which an individual is born.

Any disease, disorder, or other problem present at birth can impair an individual's health. Only a few of the disorders occurring at birth have a known genetic cause. Some are the result of environmental factors. Thus, the term *birth defects* includes not only genetic conditions but many other types of diseases and disorders that are caused by a variety of other factors.

Some birth defects are immediately observable at birth. These include physical malformations, such as cleft lip, cleft palate, and clubfoot.

FINDING HELP

Hormonal dwarfism may occur when hormone deficiency interferes with normal growth of cartilage cells. Nonhormonal dwarfism is associated with severe malnourishment. Diseases of the bowel or kidneys also may interfere with growth. For more information about dwarfism, contact:

- Little People of America
  7238 Piedmont Drive
  Dallas, Texas
  75227-9324

HEREDITY AND GENETICS **147**

L2 DISCUSSION. How can research on twins help us understand more about how our genes influence who we are?

L3 DISCUSSION. Have a student-led open discussion of how research on the function of each gene might be misused (this refers to the Human Genome Project). Consider reasons such as: discrimination against job applicants; rejection of individuals for medical insurance; manipulation of the genetic makeup of future generations.

L1 EXPLANATION. Explain why two normal carriers of the gene that causes the genetic disorder phenylketonuria (PKU) have a 25 percent chance of having a child affected by PKU.

L2 DISCUSSION. What is the role of the environment in the genetic disorder phenylketonuria (PKU)?

L2 DISCUSSION. What is the role of genetic counseling in coping with genetic disorders like Tay-Sachs and PKU?

L1 SPEAKER. Invite a representative from the March of Dimes to speak to the class regarding the agency's role in fighting birth defects.

L1 DISCUSSION. Why, for a genetic disorder like Marfan's syndrome, does it take just one parent with the gene to pass on the disorder to the children? Why must both parents be affected for a disease like cystic fibrosis to be inherited? What can you conclude about the relative frequencies of dominant and recessive disorders? (Dominant traits have the potential to be more common than recessive ones.)

L1 SPEAKER. Invite a genetics counselor from a local hospital or practice to speak to the class about genetic disorders and how they can be prevented through genetics counseling.

L1 DISCUSSION. What is amniocentesis? Why is it, along with some of the other methods of investigating the health of the fetus, controversial to some individuals and groups?

L2 DISCUSSION. What is the difference between ultrasonography and fetoscopy?

Additional Information

Down Syndrome. Down syndrome is caused by chromosome error. Instead of the normal 46 chromosomes, children with Down syndrome are born with 47. The mother's age is associated with Down syndrome. Babies born to older mothers—over age 35—have a dramatically increased risk. Scientists believe that the older egg cell is more likely to divide incorrectly.

Common in the child affected by Down syndrome are mental retardation; folded eyelids that make the eyes appear slanted; poor muscle tone; slightly dwarfed physique; low-set ears; broad, short hands; and a flat nose.

With family and professional support, Down syndrome children can work to their own potential and offer much love to a family.

L1 **SPEAKER.** Invite an obstetrician or obstetrical nurse to visit your class. Ask him or her to discuss medical tests available to monitor fetal development. What are the advantages of these tests? What are the risks? Under what conditions is each test recommended?

L1 **DISCUSSION.** What are X-linked traits? Why are males more often affected by X-linked traits, even though they have only one X chromosome?

Independent Practice

L2 **RESEARCH.** Ask students to research the number of chromosomes characteristic of other species of animals, including those closely related to humans (such as chimpanzees and gorillas) and those very distant from humans (such as reptiles and fish). Have students share the results of their research with the class.

L2 **COMMUNITY INVOLVEMENT.** Ask students to interview their friends and relatives in order to compile a list of traits commonly believed to be genetically determined. In class, discuss the list and correct misconceptions.

LEP **RESEARCH.** Ask students to count the number of pairs of twins that they know of and provide pictures of twins to show the class. Can they guess which pairs are identical twins and which are fraternal twins from the pictures? Can they observe any traits by which identical twins differ?

L1 **RESEARCH.** Have students research the process of cell division (mitosis). Ask volunteers to explain to the class how it works by drawing diagrams on the chalkboard.

L2 **READING.** Have students read scientific articles reporting current findings about the following topics: chromosomes, genes, DNA, the genetic code. Have students write summaries of their readings.

CONFLICT RESOLUTION

Jackie is a typical teen in many ways: she likes to spend time with her friends, has a crush on her favorite rapper, and is excited about her future. Jackie, however, has Down syndrome. Because her parents have helped her maximize her potential, Jackie's achievements have exceeded everyone's expectations. Yet, many of Jackie's peers can see only her disability. Their attitudes range from being overly protective to feeling uncomfortable around her. She wishes people would just accept her as she is.

How do you think Jackie can convince her peers that in many ways she's no different from them?

What would convince you?

While other congenital defects may be present at birth, testing is required to confirm their presence.

Some conditions that may be present at birth do not generate observable symptoms until the infant is several months to a year or more old. Among these are Tay-Sachs disease—a disorder causing the destruction of the nervous system, cystic fibrosis—a disorder that affects the mucous-secreting glands and the sweat glands, sickle-cell anemia—an inherited blood disorder, phenylketonuria (PKU)—an inherited enzyme deficiency, and hearing loss.

Various types of mental retardation, and minimal brain dysfunction cannot be observed until the infant begins, or fails to begin, progressing through the normal stages of physical development.

Identifying Genetic Disorders

In spite of many years of advanced research, medical scientists still are uncertain about the exact causes of many human congenital defects. Scientists do know, however, that a principal cause of birth defects is chromosomal abnormality.

Since chromosomes contain genes responsible for inherited characteristics, even the slightest abnormality can cause severe developmental problems in a fetus. Most miscarriages in early pregnancy are the result of chromosomal abnormalities.

The most serious chromosomal abnormalities are the result of fetal cells that contain more or less than the usual number of chromosomes. Down syndrome is an example. Down syndrome is a condition that results when an individual has 47 chromosomes instead of 46. Down syndrome results in abnormalities of the face and other parts of the body and physical and mental retardation.

Severe birth defects can also occur when parts of chromosomes break off and join onto other chromosomes. This interferes with the normal transmission of genetic information.

There are several methods used to investigate the health of a fetus:

- Amniocentesis, in which a syringe is inserted through the pregnant female's abdominal wall into the amniotic fluid surrounding the developing fetus. The physician removes a small amount of the fluid to examine the chromosomes, study the body chemistry, and determine the sex of the fetus. Amniocentesis is performed usually 16 to 20 weeks after fertilization.

KEEPING FIT

Dealing with Disabilities

Think of someone you know or have seen or read about who has a disability. Ask yourself the following questions, vowing to see the "differently abled" as complete human beings and to concentrate from now on on their abilities rather than on their disabilities.

- Do I see the person's disabilities first?
- What special abilities might I instead focus on seeing

and appreciating?
- How would I feel if I were seen only in terms of a disability?
- What steps can I take to help others see that disabilities does not mean inabilities?

Additional Information

Miscarriage. A miscarriage is the natural interruption of pregnancy causing the embryo or fetus to be expelled. Studies show that approximately 15 to 20 percent of all diagnosed pregnancies end in miscarriage. Most miscarriages are caused by genetic defects in the embryo or fetus or by abnormal implantation of the placenta. Infectious disease, physical trauma, or poor environment in the uterus may also cause miscarriage.

Bleeding from the vagina and low abdominal pain are early signs of impending miscarriage. Many miscarriages could be prevented if a female received good health care before and during pregnancy.

Overcoming The Odds

Jeff Barnett is 14. He is a good athlete, a good student, a good son. Some people think he is an only child, but Jeff knows better. The family photos around his house show 3 boys, not 1. Jeff is the only son who has survived. Jeff's 2 brothers, Chuckie and Michael, died of a rare genetic disorder called Leigh's disease. Jeff was 2 and 6 when his brothers died.

Chuckie Barnett became ill first. He developed fevers, muscle weakness, motor and eye problems. He gained a lot of weight. No one could figure out what was wrong—even medical specialists. Then, on a family trip, Chuckie suddenly became ill and died a short time later.

Brain tissue samples sent for testing after Chuckie's death indicated that he had Leigh's disease. For the first time, the Barnetts had a definite diagnosis.

Soon after Chuckie's death, Michael began to show the same symptoms, and for over two years, the Barnetts watched him get worse.

Jeff says, "I don't feel guilty that I'm alive. I just feel it's not right that two of the three kids in my family had this disease when it is so rare.

"I never feel low or totally down because my brothers died. I think my self-esteem is pretty high because I know I can accomplish a lot. My parents haven't treated me as if I'm their only son, either, and they haven't been as overprotective as they might have been. They've given me all the

space I've needed, and that's been just great for me."

Jeff and his parents have done a lot to pay tribute to Chuckie and Michael and to turn their double tragedy into positive action and caring for others. Jeff says, "At the preschool that Chuckie attended, there is a dogwood tree planted in his memory with a plaque next to it. At Michael's school, a greenhouse was built in his memory with a plaque and a tree was planted for him, too. Then my mother

decided she wanted to do something more about all of this."

In 1990, the Michael and Charles Barnett Center was opened at St. Christopher's Hospital for Children in Philadelphia. The Center's goals include early diagnosis and treatment for those affected by the disease.

With the help of a company called Child's Play Touring Theater, the Barnetts continue to raise funds for the Center. They have developed a program called "Child's Play" in which local school children write poems and stories, the theater company dramatizes them, and the money raised at performances goes toward their cause. In the process, they bring joy to a great many children.

Jeff understands that individuals and their families can make a difference. He says, "This project makes me feel great. Now I know that other people who have Leigh's disease may have a better chance of surviving it."

1. Many people who lose relatives feel survivor's guilt. For what reasons do you think Jeff hasn't suffered from this feeling?
2. Jeff seems to have high self-esteem. What factors in his life might have contributed to this?

- **Discussion.** What other genetic disorders lead to physical deterioration and death in childhood, as in Leigh's disease? (Tay-Sachs, which causes nervous-system degeneration and death by age 3. Sickle-cell anemia, which may lead to early death due to a defect in the blood.)
- **Discussion.** Do you think survivors feel differently if a brother or sister dies in an automobile accident than if they die from a genetic disorder, as in Jeff Barnett's family? (Most accidental deaths occur soon after the accident, if not instantly, whereas slow deterioration and great suffering may accompany a fatal genetic disorder; fault often can be placed on an individual in the case of accidental death—a higher power or bad luck may be blamed in the case of a genetic disorder.)
- **Answers**
1. Because the family paid tribute to his brothers and turned the tragedy of their deaths into help for others.
2. Being a good athlete and student and being treated as a normal child by his parents.

L2 COMMUNITY INVOLVEMENT. Assign students to find out if any research on the Human Genome Project is underway in a local university or other research facility. If so, ask them to report to the class on which piece of the puzzle is being worked on.

L1 RESEARCH. Have students research the genetic disorder Tay-Sachs. They should prepare brief reports to present to the class.

L2 COMMUNITY INVOLVEMENT. Arrange for students to tour a local Department of Health to learn about state screening programs for newborn infants.

L2 RESEARCH. Ask students to research other causes of birth defects, in addition to genetic disorders.

L1 USING THE LESSON RESOURCES. For additional student activities, refer to the lesson resources on page 144.

Overcoming Misconceptions

X-Linked Traits. It is commonly thought that X-linked traits affect only males. In reality, females are also affected—just not as often.

The reason males are affected more often is that they have only one X chromosome. If a male's one X chromosome carries a gene for a particular recessive trait, such as color blindness, that gene will be expressed.

For females, on the other hand, a recessive X-linked trait will only be expressed if it is carried on both X chromosomes. The chance of inheriting two affected X chromosomes is considerably less than the chance of inheriting just one. The result? Fewer females show X-linked traits.

Check for Understanding

- Assign and discuss the lesson review. For LD students, questions 1, 2, 3, and 5 are most appropriate. Provide names and/or articles for question 5.

Evaluate

- Administer, grade, and discuss the *Lesson 2 Quiz*.

Reteach

- Have students do a "chalk talk" in which they explain and diagram the process of heredity, showing how a simple trait is passed from parents to children.
- Ask students to complete *Reteaching Activity 19*.

Enrich

- Ask students to explore genetic engineering. Why is it controversial? What ethical questions come into consideration as scientists learn more about genetics? Ask students to summarize their findings in written reports.

Close

Tell students that in this lesson we've considered some congenital defects that are obvious at birth, including cleft palate, clubfoot, and Down syndrome. Other congenital defects, such as PKU and sickle-cell anemia, can be detected at birth with lab tests. Still other congenital defects cannot be observed until the infant fails to develop normally in some way. In order to assess whether an infant or child is developing normally, we need to know how a normal child develops. In the next lesson, we will see one view of what the normal stages of childhood development are.

DID YOU KNOW?

- A person's height is in large part determined by heredity but is also affected by environmental influences like diet. Because of better nutrition, health care, and health standards, average height of people who live in Japan, Europe, and the United States has increased steadily over the past few decades.

- Ultrasound, in which sound waves are used to project light images on a screen. The sound waves are directed at the pregnant female's abdomen and reflected onto a screen. The reflected waves act like an echo and form an image of the fetus. Ultrasound is used to determine the position of a fetus, and if there is more than one fetus in the uterus.
- Chorionic villi sampling (CVS), in which a small piece of membrane is removed from the chorion, a layer of tissue that develops into the placenta. This matter is examined for possible genetic defects. The procedure takes place around the eighth week of fetal development, so it is a procedure that can be done earlier than amniocentesis. In many cases, the results of a CVS are later confirmed by amniocentesis.

Passing on Genetic Disorders

Genetic disorders are passed on much like other physical traits; that is, there are dominant and recessive traits. The mother is the carrier of X-linked conditions. While the mother is not affected, she carries one abnormal gene and one normal gene in her sex chromosomes. There is a 50 percent risk that each male child will be affected by a disease and a 50 percent risk that each female child will be a carrier. Among the more common X-linked conditions are certain forms of color blindness, hemophilia, and muscular dystrophy.

Advances in Human Genetics

Medical professionals have gained much knowledge about genetically related diseases and disorders, and about new research techniques for diagnosing, preventing, and treating such conditions. This knowledge has produced a wide expansion of programs to deal with genetic conditions and birth defects.

One way to help prevent genetically caused birth defects is to identify carriers. Genetic counselors can advise families about the probability of having a child with a genetically related disease. They also can guide families of children with genetic disorders about possible treatment options.

LESSON 2 REVIEW

Reviewing Facts and Vocabulary

1. Define *heredity*, *chromosomes*, and *genes*.
2. List two means of identifying genetic disorders, and describe the processes involved.

Thinking Critically

3. **Analysis.** Compare fraternal to identical twins.

4. **Evaluation.** What are your views regarding the use of amniocentesis as a means of diagnosing disorders or of finding out the sex of a baby before birth?

Applying Health Knowledge

5. Write a one-page descriptive paper about the work of a noted genetic scientist.

Answers to Lesson 2 Review

1. Heredity—the passing of characteristics from parents to offspring. Chromosomes—tiny structures within the nuclei of cells. Genes—tiny protein molecules that control hereditary characteristics.
2. Answers will vary. Accept two of the following: amniocentesis; ultrasound; chorionic villi sampling. Descriptions of these methods can be found on pages 148 and 150.
3. Fraternal twins have different genetic makeup and do not look exactly alike. They may or may not be the same sex. Identical twins have the same genetic makeup.
4. Answers will vary.
5. Answers will vary.

BIRTH TO LATE CHILDHOOD

Throughout life you grow and develop physically, socially, emotionally, intellectually, and culturally. Your growth and development is predictable; it follows certain general patterns. However, you will grow and develop at a rate that is unique to you. Your growth and development are affected by your heredity, your environment, and your health decisions.

Several noted scientists have presented theories, or models, of how people develop. These models are helpful in knowing what to expect at different stages in your life.

Developmental Tasks

Experts who have studied growth and development have identified certain basic stages. For each stage, developmental tasks are identified. A **developmental task** is something that needs to occur during a particular stage for a person to continue his or her growth toward becoming a healthy, mature adult. Developmental tasks in adolescence, for example, include forming more mature relationships with peers and achieving emotional independence from parents.

A child learns to trust a parent or other adult as the needs of the child are met and satisfied by the adult.

Lesson Objectives

After studying this lesson, students should be able to:
- describe the first four of Erikson's eight stages of development

Bellringer

Write the following on the chalkboard for students to work on while attendance is being taken: *What is the value of understanding how we grow and develop?* (We can predict the type and rate of growth to be expected in normal individuals—significant deviations may indicate that there is a problem.)

Introducing the Lesson

Refer to the Bellringer. Ask volunteers to share their responses. Tell students that our physical development is well documented and very well understood, whereas our emotional and social development are not so clearly understood. Theories abound in an attempt to explain our personality development. One of the better-known and widely accepted theories of personality development is attributed to psychoanalyst Erik Erikson. His eight stages of development provide one model that explains why we are as we are. The first four of Erikson's eight stages are the focus of this lesson.

Building Vocabulary

- Ask students to find definitions for each of the following terms and then describe a situation that demonstrates that they understand each term: *initiative, guilt, industry,* and *inferiority.*
- Ask students to complete *Workbook Vocabulary Activity 20.*

BIRTH TO LATE CHILDHOOD **151**

LEP **DISCUSSION.** Collect newspaper and magazine pictures of children up to the age of adolescence to illustrate Erikson's first four stages of development. Discuss the developmental tasks associated with each stage.

L1 **DISCUSSION.** What are some ways that parents help a child develop trust versus mistrust?

L1 **DISCUSSION.** How can parents help their children develop a sense of autonomy?

L1 **EXPLANATION.** Explain what initiative means and why children may develop feelings of guilt if the questions and activities they initiate are ignored or belittled.

L1 **EXPLANATION.** Explain how feelings of inferiority and self-doubt may develop if a child's sense of industry is not reinforced.

Independent Practice

L1 **COMMUNITY INVOLVEMENT.** Divide the class into four groups and assign each group one of Erikson's first four stages of development. Ask each group to do a report on how an individual might develop healthy or unhealthy characteristics based on experiences in the stage assigned. Students should interview parents of young children to determine if they are aware of these developmental stages. Have students share the reports with the class.

L1 **PARENTAL INVOLVEMENT.** Ask students to discuss with their parents and write about the stages of development that are occurring in their nuclear and extended families.

L1 **USING THE LESSON RESOURCES.** For additional student activities, refer to the lesson resources on page 151.

Early childhood is a time of learning new skills and gaining independence.

One of the most widely accepted theories of development is presented by psychoanalyst Erik Erikson. He describes stages of development from birth through old age. Our success in each stage has much to do with our experiences during that stage. Erikson believes, however, that failure at one stage can be overcome by successes in following stages.

Stage 1: Infancy—Trust versus Mistrust

From birth to one and one-half years, you experienced the fastest period of growth in your life! Your weight tripled and your height doubled.

The developmental tasks of an infant include learning to eat solid food, beginning to walk, and learning to talk.

In the first year of life, according to Erikson, one of a child's main tasks is that of developing trust. If a child's needs are met promptly and lovingly, he or she learns to view the world as being a safe place and people as being dependable. If a child's needs are inadequately met or rejected, he or she learns to be fearful of the world and people. As you can see, a child's environment plays a major role in his or her development at this stage.

Stage 2: Early Childhood—Autonomy versus Shame and Doubt

During the second and third years of life, children develop many new physical and mental skills. They master walking, learn to climb, and can push and pull. They increase their vocabulary and even begin talking in sentences. Another important developmental task at this age is learning to control the elimination of body wastes.

Children at this age are proud of these accomplishments and personally try to do as many things as possible. Have you ever been around a 2- or 3-year-old who insisted on putting on his or her own shoes or clothes? This behavior is very typical of children's increasing desire for independence.

If parents accept the child's need to do whatever he or she is capable of, then the child will develop a sense of **autonomy,** the confidence that one can control one's own body, impulses, and environment. However, if parents insist on doing everything for the child or are critical when the child attempts things and fails, then the child will develop doubts about his or her abilities.

K E E P I N G   F I T

Modeling Healthy Behavior

Be a positive role model to the children in your life.
- Teach them safety.
- Encourage them to eat nutritious food.
- Talk to them about the importance of sharing their feelings.

Share some of your own feelings with them.
- Discuss with them the importance of treating people of all ages, races, and backgrounds with respect.
- Share with them some healthy

ways to resolve conflicts other than through violence or the use of bad language.
- Talk with them about how smoking, drinking, and drug use can harm them.

Additional Information

Personality Development. Many anthropologists, such as John and Beatrice Whiting, question the universality of Erikson's stages of development. They believe that adult personality depends on the specific child-rearing practices found in a given society, and that these, in turn, have their roots in a society's ways of meeting the basic physical needs of its members. Autonomy, for example, may be an important trait to develop in complex societies such as our own, where self-reliance and independence help ensure social and economic success. In many other societies, however, particularly farming societies, such traits conflict with the need of individuals to work for the benefit of the group.

Stage 3: Childhood—Initiative versus Guilt

During the fourth and fifth years of life, physical abilities develop to the point where a child can initiate play activities rather than merely follow other children. Children at this age often play make-believe, imagining themselves in a variety of adult roles. They copy what they see adults do. They also begin to ask many questions, a sign of intellectual growth.

If parents show approval of these new abilities and activities and encourage questions, children learn initiative, the ability to start something on their own. They also learn to be creative and explore new ideas. If, however, the parent is impatient with all the questions or makes the child think the activities are wrong, the child will likely develop a sense of guilt about self-initiated activities.

Stage 4: Late Childhood—Industry versus Inferiority

Between the ages of 6 and 11, children experience a major part of their social development—school. The developmental tasks at this age reflect social, emotional, intellectual, physical, and cultural growth.

Children learn physical skills necessary for games and activities. They develop basic skills in reading, writing, and calculating. An important task during this stage is building wholesome attitudes toward themselves. Children learn to get along with peers and learn appropriate roles in society. During this stage of development, children develop a conscience. They learn right from wrong. They also develop attitudes toward social groups and institutions.

As children in this stage begin to acquire new skills, they also develop a sense of industry. They begin to make things—cookies, kites, model planes, and the like. The child's sense of industry is reinforced if parents and teachers praise and reward these creative efforts. If, however, an adult scolds the child for making a mess or getting in the way or not following directions, feelings of inferiority and self-doubt may develop.

Late childhood is a time of expanding interests and curiosity about the environment.

LESSON 3 REVIEW

Reviewing Facts and Vocabulary

1. Define the term *developmental task,* and give two examples.
2. What are the main developmental tasks during a child's first year?

Thinking Critically

3. **Analysis.** Compare and contrast the development during the first year of life with the development from 2 to 3 years of age.

Applying Health Knowledge

4. What are some things a parent might say or do to encourage a sense of autonomy in their 3-year-old?
5. Research Jean Piaget's theory of development. How does it compare with Erikson's theory? Summarize in a one-page paper which theory you support and why.

Check for Understanding

- Assign and discuss the lesson review. Have LD students focus on questions 1 to 4.
- Assign and discuss the chapter review.

Evaluate

- Administer, grade, and discuss the *Lesson 3 Quiz.*
- Administer, grade, and discuss the *Chapter 8 Test.*
- Refer to the Performance Assessment strategy for this chapter. See pages T 23 to T 25.

Reteach

- Have students make scrapbooks to illustrate Erikson's first four stages of development. Students should select photographs from magazines that show children doing the developmental tasks for each stage.
- Ask students to complete *Reteaching Activity 20.*

Enrich

- The age 18 months to 3 years is often called the "terrible twos." Have students write an essay that discusses how Erikson's view of this age makes sense of the type of behavior attributed to the terrible twos.
- Ask students to complete *Enrichment Activity 8.*

Close

Tell students that in this chapter we've seen how the individual grows and develops from conception through childhood. We've learned how traits inherited from parents are molded by the environments in which we grow and develop. While heredity and environment usually work together to encourage normal, healthy development, one or both may sometimes lead to abnormality and ill health. Our responsibility as health-seeking individuals is to maximize both genetic and environmental influences on development. This chapter has given some guidance in that direction.

Answers to Lesson 3 Review

1. Something that needs to occur during a particular stage for a person to continue his or her growth toward becoming a healthy, mature adult. Examples will vary. See pages 151 to 153.
2. Learning to eat solid food, beginning to walk, learning to talk, developing trust.
3. Answers will vary. See page 152.
4. Accept and praise the child's attempts to do things independently, offer or suggest things the child could do, encourage the child to do more for himself or herself.
5. Answers will vary. Reports may be researched by teams but summaries should reflect an individual student's opinion.

Helping Students Improve Their Health

Using the Self-Inventory

Reinforcing Vocabulary

- **Tantrum.** A display of bad behavior.
- **Prenatal.** A stage before birth.
- **Day-care center.** A place where children of working parents are cared for while the parents are at work.
- **Self-concept.** The mental image that one has of oneself.
- **Toddler.** A young child.

Teaching Strategies

L1 EXPLANATION. Students who do not have younger siblings may inadvertently score lower than students who have had extensive experience in helping their parents with the care of younger brothers and sisters.

L1 EXPLANATION. Question 12 could be misinterpreted. Some parents may firmly enforce the idea that children are to be seen and not heard. This may be a matter of discipline and respect from which a student may have been raised.

L2 DISCUSSION. Have students discuss the rights, or lack of rights, that children experience in the United States. How are children's rights affected by the premise that children are the property of their parents?

L2 DISCUSSION. Have students debate the appropriateness of physical discipline. How may physical or mental discipline affect the developing self-esteem of the young child?

Self-Inventory

Development During the Early Years: Are You in Touch?

HOW DO YOU RATE?

Number a sheet of paper from 1 through 15. Read each item below and respond by writing either *agree* or *disagree* for each. Total the number of *agree* and *disagree* responses. Then proceed to the next section.

1. A pregnant female has a responsibility to make good health choices for her unborn child.
2. A female should seek prenatal care as soon as she discovers she is pregnant.
3. I have younger brothers, sisters, cousins, or neighbors that I have taken care of.
4. I would like to be a volunteer with an elementary school program.
5. I think any question a child asks deserves an answer.
6. I have visited a day-care center within the last year.
7. Children have a valuable contribution to make to society.
8. The way I treat a younger child has an impact on that child's self-concept.
9. I avoid picking on or teasing younger children.
10. I occasionally enjoy fun-filled, quality time with younger children.
11. Children with special needs can experience a healthy development.
12. I agree with the old saying that children should be seen and not heard.
13. If a baby was crying for no apparent reason and was not hurt, I would just let him or her cry.
14. If a toddler was throwing a tantrum in a store, I would give the child what she or he wanted just to stop the tantrum.
15. If I were taking care of a child who was struggling with a page of simple addition problems, it would be easier for me to do them than to help the child do them independently.

HOW DID YOU SCORE?

For items 1 to 11, give yourself 2 points for each *agree* answer and 0 points for each *disagree* answer. For items 12 to 15 give yourself 2 points for each *disagree* answer and 0 points for each *agree* answer. Find your total, and read below to see how you scored. Then proceed to the next section.

24 to 30
Excellent. Your understanding of child development and attitudes toward children is commendable.

16 to 23
Good. You have a general understanding of child development and the needs of children.

10 to 15
Fair. You might increase your experiences around children to better understand their developmental needs.

0 to 9
Poor. You might be missing out on some enjoyable experiences and an opportunity for a better understanding of children.

WHAT ARE YOUR GOALS?

If your score was between 16 and 30, complete the statements in Part A. If you scored 15 or below, complete the statements in Parts A and B.

Part A

1. I plan to learn more about the developmental needs of children in the following ways: ____.
2. My timetable is ____.
3. I plan to share what I've learned with others by ____.
4. The personal benefit I will receive from accomplishing this goal is ____.

Part B

5. The attitude or behavior toward children I would like to change most is ____.
6. The steps involved in making this change are ____.
7. My timetable for making this change is ____.
8. My reward for making this change will be ____.
9. I will check my progress toward this goal by ____.

Meeting Students' Needs

For students who score *Excellent*. Suggest assisting in a latch-key program or working in a day-care center during the summers or after school.

For students who score *Good*. Suggest seeking career opportunities that deal with helping children, such as teaching, day care, or coaching young children.

For students who score *Fair*. Suggest enrolling in additional high school courses in home economics that may help to develop more skills and knowlege in dealing with young children.

For students who score *Poor*. Discuss how an only child, or the youngest child in a family, may acquire skills in dealing with younger children.

Building Decision-Making Skills

Paula has just found out that her best friend is pregnant. Her friend is the star of the softball team and no one knows about the pregnancy. Her athletic activity has kept her from gaining much weight, and loose clothing helps her hide her secret from her parents, boyfriend, and others. She hopes to finish the season in the next two weeks. She has already accepted a college scholarship. She says she will tell everyone and go to the doctor right after graduation. She wants Paula to help her keep the secret.

WHAT DO YOU THINK?

1. **Choices.** What choices does Paula have?
2. **Consequences.** What are the consequences of each choice?
3. **Decision.** What do you think Paula should do?
4. **Evaluation.** How do you handle situations when people say "I have a secret to tell you, but you have to promise not to tell anyone?" How do you feel afterwards?

Jack is coaching the soccer team his 10-year-old brother plays on. At practice one day Jack overhears his brother mocking another team member because of his ethnic background.

WHAT DO YOU THINK?

5. **Choices.** List three possible choices for Jack.
6. **Consequences.** What are the possible consequences for each choice?
7. **Decision.** What should Jack do? Explain your answer.

Everyone at your table in the cafeteria is making fun of a student who has a disability. They all look at you as if to say, "Come on, join in."

WHAT DO YOU THINK?

8. **Choices.** What are your choices?
9. **Consequences.** What are the probable consequences of each choice?
10. **Decision.** What do you think would you probably do in this situation?

Sheila is seven months pregnant. She and her husband Tom are very excited about her pregnancy. Tom is hoping for a son, Sheila just wants a healthy baby. When Sheila and Tom visit Tom's parents, they go out to dinner to celebrate Tom's mother's birthday. In the restaurant the waiter asks if they want anything from the bar. Because of her pregnancy, Sheila declines. Her father-in-law orders a glass of wine for her anyway.

WHAT DO YOU THINK?

11. **Choices.** What are Sheila's choices?
12. **Consequences.** What are the probable consequences of each choice?
13. **Decision.** What should Sheila do?
14. **Decision.** Would your decision be different if you knew Sheila was aged 21? Under 21?

Discussing the Answers

Situation 1. Be certain that students understand the possible consequences of participating in an activity that could be physically dangerous. Inform students of the possible withdrawal of an academic scholarship if the athlete is pregnant.

Situations 2 and 3. Discuss with students how discrimination continues to exist in society and how one condones such behavior if one allows it to continue, even if one does not engage in such behavior oneself.

Situation 4. The best resolution in this situation may be to simply allow the alcohol to be served and to simply not drink the alcohol.

Helping Students Improve Their Health

Building Decision-Making Skills

Teaching Strategies

L1 CLASS ACTIVITY. Have students participate in a role-play situation in which Paula's friend is confiding in Paula about being pregnant.

L1 CLASS ACTIVITY. Adaptations to this role-play include: (1) How might playing softball jeopardize Paula's friend's pregnancy? (2) What lifetime consequences does Paula's friend have to face as a result of this pregnancy? (3) How will this pregnancy affect her acceptance of a college scholarship? Does Paula's friend's decision to accept this scholarship change depending on whether this is an academic scholarship or a scholarship to play softball in college?

L2 DISCUSSION. What other concerns or decisions must Paula's friend make at this time? What responsibility does she have to her parents, boyfriend, and Paula in whom she has confided? Where should Paula's friend's sense of responsibility be focused? What responsibility does this friend have to Paula, the developing fetus, her parents, or her boyfriend?

L1 DISCUSSION. Have students describe the manner in which Coach Jack should discuss his younger brother's mocking of another team member's ethnicity. When would it be most appropriate for this discussion to take place? What other forms of discrimination have students experienced or witnessed?

L1 DISCUSSION. How might someone discriminate against a person who is physically challenged?

L2 DISCUSSION. What other public situations might Sheila face at this phase of her pregnancy that could affect the health of her developing baby?

Answers to Chapter 8 Review

Using Health Terms

1. Amniotic sac
2. Fetus
3. Obstetrician
4. Dilation
5. Afterbirth
6. Fertilization
7. Labor
8. Heredity
9. Genes
10. Dominant
11. Hemophilia
12. Fraternal twins
13. Autonomy
14. Conscience
15. Initiative

Building Academic Skills

16. Lists will vary.

Recalling the Facts

17. One layer becomes the respiratory and digestive systems; one layer develops into muscles, bones, blood vessels, and skin; one layer becomes the nervous system, sense organs, and mouth.
18. Divide, reproduce, and repair itself.
19. Tissue—cells with a similar structure that do similar work; muscle and blood. Organ—two or more tissue types that perform a specific job; heart, brain, liver, lungs. Body system—a group of organs that work together to perform a common function; digestive system, cardiovascular system, reproductive system.
20. It transfers oxygen and nutrients from the mother's blood to the fetus's blood.
21. A developing baby is totally dependent on the female for oxygen, nutrition, and elimination of waste products. Whatever a pregnant female does to herself, she also does to her baby. If she eats right, exercises, avoids drugs/alcohol/tobacco, and gets regular medical care, the baby will have an excellent chance of being born healthy.
22. Low birth weight.

REVIEW

Using Health Terms

On a separate sheet of paper, write the term that best matches each definition given below.

LESSON 1

1. Thin membrane that forms around an embryo that insulates the embryo from temperature changes.
2. What the embryo is called from the eighth week of pregnancy until birth.
3. Doctor who specializes in the care of a female and her developing baby.
4. The stretching of the muscular neck of the uterus.
5. The placenta expelled after the birth of a baby.
6. The process that occurs when an ovum and a sperm cell unite.
7. Contractions preceding the birth of a baby.

LESSON 2

8. The passing on of characteristics from parents to offspring.
9. Tiny protein molecules that control the passing on of characteristics from parents to offspring.
10. Controlling or more powerful gene.
11. An X-linked genetic condition.
12. Two infants that develop at the same time in the same female from two different fertilized ova.

LESSON 3

13. The confidence that one can control one's self and environment.
14. A sense of right and wrong.
15. The ability to start something on one's own.

Building Academic Skills

LESSON 1

16. **Reading.** Read an article about pregnancy. List five to ten words that are unfamiliar to you. Using the information in the article, write definitions for each of the words on your list. Include the title, author, and source of the article.

Recalling the Facts

LESSON 1

17. What do the three layers of tissue that form in an embryo develop into?
18. What does each cell in the human body, except those that make up the nervous system, have the ability to do?
19. Define *tissue* and give two examples. Define *organ* and give two examples. Define *body system* and give two examples.
20. What is the function of the placenta?
21. How do a female's health choices affect the health of her developing baby?
22. What is the leading cause of death in an infant's first year of life in the United States?
23. Describe the three stages of birth.
24. What is the function of the umbilical cord in a developing baby?
25. What five characteristics of an infant's physical condition are assessed by the Apgar test?
26. What are three substances that are best for a pregnant female to avoid? Explain why.
27. What are some problems an infant suffering from fetal alcohol syndrome might experience?

LESSON 2

28. What will happen if a fertilized ovum divides and forms two embryos?
29. What causes most early pregnancy miscarriages in the United States?
30. What is meant by an X-linked condition?
31. How does the male determine the sex of the baby?
32. What is the relationship between dominant and recessive genes?
33. List seven genetic disorders.

LESSON 3

34. State two developmental tasks for each of Erik Erikson's first four stages of development.
35. What causes an infant to learn mistrust?
36. What leads to autonomy in childhood?

23. First—dilation: the cervix stretches to eventually allow the baby to pass through. This stage includes labor. Second—birth: the baby moves through the cervix and birth canal and out of the mother's body. Third—the expulsion of the placenta.

24. It connects the baby to the placenta. Blood vessels in the cord supply the baby with nutrients and oxygen and remove wastes.
25. Coloring, pulse, reflex irritability, activity, and respiration.
26. Drugs, alcohol, and tobacco. These substances move

from the pregnant female's blood to the blood of the fetus and can harm the fetus.
27. See pages 140 to 141.
28. Identical twins.
29. Chromosomal abnormalities.
30. It is a chromosomal abnormality carried in a female's sex chromosome.

REVIEW

Thinking Critically

LESSON 1

37. **Analysis.** Which of the following questions would be important ones for a pregnant female to ask her doctor? Explain why you chose the answers you did.
    a. Can I take something for my headaches?
    b. Do you think it is a boy or a girl?
    c. Is it all right to continue with my aerobics class?
    d. What should I do when I think I'm in labor?
38. **Evaluation.** If a pregnant female goes into a bar or restaurant and orders an alcoholic beverage, should her server refuse to bring it to her? Support your answer.
39. **Synthesis.** What advice might you give a pregnant female who says that smoking calms her worries over giving birth?
40. **Synthesis.** What advice might you give a friend who tells you she wants to get married and her parents won't give their consent so she's trying to get pregnant?

LESSON 2

41. **Synthesis.** How would you explain the similarities given for twins Jim Lewis and Jim Springer?

LESSON 3

42. **Synthesis.** For each of Erikson's first four stages of development, write two comments parents could make to their child to help him or her progress successfully through that stage.

Making the Connection

LESSON 3

43. **Science.** Research one of Erik Erikson's stages of development. Develop a report on how an individual might develop healthy or unhealthy characteristics based on experiences in the stage you're studying. You may wish to interview parents of young children to determine if they are aware of these stages. Draw conclusions on what people do to promote healthy development.

Applying Health Knowledge

LESSON 1

44. Give at least two examples of cells repairing themselves.
45. Immediately after a baby is born he or she is given an Apgar score. What might you say about a baby with a score of 8?
46. Since cigarette smoke can be harmful to a developing baby, what advice would you give to a pregnant female who finds herself in a situation where she is forced to inhale passive smoke?

LESSON 2

47. Select four traits you possess. Find out if each of these traits is dominant or recessive.
48. Sometimes DNA testing is done to identify persons accused of crimes. What is it about DNA that would make this possible?
49. How could you tell if a set of twins had developed from one fertilized egg or two?
50. Can two brown-eyed parents have a child with blue eyes? Can two blue-eyed parents have a child with brown eyes? Explain.

LESSON 3

51. Think back on the developmental tasks you have successfully completed so far. List each developmental task and give the age you were when you completed each one.

Beyond the Classroom

LESSON 1

52. **Community Involvement.** Find out what services your community provides for pregnant teenagers.

LESSON 2

53. **Further Study.** Research different tests that can be done to investigate the health of a fetus. Find out the risks, benefits, and procedures of each.

LESSON 3

54. **Parental Involvement.** Have your parents tell memories they have of you during various developmental stages.

31. An egg cell can contain only an X chromosome. A sperm cell may contain an X or a Y chromosome. When the egg cell and sperm cell unite, the sex chromosomes combine. An XX combination is a female, XY is a male.
32. If a dominant and recessive gene combine, the characteristic carried by the dominant gene will appear in the offspring. If two recessive genes combine, the recessive trait will be passed on.
33. Answers will vary. Possible answers: Cleft lip, cleft palate, clubfoot, Tay-Sachs disease, cystic fibrosis, sickle-cell anemia, phenylketonuria (PKU), hearing loss, mental retardation, Down syndrome, color blindness, hemophilia, muscular dystrophy.
34. Answers will vary. Possible answers can be found on pages 152 to 153.
35. His or her needs are inadequately met or rejected.
36. Parents and adults accepting a child's need to do whatever he or she thinks he or she is capable of doing.

Thinking Critically

37. A, C, and D. All have a direct bearing on the pregnant female's health and/or the baby's health.
38. Answers will vary but should be supported logically.
39-42. Answers will vary.

Making the Connection

43. Answers will vary but should be presented logically.

Applying Health Knowledge

44. Answers will vary. Possible answers: A cut healing, a broken bone mending.
45. The baby is doing well for a newborn and is not showing signs of distress.
46. Answers will vary. Possible answers: She could ask the smoker to put out the cigarette, or she could move.
47. Answers will vary.
48. Every individual's DNA is unique.
49. As a layperson, you couldn't tell for certain, but if the twins developed from two

eggs, they would be fraternal twins and could be same-sex or different-sex siblings and could look similar but not identical. If the twins developed from one egg, they would be identical twins and would have to be same-sex siblings and would be so similar in looks as to be indis- tinguishable from one another.
50. Yes, if each parent had a dominant and recessive gene, they would have a 25 percent chance of having a blue-eyed child. No, because blue-eyed parents have only recessive genes to pass along.
51. Answers will vary but may coincide with Erikson's stages of development.

Beyond the Classroom

52-54. Answers will vary.

Lesson Summaries

LESSON 1. Adolescence, the stage between childhood and adulthood, is a period of rapid growth. During puberty, secondary sex characteristics are developed, resulting in physical, mental, and social changes. Accomplishing developmental tasks and developing a positive self-concept or personal identity are critical during this period.

LESSON 2. Adolescence is a difficult and confusing time for many. Goals can guide adolescents during this life stage, helping them develop healthful values and decision-making skills. Peer pressure, personal expectations, and sexuality are influences and issues a teen must face.

Introducing the Chapter

To introduce this chapter, tell students that during adolescence, an individual goes through physical, mental, and social growth. Have them individually list examples of each type of growth. Write their responses on the chalkboard as students share their lists. Tell students that this chapter will explore many of the changes they mentioned, and will discuss the challenges teens face and the choices they must make as a result of these changes.

Performance Assessment ✓

Refer to pages T 23 to T 25 for a Performance Assessment strategy for this chapter. See the *Performance Assessment Activities* booklet for additional suggestions.

CHAPTER

9

ADOLESCENCE

LESSON 1
A Time of Growth and Change

LESSON 2
A Time for Understanding Yourself

158　CHAPTER 9 ADOLESCENCE

Key to Ability Levels

Teaching strategies have been coded for varying learning styles and abilities.

L1 Level 1 activities are basic activities and should be within the ability range of all students.

L2 Level 2 activities are average activities and should be within the ability range of average to above-average students.

L3 Level 3 activities are challenging activities designed for the ability range of above-average students.

LD LD activities should be within the ability range of learning-disabled students.

LEP LEP activities should be within the ability range of Limited English Proficiency students.

A TIME OF GROWTH AND CHANGE

D uring the first year of your life, your weight may have tripled and your height may have increased by as much as 50 percent! It was the most rapid growth period you will ever go through. The second fastest growth period takes place near the beginning of **adolescence**— the stage between childhood and adulthood. Growth is rapid and uneven at this time—a sign of puberty and its changes.

Puberty to Young Adulthood

Between the ages of 9 and 13, children begin to go through puberty, which is Erikson's fifth stage of development. **Puberty** marks the beginning of adolescence and is the period of time when males and females become physically able to reproduce. During puberty secondary sex characteristics begin to develop. **Secondary sex characteristics** include body hair and the development of breasts in the female and muscles in the male.

Physical Change

During puberty the feet and hands grow first and are often large in proportion to the rest of the body. This growth can cause a feeling of awkwardness and clumsiness until the arms and legs catch up. Then the muscles grow to fill out the body's framework.

Up to this stage of development, there is very little difference in the size and shape of males and females. As individuals enter puberty, and for the next four to five years, there is great variation in the size and shape of people who are all about the same age. This variation causes concern for many individuals because this is a time of comparison with others. It is important to remember that these differences are perfectly normal.

Puberty is a result of the release of hormones, chemical substances that are released into the bloodstream and travel to other organs and tissues, where they stimulate growth. The male hormone, **testosterone,** and the female hormones, **estrogen** and **progesterone,** are responsible for the physical and emotional changes that take place during puberty.

Mental Change

During adolescence the brain reaches its adult size and weight. Capacity to think and reason increases. At this age, males and females are able to predict the outcomes of many situations. Whereas during childhood they saw only one solution to a problem, during adolescence they begin to look at different ways of solving problems and making decisions. Adolescents' ability to think logically, or reason things out, increases. They begin to be able to solve more complicated problems.

A TIME OF GROWTH AND CHANGE **159**

LESSON 1 FOCUS

TERMS TO USE
- Adolescence
- Puberty
- Secondary sex characteristics
- Testosterone (te•STAHS•tuh•rohn)
- Estrogen (ES•truh•juhn)
- Progesterone (proh•JES•tuh•rohn)
- Personal identity

CONCEPTS TO LEARN
- Puberty is a time of physical, mental, emotional, and social changes in adolescents.
- Mastering developmental tasks is a significant step toward maturity for the adolescent.

ATTITUDES AND BEHAVIORS TO EVALUATE
- Self-Inventory, page 170.
- Building Decision-Making Skills, page 171.

Focus

Lesson Objectives

After studying this lesson, students should be able to:
- describe the four types of changes that occur during puberty and adolescence
- summarize the developmental tasks of adolescence
- discuss questions that are indicators of a well-developed personal identity

Bellringer

Write the following on the chalkboard for students to work on while attendance is being taken: *Write a paragraph describing adolescence.*

Introducing the Lesson

Refer to the Bellringer. Ask a few volunteers to share their responses. (Some students may describe what it is like being an adolescent, while others may give actual definitions. Others may list particular events that occur during adolescence.) Stress that the variations in growth and the changes in feelings are normal for this age group.

DID YOU KNOW?

In many cultures there are initiation rites, or rites of passage, for adolescents.

- In parts of Indonesia, young males would have to fight in wars with neighboring tribes, a practice replaced in the last few decades by simulated wars and archery contests.
- In parts of Gabon, females who begin menstruation must go into isolation.
- An Apache ceremony honors a female's first menses, or period, with a four-day celebration. She participates in a creation play and is covered with cattail pollen, which symbolizes fertility.

Resources for Lesson 1

- **Transparency** 44
- **Guided Reading** Act 21
- **Workbook** Voc Act 21

- **Reteaching** Act 21
- **Lesson 1 Quiz**
- **BARN,** Human Sexuality

- **Education in Sexuality**
- **Performance Assessment** Activity 9

ABC News InterActive Videodiscs

Teenage Sexuality, Side 1
Ch 3 Changing Bodies

Teenage Sexuality, Side 1
Ch 10 Evolution of American Attitudes

■ Have each student create a crossword puzzle or sentence completion game using all of the vocabulary words. Afterwards, ask them to exchange their puzzle or game with another student. Provide several minutes for them to complete each other's word challenge.

■ Ask students to complete *Workbook Vocabulary Activity 21.*

Teach

Guided Practice

L1 EXPLANATION. Stress that the age at which puberty begins is primarily determined by heredity, although certain aspects of development are affected by the practice of good health habits, such as good nutrition and exercise.

L1 DISCUSSION. How does physical change during adolescence differ from physical change during the first year of life?

L1 DISCUSSION. Have students discuss this statement: *In adolescence, one of the signs of mental change is the ability to see other points of view.*

L1 DISCUSSION. What are some ways that families can help children and adolescents grow mentally? emotionally? socially?

L1 SPEAKER. Invite a school counselor to speak to the class about emotional change during adolescence. Discuss how changes in their bodies may affect teens' emotions.

L1 DISCUSSION. What is a developmental task? What are some of the major developmental tasks during adolescence?

LD DISCUSSION. Have students give examples of each developmental task to demonstrate understanding.

LEP CLASS ACTIVITY. Provide newspapers and magazines, and have students find pictures that illustrate some of the developmental tasks during vadolescence. Then ask students to explain their illustrations.

Many changes occur during puberty.

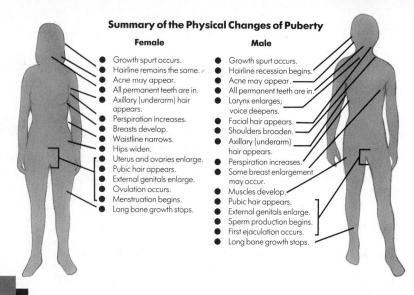

Summary of the Physical Changes of Puberty

Female	Male
● Growth spurt occurs.	● Growth spurt occurs.
● Hairline remains the same.	● Hairline recession begins.
● Acne may appear.	● Acne may appear.
● All permanent teeth are in.	● All permanent teeth are in.
● Axillary (underarm) hair appears.	● Larynx enlarges; voice deepens.
● Perspiration increases.	● Facial hair appears.
● Breasts develop.	● Shoulders broaden.
● Waistline narrows.	● Axillary (underarm) hair appears.
● Hips widen.	● Perspiration increases.
● Uterus and ovaries enlarge.	● Some breast enlargement may occur.
● Pubic hair appears.	● Muscles develop.
● External genitals enlarge.	● Pubic hair appears.
● Ovulation occurs.	● External genitals enlarge.
● Menstruation begins.	● Sperm production begins.
● Long bone growth stops.	● First ejaculation occurs.
	● Long bone growth stops.

Culturally Speaking

Rites of Passage

Many cultures publicly recognize a person's change in status. One such change is the movement from childhood to adult status. The Mbuti of Africa have a special rite that recognizes passage to adulthood. For the first time, boys and girls are separated from each other by the society. Girls are joined by friends and live in a special elima house. A festival is given by the village. Each afternoon the girls sing to the boys who sit outside. The boys respond with their own songs, and the ritual is a type of flirtation where future marriage partners may be chosen.

How does your family or culture recognize the transition to adult status?

During adolescence memory skills improve and memory span increases. This aspect of mental growth assists a person in retaining larger and lengthier bodies of information. As with other skills, mental skills improve with use. Each time teens try out new ways of thinking, reasoning, and making decisions, they gain experience that will help in making later choices. In addition, their thinking becomes more flexible.

As they begin to mature, adolescents discover that they are able to look beyond themselves to understand someone else's point of view. These new thinking skills affect a teen's life both in and out of school. Many will develop new interests and hobbies. Career goals begin to come into focus.

Remember, all of these changes do not just happen overnight; they develop over time. As you try out these new abilities, you are likely to make mistakes—everyone does. What is important is that you learn from those mistakes. For example, ask yourself: What could I have done differently? What might have happened if . . . ? By doing this simple mental exercise, you are practicing your new thinking skills and learning for the future. This skill will last you for life.

Emotional Change

Along with spurts of physical and mental change come spurts of energy and strong emotional feelings. Many teens feel that puberty is like being on a roller coaster—with emotions and feelings that go up and down quickly. It is common for teens to sometimes feel on top of the world one day and down in the dumps the next.

Friendships and family love and support are important, yet adolescents may feel unable to let others know what they are feeling and thinking. This difficulty in communicating thoughts and feelings is a normal part of development.

These extra surges of energy and emotion are caused by changes taking place in the body. The very high level of hormones that stimulate growth in the physical body cause emotional change as well.

Across the Curriculum

Language Arts. Ask students to watch a popular television show which spotlights adolescents as the main characters. Have students write about whether or not the teenagers are depicted realistically. Afterwards, have students identify (and list on the chalkboard) problems faced in the show. Ask students if these problems are the same as theirs. What else would they add to the list? Have students rank in order the problems listed. Next, take time to have students explain reasons the problems exist and what the possible solutions are. After each problem is discussed, ask students to identify who could help resolve the problem. List several possibilities.

Social Change

Social change is another important aspect of the development that occurs during puberty and the rest of adolescence. For instance, friendships and peer acceptance become very important. A growing ability to feel more deeply and to consider others' needs is also part of social development. So is the completion of a set of developmental tasks.

Developmental Tasks

Adolescence has been studied by psychologists and sociologists for more than 50 years. They have identified certain developmental tasks that can be considered basic to adolescence. A developmental task is something that needs to occur during a particular age period for a person to continue his or her growth toward becoming a healthy, mature adult. Robert Havighurst, a well-known sociologist in the field of adolescence, suggests that there are nine such tasks facing teens and, often, people in their 20s. These tasks are as follows:

- forming more mature relationships with people your age of both sexes
- achieving a masculine or feminine social role
- accepting one's physique and using one's body effectively
- achieving emotional independence from parents and other adults
- preparing for marriage and family life
- preparing for a career
- acquiring a set of personal standards as a guide to behavior
- developing social intelligence, which includes becoming aware of human needs and becoming motivated to help others attain their goals
- developing conceptual and problem-solving skills

As you can see, there is quite a lot involved in growing up. Each of these tasks is important and must be achieved before reaching maturity.

Personal Identity

Some researchers group a number of the developmental tasks into a general task of achieving a personal identity. A **personal identity** consists of the factors you believe make you unique, or unlike anyone else. The task of establishing your own personal identity has a great impact

Developing problem-solving skills and learning to use one's body effectively are two developmental tasks for teens.

K E E P I N G F I T

Facing Acne

Acne is a common problem for adolescents. In fact, 4 out of 5 teens have it. It may last for only a year or 2 or for 10 years or more. Acne is not caused by eating chocolate or greasy foods. It is usually caused by male sex hormones called androgens, which are present in both males and females. If you have acne, consider these tips:

- Avoid oil-based makeup and greasy lotions.

- Keep your face and hair clean.
- Change washcloths every day.
- Don't squeeze or scratch acne.
- Avoid sunlamps.
- For severe acne, consult your family doctor or dermatologist.

A TIME OF GROWTH AND CHANGE **161**

Overcoming Misconceptions

Myth. Physical change is the same for all teens. **Fact.** On the average, females start maturing earlier than males, usually between the ages of 8 and 13. Males usually start between the ages of 10 and 13. The development of sex characteristics typically takes four or more years. In females, changes usually progress in this pattern: breast growth, pubic hair, height spurt, first menstruation, pelvic growth, and first ovulation. For males, the order is: pubic hair, testes growth, height spurt, penis growth, voice change, semen production, and face and body hair.

Overcoming The Odds

My name is Roselyn. I'm 15. Not too long ago somebody in my neighborhood was interviewed for this book. I thought it was great, and all, that he had been able to overcome his tough situation. I'm not knocking it. But the more I thought about it the more I thought it was important to say there are lots of teens out there—lots and lots of us—who don't have to face awful tragedies, who don't get into trouble, who just go to school and do their thing and basically do what they're supposed to do. So I called up my friend and found out who to call for this book, and here I am, telling it like it is for many of us."

Roselyn continues with great energy, her hands waving as she speaks. "I have to tell you, if you read the papers, see movies, and watch the news, if you listen to all the talk about how troubled all of us teens are, well, it can get pretty depressing. And it makes me flaming mad, sometimes, too. Sure I know kids who are in trouble with drugs, kids who have sex, people who get into other kinds of trouble now and then. But that's not everybody who's a teenager. I think all those constant messages

that there's Trouble in Teenland do a lot of damage to kids' self-esteem. Do you know what I mean?

"Now if you're asking me why I'm saying all this, I say, 'cause I think it's important to make it known that not all teens are messed up, pot-smoking, window-smashing rejects. I'm 15. I go to school every day. I have a part-time job. I study whenever I can. I'm not a dropout. I don't own a handgun. I don't smoke dope. I don't even smoke cigarettes, for that matter. I'm not pregnant and feel pretty strongly about finishing my education and traveling a lot before I ever settle down."

"Sure, there is arguing sometimes in my family. Sure, there are things I'd change about my body if I could. I'd like to have one main guy in my life and I don't yet. I'd like to be better at algebra and sports and other things. But nobody's perfect. I know that. My parents love me. I know that, too. And I mostly like my brother and sisters, even though they annoy me at times. What I'm trying to say is that you could say I've overcome the odds just by being a quasi-normal, functioning teenager in this crazy, troubled world. And I know there are lots of other teens out there like me, too."

1. How does Roselyn feel about the media's portrayal of today's teens?
2. Is your self-esteem ever affected by the media's messages about teenagers in general? If so, in what ways?
3. If the effects of these messages are damaging to your self-esteem, what steps can you take to ignore, change, or overcome them?
4. What are the dangers in portraying the members of any group—including teens—as uniform, or completely alike?

Across the Curriculum

Home Economics. Adolescents are regarded as a big market by many businesses, and numerous products are marketed with adolescents in mind. Ask students to list products that are directed at adolescents and young adults. (Examples include acne medications, school letter sweaters, class rings, rock music, skateboards, etc.)

Language Arts. There are many books written for and about adolescents. Students often are made more comfortable with their own physical and emotional changes through reading experiences. Using suggestions from the librarian or other sources, have students read one of the books and, when completed, present a short oral report to the class.

on all the other developmental tasks and is centered on your self-concept. Questions such as Who am I? and What do I want to be as a person? are common during this search for identity.

Here are some questions you can ask yourself as you form your own personal identity:

- Am I carrying out my responsibilities on my own, without needing someone to remind me of them?
- Do I get my schoolwork done on time?
- Can I make decisions without my peers influencing me?
- Am I thinking about what I want to do after high school?
- Am I thinking about what I want to do after I finish my education?
- Have I examined my beliefs about what types of behavior are appropriate for males and females?
- Am I aware of the image I project as a male or a female?
- Does my behavior reflect a personal set of values and standards by which I live?
- Do I know what people like and do not like about me?
- Do I expect to work for what I want, rather than just having things done for me?

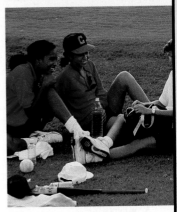

Friendship is important during adolescence. Good friends will not challenge you to do something that goes against what you believe and value.

Friends and Peers

Friendship and peer acceptance are important during adolescence. However, in the process of developing into a healthy adult, it is important for you to establish your own identity, separate from the group.

During adolescence others occasionally will challenge what you stand for, what you believe, and what you think is right or wrong. Good friends, however, will not challenge you to do something that goes against what you believe. They will not try to talk you into doing something that you do not want to do. This is one important guideline for evaluating friendships.

Assess

Check for Understanding

- Assign and discuss the lesson review. Encourage LD students to focus on questions 1, 2, and 4.

Evaluate

- Administer, grade, and discuss the *Lesson 1 Quiz.*

Reteach

- Have each student divide a sheet of paper into three vertical columns. Ask them to label the left column "mental change," and underneath, write examples of ways they have changed mentally in the past 2 years. In the second and third columns, labeled "emotional change" and "social change" respectively, have students list ways they have changed emotionally and socially in the same time period.
- Ask students to complete *Reteaching Activity 21.*

Enrich

- Have students write at least four goals or plans that they have for the next two months. (The possibilities might include getting accepted into an organization, attending a rock concert, getting their driver's license, getting a part-time job, or being able to purchase an item for which they have been saving.) Next to each goal or plan, ask them to describe how it would change or be affected if they were (1) married, (2) pregnant, or a father-to-be, or (3) a parent. Afterwards, lead students in a discussion of the importance of achieving each of the developmental tasks before taking on adult responsibilities.

LESSON 1 REVIEW

Reviewing Facts and Vocabulary

1. What is puberty? What are some of the changes that take place during this stage of development?
2. Write a one-page composition about a day in the life of an adolescent. In the composition use the terms *puberty, secondary sex characteristics,* and *hormones.*
3. Define *personal identity,* and describe the actions of someone you know who has a strong personal identity.

Thinking Critically

4. **Synthesis.** Point out the physical changes occurring during puberty that you believe are the most difficult for many teens to accept. Explain the reasons for your choices.

Applying Health Knowledge

5. Select an empty cereal or detergent box to package yourself. Create a design on the outside to represent your personal identity. On the box, list ingredients, features, and other information to tell about the unique you.

A TIME OF GROWTH AND CHANGE **163**

Answers to Lesson 1 Review

1. A stage of development that marks the beginning of adolescence and during which males and females become physically able to reproduce. Physical, mental, emotional, and social changes associated with puberty are discussed on pages 159 to 161.
2. Compositions will vary. The terms *puberty* and *secondary sex characteristics* are defined on page 159. Hormones are chemical substances that are released into the bloodstream that stimulate growth.
3. Personal identity—the factors one believes make oneself unique. Descriptions will vary.
4. Answers will vary.
5. Answers will vary.

Close

Ask students to state the most important concepts learned in the lesson.

Focus

Lesson Objectives

After studying this lesson, students should be able to:

- discuss how people's goals influence their choices in life
- explain what is meant by peer pressure and its effect on teens
- identify decisions that relate to situations facing many of today's adolescents
- outline factors to consider when making responsible sexual decisions
- describe ways to communicate a decision that they have made
- list contributing factors to teen suicide
- discuss the responsibilities of teen pregnancy and parenthood

Bellringer

Write the following on the chalkboard for students to work on while attendance is being taken: *Divide a sheet of paper into three vertical columns. Label the left column "Six Months," and list 3 goals you would like to achieve within the next 6 months. Label the center column "One Year," and list 3 goals you would like to achieve within the next year. Next, label the right column "Twenty Years Old," and list 3 goals you would like to achieve by the time you are 20 years old.*

Introducing the Lesson

Have students share their responses to the Bellringer. Explain that adolescence is an important time for setting and achieving goals. Talk about some of the obstacles to achieving goals, such as peer pressure, teen pregnancy, and parenthood.

DID YOU KNOW?

- Reports in the 1950s suggested that American youth were not as physically fit as their European peers. This led to the establishment of the President's Council on Youth Fitness in 1956 by President Dwight D. Eisenhower. Today the Council is known as the President's Council on Physical Fitness and Sports.

A TIME FOR UNDERSTANDING YOURSELF

LESSON 2 FOCUS

TERMS TO USE
- Goals
- Peers
- Abstinence

CONCEPTS TO LEARN
- Adolescence is a time for establishing goals and learning to deal with peer pressure.
- Adolescence is a time of troubles and triumphs.
- Adolescence is a time of significant change, physically, mentally, and socially.

ATTITUDES AND BEHAVIORS TO EVALUATE
- Self-Inventory, page 170.
- Building Decision-Making Skills, page

When someone asks who you are, how do you answer? Do you say something such as, "I'm Kip Martin," "I'm Maria's brother," or "I'm the class president?" Each of these may be an important part of who a person is, but none of them alone truly describes an individual.

You probably have classmates who define themselves according to their friends, their appearance, or their accomplishments. This means of establishing an identity can be a big mistake. These factors may well be important, but they are only a fraction of what makes someone tick. There is much more to understanding an individual.

The Inner You

Adolescence is often a difficult and confusing stage of life. Teenagers can be hard on themselves, and they can be hard on parents, teachers, and friends. The more you know about what is happening during adolescence, the less anxious you will be about what is going on within yourself. What you learn about yourself can assist you in making decisions and in achieving personal goals now and later in adulthood.

Your Goals

The definite plans you have in life are your **goals.** Goals help provide a mental picture of where you plan to go with your life and what you must do to get there. They guide you in the use of time, energy, and other resources.

Goals stem from dreams or hopes that you have. For instance, you may dream of becoming famous, traveling to a foreign country, or managing a business. You may also have dreams that include owning a home, having a family of your own, and helping those less fortunate.

Your dreams and goals are based on what is important to the inner you. Your values determine the kind of person you are. They affect your health practices, how you spend your time, what you decide to buy, and what friends you choose.

Some examples of values are honesty, family, religion, freedom, knowledge, health, respect for others, and respect for the environment. Examining your values will make it easier to understand your feelings and take action that is in line with those values.

Some people go through life avoiding decisions and just letting things happen. Others are pressured by their peers to make choices that are not always the best ones for them. They seem to be unable to set their own goals and to act on their dreams. Goals are rarely achieved by accident. If you want something to happen, you have to be willing to think about it, to make your own choices, and to act on those choices.

Resources for Lesson 2

- **Guided Reading** Activity 22
- **Decision-Making** Activity 9
- **Workbook** Voc Act 22, Appl Act 9
- **Reteaching** Activity 22
- **Enrichment** Activity 9
- **Health Labs** Activity 9
- **Cooperative Learning** Activity 9
- **Lesson 2 Quiz**
- **Chapter 9 Test**

Glencoe Health VHS Videos
Responsible Sexuality
ABC News InterActive Videodiscs
Teenage Sexuality, Side 2
Ch 9 Pressure From Your Peers

Choose friends whose influence will benefit your health.

Peer Pressure

Pressure from **peers,** or people your own age, is a very common part of adolescence. Peer pressure can include pressure to be like others or to do things they do.

Both peer pressure and popularity are concerns of most adolescents. Teens usually look to their peers for approval and for a measure of their success. It is normal for adolescents to depend on friends to learn more about the kind of people they are. They tend to see themselves through the eyes of their peers. Teens often judge their personalities as well as the way they look by how popular they are. Unfortunately, they can get a wrong view of themselves this way. Your peers may give you the wrong information about yourself. Peers may pressure you into making decisions that can be harmful in the long run.

Making Your Own Decisions. Everywhere you look, it seems that teens are called on to make decisions. For example, people your age usually have many interests. These may include music, sports, friends, family, school functions, movies, fashion, and dating. Each interest involves various types of decisions—some easy, some more difficult.

During adolescence many teens face decisions related to their sexual feelings. Just as hormones cause physical changes in the body, they also cause changes in feelings and in how the body begins to respond to sexual stimulation. Such stimulation could be a picture or a movie scene, or it could be holding hands or kissing. The body responds in a variety of ways. The face gets hot and flushed, the heart beats faster, the hands get clammy, and there is a fluttery feeling inside. You cannot keep this response and these feelings from happening. They are normal and healthful. However, you can and must decide what to do about these feelings. An important point to keep in mind is that these feelings do not have to be acted on.

DID YOU KNOW?

- According to one study, 13- to 15-year-old girls have an average of $3 more per week spending money than teen boys, and they are most likely to spend it on clothes.
- Boys, on the other hand, are most likely to spend their money on snacks. Girls are also more likely to buy on impulse than boys are.

A TIME FOR UNDERSTANDING YOURSELF **165**

Across the Curriculum

Language Arts. Select students to write and present a radio or TV script about several teens who are dealing with peer pressure.

Social Studies. Ask students to choose a foreign country or different culture to study. Have them use classroom and library resources to learn about adolescence in that part of the world or in that culture. After-

wards, ask them to be part of a panel to share what they learned from their research.

Speech. Ask students to develop and rehearse a variety of assertive statements to communicate decisions to another person. Have them present their statements to the class.

Make responsible decisions about sex before you become too involved to think clearly.

One factor that makes situations involving sexual stimuli difficult is the confusion surrounding one's feelings. A person may be experiencing new feelings—physical feelings of attraction to another person. If a person has not decided on a code of behavior before getting into a situation in which these feelings start to build, he or she will find it difficult to make a responsible decision. People do not think clearly when these feelings begin to build. It is much easier, and a whole lot smarter, to think through a decision about sexual behavior before getting into the situation in the first place. It is helpful to have alternatives in mind—to know just how far you are willing to go. Each person must decide what he or she wants. This decision is not an easy one, nor is it a one-time-only decision. It is a choice that people are faced with many times.

Sexual responses in the body should not be confused with love. You may have heard people say, "I have never felt this way before," "He excites me," or "Because I feel this way, I must be in love." These physical feelings of excitement have nothing to do with being in love. The feelings come about because of hormones in the body.

If you know what sexual feelings are, you can make more responsible decisions concerning them. It is easier to decide clearly about what you want for yourself—now and in the future—before you are in a situation in which these feelings have built up. Talk about them with your boyfriend or girlfriend. By talking about your feelings and your decisions, both of you can learn to understand and to respect each other.

There is nothing wrong with young people who decide that they are not ready for sex. Regardless of what you hear, not all teens are sexually active. Many teens recognize the serious risks associated with sexual activity. Many have made the decision to wait until marriage to become sexually active. These teens have chosen abstinence. **Abstinence** is choosing not to be sexually active. These teens are concerned about their futures. They have made the most healthy decision. Anyone who is thinking about being sexually active should consider the following:

- Do I feel any pressure to have sex?
- Where is the pressure coming from?
- Am I trying to prove something to someone?
- Am I trying to save this relationship by having sex?
- Have I talked with my boyfriend or girlfriend about our expectations from this relationship and how having sex might change it?
- Am I ready to deal with the possibility of being a parent?
- Have I completed my education or training for employment?
- Do I have a job and adequate finances to rear a child?
- How would being a parent affect my goals and dreams for the future?
- What would I do if I found out I had symptoms of a sexually transmitted disease (STD)?
- What would I do if I found out my partner had symptoms of an STD?
- What would my parents or family say if they knew I was having sex?
- Am I willing to accept the consequences of my decision?

Communicating Your Decisions.   Once you have decided what is right for you, you must communicate your decisions clearly.

Before getting in a sexual situation, talk to your date about your decisions and your goals and dreams. Sex is probably on both your minds. It is not easy bringing up the topic of sex and discussing it. Yet both of you are much more likely to reach an understanding and grow closer by talking about this concern.

How do you know when to say yes and when to say no? What do you do if your decision goes against what an individual or group is doing? How do you follow your values and not lose face with peers?

If your decision is no, then say no, without feeling you need to justify yourself. Be aware that others may ask you to justify why you have refused. This line of questioning should alert you that the person asking you has not really accepted your decision, so any explanation will be challenged. Again, you can repeat no. In situations like this, tell yourself that this is a good decision for you, that you will feel better when the pressure is over, and that you will not have to worry about selling yourself out because of others.

In some situations you may need to repeat yourself several times; if the person persists, leave. Avoid compromise if you feel strongly about something. Compromise can be a slow way of saying yes. Remember, good friends will not challenge you to do something that goes against what you believe. They will not try to talk you into doing something you do not want to do.

Facing Adolescence

Adolescence can be a time of joy as well as pain. Sometimes it is a period of special friendships, activity, and fun. At other times there may be loneliness, sadness, and confusion. Usually, there is a mixture of both the good and the painful during this stage of getting to know who you are and how you relate to others. Most teens turn to their family members, friends, religious leaders, and favorite teachers to lend support and comfort during good times and bad. Unfortunately, other teens sometimes turn to destructive behaviors such as drug use, casual sexual activities, or vandalism. These actions result in harm not only to the teens involved but also to others.

Teen Suicide

A much smaller number choose a more desperate action—suicide—in an attempt to deal with the troubles and challenges of adolescence. People commit suicide when they feel completely hopeless. Most are suffering from extreme depression. The depressed person sees no way out of what seems to be an impossible situation. Suicide is the eighth leading cause of death among all ages and the second leading cause of death among teens.

K E E P I N G   F I T

Five Dangerous Lines

If a teen is being pressured to have sex, one of the following lines may be used:

- Everyone's doing it.
- I'll break up with you if you don't.

- If you really love me, you'll do it.
- It will make you a real man or a real woman.
- You won't get pregnant. It will be safe.

Not everyone is having sex. Real love and caring mean getting to know someone and respecting that person's limits and rights. Even protected sex can result in pregnancy or a sexually transmitted disease.

A TIME FOR UNDERSTANDING YOURSELF **167**

Across the Curriculum

Math. The financial cost of decisions leading to pregnancy and parenthood can be quite extensive. Ask one group of students to research the cost of prenatal care and delivery. Ask a second group to find out the costs involved in caring for a child from infancy to kindergarten. Have a third group investigate the costs of education, from kindergarten through college. Request that

the three groups share their findings with the class.

Science. Besides counseling, there are medicines that are used to treat mental or physical symptoms of individuals who have attempted suicide. Have students research the types of medicines that are used and their advantages and disadvantages.

CHAPTER 9 ADOLESCENCE **167**

L1 DISCUSSION. Have students react to the following statements: Once a parent, always a parent; Parenthood never ends.

L1 CLASS ACTIVITY. As a class, have students identify roles of a parent. Next, ask each student to rank the roles from most important to least important. Later, assign students to small groups to reach consensus on the rankings. Discuss the preparedness of teens to adopt these roles.

Independent Practice

L2 COMMUNITY INVOLVEMENT. Ask students to talk with an adult whom they really like and admire. Have them ask how the person felt about him- or herself as a teenager. What were the person's self-doubts? How did the person overcome them? Does the person still have some self-doubts? What are they? Have students write a short paper summarizing their interview.

L2 COMMUNITY INVOLVEMENT. Ask students to talk with a married couple with children about the responsibilities of marriage and parenthood. Have students find out what suggestions the couple has for teens thinking of marriage and/or parenthood. Ask students to share the results of their interviews with the class.

L1 PERSONAL INVOLVEMENT. Ask students to think of one behavior they can change at home or in the community to show that they are becoming more responsible (such as doing chores without complaining, asking to take on a new chore, not talking back, volunteering their time and energy for a special cause) and have them try to implement it for at least one week. Have them write summaries of their experiences.

L1 USING THE LESSON RESOURCES. For additional student activities, refer to the lesson resources on page 164.

HELP WANTED

Teacher

We are looking for people who understand teenagers and like them anyway! We need people who know their subject matter but also realize that you don't "teach Math or English" but "teach kids." Your bachelor's degree and state certification are a must, but your interpersonal skills and dedication are what we really look for. We want to see your record of success in working with young people in some way during college. If you reflect the kind of person you enjoyed having as a teacher, you might be the person our students will enjoy having as theirs.

For more information contact:
Your local or state chapter of:
The National Education Association or
The American Federation of Teachers

Adolescence can be a time of unhappiness.

Why do young people try to kill themselves? Several contributing factors have been identified. One is a greater than normal sense of social turmoil. Competition and pressure to succeed in an increasingly complex social environment can become overwhelming.

Another factor is the loss of a love relationship. This type of loss is most often the event that leads to a suicide attempt. Other kinds of

---

HEALTH UPDATE

LOOKING AT THE ISSUES

What Should Be Done About Weapons in Schools?

A 1990 survey of high school students showed that 1 in 5 sometimes carries a weapon to school. As many as 135,000 guns are brought to schools every day in the United States, and in one recent 5-year period, at least 65 students were killed by them.

What can be done to stop students from bringing arms to school? What can be done to make students feel safe enough in school that they do not feel a need to carry weapons?

Analyzing Different Viewpoints

ONE VIEW. One of the ways schools have faced this dilemma is by increasing adult security. In New York City, a majority of schools have security-guard patrols in school halls and on school grounds.

A SECOND VIEW. A second method of cutting down on weapons in schools is to stop students from entering schools with them. Some school districts have random student searches for weapons. In other schools students are not allowed to wear baggy clothing that might conceal weapons. Other schools use metal detectors, and some have removed lockers or required see-through backpacks.

A THIRD VIEW. The approach in some schools has been to educate students about the dangers of guns and other weapons and to teach new strategies for conflict resolution and self-defense. In some schools, students trained in mediating disputes have proved effective in keeping such disputes from becoming violent.

A FOURTH VIEW. Some civil rights groups oppose student searches, claiming they infringe on people's right to privacy. Others claim that concentrating on weapons in schools is the wrong approach—that society needs to concentrate instead on the causes of violence.

Exploring Your Views

1. Which of these approaches or combination of approaches do you think might prove most effective in stopping students from bringing weapons into schools? What additional steps might be needed to protect those students who are unarmed?
2. If there are weapons in your school, what steps do you think your school should take to deal with the problem?
3. What forces in society do you think cause this problem of weapons and violence in the schools?

168 Chapter 9 Adolescence

Across the Curriculum

Home Economics. Read and discuss the following situation with the class. "When you are faced with a dilemma that demands an instant *yes* or *no,* you might consider this exercise: Imagine that you are already in the middle of doing something you have been pressured to do. Imagine that a snapshot is taken of you in the middle of the activity. Then think of personally handing the developed photo to those people you care about and value the most, such as parents, close friends, or teachers. Think about what you would feel. If there is embarrassment, guilt, shame, or fear of disappointing them when you hand over the snapshot, saying *yes* to the situation is not such a good idea."

losses, such as loss of health or loss of status because of academic or social failure, can also make a young person vulnerable to suicide.

Many teens who attempt suicide really do not want to die. They are making a plea for help. Unless you are an expert, you probably cannot tell when a depressed person is likely to commit suicide. That is why when someone you know is depressed, it is critical to get help for that person. It is also important for the entire family to receive help. People who are in danger of suicide need the love and support of family members and friends.

Teen Pregnancy and Parenthood

Adolescence is a full-time job. Add pregnancy—and the birth and care of a child—and life can become very complicated. Becoming a parent is a serious responsibility that changes a person's life. For many teens it is a consequence they did not plan.

Most teens face the pressures and decisions about having or not having sexual intercourse at some time in their lives. The only way to be absolutely certain to avoid pregnancy is not to have sexual intercourse.

From Adolescence to Adulthood

Adolescence is a time of growth. It is the next step to adulthood. Sometimes this growth is painful, and at other times it is exciting and fun. Remember, you do not have to let growth just happen. You can continue to learn about how you are changing and what to expect. Learning more about these changes will help you do the following:

- understand your own behavior and why people react to you as they do
- make appropriate decisions about who you are and who you will be in the future
- behave in ways that reflect your personal values and goals
- achieve your goals and dreams.

How will these teens' lives be affected by early parenthood?

- Assign and discuss the lesson review. Encourage LD students to focus on question 1. Modify question 2 by having students write a short story that illustrates peer pressure.
- Assign and discuss the chapter review.

Evaluate

- Administer, grade, and discuss the *Lesson 2 Quiz*.
- Administer, grade, and discuss the *Chapter 9 Test*.
- Refer to the Performance Assessment strategy for this chapter. See pages T 23 to T 25.

Reteach

- Have students list five goals. Then ask them to list, under each goal, at least one value and one decision related to that goal.
- Ask students to complete *Reteaching Activity 22.*

Enrich

- Ask students to design and administer a survey of classmates for reasons why they would or would not want to be parents now, in 5 years, and in 10 years. Have them assess how the responses differ between males and females as well as for the present versus the future. Ask them to share their findings with the class.
- Ask students to complete *Enrichment Activity 9.*

LESSON 2 REVIEW

Reviewing Facts and Vocabulary

1. What are goals? List three goals you have set for yourself.
2. Define *peer pressure*. What is its effect on someone your age?

Thinking Critically

3. **Synthesis.** Create a skit contrasting successful and unsuccessful ways of communicating yes or no when making decisions.
4. **Synthesis.** Why is it important to have a code of behavior established before getting into a situation that will require you to make a serious decision?

Applying Health Knowledge

5. Survey several teen parents who are in school to learn how their lives and responsibilities changed after having a child.
6. For a week keep a list of all the times you communicate a decision and whether you communicate the decision successfully. During the following week try to increase the number of times you are successful in your communication.

A Time for Understanding Yourself **169**

Close

Remind students that adolescence is a time for understanding themselves and for making decisions. Talk about values and goals as the basis for decisions. Stress the need to communicate effectively one's decisions to others when faced with peer pressure. Cite some sources of help to deal with challenges such as teen suicide, pregnancy, and parenthood.

Answers to Lesson 2 Review

1. Definite plans one has in one's life. Goals will vary.
2. Pressure from people one's own age. Peer pressure can cause one to get an inaccurate view of oneself or make decisions that may not be in one's best interest.
3. Skits will vary.
4. Answers will vary. Possible answer: Planning ahead can clarify issues in one's own mind. Situations requiring a serious decision may be emotionally charged and so it may be more difficult to think on the spot.
5. Answers will vary.
6. Answers will vary.

Helping Students Improve Their Health

Reinforcing Vocabulary

■ **Civic groups.** Organizational groups that are formed by members of a community to support the well-being of the community.

Teaching Strategies

L1 DISCUSSION. Have students make a list of possible future career choices that they may be interested in pursuing. Have students pick one career choice and research the job responsibilities and educational requirements. Encourage students to interview a person currently working in his or her chosen field. Have students determine how current choices may, or may not, lead to future success in their chosen career.

L2 DISCUSSION. Have students discuss the most significant issues that affect adolescents today. Have students rank in order the most important issues.

L2 CLASS ACTIVITY. Using the results obtained from the previous discussion, have students construct a questionnaire that students will use to interview their parents. Have the questions relate to issues that students' parents remember as affecting them when they were adolescents. Have students bring responses to class and share in a small group discussion.

DID YOU KNOW?

■ Late maturers may doubt their bodies will ever develop and be as well endowed as others already developing around them.
■ Early maturers may have a long period of frustration of sex drive and drive towards independence and career.

Self-Inventory

Developmental Tasks

HOW DO YOU RATE?

Number a sheet of paper from 1 through 18. Read each item below and respond by writing 3 for *definitely*, 2 for *somewhat*, or 1 for *hardly* or *not at all*. Total the numbers. Then proceed to the next section.

1. I have a picture in my mind of what kind of person I want to be as an adult.
2. I think through problems I face, looking at several possible solutions.
3. I have one or two very close friends with whom I can discuss almost anything.
4. I know of several jobs I think I would be good at as an adult.
5. I am aware of the activities of some of the civic groups in my community.
6. I have more discussions with my parents or other adults than I used to.
7. I am concerned about national and world problems in the news today.
8. I can list the four most important beliefs I have.
9. I know some of the qualities I would look for in a marriage partner.
10. People who know me know I act in a way that supports what I believe in.
11. I am usually comfortable with my behavior as a male or female in social settings.

12. I can describe some ways my life-style would change if I were married and if I had children.
13. I listen to other people's ideas, even though they may differ from my own.
14. I usually have success in making male and female friends with my peers.
15. I know and accept my physical strengths and weaknesses.
16. I do some things alone or with my friends that I used to do with my family.
17. I have several interests I would consider pursuing as career possibilities.
18. I make choices that promote my overall health and well-being.

HOW DID YOU SCORE?

Look below to see how you scored. Then proceed to the next section.

45 to 54
Excellent. You are well on your way to becoming a healthy, mature adult.

23 to 44
Good. You are making good progress on your way to becoming a healthy, mature adult.

17 to 22
Fair. You are working on some of the developmental tasks, but you need to try harder.

Below 16
Poor. You need to get serious about growing up and setting goals to achieve specific tasks.

WHAT ARE YOUR GOALS?

If your score was between 37 and 54, complete the statements in Part A. If your score was between 1 and 36, complete the statements in Parts A and B.

Part A

1. I plan to learn more about each of the developmental tasks in the following ways: ____.
2. My timetable for accomplishing this is ____.
3. I plan to share my information with others by ____.

Part B

4. The developmental task that I would like to work on the most is ____.
5. The steps involved in working on this task are ____.
6. My timetable for achieving this goal is ____.
7. The people or groups I will ask for support and assistance are ____.
8. My rewards for making this change will be ____.

Meeting Students' Needs

For students who score *Excellent* or *Good*. Encourage students to keep the lines of communication open with parents and other adults. Suggest that they continue considering future career choices. Have students construct short- and long-term goals that will help them successfully achieve their career choices.

For students who score *Fair*. Encourage students to use "I" statements when communicating feelings. Have students practice their listening and communicating skills.

For students who score *Poor*. Assist students in developing weekly goals to develop better communication skills.

Building Decision-Making Skills

K elly is a freshman cheerleader. She really enjoyed her participation in the first football game and the dance afterward, at which the captain of the team—a senior—asked her to go with him to a party the next night. Her parents said, "Sorry, you're too young to date, and especially a senior." They say Kelly can attend school functions, go out with mixed groups, or perhaps even attend school functions with boys her own age. Kelly feels her parents are treating her like a baby. She tells them all her friends date and she thinks she should be allowed to do so, too. She is thinking of sneaking out to go to the party in spite of her parents' objections.

WHAT DO YOU THINK?

1. **Situation.** Why might this be a difficult situation for Kelly?

2. **Situation.** What immediate decision needs to be made?

3. **Situation.** What other decisions need to be made later?

4. **Situation.** How much time does Kelly have to make the first decision?

5. **Situation.** What risks are involved in this decision?

6. **Choices.** What are Kelly's choices? Which of these choices is totally inappropriate? Why?

7. **Consequences.** Who will be affected by this decision and in what ways?

8. **Consequences.** How might Kelly's health triangle be affected by this decision?

9. **Consequences.** What might happen if Kelly chose to sneak out to the party?

10. **Consequences.** How might her date react if she chose to sneak out to the party?

11. **Consequences.** How might the football captain react if she tells him she can't go to the party?

12. **Consequences.** How might her parents react if she goes to the party without their permission?

13. **Consequences.** How might Kelly's self-esteem be affected by this decision?

14. **Consequences.** What reasons might Kelly's parents have for not giving her permission to attend this party?

15. **Consequences.** How might Kelly feel if she chooses not to attend the party? Might these feelings change if trouble developed at the party?

16. **Consequences.** How might Kelly convince her parents she is ready to date?

17. **Decision.** What immediate decision do you think Kelly should make?

18. **Decision.** What long-term decisions should Kelly make? Explain your answer.

19. **Evaluation.** Have you ever known someone who faced a similar situation? How was it handled? What was the outcome?

20. **Evaluation.** Many teens say they are glad their parents provide some controls on their activities. Do you agree or disagree? Why?

21. **Evaluation.** Someday you may be a parent. What rules would you establish for your teenagers in regard to dating? Would you have the same rules for your daughters as for your sons? Explain your answer.

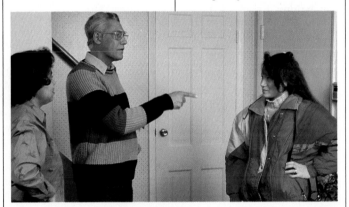

Discussing the Answers

Situation 1. Kelly is neither a child, nor an adult. She is extremely excited about being asked out by the senior captain of the football team. However, Kelly's parents object. It appears that Kelly's parents are already trying to reach some kind of compromise. Perhaps Kelly's parents would be more comfortable with this idea if they had a chance to meet this young man and get to know him better. Perhaps Kelly's parents can offer to chaperone this party. Otherwise, Kelly should not attend this party. If Kelly sneaks out and attends this party without her parents permission, Kelly may be jeopardizing her future, and the future trust of her parents.

Helping Students Improve Their Health

Building Decision-Making Skills

Teaching Strategies

L2 CLASS ACTIVITY. Divide into two groups—one group representing Kelly and the other group representing Kelly's parents. Ask students to determine arguments to support both sides. Have a class debate in which both sides are presented. Have an independent panel of guests award points to the arguments presented for both sides.

L1 CLASS ACTIVITY. Ask volunteers to role-play the part of Kelly discussing her situation with her parents. What possible compromise might Kelly and her parents be able to reach?

L2 DISCUSSION. Have students discuss the short- and long-term repercussions that Kelly might face if she sneaks out and goes to the party with the senior captain of the football team. Have students discuss why many parents object to their adolescent daughters dating males that are several years older than their daughters. What motives might the senior captain of the football team have in asking a freshman cheerleader to his party?

L1 CLASS ACTIVITY. Another possible skit pertaining to adolescence is: Jenny is an outstanding swimmer who plans to go to college someday. Last year, Jenny was recognized as an All-State swimmer. The team and her coach hold much promise for her. However, in order to pay for college, Jenny feels that she should get a job. Jenny worked all summer before her senior year and earned a lot of money. In the fall, the swim team practice began interfering with her work schedule. Now, Jenny is considering quitting the swim team. If you were Jenny's friend, what would you advise her to do?

Answers to Chapter 9 Review

Using Health Terms

1. Adolescence
2. Secondary sex characteristics
3. Hormones
4. Developmental task
5. Peers
6. Suicide

Building Academic Skills

7. A—fact; B—opinion; C—opinion.
8. Answers will vary. Possible answer: During puberty, which begins between the ages of 9 and 13, males and females acquire the ability to reproduce and secondary sex characteristics develop.
9. Paragraphs will vary.

Recalling the Facts

10. The first year of life.
11. Between 9 and 13.
12. The feet and hands grow first and are often large in proportion to the rest of the body.
13. Estrogen—female; progesterone—female; testosterone—male.
14. It reaches its adult size and weight.
15. Their ability to think logically increases; memory skills improve and memory span increases; they are able to understand someone else's point of view.
16. Answers may include but are not limited to: What could I have done differently? What might have happened if. . . ?
17. Hormones.
18. Goals help provide a mental picture of where you plan to go with your life and what you must do to get there. They guide you in the use of time, energy, and other resources.
19. Teens may make decisions that could be harmful in the long run in order to gain peer approval or popularity.
20. The body is sexually stimulated.
21. When sexual feelings begin to build, it is difficult to think clearly and to make a responsible decision.

Using Health Terms

On a separate sheet of paper, write the term that best matches each definition given below.

LESSON 1

1. The period of time between childhood and adulthood.
2. Traits such as body hair, breasts in a female, and muscles in a male.
3. Chemical substances in the body that stimulate growth, such as testosterone, estrogen, and progesterone.
4. Something that needs to occur during a particular period of life for a person to continue to grow toward becoming a healthy, mature adult.

LESSON 2

5. Other people of one's own age.
6. The intended taking of one's own life.

Building Academic Skills

LESSON 1

7. **Reading.** Tell whether each statement below expresses a fact or an opinion.
   a. During puberty males and females become physically able to reproduce.
   b. Puberty is like being on a roller coaster.
   c. Good friends are the most important thing in life.
8. **Writing.** Rosa made the following notes. She wants to combine her ideas in one sentence. Help her by writing a grammatically correct sentence that includes all of Rosa's ideas. You may need to add some words of your own.
   Puberty begins.
   between the ages of 9 and 13
   ability to reproduce
   Secondary sex characteristics develop.

LESSON 2

9. **Writing.** Write a paragraph describing one of your goals and how you plan to achieve it.

Recalling the Facts

LESSON 1

10. What is the most rapid growth period in a person's life?
11. At what age does puberty begin?
12. Why do some teens feel awkward and clumsy during the early stages of puberty?
13. Classify each of the following hormones as male or female: estrogen, progesterone, testosterone.
14. What happens to the brain during adolescence?
15. Why should adolescents be able to learn more quickly and more easily than younger students? Give three reasons.
16. What two questions can you ask yourself in order to learn from your mistakes?
17. What causes emotional changes during puberty?

LESSON 2

18. How can having goals help you in life?
19. How can peer pressure and a longing to be popular affect a teen's decisions?
20. What do the following physical signs indicate is happening to the body: the face becomes hot and flushed, the heart beats faster, the hands get clammy, there is a fluttery feeling inside?
21. Why can it be difficult to make a responsible decision while you are experiencing strong feelings of physical attraction for a member of the opposite sex?
22. What might be some unwanted outcomes of having sex to save a relationship?
23. How might becoming a parent while still in high school affect a person's plans for the future?
24. Why is it a good idea to discuss decisions about sex with your boyfriend or girlfriend before you get into a serious situation?
25. List three factors that may contribute to suicide among young people.
26. What is the only absolutely sure way to avoid pregnancy?

22. Answers may include but are not limited to: pregnancy/parenthood; sexually transmitted diseases; resentment if one or both parties felt pressured into having sex.
23. Answers may include but are not limited to: it could affect a person's educational and career goals.
24. It can help both parties reach a mutual understanding and respect.
25. A greater than normal sense of social turmoil caused by competition and pressure; loss of a love relationship; serious illness; academic failure.
26. Not having sexual intercourse.

REVIEW

Thinking Critically

LESSON 1

27. **Analysis.** Here are several physical changes that occur during puberty. Select two and analyze the impact on one's self-esteem.
    a. acne
    b. growth spurt
    c. appearance of facial hair
    d. development of breasts
    e. increase in perspiration
    f. widening of the hips
    g. narrowing of the waistline
    h. broadening of the shoulders

28. **Evaluation.** Write *strong* or *weak* to describe the personal identity of each of the following students.
    a. One day Consuela hopes to own a hair styling salon. She attends a vocational high school. In addition to courses in hair styling, she is taking business and accounting courses.
    b. Harry never begins to do his homework until one of his parents tells him to get busy.
    c. Chang wants a special set of stereo components. He is working at Burger Barn after school and mowing lawns on Saturdays to earn money to buy the set.

LESSON 2

29. **Evaluation.** Do you think there is too much sex shown on television and in the movies? Why or why not? In what ways might sex on television and in the movies influence the behavior of young people?

Making the Connection

LESSON 2

30. **Social Studies.** Compare adolescence in the 1960s with adolescence today by interviewing people who were teens during that time. What were their concerns? What were their favorite songs? Who were their role models?

Applying Health Knowledge

LESSON 1

31. Think of several possible ways in which Juan, who is 6′ 2″ tall and weighs 210 pounds, and Rich, who is 5′ 2″ tall and weighs 120 pounds, might react to being different in size from their peers?

LESSON 2

32. Zoe and Jim are seniors. They have been dating for more than a year. Zoe wants to get married after graduation, but Jim wants to go to college. Zoe feels she is ready to add sex to their relationship. Read the dialogue below, and then answer the questions that follow it.
    Zoe: Jim, I want to have sex with you.
    Jim: I don't think that's a good idea, Zoe.
    Zoe: Why not?
    Jim: You might get pregnant.
    Zoe: You could use something. Besides, I'm willing to take that chance.
    Jim: Zoe, you know I want to go to college. It's just too big a risk.
    Zoe: But, Jim, I love you so. It would bring us closer together.
    Jim: Zoe, you're putting too much pressure on me. I think we'd be making a big mistake.
    a. What motives might Zoe have for wanting to have sex?
    b. What mistake is Jim referring to?

Beyond the Classroom

LESSON 2

33. **Parental Involvement.** Talk to your parents about peer pressure they experienced when they were your age. Ask for examples of ways they were pressured. How did they respond to the pressure?

34. **Further Study.** Read an article about a famous sports figure or entertainer. Describe the goals this person set as a youth and what he or she did to achieve them.

Thinking Critically

27. Answers will vary. Possible answers: A, B, and E will probably have a negative impact on one's self-esteem because these are uncomfortable aspects of puberty. C, D, F, G, and H may have a positive impact because these are all signs of approaching adulthood.
28. A—strong; B—weak; C—strong.
29. Answers will vary but should be supported logically.

Making the Connection

30. Answers will vary.

Applying Health Knowledge

31. Answers will vary. Possible answers: Juan may feel awkward or clumsy because he is bigger than everyone else or he may feel proud to look more like an adult; Rich may feel insecure or embarrassed about being smaller than other males his age or he may feel secure about it if he has a strong personal identity.
32. Answers will vary. Possible answers: A—she may feel she will have a claim on Jim if they have sex or perhaps she hopes to get pregnant; B—he did not say *no* assertively and it sounds as though he is not sure of his decision.

Beyond the Classroom

33. Answers will vary.
34. Answers will vary.

Lesson Summaries

LESSON 1. The stages of infancy, childhood, and adolescence are brief compared to the entire life cycle. These stages are dramatic, but development occurs in every age group.

LESSON 2. The stages of life follow one another in a regular order, though they occur at different ages in different people. During early adulthood, individuals are at the peak of their physical and mental abilities, though they still must adjust to the changes a career, marriage, and family may bring. Middle adulthood often brings new insight and self-understanding with its transitions.

LESSON 3. By acting to prevent illness and premature death early on, people can also increase their quality of life. Aging, like all phases of growth and development, is predictable but very individual.

LESSON 4. Several factors influence one's attitude toward death, including personal experience, spiritual beliefs, family attitudes and values, and one's age. Elisabeth Kübler-Ross has identified five emotional stages that dying people typically pass through.

Introducing the Chapter

Tell students of the old saying, "Experience is a hard teacher." Have them analyze possible meanings of this saying. Ask them to brainstorm characteristics of adulthood. Tell them that growth and development continue through adulthood, as reaching one's potential is a lifelong process, and at each phase we have something new to learn and share.

Performance Assessment ✓

Refer to pages T 23 to T 25 for a Performance Assessment strategy for this chapter. See the *Performance Assessment Activities* booklet for additional suggestions.

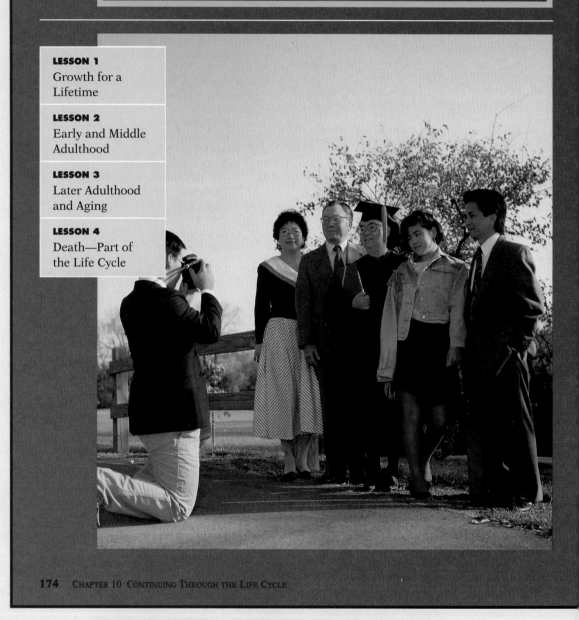

CHAPTER

10 CONTINUING THROUGH THE LIFE CYCLE

LESSON 1
Growth for a Lifetime

LESSON 2
Early and Middle Adulthood

LESSON 3
Later Adulthood and Aging

LESSON 4
Death—Part of the Life Cycle

174 CHAPTER 10 CONTINUING THROUGH THE LIFE CYCLE

Key to Ability Levels

Teaching strategies have been coded for varying learning styles and abilities.

L1 Level 1 activities are basic activities and should be within the ability range of all students.

L2 Level 2 activities are average activities and should be within the ability range of average to above-average students.

L3 Level 3 activities are challenging activities designed for the ability range of above-average students.

LD LD activities should be within the ability range of learning-disabled students.

LEP LEP activities should be within the ability range of Limited English Proficiency students.

GROWTH FOR A LIFETIME

W hen compared with the entire life cycle, the stages of infancy, childhood, and adolescence last only a short time. You and your friends may feel that the years of growing up will never end, but these years are only a small part of the rest of your life. With an average life expectancy of 76 years, you truly do have a lifetime ahead of you.

Considering the Entire Life Cycle

The study of all the years of the life cycle, beginning with a person's birth to that individual's death, is a relatively new area of research. In the past, few scientists studied life as a whole. Instead, they focused on the early years because development during infancy and childhood is so rapid. It easily falls into specific stages and is so important to later life. In fact, some scientists believed that human development ended with childhood or early adolescence. They believed there was no growth and development during adulthood. Many researchers saw the progression from birth to death much like hiking up a hill to reach adulthood and then walking across a level plateau that finally headed downward toward the end of life's journey.

Today we know that life is more dynamic than that. Even though human development is very dramatic in early life, it does not end at the age of 6 or 16. Instead, development occurs in every age group.

Developmental Tasks During Adulthood

In Chapter 9 you read about the major developmental tasks for adolescence. A **developmental task** is something that needs to occur during a particular stage for a person to continue his or her growth toward becoming a healthy, mature adult. Failure or difficulty with a task may lead to personal dissatisfaction, disapproval by society, and difficulty with later tasks.

Many of life's early developmental tasks, such as learning to walk, come about mostly as a result of physical maturation. Others, such as learning to read or learning ways to get along with others, are developed primarily from the cultural pressures of society. Still other tasks, such as choosing and preparing for a career, grow out of personal values and goals of the individual. Most developmental tasks originate from all of these factors working together.

Just as infants, children, and adolescents must complete various developmental tasks in order to grow, adults also face certain tasks that lead to maturity. These tasks focus on five major aspects of people's lives:

- occupational role
- individual identity and personal independence
- relationships with other people

LESSON 1 FOCUS

TERMS TO USE
- Developmental task
- Self-actualization

CONCEPTS TO LEARN
- All people have stages of growth and development that they must work through.
- There are clearly defined developmental tasks for each stage of life.
- Self-actualization is a continuing process of development.

ATTITUDES AND BEHAVIORS TO EVALUATE
- Self-Inventory, page 192.
- Building Decision-Making Skills, page 193.

GROWTH FOR A LIFETIME **175**

Focus

Lesson Objective

After studying this lesson, students should be able to:
- summarize the five developmental tasks of adulthood

Bellringer

Write the following on the chalkboard for students to work on while attendance is being taken: *Complete the following sentence in writing: I'll know I'm really an adult when. . . .*

Introducing the Lesson

Refer to the Bellringer. Ask volunteers to share their responses. Follow up on any responses that suggest adulthood depends on gaining maturity, knowledge, or social responsibility. Tell students that the five basic developmental tasks of adulthood will be the focus of this lesson. Review the concept of developmental task. Emphasize that attaining adulthood is not simply a matter of chronological age or the legal rights that go with it, but a matter of maturing in ways that make one a happy, productive member of society.

Building Vocabulary

- Ask students to write their own definitions of each of the following terms: *life cycle, adulthood, maturity, career, occupation, individual identity,* and *responsibility.* Ask volunteers to share their definitions.
- Ask students to complete *Workbook Vocabulary Activity 23.*

DID YOU KNOW?

As a nation, our population is changing. Consider these facts:
- There are more senior citizens than ever before.
- The over-85 group is our fastest-growing segment of the population.
- There is more cultural and ethnic diversity in our population than ever before.

Resources for Lesson 1

- **Guided Reading** Activity 23
- **Workbook** Vocabulary Activity 23
- **Reteaching** Activity 23
- **Lesson 1 Quiz**
- **Performance Assessment** Activity 10

L1 EXPLANATION. Explain how the developmental tasks of adulthood differ from many of those that must be achieved earlier in life. (They take longer to achieve, and they have to do less with physical maturation than with learning and gaining insight.)

L1 DISCUSSION. What are the first steps most young adults take to achieve self-actualization? (Leaving home, supporting themselves.) How is the ability to maintain adult relationships established? (Observation and personal experience.) Which developmental task of adulthood is usually the most difficult? (Acceptance of growing older and of the reality of death.)

LEP CLASS ACTIVITY. Have students make a bulletin board that reflects the youth-orientation of our culture. Ask them to bring in pictures from magazines and newspapers of young people and the elderly. How are the two age groups depicted differently?

Independent Practice

L1 COMMUNITY INVOLVEMENT. Have students interview adults of different ages from their families or community regarding the age at which they felt they would or did complete each of the basic developmental tasks of adulthood. Were they aware of the tasks they were completing? Work with students to develop a simple list of questions to elicit information such as this from informants.

L2 WRITING. Select students to write a paragraph on each of several different characters in TV programs. The characters should be either in their 20s or past retirement age. Both men and women should be included in each age group. Ask them to address how, if at all, the way in which men are depicted differs from the way in which women are depicted. What are the differences between young and elderly?

L1 USING THE LESSON RESOURCES. For additional student activities, refer to the lesson resources on page 175.

- relationship to society
- acceptance of growing older and of the reality of death

Each of these developmental tasks represents lessons that adults must learn to adjust to the world around them.

Establishing an Occupational Role

During adolescence many people start to form ideas about the kind of life they want as adults. An occupation or career is usually a large part of that idea or dream of the future. As they become young adults, people begin to see themselves more clearly in an occupational role. This role may occur through on-the-job training or through education beyond high school as preparation for a career. Making an occupational choice, although it may not be the final one, is one of the major developmental tasks that must be achieved on the way to adulthood.

Establishing an Individual Identity and Personal Independence

The desire for independence during adolescence is preparation for establishing an individual identity as an adult. It also is part of a continuing process, called **self-actualization,** that involves developing one's capabilities to their fullest. If people have a good understanding of their own abilities and goals and feel secure about themselves, they are able to work toward self-actualization and the establishment of an adult identity.

Until young people leave home, at least part of their identity is based on family membership. Comments such as, "He's John's son," "She's Fay's youngest," or "She's still in high school" show family ties and dependence.

Leaving home or starting to work full-time are ways that young adults can begin to achieve self-actualization. At first, they may substitute the emotional support of friends for the support they once received from parents. As their development continues, however, young adults will become more self-sufficient. In so doing, they will be continuing on the developmental path that will lead to the establishment of an individual identity and personal independence.

Choosing an occupation is part of establishing identity and personal independence.

K E E P I N G   F I T

Making a Family Fitness Contract

Consider the case of Vikki and Jason Scott, a mother-son rowing team who in 1991 competed in the Pan American Games in Cuba. Just a few years ago, Vikki Scott was an overweight, cigarette-addicted mother with no exercise routine. Inspired by her son, she took up the sport. Now they are both on the national team, rowing their way to fitness and closer family bonds.

Why not draw up a family fitness contract? Choose an exercise or sport in which everyone in your family can take part. Make up a contract that spells out when, where, and how you will exercise together and the benefits and rewards.

Overcoming Misconceptions

Societal Perceptions. Because of the baby boom, the American population has been dominated by large numbers of young people for the last several decades. This has had a tremendous influence on the way our society has perceived aging and the elderly. In our youth-oriented culture, the aged are often seen as useless scions of society.

As the baby-boom generation ages, society is increasingly dominated by individuals who are middle-aged and older. As a result, our attitudes toward aging and the elderly are also changing. More and more mass media, products, and advertising are slanted toward people over the age of 40, who are increasingly portrayed in a more positive way.

Establishing Close Relationships

This developmental task involves the ability to build close relationships with people of both sexes while still maintaining a sense of self. During this time there may be several successive romantic relationships. More time may be devoted to romantic relationships than to peer relationships. Some people give romantic relationships a sense of permanence through marriage. Others develop romantic relationships but prefer to remain single. Still others are occupied with establishing a career or defining their own identity, and the ability to develop and maintain close relationships comes later or not at all.

Establishing a Place in Society

One of the tasks of adulthood includes determining where and how a person fits into society. Political ideas, religious views, and a sense of community responsibility contribute to finding a place in society and feeling comfortable with it. Because mature adults have developed an individual identity, they find ways to share their interests in their community. They may, for example, do volunteer work, promote recycling, or join a neighborhood sports team. They take responsibility for what they are doing and what they are becoming.

Establishing an Acceptance of Growing Older and of the Reality of Death

For most people this dual task is perhaps the most difficult of all. However, individuals who have had success in their earlier developmental tasks tend to accept the inevitability of aging, physical and mental decline, and death. These individuals can be found in every community, making each day a rewarding one for themselves and others.

LESSON 1 REVIEW

Reviewing Facts and Vocabulary

1. Why is the study of the entire life cycle a relatively new area of study?
2. Define the term *developmental task;* give an example of a developmental task in adulthood.

Thinking Critically

3. **Synthesis.** Point out one or more developmental tasks that a young adult you know has achieved. Give reasons to show that the individual has worked through the task(s).
4. **Evaluation.** Rewrite the developmental tasks of adulthood in your own words. Place them in the order in which you believe they will occur in your life.

Applying Health Knowledge

5. Write a radio or television script about several adults who are dealing with some of the developmental tasks of adulthood. Share your completed script with your class.
6. Interview people of various ages. Explain the adult developmental tasks to them. Ask them to evaluate the progress they feel they are making on these tasks. Share your findings with the class.

Answers to Lesson 1 Review

1. Studies often focused on development during infancy and childhood because these stages are so rapid, readily distinguishable as stages, and clearly significant for later life.
2. *Developmental task* is defined on page 175. Examples will vary. Possible answers: Choosing and preparing for a career, deciding whether or not to marry, deciding whether or not to have children.
3. Answers will vary.
4. Answers will vary but should reflect an understanding of the developmental tasks listed as bulleted items on pages 175 and 176.
5. Answers will vary.
6. Answers will vary.

Check for Understanding
- Assign and discuss the lesson review. Encourage LD students to focus on questions 2 and 3.

Evaluate
- Administer, grade, and discuss the *Lesson 1 Quiz.*

Reteach
- Have students review the basic developmental tasks of adulthood by writing out one example of each.
- Ask students to complete *Reteaching Activity 23.*

Enrich
- Have students explore different perspectives on aging and the elderly by comparing their own culture with some other culture. Eastern and Southeast Asian cultures generally show great piety toward the elderly, so they are good ones to select for this project. Have students find out if there is an Asian American or other ethnic community in their area. Help them arrange to interview local ethnic group members if possible. They should also interview members of their own culture in different age groups to get a diverse perspective. Have them prepare a written report of their findings.

Close

Tell students that in this lesson we have come to appreciate that growth and development are processes that don't end with adulthood, but continue on throughout life. We identified and discussed five basic developmental tasks in adulthood. As they are completed, the typical individual matures into a more fulfilled and productive member of society.

Focus

Lesson Objective

After studying this lesson, students should be able to:

■ describe the major developmental tasks and transitions of early and middle adulthood

Bellringer

Write the following on the chalkboard for students to work on while attendance is being taken: *Complete the following sentences in writing: Old age starts at age. . . ; You know you're "over the hill" when. . . ; Never trust anyone over the age of. . . .*

Introducing the Lesson

Refer to the Bellringer. Ask volunteers to share their responses with the class. Use their responses to illustrate the point that for many teens, anyone over the age of 30 or 40 may seem old. Stress that these years are just the young to middle ages of adulthood, because most people in their 30s and 40s today can expect to live at least 40 or 50 years more.

Building Vocabulary

■ Ask students to describe each of the following in their own words: *intimacy, isolation, life expectancy, self-evaluation, midlife crisis, generativity,* and *self-absorption.* Clarify any misunderstandings.

■ Ask students to complete *Workbook Vocabulary Activity 24.*

DID YOU KNOW?

■ According to *Prevention's Giant Book of Health Facts,* the average woman in 1900 spent 19 years caring for her child and 9 years caring for one or more elderly parents.
■ In the 1990s, the average woman will spend 17 years caring for a child and 18 years caring for her parent or parents.

YOUNG AND MIDDLE ADULTHOOD

LESSON 2 FOCUS

TERMS TO USE

■ Transitions
■ Empty-nest syndrome
■ Cluttered-nest syndrome

CONCEPTS TO LEARN

■ Changes after childhood and adolescence occur at certain stages.
■ Crucial decisions are made during early adulthood.
■ Many transitions occur during middle age.

ATTITUDES AND BEHAVIORS TO EVALUATE

■ Self-Inventory, page 192.
■ Building Decision-Making Skills, page 193.

Legally, in many states, people are considered to be adults when they reach the age of 18. Physically, they become adults when their physical growth has been completed, around age 25. To many, adulthood is the best time of their life. To others, it is a time of stress and painful struggle. For most individuals, it is both.

Although the stages of life follow one another in a regular order, they occur at different ages in different people. Erikson's sixth and seventh stages of development are young adulthood and middle adulthood.

Young Adulthood

Young adulthood may begin as early as age 17; for most people, however, it starts at about the age of 20 and continues through the 30s. This stage of adulthood begins when individuals do not have to depend on their parents or other adults all of the time. These young adults no longer see themselves as being ruled by their parents. They are able to support themselves financially by holding down a job. Basically, they are aware of what they want from life. They tend to express their emotions in acceptable ways and know how to get along with people. They can deal with everyday situations without becoming easily upset.

Most young adults are at the peak of their physical abilities; they are stronger, quicker, and more alert than ever. Most young adults find they have an increased capacity to learn and to adjust to new situations. Their self-confidence grows as they learn to gather information and put it to use in their own lives. During this time people continue perfecting skills that make them more self-supporting and independent. They are accepted by society as full-fledged members and, in turn, are offered numerous chances to make contributions to the work force and community.

Because the years of young adulthood are the years of choice, a number of crucial decisions are made during this time. Most young adults decide what work to do. This choice may be one that was considered in adolescence or a new one.

Erikson's stage of development, intimacy versus isolation, occurs during young adulthood. This stage involves committing to another person. Many people choose to marry during this time, and the majority of these couples decide to have one or more children. Their new families bring on new responsibilities and additional lessons to learn. However, if fear of intimacy is greater than one's need for it, loneliness and isolation are more likely to occur.

At various stages during the life cycle, adults may feel as they did during adolescence. This is especially true during young adulthood. Young adults may question who they are and what they want from life. If the developmental tasks of adolescence have not been achieved, these young adults may have problems dealing with the changes that come with

Resources for Lesson 2

■ **Transparency** 40
■ **Guided Reading** Activity 24
■ **Workbook** Vocabulary Activity 24
■ **Reteaching** Activity 24
■ **Lesson 2 Quiz**

young adulthood: a career, marriage, or a family. They may not be willing or able to make the adjustments needed.

Middle Adulthood

For most of human history, and in many areas of the world today, only a tiny segment of any population has ever lived much beyond the age of 40. In many parts of the world where short life expectancy is combined with poverty, middle adulthood almost seems to disappear as a stage of the life cycle. In such situations, when people must labor unceasingly for survival, life changes very little between the beginning of adulthood and old age. In more developed parts of the world, however, people live much longer and reach the middle and later years. They come face-to-face with middle adulthood. At the age of 40, 45, or 50, people can see for themselves that they have arrived at a midpoint in the adult years. More than half of their life is gone. For some adults facing middle age, life is seen in terms of time left to live rather than time since birth. For most others, mid-life brings new insight and self-understanding. Such fresh perspectives generally come as the result of conscious self-reflection.

Some middle-aged adults tend to be concerned not only with survival and making a living, but also with thinking seriously about what they want to do with this second half of their lives. In contrast to early adulthood, in which orientation tends to be focused on a person's relationship to others, the middle years are marked by self-evaluation. This can be a period of confusion or a time for asking questions, such as Where am I going? Is this what I want to do with my life? Should I do something different? Is it too late to change direction?

The feeling that time is running out is common during middle adulthood. This feeling often surfaces as a result of the aging or death of a parent, the untimely death of a friend, the realization that children are growing up, or simply because of an increased awareness of the passage of time. All of these events emphasize the limits that time places on life. Sensing these limitations, many people may feel pressured to make changes before it is too late.

Career change, divorce, marriage or remarriage, and other changes in previously established ways of life are common during this stage. Some changes may be beneficial; others may be harmful.

You may have observed people who find it difficult or impossible to accept the passage of time. They may try to deny change by behaving as

Mid-life brings new challenges and opportunities.

K E E P I N G   F I T

Eating an Anti-Aging Diet

Though there is no known cure for aging, and no Fountain of Youth has yet been found, there are some dietary guidelines that you can follow that can help keep you healthy over time. According to the U.S. Department of

Agriculture's Human Nutrition Research Center on Aging, the following anti-aging dietary guidelines might help.
■ Eat foods rich in vitamin E, vitamin C, and beta carotene.

■ Do not get more than 30 percent of calories from fat.
■ Eat low-fat foods rich in calcium.
■ Get at least 25 to 40 grams of fiber every day.

YOUNG AND MIDDLE ADULTHOOD   **179**

Overcoming Misconceptions

Life Expectancy. Most people are familiar with the idea of life expectancy at birth— the average age an individual can expect to live. But fewer people are aware that an individual's life expectancy actually increases with age.

Life expectancy increases as we get older because a relatively large proportion of

people die shortly after birth, thereby reducing the overall average length of life. If you survive the first year of life, your chances of living to a ripe old age are quite high. For example, by the time a woman reaches age 79, which is the current life expectancy at birth for females in the U.S., she can expect to live another 5 to 10 years.

Guided Practice

LD **CLASS ACTIVITY.** Provide an outline, leaving blanks for LD students to fill in during class discussion.

L1 **CLASS ACTIVITY.** Have students compile on the chalkboard a list of characteristics and behaviors that describe the typical individual in early adulthood.

L2 **DISCUSSION.** How does college or other long-term commitment, such as military service, affect the age at which the typical characteristics and behaviors of young adulthood are attained? Does this create conflict in some people? What are the trade-offs?

L1 **DISCUSSION.** What are some of the crucial decisions that are made during young adulthood? How readily can these be changed later on?

L2 **DISCUSSION.** In what ways may early and middle adults feel as they did during adolescence? Does this knowledge help students better understand people in older generations?

L1 **DISCUSSION.** What is a mid-life crisis? Who is most likely to suffer from this difficulty?

L1 **CLASS ACTIVITY.** Ask the class to arrive at a good definition for the term *transition* and then list some of the transitions that occur during young and middle adulthood.

L1 **USING CONFLICT RESOLUTION TRANSPARENCY 40.** Refer to the Teaching Transparencies Binder.

Independent Practice

L1 **COMMUNITY INVOLVEMENT.** Ask students to find a middle-aged adult in their circle of relatives and friends who will agree to be interviewed regarding mid-life crises. Do the informants feel they are in a crisis? How do they feel differently about life now than they did in young adulthood? Why? Are they more inward-looking or outward-looking? Are they optimistic or pessimistic about the rest of their lives? How much older do they think they will live to be? Does this affect how they feel and act on a day-to-day basis?

LEP **RESEARCH.** Have students collect photos and drawings of men and women in the young and middle stages of adulthood. They should show a diversity of activities. Ask them to write a few sentences to describe the major characteristics and behaviors of each stage. Correct and discuss any misconceptions.

L1 **USING THE LESSON RESOURCES.** For additional student activities, refer to the lesson resources on page 178.

Assess

Check for Understanding
- Assign and discuss the lesson review.

Evaluate
- Administer, grade, and discuss the *Lesson 2 Quiz.*

Reteach
- Ask students to write two short paragraphs, one on young adulthood and one on middle adulthood. Students should describe the major changes in behavior and character of young adults relative to adolescents. Then they should describe the major changes of middle adulthood relative to young adulthood.
- Ask students to complete *Reteaching Activity 24.*

DID YOU KNOW?
- One recent study showed that young and middle-aged females who lift weights are also likely to lift their self-esteem.
- In the early 1960s, over 80 percent of people in their 20s drank coffee. By the late 1980s, that number had dropped to just over 30 percent.
- Up until the age of 40, the leading cause of death is accidents.

DID YOU KNOW?
- Your chances of living to be 100 or older are best in Arizona, Florida, Hawaii, Idaho, Iowa, Kansas, Minnesota, Nebraska, North Dakota, and South Dakota.
- If you think that senior citizens are confined to bed because of old age, think again. The average number of days they spend ill in bed or with their activities seriously curtailed is only 23 per year, while for those in the 45 to 64 age bracket, the average number of days infirmed is 34.

if nothing is different. Their attitudes, dress, and tastes remain the same. Some may even refuse to recognize the growing independence of their children. Refusing to recognize inner changes during middle adulthood sometimes results in emotional or physical difficulties, which may cause problems in relationships with others.

Some adults who find it difficult to accept the passage of time make drastic changes in their behavior and way of life. Sometimes this is referred to as going through a mid-life crisis. People experiencing these difficulties may imitate youthful or immature ways of living or may wear clothes designed for younger people. Since these middle-aged adults have not recognized and dealt with changes within themselves, they often find they still are not happy.

Most people progress through middle adulthood without serious problems. They adjust their hopes and dreams and adapt their life-styles to their newly experienced feelings of being in touch with themselves. Some make career changes that are more personally satisfying.

Parent-Child and Adult-Child Relationships

Many children reach adolescence at the same time one or both parents or other important adults in their lives are going through the process of self-evaluation. Because middle adulthood can be as difficult for adults as adolescence is for teens, tension and conflict may increase. Both adults and adolescents are working through stages in which many changes are taking place. As a result, the personal needs of the adult and the teen often come into conflict. An understanding of developmental tasks and an awareness of the needs of others can help keep conflicts and tensions between adolescents and adults to a minimum.

Transitions

There are a number of **transitions,** or changes, in all stages of life. A major transition during middle adulthood is based on Erikson's stage of development called generativity versus stagnation. This stage focuses on helping others, especially young people. Generativity involves a commitment to the future. This can include active concern for young people and for the society in which young people will live and work as adults. Refusal to accept and deal with changes during middle adulthood can result in self-absorption, or preoccupation with meeting only one's own needs.

KEEPING FIT

Becoming a Walking Encyclopedia

Many older adults get vigorous exercise by becoming mall walkers, track walkers, or sidewalkers. Walking is a kind of exercise that promotes maximum cardiovascular benefit with minimum risk of injury. And walking is an exercise that can benefit all ages.

Choose an older adult as a walking buddy. Exercise with the person regularly. As you walk, share your thoughts, opinions, histories, and experiences. Learn what you can from the person's life experiences. In the process, you may find that you not only become more fit, but you may become a walking encyclopedia!

180 CHAPTER 10 CONTINUING THROUGH THE LIFE CYCLE

Additional Information

Aging. Because the physical changes of adulthood occur over such a long period of time, this life stage is usually studied cross-sectionally. This means that people across the spectrum of adult ages are selected for study and measured at one point in time. Then, data for younger and older age groups are compared, and any differences between age groups are attributed to the aging process.

However, attributing all differences between younger and older individuals to aging may not be valid. While a difference in body weight, for example, between younger and older adults may be due to a real age-trend in weight gain, it also could be due to greater longevity of heavier individuals.

Middle age often brings a shift in focus in a person's life.

Another transition facing the middle-aged adult involves children leaving home and entering adulthood. This is sometimes called the **empty-nest syndrome.** If children have been the reason for a couple's staying together, divorce may take place when the couple discovers that the only factor they had in common is no longer there. However, coming to terms with themselves and aligning their dreams with reality allows many couples to reestablish close relationships as well as to grow as individuals. Single people may marry for the first time or remarry if they have been divorced or widowed. Women who have devoted their lives to home and family often go back to paid employment or begin a new career.

A recent transition involves the return of adult children to the home of their parents. The term **cluttered-nest syndrome** is often used to identify the situation in which parents must adjust, once again, to the presence of children in their lives. Many adult children return to their parents' home for economic reasons, such as insufficient income to afford both college and a place of their own or to rent or purchase housing on their own. Still others return after a divorce or the birth of a child for whom they cannot afford care.

DID YOU KNOW?

■ According to researchers at the Philadelphia Geriatric Center, people who care for invalids need breaks. New programs offer respite care—breaks from the daily caretaking. These breaks allow caregivers to do chores, get rest and, in the long run, be refreshed for future caregiving.

Enrich

■ The term *generation gap* refers to diversity in ideas and perceptions due to differences in experience and age. It is most common between teenagers and adults. Understanding and communication are key tools in bridging the generation gap. Have students work in small groups to identify specific ways in which they believe a generation gap exists between themselves and older individuals. What evidence do they have for differences in ideas and perceptions? What underlying differences in experience, whether or not due to differences in age, do they believe are responsible? How old are the youngest adults with whom they can identify a generation gap? Ask students to summarize and defend their answers in a written report.

Close

Tell students that in this lesson we have seen that several important developmental challenges face individuals in their early and middle adult years. Young adulthood is usually a time of increasing financial and emotional independence and growing responsibility. Physical and mental abilities peak, and many crucial decisions are made. Middle adulthood is a time of self-evaluation and redirection. It's time to take pride in one's accomplishments and assess the goals one still wants to attain. As individuals age and enter the elder years, more challenges and changes occur. The elder years are the focus of the next lesson.

LESSON 2 REVIEW

Reviewing Facts and Vocabulary

1. Summarize the signs indicating that a person has reached young adulthood.
2. Define the term *transition*, and give two examples of transitions people face during middle adulthood.

Thinking Critically

3. **Analysis.** Write a paragraph analyzing a crucial decision made by a young adult you know or have read about.
4. **Synthesis.** Develop two corresponding lists: concerns facing middle-aged adults who are experiencing the empty nest syndrome and concerns middle-aged adults feel as they face the cluttered nest syndrome.

Applying Health Knowledge

5. Find examples on television, in magazines, or in newspapers to illustrate people going through the stage of generativity versus stagnation.
6. Create a cartoon, bulletin board, or other illustration to show a family experiencing the empty-nest syndrome or the cluttered-nest syndrome.
7. Prepare a skit, with follow-up questions, based on someone who may be going through a mid-life crisis.

YOUNG AND MIDDLE ADULTHOOD **181**

Answers to Lesson 2 Review

1. Summaries will vary. Signs include: not depending on parents or other adults, support oneself financially, set goals, express emotions in acceptable ways, get along well with others, deal easily with everyday situations, accepted by society as full-fledged members.
2. Transition—change. Examples will vary.
3. Answers will vary.
4. Answers will vary but should reflect an understanding of the empty-nest syndrome and the cluttered-nest syndrome at the top of this page.
5. Answers will vary.
6. Answers will vary.
7. Answers will vary.

Focus

Lesson Objectives

After studying this lesson, students should be able to:

- summarize the biological changes of late adulthood
- summarize the social changes of late adulthood

Bellringer

Write the following on the chalkboard for students to work on while attendance is being taken: *Complete the following sentence in writing with as many different endings as you can. When you're an older adult you can still. . . .*

Introducing the Lesson

Refer to the Bellringer. Ask volunteers to share their responses. Point out that aging isn't all negative. Ask students to develop a list of the positive aspects of aging.

Building Vocabulary

- Ask students to demonstrate their understanding of the concepts *life expectancy* and *lifespan* by writing a paragraph that explains how the two concepts differ.
- Ask students to complete *Workbook Vocabulary Activity 25.*

DID YOU KNOW?

- Internal aging may be caused by the process of oxidation and the accumulation of "free radicals," those molecules and electrons that float around the body looking for a place to attach themselves. In doing so, they may attack or kill cells or make them open to disease.
- According to the Calorie Control Council, the peak years for dieting are among those in the 50 to 59 age bracket.
- Learning is a lifelong process. Just ask the thousands of older people who are enrolled in school.

LESSON 3
LATE ADULTHOOD AND AGING

Erikson's eighth stage of development is late adulthood. Old age is often treated more as a disease than as a stage in human development. Because our society tends to emphasize youth and economic productivity, the wisdom and experience of age are sometimes ignored. Often there is a lack of respect for the elderly and a feeling that once people reach a certain age, they are useless. These feelings and actions sometimes make it difficult for older adults to feel worthwhile.

Chronological age does not necessarily make a person old. There are many "young" people well past 70. Some 80-year-olds are in better physical condition than some much younger people. In our society age 65 was selected as the cutoff point between middle and later adulthood. This age was adopted primarily for social purposes, such as eligibility for retirement and various pensions, discounts, and services reserved for those often referred to as "senior citizens." Age 65 does not, however, indicate a magic age at which there is a decline in individual capabilities, productivity, or potential.

Late Adulthood

The trend toward better health and the resulting longer life expectancy has reshaped people's ideas of old age. The potential human life expectancy averages about 85 years of age with a maximum life duration of about 115 years. With the advances in diagnosing and treating illnesses and by practicing a healthy life-style, people can increase both their quality of life and their anticipated life expectancy.

Measures of Age

Aging, like all phases of growth and development, is predictable but very individual. **Gerontologists,** people who study and work in the area of aging, cite three measures of age. The first is **chronological age.** This is simply the number of birthdays one has had.

The second, **biological age,** is how well different parts of the body are functioning. Fitness standards for various chronological ages include how fast a person recovers from running up a flight of stairs or how fast blood clots. The rate of biological aging is influenced by heredity, life-style, and health habits, especially diet and exercise. Poisons taken in from the environment over a lifetime and the illnesses a person has had also influence biological age.

The third measure of age is **social age,** which involves a person's lifestyle. For example, at each phase of development, there are some general **age norms,** things a person is expected to be doing at a particular chronological age. For example, our society expects a 16-year-old to be going to high school, meeting and socializing with a variety of people, possibly working part-time, or preparing for a career after finishing high

---

Resources for Lesson 3

- **Guided Reading** Activity 25
- **Workbook** Vocabulary Act 25
- **Reteaching** Activity 25
- **Lesson 3 Quiz**

Science and Technology Videodisc
Human Biology, Side 2
Ch 2 Low Vision Clinic

Ch 14 Measuring Calcium Deficiency

school. These norms, which are imposed by the society in which one lives, give people a timetable, but they do not always reflect what people want to do or are able to do.

The Physical Process of Aging

You have learned that certain body cells are replaced continually. The life of a blood cell is about 120 days; that of an intestinal cell is about 1.5 days. As a person ages, this process of cell division slows. The cells that are capable of dividing and producing new cells gradually decrease activity.

As cells grow older, their nuclei change and age pigment collects in the cells. Age pigment is thought to be the result of cells becoming less efficient in processing and ridding themselves of cell wastes. With the gradual buildup of age pigment, cell function slows and cells gradually deteriorate.

As part of the aging process

- skin loses its elasticity and begins to wrinkle;
- hair turns gray;
- nails become brittle;
- hearing and vision problems may develop;
- bones gradually lose calcium, becoming more brittle;
- basal metabolism slows;
- kidney function slows;
- the endocrine system decreases its secretion of hormones;
- the body's immune system becomes less efficient;
- a loss of lean body mass occurs, often accompanied by an increase of fat tissue;
- joints become less mobile; muscular strength weakens;
- vital capacity, the total amount of air that can be exhaled from the lungs after a deep breath, lessens;
- the heart pumps blood less efficiently;
- the body's ability to use glucose diminishes, lessening the body's available energy.

Although all of these physical characteristics of aging are inevitable if a person lives long enough, they are very individual and directly related to a person's overall life-style. If people continue to be active, eat a nutritious diet, and take good mental and physical care of themselves, the function of these body parts remains more efficient.

KEEPING FIT

Developing Friendships Across the Ages

In our society, the young and old are too often segregated, or kept apart. If you have a good relationship with a senior citizen, continue to nurture it; you both have lots to gain from knowing one another. If you don't have a significant relationship with a senior citizen, develop one. Spend more time or correspond with a grandparent or other elderly relative. Get to know an elderly neighbor. Or volunteer in an organization that pairs teens with older adults. Put some time and effort into enriching the life of a senior and, in turn, have your own life enriched.

LATE ADULTHOOD AND AGING **183**

Additional Information

Pet-Facilitated Therapy. The older years can be a time of loneliness. Spouses and close friends die; children move away. For many people, Pet-Facilitated Therapy (PFT) can ease the pain and stress of loneliness.

Taking care of a pet—a dog, cat, bird, or even tropical fish—can help people who live alone feel wanted and important. Pets give much needed love, affection, and enjoyment. They bring routine and normalcy to a home life that has been disrupted by the death or disability of a spouse. Some pets offer opportunities for moderate exercise, such as walking. Researchers even have found that pets effectively allay the fears of nursing home residents.

184 CHAPTER 10 CONTINUING THROUGH THE LIFE CYCLE

Overcoming The Odds

Noel Johnson is 92 years young. He is a glowing example of how old age does not have to mean illness, dependence, or lack of fitness. He has run in marathons seven times and is now preparing to run in his eighth. "I ran my first New York marathon when I was 80 years old," he says. "I was the first 80-year-old ever to have completed the 26-mile run. I've even run two marathons just seven days apart."

Johnson works out daily and with great dedication. He says, "I just got off the exercise bike. I was on that for one hour. Then I'll be on my rebounder (trampoline) for one hour. I think that's more beneficial than running because you're going up and down every second, and it vibrates every cell in your body." He continues, "I have my light weights that I work out with 10 or 15 minutes 2 or 3 times a day." He also works out on a treadmill daily. "I'll be running the New York Marathon in November," he continues. "I run about 3 or 4 miles right now, but soon I'll run 10 miles twice a day in preparation for the race."

Noel Johnson also loves to box. He is the World Senior Boxing Champion.

Johnson was not always so

healthy or committed to fitness. At 72, he was 40 pounds overweight. He smoked cigarettes and drank alcohol, and he had a heart condition. His doctor gave him 6 months to live. In fact,

he was in such bad shape that his life insurance was canceled. "My son said I should go into a retirement home, and I said that wasn't necessary. Then he said, 'Well, will you show me you can walk?' I started walking and walking and then running, too. And that's when I began my athletic career—at age 72!"

Johnson's amazing achievements and overall fitness have been studied by health scientists. Since 1971, he has been

part of an ongoing study of master athletes over age 40 at the University of California at Davis. He is now also being studied at the University of Florida at Gainesville, where tests again show he is in superb shape. He says, "They told me in Florida after a bone scan from ankle to head that my structure was as strong and clear as anything they had examined." On a treadmill test, his pulse was 63, and researchers got it to over 200, a pulse rate that Johnson says would make the "average person drop dead."

Noel Johnson has written 2 books and is already planning his third. He has traveled and lectured in 21 countries around the world. Among his other goals: running a marathon when he reaches 100—an age, he says, "when I know I'll be in better condition than I am now."

Meeting Students' Needs

Aging. Major increases in life expectancy have occurred over the past century in the developed countries, including the United States, due to socioeconomic, technological, and medical advances. Today, far fewer people die in infancy and early childhood from infectious diseases. As a result, more and more people are living into their 80s and beyond. The average 50-year-old can now expect to live another 25 to 30 years.

It's important to stress to teenagers that the way they live their lives when they're young can influence how healthy and happy they are in their old age. It's up to them whether their old age is active, healthy, and fulfilling or fraught with pain and debility.

There are three measures of aging: chronological, biological, and social.

The Needs of the Elderly

Just like everyone else, the elderly have basic emotional needs. They need to love and be loved, to feel they are making a contribution, and to feel they are worthwhile individuals.

A variety of factors affects a person's ability to adjust to aging. For example, looking at aging as a lifelong process contributes to a better understanding and acceptance of later adulthood as a vital stage in life. People who have coped with changes all of their lives are better able to cope with the changes resulting from aging. Their attitude toward aging and their activity level have a great influence on how they adjust to getting older. People who remain active and involved tend to adjust better. Flexible policies for retirement and educational and counseling services help older adults prepare for and adapt to this stage in their lives.

Family relationships are a very important factor in helping individuals successfully adjust to aging. In some families grandparents not only care for young children but also prepare meals and do other chores so that other family members can go to work. Because older people need to feel useful and wanted, those who do not have relatives living with or near them often face the greatest difficulty in adjusting to old age.

KEEPING FIT

Finding a Mentor

Having a mentor—an older person who is an expert in an area in which you are trying to excel—can be a great source of knowledge and encouragement. Famous artists and musicians over the ages have had mentors. These days, there are mentor programs in businesses and schools.

Think of a talent or craft that you would like to learn, improve, or develop. Locate an older person who is considered competent in that area. Ask the person if you can learn from him or her. Offer to be an unpaid assistant or run errands for the person in return for his or her time and guidance.

LATE ADULTHOOD AND AGING **185**

Additional Information

Aging. In later life, you are more likely to have better emotional health; have free time to pursue hobbies and interests like reading, gardening, traveling, windsurfing, etc; eat what you want and sleep when you want; spend your free time volunteering your talents and services; enjoy younger people, including your own grandchildren; be more authentic, more true to who you are, and more likely to speak your mind; care less about what others think of you; feel less insecure; share your wisdom, knowledge, or resources; develop perspective and humor about life; appreciate your closest relationships; let the little annoyances go without getting attached to them; feel a greater sense of personal power.

Assess

Check for Understanding

- Assign and discuss answers to the lesson review.

Evaluate

- Administer, grade, and discuss the *Lesson 3 Quiz*.

Reteach

- Have students interview at least three healthy, active senior citizens. Ask students to elicit responses to this question: *What are the mental, emotional, and social benefits of aging?* Then, have students write summaries of their findings.
- Ask students to complete *Reteaching Activity 25*.

Enrich

- Ask students to research and write a brief biography of a well-known individual who lived to be at least 90 years old. Have students identify particular characteristics of the individual and his or her life-style that they believe may have contributed to longevity.

Close

While aging usually brings a gradual decline in physical capabilities, many aspects of growing old are positive changes. Most importantly, the elderly have accumulated a tremendous amount of knowledge and wisdom just through the sheer number of years they have experienced life. If they remain open-minded, healthy, and interested in life, they can continue to make an important contribution to their families and to society. It's up to the rest of us to listen and appreciate what the elderly have to offer. It's undeniable, however, that being old means facing death. Death is the focus of the next lesson.

Young and old can learn from each other.

Elderly people who maintain friendships and contact with other people after retiring cope better with aging. Programs, such as Adopt-a-Grandparent, have been started in many communities to keep the elderly involved with others, especially with young people. The rewards for such involvement are twofold. The elderly feel needed and useful, and the young people get enjoyment from sharing and learning from the elderly.

Whether living alone or with others, the elderly need to be as independent as possible. They need privacy and time to be alone to take care of their own needs, hobbies, and other interests. They need a place to keep their personal items. They need money of their own to spend without having to account for it.

Services that enable elderly people to maintain their own homes are available in some communities. These services make it possible for many elderly people to remain independent and to still make their own decisions.

LESSON 3 REVIEW

Reviewing Facts and Vocabulary

1. Define and describe the three measures of age.
2. Give examples of six physical changes that people experience as they age.

Thinking Critically

3. **Analysis.** Analyze how a person's age might measure differently based on chronological, biological, and social age scales.

4. **Synthesis.** Develop an activity program for the elderly. Discuss your reasons for each aspect of the program.

Applying Health Knowledge

5. Visit a senior citizen center and write a report on positive aspects of your visit.

186 Chapter 10 Continuing Through the Life Cycle

Answers to Lesson 3 Review

1. Chronological age—the number of birthdays one has had. Biological age—how well different parts of the body are functioning. Social age—measures a person's life-style.
2. Examples will vary. Accept six of the bulleted items on page 183.
3. Answers will vary. Possible answer: One might be middle-aged chronologically and socially but be in good physical condition and, therefore, younger biologically.
4. Programs will vary but explanations should support the program.
5. Answers will vary.

DEATH—PART OF THE LIFE CYCLE

Facing death, whether it be one's own or that of a loved one, is always difficult. People often avoid talking or even thinking about the subject of dying because of the emotions it brings up. A primary response to the prospect of dying is fear. It is quite natural to fear the unknown, and, despite the greater strides in our understanding of the process of dying, death is a subject on which no one can speak from firsthand experience. However, understanding and accepting one's feelings about death are important parts of mental health.

Clinical Death and Brain Death

Death is defined in many ways. **Clinical death** occurs when a person's body systems stop working. Sometimes clinical death can be reversed, life can be restored, and the person can make a full recovery. For example, a person could be a victim of drowning and be revived through cardiopulmonary resuscitation (CPR), a procedure to restore normal breathing and force the heart to pump blood after a cardiac arrest. If resuscitation is not successful, the brain cells do not receive the oxygen they need. Brain death can occur. **Brain death** is the loss of function of the entire brain, including the brain stem. When that happens, the person cannot be revived.

Stages in Brain Death

Among the first brain cells to die are those in the cerebral cortex. This area of the brain controls sensation and voluntary action, stores memory, and directs complex thought and decision-making processes. The victim may continue to live, but without any of these functions.

If the brain continues to be cut off from oxygen, cells in the midbrain die. This part of the brain controls emotions, alertness, and consciousness. The victim lapses into a coma, although heart function and breathing may continue.

If lack of oxygen continues, the brain stem dies. It is this area of the lower brain that stimulates the action of the heart and lungs.

Understanding and Accepting Death

Although it is often said with humor that "no one gets through this life alive," very few people know how to deal realistically with this fact. Many people do not experience the death of a loved one until late in life. Even though a large proportion of the population used to die before age 40, many more now live past age 70.

As death becomes a more foreign or distant experience, there is less opportunity for passing along lessons of how to cope with it, either to the person who is dying or to the family and friends who live afterward.

LESSON 4 FOCUS

TERMS TO USE
- Clinical death
- Brain death
- Thanatology

CONCEPTS TO LEARN
- Death is part of our life cycle.
- There are five stages in accepting death.
- Stages of grief are similar to the stages of accepting death.

ATTITUDES AND BEHAVIORS TO EVALUATE
- Self-Inventory, page 192.
- Building Decision-Making Skills, page 193.

Focus

Lesson Objective

After studying this lesson, students should be able to:
- describe the stages one goes through in accepting his or her own death or the death of a loved one

Bellringer

Write the following on the chalkboard for students to work on while attendance is being taken: *Answer the following questions in writing, keeping in mind that there are no right or wrong responses. What is the first word that comes to mind when you think of death? Do you fear death? If so, why? If you had one year to live and were guaranteed success in anything you did, what would you do? What are two things that would be important to you if you knew you were dying?*

Introducing the Lesson

Refer to the Bellringer. Ask volunteers to share their responses. Point out that people's perceptions of death will vary with their developmental stage, life experiences, and family situations. For example, young people find it particularly difficult to believe that they are mortal, especially if they have never had any personal experience with death. People without supportive family ties find facing death more difficult than do those with loving family members to rely on. Nonetheless, there are similarities in how people deal with death and grief. In this lesson we will see the stages most people go through in this process.

DID YOU KNOW?

- The nation's death rate has reached a new low except among black males, whose life expectancy has dropped for three years in a row. Among the reasons for high death rates among this group were heart disease, homicide, and AIDS.

Resources for Lesson 4

- **Transparency** 16
- **Guided Reading** Activity 26
- **Decision-Making** Activity 10
- **Workbook** Vocabulary Activity 26
- **Workbook** Application Activity 10
- **Reteaching** Activity 26
- **Enrichment** Activity 10

- **Health Labs** Activity 10
- **Cooperative Learning** Activity 10
- **Lesson 4 Quiz**
- **Chapter 10 Test**
- **ABC News InterActive Videodiscs AIDS, Side 2**
  Ch 13 What Is It Like to Face Death?

- Select students to find definitions of the following terms: *cardiopulmonary resuscitation (CPR), cerebral cortex, midbrain, brain stem,* and *coma.* Where relevant, they should use illustrations to demonstrate their understanding of the terms for the rest of the class.

- Ask students to complete *Workbook Vocabulary Activity 26.*

Teach

Guided Practice

L1 **DISCUSSION.** What are some of the reasons most people fear death?

L1 **USING LIFE MANAGEMENT SKILLS TRANSPARENCY 16.** Refer to the Teaching Transparencies Binder.

L1 **EXPLANATION.** Explain the differences between clinical death and brain death.

L1 **DISCUSSION.** What are the stages of brain death? What functions are lost as the different areas of the brain shut down? When does physical (clinical) death occur?

L1 **EXPLANATION.** Explain the stages children go through, as they get older, in their comprehension of death. How does this affect how we explain death to young children?

L1 **DISCUSSION.** How can one grieve over one's own death? Why is it important to do so? How can loved ones best help the dying individual through this stage?

L1 **DISCUSSION.** What moral dilemmas arise from medical advances that allow doctors to maintain physical life in cases of brain death?

L1 **DISCUSSION.** What experiences about death do you recall as a young child? How have your feelings about death changed as you have grown older? Why do you think your feelings have changed?

CONFLICT RESOLUTION

A recent study, which surveyed 125 youths who had lost a parent, found that those who had the greatest difficulty accepting the death had been the most shielded from dealing with their grief. As a result, they had trouble resolving the conflicting feelings that loss of a parent can bring, such as feelings of abandonment. The researchers concluded that maintaining an emotional connection to the deceased parent, rather that trying to forget about the death, usually leads to a healthier outcome.

How would you apply that advice to help a close friend deal with the loss of a parent?

At the same time, an increasing proportion of deaths occur as a result of illness such as cancer or AIDS, in which the process of dying is prolonged and emotionally painful.

Several factors influence one's understanding of and attitude toward death, including personal experience, spiritual beliefs, family attitudes and values, and one's age. Children's understanding of death increases in developmental stages. Infants up to two years have no real concept of death other than the fact that someone may be present at one moment and gone the next.

From ages 2 to 5 years, children recognize death but do not understand that it is permanent. Children may see death as being like sleep. Many children at this age have a great deal of faith in their own ability to make things happen simply by wishing.

From ages 5 to about 9, children may see death as a personification, that is, in the form of a real or imaginary person, such as an elderly man, a fairy princess, an angel, or a skeleton. They may begin to see death as being permanent, but cannot see it as something that could happen to them.

By about age 10, children may see death as final and inevitable. They are ready to deal with the reality of death, but have difficulty accepting that it can happen anytime to anyone. Such an understanding develops as children enter adolescence.

Each of these stages is general and will vary from person to person. Each stage depends on what other people have told the individuals about death and what experiences they have had with it.

Stages in Accepting Death

In recent years studies by scientists in the field of **thanatology,** from the Greek word, *thanatos,* meaning "death," have led to an understanding of what dying people go through. Their studies can greatly help the dying and their loved ones deal effectively with the situation. These researchers have learned that dying, like living, is a process. While there are different styles of dying, there are common elements and problems that all people experience as they prepare for death.

A pioneer in understanding the psychology of dying is Elisabeth Kübler-Ross, a psychiatrist, who identified five emotional stages that dying people typically pass through. For several decades she has worked with hundreds of dying patients and their families to better understand what a person goes through in coming to grips with his or her own death.

KEEPING FIT

Dealing with Grief

Losing someone that you love can be devastating. Watching someone you are close to grieve can also be very difficult.

Keep in mind the following tips:

- There is no one way to grieve. Each person has his or her own individual style and timetable for recovering from the loss of a loved one.

- Tears, anger, depression, guilt, fear, or having physical symptoms or anxiety attacks are all normal reactions to grief.

- The grieving process cannot be rushed. It generally takes years, not months.

- Talking about the person who has died rather than avoiding the subject helps everyone cope with the death.

Additional Information

The Terminally Ill. Emotional support helps people cope with imminent death. But many people feel awkward around a terminally ill person. What can you do and talk about with a grandparent, parent, or friend who is dying?

Share your emotions. It's okay to cry as well as laugh. Call to say "Hi," send cards and letters, and visit often.

When you visit, bring reminders of happy times and listen to the memories. Help the person feel useful by asking for assistance or an opinion on something. Talk about and read aloud the day's news so the dying person feels part of the present. Finally, discuss the future so he or she feels part of it now.

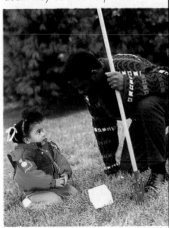
A child's first experience with death may be when a pet dies.

Visiting often and talking openly with a dying person will show that you care.

These five stages in the acceptance of death are similar to those we all experience when faced with any significant loss. However, each person's reactions are individual and will vary in degree. The stages are simply a general guideline for understanding and accepting the process of dying and death.

Stage 1: Denial. Denial is a person's initial reaction to any loss. It is the "No, not me; it can't be" stage when the patient cannot accept the fact of his or her fatal illness. This stage is an attempt to avoid reality by saying or thinking, "It is all a bad dream and will go away." During this time people often have a feeling of isolation or helplessness.

Stage 2: Anger. A person moves from denial to the second stage, anger, which is the "Why me?" stage. Anger is a natural reaction, an outlet for resentment at being a victim. Since customs often stand in the way of people's being able to vent their anger, it is often expressed in other ways. There may be an envy of others who still have life ahead of them. The patient may become hard to handle, critical, demanding, or unco-operative. Family members and friends may see this as an expression of ingratitude and respond by making their visits shorter and less frequent. As a result, the patient may possibly feel even more isolated and rejected and may become even more unpleasant to relatives, friends, and medical practitioners.

Stage 3: Bargaining. As the anger subsides and the patient begins to accept the reality of the situation, a stage of bargaining frequently follows. The dying person often tries to bargain for more time with good behavior. This stage may include attempts to postpone the end by praying, seeking better medical treatment, and promising to mend his or her ways.

Stage 4: Depression. This stage is a time of grieving for what the patient has already lost and for what will be lost. Commonly a period of silence and withdrawal, the dying person tries to become separate from all that he or she has known and loved. The patient worries about family and money. The feelings of numbness, isolation, anger, and rage felt previously are now replaced with a sense of great loss. Rather than attempting to comfort the dying person by saying that everything will be all right, loved ones should encourage him or her to grieve.

DEATH—PART OF THE LIFE CYCLE **189**

Additional Information

Mourning Rituals. Almost all societies have some culturally channeled expressions of grief and rituals of mourning for the dead. When the mourning period is over, a ritual of reintegration of mourners back into the group usually takes place. This is important because death is the most socially and emotionally disruptive event the majority of us ever experience.

Often the more important the deceased individual, the more exaggerated the mourning ritual. Worldwide, expressions of grief vary. They may include shaving the head, going unbathed, or smearing the body with clay or ashes. Mourners may tear their clothing, gash themselves, wail, or go into seclusion for varying lengths of time.

L2 RESEARCH. Have volunteers find articles about situations where a family has had to decide whether to keep a relative on life support systems, or about situations where a spouse has carried out the wish to die of a terminally ill husband or wife. How have the courts ruled in these cases? Ask students to prepare a brief report of their findings.

L1 WRITING. Have students write a case study about an individual in one of the stages of accepting death, either the individual's own death or that of a close loved one.

L1 RESEARCH. Have students research the leading causes of death among the elderly. Are there differences between men and women in the most significant causes? What life-style factors may increase the chances of dying from one of these common causes of death in old age?

L3 COMMUNITY INVOLVEMENT. Ask students to question medical professionals and other adults about the concept "dying of old age." They should get the sense that "old age" is just the category of deaths of the elderly for which no specific cause can be determined. How does this "misdiagnosis" affect our view of old age? Have them write a summary of their findings.

L1 COMMUNITY INVOLVEMENT. Ask selected students to do volunteer work in a community service for the elderly, such as Meals on Wheels, a day-care center for the elderly, a senior-citizen social center, or the Adopt-a-Grandparent program. After they have been involved in the volunteer program for a few weeks, have them prepare a brief report on what they have learned about seniors and their needs. How did the seniors respond to their volunteer efforts?

L1 USING THE LESSON RESOURCES. For additional student activities, refer to the lesson resources on page 187.

DID YOU KNOW?

■ Hospice care is family-centered health care for the terminally ill. Through team effort of loved ones, hospice nurses, home healthcare workers, and a participating physician, a dying patient can live out the rest of his or her life at home or in a home-like setting. Some hospitals even have hospice units.

■ Three-quarters of women will become widows. The average length of their widowhood will be 12 years.

Dealing with the loss of a loved one takes time.

Stage 5: Acceptance. The fifth stage of dying is that of acceptance. While the previous stage, depression, involves facing reality, it leaves a person feeling helpless. Although acceptance is not a happy or an unhappy stage, it is not a time of helplessness or resignation. Instead, it allows for action and for facing reality in a constructive way. Personal and financial matters often are taken care of during this stage.

Kübler-Ross identified another emotion that operates throughout all the stages just described. That emotion is hope. There usually is hope that there will be a cure or a remission and that death will not occur.

HEALTH UPDATE

LOOKING AT THE ISSUES

Medical Ethics

One well-known medical ethics case is that of Nancy Cruzan, who, as the result of an auto accident in Missouri, was in a coma from 1983 until 1990. In that year, the U.S. Supreme Court ruled that the family could remove her feeding and water tubes. They did so, and she died 11 days later.

In another case, 87-year-old Helga Wanglie lies in a coma in Minneapolis with no chance of recovery. The doctors want to remove life support, but her spouse refuses, saying he has no right to decide when and if she should die. Who should make life and death decisions?

Analyzing Different Viewpoints

ONE VIEW. Opinion surveys indicate that between 75 to 90 percent of the population would not want to be kept alive on life support systems if these systems could not return them to normal life.

A SECOND VIEW. Some people feel that no one has the right to terminate another's life, no matter how hopeless the medical condition of the patient.

A THIRD VIEW. Many people want to specify while they are healthy what their specific treatment requests would be should they be rendered helpless and unable to communicate their wishes. By signing a living will or a more detailed document that offers a range of choices in various medical situations, they make their wishes known.

A FOURTH VIEW. Other people argue that people without medical training cannot fully understand the choices of medical treatment and their implications. Therefore, they say, neither patients nor their families should make life and death decisions because they are unqualified to do so. Such decisions, they argue, should instead rest with medical professionals.

Exploring Your Views

1. Do you think that life support equipment should be removed in the event of irreversible brain damage or permanent coma? Why or why not?

2. Should a doctor be allowed to bring about death if the person is suffering in pain from an incurable illness?

3. Should a doctor provide the means by which an individual can take his or her own life?

Additional Information

Life After Death? Across human cultures there is an almost universal belief in the continued existence of a deceased person in the form of an immortal ghost or spirit. But this belief has numerous variations.

Some people believe in a shadowy world where the spirits of the dead reside. It may be a heaven or a hell or just a different version of reality. Others believe in a continuous cycle of reincarnation or an ultimate absorption of the soul into some kind of cosmic spirit.

In many cultures, the spirits of the dead are thought to be evil and dangerous. In others, the spirits are believed to be protectors. In still others, they are believed to be in a sort of limbo, awaiting rebirth.

Grief Experienced by Others

The family and friends of the dying person also must cope with death. Grief and mourning can develop through a series of stages much like Kübler-Ross's stages of dying. According to Kübler-Ross, survivors of a person who has died go through a stage of denial or disbelief, then a stage of anger. This anger may be directed toward the dying person or toward friends or others in the family. If there is forewarning of the death, the grieving person may bargain to prolong the dying person's life. As the grieving person realizes the futility of this, depression sets in. Later the survivors pass to a stage of acceptance as they understand that the death of the person is a reality.

When the stage of acceptance has been reached by those who are dying and by their loved ones, the process of grieving is usually shorter and less painful. Accepting the impending death of a loved one does not mean you do not care. Instead it means you care enough to make the end as pleasant as possible for all concerned, especially the person who is dying.

Experiencing grief may not be as distinct as previously defined. J. W. Worden has identified tasks of grief, in which a person can move back and forth through tasks and experience positive and negative emotions at the same time. These tasks also can overlap. The tasks include accepting the reality of the loss, experiencing the pain of the loss, adjusting to an environment in which the deceased is missing, and withdrawing emotional energy and reinvesting it in another relationship.

The death of someone you love is one of life's most shocking, and even shattering, experiences. Encouragement and comfort from others is needed to help survivors pass through their grief and mourning. In the event of sudden death, there has been little or no time for preparation. Thus, grief tends to last much longer. The real impact of the death may not surface until months later.

In order to regain physical, mental, and emotional health, the survivors need to be able to talk about what has happened and to express their feelings. Through such conversations, people can come to accept the death of their loved one and continue with their lives.

Grief is a part of life that will pass as people come to accept the death of a loved one and realize that their own lives must go on.

LESSON 4 REVIEW

Reviewing Facts and Vocabulary

1. Define *clinical death* and *brain death;* explain the difference between the two.
2. Describe the stages in brain death.

Thinking Critically

3. **Analysis.** Write a short paper pointing out how people's perceptions of death may vary with their stage in life, life experiences, and family influences.

4. **Evaluation.** Who should make the decision whether one lives or dies? Explain your reasoning.

Applying Health Knowledge

5. Using community resources, complete a course in cardiopulmonary resuscitation.
6. Write a two-page paper comparing the customs and attitudes toward death of another culture with those of your society.

Answers to Lesson 4 Review

1. Clinical death—occurs when a person's body systems stop working. Brain death—the loss of function of the entire brain, including the brain stem. Sometimes clinical death can be reversed. Brain death cannot be reversed.
2. Descriptions of each stage can be found on page 187.

3. Answers will vary. References may be made to the relationships between one's age, family ties, religious beliefs, and general health.
4. Answers will vary but should be supported logically.
5. No answer required.
6. Answers will vary.

Assess

Check for Understanding

- Assign and discuss the lesson review.
- Assign and discuss the chapter review.

Evaluate

- Administer, grade, and discuss the *Lesson 4 Quiz.*
- Administer, grade, and discuss the *Chapter 10 Test.*
- Refer to the Performance Assessment strategy for this chapter. See pages T 23 to T 25.

Reteach

- Have students talk with a grief counselor or a member of a grief support group. Ask students to find out how best to cope with grief. Using information gathered from their interviews and from this chapter, have students make a pamphlet with suggestions for people trying to cope with grief.
- Ask students to complete *Reteaching Activity 26.*

Enrich

- Have selected students, with parental permission, visit a hospice and talk both with people who are employed there and with people who stay there. Make arrangements for students to do volunteer work—reading to terminally ill patients, serving meals, etc. Ask students to keep a journal of the experience and to evaluate how their views of illness and death have changed.
- Ask students to complete *Enrichment Activity 10.*

Close

In this lesson, we focused on the last phase of the life cycle—death and dying. We learned that there are five stages in accepting our own impending death or in grieving for a loved one who has died. We saw that working through these stages with the support of loved ones is the best way of coming to terms with death and grief.

Helping Students Improve Their Health

Using the Self-Inventory

Reinforcing Vocabulary

- **Gray Panthers.** A political group that supports and protects the rights of senior citizens.
- **Stereotype.** A standard belief that is held about an entire group of people based upon common characteristics.

Teaching Strategies

L1 EXPLANATION. Some students may have very limited experience in encountering elderly individuals based upon whether grandparents are still living or whether grandparents live in close proximity to students.

L1 EXPLANATION. Be aware of students who may have suffered the recent loss of a grandparent or who may have a grandparent who is chronically ill. Students who have experienced the recent death of a grandparent, or who fear the death of a grandparent, may become upset when answering these questions.

L1 EXPLANATION. Question 11 may be sensitive to students or parents who may have a grandparent living in a nursing home. It is not always possible financially, physically, or emotionally to care for aging grandparents in one's own home.

L1 CLASS ACTIVITY. Have students brainstorm ways in which students can work cooperatively with senior citizens on community or school projects.

DID YOU KNOW?

- Brainpower doesn't lessen with age. In fact, artistic abilities are enhanced as one ages and gains in wisdom. The ability to speak and write actually improves from age 50 to 70.

Self-Inventory

Are You Up-to-Date About the Elderly?

HOW DO YOU RATE?

Number a sheet of paper from 1 through 20. Read each item below and respond by writing *yes* or *no* for each item. Total the number of *yes* and *no* responses. Then proceed to the next section.

1. Do you think young people should have a general understanding of the emotional and physical changes of aging?
2. Do you feel that most people who live to their 70s, 80s, and 90s can still contribute to society?
3. Do you think that older people can learn new things?
4. Do you believe that older people can change or readjust their lives?
5. Can you name at least five older people whose personal qualities you admire and would like to share?
6. Do you agree to allow older people to work as long as they wish?
7. Do you believe that the elderly are vital human beings?
8. Do you spend time with an elderly relative, neighbor, or friend?
9. Do you have one or more friends who are elderly?
10. Do you enjoy talking with older people?
11. Would you be willing to accept an older relative living in your home?

12. Can you name one or more older adults who lead a physically active life?
13. Have you ever volunteered your services to the elderly?
14. Have you ever experienced the death of a close friend or relative who was elderly?
15. Have you ever visited a nursing home?
16. Do you enjoy television programs, short stories, and books written about or by elderly people?
17. Can you state the major purpose of the Gray Panthers organization?
18. Do you believe that older people should continue to exercise regularly in their later years?
19. Do you occasionally take time to listen closely to an elderly person's memories of earlier times?
20. Do you avoid listening to or telling hurtful jokes that stereotype the elderly?

HOW DID YOU SCORE?

Give yourself 1 point for every *yes* answer and 0 points for every *no* answer. Add the total and read below to see how you scored. Then proceed to the next section.

15 to 20:
Excellent. Your attitudes and behaviors related to the elderly are commendable and up-to-date.

10 to 14:
Good. Your attitudes and behaviors related to the elderly are positive, but limited in scope.

5 to 9:
Fair. You need to update your attitudes and behaviors and to increase your experiences related to the elderly.

Below 5:
Needs Improvement. You're missing out on some great experiences and good friends among the elderly.

WHAT ARE YOUR GOALS?

If you received a score of 10 to 20, complete the statements in Part A. If your score was 9 or less, complete Parts A and B.

Part A

1. I plan to learn more about aging and the elderly by ____.
2. My timetable for accomplishing this is ____.
3. I plan to share my information with others by ____.

Part B

4. The attitude or behavior toward the elderly I would most like to change is ____.
5. The steps involved in making this change are ____.
6. My timetable for accomplishing this is ____.
7. The people or groups I will ask for support and assistance are ____.

Meeting Students' Needs

For students who score *Excellent*. Suggest students investigate careers that involve working with the elderly.

For students who score *Good*. Encourage students to volunteer to work for programs such as Meals on Wheels or Adopt-a-Grandparent.

For students who score *Fair*. Suggest that students visit a nursing home or retirement center and interview an elderly person about his or her hobbies and interests.

For students who *Need Improvement*. Encourage students to become friends with an elderly person in order to better understand the special contributions that senior citizens can make to area schools and communities.

Building Decision-Making Skills

K rista has made a commitment to visit her grandparents in another city over the weekend. She has always been the "apple of their eye" and has enjoyed doing things with them throughout the years. This time they are house-bound, because her grandmother is recovering from surgery. They hope Krista's visit will cheer them up. Today the boy Krista has been dating for a few months asked her to take part in a series of fun activities his family is planning for the weekend. This is appealing, not only for the fun, but because she has been trying to get to know his parents. What should Krista do?

A. Explain the commitment to her boyfriend and his parents and tell him that she doesn't want to disappoint her grandparents.

B. Ask her parents to change plans and spend only part of the weekend at her grandparents so that she can spend at least part of it with her boyfriend.

C. Ask her parents to go without her and to tell her grandparents that she is with her boyfriend and his family.

D. Tell her grandparents the situation and let them decide what she should do.

WHAT DO YOU THINK?

1. **Situation.** What decision needs to be made?

2. **Situation.** Why does a decision need to be made?

3. **Situation.** How much time does Krista have to make this decision?

4. **Choices.** What other possible choices might Krista make?

5. **Consequences.** What are the costs and benefits of each choice?

6. **Consequences.** How might Krista feel about each choice?

7. **Consequences.** How might her boyfriend feel about each choice?

8. **Consequences.** How would her parents probably feel about each choice?

9. **Consequences.** How would her grandparents probably feel about each choice?

10. **Consequences.** How might Krista's health triangle be affected by this decision? Explain your answer.

11. **Decision.** What choice do you think is best for Krista? Explain your answer.

12. **Decision.** How might Krista carry out her decision?

13. **Evaluation.** Have you found yourself torn between doing something you really want to do and something you feel committed to doing? Describe the situation, how you handled it, and what you learned from it.

Teaching Strategies

L1 CLASS ACTIVITY. Have students participate in a role-play activity in which Krista must deal with (a) keeping her commitment to her grandparents while disappointing her boyfriend or (b) disappointing her grandparents while developing her relationship with her boyfriend and his parents.

L1 CLASS ACTIVITY. Have students brainstorm in order to determine the different ways in which Krista may be able to handle this situation. Discuss what the consequences and benefits of each situation may be.

L1 CLASS ACTIVITY. Other possible role-plays pertaining to the life cycle include: (1) Your grandparents are angry with your father and have not spoken to him for years. You want very much to visit your grandparents, but your father forbids it. (2) You have become very close to an elderly neighbor and spend a lot of time with this person. Your parents object because they think that you do not socialize enough with people your own age.

L2 DISCUSSION. Debate the pros and cons of a mandatory retirement age.

L1 DISCUSSION. Have students discuss experiences they have had with the elderly. Have students make a list of advantages and disadvantages of having a grandparent live with them.

Discussing the Answers

Situation 1. Krista is fortunate in that whatever she chooses, something positive should develop. Unfortunately, Krista must also risk the possibility of hurting her grandparents, or not participating in an activity which appears to be her preference. Obviously, the choice comes down to priorities. It would be ideal if Krista could participate in both activities. However, more realistically, she will most likely have to make a choice. It is possible that the best solution to this dilemma will have Krista visiting her grandparents. Sometimes it is a matter of integrity to keep one's promise, even if a better opportunity comes along. In the long run, Krista's boyfriend should respect her for this decision.

DID YOU KNOW?

■ Sociologists refer to many of the parents of today's teens as the "sandwich generation"—grown-ups squeezed between dependent kids and dependent parents. They must take care of aging parents—and their teenage children may get less attention as a result.

Answers to Chapter 10 Review

Using Health Terms

1. Occupational role
2. Self-actualization
3. Developmental tasks
4. Young adulthood
5. Transitions
6. Middle adulthood
7. Self-absorption
8. Empty-nest syndrome
9. Gerontologists
10. Chronological age
11. Age norms
12. Clinical death

Building Academic Skills

13. Answers will vary.
14. Answers will vary.

Recalling the Facts

15. So a person can continue to grow and develop into a healthy, mature adult.
16. Physical maturation, cultural pressures, personal values and goals.
17. Family membership.
18. Beginning with birth and ending with death.
19. Answers may include but are not limited to: Volunteer work, promoting recycling, joining a neighborhood sports team.
20. Seventeen to 20 years of age, continuing through the 30s.
21. Intimacy versus isolation—involves committing to another person. If one fears commitment, loneliness and isolation are more likely to occur.
22. Answers will vary. Possible answers: Divorce, marriage or remarriage, career change, empty-nest syndrome, cluttered-nest syndrome.
23. Answers will vary. Possible answers: The aging or death of a parent, the death of a friend, the realization that one's children are growing up, or an awareness of the passage of time.
24. Young adulthood, middle adulthood, late adulthood.
25. Biological.
26. Answers will vary. Accept three of the following: Seeing the aging process as a lifelong process, the ability to

Using Health Terms

On a separate sheet of paper, write the term that best matches each definition given below.

LESSON 1

1. Preparation for a career.
2. Realization that one has developed in all ways to one's fullest.
3. Need to be accomplished in order for one to become a healthy, mature adult.

LESSON 2

4. The stage that may begin as early as age 17.
5. Changes.
6. A stage experienced by adults about 40 to 50 years old.
7. Being completely involved with one's own wants or needs.
8. A change caused by children leaving home and entering adulthood.

LESSON 3

9. People who study aging.
10. The number of years one has lived.
11. Acceptable behaviors of a certain age group.

LESSON 4

12. Type of death that occurs when one's heart stops beating.

Building Academic Skills

LESSON 1

13. **Writing.** Write several paragraphs describing skills you have developed through the years that have depended on your physical maturation.

LESSON 2

14. **Writing.** As you approach young adulthood, you are probably making plans and setting goals for your future. Write a letter to yourself that you will read when you turn 40. Include your thoughts about aging and your plans for the future.

Recalling the Facts

LESSON 1

15. Explain why developmental tasks need to occur.
16. What three factors influence the completion of developmental tasks?
17. Before a young person leaves home, on what is his or her identity usually based?
18. Life is like a journey beginning with what and ending with what?
19. In what ways might adults show an interest in their community?

LESSON 2

20. What is the approximate age range of young adulthood?
21. What stage of development did Erikson identify as occurring in young adulthood? Describe this stage.
22. What are two changes that may occur in middle adulthood?
23. Name at least two circumstances that might cause a person in middle adulthood to begin to feel that life is coming to an end.
24. What are the three stages of life that follow childhood and adolescence?

LESSON 3

25. What type of aging is determined by the functioning of body parts?
26. List at least three factors that affect a person's ability to adjust to aging.
27. Who are gerontologists?
28. What is social age?
29. How might one's biological aging process be slowed down?

LESSON 4

30. List in order and explain the five stages of dying as identified by Elisabeth Kübler-Ross.
31. How do the stages of dying differ for the person dying and his or her loved ones?
32. What is needed for survivors to be able to work through their grief and mourning?

cope with changes, one's attitude toward aging, activity level, feeling useful and wanted, maintaining friendships, contact with other people, maintaining some level of independence.

27. Gerontologists are persons who study and work in the area of aging.

28. A measure of age as determined by one's life-style.
29. By practicing healthful habits such as proper diet and exercise.
30. Denial, anger, bargaining, depression, acceptance. Explanations can be found on pages 188 to 190.
31. For the person dying and his or her loved ones, the

five stages of dying do not differ significantly.
32. Encouragement from others to talk and express their emotions.

Thinking Critically

33. Answers will vary.
34. Answers will vary but might include: In young adulthood, one might be

REVIEW

Thinking Critically

LESSON 1

33. Synthesis. Self-esteem increases as one experiences success. What are some successes you have had in your life?

LESSON 2

34. Analysis. Compare concerns one might have in young adulthood to concerns in middle adulthood.

35. Analysis. What are some advantages of deciding not to marry in young adulthood? What are some disadvantages?

36. Evaluation. What advice would you give to someone who is suffering from the empty-nest syndrome? What advice would you give someone experiencing the cluttered-nest syndrome?

LESSON 3

37. Analysis. Review some of the ways your body changes as you approach old age. What could you be doing now to help slow down your body's aging process?

38. Synthesis. What needs do all age groups share?

LESSON 4

39. Analysis. Think about how you and your family deal with the issue of dying. What factors affect the way you view death in your family?

40. Evaluation. Some people feel that a person's bodily functions should not be sustained by machines once the brain is dead. What is your opinion of this?

Making the Connection

LESSON 3

41. Science. Volunteer to help conduct exercise classes at a retirement or nursing facility. Differentiate between a program designed to meet the physical health needs of the elderly and one designed to meet the physical health needs of a teenager.

Applying Health Knowledge

LESSON 1

42. Being unable to successfully complete developmental tasks can lead to difficulty in later stages in life. Discuss what might get in the way of an adolescent being able to complete developmental tasks.

LESSON 2

43. You notice that your dad has started to dress like you and your friends. How do you feel about this? What do you think is causing this behavior? What would you do about it?

LESSON 3

44. Your grandmother is going to live with you. What do you think you could do to make your grandmother comfortable?

45. Many older people are placed in nursing homes when they need a great deal of care. Visit a nursing home and describe what you saw. Do you feel this is a place you would someday want to call home? Why or why not?

LESSON 4

46. Imagine that a classmate has just been killed in a car crash. What would you say to that person's parents and siblings? In what way could you help them cope with their grief?

Beyond the Classroom

LESSON 2

47. Parental Involvement. Interview your parents, asking questions about the dreams, hopes, plans, and goals your parents set for themselves when they were your age. Find out why they made the plans they did and how they feel about what they have actually accomplished.

48. Further Study. Research Erik Erikson's stages of development. Give examples of feelings one might have at each stage.

concerned with choosing a career, but one in middle adulthood may be trying to decide whether or not to change careers. Other concerns might be family, personal identity, money, relationships, and for one in middle adulthood—health.

35. Answers will vary. Possible answers: Advantages—time to develop sense of self, concentrate on career, attain higher education, save money, enjoy a variety of life experiences and relationships. Disadvantages—may run out of time to have a family, may miss the opportunity to marry that one right person.

36. Answers will vary. Possible answers: Try to find a job, develop hobbies, do volunteer work. Don't make life easy for children moving back into home—demand help with housework and laundry, have them pay rent, expect their actions to reflect your values and morals, provide emotional support so grown children can live on their own.

37. Answers will vary. Possible answers: Eat a balanced diet, get plenty of calcium, stay out of the sun or use sunscreen, get regular checkups for eyes/ears/body, exercise regularly.

38. Answers will vary. Possible answers: To love and be loved, acceptance, to feel useful.

39. Answers will vary but students may mention their families' religious beliefs, prior experiences with death, native cultural beliefs, and fears concerning death and dying.

40. Answers will vary.

Making the Connection

41. Answers will vary.

Applying Health Knowledge

42. Answers will vary. Possible answers: Difficulties at home such as divorce, physical or sexual abuse, drug or alcohol use.

43. Answers will vary, but students should mention that the father is in middle adulthood and may be having an identity crisis.

44. Answers will vary. Possible answers: Give her some physi-

cal and psychological space so she can be independent, engage her in conversations, ask her opinion, include her in social outings.

45. Answers will vary.

46. Answers will vary but appropriate comments will be positive and relay how the classmate was special or share a pleasant memo-

ry. Do not say: anything negative, platitudes such as "Time heals all wounds," anything about problems the classmate may have been having.

Beyond the Classroom

47. Answers will vary.
48. Answers will vary.

Lesson Summaries

LESSON 1. The integumentary system includes the skin, hair, nails, and sweat glands. Skin is the primary organ of the system. It has a great number of functions and affects one's overall appearance. In addition to the integumentary system's function, its structure, potential problems, and skin care are discussed.

LESSON 2. The skeletal system is the body's framework and can be divided into two main parts: the axial skeleton, which serves to primarily protect vital organs, and the appendicular skeleton, which allows for movement. A discussion of the skeletal system's structure, problems associated with the system, and its care are presented.

LESSON 3. There are three types of muscles—smooth muscles, skeletal muscles, and cardiac muscle. The function, structure, problems associated with the muscular system, and ways to care for the system are presented.

Introducing the Chapter

Tell students that the body systems they are about to study have a great impact on their appearance, ranging from complexion to posture and physique or body build. At the same time, they are vital to life. Have students preview the chapter and set up a chart with these categories: *structure, function, problems,* and *care* for each body system. Have them fill the chart in as a study aid as they read the chapter.

Performance Assessment ✓

Refer to pages T 23 to T 25 for a Performance Assessment strategy for this chapter. See the *Performance Assessment Activities* booklet for additional suggestions.

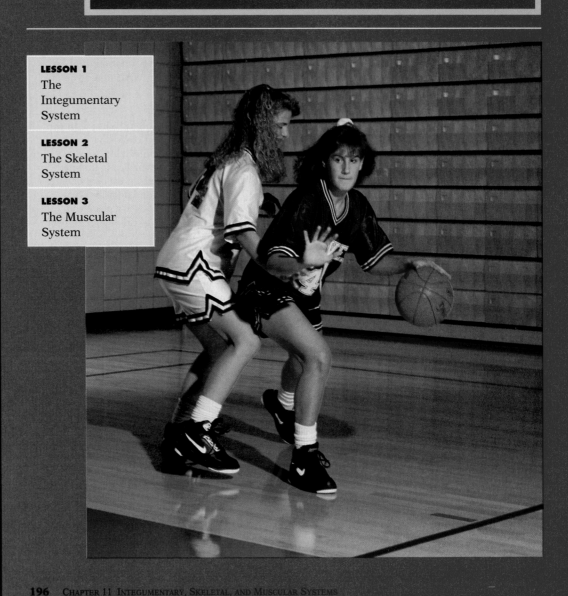

CHAPTER

11

INTEGUMENTARY, SKELETAL, AND MUSCULAR SYSTEMS

LESSON 1
The Integumentary System

LESSON 2
The Skeletal System

LESSON 3
The Muscular System

196   CHAPTER 11 INTEGUMENTARY, SKELETAL, AND MUSCULAR SYSTEMS

Key to Ability Levels

Teaching strategies have been coded for varying learning styles and abilities.

L1 Level 1 activities are basic activities and should be within the ability range of all students.

L2 Level 2 activities are average activities and should be within the ability range of average to above-average students.

L3 Level 3 activities are challenging activities designed for the ability range of above-average students.

LD LD activities should be within the ability range of learning-disabled students.

LEP LEP activities should be within the ability range of Limited English Proficiency students.

THE INTEGUMENTARY SYSTEM

Your **integumentary system** includes your skin, hair, nails, and sweat glands. Your skin is the primary organ of your integumentary system. Besides being the largest organ of the body, it probably has the greatest number of functions. Your skin also has a great effect on your overall appearance because so much of it is visible.

Functions of Your Skin

Your skin's main function is to serve as a watertight covering. It helps protect internal tissues and organs and is the body's first line of defense against invading pathogens. It provides protection against the ultraviolet rays of the sun.

Another important function of the skin is the regulation of body temperature. Your skin has an enormous supply of tiny blood vessels just beneath the surface. When your internal temperature rises, circulation to these blood vessels increases. As internal heat is circulated through these surface vessels it is lost by the process of radiation. Increased internal heat causes the sweat glands in the skin to become more active, releasing perspiration through pores onto your skin. As perspiration evaporates, your skin cools. If the internal temperature of the body drops, circulation to the blood vessels in the skin slows down, sweating stops, and body heat is conserved.

The skin is also a major sense organ, serving as a means of communication with your outside environment. Nerve endings in your skin are responsive to pain, pressure, changes in temperature, and texture.

Structure of the Skin

Your skin has two main layers. The outside layer is the epidermis; the inner layer is the dermis. Below the dermis is tissue called the hypodermis. The hypodermis is not part of your skin, but it attaches your skin to bone and muscle.

Epidermis

The **epidermis** is the outer, thinner layer of skin and is made up of both dead and living cells. Most cells of the epidermis contain a protein called keratin. Keratin helps waterproof and protect the cells.

There are many levels of cells in the epidermis. Dead cells make up the outermost level. These cells slough off or shed when clothing rubs your skin or when you wash. Through this shedding, your outer skin is replaced about once a month. New cells rise to the surface to replace the old ones.

LESSON 1 FOCUS

TERMS TO USE

- Integumentary system
- Epidermis (ep•uh•DUR•mihs)
- Dermis (DUR•mihs)
- Sebaceous (sih•BAY•shuhs) glands
- Sweat glands
- Follicle
- Athlete's foot

CONCEPTS TO LEARN

- Every living organism is protected from the environment by a protective covering.
- The skin has functions that are important to your health.
- Problems of the skin require varying degrees of attention.
- Healthy skin can be promoted by following healthy habits.

ATTITUDES AND BEHAVIORS TO EVALUATE

- Self-Inventory, page 216.
- Building Decision-Making Skills, page 217.

Lesson Objectives

After studying this lesson, students should be able to:
- define the structure and function of the skin
- describe problems of the skin
- describe proper skin, hair, and nail care

Bellringer

Provide students with quarter sheets of white paper and ink pads. Write the following on the chalkboard for students to work on while attendance is being taken: *On the paper provided, make an imprint of your forefinger of your left hand and write your name beneath it.*

Introducing the Lesson

Refer to the Bellringer. Ask students to compare the prints of all students near them and determine in what ways they are alike. How do they differ? Discuss the use of fingerprints for identification. What other area of the body has an identifiable imprint? (Foot.) Why are babies' footprints taken immediately after birth?

Building Vocabulary

- Write the word *skin* on the chalkboard. Ask students to think of words they associate with skin. Draw a semantic map linking their responses to the word *skin*. Typical responses may include: *sweat, zits, color, tan, feeling, rash*, etc. List the lesson's vocabulary words on the chalkboard. Ask students to relate the terms to the words on the map.
- Ask students to complete *Workbook Vocabulary Activity 27*.

THE INTEGUMENTARY SYSTEM **197**

Resources for Lesson 1

- **Transparency** 45
- **Guided Reading** Act 27
- **Workbook** Voc Act 27
- **Reteaching** Activity 27
- **Lesson 1 Quiz**
- **Performance Assessment** Activity 11

Science and Technology Videodisc
Human Biology, Side 2
Ch 6 Hearing by Touch

Ch 8 Treating Motion Sickness

DID YOU KNOW?

- To remove chlorine from hair after swimming, rinse hair with club soda.

Guided Practice

LD CLASS ACTIVITY. Provide an incomplete outline for students to fill in during class discussions.

L2 CLASS ACTIVITY. Ask: Where can you write for information about dermatology and dermatologists? What questions would you ask in letters to the associations? Select several students to write to professional associations requesting information for the class about careers in dermatology. Share the letters with the class, requesting input, before the letters are mailed. Afterwards, share and discuss each of the responses with the class.

L1 USING BODY SYSTEMS TRANSPARENCY 45. Refer to the Teaching Transparencies Binder.

L1 EXPLANATION. Apart from its many other functions, the skin remains one of the most reliable diagnostic tools in the treatment of hay fever and other seasonal allergies. When sensitivity to an allergen is suspected, a doctor will administer a "scratch test." The test consists of a series of surface injections of plant extracts and other possible immunosensitive culprits. Depending on the substance, a positive response will register in the form of a blotch or bump—either one is a sign that immunotherapy is called for.

L2 DEMONSTRATION. Purchase a 2-inch cube of suet (fat) and a cube of lean meat exactly the same size. Leave them out of the refrigerator for at least half a day. Check two thermometers for accuracy before beginning the demonstration. Insert one thermometer into the cube of fat so the metal tip reaches the center. Push the second thermometer into the cube of meat. Set both cubes in a refrigerator or pack in ice and check the temperature every 10 minutes. Which cube gets colder faster? (Meat.) After an hour bring both cubes out so they can reach room temperature. Which warms faster? (Meat.) Why is it advantageous to have a layer of fat under the skin? (Insulator to heat and cold.)

Culturally Speaking

Skin Color and Vitamin D

Skin color in humans is determined largely by the amount of the pigment melanin in the skin. The melanin in dark skin absorbs most of the sun's ultraviolet rays in tropical areas where the sun's rays are intense. However, enough of the rays still get through so the body can produce vitamin D. Vitamin D is necessary for proper bone growth and to prevent rickets. In areas with less intense sun rays, such as in northern latitudes, light skin allows sufficient amounts of ultraviolet rays into the body so it can produce vitamin D. The melanin in dark skin in northern latitudes may absorb too much of the ultraviolet rays, and the body is not able to produce vitamin D. People with dark skin who live in northern areas need to drink vitamin D-enriched milk or eat foods rich in vitamin D to avoid rickets.

The skin is a waterproof shield, a regulator of body temperature, and a barrier to pathogens.

The new cells are produced in the inner level of the epidermis. It is here that cells containing melanin are found. Melanin gives the skin its color—the more melanin, the darker the skin—and helps protect it from the sun's radiation. The production of melanin is increased when you are out in the sun, causing the skin to tan. Freckles are small spots of melanin.

The epidermis on your fingers, palms of your hands, toes, and soles of your feet contain ridges that form a unique pattern. Your footprint may be on your birth certificate. Footprints are used for identification of newborn babies. Your unique fingerprint identifies you. No two people, not even identical twins, have the same print. If you cut or injure your toes or fingers, the skin will heal, forming the same print.

Nails. Your fingernails and toenails are dead cells that grow out of the epidermis. Living cells extend from the root of the nail, below the epidermis, to just above the base of the nail. As living cells die and are replaced, they are pushed up forming the rest of the nail. The nail is surrounded by the cuticle, the nonliving epidermis surrounding the edges of your fingernails and toenails. If you have ever lost a nail, you probably grew another one. New nails will grow as long as the root is still alive.

Dermis

The **dermis** is the inner, thicker layer of skin. Differences in total skin thickness are due to the thickness of the dermis. For example, skin on your back has more dermis than skin on the back of your hand.

The dermis has protein fibers that give the skin its elasticity, or spongy, flexible quality. As a person ages, the skin loses some of its elasticity, resulting in wrinkles. Nerve endings, glands, and hair follicles extend into the dermis.

Glands. There are two main kinds of glands in the skin, sebaceous glands and sweat glands. **Sebaceous glands** connect to hair follicles and produce an oily secretion called sebum. Sebum oils the skin and

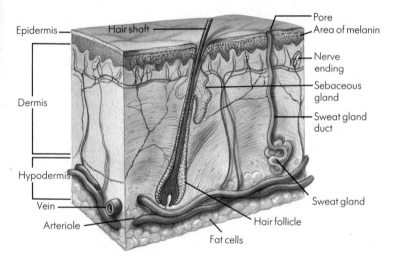

Additional Information

Heat Reaction. The heat is on and keeping "cool" means more than an attitude. Your skin can help by sweating, allowing the subsequent evaporation of the moisture to lower body temperature, but that may not be enough. When the body is exposed to temperatures 97 degrees and above for a period of time, it can raise body temperature and hinder body functions. Runners, joggers, or other sports enthusiasts who expose themselves to intense exercise during hot weather place themselves at risk of heat reactions.

Drinking adequate amounts of water, restricting activity, and wearing light-colored, loose clothing in hot, sunny weather can help lower the incidence of heat reactions.

hair, preventing drying and helping protect against some pathogens. Overactive oil glands, however, can result in oily skin and hair. Oil glands prevent the skin from absorbing too much water.

Sweat glands secrete perspiration through ducts to pores on the surface of your skin. Sweat glands are found in most areas of your body, but they are most numerous in the soles of your feet and the palms of your hands. When your body gets hot, pores in your skin open up and perspiration is released. Perspiration is a mixture of water and waste products. Some sweat glands are affected by emotional stress, such as fear, anxiety, or pain. At such times, they produce more perspiration than usual.

Many people think perspiration causes body odor. Perspiration itself does not cause an odor. Bacteria acting on perspiration cause an odor. Sweat glands are numerous under the arms, which is the reason body odor tends to be a problem in that area.

Hair. Humans have hair present on almost all skin surfaces of their bodies. You have between 100,000 and 200,000 hairs on your head! The roots of hairs are made up of living cells and grow out of the dermis. A hair root grows out of a **follicle,** which is a small pocket that holds the root in the dermis.

Through the follicle the root is supplied with blood and nerve tissue. As new hair cells are made, old hair cells are pushed up and out of the hair follicle and die. The hair visible on your head is made up of such dead cells.

Hair normally grows at a rate of about 6 inches (15 cm) per year. Each hair on your head grows for about 4 years, rests a few months, and then falls out. You lose between 25 and 100 hairs a day.

Hypodermis

The hypodermis attaches your skin to bone and muscle. Blood vessels and nerves that supply your skin pass through the hypodermis. This layer is made up of fatty tissue and serves as the body's natural insulation against heat and cold. It also acts as an inner cushion to protect internal organs from injuries.

Problems of the Integumentary System

Many problems of the integumentary system are not life-threatening. Nevertheless, they can affect how a person looks and how a person feels about him- or herself. Some of these problems are temporary. Following healthy habits may help eliminate some of these problems.

Skin Problems

Acne, which is a clogging of the pores of the skin, is the most common skin problem during adolescence.

During adolescence the increase in hormone production causes oil glands to enlarge and produce more sebum. Excess sebum makes the skin oily, providing an ideal place for bacteria to grow. Since there are more oil glands in the area of the face than in other parts of the body, acne occurs there.

It takes many years and extra care to grow and maintain long hair.

THE INTEGUMENTARY SYSTEM **199**

Ringworm sores usually have a circular or ringlike appearance.

The oil secreted by the oil glands moves out through pores in the skin. Excess sebum can clog these pores and cause the following conditions:

- A whitehead results when sebum gets trapped in a pore and plugs it.
- A blackhead develops if this plug of sebum becomes exposed to air and dead skin and sebum become dark.
- A pimple is formed if bacteria get into the clogged pore and infect it. The infected pore fills with pus.

Picking or squeezing pimples can spread the infection, possibly leaving the skin scarred. There is no cure for acne at this time. Keeping the skin clean is most important. Washing with warm water will help rid excess oils from the skin.

Another skin problem can be caused by ringworm. Ringworm is a common fungal infection that affects different parts of the body. It gets its name from the fact that it appears as a whitish ring. The ringworm fungus causes **athlete's foot,** which is an infection of the skin between the toes. The redness and itching can be treated with talcum or antifungal powders. Athlete's foot is very contagious. That is the reason it is important to wear a foot covering in locker rooms and showers.

Jock itch is another common skin infection caused by the ringworm fungus. Jock itch mainly occurs in the groin area.

Washing, drying carefully, and dusting with talcum or an antifungal powder will usually clear up the condition. Avoid using ointments, because they can make the condition worse by holding in moisture. To help relieve the discomfort of jock itch, wear loose cotton clothing to allow proper ventilation. Since jock itch can be spread easily, always use your own soap and towels.

Boils are skin infections that result in swelling, redness, and the formation of pus. They are caused by bacteria and can destroy skin tissue. Boils can be serious infections and should be treated by a doctor. Like acne, boils should not be squeezed. They are infections, which means that the bacteria that cause them can spread and form other boils on the body. Keeping skin clean helps prevent boils.

Warts are small growths caused by viruses. Warts appear as raised growths on the outer layer of the skin. Most warts are painless and harmless, but the virus that causes them can spread and form more warts. If that happens, or if there is any change in the size or color of a wart, see your doctor immediately. Color change may indicate a more serious problem.

Moles are small, round, slightly thick places on the skin. They may be black or brown and are present from birth. Moles are not usually dangerous, but if they start to change color, a doctor should be consulted immediately.

Psoriasis is an ailment in which red patches appear on the skin, followed by the skin's turning white and flaking off. Psoriasis should be treated by a doctor and is usually lessened with the use of medicinal creams. The cause is not known.

Vitiligo is probably caused by an absence of melanin in certain patches of skin. This skin turns whitish to pinkish. There is no cure for vitiligo, but it appears to be harmless. The affected area should be kept away from direct sunlight.

Blisters are raised areas that are filled with a watery liquid. They are usually the result of skin being rubbed, injured, or burned. Blisters can

---

Across the Curriculum

Social Studies. Have students discuss grooming standards in other countries. Include topics such as frequency of showering, perms for men, and women shaving. Foreign exchange students are excellent resource people.

Science. Invite a nurse, therapist, or doctor from a burn unit to speak to the class about skin burns. Include information about caring for minor burns at home as well as care for severe cases.

Language Arts. Periodicals offer many articles dealing with self-improved appearance. Ask each student to find, read, and summarize at least one article of this kind.

form anywhere on the body. A blister should be protected so that it will not break. A broken blister can become infected.

A callus is a hard, thickened layer of skin that forms as a result of continued friction or rubbing. Calluses are common on the soles of the feet. Many musicians have calluses on their fingers from playing string instruments. Calluses are annoying, but not harmful. They can be reduced by using a pumice stone, which is a porous stone.

Friction can also form a corn. A corn usually has a hard inner core that can be painful. Corns usually appear on or between toes. Corns may be softened by soaking them in water. Wearing shoes that fit properly is the main way to prevent calluses and corns on the feet.

Hair Problems

Dandruff is one of the most common hair and scalp problems. Dandruff is caused by the flaking of the outer layer of dead skin cells covering the skull. It is noticeable on the head because the flakes of skin can cling to the hair. Regular, thorough washing of hair can control ordinary dandruff. However, special shampoos also are available. Sometimes what appears to be dandruff is actually a skin infection. If itching and scaling persist, a health professional should be consulted.

Head lice are insects that attach themselves to human hair and skin and feed off blood. Lice make the scalp itchy and uncomfortable and can cause infection. Lice can usually be killed by medicinal shampoos.

Head lice can spread from one person to another. Therefore, it is wise not to use other people's combs, brushes, towels, or hats.

Nail Problems

Hangnails are bits of loose cuticle around the base or side of the fingernail. If hangnails are not removed, they can become infected. Do not pull or bite a hangnail. Cut off the major part and cover with a bandage. Hangnails can be prevented by pushing the cuticle back gently each time you wash your hands.

An ingrown toenail results when the nail pushes into the skin and cuts it. Trimming your toenails carefully will prevent this condition.

Care for the Skin, Hair, and Nails

Caring for your skin, hair, and nails is a lifelong process. You can promote your health by following healthy grooming habits.

Warts are common viral infections. Treatment depends on the area of the body where they appear.

KEEPING FIT

Avoiding Toenail Torment

An ingrown toenail occurs when your toenail—often the one on your big toe—begins to rub on and cut into the surrounding skin. The result can be very painful. Sometimes, the irritated or swollen area can even become infected. To prevent ingrown toenails:
- Don't wear shoes that are too tight.
- Try not to "put the brakes on" too much when you play sports by screeching to a halt and shoving your toes against the tips of your shoes.
- Keep your toenails clipped, but don't clip them too short.
- Keep them cut straight across rather than rounded.

THE INTEGUMENTARY SYSTEM **201**

L1 EXPLANATION. To stop nail biting, tell students to try polishing nails with the bitter-tasting coatings used to discourage thumb-sucking; try to grow just one nail at a time, rewarding themselves after each success; or make a no-nail-biting contract with a fellow nail biter, offering each other support as they try to break the habit.

L1 CLASS ACTIVITY. Place several hair and nail care aids (such as emery board, nail clippers, shampoo conditioner, nail hardener, etc.) on a tray. Number each item. Include some items students may not be familiar with. Ask students to identify each numbered item on the tray by its name and use. Be prepared to discuss their answers.

L1 CLASS ACTIVITY. Have students design and set up a display of various kinds of bath soap. Ask students to research the difference in the effectiveness of deodorant soap compared to ordinary bath soap.

DID YOU KNOW?

■ "To get in someone's hair" means to get in someone's way or to irritate them as much as lice and other hair-inhabiting insects do.

Independent Practice

L2 WRITING. Select students to write an original story about a person suffering from psoriasis or vitiligo, emphasizing the effects of the ailments on the individual and the family. Have students research the skin conditions so they can include facts about it in their story.

L2 RESEARCH. Have students collect examples of newspaper and magazine advertising, brochures, and product inserts for items designed to aid the skin's elasticity. Have students research the effectiveness of these products.

L2 READING. Have students read articles about various acne preparations, such as Accutane, retinoic acid, tetracycline, and benzoyl peroxide. Discuss the effectiveness of the products and their side effects.

Additional Information

Technology. The development of synthetic skin has been stimulated by doctors treating burn patients. Researchers at a number of institutions are developing synthetic skin. Dr. John Hansbrough has developed skin made from two types of human cells, fibrocyst and keratinocyst. The skin is grown as a polymer mesh using these cells. At this point, new skin is made from a healthy donor's cells, meaning the patient's body may reject the skin. Eventually though, it is hoped that cells from the burn patient can be used to create skin reducing rejection and increasing the skin's chances of growing.

L1 **RESEARCH.** Have students research the costs of skin products used to control acne. Ask them to list the skin products in order of best buy per quantity.

L2 **RESEARCH.** Ask for volunteers to research the safety of tanning salons. Have other students determine the costs of tanning sessions and the precautions required or suggested by tanning businesses to protect their clients.

L3 **RESEARCH.** Select students to research ingredients in products for treating acne. Ask them to report their findings to the class.

L2 **WRITING.** Have students write public service announcements directed to teenagers about ways to control acne. Have students videotape the announcements, using music and illustrative materials. Play the announcements back to the entire class.

L3 **RESEARCH.** Select students to research the protective effect of atmospheric ozone against sunburn. Assign others to report on current scientific concerns about the destruction of ozone occurring today and the reasons for its destruction.

L2 **RESEARCH.** Have students conduct experiments comparing the effects of the sun on the skin to its effects on various materials such as fabric, plastic, and paper. Ask students to share their experiment results with the class.

L1 **USING THE LESSON RESOURCES.** For additional student activities, refer to the lesson resources on page 197.

DID YOU KNOW?

■ A large percentage of household dust is composed of dead skin cells.
■ By the age of 70, the average human being sheds about 100 pounds of dead skin.

CONFLICT RESOLUTION

Andrew has tried repeatedly to get his parents' permission to go to a tanning salon. He's not convinced by their claim that the radiation is harmful. Andrew has heard that the new tanning beds mostly use UV-A radiation, which causes the skin to burn more slowly than UV-B rays.

As Andrew's friend, what comments would you make to him about this topic?

Healthy Skin

Every morning and evening wash your face with soap and water. If your face is very oily, wash it once more during the day. Pat your skin dry with a clean towel. If you use creams and cosmetics, select them carefully and avoid greasy preparations. Eat a well-balanced diet. Vitamin A helps promote healthy skin. Milk, egg yolks, liver, green and yellow vegetables, and yellow fruits are good sources of vitamin A. Get plenty of rest and exercise. Try to keep your hands away from your face.

Thorough washing with soap and water on a daily basis slows bacterial growth and helps control body odor. Deodorants and antiperspirants can help mask body odors or reduce the amount of perspiration.

Skin and the Sun. Understanding the sun's effect on the skin and knowing some protective steps to take can help you better care for your skin. The sun does not have the same effect on everyone. Some people tan more easily than others. Some people with fair skin may never tan; they may just burn.

Ultraviolet rays are light rays that come from the sun. Two types of ultraviolet rays are important in considering the sun's effects on the human body. The shorter rays, most intense in the middle of the day, are the main cause of sunburn. The longer rays, in the morning and late afternoon, are less strong in terms of sunburn.

Do not be fooled on a hazy or cloudy day. Up to 80 percent of ultraviolet rays can penetrate haze, light clouds, or fog. Ultraviolet rays can also be reflected upward from the ground, sand, and water. Snow is an excellent reflector, sending back more than 85 percent of the rays.

Do not judge a sunburn by how red you look while you are still out in the sun. It takes about 2 to 8 hours after exposure for a sunburn to show. The pain from the burn is greatest about 6 to 48 hours after exposure.

In addition to causing sunburn, exposure to the sun's ultraviolet rays can permanently destroy the elastic fibers that keep the skin tight. The sun causes the skin to age prematurely, that is, before its time. The layers of skin cells also thicken with repeated sun exposure. This gives the skin a hard, leathery texture.

K E E P I N G   F I T

Sunscreens

Follow these guidelines in regard to sunscreens.
■ Wear a sunscreen that is water-resistant and waterproof.
■ Apply liberally 15 to 30 minutes before you go out into the sun.
■ Reapply at least every 2 hours.

■ Don't forget places like ear lobes, nose, and balding spots.
■ Wear a sunscreen with an SPF of 15 or higher. *SPF* stands for *sun protection factor.* Sunscreens are rated by number from SPF 2 to SPF 50. The

numbers indicate the sunscreen's ability to screen out the sun's harmful ultraviolet rays, which are known to cause skin cancer.
■ Stay out of the sun between 10 A.M. and 3 P.M. if possible.

Additional Information

Balding. New research on hair-growing medication has shown promise. Minoxidil is the first medicine to be proven effective in growing hair on balding heads. This medication was initially given to treat hypertension and it was noted that patients taking the medicine grew body hair. The company researched the medicine further and created a form to be applied topically. It seems a miracle for the 30 million men and 20 million women plagued by thinning and balding hair. Patients under 40 do best with the treatment. The major drawback of minoxidil is that it is not effective for everyone.

Ultraviolet radiation also damages the deoxyribonucleic acid (DNA), the genetic material in skin cells. Accumulated DNA damage can result in the formation of cancerous cells. Excessive sun exposure is the primary cause of certain types of skin cancer. Therefore, you should protect your skin. Use a sun block if you are going to be in the sun for a prolonged period of time. Sun blocks stop the sun's rays by reflecting them.

The effects of the sun on your skin may not show up for years and cannot be stopped by any cosmetic ointments. These effects are cumulative, or increasing, and the damage is irreversible. The healthiest behavior is prevention. Avoid overexposure to the sun's ultraviolet rays.

Healthy Hair

Your hair has a great impact on your appearance. Wearing a style that fits your features and type of hair and taking proper care of your hair are important aspects of total health.

Brushing your hair helps keep dirt from building up and helps evenly distribute the natural hair oils. These oils keep the hair soft and give it its shine. Overbrushing can cause hair to pull out or break off. A good brushing once a day is enough. Massaging the scalp along with brushing helps increase circulation in the scalp.

Washing your hair regularly is necessary for healthy hair. If possible, let your hair dry naturally. Try to avoid using blow dryers because the heat can damage your hair. Heat from electric curlers or curling irons also dries out hair, causing the ends to break or split.

Healthy Nails

Good nail care includes keeping nails clean and evenly trimmed. Keep cuticles pushed back and clip hangnails with a nail clipper. You should cut toenails straight across, leaving the nail just at or slightly above skin level. If you cut the nails too low, you increase your risk of skin infection and ingrown nails.

Fingernails should be slightly rounded. Use a nail file or emery board to shape the nails. Always file in the same direction, rather than using a sawing motion. Clean, trimmed nails add to your overall appearance.

Taking care of your skin takes time and effort but it will contribute to your overall appearance.

LESSON 1 REVIEW

Reviewing Facts and Vocabulary

1. What are the functions of the skin?
2. Explain the unique characteristics of the epidermis.
3. What effect does the sun have on skin?

Thinking Critically

4. **Analysis.** Analyze the following statement: "I look healthier with a good tan."

Applying Health Knowledge

5. Think of the healthy grooming habits you have established. Which are the most important to you? What are your least favorite grooming activities? What changes might you make in your routine to make these activities less bothersome?
6. Design a poster about the dangers of the sun's ultraviolet rays and their effects on the human body.

THE INTEGUMENTARY SYSTEM **203**

Answers to Lesson 1 Review

1. Watertight covering, protects internal tissues and organs, defense against invading pathogens, regulation of body temperature, serves as a sense organ.
2. Contains both dead and living cells, keratin, melanin, and ridges which form unique patterns.
3. It causes the skin to tan or burn, destroys the elastic fibers, causes pre-

mature aging, thickens skin, damages genetic material in the skin cells which can lead to skin cancer.
4. Answers will vary.
5. Answers will vary.
6. Posters will vary but should include sunburn, change in skin texture, and skin cancer.

204 CHAPTER 11 INTEGUMENTARY, SKELETAL, AND MUSCULAR SYSTEMS

Focus

Lesson Objectives

After studying this lesson, students should be able to:
- define the function of the skeletal system
- describe the structure and function of bones
- compare the various types of joints
- describe problems of the joints and bones
- identify ways to care for the skeletal system

Bellringer

Write the following on the chalkboard for students to work on while attendance is being taken: *Write as many words or terms as you can that relate to the skeletal system.* Ask volunteers to share their responses.

Introducing the Lesson

Refer to the Bellringer. Use a skeletal model or diagram to point out the various bones that students listed. Follow this activity by asking students which bones they think are most often broken due to falls or other accidents. What types of padding are worn in sports to reduce the chance of breaking bones?

Building Vocabulary

- Ask students to work in teams to create crossword puzzles using the vocabulary terms. The clues to the word placement should be the definitions or descriptions of the terms.
- Ask students to complete *Workbook Vocabulary Activity 28.*

DID YOU KNOW?

- "To bone up for a test" means to study so hard that the material seems almost a part of you. The phrase originated as part of an advertising campaign for the Bohn Publishing Company which, between 1860 and 1910, published translations of Greek and Latin classics to help students with their studies.

THE SKELETAL SYSTEM

LESSON 2 FOCUS

TERMS TO USE
- Axial (AK•see•ul) skeleton
- Appendicular (ap•en•DICK•u•lar) skeleton
- Cartilage
- Ossification (os•seh•fuh•KAY•shun)
- Ligaments
- Tendons

CONCEPTS TO LEARN
- Bones have four main functions.
- The skeleton gives stability to the body.
- A healthy diet is essential to maintaining healthy bones.

ATTITUDES AND BEHAVIORS TO EVALUATE
- Self-Inventory, page 216.
- Building Decision-Making Skills, page 217.

You might think of the skeletal system as the girders and cross-beams that make up the framework of a building. The muscular system is like the bricks and mortar that cover the framework.

Functions of Your Skeletal System

Unlike a building, which cannot move, your skeletal and muscular systems work together to allow you to walk, run, jump, bend, lift, and carry. The skeletal system not only allows movement, it also provides a supporting framework for your body. This system protects delicate, internal organs. Bones are the principal storage place for essential body minerals, such as calcium and phosphorus. Calcium is one of the minerals that promotes strong bones. Another important function is the production of red and white blood cells in the red marrow of bones.

Structure of the Skeletal System

Your skeletal system is divided into two main parts. The **axial skeleton** includes the bones of the skull, the sternum (breastbone), the ribs, and the vertebrae (spine).

The bones of the skull protect the brain and form the shape of the face. The 12 pairs of ribs attach to the sternum in your chest area and to vertebrae in your back. These bones protect your lungs and heart. The 33 small bones that make up your spine are called vertebrae. Vertebrae protect your spinal cord.

The **appendicular skeleton** includes the 126 bones of the shoulders, arms, hands, hips, legs, and feet. The appendicular skeleton helps you perform a wide range of movement. Refer to the illustration on page 205 to identify the two main divisions of the skeleton.

Your body's framework is made up of both bone and **cartilage,** a strong, flexible material that provides a smooth surface that makes movement at a joint smooth. Cartilage supports the nose and ears, connects the ribs to the sternum, and acts as a cushion between adjoining vertebrae.

A baby's skeleton is mostly cartilage. As the body grows, cartilage cells are replaced by bone cells and minerals through a process called **ossification.**

The periosteum is a tough membrane that adheres tightly to the outer surface of bone. This living membrane is richly supplied with blood vessels that branch into the bone at various points. The periosteum is vital in nourishing the bones and in producing bone cells. It contains bone-forming cells called osteoblasts, which are important in bone growth and repair.

Adults have about 206 bones in their skeletal system. Bones range in size from the smallest bone, the stapes in the middle ear, which is about

---

Resources for Lesson 2

- **Transparency** 46
- **Guided Reading** Act 28
- **Workbook** Voc Act 28
- **Reteaching** Activity 28
- **Lesson 2 Quiz**

Science and Technology Videodisc
Human Biology, Side 2
Ch 14 Measuring Calcium Deficiency

Ch 21 Orthopedic Implants

0.1 inch (3 mm) long, to the longest bone in the body, the femur, or thighbone, which is usually about 27 percent of a person's total height.

Types of Bones

Bones are grouped according to their shapes. There are four basic types in the human body.

■ Long bones, like the femur, are found in the arms and legs. The shafts of a long bone are called the diaphyses. The ends of long bones are called epiphyses. Long bones are very strong. The inner cavity of long bones contains yellow marrow, which is a fatty tissue. The epiphyses of long bones form joints with other bones. Epiphyses are composed mainly of spongy bone tissue. The enlarged ends give stability to joints. Muscles attach to the epiphyses. The inner parts of the epiphy-

The axial skeleton is shown here in yellow. The appendicular skeleton is shown in green.

The Two Divisions of the Skeletal System

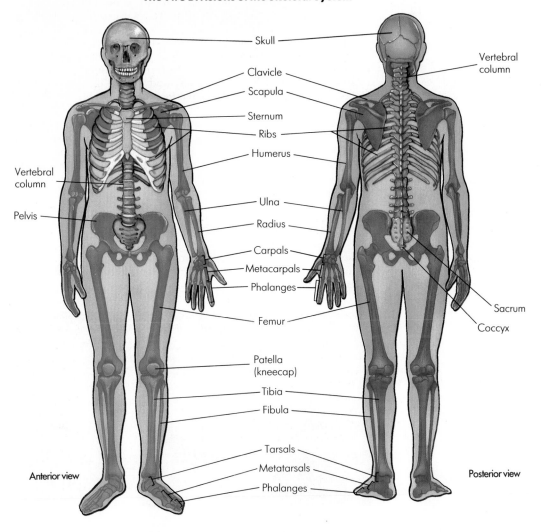

Skull

Clavicle

Scapula

Sternum

Ribs

Humerus

Vertebral column

Pelvis

Ulna

Radius

Carpals

Metacarpals

Phalanges

Femur

Vertebral column

Sacrum

Coccyx

Patella (kneecap)

Tibia

Fibula

Tarsals

Metatarsals

Phalanges

Anterior view

Posterior view

THE SKELETAL SYSTEM **205**

Teach

Guided Practice

L1 **CLASS ACTIVITY.** Using a skeletal model, detail for the class the parts of the axial and appendicular skeleton. There are 80 bones in the axial skeleton. The appendicular skeleton consists of 126 bones. The word *appendicular* refers to a structure and its connection to the body's axial skeleton. In humans, appendages attach to the axial skeleton at the shoulder or pectoral girdle and the hip or pelvic girdle. The skull has 8 cranium bones, which are mostly flat, and 14 facial bones, which are irregularly shaped; there are 3 bones in the inner ear, and a single bone in the neck called the hyoid bone. The last is the only bone in the body that does not connect to any other bone. It serves as an attachment for the tongue muscles. The vertebral column is made up of 26 individual bones linked together by cartilage and ligaments.

L1 **USING BODY SYSTEMS TRANSPARENCY 46.** Refer to the Teaching Transparencies Binder.

L1 **CLASS ACTIVITY.** Using models from the science department, ask students to compare the skull size of an infant and an adult. What is the relationship of the size of the head to the rest of the skeleton in a child and in a adult?

L2 **CLASS ACTIVITY.** The bones protect internal organs. Ask students to identify organs protected by bones. Then ask them to name the specific bones involved.

LD **DEMONSTRATION.** Demonstrate each type of joint. Provide a diagram if available.

L2 **CLASS ACTIVITY.** Skeletal injuries, especially knee, cartilage, and ligament injuries, are of interest to athletes. Have students find out what happens when there is cartilage or ligament damage. They can research the newest ways of treating these injuries.

Across the Curriculum

Science. In a science lab, cut cross sections of the bones of a pig, cow, lamb, and chicken. Have students compare the structure for differences and similarities. The bone sections should be comparable in function, i.e., long bones of the legs.

Home Economics. Ask a home economics teacher to present information on the history of rickets. Have the teacher share how

it was discovered, what the treatment was, and prevention strategies.

Physical Education. Ask a physical education teacher to discuss the problems of rapid growth and the ability to coordinate body movements. What other complications may temporarily interfere with normal growth?

L1 **CLASS ACTIVITY.** Using the skeletal model on page 205, have students identify long bones, short bones, and flat bones. Which group has the greatest number?

L1 **DISCUSSION.** Calcium is an important ingredient in the diet throughout life. What measures can students employ to assure that they and their family members receive enough calcium?

L2 **CLASS ACTIVITY.** Dietary calcium additives are popular in today's advertising. Ask students to prepare a collage of ads for these products and the varying claims. Is there scientific evidence of product efficacy?

L2 **DISCUSSION.** Ask students why the body needs phosphorus. Then ask them to list foods that are high in this mineral. (Cereals, meats, poultry, fish, eggs, dried beans and peas, milk and milk products.)

L2 **DISCUSSION.** Tell sudents that the ribs are the flat bones that protect the lungs. How does a fractured rib affect the functioning of the lungs? Is this the same as the impaired function of the brain when the skull is fractured?

L1 **CLASS ACTIVITY.** Identify with the class those areas in the body where pivot (head and neck), hinge (elbow), and ball-and-socket (shoulder) joints are found.

L1 **DISCUSSION.** Have students develop a comparison of the body's hip joints with shock absorbers on a motor vehicle.

L1 **CLASS ACTIVITY.** Ask a doctor or local hospital for copies of X rays showing bone fractures. Show these to the class either by holding them up to a window or by using a projector. As you point to each X ray, ask students to identify what kind of fracture has occurred.

L1 **DISCUSSION.** Ask students to share their personal experiences, or those of their family members, with broken bones. How were the fractures treated? At what age and under what circumstances did the fracture occur?

Connectors

— Tendon

Patella

Femur —

Cartilage

Ligament —

Tibia —

Ligaments, tendons, and cartilage are types of connective tissue. Ligaments connect bones to bones. Tendons connect muscles to bones.

ses contain red marrow. Red marrow produces red blood cells and most of the white blood cells in the blood.

- Short bones, like those in the wrists and ankles, are as broad as they are long. Over half of all the short bones in the body are in the hands and feet.
- Flat bones, like the ribs and skull bones, have a thin, flat shape. These bones generally serve to protect vital body organs.
- Irregular bones, like vertebrae, have a shape that does not fit with the other types of bones.

Joints

The point at which two bones meet is called a joint. Most joints allow movement of the body framework. Imagine that you did not have a joint at the point where your arm bones meet at your elbow. What kinds of activities would be restricted?

Bones in the skull form immovable joints. The joints that are formed by vertebrae are slightly movable. However, most of the joints in the body are freely movable.

Ball-and-socket joints, such as the shoulder joint, allow you the most range of movement. Hinge joints, such as the knee joint, allow movement back and forth in one plane. Pivot joints occur when one bone rotates around another, such as your head turning on your spine. In gliding joints, such as in the hand and foot, bones are able to slide over one another.

At joints where movement occurs, bones are bound together by ligaments and muscles. **Ligaments** are strong bands or cords of tissue that connect the bones to one another at a moveable joint. Ligaments hold the bones in place. **Tendons** are bands of fiber that connect muscles to bones. Drum your fingers on your desk. The movement you see in the back of your hand is from the action of tendons.

Problems of the Skeletal System

Skeletal system disorders and injuries to bones can be the result of many factors, including sports and recreational mishaps, viral infections, poor diet, and poor posture.

Body braces can be used to halt and correct a curvature of the spine.

Additional Information

Knee Injuries. Cut the risk of developing knee injuries by following these guidelines:
- Wear good athletic shoes that cushion the shock of your body's weight.
- Don't do strenuous exercises unless you have stretched for at least 5 minutes.
- If you are overweight, try to lose weight (in a sensible way) to take some of the pressure off your knees.

- Don't sit cross-legged.
- Try walking instead of jogging.
- If you jog, be sure to give your knees some days off.
- If you go biking, make sure your bike seat is at the right height.

Bone Fractures

Fractures are any type of break in a bone. Following are descriptions of some types of fractures.

- closed fracture—the broken bone does not protrude, or stick out, through the skin
- open fracture—the broken bone protrudes through the skin
- complete fracture—the bone is broken in two or more fragments
- incomplete fracture—the fracture is not completely across the bone
- hairline fracture—the fracture is incomplete, and the two parts of the bone do not separate

Scoliosis

Scoliosis is a lateral, or side-to-side, curvature of the spine. It usually develops during puberty. Most schools have scoliosis screening programs, usually conducted by the school nurse. Depending on the severity of the curvature, treatment may include exercise, a special brace, or surgery. If left untreated, a person may experience serious back problems in adulthood.

Osteoporosis

Osteoporosis is a condition that results from a loss of calcium in the bone. The bones become weakened and can break easily. In addition, the back may become hunched. Osteoporosis is most commonly found in older females. Exercise and a diet high in calcium can help prevent osteoporosis.

Osteomyelitis

Osteomyelitis is a term given to inflammation of the soft inner surface of the bones. Many times this inflammation is caused by bacteria. Antibiotics, such as penicillin, are used to treat the infected bones. Surgery is sometimes necessary to remove damaged bone tissue.

Injuries to Joints

Sprains are the most common injury to joints. A sprain occurs when tissue around a joint is twisted or receives too much pressure. The ligaments around the joint are stretched or torn, resulting in swelling and pain

KEEPING FIT

Too Much of a Good Thing

Practicing the same sport and the same motions within that sport every day for at least two hours can greatly increase your risk of injuries from overuse. The repeated motions that some sports require—such as throwing in baseball—can wear down both your ligaments and your tendons. This can cause tissues to tear and even cause bones to break. So don't overdo it.

THE SKELETAL SYSTEM **207**

Additional Information

Fractures. Broken bones may not heal as easily as we assume. Circumstances often influence how a bone heals. Younger people heal more quickly than older people. Mental stress, fatigue, and other physical problems as well as some medications may influence healing rates. Any serious disease will cause healing problems, as we know, but people who seem reasonably healthy sometimes find that a break just won't heal.

Techniques to assist the healing process include placement of pins and replacement of an entire joint or bone with synthetic bones.

L1 SPEAKER. Contact an orthopedic technician at a local hospital and ask him or her to make a presentation to your class about cast application and cast care. Encourage students to develop a list of questions prior to the presentation.

L1 DISCUSSION. Ask students to imagine they have broken a forearm and must wear a cast for several months. Ask them to describe the effect on the bones in the arm.

L3 CLASS ACTIVITY. Ask selected students to research the current first-aid treatment for joint pain and fractures. Plan a demonstration of proper splinting of long bone fractures. Include information about over-the-counter preparations for joint pain, including both pills and ointments. Is cold or heat considered the safer treatment for sprains?

L3 DISCUSSION. Identify the word parts used to designate diseases of the skeletal system: -itis (inflammation), osteo- (bone), -emia (lack). Familiarize students with the universal use of these prefixes and suffixes to identify conditions within the body.

L1 SPEAKER. Ask a doctor of osteopathy to visit your class. Encourage him or her to describe in detail how his or her practice differs from that of a doctor of medicine.

L2 CLASS ACTIVITY. Contact the local chapter of the American Cancer Society and ask for current information about leukemia and its treatment. Help students understand the effects and long-term consequences of this disease.

Independent Practice

L1 PERSONAL INVOLVEMENT. Many broken bones result from accidents within the home. Suggest that students conduct a home safety check for throw rugs, loose cords, blocked stairways, toys in poor repair. Have students identify both good and poor safety practices in their homes, and then make correlations of their findings to school safety concerns.

- Stress fractures can appear in any bone in the body, but are most common in the feet, lower legs, and spine. They are sometimes not detected by X rays and need to be diagnosed by a bone scan.
- Housemaid's Knee is a condition in which those sacs filled with fluid that cushion shocks in the knee area swell up and cause pressure. People who kneel and scrub for long periods, such as gardeners, bricklayers, etc., are subject to developing the condition.
- The knee is the body's largest and heaviest joint and is more susceptible to injury than any other joint in the body.
- Women are more likely to suffer knee injuries than men are. Among a study of college basketball players, women players suffered 60 percent more injuries than men players, took longer to heal, and were more likely to need surgery.

L2 RESEARCH. Ask students to research the causes of osteoporosis. Who is most susceptible? Why? Is the condition hereditary? What are its symptoms and how is it treated? Can it be prevented? How? Ask students to illustrate their findings in a poster.

L1 RESEARCH. Have students visit a sporting goods store and examine the various types of knee, wrist, and ankle supports available. Have them ask a salesperson how effective the devices are and what other safeguards against injury are recommended.

L1 USING THE LESSON RESOURCES. For additional student activities, refer to the lesson resources on page 204.

around the joint. If blood vessels are injured, too, there may be discoloration of the skin. Sprains occur most often in the joints with a wide range of movement, like the wrist and ankle. Although sprains usually heal by themselves, it is a good idea to see a doctor.

A dislocation results when a bone slips from its normal position at a joint. A doctor must put the bone back in place and immobilize the joint so that the tissue can heal.

You have probably read of athletes who have torn a cartilage in the knee. A torn cartilage is a serious joint injury. It can result from a sharp blow or severe twisting of a joint. Doctors can now repair some cartilage tears with arthroscopic surgery.

A bunion is a painful swelling of the bursa in the first joint of the big toe. The cause of bunions is wearing tight or high-heeled shoes, which cram the toes and cause them to bend in an abnormal way. It is important to wear shoes that fit properly. Special exercises may also be recommended by a doctor. In severe cases, surgery may be required.

Bursitis is a painful condition that occurs when the bursa in a joint becomes inflamed. It is common in the shoulder and knee joints. Bursitis may result from an injury, or an infection or from overuse of the joint. Mild cases of bursitis are treated by resting the joint.

HEALTH UPDATE

LOOKING AT TECHNOLOGY

Arthroscopic Surgery

Until the early 1970s when the arthroscope was developed, knee surgery involved a large incision, lengthy hospitalization, and a long recovery time. Now advances in knee surgery are making prospects better for knee-injured athletes, particularly for those without major knee damage.

Arthroscopic surgery is the name of the procedure now often used to repair these injuries to the knee. The arthroscope, a tiny fiber-optic camera, allows the surgeon to look inside the knee and perform the needed procedure. *Arthro* means "joint" and *scope* means "to view," and the device does just that—allows the surgeon to view the damaged joint. The arthroscope actually has three parts: a fiber-optic light source, a tube, and magnifying lenses.

Before the procedure, the patient is given local or general anesthesia. Then a few small incisions, called portals, are made around the knee. A sterile saline solution is injected through one of these portals to expand the joint, while the surgeon inserts the arthroscope into the others to examine the knee completely. Looking through the eyepiece or at a TV monitor, the doctor has a clear view to most areas of the knee. Tiny instruments can be inserted through separate portals to perform the operation. A biopsy may be taken, tissues can be examined, and repair to or removal of damaged ligaments and cartilage can take place.

Arthroscopic surgery rarely takes more than an hour and recovery time is greatly reduced. Though rest is recommended after the procedure, many athletes who have the procedure are back on the playing field in no time at all.

- The thigh bone is the longest bone in your body.
- The stapes bone, which is in your middle ear, is the smallest bone in your body.
- Bones are lightweight; they comprise about 14 percent of your total body weight.
- At birth, everyone has 350 bones. Many of these join, as you grow. By adulthood, you have 206 bones.

208 CHAPTER 11 INTEGUMENTARY, SKELETAL, AND MUSCULAR SYSTEMS

Overcoming Misconceptions

Fractures and Osteoporosis. Elderly people, particularly women, often fall and break their hips. Is this always true or could the hip bone fracture first and cause the person to fall? As women age and go through menopause, the hormones change, making the absorption of calcium less efficient. The result is bones becoming thinner and porous, causing a condition called osteoporosis. As the bones become increasingly brittle they break easily. A jarring movement or an effort to lift something is sometimes enough to break a fragile hip. Many women take supplemental calcium in an effort to forestall the onset of this condition. Exercise also helps maintain bone density. Estrogen therapy may be necessary for some women following menopause.

Arthritis is an inflammation of the joints. Its cause is not completely known, and it affects people of all ages. Arthritis can be very painful and can restrict movement.

Care of the Skeletal System

Like other cells of the body, bone cells get the nutrients and oxygen they need as blood circulates in bones. With proper health care, bones can be strong and healthy.

Essential Minerals for Bones

In order to grow, harden, and repair, bones must have an adequate supply of minerals, especially calcium and phosphorus. Bones store these two minerals. If you have enough calcium and phosphorus in your daily diet, your body does not use the deposits in bones.

However, if you have a mineral deficiency in your diet, your body takes away some of the mineral supply in the bones to provide minerals to the blood, muscles, and nerves. This can cause weakening of the skeleton and increases a person's chance of bone fractures.

Caring for your bones and joints means including in your diet foods that contain minerals and vitamins that promote bone growth. The mineral calcium is a building material for bones. Sources of calcium include dairy products and leafy vegetables. Phosphorus combined with calcium gives rigidity to bones. Sources of phosphorus include peas, beans, milk, liver, meat, cottage cheese, broccoli, and whole grains. Vitamins A and D work to utilize calcium and phosphorus in bone formation. Sources of vitamin A include milk and other dairy products, green vegetables, carrots, and animal liver. Sources of vitamin D include fish oils, cream, butter, egg yolks, milk, and liver. Vitamin D is produced in the skin with exposure to ultraviolet rays in sunlight.

Regular physical activity, especially weight-bearing exercises, increases bone mass. While exercising, make sure that you use proper equipment and wear shoes and clothing for the particular activity you choose. Doing so can help prevent injuries and protect the skeletal system.

FINDING HELP

Too many people think that because there is no cure for arthritis, nothing can be done to treat it. That is a false assumption. The Arthritis Foundation has many programs including some self-help courses and exercise classes. For free information on how to cope more effectively with arthritis, contact the Arthritis Foundation, P.O. Box 19000, Atlanta, Georgia 30326

LESSON 2 REVIEW

Reviewing Facts and Vocabulary

1. What are the two main divisions of the skeletal system?
2. What are three functions of bones?
3. Describe two injuries or diseases of the skeletal system.
4. Classify and give examples of four freely moveable joints.

Thinking Critically

5. **Analysis.** What might happen if a young person did not include enough minerals, especially calcium, in his or her diet?

Applying Health Knowledge

6. At the grocery store ask the butcher for soup bones. Try to get a long bone. Ask the butcher to saw it in half for you. Identify the periosteum, yellow marrow and epiphyses, spongy bone tissue, and red marrow.

Answers to Lesson 2 Review

1. Axial—skull, ribs, sternum, and vertebral column; appendicular—bones of the shoulders, arms, hands, hips, legs, and feet.
2. Allows movement, provides a supporting framework that protects internal organs and stores essential body minerals, produces red and white blood cells in the red marrow.
3. Answers will vary. See pages 207 to 208.
4. Ball-and-socket—shoulder, hip; hinge—knee, elbow, jaw, toe, finger; pivot—forearm, head; gliding—vertebrae, wrist, ankle.
5. Eventually the bones will weaken and chances of a bone fracture increase.
6. Students may bring labeled bones to class.

THE MUSCULAR SYSTEM

Bones form the body's framework. Bones alone, however, cannot produce movement without the muscles that are attached to bones.

Functions of Your Muscular System

All body movements depend on characteristics of muscle tissue—the ability to contract, or shorten; the ability to extend, or stretch; and the ability to return to the original shape after contraction or extension. Muscles in your body are responsible for moving bones, pumping blood, moving food through the digestive system, and controlling air movement in and out of your lungs.

What Makes Muscles Contract?

Muscle contraction is started by the triggering action of nerve impulses. Nerves supplying most of the skeletal muscles that provide movement originate at the spinal cord. At the point where the nerve enters a muscle, it breaks up into numerous nerve endings, which, in turn, stimulate muscle fibers by means of tiny buttonlike endings called motor end plates. A neuron may branch to supply many muscle fibers.

Muscle Tone

All muscle fibers do not contract at the same time. While some are contracting, others are relaxing. Even when you are sleeping, some fibers are in a state of contraction, bringing about a certain degree of firmness, or tone, to your muscles. In the case of aging or poor health, muscles lose some or all of their tone. When you are in good health, a constant flow of impulses from nerves maintains muscle tone. Tone is essential for maintaining posture. Exercise and good nutrition improve muscle tone.

Structure of the Muscular System

A muscle consists of a mass of fibers grouped together. Almost all of the individual muscle fibers a person will ever have are present at birth. General muscle growth is an increase in the size rather than the number of the muscle fibers.

Muscle fibers are made of smaller fibers called myofibrils. Thick and thin filaments make up each myofibril. The thick filaments are made up of the protein myosin. The thin filaments are made up of the protein actin. Myofibrils are divided into sections called sarcomeres. When a muscle fiber receives an impulse from a nerve, actin filaments slide over the myosin filaments and move toward the center of the sarcomeres and

Resources for Lesson 3

- **Transparency** 47
- **Guided Reading** Activity 29
- **Decision-Making** Activity 11
- **Workbook** Vocabulary Activity 29
- **Workbook** Application Activity 11
- **Reteaching** Activity 29

- **Enrichment** Activity 11
- **Cooperative Learning** Activity 11
- **Health Labs** Activity 11
- **Lesson 3 Quiz**
- **Chapter 11 Test**

toward each other during contraction. When the muscle relaxes, the actin filaments return to their original positions.

Types of Muscles

Your body has three basic types of muscle tissue. These types are smooth muscle, skeletal muscle, and cardiac muscle.

Skeletal muscles give shape to the body and are essential in performing physical movements.

The Skeletal Muscles

Trapezius
Rhomboid
Teres
Triceps
Biceps (of arm)
Latissimus dorsi
External oblique muscle of abdomen
Gluteus maximus
Abductor muscles (pull legs away from body)
Biceps (of thigh)
Semitendinosus
Gastrocnemius
Peroneus
Achilles tendon

Facial muscles
Frontalis
Temporalis
Orbicularis oculi
Masseter
Orbicularis oris

Extensor muscles (dorsal surface)
Biceps
Deltoid
Serratus anterior
Sternocleidomastoid
Pectoralis major
External oblique
Flexor muscles (inside of arm)
Sartorius
Adductor muscles (pull legs toward body)
Quadriceps muscles
Patella (kneecap)
Peroneus
Anterior tibial

Gastrocnemius
Soleus

THE MUSCULAR SYSTEM **211**

Overcoming Misconceptions

Steroids. Short-term and low-dose steroid use won't hurt you. If students believe this, they will be in trouble. Though illegal in many states, steroids are still heavily promoted and sold through gyms and body-building magazines.

It only takes one sharing of a needle from someone who may not even know that he or she has HIV to pass the disease to a casual steroid user.

Steroid users ignore side effects of stunted growth, shrinking of sexual organs, liver and kidney disease, and mood swings. "Roid mania" is not uncommon and is sometimes a first clue that a person is using steroids.

Building Vocabulary

- Have students form groups of four to review the vocabulary terms. Using these terms they should write a sports story. One group member begins by writing an introductory sentence with a vocabulary term from the list. The next group member reads the sentence aloud and adds another sentence with another vocabulary term. Group members pass their paper around until all the vocabulary terms are used. Each time the paper is passed, the new writer should read the whole story so that coherence can be maintained. If someone gets stuck, other group members should help out. Encourage humor and creativity; but advise students that they must use the vocabulary terms correctly.
- Ask students to complete *Workbook Vocabulary Activity 29.*

Teach

Guided Practice

L1 **USING BODY SYSTEMS TRANSPARENCY 47.** Refer to the Teaching Transparencies Binder.

L2 **EXPLANATION.** Introduce the term *antagonistic.* Explain that the paired muscles described in the lesson introduction were antagonistic pairs. If both were to contract equally at the same time, no movement could take place. Tell students that actually when a muscle relaxes, some tension is maintained to control the movement at a joint.

L1 **CLASS ACTIVITY.** To see how certain muscles work, students can observe the action of tendons by drumming their fingers on the desk and watching the backs of their hands.

L1 **DISCUSSION.** Using a large chart, identify for the class the major muscle groups. Ask students if the location of the muscle affects its function.

L1 **CLASS ACTIVITY.** Ask students to evaluate the function of their large muscle groups. Which groups are adequately developed? Which need additional toning?

Smooth muscle, sometimes called unstriated muscle, is located in such places as the intestines and blood vessels. Smooth muscles are involuntary because they work without a person's conscious control.

Skeletal muscles are attached to bones and cause body movement. Skeletal muscles are voluntary. They are under conscious control. Skeletal muscles account for about 40 percent of body weight.

Skeletal muscles work in pairs. While one contracts, its counterpart extends. When a skeletal muscle contracts, bones are pulled by tendons, which attach muscles to bones. The tendons that connect a muscle to a bone must be connected to another bone, so that there is something to pull against when the muscle contracts. Muscles that bend a limb at the joint are called **flexors;** those that straighten a limb are called **extensors.** If the flexors and extensors both contracted at the same time, they would work against each other, and there would be no movement.

Cardiac muscle is a special type of striated tissue that forms the walls of the heart. This muscle pumps blood through your cardiovascular system. Cardiac muscle is involuntary muscle.

Your heart is the most important muscle in your body. It works continuously, day and night. Just like other muscles, the more exercise the heart gets, the stronger it becomes. A strong heart works more efficiently; that is, it does the same amount of work with less effort.

Problems of the Muscular System

You have probably experienced sore muscles after overworking them. This condition is temporary. Many other conditions of the muscular system are not temporary. They have an impact on a person's health and life-style.

Muscle Strain

A muscle strain is one of the most common injuries to muscles. A strain, or a "pulled muscle," is a sudden, painful stretching or tearing of muscle fibers. Strains usually occur in large muscles and are a result of overexertion. A strained muscle needs to be rested in order to heal. Ice

Muscles that are exercised and cared for are flexible and allow extraordinary movement.

Additional Information

Anaerobic and Aerobic Processes. Adenosine triphosphate (ATP) is a molecule that results in the breakdown of glucose. ATP stores energy in cells. When ATP is broken down chemically, energy is released. ATP is not stored in large quantities in muscle cells. Therefore, it must be replaced. When glucose is broken down, it is stored as glycogen in the liver and in the muscles, and it provides some ATP molecules. This process does not require the presence of oxygen and, therefore, is called anaerobic. In the presence of oxygen, however, a glucose molecule is completely broken down, producing 18 to 20 times more ATP than does the anaerobic process. This aerobic process results in a higher yield of energy.

Flexor

Tendon

Extensor

Muscle relaxed

Muscle contracted

Muscle tone maintained

Muscles work in a seesaw pattern around a joint. As one muscle pulls, or contracts, another stretches, or relaxes.

should be applied to a strain for the first 24 hours. After that, heat should be applied to the strain.

Muscle Cramp

Have you ever been swimming and had a muscle cramp? A cramp occurs when a muscle contracts spasmodically and involuntarily. The muscle feels tense, knotted, and painful. A cramp may occur from using certain muscles for too long a period of time. Have you ever been writing for a long time and had your hand develop a cramp? Cramps also result from overworking in the heat. Cramps can be treated by gently stretching the muscle and firmly massaging the knot out of the muscle. Heat may also be used to help the muscle relax.

Myasthenia Gravis

Myasthenia gravis is a disease that is characterized by muscles that are weak and easily fatigued. The most commonly affected muscles are

DID YOU KNOW?

- Muscular strength reaches its peak between the ages of 20 and 30.
- Muscles give off large quantities of heat. According to one estimate, in one hour, one's body muscles can give off enough heat to boil a quart (.9 l) of water.

KEEPING FIT

A Foot Massage

A foot massage relaxes the muscles of your foot and relieves stress.
- Wash your hands and your feet.
- Place your right foot on your left knee.
- Hold your foot there with your right hand.

- Place your thumb on the sole of your foot.
- Place your fingers up toward your toes.
- Put firm pressure on your foot.
- Moving your thumb in a circular motion, massage from the

heel up toward your toes.
- Rub each toe with a circular motion between the thumb and the index finger.
- Repeat the process, working from the toes to ankle.
- Now switch feet.

THE MUSCULAR SYSTEM **213**

Additional Information

The Heart. The heart is a muscle that responds to an increase in anaerobic and aerobic activity. An increase in aerobic activity makes the muscle more efficient and stronger.

The ventricles are the stronger muscles of the heart. They force blood out of the heart to all parts of the body.

Because the heart is a muscle, it requires

nutrients, oxygen, and removal of wastes. It has its own system of veins and arteries to do the job efficiently.

The heart responds to hormones by accelerating or decelerating its beating. Control of the beating mechanism is within the medulla of the brain.

Drug overdose can disrupt this connection and cause death.

L1 **CLASS ACTIVITY.** Walking is an excellent exercise to tone muscle groups. Arrange for regular walking tours as part of the students' daily or weekly activities.

L1 **DISCUSSION.** The cardiac muscle extends to receive blood from the veins. Oxidation permits contraction of the cardiac muscle to pump blood into the arteries. Discuss other examples of this process in the body systems, such as stomach, bladder, diaphragm.

L1 **CLASS ACTIVITY.** Take the class to visit the auto shop on campus. Ask a shop teacher to illustrate car engine stroke volume for the class. Then have students write paragraphs comparing the engine stroke volume to the stroke volume of the human heart. Do all hearts have stroke volume?

L2 **LAB.** From the science department in your school, borrow microscopes and prepared slides of cardiac muscle, striated or skeletal muscle, and smooth muscle. Ask students to observe these slides and make drawings of the differences they observe between the three types of muscle tissue.

L1 **EXPLANATION.** Tell students because muscle tissue responds to increased work loads by increasing strength, endurance, and efficiency, all muscle types can be trained to work more efficiently and with less strain. As muscles become stronger, their tendons also become stronger.

L1 **EXPLANATION.** Explain that tendons act as a secondary bracing system for joint ligaments. When a ligament is damaged, a strong tendon can take over the job of providing joint stability.

L2 **CLASS ACTIVITY.** Home injuries are one of the most frequent causes of muscle pain. Ask students to write descriptions of ways to prevent muscle strain when moving, lifting, pulling, or carrying heavy objects. Have students share the reports in class.

L1 **SPEAKER.** Ask a member of your community who suffers from muscular dystrophy to speak to the class. How has the disease affected his or her life and participation in daily activities?

■ **Discussion.** What helped Jill improve her self-esteem? How did that improve her outlook and happiness? What did she see as the most important way to achieve self-acceptance? (Most important in improving Jill's self-esteem was being in an environment of other differently abled people. This helped her feel accepted and normal. Jill felt that taking responsibility for her own life was the best way to feel good about herself.)

■ **Explanation.** Explain how Jill inherited muscular dystrophy even though her parents didn't have the disease. (Muscular dystrophy is a recessive inherited disorder—inheriting one gene from each parent produces an affected child, like Jill, with two genes for muscular dystrophy. Because the parents each have just one gene for muscular dystrophy, they aren't affected by the disease.)

■ **Answers**
1. She lives alone and supports herself; she's been willing to get help doing things she's too small or physically weak to do.
2. Remind yourself that others feel the same way you do.

Independent Practice

L2 RESEARCH. Every community has various groups that attempt to raise funds for worthy organizations. Some of these are the Muscular Dystrophy Association, the Heart Association, the Diabetes Association, the March of Dimes, etc. Ask students to contact these groups to find out what activities they sponsor in your community. What percentage of the money they collect stays in the community? Where are the other funds expended? Is research or prevention emphasized?

L1 COMMUNITY INVOLVEMENT. Have students contact the local Muscular Dystrophy Association to learn more about the effects of muscular dystrophy. Does this association assist individuals with disorders other than muscular dystrophy?

Overcoming The Odds

Jill Eshleman is 23. She has a very rare form of muscular dystrophy. She says, "When I was born, there was no indication of a problem. Then, at age 4, I had heart failure from the disease, but they didn't know why. At 6, I had pneumonia. That's when I had surgery that made an opening into my trachea. I called it my 'trach'. They knew I was a very sick child, and they gave me 2 months to live. My spine had curved because the muscles were not strong enough to hold it straight. I had scoliosis, and my mom and dad designed a special walker. I was too sick to go to school, so I was tutored at home until 8th grade.

"Then my health stabilized and I tried four classes a day in the public school. I still had my trach. School was tough. In ninth grade it was better than being tutored at home, but it was not a good experience. I was painfully shy. The kids were hesitant, so they didn't really approach me. I had one good friend and the rest of the time I stayed by myself. I felt very self-conscious of what other kids thought."

After high school, Jill went to a community college and then completed a computer program for the disabled. "That's when I blossomed—when I got around people who were just like me," she says.

"Recently, I moved out on my own permanently. I love living alone," she says. "I was able to buy a house right up the road from my mom. I've

been working for three years. I started out in customer service and now I do bookkeeping for a company that imports Australian coats. I'm still using my special homemade walker. I have my driver's license. I'm learning to play an electric keyboard. My kitchen counters are low so that I can cook for myself. And I have friends now."

Jill is 4 feet 8 inches tall and weighs 52 pounds. Yet, she says, laughing, "My current health problem is pimples."

Jill has signed up with an organization called Canine Partners for Life, Inc. in Cochranville, Pennsylvania. Soon they will provide her with a special canine friend to help her. "They train dogs for your special needs," she says. "My dog will be able to pick up things off the floor, open heavy doors, retrieve a cordless telephone, and help me with steep ramps. He's an Australian sheep dog named Money. The dogs are trained for a year with a family, then at the Canine Partners kennel for a second year."

Jill concludes, "These days I feel good about myself. I would say to other people, set a goal so that when you feel frustrated you can think about it and get inspired. I really feel you have to inspire yourself. No one else is going to do it for you."

1. In what ways has Jill achieved independence? In what ways has she been willing to get help when she needs it?
2. Jill says that in high school other students felt hesitant about approaching her and she about approaching them. Do you ever have such reactions to people who are different from you? How can you overcome such hesitancy?

Across the Curriculum

Science. Examine specimens of animal hearts available in a laboratory. Compare the size of the heart to the animal's size. How does this compare to the size of a human heart and the size of a human body? Ask students to summarize their findings in writing.

Physical Education. Muscle strains are frequently treated with the RICE method (rest, ice, compression, and elevation). Ask students to describe how to treat muscle strains in various locations, such as thigh, calf, shoulder, via the RICE method.

Physical Education. Work with the physical education staff to develop and promote muscle toning activities daily on campus.

the eye muscles, which may result in drooping eyelids and double vision. Symptoms can be relieved with medicines.

This disease can affect anyone, but for reasons unknown, it is most common in women of childbearing age. The disease may occur during pregnancy or following an infection.

Muscular Dystrophy

Muscular dystrophy is a crippling disease characterized by a progressive wasting away of skeletal muscles. Muscular dystrophy is usually inherited.

With this disease the muscle cells are unable to function properly and are replaced by fatty tissue. The symptoms of muscular dystrophy vary depending on the part of the body that is affected. A person may experience muscle weakness, difficulty standing or walking, or frequent falls. Early detection of muscular dystrophy is crucial because, even though the disease cannot be cured, muscle weakening can be delayed. Exercise can help maintain flexibility.

Care for the Muscles

The more you use your muscles, the more efficient and strong they become. A program of regular exercise with stretching, warm-up, and cool down increases muscular strength and flexibility. Exercise increases muscle mass and stamina. By including an activity that promotes balance and coordination, falls and injuries can be reduced. Proper equipment and clothing can help protect muscles during exercise. Practicing good posture can help strengthen back muscles. Remember, your heart is a muscle and benefits from exercise just as other muscles do. Regular exercise strengthens the heart and makes it work more efficiently by increasing the amount of blood pumped in a single beat. As a result, the heart can pump fewer times and has more time to rest between beats. As with all other body cells, a healthy diet is important to the health of all your muscles.

LESSON 3 REVIEW

Reviewing Facts and Vocabulary

1. What are two important characteristics of muscle tissue?
2. What are the three types of muscles?
3. Describe two injuries or diseases related to the muscular system.

Thinking Critically

4. **Synthesis.** What possible benefits to muscles may be derived from warming up and stretching before exercise?

5. **Synthesis.** Suggest ways that a person can prevent injury to skeletal muscles.

Applying Health Knowledge

6. Get a chicken drumstick and thigh that are still attached. Pull back the skin and flex the leg. Watch which muscles contract and flex. Cut through the tendons at the base of the leg and separate the muscle groups. How many muscle groups are there? Can you identify the large blood vessels and the ligaments?

THE MUSCULAR SYSTEM **215**

Answers to Lesson 3 Review

1. Answers will vary. Accept two of the following: the ability to contract; the ability to extend; the ability to return to the original shape after contraction or extension.
2. Smooth muscle, skeletal muscle, cardiac muscle.
3. Answers will vary. Accept two of the injuries or diseases described on pages 212 to 215.
4. Stretching loosens up the muscles and tendons and reduces the risk of injury.
5. By following a regular exercise program that includes stretching, warming up, and cooling down; participating in activities that promote balance and coordination; wearing proper equipment and clothing during exercise; practicing good posture.
6. Answers will vary.

L1 **USING THE LESSON RESOURCES.** For additional student activities, refer to the lesson resources on page 210.

Assess

Check for Understanding

- Assign and discuss the lesson review.
- Assign and discuss the chapter review.

Evaluate

- Administer, grade, and discuss the *Lesson 3 Quiz*.
- Administer, grade, and discuss the *Chapter 11 Test*.
- Refer to the Performance Assessment strategy for this chapter. See pages T 23 to T 25.

Reteach

- Ask students to recall the three types of muscles. Have them describe similarities and differences and provide an example and location of each type.
- Ask students to complete *Reteaching Activity 29*.

Enrich

- Have students investigate the anaerobic and aerobic processes of muscles. Ask them to explain how both systems operate during exercise.
- Ask students to complete *Enrichment Activity 11*.

Close

Tell students that they have studied the function, structure, problems, and the care of muscles.

Helping Students Improve Their Health

Using the Self-Inventory

Reinforcing Vocabulary

- **Sunscreen.** A substance that protects the skin from excessive ultraviolet radiation.
- **Vitamin A.** A nutrient that the body needs found in orange-yellow vegetables.
- **Calcium and phosphorus.** Two important minerals that develop strong bones and teeth.
- **Sprain.** A damaged ligament.

Teaching Strategies

L1 EXPLANATION. Students who exhibit poor hygiene practices are not always aware of the problem. Also, what is perceived as poor hygiene may be in reality a medical condition that may or may not be diagnosed. Use care and sensitivity when approaching students with these problems.

L1 EXPLANATION. Occasionally students may ask about losing weight from a particular body part, such as the stomach. Individuals lose weight according to the intake of calories and one's expenditure of energy. One cannot choose from exactly where on the body weight will be lost. This is dependent upon heredity and one's own personal body type.

L1 CLASS ACTIVITY. Plan a visit to your school's weight training facility. Allowing the students to actually see specific muscles contracting during a certain movement will aid in student comprehension and retention.

DID YOU KNOW?

- The SPF number on sunscreen tells you how long you can stay in the sun without burning—if you normally burn in 10 minutes, an SPF of 15 lets you stay in the sun 150 minutes.

Self-Inventory

Care of Your Integumentary, Skeletal, and Muscular Systems

HOW DO YOU RATE?

There are many things you can do to promote these three body systems. Take the following self-inventory, and rate yourself on your health behaviors. On a separate sheet of paper, answer *always*, *sometimes* or *never* to the following questions.

Integumentary System

1. I keep my hair clean, cut, and styled in a way that fits my features and type of hair.
2. I keep my nails clean and evenly trimmed.
3. I avoid prolonged exposure to the sun.
4. When I am in the sun, I use an appropriate sunscreen.
5. I wash my face twice daily and use only creams and cosmetics appropriate for my skin type.
6. I avoid picking at acne.
7. I eat a well-balanced diet that includes an adequate source of vitamin A.

Skeletal System

8. My diet includes food sources of calcium and phosphorus.
9. My physical activity includes weight-bearing exercises.
10. I wear proper equipment for the activities I participate in.
11. I know how to care for a sprain.

12. I wear proper shoes for the activities I participate in.

Muscular System

13. I exercise three to five times a week.
14. I warm up and stretch before beginning to exercise.
15. I work to increase my muscular strength.
16. I know how to care for a muscle cramp.
17. I practice good posture in order to strengthen my back muscles.
18. I cool down after exercising.
19. I participate in activities that increase my balance and coordination.
20. I choose a healthy diet.

HOW DID YOU SCORE?

Give yourself 2 points for each *always* response, 1 point for each *sometimes* response, and 0 points for each *never* response. Total your score. Then proceed to the next section.

31 to 40
Excellent. Your health choices show you are taking care of these systems.

21 to 30
Good. However, there are some things you could do better to promote these systems.

Below 21
Look out! You may be taking unnecessary risks that could affect your health.

WHAT ARE YOUR GOALS?

Identify an area in which your score was low, and use the goal-setting process to begin making a change.

1. The behavior I would like to change or improve is ____.
2. If this behavior were completely changed, I would look, feel, and act differently in the following ways: ____.
3. The steps involved in making this change are ____.
4. My timetable for accomplishing this is ____.
5. People I will ask for support or assistance are ____.
6. The benefits I will receive are ____.
7. The rewards for making this change will be ____.

Meeting Students' Needs

For students who score *Excellent*. Suggest that students involve themselves in appearance or fitness-oriented careers, such as weight training, coaching, physical education, modeling, or cosmetology.

For students who score *Good*. Suggest that students examine their own personal level of fitness and design a fitness program in order to improve in certain areas.

For students who need to *Look out!* Suggest that students enroll in fitness workshops that may help them become more knowledgeable in maintaining health and well-being through reasonable exercise and diet practices.

Building Decision-Making Skills

N ick has had close family members die of muscular dystrophy and feels very strongly about raising funds for the muscular dystrophy telethon. He is forming an organizing committee in his homeroom for a dance at his school to benefit the charity. A couple of friends start making jokes about "Jerry's kids" and suggest that any fund-raising dance should benefit the students of their school, not people they don't even know. What should Nick say to his friends?

WHAT DO YOU THINK?

1. **Situation.** Why does Nick need to make a decision?

2. **Choices.** Should Nick respond to these students? If so, what are his possible approaches?

3. **Choices.** Should Nick relate his response to his personal situation? Explain your answer.

4. **Consequences.** What will probably happen if Nick does not make a decision?

5. **Consequences.** What will probably happen if Nick changes his plan and organizes a dance to raise money for the senior class trip or some other school activity?

6. **Consequences.** How might Nick's self-esteem be affected by this decision?

7. **Consequences.** How might Nick's health triangle be affected by this decision?

8. **Consequences.** How will Nick's family be affected by this decision?

9. **Consequences.** Should school fund-raising activities benefit only students?

10. **Consequences.** What are the benefits of participating in an event that benefits a particular charity?

11. **Decision.** What do you think Nick should do? Explain your answer.

12. **Evaluation.** Have you ever been in a similar situation? If so, how did you handle it? Would you handle it differently now?

S cott's friends on the football team have grown considerably in the past year and have earned spots on the varsity football team, which is one of the most successful in the state. In addition to status in school, some varsity players on this team are virtually assured of college scholarship opportunities. Scott is very talented and dedicated, but just not big enough. His friends have told him the answer is simple—just do as they did and use steroids, which they got from older players. Scott knows the dangers of using steroids and he doesn't want to take those risks. What should he tell his friends?

WHAT DO YOU THINK?

13. **Situation.** If Scott didn't know the facts about steroids, where could he find them?

14. **Situation.** What difference does it make what he tells his friends?

15. **Situation.** What might make this a difficult decision?

16. **Choices.** What choices does Scott have?

17. **Consequences.** What are the costs of each choice?

18. **Consequences.** What are the benefits of each choice?

19. **Consequences.** How can Scott accept the fact that he's too small to get a college football scholarship?

20. **Consequences.** If money is a problem, how might Scott go to college if he doesn't get the football scholarship?

21. **Consequences.** How might Scott's parents help him accept the fact that he won't get a football scholarship?

22. **Consequences.** Are there any circumstances under which you would suggest that Scott take the steroids? Explain your answer.

23. **Decision.** What do you think Scott should do? Explain your answer.

Discussing the Answers

Situation 1. Perhaps a solution can be found by using humor. Nick will be successful in his cause if he can educate his friends about muscular dystrophy and have his friends come to see this problem as he sees it. Another possible solution would be to have funds that are raised benefit students of their school and MDAA.

Situation 2. The only healthful solution to this problem would be to have Scott say *no* to using steroids. By practicing saying *no*, students can become capable of resisting negative peer influence. It would be ideal if Scott could care enough about his friends to get them help. By contacting a coach, guidance counselor, or the parents of his friends, Scott may be acting as a true friend.

Helping Students Improve Their Health

Building Decision-Making Skills

Teaching Strategies

L1 CLASS ACTIVITY. Have students role-play Nick encountering his fellow classmates. How can Nick include these students in his project, rather than alienating them? Should Nick compromise with these students by having a share of the proceeds benefit their school, while at the same time having a share of the proceeds going to MDAA?

L1 CLASS ACTIVITY. Have students role-play the part of Scott being pressured to use steroids in order to become big enough to play on the varsity football team. How will the use of steroids affect Scott's friends' health? What are the legal repercussions of using steroids? How might using steroids jeopardize one's college scholarship? How might mandatory testing of steroid use affect the football team for which these students play?

L1 CLASS ACTIVITY. Other possible role-plays pertaining to the integumentary, skeletal, and muscular systems include: (1) A friend who has severe acne is told that a tanning bed will clear up her skin. (2) An obese friend is following a fad diet that makes claims of fast weight loss. Your friend has nearly fainted after being on this fad diet for just two days. (3) Your five-year-old brother wants to play little league football in a league that does not provide protective equipment. You have learned that trauma can cause bones to fuse early in life, stunting growth and leading to deformity. Your parents are ready to let him play and you are afraid for your little brother.

L2 DISCUSSION. Debate the use of illegal anabolic steroids that build muscle for athletics. What are the legally sound medical purposes for using steroids? What are the physical and emotional costs involved in illegal steroid use?

Answers to Chapter 11 Review

1. Epidermis
2. Dermis
3. Perspiration
4. Ringworm
5. Dandruff
6. Cartilage
7. Ossification
8. Joint
9. Scoliosis
10. Osteoporosis
11. Muscle
12. Cardiac

Building Academic Skills

13. Increasing by repeated exposure.
14. About 3.9 percent.

Recalling the Facts

15. The skin.
16. When internal body temperature rises, heat is carried to the surface of the skin by the blood, and body heat is lost by radiation. Sweat glands also affect body temperature as they release perspiration. When internal body temperature drops, circulation of the blood to the surface of the skin slows down, and heat is saved inside the body.
17. They shed when clothing rubs one's skin or when one washes.
18. The inner layer of the epidermis.
19. Bacterial growth on the skin.
20. Answers will vary. Accept two of the following: attaches the skin to bone and muscle; serves as the body's natural insulation; acts as an inner cushion to protect internal organs.
21. Skin cancer.
22. Brushing keeps dirt from building up and helps evenly distribute the natural hair oils.
23. It is caused by a fungus and can be avoided by wearing foot coverings in locker rooms and showers.
24. Keep nails clean and evenly trimmed, push back cuticles, clip hangnails.
25. The stapes in the middle ear. The femur.

26. Long bones—femur; short bones—as in wrists and ankles; flat bones—ribs and skull bones; irregular bones—vertebrae.
27. Older females.
28. Calcium and phosphorus.
29. A—yes; B—yes; C—no; D—yes; E—yes; F—yes; G—no.
30. Smooth, skeletal, cardiac.
31. The heart.
32. By using them.

Using Health Terms

On a separate sheet of paper, write the term that best matches each definition given below.

LESSON 1

1. The outer, thinner layer of skin made up of both living and dead cells.
2. The inner, thicker layer of skin.
3. Water and other waste products secreted from the sweat glands.
4. Disease of the skin caused by a fungus and symptomized by a whitish ring.
5. A common hair and scalp problem symptomized by flakes of skin.

LESSON 2

6. A strong material that gives support and flexibility to the body's framework at the joints.
7. A process by which cartilage becomes bone as the body matures.
8. The point at which two bones meet.
9 A curvature of the spine that may develop during puberty.
10. A condition that results from a loss of calcium in the bones.

LESSON 3

11. A mass of fibers grouped together.
12. Kind of muscle that forms the walls of the heart.

Building Academic Skills

LESSON 1

13. **Reading.** Use the context clue in the following sentence to define the word *cumulative.* The increasing effect of the sun on your skin is cumulative, and the damage is irreversible.

LESSON 2

14. **Math.** Four bones make up the human leg: the femur, the patella, the tibia, and the fibula. The bones in both legs make up what percentage of the 206 bones found in the adult skeletal system?

Recalling the Facts

LESSON 1

15. What is the largest organ in the body?
16. Explain the process by which your skin helps regulate body temperature.
17. What eventually happens to dead cells in the epidermis?
18. In what part of the skin are new cells formed?
19. What causes body odor?
20. Name two functions of the hypodermis.
21. What can be a serious result of excessive exposure to the sun over a period of time?
22. How does regular brushing benefit your hair?
23. What causes athlete's foot and how can it be avoided?
24. What are some basic procedures to follow for good nail care?

LESSON 2

25. What is the smallest bone in the body? The longest?
26. Name the four kinds of bones in the human body and give an example of each.
27. In what part of the population is osteoporosis most common?
28. What two minerals are important for your bones to grow, harden, and repair?
29. For each condition below, write *yes* if it affects a joint. Write *no* if the condition affects some other part of the skeletal system.
    a. sprain
    b. dislocation
    c. fracture
    d. torn cartilage
    e. bursitis
    f. arthritis
    g. osteoporosis

LESSON 3

30. What are the three types of muscles?
31. What is the most important muscle in the body?
32. What is the best way to keep your muscles strong and working efficiently?

Thinking Critically

33. The skin of each person's fingers forms a unique pattern of ridges so no two are alike.
34. Too little results in dry skin and hair; too much results in oily skin and hair.
35. Ringworm because the fungus that causes ringworm can spread.
36. The sun's rays are shorter and more intense between 11 A.M. and 1 P.M. than they are in the late afternoon and early evening.

REVIEW

Thinking Critically

LESSON 1

33. **Analysis.** Why is it not possible for two people to have the same fingerprints?
34. **Analysis.** Compare the results of too much and too little sebum being produced by the sebaceous glands.
35. **Synthesis.** Jackie has ringworm. Sandra borrows Jackie's comb every morning before school. What problem is Sandra likely to develop and why?
36. **Synthesis.** Sally was at the beach from 4 o'clock to 6 o'clock on Tuesday afternoon and did not get a sunburn. On Wednesday, she was at the beach from 11 o'clock in the morning to 1 o'clock in the afternoon and did get a sunburn. Why did she burn on Wednesday and not on Tuesday?
37. **Analysis.** Review this statement: "To avoid the sun, I'm going to a tanning booth."

LESSON 2

38. **Synthesis.** Devise and write out a plan for a person who has a deficiency in calcium and phosphorus.
39. **Analysis.** How are ligaments and tendons alike? How are they different?

LESSON 3

40. **Analysis.** Compare flexor and extensor muscles.
41. **Synthesis.** Compare and contrast the three basic types of muscles.

Making the Connection

LESSON 2

42. **Language Arts.** Interview several people who work in the sports or exercise field. Examples include a physical therapist, a trainer, or a dance instructor. Write a two-to three-page report that describes the academic preparation necessary for that career and the individual's personal characteristics that would be necessary to be successful in that field.

Applying Health Knowledge

LESSON 1

43. What phrases in skin product ads should be viewed with skepticism?
44. John spends a lot of time working on his tan. What can you tell him about the harmful effects of the sun on skin?
45. You have a mole on the left side of your neck. Recently you noticed that it has changed color from light brown to black. What should you do?
46. You have noticed white flakes in Ted's hair and on the shoulders of his dark shirts. What might Ted's problem be?
47. Duane shoveled snow for two hours on Friday afternoon. The day was bright and sunny. Now Duane appears to have a sunburn. How could Duane get a sunburn in the winter?
48. Explain how your overall appearance makes a statement about how you feel about yourself.

LESSON 2

49. Celia, who is 8, and her grandmother, who is 63, went roller skating together. They both fell down. Celia's grandmother broke her wrist, but Celia was uninjured. Why do you think Celia's grandmother broke a bone?

LESSON 3

50. Julio strained a muscle during wrestling practice. What should he do for it?
51. Shirley sometimes experiences muscle cramps during swimming practice. What advice would you give her for the next time this happens?

Beyond the Classroom

LESSON 3

52. **Community Involvement.** Contact your local chapter of the Muscular Dystrophy Association. Find out what this organization is doing to help people who have this disease.

37. The effects of a tan are the same no matter how one gets it.
38. Answers will vary but plans should include dairy products and leafy vegetables for calcium and peas, beans, milk, liver, meat, cottage cheese, broccoli, and whole grains for phosphorus.
39. Both connect. Ligaments connect bones together at a joint; tendons connect muscles to bones.
40. Flexors bend a limb at a joint; extensors straighten a limb at a joint.
41. Refer to page 212.

Making the Connection

42. Answers will vary.

Applying Health Knowledge

43. Answers will vary but should include claims that seem to promise perfect skin and beauty.
44. Refer to pages 202–203.
45. See a doctor.
46. It is probably dandruff.
47. Snow reflects more than 85 percent of the sun's ultraviolet rays.
48. Answers will vary. Possible answers: If one's appearance is unkempt, it may indicate low self-esteem and that one does not feel like taking time for oneself. It may indicate that one's personal appearance is not a high priority for that person.
49. In later adult years, bones become more brittle, breaking more easily.
50. Rest the muscle, apply ice to the area for 24 hours, then apply heat.
51. Gently stretch the muscle and firmly massage the knot out of the muscle.

Beyond the Classroom

52. Answers will vary.

Lesson Summaries

LESSON 1. The nervous system is the body's communication network and control center. It has two main divisions—the central and the peripheral nervous systems. The structure and function of each of these divisions is presented in this lesson.

LESSON 2. Normal functioning of the nervous system can be impaired by infectious diseases, accidents, or the use of illegal drugs, particularly alcohol. Genetic disorders can also affect this system. Daily exercise, proper nutrition, and adequate sleep will keep this system functioning well.

LESSON 3. The endocrine system is made up of glands that secrete hormones that affect the autonomic nervous system and hypothalamus. Most disorders are related to the glands producing too much or too little of a hormone. Good health habits can help maintain this system.

Introducing the Chapter

Students are probably familiar with the analogy that likens the brain to a computer. It receives, processes, stores, and finds information and transmits messages to all parts of the body. The nervous system, in fact, coordinates and regulates all of the body's functions. Tell students that the endocrine system works closely with the nervous system in regulating certain activities in the body and that these two body systems will be studied in this chapter. Have students add the body systems discussed in this chapter to the chart they developed for Chapter 11, providing each system's structure, function, problems, and care as they read the chapter.

Performance Assessment ✓

Refer to pages T 23 to T 25 for a Performance Assessment strategy for this chapter. See the *Performance Assessment Activities* booklet for additional suggestions.

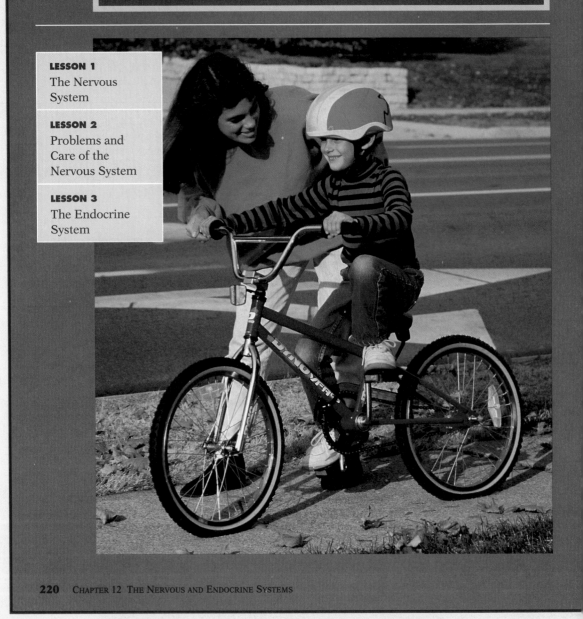

CHAPTER

12 THE NERVOUS AND ENDOCRINE SYSTEMS

LESSON 1
The Nervous System

LESSON 2
Problems and Care of the Nervous System

LESSON 3
The Endocrine System

220 CHAPTER 12 THE NERVOUS AND ENDOCRINE SYSTEMS

Key to Ability Levels

Teaching strategies have been coded for varying learning styles and abilities.

L1 Level 1 activities are basic activities and should be within the ability range of all students.

L2 Level 2 activities are average activities and should be within the ability range of average to above-average students.

L3 Level 3 activities are challenging activities designed for the ability range of above-average students.

LD LD activities should be within the ability range of learning-disabled students.

LEP LEP activities should be within the ability range of Limited English Proficiency students.

THE NERVOUS SYSTEM

Think of the series of events that take place when you eat a meal. Your eyes register that food is on your plate. Your hands move to pick up a utensil. You pick up the food. You then raise the food to your mouth, which opens at just the right time. You put the food in your mouth and start chewing. Your mouth has already begun secreting saliva to begin the digestive process.

You perform this act so regularly that it may seem automatic, but it is not. Eating is just one of many body functions that require coordinated responses and movements. The nervous system, along with the endocrine system, controls the coordination of all body functions. These two systems work together in such a way that the body is regulated and integrated and acts as a unit.

Functions of the Nervous System

Your nervous system is your body's communication network and control center. This system transmits information by nerve impulses from one nerve cell to another throughout your body. Your nervous system senses changes not only within your body but also outside your body in your environment. Those changes are interpreted and you respond to them. This happens in split seconds so that your body adjusts quickly to any internal or external changes. For example, when you touch a hot object in your external environment, how quickly do you respond?

Functions of Neurons

Nerve cells, which are called **neurons,** are the functional and structural parts of the nervous system. Neurons are classified according to their functions. There are three main types of neurons: sensory neurons, interneurons, and motor neurons.

- Neurons that have specialized receptor ends and are located in the skin and other sensory organs are called **sensory neurons.** Sensory neurons receive stimuli, such as sounds, and send impulses to your spinal cord and brain. You have sensory receptors for heat, cold, pain, hearing, taste, sight, smell, touch, and balance.

- Neurons within the brain and spinal cord that relay impulses from sensory neurons to motor neurons are called **interneurons.**

- Neurons that carry impulses from interneurons to muscles and glands are called **motor neurons.** When you touch a hot object you lift your hand away. When you are in an emergency situation your adrenal glands release adrenaline and you have extra energy. You will learn more about neurons later in this chapter.

THE NERVOUS SYSTEM **221**

Focus

Lesson Objectives
After studying this lesson, students should be able to:
- describe the functions and characteristics of neurons
- describe the central nervous system
- describe the functions of the parts of the brain
- describe the peripheral nervous system
- explain the reflex action

Bellringer
Write the following on the chalkboard for students to work on while attendance is being taken: *Make a list of the things you do that do not involve the use of the nervous system.*

Introducing the Lesson
Refer to the Bellringer. Ask volunteers to share their responses. Stress that there is absolutely nothing that they do that does not involve the nervous system. Ask students to think about many actions taking place inside their bodies right now, such as breathing, seeing, heartbeat, etc. Tell students that this lesson will explain how all body activities are controlled by the nervous system.

DID YOU KNOW?
- Room No. 19 of the Brain Research Institute in Moscow holds the brain tissue of many famous dead Soviet figures—from politicians to poets. Included in the collection are brain-tissue slides of long-dead leaders Lenin and Stalin, poet Mayakovsky, and scientist Pavlov. For more than 60 years, such slides have been examined at the Institute to see if there are structural differences between the brains of those considered famous or great and less prominent people. Their findings? There are no such verifiable differences.

Resources for Lesson 1

- **Transparencies** 48 and 49
- **Guided Reading** Act 30
- **Workbook** Vocabulary Act 30
- **Reteaching** Activity 30
- **Lesson 1 Quiz**
- **Performance Assessment** Activity 12

Science and Technology Videodisc
Human Biology, Side 1
Ch 19 PETT Scanner

Ch 20 Panic Disorder and Brain Activity

Building Vocabulary

- Instruct students to assign points as follows to each category of terms in the vocabulary list:

  4 points for each term representing a group of parts working together;

  3 points for each term that is a part of the body;

  2 points for each term that relates to transmitting or receiving messages or signals. Have students total the points in each group.

- Ask students to complete *Workbook Vocabulary Activity 30.*

Teach

Guided Practice

L1 USING BODY SYSTEMS TRANSPARENCY 48. Refer to the Teaching Transparencies Binder.

L2 DEMONSTRATION. Using a skeletal model, have students locate cervical (neck), thoracic (chest), and lumbar (lower back) vertebrae that are the origin of nerves. Compare the sizes of these bones. Are larger nerves associated with larger vertebrae?

LD EXPLANATION. Try to narrow down the information you expect LD students to learn. Provide easy-to-follow diagrams of the components of the nervous system.

L2 EXPLANATION. Explain to students what causes us to feel hungry, sick, etc. Sensory receptors receive messages about digestion, hunger, illness, etc. All of these receptors send messages toward the brain or spinal cord.

L2 DISCUSSION. Have students describe the spectrum of sensations that produce pleasure or pain from the receptor neurons. (Examples: music and shrill sirens, caress and pinch, aroma of fresh bread and smell of a skunk.)

The central nervous system consists of the brain and spinal cord. The peripheral nervous system consists of the cranial and spinal nerves that branch from the brain and spinal cord.

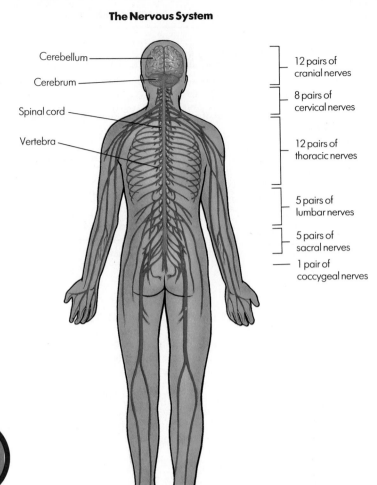

The Nervous System

Cerebellum

Cerebrum

Spinal cord

Vertebra

12 pairs of cranial nerves

8 pairs of cervical nerves

12 pairs of thoracic nerves

5 pairs of lumbar nerves

5 pairs of sacral nerves

1 pair of coccygeal nerves

FINDING HELP

Cerebral refers to the brain, and *palsy* to a disorder of movement or posture. Cerebral palsy is neither progressive nor communicable. It also is not curable in the accepted sense, although training and therapy can help.

To learn about cerebral palsy services in your community, contact your doctor; your local United Cerebral Palsy affiliate; or write to United Cerebral Palsy Associations, Inc. 66 East 34th Street New York, NY 10016

Structure of the Nervous System

Two main divisions of the nervous system are the central nervous system (CNS) and the peripheral nervous system (PNS). The CNS includes the brain and spinal cord. The PNS connects the CNS to other parts of the body by 43 pairs of nerves that extend from the CNS. The PNS consists of nerves and ganglia, which are groups of nerve cell bodies.

Structure of Neurons

Neurons are the structural parts of both the CNS and the PNS. Neurons have three basic parts: a cell body, dendrites, and an axon.

The Cell Body. The cell body has a nucleus and is the center for receiving and sending nerve impulses. It also is the center for making proteins

222 CHAPTER 12 THE NERVOUS AND ENDOCRINE SYSTEMS

Additional Information

Sensory Neurons. Sensory neurons in the cerebrum allow a sensation—seeing, hearing, feeling, smelling, or tasting something—to trigger the re-creation of a past experience.

Sensory neurons located in muscles are triggering mechanisms for the stretch reflex. The body reacts to overstretching with muscle contractions and pain.

Sensory neurons in the walls of the stomach send us "hunger pangs" when the stomach is empty and ready to be filled.

Sensory neurons in the esophagus and pharynx signal the gag reflex when contacted, causing the stomach to contract and regurgitate its contents.

and using energy for the maintenance and growth of the neuron. The shape of the cell body varies according to the type of neuron. Some sensory neurons are round, those on the surface of the brain are diamond-shaped, and motor neurons are star-shaped.

Dendrites. Dendrites are threadlike extensions of the cell body. They are usually short and have many branches. Dendrites receive and carry impulses toward the cell body. Some neurons may have many dendrites, others may have only one dendrite, while some may have no dendrites.

Axons. Each neuron has only one axon. An axon is a threadlike extension of a cell body that carries impulses away from the cell body. An axon of one neuron may have enough branches to make contact with as many as 1000 other neurons. Axons vary in length from a few millimeters to more than 1 meter. In the PNS, however, axons are longer. Some axons extend from the spinal cord to muscles in the fingers and are as long as 40 inches (102 cm).

Many axons in the PNS have a whitish coating or sheath of fatty material, called myelin, around them. The myelin sheath insulates the nerve fiber and speeds the transmission of impulses.

The Nerve Impulse

Neurons are unique body cells. Unlike other cells, neurons cannot replace themselves. Damage to neurons is permanent. Neurons are unique also in that they are very sensitive and can react to even the slightest stimulus. Once excited, a neuron can rapidly send an electrical charge from the point of stimulation to the brain or spinal cord. This charge can travel as fast as 248 miles (399 km) per hour!

A nerve impulse is an electrical charge that races along neurons from the point of stimulation to the brain or spinal cord. The more myelin a neuron has, the faster the impulse travels. Suppose you are walking home with a friend. At an intersection the "Don't Walk" sign lights up. You stop, wait for the "Walk" sign, and proceed. But during this time,

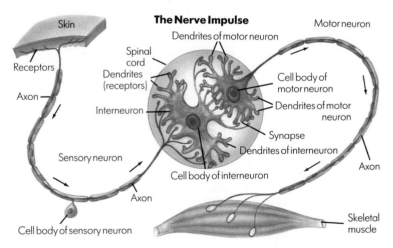

The Nerve Impulse

Skin
Receptors
Axon
Spinal cord
Dendrites (receptors)
Interneuron
Sensory neuron
Axon
Cell body of sensory neuron
Cell body of interneuron
Dendrites of motor neuron
Motor neuron
Cell body of motor neuron
Dendrites of motor neuron
Synapse
Dendrites of interneuron
Axon
Skeletal muscle

A nerve impulse travels from the receptors of a sensory neuron across an interneuron to a motor neuron to muscle fibers.

THE NERVOUS SYSTEM **223**

Additional Information

Body System Regulation and Communication. "Slow and easy" could describe regulation by chemicals in animals, because a time lag of seconds to days may occur between the release of a chemical messenger and a response by cells sensitive to it.

Nervous systems, by contrast, act far more rapidly and often even more specifically, usually transmitting information about events in one part of an animal instantaneously to other body parts. While chemical control of some kind operates in all living things, nervous systems are found only in animals.

In both systems of communication and regulation, the structure or process being controlled may be away from the control center.

Culturally Speaking

Acupuncture

Acupuncture is the ancient Chinese method of treating disease and relieving pain through the use of fine, sharp needles inserted into specific body points then gently twirled.

Doctors around the world have experimented with this method to treat problems such as migraines, asthma, arthritis, and weight gain. Acupuncture also has been used to prevent pain during surgery. Scientists speculate that acupuncture increases the brain's output of natural painkillers or that it sends signals in the nervous system that interrupt pain messages headed for the brain.

you never stop talking with your friend. It sounds simple enough, but the event of stopping and waiting involves millions of nerve cells.

Sensory receptors in your eyes are stimulated by the signal light and translate the stimulation into a nerve impulse. Now each sensory neuron begins a series of electrical and chemical changes to transmit the impulse. The impulse moves from the receptor ends of dendrites to the cell body and along the axon to the dendrites of another sensory neuron. The impulse has to cross a very narrow gap called a synapse, the junction between the axon end of one neuron and the dendrite of another neuron.

The impulse is transmitted in this way to your spinal cord, where interneurons carry the impulse to your brain. Your brain translates the message and sends an impulse back through motor neurons to muscles in your legs. You stop at the corner. The process repeats itself when the sensory receptors in your eyes receive the stimulus of the "Walk" light. This time you start walking across the street.

The Central Nervous System

In one way or another, every body function involves the central nervous system (CNS). Remember, the spinal cord and brain make up this control center, which is one of the two divisions of the nervous system.

The Spinal Cord

The spinal cord is about the same diameter as your index finger, is less than 2 feet (61 cm) long, and contains about 10 billion nerve cells. The spinal cord is protected by the vertebrae, the bones that make up your spine. It is also protected by cerebrospinal fluid that acts like a shock absorber, and by three layers of connective membranes called the spinal meninges.

The Brain

Cerebrum
Midbrain
Pons
Medulla oblongata
Cerebellum
Spinal cord

Your brain has three main divisions: the cerebrum, the cerebellum, and the brain stem.

Additional Information

The Brain. Two pioneers in the study of aphasias, the disorders of speech, have contributed greatly to our knowledge.

Paul Broca, a 19th-century Frenchman, observed that when a certain part of the left side of the brain (now called "Broca's area") was damaged, an individual's speech was slow and labored, even though

his or her understanding of language was complete. Broca's area apparently coordinates the muscles that produce speech.

Another student of aphasia, named Wernicke, discovered the region of the brain (now called "Wernicke's area") crucial for comprehending spoken language.

The Brain

The brain is the largest, most complex part of the nervous system. Your brain helps you receive messages—think, remember, and reason—and coordinates your muscular movement. Your brain is involved in your emotions and everything you sense. It weighs about 3 pounds (1.4 kg) and contains almost 100 billion neurons. At birth, the brain weighs about 1 pound (0.5 kg). In humans, it reaches full size by age 6.

The brain is supplied with the food and oxygen it needs from a vast network of blood vessels. Although the brain makes up only about 2 percent of your total body weight, it uses 20 percent of the oxygen you inhale. The brain can be without oxygen for only 4 to 5 minutes before suffering serious and irreversible damage.

The brain is protected by eight cranial bones which form the skull, and three layers of membranes called cranial meninges. Cerebrospinal fluid between the meninges cushions the brain from injury.

The work of the brain is similar to that of a computer or a chemical factory. Brain cells produce electrical signals and send them along pathways called circuits. These circuits receive, process, store, and retrieve information much like a computer does. Unlike a computer, however, the brain creates its electrical signals by chemical means. The proper functioning of the brain depends on the many complicated chemical substances that brain cells produce.

The brain has three main divisions: the cerebrum, the cerebellum, and the brain stem.

The Cerebrum. The largest, most complex part of the brain is the **cerebrum.** The cerebrum is divided into two identical halves called the cerebral hemispheres. The right hemisphere controls muscular activity and receives sensory input from the left half of the body. The left hemisphere controls the muscular activity and receives sensory input from the right half of the body.

Each hemisphere has four lobes. Each lobe is named after the bone in the skull that protects it:

- The frontal lobe controls voluntary movements, motivation, mood, and aggression.
- The parietal lobe is involved with a wide variety of sensory information—heat, cold, pain, touch, and body position in space.
- The occipital lobe contains the sense of vision.
- The temporal lobe contains the senses of hearing and smell, as well as memory, thought, and judgment.

L1 CLASS ACTIVITY. Have students compare the function of a telephone network to the nervous system. (Both carry messages, have control centers.)

L2 CLASS ACTIVITY. Ask students to describe how an EEG is analogous to an EKG that is taken for the heart. (An EEG shows activity in the brain; an EKG shows activity in the heart.)

L2 DISCUSSION. Ask students to discuss how an understanding of the nervous system relates to decision making.

L1 CLASS ACTIVITY. Have students trace the drawing of the brain. Then have them use colored pencils or crayons to shade the cerebrum blue, the cerebellum red, and the brain stem yellow.

L1 CLASS ACTIVITY. Have students write paragraphs or poems describing what life might be like if they lost one of the five senses.

L2 DISCUSSION. Ask students to give examples of how a person with poor vision can compensate with other sense organs.

L2 CLASS ACTIVITY. Ask students to determine what happens when the sense of smell is impaired. Have students pinch their noses. Then give each student something to eat or taste. Ask students to share with the class a description of what it is like to eat something, yet not be able to smell it.

KEEPING FIT

Moving Your Body, Moving Your Mind

When you sit in the same position for a long time, a main nerve in your leg gets squeezed and stops sending information to your brain. When this happens, you may feel "pins and needles," and your foot may seem "asleep." If you move around, you will quickly take the pressure off the nerve and "wake up" your leg and foot.

Getting up and changing position may be good for your mind, too. By standing, you increase circulation. One new study suggests, in fact, that just standing up periodically, will help improve your thinking. Taking deep breaths will increase the oxygen supply to your brain, increasing your mental capacity.

Across the Curriculum

Psychology. Ask a psychology teacher in your school to help students research the right-brain and left-brain theory. Have students make a notebook about the theory. Include articles from newspapers or magazines relating to the theory.

Ask each student to determine whether he or she is right-brain or left-brain dominant. Have students provide an assessment from their research to determine right- or left-brain dominance.

Ask students to include information relating to the theory that "we can all draw." What would it imply for those who can't draw? (They have not developed that part of the brain.)

226 CHAPTER 12 THE NERVOUS AND ENDOCRINE SYSTEMS

L2 EXPLANATION. Much interesting research has been done on right- and left-brain thinking. The two frontal hemispheres of the cortex function in separate, almost opposite, ways. The right hemisphere is described as playful, spontaneous, flexible, creative, intuitive, irrational, illogical. The left side is characterized as logical, rational, knowledge-seeking, factual, serious, rules and order. We all function using both hemispheres, but scientists believe we each have a dominant side.

L2 CLASS ACTIVITY. Using a cranial cross-section model, ask the class to identify the parts of the cerebrum. How does one distinguish the cerebrum from other parts of the brain? What is special about its size? shape? color? texture?

L2 CLASS ACTIVITY. Divide the class into two teams. Provide one team with activities performed by the lobes of the cerebrum. Have the other team identify the proper lobe for each activity. Examples: speech (frontal), sight (occipital), pain (parietal), smell (temporal).

L2 DISCUSSION. Explain to students that they have touched something hot. Discuss the pathway of a nerve impulse from the fingers to the central nervous system and back in a reflex action that draws the fingers away from the hot object.

L2 CLASS ACTIVITY. Tell students that the best demonstration of the nervous system is through actions called reflexes. Then have them work in pairs to demonstrate the patellar (knee-jerk) reflex. One student sits in a chair and, in a relaxed way, crosses his or her legs. The other student uses the side of an extended hand to strike the soft area just under the kneecap of the first student's crossed leg. Then, have students switch roles. Have students discuss the reflex, describing what happened and what caused it. Have students get into groups and make a poster that demonstrates other reflex actions. Draw and explain the reflex arc. Display it in the class.

Each hemisphere of the brain is divided into four lobes. Each lobe is involved in different functions.

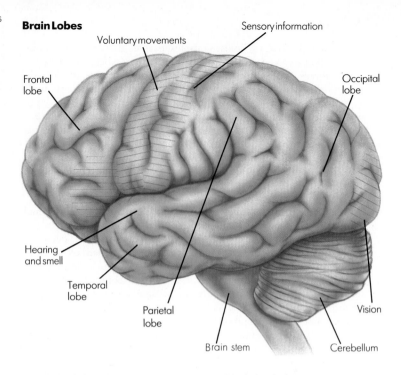

Brain Lobes

Voluntary movements
Sensory information
Frontal lobe
Occipital lobe
Hearing and smell
Temporal lobe
Parietal lobe
Brain stem
Cerebellum
Vision

The Cerebellum. The cerebellum is the second largest portion of the brain. It is situated beneath the occipital lobes of the cerebrum. The cerebellum is also divided into two hemispheres.

The **cerebellum** functions as a center for the coordination of skeletal muscle movement. It receives impulses from the balancing centers of the inner ear, from muscles, and from the motor areas of the brain. The cerebrum determines what movements the body will make, initiating the nerve impulses that activate the muscles. The cerebellum coordinates these nerve impulses to ensure accurate, controlled, and rapid movements. The cerebellum also maintains equilibrium during movements as it receives information from the sensory organs.

The Brain Stem. The **brain stem** connects the spinal cord to the brain. The brain stem includes the medulla oblongata, pons, midbrain, and interbrain.

KEEPING FIT

Headaches

There are many different kinds of headaches, including tension headaches that throb and occur on both sides of the head; migraines, that may cause severe pain and nausea; and cluster headaches, that may cause pain around or behind one eye. According to one recent survey, the following major causes of headaches were identified: sinus infections, job or school stress, eye problems, weather, allergies, and the use of certain foods.

Getting too much sleep may also result in headaches.

If you suffer from frequent headaches, try to determine what triggers them. If they are very frequent, very intense, or last over long periods, consult a physician.

Overcoming Misconceptions

Biased Research. At the turn of this century, the noted biostatistician, Samuel Morton, collected human skulls representing various races. He filled each skull with sand and then weighed the sand—thus obtaining an estimate of "endocranial volume," an approximate indicator of brain size. By Morton's calculations, Europeans and Euro-Americans had larger brains, on average, than those of any other race.

A re-study of Morton's collection by Stephen Gould, using similar methods, revealed no significant differences in skull size among any of the racial groups. Gould's conclusion? Morton's racial misconceptions biased his research—he found what he expected to find.

Overcoming The Odds

Eric Meneely is 21. School, sports, friends, and playing piano were all important to him. Then, he almost lost it all.

Eric was on his motorcycle. Distracted by some girls playing soccer, he didn't see that the car in front of him had stopped. He says, "I swerved and my head went crashing through his back windshield, then I rolled over the roof of the car, and my feet broke the front windshield. Luckily, I was wearing a helmet. If I hadn't been, I'd have been all over the road. It was all my fault.

"Miraculously, I had few external injuries. However, I had a brain injury. I apparently hit the right side of my brain. That affected what the left side of my body can do. Also, my right eye has a palsy of the optic nerve. This makes my eye go off to the right." Doctors have told him that surgery can repair his eye problem. However, there are other enduring problems. Eric says, "I slur my speech a little bit. And I can't drive until my eye is fully functioning again.

"I went against my parents'

wishes when I bought the motorcycle. They were quite upset, but I was on the big teen immortal kick. I thought accidents happened only to other people."

Meneely says that after the

accident, his self-esteem suffered. "I felt like such a fool for buying the motorcycle and going against my parents. And I felt incompetent." These days, however, he is rebuilding his confidence by learning to compensate. "The memory is a little shaky, so I either write things down or tell one of my friends to remember for me.

My running is shaky, too, but I do it. As for playing the piano, I can't explain how I compensate, but I do."

Eric is back in college now. He is studying to become a physical therapist to help people who have injuries like his own. "It's not the way I would have chosen to get on-the-job training," he says, "but my own therapy and rehabilitation have served just that way. Because of what I've been through, I think I'll have greater insight and a more in-depth understanding of what patients go through. I think that most of what we worry about is trivial. You don't realize how important some things are until you almost lose it all."

1. How does Eric plan to put his near-tragic experience to good use in the future?
2. How did the accident affect Eric's self-esteem?
3. What concerns do you have right now that deeply upset you and hurt your self-esteem but might actually prove to be rather trivial?
4. If there are things about yourself that eat away at your self-esteem, what changes can you make? How can you compensate, as Eric learned to do?

■ **Explanation.** Explain why the left side of Eric's body was affected by the injury on the right side of his head. (The two hemispheres of the brain house the nervous system controls for the opposite two halves of the body.)

■ **Discussion** What helped to protect Eric's brain from injury? (In addition to his helmet, Eric's brain was protected by eight cranial bones, which are relatively thick and hard, as well as by spinal fluid between the membranes covering the brain.)

■ **Answers**
1. To become a physical therapist and help other injured people.
2. It was lowered because he felt foolish and incompetent.
3. To gain perspective, students should compare a major loss, like the death of a parent, with their current concerns.
4. Learn to identify and exploit your strengths.

Additional Information

Brain Size. Many people believe that the most significant human characteristic is our big brain—larger for our body size than the brain of virtually any other animal.

Our big brain evolved relatively recently. Our most distant ancestors of 4 million

years ago, the Australopithecines, had chimp-sized brains. Our direct ancestor of less than 1 million years ago still had a brain little more than half the size of the modern human brain.

DID YOU KNOW?

- People who are right-handed are usually left-brain dominant while people who are left-handed may be right-brain dominant or have mixed dominance.
- People who are left-brain dominant may be more logical and verbal than their right-brain counterparts.
- People who are right-brain dominant may be gifted mathematically, musically, or artistically.
- One in ten persons is left-handed, and the tendency may be inherited.

The medulla is the lowest part of the brain stem. It contains control centers that regulate heartbeat, breathing, and the diameter of the blood vessels. The control centers for vomiting, sneezing, swallowing, hiccuping, and coughing are also located in the medulla.

Just above the medulla, the brain stem enlarges to form the pons. The pons serves mainly as a pathway for nerve impulses passing to and from the cerebrum. It contains nerve fibers that link the cerebrum and the cerebellum. The pons also plays a part in controlling respiration.

The shortest part of the brain stem is the midbrain, which lies just above the pons. The midbrain connects the brain stem with the fibers from the cerebellum. Its nerve centers help control movements of the eyes and the size of the pupils.

Located above the midbrain is the interbrain. The interbrain consists of two parts—the thalamus and hypothalamus. The thalamus is like a relay station for incoming sensory impulses, such as vision. The thalamus also influences mood and movement related to fear or anger.

The hypothalamus has nerve centers that control different body processes and keep body conditions balanced. For example, nerve centers in the hypothalamus regulate body temperature and food and water intake. Neurons from the hypothalamus stimulate the pituitary gland to release hormones that control many body functions, such as metabolism and sexual development. The hypothalamus also plays an important role in emotional responses.

The Peripheral Nervous System

Peripheral means "located away from the center." The peripheral nervous system (PNS) consists of nerves that branch from the central nervous system. The PNS carries messages between the CNS and the rest of the body. The PNS consists of 12 pairs of cranial nerves that branch from the brain, and 31 pairs of nerves that branch from the spinal cord. The PNS is composed of two subdivisions—the somatic nervous system and the autonomic nervous system:

- The somatic system includes cranial and spinal nerves that transmit impulses from the CNS to skeletal muscles. This involves voluntary responses—responses under your control.
- The autonomic system includes nerve fibers that connect the CNS to smooth muscles, such as the intestines, to the heart, and to glands. This system produces responses in involuntary muscles and glands.

K E E P I N G   F I T

The Headache/Food Connection

If you have frequent headaches, try to determine if your headaches are induced, or brought on, by specific foods. Try eliminating these foods from your diet one at a time. The following are common headache triggers: seafood, citrus fruits, milk, caffeine, fatty food, and onions.

Foods that contain MSG, (which is often found in processed food), nitrites, (which are used in lunchmeat), and the amino acid tyramine, (which is found in chocolate), are also common headache triggers. Other foods that contain tyramine include sour cream, yogurt, and vinegar.

Additional Information

Brain Collection. The Armed Forces Institute of Pathology in Washington, D.C., houses one of the most interesting collections of neuroanatomical data in the world. It's the Yakovlev Collection—an immense museum of human brains (close to 1,800 in all), which have been dried, thin-sliced, and mounted on glass slides. Each brain occupies about 4,000 slides, and the entire weight of glass mounts is 35 tons!

The oldest brain in the collection belonged to a 98-year-old man, the youngest to a 6-week-old fetus. The largest brain belonged to a housepainter, weighing in at an impressive 4.2 pounds (the average is about 3 pounds). Normal brains as well as brains of individuals with a variety of neurological disorders are included.

The Autonomic Nervous System (ANS)

The autonomic nervous system's constant regulation of internal body processes enables the body to maintain a stable internal environment. There are two divisions of the ANS—the sympathetic division and the parasympathetic division. These two divisions affect the same organs, but basically produce opposing effects.

The Sympathetic Division. The sympathetic division responds to the body's needs during increased activities and in emergencies. For example, when you are excited, the sympathetic division would cause your heart to beat faster and your breathing rate to increase. Sympathetic nerves lead to all of the vital organs and glands, including the liver, heart, kidneys, pancreas, stomach, and salivary, sweat, and adrenal glands.

The Parasympathetic Division. The parasympathetic division generally opposes the actions of the sympathetic system by slowing body functions. It slows down the heartbeat, opens blood vessels, and lowers blood pressure. The balance of activity between the sympathetic and parasympathetic divisions is controlled by the CNS.

ACTION OF THE AUTONOMIC NERVOUS SYSTEM

Organ	Action of Sympathetic Division	Action of Parasympathetic Division
Heart	Increases heartbeat	Slows heartbeat
Arteries	Raises blood pressure by constricting arteries	Lowers blood pressure by dilating arteries
Stomach and intestines	Slows movement	Speeds up movement
Sweat glands	Decreases activity Increases secretion of sweat	Increases activity Decreases secretion of sweat
Muscles of iris	Dilates pupil	Constricts pupil

Reflex Action

A **reflex** is a spontaneous response of the body to a stimulus. It occurs automatically, without conscious thought or effort. You cannot stop or keep some reflex actions from happening. In what ways do these reflex actions serve as protection?

L1 WRITING. Assign each student a body part, such as heart, lungs, intestines. Then ask each student to write a paragraph describing the functions of the sympathetic and parasympathetic nervous systems on this organ. What are the physical signs that show the effects of the nervous system response?

L2 RESEARCH. Divide the class into groups. Assign each group a type of drug that affects the nervous system such as alcohol, codeine, caffeine, or tobacco. Ask students to research how each drug affects the nervous system. Have each group make a chart or poster and share it with the class.

L3 RESEARCH. Research medicines that can reduce or eliminate pain. Explain how these medicines affect the release of cholinesterase in the transmission of the signal of pain to the central nervous system.

L1 USING THE LESSON RESOURCES. For additional student activities, refer to the lesson resources on page 221.

Additional Information

The PNS. Did you know you are using all five senses when you eat popcorn? Share this sequence of events with students. First you see the popcorn, then you touch it as you put it in your mouth, you smell the popcorn, you taste the popcorn as you eat it, and hear the crunch of the popcorn as you chew it. You are able to experience all of these senses because of special receptor neurons. These neurons receive the information and then transmit it through sensory neurons to your spinal cord and brain. Your brain then responds and sends the impulses on motor neurons, allowing you to respond to the initial information.

Check for Understanding

- Assign and discuss the lesson review. Encourage LD students to focus on question 2.

Evaluate

- Administer, grade, and discuss the *Lesson 1 Quiz*.

Reteach

- Ask students to find facts in this lesson that support the following generalization: *The nervous system is the body's communication network and control center.* Ask them to write lists of the facts they find.
- Ask students to complete *Reteaching Activity 30*.

Enrich

- Have students research phantom limbs or phantom pain. What is it? How do scientists explain this unusual sensory phenomenon? Ask students to summarize their findings in written reports.

Close

Ask students to state the most important concepts learned in this lesson. Ask students to discuss why a computer can never replace the human brain.

DID YOU KNOW?

- Most of your brain's weight is made up of the cerebrum, the part of the brain associated with thinking and memory.
- The human skull is made up of 29 different sections.
- Among invertebrates, or animals without backbones, the octopus has the most highly developed brain.

The knee-jerk reflex is an example of a simple reflex. Tapping a ligament just below the kneecap initiates the reflex.

A simple reflex, such as occurs when the doctor taps the ligament below your knee, involves the interaction of only two neurons—a sensory neuron and a motor neuron. The doctor's tap is the stimulus that initiates the nerve impulse. The impulse travels along sensory neurons to the spinal cord. Here the impulse moves across the synapse to the dendrites of a motor neuron. The impulse travels back to leg muscles, causing them to contract and the knee to jerk.

In other reflexes, when a receptor is stimulated (for example, when your hand touches a hot stove), the axon of the sensory neuron makes contact with a connecting neuron in the spinal cord. This neuron, in turn, contacts a motor neuron that sends an impulse down its axon to the muscles. The muscles respond by pulling the hand away from the stove. All of this happens in a split second, even before pain is perceived by the brain.

The nerve chain of sensory and motor neurons involved in the reflex action is called a reflex arc.

LESSON 1 REVIEW

Reviewing Facts and Vocabulary

1. Describe the three types of neurons.
2. What is the difference between the sympathetic and parasympathetic divisions of the autonomic nervous system?

Thinking Critically

3. **Analysis.** How does the central nervous system compare with the peripheral nervous system?

Applying Health Knowledge

4. Make a diagram to show the parts of the brain, listing examples of what each part controls.
5. Test your reflex reaction. Have someone hold a dollar bill above your thumb and index finger. As he or she releases the dollar, trap it using only your thumb and index finger, without moving your arm. Mark where you caught the dollar. Repeat several times. Chart your reaction times.

230 CHAPTER 12 THE NERVOUS AND ENDOCRINE SYSTEMS

Answers to Lesson 1 Review

1. The three types of neurons are sensory neurons, interneurons, and motor neurons. Descriptions are given on page 221.
2. The sympathetic division responds to the body's need during increased activities and emergencies. The parasympathetic division opposes the sympathetic by slowing body functions.
3. The PNS carries messages from the CNS to the rest of the body. These two sys-

tems receive messages, relay and interpret the messages, and send back responses.
4. Diagrams should include: cerebrum—frontal, parietal, occipital, and temporal lobes; cerebellum; brain stem—medulla oblongata, pons, midbrain, and interbrain. For examples of what each part controls, see pages 225 to 226 and 228.
5. Charts will vary.

PROBLEMS AND CARE OF THE NERVOUS SYSTEM

The normal functioning of the nervous system can be disturbed in a number of ways. An infectious disease, such as syphilis, can attack and destroy nerve tissue in the brain or spinal column. Accidents can damage or destroy nerve tissue. Illegal drug use, including alcohol use, can destroy brain cells and lead to a variety of nervous system disorders.

In general, problems with the nervous system can be divided into four categories: injuries, degenerative diseases, communicable diseases, and genetic disorders.

Injuries

Each year many young people suffer brain injuries resulting from motor vehicle accidents, falls, sports, and physical abuse. In addition, many people suffer spinal cord injuries.

Head Injuries

The brain is protected by the skull bones and the fluid that surrounds it. However, any direct blow to the head can lead to possible brain injury. A person may experience a concussion, a temporary disturbance of the brain's ability to function. A concussion is caused by a sharp blow to the head. Concussions are the most common and mildest kind of brain injury.

Concussions usually result in a temporary loss of consciousness and a memory loss of events just before and after the injury. Mild concussions, however, may not result in either loss of consciousness or memory loss.

A more serious injury to the brain is a contusion. A contusion of the brain is a bruise caused by a head injury. This bruising may cause swelling of the brain. In the brain stem, contusions produce severe neurological damage. A severe contusion could result in a coma, a state of unconsciousness resulting from an injury to the brain. A coma indicates that there has been serious damage to nerve tissue.

Depending on which brain cells are damaged, and how serious the injury is, the person will lose the ability to perform certain functions. If the cerebellum is damaged, a person may suffer from lack of balance or lack of muscular coordination. Damage to the brain stem could result in a loss of the sense of pain or in loss of the body's ability to regulate temperature.

Spinal Cord Injuries

The spinal cord is surrounded by protective membranes, shock-absorbing fluid, and the backbone. These defenses protect it from the

PROBLEMS AND CARE OF THE NERVOUS SYSTEM **231**

LESSON 2 FOCUS

TERMS TO USE
- Parkinson's disease
- Multiple sclerosis
- Meningitis
- Poliomyelitis
- Rabies
- Down syndrome
- Epilepsy
- Cerebral palsy

CONCEPTS TO LEARN
- The nervous system can be damaged by injuries, degenerative diseases, communicable diseases, and genetic disorders.
- Any damage to the nervous system disturbs the impulse pathways to and from the brain and spinal cord.
- By following basic rules of safety, many head and spinal injuries can be prevented.

ATTITUDES AND BEHAVIORS TO EVALUATE
- Self-Inventory, page 244.
- Building Decision-Making Skills, page 245.

Focus

Lesson Objectives
After studying this lesson, students should be able to:
- identify symptoms, causes, and treatment of various injuries, diseases, and disorders of the nervous system
- discuss care of the nervous system

Bellringer
Write the following on the chalkboard for students to work on while attendance is being taken: *Write an explanation of the differences in these terms:* degenerative, infectious, genetic. (*Degenerative* refers to a breakdown or deterioration of the structure of an organ or tissue; *infectious* involves pathogens, or germs; and *genetic* involves inherited characteristics passed on through genes.)

Introducing the Lesson
Refer to the Bellringer. Ask volunteers to share their responses. Correct any misconceptions. Explain to students that this lesson will provide information on degenerative, infectious, and genetic diseases or disorders that relate to the nervous system. In addition, the lesson will address injuries to the nervous system and how to protect the nervous system.

DID YOU KNOW?

- Nearly 80 percent of all bicycle fatalities are due to head injuries.
- Since the 1960s, it's been required by law that all newborns be tested for phenylketonuria. This has prevented thousands of cases of mental retardation.

Resources for Lesson 2

- **Transparencies** 48 and 49
- **Guided Reading** Act 31
- **Workbook** Voc Act 31
- **Reteaching** Activity 31
- **Lesson 2 Quiz**

Science and Technology Videodisc
Human Biology, Side 1
Ch 18 Detecting the Body's Magnetic Fields

Ch 21 Brain By-Pass Surgery

Human Biology, Side 2
Ch 20 Tricycle for the Handicapped

- Ask each student to divide a sheet of paper into four sections. Label one section "injuries," another "degenerative," another "infectious," and another "genetic." Have students write under each section the vocabulary words from this lesson that belong there. Have them also explain why they placed the words as they did.
- Ask students to complete *Workbook Vocabulary Activity 31.*

Teach

Guided Practice

LD CLASS ACTIVITY. Provide a list of the many afflictions of the nervous system with brief descriptions of each for LD students to follow during class discussion.

L2 CLASS ACTIVITY. Have students list three ways to avoid injuries to the nervous system. (Explain how the use of alcohol and other drugs can affect the nervous system.)

L2 CLASS ACTIVITY. Cranial and spinal injuries can be fatal. Ask the class to prepare a bulletin-board display to promote safe practices to protect the brain and spinal cord. (Examples: seat belts, helmets, good posture, muscle-strengthening exercises.)

L2 DISCUSSION. Cartilage cushions the space between bones. When it is injured, bone rubs against bone, causing pain. Have students discuss ways in which spinal cord alignment can be protected and preserved. Be sure to emphasize good posture.

L2 CLASS ACTIVITY. Ask students if they have known anyone or seen a movie or a TV program about someone who suffered brain damage. Discuss some of the symptoms the victims might exhibit. (Victims might be paralyzed or comatose.)

L2 EXPLANATION. Stress that cranial symptoms—dizziness, headache, double vision—are indicators of problems in the central nervous system. These symptoms should be reported promptly to a doctor.

The consequences of a spinal injury will depend on the amount of damage to the spinal cord.

bumps and falls common in everyday life. However, they often are not enough to protect it from more serious accidents.

One of the most common injuries to the spinal cord is a pinched nerve. This occurs when one of the cartilage disks that separates the vertebrae moves slightly as a result of a sudden jerking of the body, a blow, a fall, or a jolt. The disk can press on or pinch a nerve, causing discomfort and often great pain.

Remember that all messages to and from the brain go through the spinal cord. Injury to the spinal cord means that these messages cannot get through. Depending on the severity and location of the injury, this breakdown in communication could be mild or serious, or could result in death. An injury anywhere on the spinal cord could cause paralysis.

In general, injury to the upper part of the cord causes more extensive damage. An injury at the neck level, for example, may cause paralysis in both the arms and the legs. Someone with such an injury is called a quadriplegic. Injury at the chest level or lower affects the legs and lower body. Someone whose lower body is paralyzed is called a paraplegic.

Some spinal injuries require people to wear a neck collar or a special corset to support the back. Other injuries require traction, in which weights are used to balance out parts of the spinal cord, to give relief from pain. Surgery is the last resort to correct spinal injuries.

HEALTH UPDATE

LOOKING AT TECHNOLOGY

New Hope and Better Care

There are many new and exciting medical and technological advances that may offer new hope and better care to people with brain and spinal cord diseases and injuries.

MAPPING THE BRAIN. Through the BrainMap Project, researchers at Johns Hopkins University in Maryland and the Research Imaging Center at the University of Texas Health Science Center in San Antonio are trying to make the first comprehensive map of the brain. Using computers and other imaging techniques, they are compiling data about the brain that may be used by doctors and researchers around the world. Very soon, the project will result in a comprehensive system of information about the brain. A doctor who has a patient with a rare or difficult brain problem can feed information about that problem into the system and learn the latest data and research regarding it.

COMPUTERIZED LEG BRACES. Researchers at the Massachusetts Institute of Technology are studying special computerized leg braces that may prove helpful to people such as those with multiple sclerosis.

STAND-UP WHEELCHAIRS. Newly designed wheelchairs called "standing wheelchairs" are now being made available. They allow a paralyzed person to stand up and say hello face-to-face, reach for things in high places, or even dance cheek-to-cheek.

Additional Information

The Spinal Cord. Epidural anesthesia, sometimes called a spinal block, is used for surgery and in childbirth. The person is awake during the procedure and will feel no pain in the area. The anesthesia is injected into the spine between vertebrae. The anesthesia numbs all spinal sensation of pain below the point of injection. This procedure is preferred in childbirth when the patient does desire an anesthesia during the final hours of labor.

Spinal disorders that occur in the alignment of the vertebrae (scoliosis, kyphosis, lordosis, etc.) can create pressure on the spinal cord and on peripheral nerves extending to limbs and organs of the body.

Degenerative Diseases

Degeneration means a breakdown or deterioration of function or structure. Three common degenerative diseases of the nervous system are Parkinson's disease, multiple sclerosis, and Alzheimer's disease.

Parkinson's Disease

Parkinson's disease, first described in the 1800s by James Parkinson, usually affects people between the ages of 50 and 75.

The exact cause of Parkinson's disease is not known. **Parkinson's disease** is a disease that interferes with the transmission of nerve impulses from the motor areas of the brain. It is a progressive disorder, meaning that it gradually involves more and more nerves. The result is uncoordinated muscular movement. This disease is characterized by slow voluntary movements and tremors.

With the discovery of new medicines, the effects of this disease have been dramatically controlled in many patients.

Multiple Sclerosis

Multiple sclerosis (MS) is the progressive destruction of the myelin sheath that surrounds nerve fibers. This coating is gradually destroyed and scar tissue forms in its place. Neurons become permanently damaged. The scar tissue interferes with the ability of the nerve fibers to send impulses. The impulses may even be blocked completely. Voluntary control of muscles gradually decreases.

The effects of MS depend upon which nerves are involved. MS is quite unpredictable. Symptoms may occur and disappear in random patterns. They may occur once and never reappear. There is no known cure for MS. Therapy is directed at managing the complications. Many patients are able to lead full, productive lives.

Alzheimer's Disease

Alzheimer's disease was first described by Alois Alzheimer in the early 1900s. It is a progressive, degenerative disease that generally affects people over 60 years old. About $2^1/_2$ million Americans suffer from this disease. It is the fourth leading cause of death in adults, after heart disease, cancer, and stroke.

FINDING HELP

You can get more information about disorders of the nervous system by contacting the following organizations:

- Alzheimer's Association
  70 East Lake Street
  Suite 600
  Chicago, IL 60601
- American Parkinson Disease Association
  60 Bay Street
  Suite 401
  Staten Island, NY 10301
- Epilepsy Foundation of America
  4351 Garden City Drive
  Landover, MD 20785
- National Multiple Sclerosis Society
  205 East 42nd Street
  New York, NY 10017

KEEPING FIT

Rethinking Disabilities

Next time you get caught in the trap of thinking an amputee or a person in a wheelchair can't perform, think of the following trio, all winners of the Victory Awards at the National Rehabilitation Hospital in Washington, D.C.:

- Skip Wilkins had his spinal cord cut in a water skiing accident, but that didn't stop him. He now stars in all kinds of wheelchair athletic events.
- Joni Tada, paralyzed from the neck down after a diving acci-

dent, creates her drawings with a pencil between her teeth.
- Bruce Demby had his leg blown off in Vietnam. He now competes and wins in special track-and-field events and also serves as a ski instructor.

Additional Information

Injuries to the CNS. Concussion occurs when the brain absorbs external forces and collides with the cranium, causing the brain to bruise. The bruise usually occurs on the side opposite the initial impact. Symptoms usually appear within 24 hours of the injury and include loss of recent memory, disorientation, loss of balance, blurred vision, and minor to extreme levels of unconsciousness.

Sciatica (low back pain) is caused when the sciatic nerve is obstructed or pressured, causing pain to radiate down one or both legs. The upper sections of the spine (cervical, thoracic, and lumbar) have freedom of movement, while the lower sacral and coccygeal sections have little or no movement abilities.

L1 SPEAKER. Invite a paraplegic to speak to the class about spinal cord damage. Some communities have wheelchair-basketball teams that play games as fund-raising programs. Often, these people are willing to speak to groups and perform demonstrations.

L1 SPEAKER. Contact a local chapter of the Veterans Administration or a VA hospital to invite a representative to speak to the class about the sorts of therapy and other treatment undergone by patients who have suffered injuries to the brain or spinal cord.

L2 DISCUSSION. Ask students to think about any scars they have on their bodies from accidents or surgery. How do these affect their use of the scarred body part—pain, stiffness, lack of sensation? Compare these symptoms to a scar on a nerve. Can students describe how their body part might be affected by a nerve scar, as seen in multiple sclerosis?

L1 SPEAKER. Invite a speaker from the MS Society, Cerebral Palsy Association, or Association of Retarded Citizens to talk about these diseases or disorders and the agency's services. How does the disease or disorder affect the individual? How does it affect family life?

L1 DISCUSSION. Ask students to share personal experiences or reports in the media about individuals with Alzheimer's disease.

L1 SPEAKER. Contact your community representative for the Alzheimer's Association and ask him or her to make a class presentation about this disease and its effects on the community. Do class members know anyone suffering from this disease?

L2 CLASS ACTIVITY. Explain that antibiotics are used to treat meningitis. Ask students to list the types of precautions that should be observed when receiving medications. (Dosage, side effects, completion of a series of medicines, compliance with instructions, reporting to the doctor.)

Caregivers are important to a person who has Alzheimer's disease. This man cares for his wife who has Alzheimer's.

Alzheimer's disease causes general mental deterioration. Patients gradually lose their memory and powers of judgment. Speech and body coordination may also be affected. Although there is no cure, researchers continue to search for effective treatment for the symptoms of the disease.

Communicable Diseases

Communicable diseases of the nervous system are caused by pathogens that can enter the brain in several ways. They may enter directly through a fracture in the skull. Others may be spread from ear and sinus infections. They may also be carried from some other part of the body to the brain through the bloodstream. Some, such as the virus that causes rabies, move through a peripheral nerve to the brain.

Encephalitis, meningitis, poliomyelitis, and rabies are communicable diseases that may result in damage to the nervous system.

Encephalitis

Encephalitis is an inflammation of the brain caused by a virus and sometimes by bacteria. Neurons in the brain may be damaged. Symptoms may include headaches, fever, and sometimes convulsions. Although most patients recover from encephalitis, some suffer permanent brain damage.

Meningitis

What word does *meningitis* resemble? What part of the nervous system do you think this disease affects? **Meningitis** is an inflammation of the meninges. It can be caused by bacteria or viruses. Symptoms include severe headaches, high temperature, vomiting, and sore or tight neck muscles. Antibiotic medicines are used to treat meningitis when it is caused by bacteria, making the chances for recovery excellent. Antibiotic medicines are ineffective, however, when the source of the infection is viral.

234 CHAPTER 12 THE NERVOUS AND ENDOCRINE SYSTEMS

HELP WANTED

EEG Technician

If you have been working successfully as a laboratory aide, or licensed practical nurse, and are looking for the opportunity to "move up," we are seeking caring, patient, personable workers with good judgment. We will provide on-the-job training and some classroom instruction. You might be comfortable working with sophisticated electronic equipment, which runs important diagnostic tests on the brain. You will receive a competitive salary and benefits, security, and the chance for continued training that can result in certification and possibly supervisory opportunities.

For more information contact:
American Hospital Association
850 N. Lake Shore Drive
Chicago, IL 60611

Across the Curriculum

Science. Ask a science teacher to help students research genetic disorders related to the central nervous system. Have students learn about the following: genetic mapping, amniocentesis (a test to check the genetic code of the embryo/fetus), genetic disorders resulting from the age of a woman during pregnancy, genetic disorders that are a result of poor prenatal care during the first trimester of pregnancy, and how the use of chemicals (marijuana, cocaine, alcohol, etc.) have been shown to produce strong genetic-code dysfunction of the central nervous system. Work with the March of Dimes to learn more about genetic disorders.

Poliomyelitis

Poliomyelitis, or polio, is a viral infection that affects motor neurons in the spinal cord and brain stem. The virus enters the body through the mouth, reaches the bloodstream through the stomach and lungs, and then attacks the central nervous system. This infection can result in paralysis of one or more limbs, usually the legs. If nerves controlling the diaphragm become infected, the respiratory system may become paralyzed. Polio epidemics occurred in the 1940s and early 1950s. The development of the Salk and Sabin vaccines in the 1950s has brought this once life-threatening disease under control.

Rabies

Rabies is a viral infection of the brain and spinal cord. Humans become infected if they are bitten by an animal infected with the virus. Symptoms of rabies include restlessness, mental depression, and painful throat spasms. Rabies is a life-threatening disease. There is a vaccination for rabies that consists of a series of injections after a person has been bitten.

Genetic Disorders

Some diseases of the nervous system are hereditary, they are passed from parent to child through inherited genes. These disorders include phenylketonuria and Down syndrome.

Phenylketonuria

Phenylketonuria (PKU) is rare, occurring in about 1 out of every 15,000 babies born in the United States, and is transmitted by a recessive gene. PKU is characterized by an inability of the body to break down a substance found in some foods called phenylalanine. The resulting buildup of this substance in the body interferes with the normal development of the brain. Symptoms of PKU appear in the first few weeks of life. PKU can be detected by a blood test even before any symptoms appear. With early treatment, mental retardation can be prevented. Treatment consists of a special diet that restricts any foods that contain phenylalanine.

> **CONFLICT RESOLUTION**
>
> Jamahl will be 16 next week and has been eagerly waiting to get his driver's permit. Until yesterday, his parents had agreed he could get it on his 16th birthday. Then Jamahl was diagnosed with epilepsy. Now his parents say getting a driver's permit is out of the question because it may not be safe for him to drive. They're afraid he might have a seizure while driving. Jamahl's doctor says that the right dose of medication should keep the seizures under control. Jamahl thinks his parents are overreacting to his disease.
>
> *Can you think of a way to resolve the conflict between them?*

KEEPING FIT

New Strides for the Disabled

There are about 43 million Americans with disabilities. The Americans With Disabilities Act now requires that hotels offer special telephones with phone flashers, tape-recorded safety instructions, and other features for the speech and hearing impaired. A new hotel in Florida has also included roll-in showers for people in wheelchairs, talking alarm clocks, and special training for employees that gives them a view of what it is like to have a disability.

Is your school user-friendly for people with handicaps? Think of ways that you can help make your school environment better for those people. If you have a disability, why not lead the effort?

Additional Information

Epilepsy. Epilepsy can occur at any time during a person's life. These individuals have special needs that should be considered by teachers and students.

Because people with epilepsy do not always know when a seizure will occur, they live in uncertainty. These individuals cannot get driver's licenses or operate motor vehicles. They cannot participate in some athletic events involving contact. They are often embarrassed after a seizure, because people stare and think they are ill. Some believe these people have a mental illness, and the stigma affects the self-esteem of the individuals.

L1 EXPLANATION. Explain to the class that in the past, it was recommended that if someone was having a grand mal seizure to put something in their mouth to prevent them from chewing or swallowing their tongue. Explain the first-aid procedures for someone having a seizure.

L2 DISCUSSION. Cerebral palsy may result from a lack of oxygen to the brain before or during birth. Ask students to discuss those things that are known to affect the newborn and its central nervous system. (Drugs, genes, smoking, infections.) What responsible behaviors should be demonstrated during pregnancy?

L2 COOPERATIVE LEARNING. Place students in small groups. Assign each group a disease or disorder of the nervous system. Have students write a paragraph about the disease or disorder to put on a poster. Ask other students to cut and paste pictures for the poster that relate to the disease or disorder. Have students consider prevention, treatment, and special needs.

L2 EXPLANATION. Explain how genetic counseling relates to the prevention of genetic diseases and disorders.

L1 CLASS ACTIVITY. Have students bring in magazine and newspaper ads for sports safety equipment and headgear. Ask them to discuss why they would or would not wear such gear. (They might wear the gear because it protects them or because it is the law in your state. They might not wear the gear because it is hot or uncomfortable. It might restrict their vision or movement, or their friends might tease them.) Discuss what might happen if they choose not to wear protective gear. Then ask how they could make the equipment more comfortable or less restrictive.

Independent Practice

L2 RESEARCH. Some individuals suffer neurological damage due to accidents. "Patterning" exercises have helped restore some neurologic functioning. Ask a volunteer to research these exercises and report the findings to the class.

Down Syndrome

Down syndrome is characterized by mild to serious mental retardation and short stature. It is the result of a chromosomal abnormality. Humans normally have 46 chromosomes, 23 pairs in each body cell. A child with Down syndrome has 47 chromosomes in each body cell, with the extra chromosome being with the twenty-first pair. The cause of the extra chromosome is not completely understood. The incidence of having a baby with Down syndrome increases with the age of the mother. There is no cure for Down syndrome. Special education can enhance what a Down syndrome child can achieve.

Other Disorders of the Nervous System

Although many disorders of the nervous system have known causes, some may have many possible causes. In some cases, the cause is unknown. Epilepsy and cerebral palsy are two such disorders.

Epilepsy

The term *epilepsy* comes from a Greek word meaning "seizure." **Epilepsy** is a disorder of the nervous system that is characterized by a sudden burst of nerve impulses in the brain. This sudden burst of impulses is transmitted to the muscles and results in a seizure, a physical reaction that may be slight or intense.

The reason for this sudden discharge of nerve impulses is not completely understood. It may be the result of a chemical imbalance in the brain, a tumor, or an injury to the brain before or during birth. There may be other causes, such as a high fever in childhood or an infection. Sometimes children who have epilepsy simply outgrow it as they reach their teenage years.

There are two types of seizures—grand mal and petit mal.

- Grand mal seizures usually last about 2 to 5 minutes, and the person may fall to the floor, losing consciousness. During the seizure, the muscles become tense causing the body to shake. The person may be sleepy after the seizure, but usually has no memory of it.
- Petit mal seizures are so slight that they often pass unnoticed. The person may go into a daze or have a blank stare for about 30 seconds. He or she may experience slight dizziness or faintness.

There is no present cure for epilepsy, even though there are medicines that control most seizures. Persons with epilepsy generally live a normal, healthy life. The disorder does not affect their intelligence or ability to function.

Cerebral Palsy

Cerebral palsy refers to a group of nonprogressive neurological disorders that are the result of damage as the brain is developing. Damage may occur before or during birth if oxygen to the brain is decreased or cut off. Pressure to a baby's head during birth can cause damage to the cerebrum. Accidental injury, lead poisoning, and certain illnesses can also cause cerebral palsy.

A child with Down syndrome can learn skills that were once thought to be beyond the capacity to learn.

236 CHAPTER 12 THE NERVOUS AND ENDOCRINE SYSTEMS

Diving into water that is too shallow is a risk behavior. Always check the depth of the water before you dive into it.

The effects of cerebral palsy vary, depending on which part of the cerebrum is damaged and the extent of the damage. The effects are mainly physical and include muscular spasms, poor coordination and balance, or hearing, sight, and speech problems. Persons who have cerebral palsy can have normal or above-normal intelligence. Physical therapy programs, braces, and walking aids all help these persons lead full, active lives.

Care of the Nervous System

Your nervous system is the control center of your body and it is important to keep it healthy. Exercise, proper nutrition, and adequate sleep will keep the nervous system functioning well. Avoid using alcohol and other drugs, which can cause permanent damage to the nervous system.

Many head and spinal cord injuries can be prevented by following basic safety rules. Wearing a seat belt gives you added protection in case of an accident. Before diving into a pool or lake, you should always check the depth of the water.

You can protect your head from injuries by wearing a helmet whenever you ride a bike, moped, or motorcycle or play contact sports.

LESSON 2 REVIEW

Reviewing Facts and Vocabulary

1. Describe injuries that might result from a sharp blow to the head.
2. What is the effect of multiple sclerosis on the body?

Thinking Critically

3. **Analysis.** What is the difference between degenerative diseases and communicable diseases? Give an example of each.

4. **Synthesis.** What might a person do to prevent a communicable disease of the nervous system?

Applying Health Knowledge

5. Find out whether there is a helmet law in your state. If there is, find out how the number of head injuries has changed since the law was enacted.

Answers to Lesson 2 Review

1. Concussion—a temporary disturbance of the brain's ability to function; contusion—bruising of the brain.
2. The myelin sheath that surrounds nerve fibers is destroyed, and scar tissue forms in its place. This interferes with the ability of the nerve fibers to send impulses, thus decreasing muscle control.
3. See pages 233 to 235.
4. Answers will vary. Possible answers: Follow safety measures to prevent skull fractures, get vaccinated against polio, avoid unfamiliar animals.
5. Answers will vary.

Assess

Check for Understanding

- Assign and discuss the lesson review. Questions 1 and 2 are appropriate for LD students.

Evaluate

- Administer, grade, and discuss the *Lesson 2 Quiz*.

Reteach

- Have students prepare an outline on problems of the nervous system. Ask them to provide supporting facts for each of these categories, relying on the text for the information.
- Ask students to complete *Reteaching Activity 31*.

Enrich

- Ask students to find out what a myelogram is. What is it used for? How is it performed? How has it been improved in recent years? Also have them find out about CAT scans and MRI—magnetic resonance imaging—two diagnostic tools that neurologists now often use. What are they? How and in what kinds of situations are they used? What kinds of information can they provide that other diagnostic tests cannot? Ask students to summarize their findings in written reports.

Close

Ask students to state the most important concepts learned in this lesson. Have each student list two short-term and two long-term advantages of making choices that promote health of the nervous system.

DID YOU KNOW?

- About 80 percent of spinal cord injuries happen to men.
- Each year in the U.S., some 10,000 Americans are left paralyzed by spinal cord injuries.

THE ENDOCRINE SYSTEM

Y ou already know that the nervous system coordinates and regulates all of the functions of the body. The endocrine system works closely with the nervous system in regulating body functions.

Functions of the Endocrine System

The **endocrine system** is made up of ductless glands and the hormones they produce. Endocrine hormones are carried in the blood to various parts of the body and activate these parts in specific ways. You have no conscious control over your endocrine glands.

Glands

A gland is a cell, a group of cells, or an organ that secretes a substance. There are two types of glands in the body. Some glands secrete substances into ducts, or tubes, to be carried to a specific area of the body. These glands are called exocrine glands. Sweat glands and salivary glands are examples of exocrine glands. Other glands are ductless, or tubeless. They release their secretions directly into the bloodstream. **Endocrine glands** are ductless glands that secrete substances called hormones into the bloodstream.

Hormones

Hormones are substances released by ductless glands that regulate the activities of different body cells. They are often referred to as chemical messengers. The word *hormone* comes from the Greek word *horman*, meaning "to excite, or set in motion." Some hormones are produced continually in the body. Others are produced only at certain times.

Structure of the Endocrine System

Endocrine glands are scattered throughout the body. They work independently of each other, but together they control body activities. The pancreas functions both as an exocrine and endocrine gland. For example, the pancreas produces digestive enzymes that flow through a duct directly to the small intestine. The pancreas also produces the hormone insulin, which has a function in the metabolism of sugar. You will learn more later about the pancreas.

Some of the major glands of the endocrine system are the pituitary, the thyroid, the parathyroid, the adrenals, the pancreas, and the ovaries and testes.

The Endocrine System

Pituitary gland

Pineal body

Thyroid gland

Parathyroid glands

Thymus gland

Adrenal glands

Ovaries
(in female)

Pancreas

Testes
(in male)

Glands of the endocrine system are situated in different parts of the body.

The Pituitary Gland

The **pituitary gland** is about the size of an acorn and is situated at the base of the brain. Because the pituitary gland regulates other endocrine glands, it is often referred to as the master gland.

The pituitary gland has three lobes. The anterior lobe and the posterior lobe secrete various hormones and have a great effect on the other glands. The intermediate lobe is still not completely understood.

The Anterior Lobe of the Pituitary. The hormones released from the anterior lobe control a range of body functions. They regulate metabolic activities of cells and stimulate other endocrine glands. The anterior lobe produces at least five different hormones. They are as follows:
- The somatotropic hormone, also known as the growth hormone,

DID YOU KNOW?

- Scientists have identified over 30 different hormones in the human body.
- Since the 1940s, scientists have been able to create synthetic hormones in the laboratory.
- The tallest man on record was Robert Pershing Wadlow, who was 8 feet, 11 inches in height.

Across the Curriculum

History. Ask students to research hormone therapy. Find out when and where each hormone was isolated by scientists. Investigate the discovery of insulin in 1921 by two Canadian scientists, Frederick G. Banting and Charles H. Best. What happened to children with diabetes then? Pose the following questions: Are all hormones currently produced synthetically? How were the names of each derived? Who invented the insulin pump, and how is it used today? Have students make a poster illustrating the history of hormone therapy.

Building Vocabulary

- Write the vocabulary words, as well as their pronunciations, on the chalkboard. (Pronunciations are given in the lesson text and in the Glossary at the back of the book.) Ask volunteers to pronounce each of the terms. After all terms have been pronounced correctly, have the entire class repeat each pronunciation.
- Ask students to complete *Workbook Vocabulary Activity 32.*

Teach

Guided Practice

L1 USING BODY SYSTEMS TRANSPARENCY 50. Refer to the Teaching Transparencies Binder.

LD CLASS ACTIVITY. Provide LD students with short, easy-to-understand explanations of major concepts.

L1 SPEAKER. Ask an endocrinologist to visit the class. Have him or her discuss disorders and diseases of the endocrine system, prevention, and treatment.

L1 CLASS ACTIVITY. Ask students to describe in their own words the shape of each endocrine gland and its relation to other body parts such as the stomach, intestine, or mouth.

L2 DISCUSSION. Since hormones "set things in motion," ask students to describe in their own words which of the endocrine glands they feel is most vital; which one is least vital. Ask them to explain their choices.

L2 DISCUSSION. Ask students to discuss the relationship of hormones to the nervous system.

L2 CLASS ACTIVITY. Ask students to recall emergency situations in which they found themselves. Following this reflection, ask each person to make a written identification of their autonomic responses to hormone stimulation.

L2 **CLASS ACTIVITY.** Using an anatomical model of the brain, or a chart showing a cross section of the cranium, have students identify the pineal and pituitary glands. Ask students if these glands are related to each other in structure or function.

L2 **EXPLANATION.** Hormone therapy can be used to speed or slow body processes. Explore with the class several common hormone treatments, such as thyroid replacement, insulin, cortisone, birth-control pills, diuretics. What are the benefits and hazards of these treatments?

L1 **EXPLANATION.** There is much new research available on the varying levels of hormones in the body, especially during adolescence. Hormonal activity related to puberty and sexual development is very low to non-existent in children. It is higher, but level, in adults (except during pregnancy). During puberty and adolescent years, it might be at a child's level 1 minute and 20 minutes later at an adult level. These "ups and downs" help explain the mood swings and extreme "highs and lows" experienced during these years.

L2 **CLASS ACTIVITY.** On the chalkboard, draw a schematic of the lobes of the pituitary gland. Have students name the hormones produced by each lobe by writing the hormone's name and making an arrow to the producing lobe.

L1 **CLASS ACTIVITY.** Draw the endocrine system on the chalkboard. Have students label the parts and describe their functions to the class.

L1 **CLASS ACTIVITY.** Have students write paragraphs to explain why the pituitary is called "the master gland." Do they agree with this designation? Why or why not?

L2 **DISCUSSION.** Abnormal physical growth is a condition that can be treated through hormone replacement in some cases. Prompt medical attention and adherence to a medical regime are recommended. What other kinds of diseases or disorders can the class recall that require long treatment periods? (Diabetes, epilepsy, paralysis, etc.)

DID YOU KNOW?

- Graves' disease, or hyperthyroidism is an autoimmune ailment that causes the thyroid gland to be over-stimulated. The fact that former President George Bush and his wife Barbara Bush both suffer from the disease and their dog Millie also had an autoimmune disease suggests that there may be some environmental or viral link that helps trigger the disease.

---

influences growth in most body tissues. It especially influences the skeleton and skeletal muscles.

- The thyroid-stimulating hormone (TSH) regulates both the size and activity of the thyroid gland.
- The adrenocorticotropic hormone (ACTH) controls the manufacture and secretion of hormones produced in the outer layer of the adrenal glands.
- Two gonadotropic hormones control the growth, development, and functions of the gonads, which is another name for the ovaries and testes. In females, the follicle stimulating hormone (FSH) triggers the development of egg cells, or ova, in the ovary. FSH also stimulates cells in the ovary to produce estrogens, female sex hormones. In males, FSH stimulates the testes to produce sperm cells.

In females, the leuteinizing hormone (LH) is responsible for ovulation, or the release of a mature ovum from the ovary. LH also stimulates cells in the ovaries to produce progesterone, a female sex hormone. In males, LH stimulates cells in the testes to produce testosterone, a male sex hormone.

The Posterior Lobe of the Pituitary. The posterior lobe of the pituitary gland secretes two hormones, antidiuretic hormone (ADH) and oxytocin.

ADH's principal effect on the body is to regulate the balance of water in the body. It stimulates the kidneys to retain water by returning it to the blood. If the kidneys did not return water to the blood, a person would have excess water in the urine and experience a serious internal water shortage. Oxytocin stimulates the smooth muscles in the uterus of a pregnant female causing contractions during the birth of a baby.

The Thyroid Gland

The **thyroid gland** is one of the largest glands of the endocrine system. It is a twin mass, consisting of a left and right lobe, located in the neck at the junction of the trachea and larynx. Thyroxine contains iodine, and is the principal hormone produced by the thyroid gland.

Thyroid hormones regulate the metabolism of carbohydrates, fats, and proteins in body cells. **Metabolism** is the sum total of all chemical reactions within a cell. The metabolism of nutrients within a cell is important in providing the cells with a source of energy.

The Parathyroid Glands

The **parathyroid glands** are the smallest glands of the endocrine system and are situated on the lobes of the thyroid gland. The hormone from these glands, parahormone, regulates the body's calcium and phosphorus balance. These minerals are necessary for normal functioning of muscle and nerve tissue.

The Adrenal Glands

The two adrenal glands are located on each kidney. The **adrenal glands** consist of two parts—the outer portion, called the adrenal cortex, and the inner portion, called the adrenal medulla.

Additional Information

Hormones. When hormones such as cortisone are taken in amounts larger than that produced by the body, they can act as drugs. They may reduce swelling, but they might also suppress the immune system. Short-term use can be beneficial in a variety of conditions, but long-term use may lead to lowered immunities, fat deposits in the face—causing a moon face, weakening of the bones, and high blood pressure. Doctors have recently discovered that serious side effects can be avoided by prescribing low doses or giving higher doses on alternate days.

The Adrenal Cortex. The adrenal cortex, which is absolutely essential for life, secretes a mixture of hormones that affects numerous body functions. Hormones from the pituitary gland stimulate the adrenal cortex.

Aldosterone is the principal, most potent hormone that the adrenal cortex produces. Its function is to conserve the body's sodium and water balance.

The inner layer of the cortex produces a group of hormones that affect metabolism. Cortisone affects the metabolism of carbohydrates and proteins. Other hormones secreted from the cortex help a person cope with stress.

The Adrenal Medulla. The adrenal medulla is highly dependent upon the hypothalamus and the autonomic nervous system for regulation. It secretes the hormone epinephrine, more commonly called adrenaline, which increases heart action, raises blood pressure, increases respiration, and suppresses the digestive process.

This hormone is also known as the emergency hormone because it is released into the blood in greater amounts during highly emotional states, such as when a person experiences fear or anger.

The Pancreas

The **pancreas** is a gland that serves two systems—the digestive and the endocrine. This elongated, flattened organ lies behind the stomach, attached to the first section of the small intestine by a duct that transports its digestive juice to the intestine.

Scattered throughout the pancreas are small clusters of cells that are separate from the exocrine portion of the gland. These clusters make up the endocrine part of the pancreas. They are called the islets of Langerhans for Paul Langerhans, a German scientist who first noticed them in 1869. There may be as many as a million of these clusters that produce two hormones affecting the metabolism of glucose (blood sugar).

One hormone, glucagon, helps maintain the sugar level of the blood by stimulating the liver to convert glycogen to glucose, thus raising the blood sugar level. Glycogen is a storage form of glucose in the liver and muscle cells. The other hormone, insulin, tends to decrease blood sugar levels. Insulin stimulates the liver to form glycogen from glucose. Insulin is a complex protein substance and is essential to life.

K E E P I N G   F I T

What to Do If Your Size Is a Problem

If your size or rate of development is different from that of most of your peers, consider these thoughts:
- There is a wide range in the rates at which teens develop and grow. What may appear to be slow may in fact still be considered normal.
- Some hormonally based size differences may be associated with other medical problems, so it is important to have medical supervision and advice.
- Learn to see yourself in terms of your assets and talents. Remind yourself that a person's true value is not related to his or her size.

Meeting Special Needs

Gland Disorders. Thyroid conditions can cause behavioral changes ranging from excitability to lethargy. They can also cause individuals to be overweight or very thin. Such individuals are self-conscious about their weight and are not always aware of the cause of the problem.

Diabetics do not need others to consider their condition in a negative way. They are aware of the medicine, diet, and exercise available to control the disorder. As a teacher, you should be aware of diabetics in your class, and recognize the special needs of students with hypoglycemia.

L2 **SPEAKER.** Ask a school nurse or someone you know that has diabetes to visit your class. Have the visitor demonstrate how to use a glucometer in determining blood sugar/glucose levels in the blood. Demonstrate an insulin kit and explain why insulin must be taken and when. Have the class prepare a list of pertinent questions prior to the presentation. How does someone with diabetes manage medication, diet, and exercise? Is diabetes hereditary?

L2 **EXPLANATION.** The parathyroids, although very small, are essential to life. The two parts act as two separate glands, controlling separate activities.

L2 **CLASS ACTIVITY.** Ask students to differentiate between diabetes and hypoglycemia in a one-page report.

L2 **COOPERATIVE LEARNING.** Divide the class into eight groups and assign each a different gland. Each group is to develop a 5- to 8-minute presentation to teach a lesson regarding its assigned endocrine gland. Presentations should include illustrations, problems with the gland, new research, and interesting facts. Allow class time for presentations.

L2 **DISCUSSION.** Malfunction of glands of the endocrine system can cause serious and often grotesque physical changes and emotional scars. Explore with students the area of individual differences. Ask them to develop a list of things that promote individual worth and self-esteem.

L2 **DISCUSSION.** Since a dietary deficiency of iodine can cause a goiter, ask students to discuss actions taken to prevent this disease in the U.S. (Iodized salt, and water treatment.)

L2 **DISCUSSION.** Remind students that the need for a good diet was mentioned in connection with the health of every body system discussed in this chapter. Have students give reasons that diet is so essential to good health. (Each body system needs specific nutrients, vitamins, and minerals.)

L2 **CLASS ACTIVITY.** Steroids are being used by some athletes to improve strength and endurance. Ask students to relate steroids to the endocrine system. Have students relate the potential dangers of these drugs to the body. What are some beneficial uses for steroids under the supervision of a doctor?

Independent Practice

L3 **RESEARCH.** For extra credit, have students research the thyroid gland. They should find out what happens to the body when there is a thyroid deficiency or an overactive thyroid. Have them summarize their findings in writing.

L3 **READING.** Ask students to read an article or book that describes an endocrine disorder found in another country. How is the condition treated there? Is the United States helping this country deal with this medical problem? If so, how?

L2 **PARENTAL INVOLVEMENT.** Have students ask their parents if anyone in their family has had to take artificial hormones and if so, why.

L2 **RESEARCH.** Ask students to research the use of adrenaline and cortisone for severe allergic reactions. How is thyroxin used for thyroid conditions such as hyperthyroid or hypothyroid? Do these conditions have any effect on weight control?

L1 **USING THE LESSON RESOURCES.** For additional student activities, refer to the lesson resources on page 238.

DID YOU KNOW?

■ Taking hormones can be a mixed bag. Estrogen, for example, when given to women after menopause, helps prevent both osteoporosis and heart attacks. Yet, it may slightly increase a woman's chance of developing breast cancer.

The Ovaries and the Testes

The ovaries in the female and the testes in the male are part of the reproductive system. The ovaries produce and release ova, and the testes produce and release sperm. Both the ovaries and testes are endocrine glands.

As endocrine glands, the ovaries and the testes produce hormones that are responsible for the development and maintenance of secondary sex characteristics. The secretion of the hormones progesterone and estrogen by the ovaries is stimulated by hormones from the pituitary gland. Hormones from the pituitary gland stimulate the testes of the male to produce and secrete the hormone testosterone.

Disorders of the Endocrine Glands

Most disorders of the endocrine glands are related to the production of too much or too little of a hormone. There are other possible causes, however. Following is a description of some problems associated with endocrine glands.

The Pituitary Gland

If, during the growing years, the anterior lobe of the pituitary gland does not produce enough of the growth hormone, a person does not grow. The person's stature is short because of delayed bone growth. Bones are usually normal in shape, however. If this condition is diagnosed early, proper treatment can be prescribed. With early treatment, a child may reach full height.

If too much of the growth hormone is produced during the growing years, the bones lengthen abnormally, resulting in a condition called giantism. If too much of this hormone is produced after the growing years, the bones thicken instead of lengthen. In this rare condition, called acromegaly, the soft tissue over the bones enlarges, making the face look massive and the hands and feet look large and awkward.

If the posterior lobe of the pituitary does not function, a person will experience a very large increase in the output of urine, a condition known as diabetes insipidus. This disease is rare and is not related to the more commonly known diabetes.

The Thyroid Gland

The metabolic action of thyroid hormones is very important during the growth years. A lack of thyroid hormones during the early growing years results in cretinism. This condition results in arrested growth, mental retardation, slow heart rate, and dry, yellowish skin.

Myxedema is a condition that results from lack of thyroid hormones. The metabolic rate drops, and mental and physical activity becomes sluggish. By administering thyroid hormones, all symptoms of myxedema usually disappear within a few weeks.

A simple goiter is an enlarged thyroid gland. It is caused by a dietary deficiency of iodine. Goiters are not a very common problem in the United States because of the availability and use of iodized salt.

Across the Curriculum

Language Arts. Have students ask a language arts teacher to help them write reports on hormone deficiencies that alter the size of an individual. Explain that a condition called acromegaly results from an overproduction of the growth hormone. The bones thicken and the nose, jaw, hands, and feet become enlarged. An underproduction of the growth hormone can cause dwarfism. Have students contact the organization Little People of America to find out more about dwarfism in this country. A deficiency of thyroid hormones can cause cretinism.

The Parathyroids

Underproductive parathyroids cause the level of calcium in the blood to drop. This results in muscle spasms, called tetany, which can be painful. Overproductive parathyroids cause calcium to be withdrawn from the skeleton, leaving bones weak and susceptible to fracture.

The Adrenal Glands

Addison's disease is caused by underproductive adrenal glands. Persons with Addison's disease lose excessive amounts of salt through the kidneys. They may experience a serious drop in blood pressure. Adrenal cortex hormones are used to treat Addison's disease.

Overproduction of adrenal hormones can result in Cushing's disease. The person may be weak and tired and have an excess of fatty deposits in the face.

The Pancreas

If insulin is not being produced or is not functioning, glucose accumulates in the blood and tissues and is passed out of the body through the urine. The result is a loss of nutrients and energy the body needs to carry out its basic activities. This condition is called diabetes mellitus.

Care of the Endocrine System

The glands of the endocrine system work together to keep your body healthy. This system usually takes care of its own chemical balance. However, as with other body systems, good health habits are important. For example, because the thyroid gland needs iodine, this mineral must be part of your diet. This kind of care is especially important in the teen years because the body is growing and changing so rapidly.

This female is using a pen-like device to inject herself with insulin. This injection helps her keep her blood sugar level within a normal range.

LESSON 3 REVIEW

Reviewing Facts and Vocabulary

1. Why is the pituitary gland called the master gland?
2. Make a chart showing the hormones produced by the pituitary gland. Include what they do.
3. What happens if the thyroid gland does not function properly?

Thinking Critically

4. **Analysis.** Compare the ovaries and testes.
5. **Synthesis.** What endocrine gland would you predict is not functioning properly if the following conditions exist?

a. excess sugar in the urine
b. impaired growth, causing a person to be abnormally small for his or her age
c. muscle spasms
d. vomiting, weakness caused by a serious drop in blood pressure

Applying Health Knowledge

6. Find out which hormones can be made synthetically. For what are these hormones used?
7. Research what an endocrinologist does. Write a narrative report describing this person's work.

Answers to Lesson 3 Review

1. It regulates other endocrine glands.
2. Charts will vary, see pages 239 to 240.
3. It could lead to cretinism, myxedema, or goiters.
4. Both are part of the reproductive system and are endocrine glands. They produce hormones responsible for secondary sex characteristics.
5. A—pancreas or islets of Langerhans; B—anterior lobe of the pituitary; C—parathyroids; D—adrenal glands.
6. Answers will vary.
7. Reports will vary.

Check for Understanding
- Assign and discuss the lesson review. Encourage LD students to focus on questions 1 and 3.
- Assign and discuss the chapter review.

Evaluate
- Administer, grade, and discuss the *Lesson 3 Quiz*.
- Administer, grade, and discuss the *Chapter 12 Test*.
- Refer to the Performance Assessment strategy for this chapter. See pages T 23 to T 25.

Reteach
- Have students write paragraphs explaining the role of the endocrine system and make a chart with the name of each endocrine gland in the left column and its function in the right column. Ask students to describe the effects of too much or too little hormone production in the endocrine glands. Encourage them to use the text and an encyclopedia.
- Ask students to complete *Reteaching Activity 32*.

Enrich
- Ask each student to select one gland in the endocrine system and to find out what happens if it malfunctions, whether a person can live without it, how malfunctions can be treated, and whether there are side effects from this treatment. Have each student summarize his or her findings in a written report.
- Ask students to complete *Enrichment Activity 12*.

Close

Ask students to state the most important concepts learned in this lesson.

Helping Students Improve Their Health

Reinforcing Vocabulary

■ **Basic safety rules for cycling.** Rules to follow in order to ensure the highest possibility of safety, such as using hand signals, wearing a helmet, and always wearing bright, reflective clothing.

Teaching Strategies

L1 EXPLANATION. Students frequently believe that they are invincible when it comes to accidents or injuries. Adolescents usually do not believe that they may be victims of accidents that result in permanent paralysis or even death. Often, damage to the nervous system results from carelessness or recklessness. Encourage students to examine reasons that accidents occur. Encourage students to examine how they can help prevent themselves and others from being an accident statistic.

L1 EXPLANATION. Question 2 may be misinterpreted by parents. Some people firmly believe that motorcycles are dangerous to ride, regardless of wearing protective equipment. Number 2 may be interpreted as meaning that wearing a helmet will ensure one's safety on a motorcycle. This is not the case.

L2 DISCUSSION. Have students list the top 10 causes of injury or death for adolescents. How many of these causes are related to nervous-system trauma? Have students determine the behaviors that helped contribute to these accidents. What can students do to reduce their chances of suffering an injury to the nervous system?

L2 SELF-ESTEEM. Discuss how a person's self-esteem affects decisions to protect the nervous system. Use examples such as wearing a helmet or using a seat belt when no one else is.

Self-Inventory

Care of the Nervous System

HOW DO YOU RATE?

Number a sheet of paper from 1 through 10. Read each item below, and respond by writing *always*, *sometimes*, or *never* for each item. Total the number of each type of response. Then proceed to the next section.

1. I wear a seat belt when traveling by car.
2. I wear a helmet when riding a bicycle, skateboard, rollerblades, or motorcycle.
3. I wear protective headgear whenever I participate in a contact sport.
4. I follow basic safety rules when cycling.
5. I get at least 8 hours of sleep each night.
6. I exercise regularly.
7. I avoid alcohol and other drugs.
8. I determine the depth of water in a pool or lake before diving.

9. I wear safety goggles when required for class or sports.
10. I avoid injuries to the spinal cord by lifting and carrying objects properly.

HOW DID YOU SCORE?

Give yourself 3 points for each *always* response, 1 point for each *sometimes* response, and 0 points for each *never* response. Find your total, and read below to see how you scored. Then proceed to the next section.

20 to 30
Excellent. Your health choices show you are taking care of your nervous system.

10 to 19
Good. You have a good understanding of ways to protect the nervous system, but you could use more caution.

Below 10
Needs Improvement. You may be taking unnecessary risks with your most vital body system.

WHAT ARE YOUR GOALS?

If you scored between 20 and 30, complete the statements in Part A. If your score was under 20, complete Parts A and B.

Part A

1. I plan to learn more about the care of the nervous system in the following ways: ____.
2. My timetable for completing this is ____.

Part B

3. The behavior I would like to change or improve is ____.
4. The steps involved in making this change are ____.
5. My timetable for making this change is ____.
6. The people or groups I will ask for support are ____.
7. My rewards for making this change will be ____.

Meeting Students' Needs

For students who score *Excellent*.
(1) Have students give safety talks to elementary school children on how to prevent nervous-system accidents from occurring. (2) Suggest that students pursue a summer-intern position or career that deals in the care and prevention of nervous-system injuries.
For students who score *Good*.

Suggest that students take a field trip to a local hospital and interview doctors and patients who suffer from head and spinal cord injuries.
For students who *Need Improvement*.
Suggest that students examine their behavior and how it may lead to injury or death. Present a real-life nervous-system injury situation to students in a relevant manner.

Building Decision-Making Skills

Jenna's brother, Michael, is a mildly retarded Down syndrome child. Michael attends classes for developmentally handicapped youngsters. Lately Michael has talked with Jenna about his desire to join a regular third-grade class. He wants Jenna to help him convince his parents to talk with school administrators about making the switch to regular classes. Jenna is concerned about the social, intellectual, and emotional difficulties Michael might face in a regular classroom. She feels he might be better off staying where he is. What should Jenna do?

A. Support Michael in whatever he chooses to do.

B. Leave the decision up to their parents and the school administrators.

C. Get an opinion from one of Michael's teachers or from a specialist in the field of developmentally handicapped children.

D. Talk with Michael about waiting until next year when he may be more capable of accepting the challenges in a regular classroom.

WHAT DO YOU THINK?

1. **Choices.** What other choices can you think of for Jenna?

2. **Consequences.** What are the costs and benefits of each choice?

3. **Consequences.** Who will be affected by Jenna's decision?

4. **Decision.** What do you think Jenna should do? Explain your answer.

5. **Evaluation.** Have you ever been asked to do something that you knew might not be best for the person who asked? How did you handle the situation?

Your friend, Lauren, has been looking very tired lately. Her grades are dropping, because she falls asleep in class. Her relationships with her family and friends are deteriorating because she is so irritable. Her new job at the pizza shop requires her to work from 8 P.M. to midnight five days a week. You know that she doesn't really need the money.

WHAT DO YOU THINK?

6. **Situation.** Does Lauren need to make a decision?

7. **Choices.** What are her choices?

8. **Consequences.** What are the consequences of each of the choices?

9. **Decision.** What do you think Lauren should do? Explain your answer.

James is caught in a downpour on the way home from school one afternoon. His friend, Will, drives by on his motorcycle and stops to offer James a ride. The only problem is that James doesn't have a helmet. He is getting soaked. What should he do?

A. Tell Will "No, thanks," and hurry on his way.

B. Accept the ride and, just this once, ride without a helmet.

C. Accept the ride, but ask Will if he can wear his helmet.

WHAT DO YOU THINK?

10. **Choices.** Can you help James come up with some other possible solutions?

11. **Consequences.** What are the advantages and disadvantages of each choice?

12. **Decision.** What should James do?

Discussing the Answers

Situation 1. Perhaps the best resolution would be to have Jenna give her full support to Michael as he attempts to join a mainstreamed third-grade class. If Jenna helps educate the third-grade students about Down syndrome, Michael can have a very positive experience.

Situation 2. A friend should choose a time to talk to Lauren when Lauren is under the least amount of stress. Lauren would be more receptive at that time. Suggest that Lauren begin by decreasing the number of hours that she works.

Situation 3. The best decision is to have James respect the law. It is illegal to be a passenger on a motorcycle and not wear a helmet. It is better to have James get soaked than to risk losing his life.

Helping Students Improve Their Health

Building Decision-Making Skills

Teaching Strategies

L2 CLASS ACTIVITY. Have students determine the best two answers for each scenario and debate the pros and cons for each situation.

L1 CLASS ACTIVITY. Have students role-play the part of the friend who approaches Lauren concerning her late-night job. Have students discuss the effect that a lack of sleep is having on Lauren's schoolwork and social life. In what manner should this friend approach Lauren so that Lauren listens and does not get resentful?

L1 CLASS ACTIVITY. Have students role-play the following situation: While visiting your grandparents, you notice that your grandfather has become increasingly forgetful. One moment he appears fine; the next moment he seems to not even know who you are. You fear that perhaps these are symptoms of an early stage of Alzheimer's disease. Your suspicions would devastate your grandmother. You wonder if you should keep your fears to yourself.

L2 DISCUSSION. Have students debate whether people who have had a history of epilepsy should be permitted to drive a motor vehicle.

L1 DISCUSSION. Have students discuss how the image of Down syndrome has possibly changed, following the introduction of the character "Corky" on the TV show "Life Goes On."

DID YOU KNOW?

■ Down syndrome can be detected during pregnancy by either chorionic villi sampling or amniocentesis. Both tests sample fetal cells to determine if there is an extra chromosome—number 21—the cause of the disorder.

Answers to Chapter 12 Review

Using Health Terms

1. Myelin
2. Synapse
3. Spinal meninges
4. Brain stem
5. Reflex
6. Cerebrum
7. Paralysis
8. Multiple sclerosis
9. Down syndrome
10. Coma
11. Pituitary
12. Metabolism
13. Islets of Langerhans
14. Epinephrine or adrenaline

Building Academic Skills

15. Answers will vary.

Recalling the Facts

16. The brain and spinal cord.
17. Nerves and ganglia.
18. A receptor is stimulated. The axon of the sensory neuron makes contact with a connecting motor neuron in the spinal cord. The motor neuron transmits an impulse to muscles.
19. Cerebrum, cerebellum, brain stem.
20. It constantly regulates internal body processes, enabling the body to maintain a stable internal environment.
21. The sympathetic division.
22. Examples will vary. Accept any two examples shown on the chart on page 229.
23. Answers will vary. Accept two of the following: Parkinson's disease—slow, involuntary movements and tremors; multiple sclerosis—loss of voluntary control of muscles, damage to neurons; Alzheimer's disease—loss of memory and powers of judgment, speech and body coordination become impaired.
24. Answers will vary. Accept two of the following: encephalitis—headaches, fever, convulsions; meningitis—severe headaches, high temperature, vomiting, sore or tight neck muscles; rabies—restlessness, mental depression, painful throat spasms.

Using Health Terms

On a separate sheet of paper, write the term that best matches each definition given below.

LESSON 1

1. Fatty material that coats axons and speeds the transmission of an impulse.
2. Narrow gap between the axon of one neuron and dendrite of another neuron.
3. Connective membranes surrounding the spinal cord.
4. Connects spinal cord to brain.
5. Spontaneous response of the body to a stimulus.
6. The largest and most complex part of the brain.

LESSON 2

7. The inability to move.
8. A degenerative disease of the nervous system in which the myelin sheath surrounding nerve fibers is destroyed.
9. A genetic disorder of the nervous system in which one has inherited an extra chromosome, resulting in mental retardation.
10. A state of unconsciousness caused by an injury to the brain.

LESSON 3

11. Gland at the base of the brain, often called the "master gland."
12. The sum total of all chemical reactions within a cell.
13. The clusters of cells in the pancreas that produce insulin.
14. A hormone secreted by the adrenal medulla and known as the "emergency hormone."

Building Academic Skills

LESSON 2

15. **Reading.** Read several current magazine articles about people who have suffered paralysis as a result of injuries received in accidents. What generalizations can you make about the quality of life these people have had since their accidents?

Recalling the Facts

LESSON 1

16. What are the two parts of the central nervous system?
17. What does the peripheral nervous system consist of?
18. Explain the action of a reflex.
19. List the three main divisions of the brain.
20. What is the function of the autonomic nervous system?
21. What division of the autonomic nervous system responds to the body's needs during increased activities?
22. Give two examples of the opposing actions of the sympathetic and parasympathetic divisions of the autonomic nervous system.

LESSON 2

23. Name two degenerative diseases of the nervous system. Describe the symptoms.
24. Name two communicable diseases of the nervous system. Describe the symptoms.
25. What is PKU? How is it diagnosed? How is it treated?
26. Tell what a concussion is and what the results of a concussion might be.
27. Tell what a contusion is and what the results of a contusion might be.
28. What causes a pinched nerve?

LESSON 3

29. What are hormones and what is their function?
30. What is the difference between endocrine glands and exocrine glands?
31. Describe why the ovaries and testes are regarded as endocrine glands.
32. Which endocrine gland affects the body's response to stress? How?
33. What is the largest gland in the endocrine system and what does it do?
34. Which gland secretes insulin? What is the function of insulin in the body?
35. Name three disorders associated with an improperly functioning pituitary gland.

25. Phenylketonuria is a rare genetic disorder of the nervous system, characterized by the body's inability to break down phenylalanine. It is diagnosed in infants through a blood test and is treated with a special diet.
26. It is a temporary disturbance of the brain's ability to function. It may result in loss of consciousness and/or short-term memory loss.
27. It is a bruising of the brain. It may result in coma or a loss of ability to perform certain functions.
28. A pinched nerve results when a cartilage disk between vertebrae moves.
29. Hormones are substances released by ductless glands that regulate the activities of different body cells, often referred to as chemical messengers.
30. Endocrine glands do not have ducts, and secrete hormones into the bloodstream. Exocrine glands secrete substances into ducts to be carried to a specific area of the body.

REVIEW

Thinking Critically

LESSON 1

36. **Synthesis.** Suppose your frontal lobe was injured and you began to suffer from mood swings. How do you think your life might change?

LESSON 2

37. **Evaluation.** Why do you think people continue to experiment with drugs, knowing the risks to the nervous system?

38. **Evaluation.** In some states, parents are required by law to have their child immunized against polio before the child enters school. Do you think parents should be required by law to do this? Why or why not?

39. **Synthesis.** Summarize reasons for the stigma that has historically been attached to epilepsy.

40. **Analysis.** Think of the different tasks you perform in a day. Decide which of these tasks you think you could still perform if you became a paraplegic. Which tasks would require retraining in order to accomplish them? Which of your daily tasks could you still perform without retraining if you became a quadriplegic?

LESSON 3

41. **Synthesis.** Your friend has not been growing properly and has just found out that her pituitary gland is not producing enough growth hormone. What might happen to your friend? What treatment may your friend receive?

Making the Connection

LESSON 1

42. **Language Arts.** Research scientific discoveries about how the left brain and right brain work. Which of these sides affects writing and other language functions? Of interest may be studies done with individuals who have suffered brain damage.

Applying Health Knowledge

LESSON 1

43. Imagine that you are approaching a busy intersection. When you are about 10 yards away, you notice a 4-year-old on a bike heading right for the street. Which part of your autonomic nervous system will respond? How do you know?

44. You know that to perform even the simplest task your nervous system goes through a series of events. List the events your nervous system goes through when you copy information from the chalkboard.

45. Imagine that your friend recently had a head injury. When you talk with your friend, he tells you that he is having trouble feeling things and that he has already cut himself and didn't know it until he saw the blood. What part of your friend's brain may have been damaged? How do you know?

LESSON 2

46. Find out how each of the communicable diseases discussed in this chapter are transmitted. What can you do to protect yourself from getting each disease?

LESSON 3

47. Find out more about diabetes insipidus. What medical help might a person suffering from this disorder be able to get?

Beyond the Classroom

LESSON 2

48. **Further Study.** Sometimes a disease is named for a famous person who has been affected by it. Lou Gehrig was a player for the New York Yankees. In 1941 he died of a disorder that has since been called Lou Gehrig's disease. Find out what this disease is and how it affects a person.

49. **Futher Study.** Make a report showing medical progress during the past 25 years of any disorder discussed in this chapter.

31. As endocrine glands, the ovaries and testes produce hormones that are responsible for secondary sex characteristics.

32. The adrenal cortex produces hormones that help a person cope with stress.

33. The thyroid gland produces thyroxine and regulates the metabolism of carbohydrates, fats, and proteins.

34. Pancreas. Insulin decreases blood-sugar levels and stimulates the liver to form glycogen from glucose.

35. Giantism, acromegaly, diabetes insipidus.

Thinking Critically

36. Answers will vary. Possible answers: Lose friends, embarrass oneself in public, disrupt functions, hurt oneself or others, become aggressive or despondent.

37. Answers will vary. Possible answers: To escape, peer pressure, ignorance of the facts.

38. Answers will vary but should be supported logically.

39. Answers will vary.

40. Answers will vary.

41. She will probably be a person of short stature. Answers will vary as to what one might say to her. The friend may get help from a doctor who specializes in functions of the endocrine system.

Making Connections

42. Answers will vary.

Applying Health Knowledge

43. The sympathetic system will respond because this is an emergency situation.

44. Your eyes register the information to be copied. A message is sent to your brain that this information needs to be written down. Your brain sends a message to your hand and arm muscles that respond by writing what your brain tells you that you are seeing.

45. His parietal lobe. That is the part that is involved with sensory information.

46. Polio is transmitted by direct contact when the virus is swallowed. Washing one's hands frequently may help prevent the spread of polio. Encephalitis is transmitted in

the birth canal, by ticks and mosquitoes, and after vaccination. Using bug repellent when going outdoors may help prevent the spread. Meningitis is transmitted through direct contact with infected persons. If one has been exposed to bacterial meningitis, one may be vaccinated or given antibiotics. Rabies is transmitted when the saliva from an infected animal gets into a break in the skin. If bitten, wash the bite site and see a doctor immediately.

47. Diabetes insipidus is caused by a lack of vasopressin. Vasopressin can be made synthetically, so a person suffering from diabetes insipidus can take

vasopressin to control it.

Beyond the Classroom

48. Lou Gehrig died of amyotrophic lateral sclerosis, a progressive neurological disorder of unknown cause.

49. Answers will vary.

Lesson Summaries

LESSON 1. The cardiovascular system moves blood throughout the body. It includes the heart, blood vessels, and blood. The action of the heart is critical to cardiovascular function, as it pumps blood through two major pathways allowing for pulmonary and systemic circulation.

LESSON 2. Many problems of the cardiovascular system exist. Choices and behaviors affect the health of the system.

LESSON 3. The lymphatic system helps the body maintain its fluid balance by carrying fluid away from tissues. The system primarily consists of lymphatic vessels, lymph nodes, lymph, and lymphocytes. Problems of the system relate to infection, and it can be cared for by following general health practices.

LESSON 4. The respiratory system functions externally to take in air and give off carbon dioxide. Internally, it exchanges gases between the blood and body cells, releasing oxygen and taking in carbon dioxide.

Introducing the Chapter

Tell students that the circulatory system is the primary transportation system of the body, delivering needed nutrients and carrying away waste products from the body's cells. Have students add the body systems discussed in this chapter to the chart they developed for Chapter 11. Ask them to provide information regarding system structure, function, problems, and care.

Performance Assessment ✓

Refer to pages T 23 to T 25 for a Performance Assessment strategy for this chapter. See the *Performance Assessment Activities* booklet for additional suggestions.

CHAPTER

13

CARDIOVASCULAR, LYMPHATIC, AND RESPIRATORY SYSTEMS

LESSON 1
The Cardiovascular System

LESSON 2
Problems and Care of the Cardiovascular System

LESSON 3
The Lymphatic System

LESSON 4
The Respiratory System

248 CHAPTER 13 CARDIOVASCULAR, LYMPHATIC, AND RESPIRATORY SYSTEMS

Key to Ability Levels

Teaching strategies have been coded for varying learning styles and abilities.

L1 Level 1 activities are basic activities and should be within the ability range of all students.

L2 Level 2 activities are average activities and should be within the ability range of average to above-average students.

L3 Level 3 activities are challenging activities designed for the ability range of above-average students.

LD LD activities should be within the ability range of learning-disabled students.

LEP LEP activities should be within the ability range of Limited English Proficiency students.

LESSON 1

THE CARDIOVASCULAR SYSTEM

Your cardiovascular system moves blood throughout your body. Think of this system as a transport system serving body cells as a delivery and pick-up system.

Functions of the Cardiovascular System

The major function of the cardiovascular system is to maintain an internal body environment in which all body cells are nurtured. As your heart pumps blood, blood vessels carry oxygen and nutrients to body cells. Oxygen and nutrients pass from the circulating blood into cells. At the same time, carbon dioxide and other wastes are picked up by the blood and distributed to the lungs and kidneys where they are released from the body. Your body cells could not function without these two processes occurring.

Structure of the Cardiovascular System

Your cardiovascular system includes your heart, blood, and a network of branching blood vessels.

The Heart

Your heart is one of the most vital organs in your body. It started beating before you were born and it has been beating every minute of your life. Your heart is a pear-shaped muscular organ about the size of your fist. It is enclosed in a loose-fitting sac called the pericardium. The pericardium protects the heart.

Chambers of the Heart. The heart is divided into four chambers, two on the left side and two on the right side. The two upper chambers are called atria. The two lower chambers are called ventricles. The heart chambers are referred to as the left atrium, the left ventricle, the right atrium, and the right ventricle. The two halves of the heart are separated by a wall called the septum. A valve separates each atrium and ventricle. The valves keep the blood flowing in the proper direction.

Your heart is a pump that moves blood through two major pathways. **Pulmonary circulation** is the flow of blood from the heart to the lungs and back to the heart. Two major veins return blood that carries wastes from body cells to the right atrium. As the right atrium fills, it contracts and blood flows into the right ventricle. This ventricle pumps the blood to the lungs through the pulmonary arteries. In the lungs, carbon dioxide and oxygen are exchanged. The blood picks up oxygen from inhaled air in

THE CARDIOVASCULAR SYSTEM **249**

LESSON 1 FOCUS

TERMS TO USE
- Pulmonary circulation (PUL•muh•NER•ee)
- Systemic circulation
- Plasma
- Hemoglobin
- Platelets
- Arteries
- Capillaries (KAP•uh•LER•eez)
- Veins

CONCEPTS TO LEARN
- The continuous flow of blood through the circulatory system depends on the heart.
- To maintain all the cells that make up the human body, there must be a continuous stream of nutrients from the outside world and a continuous removal of waste products from the cells.

ATTITUDES AND BEHAVIORS TO EVALUATE
- Self-Inventory, page 270.
- Building Decision-Making Skills, page 271.

Focus

Lesson Objectives
After studying this lesson, students should be able to:
- describe the pathways of pulmonary and systemic circulation
- explain the purposes of arteries, capillaries, and veins

Bellringer
Write the following on the chalkboard for students to work on while attendance is being taken: *Write a definition for the term cardiovascular system. (Cardiovascular refers to the entire circulatory system, including the heart, the blood vessels, and the blood.)*

Introducing the Lesson
Tell students that without a healthy circulatory system the body could not function. Refer to the Bellringer and have volunteers define the term *cardiovascular system.* Tell students that in this lesson they will learn about the heart, what makes it work, and what influences its action.

Building Vocabulary
- Ask students to work in teams to create a crossword puzzle using the vocabulary words.
- Ask students to complete *Workbook Vocabulary Activity 33.*

DID YOU KNOW?

- *To breed bad blood* means to create conflict between people. It derives from the medieval idea that behavior comes from the balance or imbalance of the body's fluids, and blood was the fluid deemed responsible for negative emotions such as anger.

Resources for Lesson 1

- **Transparency** 51
- **Guided Reading** Act 33
- **Workbook** Voc Act 33
- **Reteaching** Activity 33
- **Lesson 1 Quiz**
- **Performance Assessment** Activity 13

Science and Technology Videodiscs
Human Biology, Side 1
Ch 2 Modeling Blood Flow

Ch 3 Measuring Blood Pressure

Ch 16 Natural Time-Release Capsules

Guided Practice

LD **CLASS ACTIVITY.** Provide LD students with a skeletal outline of the chapter. Ask them to fill in notes during class discussions.

L1 **DISCUSSION.** Using a heart model, clarify for students the direction of blood flow through the heart. Which chamber has the thickest wall in order to pump blood to the body? (Left ventricle.) Explain that heart valves permit blood to flow only in one direction: atrium to ventricle, ventricle to vessels.

L1 **CLASS ACTIVITY.** Ask each student to draw a picture of the heart and to label the atria, the ventricles, and the layers of the heart muscle.

LD **CLASS ACTIVITY.** Provide a labeled diagram of the heart and have LD students write notes under each label.

L2 **CLASS ACTIVITY.** Have each student take his or her pulse for one minute. Using that figure, have the student determine how many times his or her heart beats per day, week, month, and year. Then tell the class the heart pumps an average of 5.3 quarts of blood every minute. Have students determine how many quarts of blood their hearts pump in a day, a week, and a month.

L3 **CLASS ACTIVITY.** Using laboratory samples, have students examine the chambers of animal hearts. Do all hearts have four chambers? Are all hearts the same size?

L1 **EXPLANATION.** Tell students that in 1 day a human heart beats about 100,000 times. Have students guess and then calculate approximately how many times their heart has beaten since they were born. (In 1 year, the heart beats approximately 36,500,000 times. In 1 month, the heart beats approximately 3,000,000 times.)

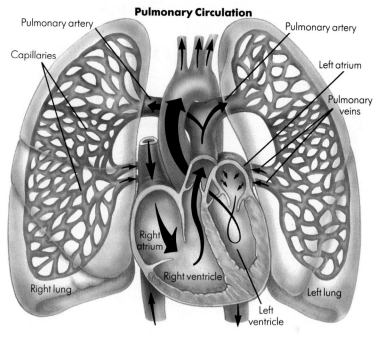

Pulmonary Circulation

Blood low in oxygen is pumped from the right ventricle to the lungs through the pulmonary arteries (shown in blue). Blood rich in oxygen returns to the left atrium through the pulmonary veins (shown in red).

Pulmonary artery
Capillaries
Pulmonary artery
Left atrium
Pulmonary veins
Right atrium
Right ventricle
Right lung
Left ventricle
Left lung

the lungs and releases carbon dioxide into the lungs. When you exhale, you get rid of the carbon dioxide. Blood with a fresh supply of oxygen returns to the left atrium in the pulmonary veins.

Systemic circulation moves blood to all body tissues except the lungs. The oxygenated blood flows from the left atrium to the left ventricle. The left ventricle is the most muscular part of the heart. It pumps blood through the aorta, the largest artery, to all of the parts of the body. This blood supplies body cells with nutrients and oxygen. Blood returns to the heart from the body through major veins called the inferior and superior vena cava. The systemic circulation includes circulation through the coronary arteries to nurture the heart muscle.

Blood

Blood is the fluid that transports all of the substances that the body needs to sustain life. Blood delivers oxygen, hormones, and nutrients to the cells and carries away wastes that the cells produce. The blood also contains certain cells that help fight infection. Blood is made up of a liquid called **plasma** in which the other parts—red blood cells, white blood cells, and platelets—are suspended.

Plasma. About 55 percent of the total volume of your blood is plasma, which is about 92 percent water. Plasma transports dissolved nutrients, waste products, and mineral salts as well as hormones, enzymes, and vitamins.

Red Blood Cells. Red blood cells carry oxygen from the lungs to all body cells. The oxygen-carrying substance in red blood cells is known as

---

DID YOU KNOW?

- If you could connect your blood vessels end to end into a rope, you could wrap that rope around the world almost two and one-half times.
- The heart of an average adult forces out more than two ounces of oxygen-rich blood every time it beats. That amounts to slightly more than five quarts each minute.
- The first heart transplant in the world was performed in South Africa in 1967 by Dr. Christiaan Barnard and a team of 30. The recipient died just over two weeks after the operation.

Additional Information

Heart Rate. Instruct students on how to take their own pulse by putting their middle and ring fingers from one hand on the inside of the wrist of the other hand. Tell them to count the number of beats for 15 seconds and multiply by 4 to find out the number of beats per minute. Then have students take their pulse and record the result. Next, instruct them to jog in place for 2 minutes and record their pulse every 2 minutes for the next 6 minutes. What do they find? (Light activity causes an increase in heart rate, which gradually returns to normal once activity ceases.) What can they conclude about vigorous exercise? (Warming up and cooling down are important.)

The Cardiovascular System

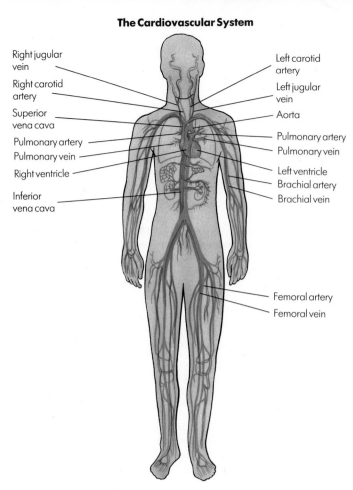

Right jugular vein
Right carotid artery
Superior vena cava
Pulmonary artery
Pulmonary vein
Right ventricle
Inferior vena cava

Left carotid artery
Left jugular vein
Aorta
Pulmonary artery
Pulmonary vein
Left ventricle
Brachial artery
Brachial vein

Femoral artery
Femoral vein

The cardiovascular system is a closed system of vessels through which blood, pumped by the heart, maintains the health of body cells by providing constant oxygen, nutrition, and removal of waste products.

There is no risk of infection when giving blood. New disposable needles are used each time.

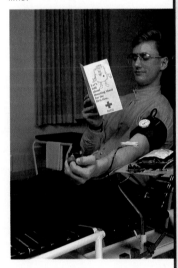

hemoglobin. It is a protein compound that is rich in iron. Hemoglobin is a pigment that gives blood its red color. Red blood cells also carry carbon dioxide, a waste product from body tissues, to the lungs. Red blood cells are the most numerous cells in blood. New red blood cells are continually being produced in bone marrow.

White Blood Cells. The main function of white blood cells is to destroy invading pathogens. Some white blood cells surround pathogens and ingest them. White blood cells are produced in red bone marrow. Production of white blood cells increases when there is an infection in the body. Normally, there are fewer white blood cells than red blood cells in a person's blood.

Platelets. Blood **platelets** are the smallest parts of the blood. Platelets are crucial in preventing the body's loss of blood. They initiate a chain of reactions that results in the clotting of blood. Platelets produce small fibers, called fibrin, that trap red blood cells at the site of a cut or a broken surface. These trapped cells form a clot, which helps prevent more blood loss.

THE CARDIOVASCULAR SYSTEM **251**

L1 CLASS ACTIVITY. Students can simulate the work a heart does by squeezing a tennis ball 70 times in 1 minute. The force needed to squeeze the tennis ball is about the same as the force needed to squeeze blood from the heart, which the heart does about 70 times a minute.

L1 DISCUSSION. What role does blood play in the body? (It transports all the substances that the body needs to sustain life.)

L1 USING BODY SYSTEMS TRANSPARENCY 51. Refer to the Teaching Transparencies Binder.

L1 CLASS ACTIVITY. Ask a volunteer to list on the chalkboard the four blood types. (A, B, AB, and O.) Then write *Rh negative* and *Rh positive* on the board. Have students list all the possible blood-type combinations. (There are eight: A+, A−, B+, B−, AB+, AB−, O+, O−.)

L2 CLASS ACTIVITY. Ask student volunteers to take a sample of their blood using a pin stick. (Do not allow students to share pins.) Place their drops of blood on glass slides for examination under the microscope. Have them examine the blood every 3 minutes. Ask them to watch for the formation of fibrins as the clotting begins. Have them look at their finger where the pin prick occurred. Is it still bleeding? Why not? What impedes the normal clotting factors? medications? hereditary factors? lack of certain vitamins?

L1 DISCUSSION. Ask students if they have ever noticed their own blood clotting. When? (Whenever their blood forms a scab.) Ask students to describe what happens when blood clots.

L2 SPEAKER. Arrange for a representative from the local blood bank to speak to the class about the current available blood supply. Is it sufficient? insufficient? overabundant? Approximately how many people donate blood in a week? Are certain times of the year more likely to bring donations? More likely to result in insufficient supplies? Ask students to summarize the presentation in writing.

Additional Information

Hypothermia. Students may not be aware of the relationship between the heat provided to our bodies by circulating blood and the effect of prolonged exposure to cold. Circulation is significantly suppressed by this exposure, causing hypothermia— a condition in which the body is unable to maintain normal body temperature. Many young people do not realize how quickly this life-threatening condition can occur.

Invite a knowledgeable member of an outing club to instruct your class on hypothermia.

Encourage students to investigate techniques for dressing warmly and new fabrics designed for outerwear in cold climates.

DID YOU KNOW?

- Beginning early in pregnancy, every Rh-negative female should have her blood checked regularly. If she has received an Rh-positive blood transfusion or if the father of the baby is Rh-positive, there could be problems when the antibodies from the mother cross the placenta and attack the baby's red blood cells. Fortunately a serum called RhoGAM can be given to the Rh-negative mother to prevent the buildup of antibodies.

Do you know your blood type? This information could be very important if you needed a blood transfusion in an emergency. Tests for human blood types classify red blood cells as type A, type B, type AB, or type O.

A person who has type O blood is referred to as a universal donor because that person can give blood to a person with any blood type. On the other hand, a person who has type AB blood is referred to as the universal recipient because he or she can receive any type of blood.

For transfusions to work, the blood types must match. Hospitals and blood banks take extreme care in checking blood types before giving transfusions.

BLOOD BANKS

Many cities have blood banks where blood is collected from healthy donors and stored. Blood banks store whole blood—blood that still contains both plasma and blood cells. Whole blood can be frozen and kept for long periods of time. When refrigerated, whole blood can be stored for several weeks. Transfusions of whole blood are given most often when a patient has suffered a severe loss of blood.

In some cases, such as those involving burn victims, the need may be for blood volume rather than blood cells. Plasma transfusions are given in these situations. Plasma is separated from whole blood by a centrifuge machine. This machine whirls the blood at a high speed, causing the blood cells to settle to the bottom, leaving a layer of plasma on the top.

Rh Factor. About 85 percent of the United States population has certain proteins in the blood, called Rh factors. These people are said to be Rh-positive. The remaining 15 percent of the population lack these proteins and are Rh-negative. What significance does the Rh factor have for your health?

A person with Rh-negative blood should not be given Rh-positive blood. Mixing the two causes antibodies to be produced. Rh-negative blood containing Rh antibodies causes the red blood cells of the Rh-positive blood to clump together. This mixing can occur when an Rh-negative person receives Rh-positive blood through a transfusion. This can cause serious complications and even result in death.

KEEPING FIT

Knowing About Cholesterol

For people 20 years of age and older, a desirable blood cholesterol level is less than 200. From 200–239 levels are considered borderline high. 240 and above is high. Now, even children are tested if there is a family history of high cholesterol.

Most people can reduce cholesterol levels by taking these steps:
- Reduce the intake of cholesterol-containing foods and fat.
- Increase the intake of soluble fiber.
- Maintain ideal weight; if overweight, lose that weight.
- Get regular aerobic exercise.
- Don't smoke.

Across the Curriculum

Science. Obtain slides that will permit students to see under a microscope the various blood components.

Science. Ask students to discover which classmates could donate blood for them. For which students could they donate blood? (Make arrangements with the science department for students to determine their blood type.)

Science. From the science department in your school, borrow microscopes and prepared slides of white blood cells, red blood cells, and platelets. Ask students to observe the differences and to draw sketches of what they see. Ask them to speculate about how the sizes and shapes of the cells are related to their functions.

Overcoming The Odds

Carmella Garcia is 15. She plays the trumpet, likes soccer, and has a part-time job walking dogs. She is also president of her class. She loves to run, and she has set two track records at her school in the past year. "I've always loved to run," she says. "It's like I was born with running shoes. My dad was the same way when he was younger. But it was what happened to my mom that really got us all more focused on being fit."

What happened to her mom was a heart attack. "Mom is only 52, so it was really a surprise. She was at work when it struck. I'll never forget that call from the hospital. My dad's face turned to stone. The next thing I knew, we were all there. It seemed like we lived at the hospital.

"Later they did coronary bypass surgery on her. When I saw her after the operation, I thought I was going to pass out. She looked so old.

"My mom wasn't fat or anything like that but she was a little overweight and she smoked. She's a nervous type of person like my sister, and I think that's part of what happened. Plus, she loves to cook, and she loves to eat.

"Well, the medical center where she had her operation had this program called

Lifestyle II, a program for heart patients and their families. So when my mom was stronger all five of us started to go to the two-hour sessions every week. We all had our cholesterol tested. My mom's

had been real high. Mine was okay. My dad's was a little elevated. My brother's was okay. But my sister's, well, that was the surprise. Hers was over 300. And she's even thin. My sister's cholesterol and my mom's and dad's are being watched really carefully. My sister may even go on medication if our home plan doesn't lower her cholesterol enough.

"They taught us in the classes how changing our life-style as a family could help not just our mom but all of us to live

longer and healthier. We had classes about low-fat diets, stress management, and regular exercise. They gave us this chart to keep track of how far and often we walk—as well as our pulse rates. My mom has given up cigarettes and coffee.

"I guess when that phone call came in about my mom, I thought that could be it. It was a low point in my life. But I guess now I am grateful in a funny kind of way that it all happened because it has brought us so close and it has made us all so much more aware of how important family and staying fit are. Lifestyle II is a good name for the program, I think, because it's like we've all been given a second chance. And we're taking it."

1. Carmella's family had to be shaken up by a heart attack to make the necessary life-style changes. Why do you think it often takes a scare for people to begin caring for their cardiovascular health?
2. What steps can you take to improve your cardiovascular health? What steps can you take to help your family members become more fit?
3. How do you think taking such steps might affect your self-esteem? Your family relationships?

DID YOU KNOW?

- The rarest type of blood in the ABO system is type AB. The rarest subgroup of a blood type has been found in only three people—one in the former Czechoslovakia and two (a brother and sister) in Massachusetts. Because of the rarity of the subtype, the brother has founded his own blood bank.

Blood pressure is the measure of the force of blood on the walls of blood vessels.

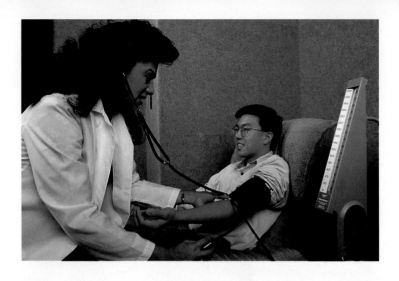

DID YOU KNOW?

- Men have more blood and more blood vessels than women do.
- The aorta is the largest blood vessel in the body. It is about 1 inch in diameter.
- There are about 10 billion capillaries in your body.
- The average heart pumps about 70 times per minute.
- A well-conditioned athlete can have a resting pulse as low as 45.

BLOOD PRESSURE

As blood flows from the arteries into the capillaries, blood pressure lowers. Blood pressure is the force of blood on the walls of blood vessels. By the time blood reaches the venules, it has lost all but about one-twelfth of its pressure. This low pressure is necessary because the thin, tiny capillaries could not withstand the force at which blood is pumped through the arteries. Blood pressure is reduced even more as the veins get larger. Muscular activity is necessary to maintain the blood flow through the veins.

Blood leaves the ventricles under a high pressure. As you might expect, pressure is greater in the left ventricle and aorta than in the right ventricle and pulmonary artery. Blood pressure is greater in the left ventricle because blood must be pumped with enough force to send it throughout the body. The right ventricle sends blood a shorter distance—to the lungs.

Each time the ventricles contract, blood surges through the arteries with such a force that the walls of the arteries bulge. At this point in the cycle of heart action, arterial pressure is at its greatest and is called systolic pressure. As the ventricles relax to refill with blood, arterial pressure is at its lowest and is called diastolic pressure.

A sphygmomanometer is an instrument used to measure blood pressure. You have probably had your blood pressure measured during a checkup. To have this done, a health professional wraps a blood pressure cuff around your arm just above the elbow. The cuff is then inflated with air until circulation in your arm is blocked. As air is slowly released from the cuff, the health professional uses a stethoscope to hear the sound of the blood beginning to move through the constricted area again. He or she listens for the return of a pulse in the artery. The number on the sphygmomanometer gauge at this point represents your systolic blood pressure. It is the upper number of the fraction representing your blood pressure and is usually between 110 and 140.

As air continues to be released, the person taking the reading listens for a change in the tone of your pulse or for the sound of the pulse to disappear completely. The number on the gauge at this point represents your diastolic blood pressure. It is the lower number of the fraction and is usually between 70 and 90.

Additional Information

Blood Types. Variation in ABO and Rhesus blood types is studied through immunological reactions, which can best be understood by considering a specific example.

If someone has type A blood, the red blood cells bear the A antigen and the serum contains anti-B antibodies. Someone with type B blood, on the other hand, will have the B antigen and anti-A antibodies.

When red blood cells with A antigen (from the type A individual) are mixed with serum containing anti-A antibodies (from the person with type B blood), an antigen-antibody reaction occurs—pairs of antibodies and antigens each fit together like a key in a lock—leading to agglutination, or clumping, of the red blood cells.

Blood Vessels

Your blood vessels make it possible for blood to be distributed throughout your body. There are over 60,000 miles (96,540 km) of blood vessels in your body. They are divided mainly into arteries, capillaries, and veins.

Arteries. The largest blood vessels, called **arteries**, carry blood away from the heart. As part of the systemic circulation, the left ventricle pumps oxygenated blood through the largest artery, the aorta. As part of the pulmonary circulation, the right ventricle pumps blood that is low in oxygen through the pulmonary arteries to the lungs. Arteries branch into smaller vessels called arterioles. These microscopic branches regulate the flow of blood into capillaries.

Capillaries. The smallest blood vessels are called **capillaries.** Some capillaries are 50 times thinner than a single strand of hair. Nutrients and oxygen from the blood pass to body cells through capillary walls. Waste products from the cells move into the blood through capillary walls.

Veins. The system of capillaries leads into tiny branches of veins called venules. These venules lead to **veins**, the vessels that carry the blood back to the heart. Veins become thicker and larger in diameter as they get closer to the heart. The walls of veins are thinner than those of arteries.

Veins do not have to withstand the great pressure the arteries do. Another difference between veins and arteries is that the inner lining of the veins forms valves that help direct the flow of blood. These valves prevent blood from flowing back into the capillaries. Regulating blood flow is especially important in the legs and feet where the blood must flow against the force of gravity to return to the heart.

FINDING HELP

Heart disease is America's number one killer. In fact, an adult's chances of dying from it are very high. For more information about cardiovascular health and disease, check to see if there is an office of the American Heart Association in your community. If not, write to the American Heart Association 7320 Greenville Avenue Dallas, TX 75231

Assess

Check for Understanding
■ Assign and discuss the lesson review. Encourage LD students to focus on questions 1, 2, 3, 4, and 7.

Evaluate
■ Administer, grade, and discuss the *Lesson 1 Quiz.*

Reteach
■ Ask students to write questions about the lesson's key points. Compile the questions and use these as a basis for discussion.
■ Ask students to complete *Reteaching Activity 33.*

Enrich
■ Ask students to research new advances in the development and use of artificial hearts. Ask them to read about and report on the case of Barney Clark, the first artificial heart recipient. Ask students to decide whether or not they would have opted for the operation he had and to explain their decisions.

LESSON 1 REVIEW

Reviewing Facts and Vocabulary

1. In what ways is the cardiovascular system a transport system?
2. Describe the changes in pressure as blood flows through the blood vessels. What is meant by systolic and diastolic pressure?

Thinking Critically

3. **Analysis.** Compare the pathways of pulmonary and systemic circulation.
4. **Analysis.** When might a blood pressure reading be a health concern?

5. **Evaluation.** Why do you think the body has more red blood cells than white blood cells? When would you expect the body to make more white blood cells?

Applying Health Knowledge

6. Write a paragraph describing a typical day in the life of your heart.
7. Have your blood pressure checked in class by the school nurse. What is the average blood pressure for the class? How does the blood pressure of students who exercise regularly differ from those who do not?

Close

Write the lesson's major concepts on numbered, separate slips of paper. Place the slips in a box, and let each student draw one. Next, going in numerical order, have students define and summarize the concept written on the slip of paper they selected.

DID YOU KNOW?

■ The word *artery* derives from the Greek word *arteria,* meaning "air pipe." Ancient Greeks reasoned that since the arteries of the dead appeared empty, they must have been used for transporting air through the body.

Answers to Lesson 1 Review

1. It carries oxygen and nutrients to body cells and picks up waste products for disposal by the lungs and kidneys.
2. Changes in pressure and systolic and diastolic pressure are discussed on page 254.
3. The pathways of pulmonary and systemic circulation are discussed on pages 249 and 250.
4. A reading outside the range of 110 to140 for systolic pressure and 70 to 90 for diastolic pressure may be a health concern.
5. Answers will vary. Possible answer: Red blood cells must carry oxygen throughout the body. White blood cells increase when one has an infection.
6. Paragraphs will vary.
7. Answers will vary.

Focus

Lesson Objectives

After studying this lesson, students should be able to:

- describe problems that affect the cardiovascular system
- explain causes of congenital heart disease
- list risk factors related to heart disease that are within a person's control

Bellringer

Write the following on the chalkboard for students to work on while attendance is being taken: *List as many diseases and disorders of the cardiovascular system as you can.*

Introducing the Lesson

Refer to the Bellringer. Have students share their lists. Tell students that many of the diseases and disorders of the cardiovascular system have very serious consequences. Sickle-cell anemia, leukemia, and hemophilia are blood diseases. Heart murmur, varicose veins, and thrombosis affect the heart and blood vessels. Anemia is a blood disorder. Tell students that this lesson allows them to take a more detailed look at these diseases and disorders.

Building Vocabulary

- Ask students to provide verbal explanations for each vocabulary word and to use each word in a sentence.
- Ask students to complete *Workbook Vocabulary Activity 34.*

DID YOU KNOW?

- About 46 percent of the world's people have blood type O. However, in certain parts of the world, another blood type might be more common. For example, in Norway, type A blood is most common.

PROBLEMS AND CARE OF THE CARDIOVASCULAR SYSTEM

LESSON 2 FOCUS

TERMS TO USE
- Congenital
- Thrombosis
- Embolus

CONCEPTS TO LEARN
- Genetic, environmental, and life-style problems can affect the cardiovascular system.
- Congenital heart disease covers a wide variety of conditions.
- Many of the risk factors related to heart disease are within your control.

ATTITUDES AND BEHAVIORS TO EVALUATE
- Self-Inventory, page 270.
- Building Decision-Making Skills, page 271.

There are a variety of problems that can affect the cardiovascular system. With proper care, some problems can be avoided; others can be treated.

Problems of the Cardiovascular System

In this lesson, you will read about congenital heart disease, heart murmurs, varicose veins, thrombosis, anemia, sickle-cell anemia, leukemia, and hemophilia. In Chapter 29 you will read about other diseases of the heart.

Congenital Heart Disease

Before birth the heart begins as a single tube. It enlarges and divides into chambers. This process involves a progression of developmental steps. A disruption in this process can result in a defect in the heart. Babies born with such a defect have congenital heart disease. The term **congenital** means "occurring at birth."

Congenital heart disease covers a wide variety of conditions. The heart may have a hole between two chambers. The valves may not function properly, or there may be a blockage of the blood flow. The defect may be in the blood vessels leading to and from the heart. Certain types of defects may not be noticed right away. In some cases the defect heals itself as the heart grows following birth. Other defects may require surgery.

There are numerous causes of congenital heart disease. Only a small percentage of these defects have a genetic cause. Some defects result from a viral infection during the early months of pregnancy, illegal drug use, or a vitamin deficiency. Most cases can be treated or corrected with surgery.

Heart Murmurs

Have you ever used a stethoscope to listen to your heart? Blood makes strong, clear sounds as it passes through a healthy heart. If the heart is not functioning properly, other noises may be heard as blood moves through the chambers.

A heart murmur is an abnormal sound. The major cause of heart murmurs is a defective valve in the heart. A valve that is too narrow causes the blood to be pushed through the restricted opening with more force. A valve that does not close properly allows blood to leak back through it. Both situations cause the sound labeled a "murmur". Most murmurs are slight and do not need correction. More serious murmurs may require treatment.

256 CHAPTER 13 CARDIOVASCULAR, LYMPHATIC, AND RESPIRATORY SYSTEMS

Resources for Lesson 2

- **Transparency** 51
- **Guided Reading** Act 34
- **Workbook** Voc Act 34
- **Reteaching** Activity 34
- **Lesson 2 Quiz**

Science and Technology Videodisc
Human Biology, Side 1
Ch 5 Blood Clot Treatment

Ch 8 Computer-Aided Heart Surgery

Ch 12 Heart Rehabilitation

A Congenital Heart Problem

- Aorta
- Pulmonary artery
- Pulmonary artery
- Pulmonary vein
- Pulmonary vein
- Left ventricle
- Opening in septum
- Right atrium
- Right ventricle
- Septum

A common congenital heart problem involves an abnormal opening in the septum, the wall that divides the right and left chambers of the heart. The oxygen-rich blood in the left ventricle can mix with the deoxygenated blood in the right ventricle. The result is that blood circulating through the baby's body does not have the level of oxygen it needs. The baby will have a "bluish" appearance. This problem can be corrected surgically.

Varicose Veins

Varicose veins are swollen and enlarged veins, especially in the legs. Varicose veins develop when the valves in the veins are weakened. This condition may affect both sexes and all ages. Some people inherit the tendency to develop varicose veins. Other contributing factors include the following:

- prolonged periods of standing
- obesity
- pregnancy
- wearing very tight clothing
- aging, which can cause veins to lose their tone and elasticity

---

K E E P I N G   F I T

Blood Donors

Requirements for blood donors vary from state to state. Generally there are minimum age and weight requirements. In addition, general good health is required and donors should not have active colds, sore throats, other infections, or have had recent surgery. To find out about your state's requirements for donating blood call your local Red Cross chapter, hospital, or blood bank.

PROBLEMS AND CARE OF THE CARDIOVASCULAR SYSTEM **257**

Additional Information

The Cardiovascular System. Veins are closer to the body surface than are arteries. The veins appear bluish in color. Consider these other characteristics of veins and arteries:

- When an artery bleeds, the blood appears to be pumping out in spurts. This is due to the heart muscle contracting.

- When a vein bleeds, the blood appears to be oozing out of the body.
- Arterial bleeding is more serious because a larger amount of blood is lost more quickly.

Direct pressure or pressure-point pressure will slow down either type of bleeding.

Guided Practice

L2 DISCUSSION. Discuss congenital heart disease. What can be done prior to birth for infants with heart defects? after birth? What is their prognosis for a healthy life? What types of new specialties in medicine are resulting from the need to save the lives of infants?

L2 CLASS ACTIVITY. Ask a cardiologist to give you a tape of the sounds of a heart that is not functioning correctly. Play the tape for the class and have students compare these sounds to healthy heart sounds. Ask students what a doctor can tell from listening to heart sounds through the stethoscope. What are the limitations of checking your own heart sounds?

L2 DISCUSSION. Have students analyze the conditions under which a person might develop varicose veins or phlebitis. What could be done to treat the condition? What could be done to prevent the condition?

L2 DISCUSSION. Ask students if they know of anyone who is likely to develop varicose veins. Ask them to explain their answers.

L2 DISCUSSION. Review with the class the structure and size of the coronary arteries. A thrombus or embolus (a clot) in an artery can cause death of tissue and this can have fatal results. What are the symptoms of a heart attack?

L3 DEMONSTRATION. Visit a hospital that performs angioplasty. Ask if you can borrow a catheter used in the procedure to show the class and some film footage of how this is performed by doctors. If a doctor or technician can come to the classroom and explain the procedure, it would be ideal.

L2 DISCUSSION. Ask students to compare the size of a drinking straw to the size of an aortic catheter. Are all catheters the same size? Can one catheter be used in all blood vessels?

Blood flow in the veins from the legs to the heart goes against gravity. When the valves in the veins are weak, they cannot close tightly to prevent the backflow of blood. Blood then collects in the veins. As a result, veins become dilated and valves cannot function efficiently. This condition can be very painful.

Exercise is not only a means of prevention but also a recommended treatment for varicose veins. Through exercise, circulation in the legs and back to the heart is improved. Exercise also massages the walls of the veins and helps them regain their elasticity. If necessary, final treatment is surgical removal, or stripping, of the veins.

Thrombosis

Thrombosis is the presence or formation of a blood clot within a blood vessel. A blood clot, called a thrombus, occasionally occurs in blood vessels, and usually remains attached to its place of origin. Clots can interfere with blood flow through the vessels.

A clot that becomes dislodged from its place of origin is called an **embolus.** An embolus can travel to other parts of the body, blocking important blood vessels. A coronary embolism is the result of an embolus that blocks an artery in the heart. A pulmonary embolism results when an embolus blocks a blood vessel in the lungs. Clots in the arteries to the brain cause a stroke. When the brain's supply of oxygen is blocked, brain cells are damaged.

Anemia

Anemia is a condition caused by a deficiency of red blood cells or by a low concentration of hemoglobin in the red cells. With a low level of hemoglobin, body cells do not receive a sufficient amount of oxygen. Treatment depends on the specific cause. The three main causes are as follows:
- a serious loss of blood
- a decrease in the production of red blood cells because of malfunctioning red bone marrow
- a nutritional deficiency, such as a lack of iron in the diet

Red blood cells are normally round. Sickle cells have a crescent shape because of the action of the hemoglobin they contain.

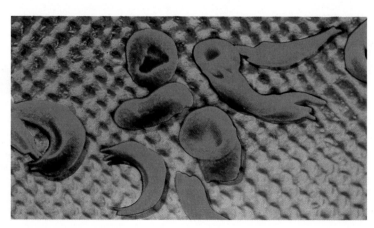

Additional Information

Heart Disease. Pain that a person experiences that radiates and becomes gradually stronger focusing on the left side of the body is a sure sign of a heart attack. If the pain instead fades and recurs, it is probably angina, not a heart attack.

Angina is the body's way of signaling that something is happening to the heart. It is a warning that a heart attack may be next. During angina, the heart muscle cells are being deprived of oxygen-carrying blood. Years of overeating or eating high-fat foods may be the cause for many angina attacks. Such diets cause plaque and cholesterol to line the interior of the coronary arteries.

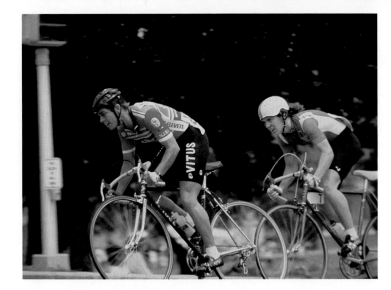

Sickle-Cell Anemia

Sickle-cell anemia is an inherited condition, resulting from a defect in the hemoglobin within red blood cells. The red blood cells develop a sickle shape and clump together, obstructing blood flow to the tissues. This obstruction leads to the death of tissues because they are deprived of oxygen. The symptoms of sickle-cell anemia are severe joint and abdominal pain, weakness, and chronic kidney disease. There is no cure for sickle-cell anemia. However, it can be treated with blood transfusions and pain-relieving medicines.

Leukemia

Leukemia is a type of cancer that is the result of abnormal production of one or more types of white blood cells. These cells are immature and are not able to help fight pathogens. A person with leukemia is highly

---

K E E P I N G   F I T

Leg Pain: When Calves Speak

Leg pain can be caused by many factors, many of them not serious. However, some leg pain may indicate hardening of the arteries, which can put a person at increased risk of heart attack or stroke. Blocked arteries cannot supply needed blood to the body's extremities, and pain results.

If a parent or grandparent shows the following signs, urge him or her to see a doctor:

- pain that occurs when walking
- pain that occurs after walking
- pain that increases with distance walked
- pain that stops when standing or after a short rest

PROBLEMS AND CARE OF THE CARDIOVASCULAR SYSTEM **259**

Additional Information

Sickle-cell Genes. In some parts of the world, having one of the genes that cause sickle-cell anemia can be an advantage—even though having two of them is a lethal combination.

People who have one sickle-cell gene and one normal gene have enough normal hemoglobin in their blood to function normally.

If they live in a tropical region where malaria is prevalent, such as West Africa or the Caribbean, their sickle-cell hemoglobin helps protect them from serious malaria infection. The reason? The microscopic malaria parasite spends most of its life cycle in the human host's red blood cells. Sickle-cell hemoglobin distorts the red cells, causing them to die prematurely—taking many of the parasites with them.

Hypertension, or high blood pressure, is a common condition often characterized as dangerous if undetected or untreated. Low blood pressure, however, may also present health risks. Have students investigate the following questions. What are these risks? What are the symptoms of low blood pressure? What is the treatment? What percentage of the population suffers from chronic low blood pressure? from chronic high blood pressure? What is your blood pressure? Ask students to present the answers to all of these questions in well-researched oral reports.

L2 PERSONAL INVOLVEMENT.
Have an American Heart Association "Save a Sweetheart Day." This is one day when students help their significant male or female friends stop behaviors that make them at risk of heart disease. February is a good time for this activity. Materials are free from the American Heart Association.

L2 PERSONAL INVOLVEMENT.
Work with students to set up a school walk for faculty and staff to get cardiovascular exercise. The walk can be inside or outside. It should be measured and include a plan for slow warm-up and cool down. The American Heart Association would be a good resource for the walk planners.

L1 USING THE LESSON RESOURCES. For additional student activities, refer to the lesson resources on page 256.

DID YOU KNOW?

■ The gene for hemophilia is on the X chromosome. For females to have the disease, they must inherit two copies of the gene, which is unlikely because it's rare. Males need only inherit one copy of the gene, so hemophilia is much more common in males than females.

HELP WANTED

Cardiology Technician

Do you handle pressure well? When you are in a hospital and hear a "code blue," do you wish you were one of those rushing into action? Well, now is your chance. As a cardiology technician you can save lives. You must be able to handle the emotional highs and lows, must be physically and mentally sharp, and must be able to perform precisely when the pressure is on. Excellent pay, benefits, and opportunity for advancement are some of the rewards you will receive as a cardiology technician. For more information contact:
National Association of Cardiovascular Pulmonary Technology
Suite 1100
1101 14th Street N.W.
Washington, DC 20005

HEALTH UPDATE

LOOKING AT TECHNOLOGY

Some Heartening News About Hearts

There are many new technological advances that are now available or are soon to be available to people with heart diseases and disorders.

■ Blood and urine tests are now available to quickly alert doctors to which high blood pressure patients are most likely to have heart attacks.

■ Doppler ultrasound is now being used by cardiologists to show trouble in blood vessels before they develop into major problems. The test, which uses sound waves, is less expensive and faster than other methods of diagnosis.

■ Clotbusters, medicines given to heart attack victims right after their attacks, can prevent much of the damage associated with the attacks.

■ The use of aspirin, given immediately following a heart attack, has been found to be helpful in preventing thrombus formation for some patients. Aspirin decreases the tendency of blood platelet cells to adhere to the blood vessel walls. Some studies show that aspirin therapy may be more effective in men than in women.

■ Heart-defibrillators are now being used in some locations by fire fighters, lifeguards, and police. The devices, which administer electric shocks to heart attack victims on the scene before medical help can arrive, have already saved many lives. New plans to place them in sports arenas, schools, and other public places are now being considered.

■ Atherectomy is a new, less expensive, and less complicated way of removing blockages in arteries and blood vessels. Guided by an X-ray image, a stiff tube is inserted into the blocked area. Then, a small tool similar to a drill is threaded into the blocked area, and the plaque causing the blockage is shaved or chipped away. The procedure may be a better alternative to angioplasty, the balloon technique now used to clean out arteries, which tend to narrow again.

■ The ventricular assist device, now being tested, is a permanently implanted device that mechanically takes on the work of the heart's major pumping chamber.

■ Total artificial heart is a mechanical pump that will be available within 20 years to replace damaged hearts. Unlike earlier heart replacements, this one will not have to be connected to tubes or wires running outside the patient's body. Instead, electrical impulses sent through the skin to implanted receivers will do the work that the heart once was able to do.

---

susceptible to infection. In addition, the large numbers of white blood cells interfere with red cell and platelet production. Leukemia can result in the following conditions:

■ anemia and a general feeling of being tired resulting from lack of red blood cells

---

Across the Curriculum

Home Economics. Some anemias are a direct result of an iron-deficient diet. Have students research and list five foods that are good sources of iron. (Some examples are meat—especially liver, kidneys, and heart—peas, leafy green vegetables, potatoes, dried fruits, beans, egg yolks, and whole-grain and enriched cereals and breads.) Have students report their findings to the class. As a follow-up activity, have students consult cookbooks for recipes using iron-rich foods and collect these in a booklet.

Science. Using a microscope, have students view slides of healthy cardiac tissue and cadaver tissue taken from someone who suffered a fatal embolism. Have them compare color and character of the tissues.

- abnormal bleeding from cuts or bruises, caused by insufficient platelets to help clot the blood
- general openness to infection, since the white blood cells that stimulate antibody production are underproduced

The causes of leukemia, the most common type of cancer in children, are largely unknown. Some subtypes of the disease seem to be genetic; others may be traced to a virus.

Bone marrow transplants have been very successful in treating some types of leukemia. Certain medicines and radiation may slow down the rate of the disease. However, the death rate is still high.

Hemophilia

Hemophilia is an inherited disease in which a clotting factor is absent or abnormal. This causes the blood to clot very slowly or not at all. A person who has hemophilia can bleed to death very easily. Treatment involves giving the patient an injection of the clotting factor. If too much blood is lost, a complete transfusion may be done.

Care of Your Cardiovascular System

Most of the risk factors related to cardiovascular problems are within your control. Your choices and behaviors affect the health of your cardiovascular system.

You probably know that smoking puts added stress on the cardiovascular system. Nicotine in cigarettes increases blood pressure and heart rate. Not smoking as well as avoiding the smoke of others is a healthy choice. Being overweight causes the heart to pump more blood through more blood vessels. It's important to eat a healthy diet. Limiting your intake of foods high in fat, cholesterol, and salt will protect both your heart and blood vessels. In addition, a regular exercise program will strengthen the heart, making it work more efficiently. Exercise will also help circulation. Finally, having regular medical checkups enables your doctor to monitor the health of your cardiovascular system and encourage healthy behaviors.

> **CONFLICT RESOLUTION**
>
> Although heart disease is the number one killer of both males and females, it tend to affect females later in life. This fact often results in a myth that females don't get heart disease. This myth is one reason researchers routinely have omitted females from heart-disease studies.
>
> *How does this gender bias in research put females' health at risk?*

LESSON 2 REVIEW

Reviewing Facts and Vocabulary

1. Define two problems of the cardiovascular system.
2. Explain how a defective valve in the heart could affect blood flow.

Thinking Critically

3. **Analysis.** Compare a thrombus and an embolus.

Applying Health Knowledge

4. Make a list of health behaviors you practice to promote care of your cardiovascular system. Make a separate list of additional behaviors that you want to practice. Write an essay describing how you plan to care for your cardiovascular system now, in 10 years, and in 20 years.

Check for Understanding

- Assign and discuss the lesson review.

Evaluate

- Administer, grade, and discuss the *Lesson 2 Quiz.*

Reteach

- Write or call your local chapter of the American Heart Association and ask for free pamphlets about cardiovascular diseases and caring for the cardiovascular system. Ask each student to select one pamphlet and rewrite it in his or her own words. Ask students to display both the original and the paraphrased versions.
- Ask students to complete *Reteaching Activity 34.*

Enrich

- Ask students to research bone marrow transplants. Why are they needed? What does bone marrow do? Is the surgery usually successful? Who can donate bone marrow? Ask students to summarize their findings in writing.

Close

Tell students they will study in later chapters more about cardiovascular diseases and ways to lower their risks.

Answers to Lesson 2 Review

1. Answers will vary. Accept definitions for two of the following: congenital heart disease, heart murmurs, varicose veins, thrombosis, anemia, sickle-cell anemia, leukemia, hemophilia. Definitions can be found on pages 256 to 261 or in the Glossary.
2. A valve that is too narrow causes blood to be pushed through the restricted opening with more force. A valve that does not close properly allows blood to leak back through it.
3. Both are blood clots. A thrombus remains attached at its point of origin. An embolus becomes dislodged and can travel to other parts of the body.
4. Answers will vary.

Focus

Lesson Objectives

After studying this lesson, students should be able to:

- explain the function of the lymphatic system
- describe how the two main types of lymphocytes help your body fight pathogens

Bellringer

Write the following on the chalkboard for students to work on while attendance is being taken: *List as many details about the lymphatic system as you can recall. What does the system do for your body?*

Introducing the Lesson

Refer to the Bellringer. Ask students to share their responses. Write their responses on the chalkboard. Tell them that the lymphatic system is often overlooked because its functions have not always been clearly understood as it operates within the greater cardiovascular system. This lesson will present the many ways that this system contributes to maintaining good health.

Building Vocabulary

- Write the vocabulary terms on the chalkboard and pronounce them for students. Have students preview the lesson to find each term's definition. Record the definitions on the board.
- Ask students to complete *Workbook Vocabulary Activity 35.*

DID YOU KNOW?

- Every year in the United States, Americans suffer an estimated 700 million infections.
- In 1918, one flu epidemic hit many locations around the globe, killing 21 million people.

THE LYMPHATIC SYSTEM

LESSON 3 FOCUS

TERMS TO USE

- Lymph
- Lymph nodes
- Lymphocytes

CONCEPTS TO LEARN

- Your lymphatic system helps your body maintain its fluid balance by carrying fluid away from tissues.
- Lymphocytes are valuable in helping your body fight pathogens.

ATTITUDES AND BEHAVIORS TO EVALUATE

- Self-Inventory, page 270.
- Building Decision-Making Skills, page 271.

The cardiovascular system moves blood throughout the body to nourish cells and remove waste products. The lymphatic system transports a fluid called lymph. **Lymph** is a clear yellow fluid that fills spaces around cells. Lymph is present in all body tissues.

Functions of the Lymphatic System

Your lymphatic system helps your body maintain your body's fluid balance by carrying excess fluid away from tissues. Lymph moves through lymphatic vessels and returns to your bloodstream. If this fluid were to remain in the spaces around cells, swelling of your tissues would result. This system also helps your body defend itself against pathogens.

Structure of the Lymphatic System

The lymphatic system consists of lymphatic vessels, lymph nodes, lymph, and lymphocytes. The spleen, tonsils, and thymus gland also play a part in the functioning of the lymphatic system.

Lymphatic vessels are distributed throughout the body much the same as blood vessels. Lymphatic vessels form a network that carries lymph to two lymph ducts, one in the neck area and the other in the chest area. These ducts empty into veins of the cardiovascular system.

At certain places in the body, lymph passes through lymph nodes. **Lymph nodes** are masses of tissues that filter lymph before it returns to the blood. They are located along lymph vessels, mostly in the neck, groin, and armpits. **Lymphocytes** are a type of white blood cell that multiply in lymph nodes and lymph tissue to destroy invading pathogens.

Types of Lymphocytes

There are two main types of lymphocytes—T cells and B cells. T cells are produced in bone marrow and are transported to the thymus gland, which is located behind the sternum. T cells can release a toxin that weakens a pathogen so that it can be ingested. T helper cells are a type of T cell. These cells stimulate the other type of lymphocyte, B cells, to produce antibodies that destroy or neutralize invading pathogens. Antibodies help destroy pathogens. They can attach themselves to pathogens so that they can be ingested by white blood cells.

Lymphatic Organs

Have you ever been sick and felt swollen areas just below your ears? You were feeling swollen lymph nodes. They swell when the body is fighting an infection and producing more lymphocytes.

262   CHAPTER 13 CARDIOVASCULAR, LYMPHATIC, AND RESPIRATORY SYSTEMS

Resources for Lesson 3

- **Transparency** 52
- **Guided Reading** Act 35
- **Workbook** Voc Act 35
- **Reteaching** Activity 35
- **Lesson 3 Quiz**

Science and Technology Videodisc
Human Biology, Side 1
Ch 14 White Cells in Action

Ch 15 Combined Immune Deficiency

The Lymphatic System

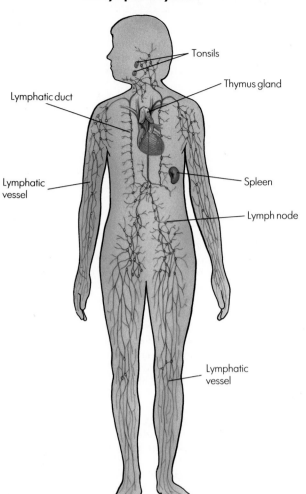

- Tonsils
- Thymus gland
- Lymphatic duct
- Spleen
- Lymphatic vessel
- Lymph node
- Lymphatic vessel

Lymph vessels are present in most body tissues.

The spleen is an organ located slightly behind the stomach on the left side of the body. The spleen plays an important role in keeping the blood free of foreign substances and also in storing B cells.

Tonsils are a mass of lymphatic tissue in the back of the throat. The adenoids are similar masses. Tonsils and adenoids trap and filter out pathogens that enter the body through the mouth and nose. When the body has been invaded by pathogens, the tonsils swell as they produce lymphocytes to kill the pathogens.

The thymus gland produces lymphocytes in infants and children and is important in the development of the body's defense system.

Problems of the Lymphatic System

Several problems can affect the lymphatic system. Some can usually be cured; others have no cure.

> **DID YOU KNOW?**
>
> - A study at the University of Virginia suggests that colds are more likely spread by fingers and hands (skin-to-skin contact) than through sneezes or coughs. Hand washing, then, might be the best preventive measure when someone in your family has a cold.
> - A hefty allergic sneeze can throw water particles out across the room at speeds up to 100 miles an hour.

THE LYMPHATIC SYSTEM **263**

L1 PERSONAL INVOLVEMENT. Have students develop a system to use in keeping personal medical records.

L1 USING THE LESSON RESOURCES. For additional student activities, refer to the lesson resources on page 262.

Assess

Check for Understanding

- Assign and discuss the lesson review. Encourage LD students to focus on questions 1 and 2.

Evaluate

- Administer, grade, and discuss the *Lesson 3 Quiz*.

Reteach

- Have students trace the lymphatic system and explain how it interrelates with the blood circulatory system.
- Ask students to complete *Reteaching Activity 35*.

Enrich

- Assign students to research the relationship, if any, between smoking and the frequency of colds and flu. Have them discuss their findings with the class.

Close

Tell students they have studied the cardiovascular and lymphatic systems—two systems that closely interrelate. Tell them a third system, the respiratory system, is also associated with the cardiovascular and lymphatic systems. The combined systems are sometimes referred to as the cardiorespiratory system. Tell them they will study the respiratory system in the next lesson.

> **DID YOU KNOW?**
> - Many of the infections associated with the common cold are caused by a large group of viruses called rhinoviruses.
> - When you have a cold, you should drink at least 8 ounces of juice or water every 2 hours.
> - The incubation period of the common cold is usually 18 to 48 hours. Colds often last between 4 and 10 days.

Tonsillitis

Tonsils can become infected even when they are helping to fight infections in other parts of the body. When they are infected, tonsils become inflamed and tender. Symptoms are a sore throat and fever. Infected tonsils may be treated with antibiotics. In some cases, tonsils are surgically removed.

Hodgkin's Disease

Hodgkin's disease is cancer of lymph tissue. The cancer cells spread quickly through the lymphatic system. Hodgkin's disease is treated with radiation for localized areas and chemotherapy when the disease has spread. The cure rate is high for localized areas.

Immune Deficiency

Your body protects itself against anything that might enter it and cause it harm. T cells are an important part of that defense system. T cells stimulate B cells to produce antibodies that fight pathogens and give you immunity to many diseases. If there is any disruption of T cell activity, an immune deficiency results.

For example, HIV, the virus that causes AIDS, destroys T cells. As a result, a person who has been infected with HIV cannot fight other pathogens effectively. An HIV-infected person will eventually develop AIDS. However, in the meantime, he or she will have many infections that would ordinarily be controlled by a healthy defense system. Eventually, one of these infections will cause the person to die.

Care of the Lymphatic System

Taking care of your lymphatic system involves helping your body fight disease. This means making sure that you care for your total health by eating properly, exercising regularly, and getting enough sleep. Having regular medical checkups and staying up-to-date on your immunizations are other important steps you can take.

LESSON 3 REVIEW

Reviewing Facts and Vocabulary

1. Describe the function of lymphocytes.
2. What are the functions of the lymphatic system?

Thinking Critically

3. **Analysis.** Compare the components of the lymphatic system.

Applying Health Knowledge

4. Gather statistics and information about Hodgkin's disease. What age groups are affected? What are the rates of recovery?

Answers to Lesson 3 Review

1. Lymphocytes are a type of white blood cell that multiply to destroy invading pathogens.
2. It helps one's body maintain fluid balance by carrying excess fluid away from tissues and helps one's body defend itself against pathogens.
3. Answers will vary. Possible answer: All components work together to help keep the body healthy. Lymphatic vessels carry lymph to lymph ducts. Lymph is a fluid that fills spaces around the cells. Lymph nodes filter lymph. Lymphocytes are white blood cells that multiply in lymph nodes and lymph tissues.
4. Answers will vary.

THE RESPIRATORY SYSTEM

W hile reading this paragraph, you will inhale two or three times without even thinking about it. Have you ever counted the number of times you inhale in a minute?

Functions of the Respiratory System

Respiration is the exchange of gases between you and your environment. There are two major parts to respiration. **External respiration** is the exchange of oxygen and carbon dioxide between the blood and the air in the lungs. As you breathe, you inhale air that contains oxygen into your lungs. Oxygen moves from your lungs to your blood. Carbon dioxide moves from your blood to your lungs. **Internal respiration** is the exchange of gases between the blood and the body cells. Oxygen moves from your blood to your cells. Carbon dioxide moves from your cells to your blood. Without the oxygen you could live only a few minutes.

Structure of the Respiratory System

The main parts of the respiratory system are the nasal cavity, pharynx, larynx, trachea, bronchi, and lungs.

The Nasal Cavity

Air enters the body primarily through the nasal cavity, which is the inner nose. Here the air is warmed and cleaned by mucous membranes and tiny hairs called cilia that line the nose. The mucous membranes also secrete mucus, which adds moisture to the air. All the upper air passages are lined with mucous membranes.

The Pharynx and the Larynx

From the nasal cavity, air moves through the **pharynx,** or throat, the **larynx,** or voice box, and into the **trachea,** or windpipe. The larynx contains two pairs of ligaments called vocal cords. As air passes over these cords, the cords vibrate and sound is produced.

The epiglottis is a flap of tissue that covers the larynx. When you swallow, it closes, covering the opening of the larynx. This covering prevents solids and liquids from getting into your larynx and trachea. The epiglottis opens when you breathe to allow air to pass into the lungs.

The Trachea and the Bronchi

The trachea is lined with a mucous membrane and covered with cilia. Cilia are in constant movement, keeping foreign particles from reaching

THE RESPIRATORY SYSTEM **265**

LESSON 4 FOCUS

TERMS TO USE
- External respiration
- Internal respiration
- Pharynx (FAIR•inks)
- Larynx (LAIR•inks)
- Trachea (TRAY•key•uh)
- Bronchi
- Diaphragm (DIE•uh•FRAM)

CONCEPTS TO LEARN
- Respiration takes place at different levels within the body.
- Respiration is the exchange of gases between you and your environment.
- Polluted factors in the environment negatively affect the quality of respiration.
- Respiration is vital to life.

ATTITUDES AND BEHAVIORS TO EVALUATE
- Self-Inventory, page 270.
- Building Decision-Making Skills, page 271.

Lesson Objectives
After studying this lesson, students should be able to:
- explain the function of respiration
- tell where the oxygen and carbon dioxide exchange takes place

Bellringer
Write the following on the chalkboard for students to work on while attendance is being taken: *What is the difference between breathing and respiration?*

Introducing the Lesson
Discuss student responses to the Bellringer. Point out that respiration encompasses breathing and involves the overall exchange of gases by the body. Explain that breathing properly is critical to respiration. Have students sit erectly with their backs straight, their heads up, and their hands in their laps. Ask them to take slow, deep breaths. Talk students through the breathing process so that they can feel what is taking place: Feel the air entering the body through the nasal cavity. As you inhale, the diaphragm is lowered and the ribs are pulled upward and outward, thus enlarging the chest cavity. As you exhale, the diaphragm rises and the ribs move inward, forcing air out the mouth and nose.

Building Vocabulary
- Ask students to work in teams to create a crossword puzzle using the vocabulary terms.
- Ask students to complete *Workbook Vocabulary Activity 36.*

Resources for Lesson 4

- **Transparency** 53
- **Guided Reading** Activity 36
- **Decision-Making** Activity 13
- **Workbook** Voc Act 36, Appl Act 13
- **Reteaching** Activity 36
- **Enrichment** Activity 13
- **Health Labs** Activity 13
- **Cooperative Learning** Activity 13
- **Lesson 4 Quiz, Chapter 13 Test**

**Science and Technology Videodisc
Human Biology, Side 2**
Ch 15 Nicotine and the Lungs

Ch 16 Children and Smog

DID YOU KNOW?

- In a lifetime, you breathe about 13 million cubic feet (390,000 cubic meters) of air.
- In one day in a city, you might inhale 17,000 pints of air that might contain about 20 billion particles of dust and dirt.

Teach

Guided Practice

L2 DISCUSSION. Ask students to compare the organs of the respiratory system to a tree. What are the similarities? differences?

L1 DISCUSSION. Ask students to list conditions and situations that can affect the proper functioning of the respiratory system. What can cause problems with the functioning of the respiratory system? (Examples of conditions and situations are smog, pollution, infections, allergies, smoking, heredity, genetic defects, drug abuse—particularly cocaine.)

L1 DEMONSTRATION. Using a cranial model, detail for the class the location of the respiratory organs in the head. Clarify the size and shape of the sinus cavities.

L1 CLASS ACTIVITY. Have students trace the path of air from outside the body to the alveoli, describing what happens along the way. Then, using what was learned in the discussion on blood, have them continue to trace the path of oxygen to a body cell.

L1 DEMONSTRATION. Locate a plastic soft drink container and remove the bottom. Drill a hole through a cork, then insert a Y-shaped glass tube. On the ends of each fork of the Y, place a balloon to serve as the lungs. Place the cork in the top of the container with the balloon inside. A piece of inner tube or sheet rubber should be fastened over the bottom of the plastic container to mimic the diaphragm. Push the "diaphragm" up into the plastic container with your clenched fist. The muscle is in this position (domed-shaped) when it is relaxed. Release the pressure on the diaphragm. Discuss with students that this shows what happens as you breathe. As the diaphragm contracts, you take in air. When it relaxes, you expire air.

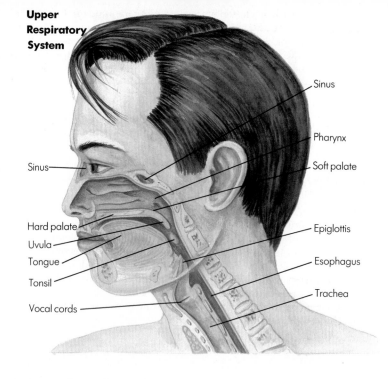

The air you inhale is cleaned, moistened, and warmed as it moves through the upper respiratory passages.

Upper Respiratory System

Sinus
Pharynx
Soft palate
Sinus
Hard palate
Epiglottis
Uvula
Esophagus
Tongue
Tonsil
Trachea
Vocal cords

the lungs. The trachea extends into the chest area and divides into two branches called **bronchi,** or bronchial tubes that lead into the lungs.

The Lungs

The lungs are two cone-shaped organs that are enclosed and protected within two layers of membranes, called pleura. Each lung is divided into sections called lobes. There are three lobes in the right lung and two lobes in the left lung. Within the lungs, each bronchus divides and then subdivides, forming a network of tubes that resemble tree branches. These divisions of the bronchial tubes are called bronchioles.

At the end of each bronchiole is a cluster of thin-walled air sacs called alveoli. There are about 300 million alveoli in the lungs.

The alveoli are covered with a vast network of capillaries. Thin capillary walls and equally thin alveolar walls allow the exchange of oxygen and carbon dioxide to take place.

Air is constantly being drawn into and expelled from the lungs by successive changes in pressure within the chest. However, the lungs do not do this work—the diaphragm and chest cavity do. The movement of air into and out of the lungs is regulated by changes in air pressure—both within the lungs and outside the body. Muscles in the rib cage and the diaphragm make this movement possible. The **diaphragm** is a muscle that separates the chest and abdominal cavities.

When you inhale, your rib muscles and diaphragm contract. The diaphragm moves downward and the ribs are pulled upward and outward. This action enlarges the chest cavity, creating lower pressure in

> ### DID YOU KNOW?
> - About 44 million Americans suffer from allergies and asthma.
> - About 11 million have asthma, including 3 million children.
> - About half a million people are admitted to hospitals in the U.S. each year because of asthma.
> - Between 50 percent and 90 percent of the people with asthma have asthma that is caused by allergies.
> - The number of asthma-related deaths in the U.S. has doubled over the past 20 years.

Additional Information

Colds. Researchers have found that hundreds of viruses cause colds, not one as once thought. The rhinovirus family is predominant in the winter, but is active all year. Occurrence is more frequent when school starts and children gather in closed spaces. Research for preventions has included covering the nose with masks to keep the viruses from entering the main receptor. Use of antiviral drugs in nasal sprays and blocking proteins that may produce cold symptoms have opened new possibilities. Since the spread of rhinovirus is through air particles, some research is being done to develop an air filtering system that interrupts the spread of the viruses.

266 CHAPTER 13 CARDIOVASCULAR, LYMPHATIC, AND RESPIRATORY SYSTEMS the lungs. Air rushes into the lungs to equalize the pressure between the lungs and the outside environment.

Just the reverse happens when you exhale. The diaphragm relaxes, moving upward, and the ribs move inward, increasing the pressure within the lungs. Air moves from the higher pressure within the lungs to the outside environment where the pressure is lower.

Problems of the Respiratory System

The respiratory system is a common site of infection in the body. Pathogens have easy access into the body through the mouth and nose. Colds and sore throats are common problems with the upper respiratory tract. More serious respiratory infections are those that affect the lower respiratory tract. These include bronchitis, pneumonia, pleurisy, bronchial asthma, tuberculosis, and emphysema.

Bronchitis

Bronchitis is an inflammation of the lining of the bronchial tubes. Bronchitis can be either acute or chronic.

Acute bronchitis often develops as a result of a severe cold. A person usually experiences fever and coughing. Acute bronchitis can last for several weeks.

Chronic bronchitis is a longer-lasting, recurring disease. It can get progressively worse. A person may experience long coughing spasms, shortness of breath, wheezing, and long-lasting colds. Most important in the treatment of chronic bronchitis is avoiding respiratory irritants, such as dust, fumes, smoke, or other air pollutants.

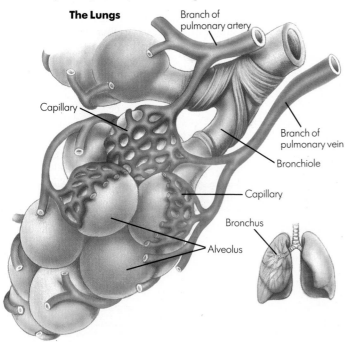

The Lungs

Branch of pulmonary artery

Capillary

Branch of pulmonary vein

Bronchiole

Capillary

Bronchus

Alveolus

The alveoli are surrounded by a network of capillaries. External respiration takes place in the alveoli.

THE RESPIRATORY SYSTEM **267**

L1 USING BODY SYSTEMS TRANSPARENCY 53. Refer to the Teaching Transparencies Binder.

L1 DISCUSSION. Ask students to describe the shape of the lobes of the lungs. Emphasize that there are three lobes on the right (upper, middle, and lower), but only two on the left (upper and lower) due to the placement of the heart. Ask students to tell how the lungs are protected by the body. (Rib cage.)

L1 LAB. Have students compare their lung capacities by taking in as much air as they can and exhaling into balloons. Compare sizes of the balloons.

L1 CLASS ACTIVITY. Have students record their voices into a tape recorder by saying their names. Listen to the replay and discuss why the voices sound different from one another.

L1 DISCUSSION. Discuss the disorders of the respiratory system, emphasizing connections with smoking—especially in regard to chronic bronchitis and pulmonary emphysema.

L1 DISCUSSION. Ask students to describe the symptoms of asthma. Make a list of agents known to aggravate the disorder. How do people with asthma treat it? (inhalers, medication, respiratory therapy)

L1 DISCUSSION. Skin testing for tuberculosis is routinely done in many communities. What are the implications of a positive test? How is the current treatment for tuberculosis different from the treatment of 30 years ago?

L2 SPEAKER. Invite a representative from the American Lung Association to talk to the class about emphysema. In addition to smoking, what are other causes?

L1 DISCUSSION. Have students explain what happens when someone chokes.

Additional Information

Asthma. Each year asthma costs over $4 billion and causes over 100 million days of restricted activity.

From 1979 to 1987, the percentage of the U.S. population with asthma increased by a third, and the number of asthma-related hospitalizations rose by 43 percent. It's believed that environmental factors, such as ozone and other air pollutants, are primarily responsible for this increase in morbidity from asthma.

The proportion of African Americans with asthma is only slightly higher than that of whites, but African Americans with asthma are more likely to be hospitalized for it, and they're three times as likely to die from it. The reasons? Worse environments and poorer medical care.

Pneumonia

Pneumonia is an infection of an area of the lungs. Pneumonia can be caused by bacteria or viruses. The infection may involve parts of the lungs, such as the bronchioles or an entire section or lobe.

Pneumonia often affects a person whose resistance is already low because of another illness. Bronchial pneumonia causes difficult and painful breathing. A person may also have a severe cough. Medical care is important because of the risk of complications and the possibility of a recurrence.

Lobar pneumonia is an infection affecting one or more lobes of the lungs. Prior chronic respiratory or heart disease, poor nutrition, alcoholism, and exposure to sudden changes in temperature are all factors that make a person more susceptible to developing this type of pneumonia. Chills, high fever, coughing, chest pains, and difficult breathing are all symptoms of lobar pneumonia. Because this disease can have serious complications, medical treatment is important. Hospitalization is often necessary.

Pleurisy

Pleurisy is an inflammation of the pleural membrane, a double-wall lining that covers the lungs. Pleurisy usually results as a complication from another disease, such as pneumonia. A person may experience shortness of breath and sharp pains in the chest.

Bronchial Asthma

Bronchial asthma is a condition that can result from a sensitivity to pollen, dust, certain foods, or animal hair. Strong emotional responses also can bring on the attack of bronchial asthma. These irritants and emotional stresses cause the linings of the bronchioles to produce large amounts of thick mucus. The bronchioles constrict and breathing is difficult. An attack of bronchial asthma is characterized by wheezing and coughing as air moves through the narrowed bronchioles.

Tuberculosis

Tuberculosis is an infectious bacterial disease of the lungs characterized by the growth of tubercles, or nodules, on the lungs. Tuberculosis

A bronchodilator helps reduce the swelling and production of mucus in the bronchial tubes of someone with asthma.

K E E P I N G   F I T

Posture and Breathing

When you stand erect, sit erect, or walk erect, you give the breathing mechanisms in your body the best opportunity to do their work. By slouching, you hinder efficient breathing. Practice sitting with your back straight in a chair that supports your head and back. Stand with your head up, neck straight, shoulders down and back, stomach and buttocks in, but hold yourself naturally, not stiffly. Also try standing with your arms down at your sides, then inhaling deeply as you raise your arms outstretched to shoulder level. Breathe out fully as you lower your arms.

Additional Information

Respiratory System Care. Aerobic exercise maintained for at least 30 minutes, 3 to 4 times a week, will develop and maintain the endurance necessary for an efficient respiratory system.

Smoking restricts the ability of the lungs to absorb oxygen and decreases the lungs' flexibility and absorbency.

Extreme hot or cold temperatures can place stress upon the respiratory system. During extremely cold weather, athletes who train or compete outdoors should cover their nose and mouth.

bacteria attack the alveoli and cause inflammation of tissues and organs. Symptoms include fever, weakness, loss of appetite, and severe coughing. Chest X rays detect tuberculosis, which used to be one of the principal causes of death. Most cases of tuberculosis can be treated successfully with antibiotics. However, medicine-resistant forms of tuberculosis have recently become more prevalent.

Emphysema

Emphysema is a disorder that causes the alveoli to disintegrate and to lose their elasticity, making it difficult for air to pass out of the lungs. The normal exchange of carbon dioxide and oxygen in the alveoli is disrupted. This condition cannot be reversed. Emphysema is caused by breathing in foreign matter such as smoke and smog particles over a long period of time. Inhaled smoke from burning cigarettes is the primary cause of emphysema. Symptoms include difficult breathing and coughing.

Care of the Respiratory System

Since the respiratory system is highly susceptible to infection, you should pay close attention to any nasal or sinus condition, or to coughing or wheezing that lasts more than a few days. Hoarseness or loss of voice can also be a sign of a respiratory infection.

Try to keep nasal passages open during a cold or respiratory infection. Keep in mind that respiratory passages are very delicate. Avoid blowing your nose too hard or trying to hold back a cough or sneeze.

A regular program of exercise helps keep the lungs working efficiently. Exercise strengthens the lungs and helps keep the other parts of the respiratory system clear. Avoiding polluted air, as well as never smoking yourself, help promote the health of your respiratory system.

DID YOU KNOW?

You can lessen the effect of pollution if you
- avoid breathing the cigarette smoke of others.
- ask smokers in your family to confine their smoking to one room or to smoke outside. Avoid exercising in dusty or heavily polluted areas.
- avoid areas where there are heavy exhaust fumes when walking, running, or biking.
- work on a vehicle in a well-ventilated area.
- cover your mouth and nose with a handkerchief or tissue whenever you are outside in a dust storm.

LESSON 4 REVIEW

Reviewing Facts and Vocabulary

1. What function does the nasal cavity serve as part of the respiratory system?
2. Describe the process that takes place in the alveoli.
3. What is the difference between acute and chronic bronchitis?

Thinking Critically

4. **Analysis.** Compare external and internal respiration.

Applying Health Knowledge

5. Interview three smokers and three non-smokers. Ask them how often they experience respiratory infections, sore throats, and colds. Draw some conclusions.

Answers to Lesson 4 Review

1. Air is warmed, cleaned, and moistened in the nasal cavity.
2. Thin alveolar walls are covered with thin-walled capillaries, which allows the exchange of oxygen and carbon dioxide to take place.
3. Acute bronchitis usually develops as a result of a severe cold and can last several weeks. Chronic bronchitis is a longer-lasting, recurring disease that can get progressively worse.
4. External respiration is the exchange of oxygen and carbon dioxide between the blood and air in the lungs. Internal respiration is the exchange of oxygen and carbon dioxide between the blood and body cells.
5. Conclusions will vary.

Assess

Check for Understanding

- Assign and discuss the lesson review. Provide LD students with page numbers to facilitate their answering questions 1, 2, and 3.
- Assign and discuss the chapter review.

Evaluate

- Administer, grade, and discuss the *Lesson 4 Quiz.*
- Administer, grade, and discuss the *Chapter 13 Test.*
- Refer to the Performance Assessment strategy for this chapter. See pages T 23 to T 25.

Reteach

- Ask students to work in small groups. Have each group use clear plastic pages and markers to make a series of transparencies that show the major parts of the respiratory system. Ask them to draw one major system part on each sheet and organize the transparencies so that when they are all placed on top of one another, they look like a diagram. Ask them to make a final transparency showing a respirator hooked up to the respiratory system. Have each group show the transparencies to the class and explain the respirator and its uses.
- Ask students to complete *Reteaching Activity 36.*

Enrich

- Have students research how respiration is affected by high altitudes, space travel, and being underwater. What adaptations are required in each situation? Have them report their findings to the class.
- Ask students to complete *Enrichment Activity 13.*

Close

Ask students to describe the interdependence of the cardiovascular and respiratory systems studied in this chapter.

Helping Students Improve Their Health

Using the Self-Inventory

Reinforcing Vocabulary

- **Stress.** Events that cause tension or an individual's perception of such events.
- **Blood pressure.** Pressure that is exerted by blood upon the walls of blood vessels.
- **Cholesterol.** A chemical substance found in animal cells and body fluids that is important in physiological processes; factor that increases the risk of heart disease when present in excessive amounts.
- **Ideal weight.** The amount that one should weigh in order to maximize one's health; varies according to one's age, gender, height, and bone structure.
- **Immunizations.** Inoculations that prevent the contraction of specific diseases.

Teaching Strategies

L1 SELF-ESTEEM. Many of the self-inventory questions are directly related to choices students make that promote the health of their body systems. Discuss how self-esteem relates to those choices and influences students to take good care of themselves.

L2 DISCUSSION. Have students discuss how chronic illnesses tend to affect society today more so than in past decades. Have students determine life-style practices that can increase or decrease a person's chances of dying from a chronic illness.

Self-Inventory

Care of the Cardiovascular and Respiratory Systems

HOW DO YOU RATE?

Number a sheet of paper from 1 through 20. Read each item below, and respond by writing *always*, *sometimes*, or *never* for each item. Total the number of each type of response. Then proceed to the next section.

1. I eat a well-balanced diet.
2. I get at least 20 minutes of aerobic exercise 3 times a week.
3. I manage the stress in my life.
4. I avoid foods high in fat.
5. I limit the amount of salt I put on my food.
6. I do not smoke.
7. I avoid breathing in others' smoke.
8. I stay within 5 pounds (2.2 kg) of my ideal weight.
9. I regularly have my blood pressure checked.
10. I know my cholesterol level.
11. I avoid foods high in cholesterol.
12. I eat foods rich in iron (liver, green leafy vegetables, dried fruits, enriched cereals) daily.
13. I study or work in a well-ventilated area.
14. I sleep 7 to 8 hours every night.
15. I keep records of my immunizations.
16. My immunizations are up-to-date.

17. When possible, I avoid pollen, dust, and animal hair.
18. When I have a choice, I ask for a seat in the nonsmoking section in a restaurant.
19. I avoid blowing my nose too hard when I have a cold.
20. I don't try to hold back a cough or sneeze.

HOW DID YOU SCORE?

Give yourself 2 points for every *always* answer, 1 point for every *sometimes* answer, and 0 points for every *never* answer. Find your total, and read below to see how you scored. Then proceed to the next section.

26 to 40
Excellent. Your health choices show you are taking care of your cardiovascular and respiratory systems.

11 to 25
Good. Your health choices are good, but you could work to better promote a healthy cardiovascular and respiratory system.

Below 11
Look out! You may be taking unnecessary risks that could affect the health of your cardiovascular and respiratory systems.

WHAT ARE YOUR GOALS?

Identify an area in which your score was low, and use the goal-setting process to begin making a change.

1. The behavior I would like to change or improve is ____.
2. If this behavior were completely changed, I would look, feel, or act differently in the following ways: ____.
3. The steps involved in making this change are ____.
4. My timetable for accomplishing this change is ____.
5. People I will ask for support or assistance are ____.
6. The benefits I will receive are ____.
7. My reward at the end of each week will be ____.

Meeting Students' Needs

For students who score *Excellent*. Suggest that students organize and manage a creative contest in which the entire school population will participate. The goal of this contest is to have students focus on ways to improve their attitudes towards health.

For students who score *Good*. Encourage students to design a healthful-habits con-

tract that will allow students to work on achieving attainable healthful goals. Have students share a contract with another person, such as a friend or parent.

For students who *Need to Look Out!* Suggest that students choose one self-inventory item in which they will try to improve within a specified period of time.

Building Decision-Making Skills

T omorrow is the school blood drive, which is part of a competition between schools in the area to see who can donate the most blood to send to victims of the disaster in the next county. Chung, the captain of the football team, really supports the cause. In fact, he personally knows people who will benefit from the drive. His friends are all signing up and encouraging him to join them. He just turned 17 and this is the first year he is eligible to donate. Although he is really queasy about the whole idea, he feels pressure from his friends to be "macho" and to participate in this blood drive.

WHAT DO YOU THINK?

1. **Situation.** Why do you think Chung feels the pressure to donate?

2. **Situation.** What questions do you think Chung might have about donating blood?

3. **Situation.** Where might Chung find out what it's really like to donate blood?

4. **Choices.** What are Chung's choices?

5. **Choices.** If Chung decides not to participate in the blood drive, what choices does he have for handling the situation?

6. **Consequences.** What are the pros and cons of each choice?

7. **Consequences.** How might Chung's self-esteem be affected by this decision?

8. **Consequences.** How might his peers be affected by this decision?

9. **Consequences.** How might his family be affected by this decision?

10. **Consequences.** What's the worst thing that might happen to Chung if he donates blood? How could he prepare for these possibilities?

11. **Consequences.** What positive outcome can he expect from donating blood?

12. **Decision.** What do you think Chung should do? Explain your answer.

13. **Evaluation.** How will he know if he made a good decision?

B enson knows that his friend has high blood pressure, but every day at lunch his group ends up going to a fast-food restaurant that serves all "the wrong kinds of food." His friend also eats desserts that only add to his weight problem, and thus, his blood pressure problem. Benson wants to help his friend.

WHAT DO YOU THINK?

14. **Choices.** What might Benson do to help his friend? What can't Benson do to help his friend?

15. **Consequences.** What are the advantages of each choice?

16. **Consequences.** What are the disadvantages of each choice?

17. **Consequences.** What risks are involved in this decision?

18. **Consequences.** How might Benson's health triangle be affected by this decision?

19. **Consequences.** How might the friend's health triangle be affected by this decision?

20. **Decision.** What should Benson do? How should he implement the decision?

21. **Decision.** How might Benson handle the situation if he makes a suggestion and his friend refuses to accept it?

22. **Evaluation.** Have you ever been in a similar situation? How did you handle it? What did you learn that could be applied to this situation?

Discussing the Answers

Situation 1. Perhaps the best resolve would be for Chung to evaluate and prioritize his true feelings. Perhaps Chung could help with the blood drive by assisting the blood drive nurses, processing any paperwork, or caring for those who donate blood, instead of donating blood himself. Chung could feel proud of his contribution to the blood drive effort and still resist the peer pressure to do something that makes him feel uneasy.

Situation 2. Benson could help by being a role model for his friend. Perhaps Benson could suggest that he and his friend not eat lunch at the fast-food restaurant the next day and that they instead eat in the school cafeteria. By being a role model, Benson's actions could speak louder than his words.

Helping Students Improve Their Health

Building Decision-Making Skills

Teaching Strategies

L1 DISCUSSION. Many people are afraid of needles. Chung is no different. Have students discuss how Chung may participate in this event without actually donating blood. Is it possible to play a vital role in a blood drive and not actually donate blood? Have students discuss whether Chung should participate in this activity while he feels unsure. Would it be a sign of strength or weakness for Chung to participate in the blood drive because of pressure from his friends?

L1 CLASS ACTIVITY. Have students role-play the character of Benson as he approaches his friend to discuss their lunchtime menus. Should Benson become involved in discussing his friend's eating patterns and medical condition?

L1 CLASS ACTIVITY. Other possible role-plays pertaining to cardiovascular and respiratory health include: (1) Your mother is extremely obese. A few years ago she was diagnosed as having high blood pressure. Recently, she has been diagnosed as having diabetes. You are aware of the health risks involved with both these conditions. Your family has a history of heart problems, which is also a concern. You feel that your mother is a walking time bomb and may die before her time if she does not lose weight. (2) Your father had a heart bypass operation a few years ago. Since that time he has stopped smoking, lost weight, and has begun exercising. Recently, however, he has begun to let himself go. You wonder if you should say anything.

L2 DISCUSSION. Have students divide into small groups and share their families' medical histories of cardiovascular and respiratory problems. Allow students to discuss with fellow classmates their plans for life for combating heart disease.

Answers to Chapter 13 Review

Using Health Terms

1. Blood pressure
2. Hemoglobin
3. Fibrin
4. Pulmonary circulation
5. Embolus
6. Congenital
7. Heart murmur
8. Thrombosis
9. Lymph
10. Lymph nodes
11. Lymphocytes
12. Hodgkin's disease
13. Mucous membranes
14. Epiglottis
15. Hyperventilation
16. Diaphragm

Building Academic Skills

17. Pints—340, quarts—170, gallons—42.5. Pints—4,200, quarts—2,100, gallons—525. Pints—1,880, quarts—940, gallons—235.

Recalling the Facts

18. It is the liquid part of the blood. It is about 55 percent of the total blood and about 92 percent water.
19. Delivers oxygen, hormones, and nutrients to cells; carries away wastes given off by body cells, helps fight infections.
20. Descriptions for pulmonary circulation and systemic circulation can be found on pages 249 to 250.
21. Right atrium, right ventricle, left atrium, left ventricle.
22. Platelets cause the blood to clot so, without platelets, one could bleed to death from a minor cut.
23. To match for a transfusion.
24. See pages 250 to 251.
25. Do not smoke; watch your weight; eat healthy foods that are low in fat, cholesterol, and salt; exercise; have regular medical checkups.
26. Varicose veins develop when the valves in veins are weakened.
27. Answers will vary. Accept two of the following: a hole between chambers of the heart; malfunctioning valves; blockage of the blood

REVIEW

Using Health Terms

On a separate sheet of paper, write the term that best matches each definition given below.

LESSON 1

1. The force of blood on blood vessel walls.
2. Blood component made up of protein and iron and carried in red blood cells.
3. Small fibers produced by platelets that trap red blood cells and form a clot.
4. Circulation through the lungs.

LESSON 2

5. A blood clot that becomes dislodged from its place of origin.
6. Term that means "occurring at birth."
7. An abnormal sound in the heart.
8. Presence of a blood clot in a blood vessel.

LESSON 3

9. Fluid that enters lymphatic capillaries before returning to the blood.
10. Masses of tissues that filter lymph.
11. White blood cells that multiply in lymph tissues to destroy pathogens.
12. Cancer of the lymph nodes.

LESSON 4

13. Membranes that line the nasal cavity.
14. A flap of tissue that covers the larynx.
15. Breathing too quickly, thereby lowering the level of carbon dioxide in the blood.
16. Muscle that separates the chest cavity from the abdomen.

Building Academic Skills

LESSON 1

17. **Math.** If your heart beats 70 times a minute, and pumps 5 quarts of blood each minute, how many pints, quarts, and gallons of blood would your heart pump in 34 minutes? How many in the course of a 7-hour school day? During exercise, if your heart pumps 20 quarts per minute, how many pints, quarts, and gallons of blood would your heart pump in 47 minutes?

Recalling the Facts

LESSON 1

18. What is plasma?
19. What are the functions of the blood?
20. Describe two types of circulation.
21. What are the chambers called in the human heart?
22. Why are platelets important to your health?
23. Why is it important to know your blood type?
24. What are the components of blood and what function does each one serve?

LESSON 2

25. How can one lower his or her risk of heart disease?
26. What causes varicose veins?
27. Describe two conditions that are examples of congenital heart disease.
28. Explain why sickle-cell anemia is a serious condition.

LESSON 3

29. Explain the function of the lymphatic system.
30. List the organs that make up the lymphatic system.
31. How can one care for his or her lymphatic system?
32. Why do lymph nodes swell when a person has an infection?

LESSON 4

33. What are the functions of mucous membranes and tiny hairs in the nose?
34. What are causes and symptoms of hyperventilation?
35. What are some respiratory irritants?
36. Name and briefly describe three serious respiratory infections.
37. What regulates the movement of air in and out of the lungs?
38. Explain why food does not usually get into the trachea.
39. What are the main parts of the respiratory system?
40. What causes sound when you speak?

flow; a defect in the blood vessels.
28. Red blood cells cause obstructions that lead to the death of tissues, and there is no cure for sickle-cell anemia.
29. It helps one's body maintain its fluid balance and defend itself against pathogens.
30. Lymphatic vessels, lymph

nodes, lymph, and lymphocytes.
31. Eat properly, exercise regularly, get plenty of rest, get regular medical checkups.
32. They are producing more lymphocytes to fight the infection.
33. Add moisture to the air, clean the air.
34. Hyperventilation occurs when one takes too many

breaths too quickly, thus lowering the level of carbon dioxide in the blood. Symptoms—dizziness, tingling in the skin, cramps in the hands, a panicky feeling.
35. Dust, fumes, smoke, air pollutants.
36. Answers will vary. Descriptions can be found on pages 267 to 269.

REVIEW

Thinking Critically

LESSON 1

41. **Synthesis.** If a person who has blood type B and is Rh-positive needs a transfusion, what types of blood can he or she safely be given? To what types could this person safely donate blood? What if the person is type A and Rh-negative? What types could this person safely be given? To what types could he or she donate blood?

LESSON 2

42. **Synthesis.** How might suffering from anemia affect your life?

43. **Evaluation.** When one suffers from leukemia, it is sometimes necessary to have a bone marrow transplant in order to survive. A blood relative is often the best match for a successful transplant. In order to obtain such a match, parents have been known to have a baby to save their other child's life. The hope is that the new baby's bone marrow would exactly match that of the leukemia patient. What do you think about this situation and all the implications for the leukemia sufferer, the parents, and the baby?

LESSON 3

44. **Analysis.** What is the relationship between the cardiovascular and lymphatic systems?

LESSON 4

45. **Evaluation.** Some workplaces are smoke-free. What are some advantages and disadvantages of this policy? Judge the appropriateness of such a policy.

46. **Analysis.** What is the difference between external and internal respiration?

Making the Connection

LESSON 1

47. **Math.** Compare survival rates of various kinds of leukemia a generation ago with those today. Prepare a bar graph that shows your findings. Interpret these statistics and suggest reasons for the changes.

Applying Health Knowledge

LESSON 1

48. Take your heart rate by counting your pulse for 10 seconds and multiplying by 6. This is your heart rate for a minute. The average heart rate is 72. How does your heart rate compare? What might affect your heart rate?

49. Give three situations in which one's sympathetic nervous system might speed up one's heart rate.

50. What can a person do to keep his or her blood pressure normal?

LESSON 2

51. When might medical personnel type a person's blood?

52. Categorize the following food items as being generally healthy or unhealthy for your heart: potato chips, broccoli, cheese, apple pie, coffee, fish, bagels, butter.

LESSON 3

53. What might happen if one's lymphatic system shut down?

LESSON 4

54. Research the respiratory infection known as walking pneumonia. What is it and why is it called that?

55. When one stops smoking, the lungs begin to improve. What implications does this have for smokers?

Beyond the Classroom

LESSON 1

56. **Further Study.** Identify a health agency that focuses on some aspect of cardiovascular disease or fitness. Find out what this organization does for public education.

LESSON 4

57. **Community Involvement.** Interview a number of people to find out what home remedies they have heard of or use to cure hiccups. Compile a report reflecting what you have learned.

37. Changes in air pressure inside and outside the body.
38. The epiglottis closes over the trachea when one swallows.
39. Nasal cavity, pharynx, larynx, trachea, bronchi, lungs, alveoli.
40. Air passing over the vocal cords.

Thinking Critically

41. Could receive only Rh-positive blood type O or B. Could donate to Rh-positive types B and AB. Could receive only Rh-negative blood type A or O. Could donate to Rh-negative types A and AB.
42. Answers will vary. Possible answers: One may sleep a lot and/or be too tired to perform normal activities. School performance could suffer. One may need to seek medical supervision.
43. Answers will vary.
44. Both are involved with maintaining an internal environment that nurtures all body cells.
45. Answers will vary. Possible answers: Advantages—fewer employee absences due to respiratory infections, cleaner air, better nonsmoker attitudes, reduced health insurance costs. Disadvantages—employee dissension, smokers spend more time away from their work stations to reach designated smoking areas, smoker irritation due to withdrawal. Opinions will vary.
46. See page 265.

Making the Connection

47. Answers will vary.

Applying Health Knowledge

48. Comparisons will vary. Age, sex, level of stress, weight, and activity prior to taking heart rate all affect one's heart rate.
49. Answers will vary. Possible answers: Any situation that induces fear; exercise; any situation that induces ecstasy.
50. Answers will vary. Possible answers: Maintain optimum weight; avoid stress; follow a healthy diet; exercise regularly; do not smoke.
51. Answers will vary. Possible answers: Before surgery; when one wishes to donate blood; during pregnancy.

52. Healthy—broccoli, cheese, fish, bagels (all in moderation). Unhealthy—potato chips, apple pie, coffee, butter.
53. Answers will vary. Possible answers: Tissues would swell from accumulating too much fluid; the body would be unable to fight infections.

54. Walking pneumonia is caused by a virus. People with walking pneumonia often do not know they have it and continue to function as they normally would.
55. Answers will vary. Possible answer: No matter how long one has been smoking, the health of the lungs will improve if one quits before cancer sets in.

Beyond the Classroom

56. Answers will vary.
57. Answers will vary.

Lesson Summaries

LESSON 1. The digestive system breaks down food into microscopic molecules to be carried in the blood to body cells. This is achieved through mechanical and chemical processes. Digestion, absorption, and elimination are discussed in this lesson.

LESSON 2. The complicated digestive system normally functions as it should, though a variety of problems are associated with it. Common digestive problems, digestive disorders and diseases, and ways to care for the digestive system are presented in this lesson.

LESSON 3. The urinary system, consisting of two kidneys, two ureters, a bladder, and the urethra, removes water-soluble waste from the blood, tissues, and cells. The system's structure, function, problems, and care are presented in this lesson.

Introducing the Chapter

Ask students to recall how they, as very young children, viewed the process of digestion. Most likely they once thought that the food they ate retained its form as it was used to supply the body with energy. Tell them as young adults, they learned the process is much more complex and that in this chapter they will study the process and the body's way of ridding waste products in more detail.

Encourage students to continue to fill in the body systems study chart that was introduced in Chapter 11, filling in the structure, function, problems, and care for each system presented in this chapter.

Performance Assessment ✓

Refer to pages T 23 to T 25 for a Performance Assessment strategy for this chapter. See the *Performance Assessment Activities* booklet for additional suggestions.

CHAPTER 14
DIGESTIVE AND URINARY SYSTEMS

LESSON 1
The Digestive System

LESSON 2
Problems and Care of the Digestive System

LESSON 3
The Urinary System

Key to Ability Levels

Teaching strategies have been coded for varying learning styles and abilities.

L1 Level 1 activities are basic activities and should be within the ability range of all students.

L2 Level 2 activities are average activities and should be within the ability range of average to above-average students.

L3 Level 3 activities are challenging activities designed for the ability range of above-average students.

LD LD activities should be within the ability range of learning-disabled students.

LEP LEP activities should be within the ability range of Limited English Proficiency students.

THE DIGESTIVE SYSTEM

Digestion is the breaking down of food into simpler substances to be carried in the blood to body cells. This process is both mechanical and chemical. The mechanical portion involves chewing, mashing, and breaking food into smaller pieces. The chemical portion involves changing food into simpler substances by digestive enzymes. Enzymes are proteins that affect the rate of many body processes. Digestive enzymes speed up the breakdown of food. Many enzymes are produced in the body.

Functions of the Digestive System

The digestive system performs three different functions:

- The first is **digestion**—the physical and chemical breakdown of foods into smaller pieces.
- The second is **absorption**—the passage of digested food from the digestive tract into the circulatory system.
- The third is **elimination**—the expulsion of undigested food or body wastes.

Structure of the Digestive System

Digestion takes place in the gastrointestinal tract, which includes the mouth, esophagus, stomach, small intestine, and large intestine.

The Mouth and Teeth

Food enters the gastrointestinal tract through the mouth, which is lined with many nerve endings that respond to heat, cold, pain, and pressure. The mouth is the only part of the digestive system that has this sensitivity.

What happens when you take a bite of pizza or hamburger? The teeth and the tongue make the first contact. The primary function of teeth is to break the food into smaller pieces. This process of chewing, called **mastication,** prepares the food to be swallowed.

The Salivary Glands

Secretions are added to food as it moves through the digestive tract. This process starts in the mouth. Three pairs of salivary glands secrete saliva. Saliva is a watery solution that contains an enzyme that starts the digestion of carbohydrates.

THE DIGESTIVE SYSTEM **275**

LESSON 1 FOCUS

TERMS TO USE

- Digestion
- Absorption
- Elimination
- Mastication (mas•tuh•KAY•shuhn)
- Peristalsis (per•uh•STAWL•suhs)
- Chyme (kym)
- Gastric juices
- Bile

CONCEPTS TO LEARN

- Digestion is both a mechanical and a chemical process.
- Each organ of the gastrointestinal tract has its own specific and unique function.

ATTITUDES AND BEHAVIORS TO EVALUATE

- Self-Inventory, page 292.
- Building Decision-Making Skills, page 293.

Focus

Lesson Objectives

After studying this lesson, students should be able to:
- describe digestion
- identify and explain the function of each organ of the digestive system

Bellringer

Write the following on the chalkboard for students to work on while attendance is being taken: *Describe in your own words the purpose of the digestive system.* (The digestive system is an extremely complex system that involves both the chemical and the physical breakdown of food. Beginning in the mouth, digestion prepares food to be in a form that all cells of the body can use.)

Introducing the Lesson

Introduce this lesson by stating that digestion takes place mainly in the stomach and the small intestine, but that these two organs need other organs to make their efforts successful. The liver, the gallbladder, and the pancreas have important roles to play in the digestion process. The large intestine and the kidneys are of prime importance in the elimination of body wastes. This lesson will explain the function of each organ as well as the processes of digestion and elimination. Refer to the Bellringer and ask volunteers to share their responses.

DID YOU KNOW?

- Another name for the throat is pharynx. The pharynx is a muscular tube that is 5 inches (12.7 centimeters) in length. It acts as a passageway for both food and air.

Resources for Lesson 1

- **Transparency** 54
- **Guided Reading** Activity 37
- **Workbook** Vocabulary Activity 37
- **Reteaching** Activity 37
- **Lesson 1 Quiz**
- **Performance Assessment** Activity 14

Building Vocabulary

- Using the vocabulary terms below, have students make a schematic outline of the digestive process, illustrating the relationship of the process with the organs or glands. Have students first put the terms in the order they would appear in describing the process and then write brief definitions. (*Digestion, absorption, elimination, mastication, salivary glands, saliva, esophagus, peristalsis, chyme, gastric juices, small intestine, duodenum, jejunum, ileum, bile, trypsin, amylase, lipase, large intestine, colon, feces, anus, papillae, liver, urea, gallbladder, pancreas.*)
- Ask students to complete *Workbook Vocabulary Activity 37.*

Teach

Guided Practice

LD **EXPLANATION.** LD students may have difficulty with this chapter due to the complex subject matter and high-level vocabulary. You may need to provide a very basic summary of each lesson and test them only on that material.

L1 **USING BODY SYSTEMS TRANSPARENCY 54.** Refer to the Teaching Transparencies Binder.

L2 **CLASS ACTIVITY.** Give each student a soda cracker and point out the dryness of that cracker. Ask students to take a bite of the cracker and chew it thoroughly. As they are chewing, have them notice the action that their teeth and tongue undergo. Point out that saliva moistens and dissolves the cracker so it can be tasted. As they swallow, ask them to take note of the tongue action forcing the food into the esophagus. Explain that this is the first stage of digestion.

Saliva softens and moistens food, making it easier to chew and swallow. Saliva cleanses the teeth and helps neutralize acids in the mouth. Saliva also helps keep the mouth moist and flexible, which is important for speech. The autonomic nervous system controls the secretion of saliva.

The Tongue

The tongue is a muscular organ that plays a primary role not only in tasting and speech, but also in chewing and swallowing. In order for you to recognize the flavor of a food, it must be in the form of a solution.

The velvetlike look of the tongue is a result of small projections, called papillae, that cover the tongue's surface. Taste buds, about 9,000 of

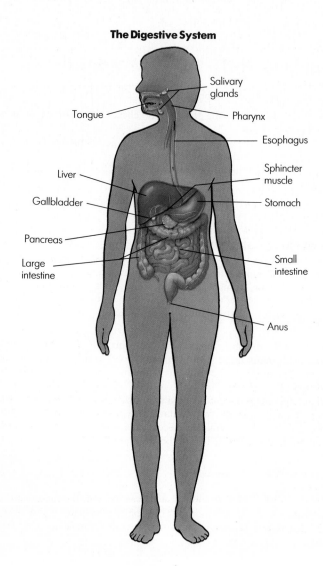

The Digestive System

Salivary glands

Tongue

Pharynx

Esophagus

Liver

Sphincter muscle

Gallbladder

Stomach

Pancreas

Large intestine

Small intestine

Anus

The organs of the digestive system form a continuous passageway.

276 CHAPTER 14 DIGESTIVE AND URINARY SYSTEMS

Additional Information

Role of Teeth in Digestion. Not only in humans but in most other mammalian species as well, teeth are the prime agents of mechanical digestion. Unlike other animals with dentition, mammalian teeth reflect their specialization for chewing. Mammals usually have several different types of teeth, each type suited for a particular function. In general terms, incisors shear food, canines rip, and molars grind.

For most mammals the volume of food is not reduced significantly by chewing. However, by breaking up food into small particles, chewing greatly increases the surface area of food that's exposed to digestive juices. This makes us very efficient at getting the greatest amount of energy from what we eat.

them, cover the tongue but are most heavily concentrated around the papillae. There are at least four different kinds of taste buds. Each kind is located in a different area of the tongue. The four are sweet, sour, salty, and bitter.

Swallowing. In your mouth your tongue forms the food into a ball to prepare for swallowing. Swallowing involves numerous muscles in your mouth and pharynx.

As you begin to swallow, the tip of the tongue slightly arches, pushing the food to the back of the mouth. The back of the tongue elevates, and a wave of muscular contractions passes over the tongue, forcing food into the pharynx.

At the same time, the uvula, a small muscular flap of tissue suspended at the back of the mouth, closes the opening to the nasal passages. The epiglottis, the flap of tissue covering the trachea, closes to keep the food from entering the respiratory system. However, if you talk or laugh while swallowing, the epiglottis will open and food may enter the windpipe. When this happens, you have a reflex response. You choke and cough to force the food out of the windpipe.

Your body has another built-in protection system to keep the food from entering the respiratory system. When you are swallowing, the nerve impulses that are responsible for breathing stop, making it almost impossible to swallow and breathe at the same time.

The Esophagus

When you swallow, food enters the esophagus, which is a muscular tube that extends from the pharynx to the stomach and is situated behind the trachea and heart. It is about 10 inches (25 cm) long. A series of involuntary muscular contractions—a process called **peristalsis**—moves food through the esophagus. It takes solid food about nine seconds to move through the esophagus. Food moves through the entire digestive tract as a result of peristalsis.

A sphincter muscle, which is a circular muscle at the entrance to the stomach, allows food to move from the esophagus into the stomach. When the muscle is relaxed, it forms an opening. When the muscle contracts, the opening closes. Sphincter muscles located along the digestive tract prevent food from backing up as it moves through the digestive process.

The Stomach

The stomach is a very muscular organ. Refer to the illustration on page 278 and note the three layers of muscles. The outer layer is longitudinal; the middle layer is circular; the inner layer is oblique, or at an angle.

The three main activities that take place in the stomach are listed below.

- temporary holding or storage of the food until it is ready to enter the small intestine
- mixing of the food and gastric juices together to form a substance called **chyme**
- control of the rate at which food enters the small intestine

Culturally Speaking

Fiber from Many Cultures

Many wonderful high-fiber foods common in other parts of the world are now becoming available for the American diet.

- Beans. High in fiber and low in fat, they are being used as substitutes for meat in a number of international ways. For example, many restaurants now offer dahl, a spicy lentil from India; falafel, a Mideastern dish of mashed and fried chick peas; and nuñas, popping beans currently very popular in South America.
- Pea fiber. Used in Denmark and now by bakers in the U.S., this is a powder that resembles wheat flour and contains 90 percent insoluble fiber.
- High-fiber drinks. These are on their way, experts say. Already the rage in Japan, these drinks contain large amounts of pectin, the nature "binder" found in fruit.

L2 DISCUSSION. Using a denture model or diagram, explain the function of the 32 permanent teeth. Point out the incisors (cut and bite) and molars (grind). Describe the difference in mastication for an infant, a young child, and a teenager.

L2 CLASS ACTIVITY. Following a discussion of mastication and swallowing, ask students to develop a chart of the sequential steps, identifying the other body systems that help carry out this process—nervous, circulatory, muscular, endocrine.

L2 EXPLANATION. A sphincter muscle controls the entrance to the stomach. Identify for the class other sphincters or valves that regulate flow—oral, intestinal, cardiac.

L2 EXPLANATION. Food may stay in the stomach 2 to 6 hours. Carbohydrates leave first, proteins next, and fats remain the longest.

LEP CLASS ACTIVITY. Select certain students to pretend they are different parts of the digestive system. Have them form a line with each part in its proper place for digestion to take place. Ask a student to volunteer to be the food. As this student moves through the line, ask him or her to identify each part of the digestive system represented. Ask students to actually depict the action of each part of the digestive system in some way.

L2 COOPERATIVE LEARNING. Divide the class into groups. Provide each group with a poster. Ask the students to prepare a chart of the organs of the digestive tract, the enzymes produced in each organ, and the types of food digested in each organ. Have students list the organs in order, from the oral cavity to the anal cavity. Display the posters in the classroom.

L2 SPEAKER. Invite a coach into the class to discuss the types of foods recommended for athletes on a game day. Ask him or her to discuss foods that are not recommended before a game. Have the coach explain why athletes must eat several hours before participating in a game.

Additional Information

The Digestive System. Smooth muscles contract to move food down the esophagus and along the rest of the digestive tract.

Stomach walls contain small pressure sensors that tell the body when the stomach is empty. These sensations are commonly called hunger pangs.

The stomach is a storehouse for food where acids break down contents into simpler components that are absorbed in the small intestine.

Alcohol doesn't need to be broken down chemically before it is absorbed into the bloodstream.

The presence of food in the stomach slows down the absorption of alcohol. Even so, food in the stomach will not keep one from being intoxicated.

L2 DEMONSTRATION. Using a torso model, trace the process of digestion for the class. Have students handle the parts of the digestive system and replace them properly within the model.

L2 CLASS ACTIVITY. Ask students to list the foods they ate at the meal prior to class. Have them identify which digestive organ is the site of the digestion of that particular carbohydrate, protein, or fat.

LD CLASS ACTIVITY. Have students diagram the digestive system, providing labels.

L2 CLASS ACTIVITY. Ask students to trace the outline of the body and use various objects to illustrate the digestive system, such as one-half of a potato for stomach, spaghetti for intestines, etc. An alternative is to have students make a dough model of the digestive system.

L2 LAB. Working with a member of the science department, prepare a demonstration showing the action of hydrochloric acid on a protein, a fat, and a carbohydrate. Ask students to compare the time and type of digestion that takes place. Do animal gastric juices contain hydrochloric acid?

L2 EXPLANATION. Explain to students that food must undergo both physical and chemical changes before it can be used in the body. Have students explain the meaning of this statement.

L3 CLASS ACTIVITY. Ask a student to work with the science department to microscopically compare available tissue samples from the digestive tract. Ask the student to report to the class the variance in wall size and muscle structure in the organs.

DID YOU KNOW?

- Though amounts may differ from person to person, on average, the human stomach can hold slightly more than one quart (0.9 l) of food.
- Any food that you eat takes a 30-foot (9.1-m) journey.
- The hydrochloric acid in your stomach is strong enough to dissolve razor blades. This acid works to destroy any bacteria in the food that reaches your stomach.

After a meal, food stays in the stomach for about three to four hours. The rate at which the stomach empties varies considerably. Liquids pass through rapidly. Solids remain until they are well-mixed with gastric juices. The stomach's capacity for food is about 1 quart (0.9 l).

The stomach is lined with mucous membranes and glands that secrete gastric juices. **Gastric juices** contain hydrochloric acid, digestive enzymes, and mucus. Gastric juices start the digestion of proteins.

As the stomach fills, muscular contractions churn and mix the food with gastric juices and move it toward the small intestine. The chyme moves into the small intestine as a result of peristalsis. Very little food is absorbed into the blood from the stomach. Food has not been broken down enough for absorption. However, some medicines and drugs, such as aspirin and alcohol, are absorbed into the blood from the stomach.

The Small Intestine

The major part of digestion and absorption occurs in the small intestine, which is about 20 feet (6 m) in length and 1 inch (2.5 cm) in diameter. It consists of three parts: the duodenum, the jejunum, and the ileum. Chyme enters the duodenum from the stomach. The ileum opens into the large intestine.

Peristalsis moves chyme through the small intestine at a relatively slow rate for approximately three to five hours. Chyme that enters the small intestine includes partially digested carbohydrates and proteins and undigested fats. Intestinal juices produced by glands in the lining of the small intestine, along with secretions from the liver and the pan-

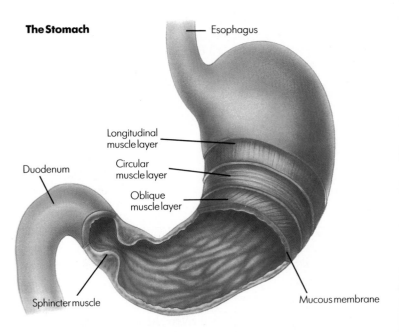

The Stomach

Esophagus

Longitudinal muscle layer

Duodenum

Circular muscle layer

Oblique muscle layer

Sphincter muscle

Mucous membrane

As the muscular wall of the stomach contracts and expands, chyme is formed as food mixes with gastric juices.

Additional Information

Diet and Dentition. The relationship between diet and dentition is a complex one—but it's clear that your teeth reflect what you eat.

Paleontologists study wear patterns on teeth to get an idea of the type of food extinct species ate regularly. They compare microscopic scratches and signs of wear on fossilized teeth with those on the

teeth of living animals whose diets are known.

Diets are also reflected by orthodontic problems. In populations like ours that eat relatively soft foods, the mechanical force of chewing is often insufficient to keep teeth aligned. In people who eat a coarser, tougher diet, fewer problems of alignment are found.

creas, complete the chemical breakdown of all food. You will learn more about the liver and pancreas later in this lesson.

The small intestine is lined with millions of fingerlike projections called villi. Each villus has a network of capillaries. Digested food particles are absorbed from the small intestine into the capillaries in the villi. Villi, especially those in the jejunum, increase the surface area for the absorption of digested food particles about 600 times. Food particles enter capillaries in the villi and are then carried throughout the body by the blood. Undigested food materials move by peristalsis into the large intestine.

The Large Intestine

The lower part of the digestive tract is the large intestine, or colon. It is about 2 1/2 inches (6 cm) in diameter and 5 to 6 feet (1.5 to 1.8 m) long. Movement through the large intestine is very slow. The main functions of the large intestine are the absorption of water and the elimination of undigested food.

The undigested food that moves to the large intestine is in a very watery state. The walls of the large intestine absorb most of the water from the undigested food and return the water to the bloodstream. This action is important in maintaining the water balance in the body.

Many harmless bacteria normally live in the large intestine. They serve a useful purpose by acting on the undigested food. The action of the bacteria changes the consistency to a semisolid waste, called feces. Feces pass from the body through the anus, as a bowel movement.

Organs That Help Digestion

The liver, the gallbladder, and the pancreas are organs that contribute to the digestive process. Juices are secreted into the digestive tract that are essential for completing the digestion of carbohydrates, proteins, and fats.

The Liver. Besides being the largest gland in the body, the liver is perhaps the most versatile. The liver of an average adult weighs about 3 1/2 pounds (2 kg) and is a dark reddish-brown color. Scientists have identified over 500 functions of the liver.

KEEPING FIT

Understanding Fiber

Soluble fiber, which dissolves in water, may lower cholesterol; insoluble fiber, which does not dissolve, may help protect you from colon cancer and other bowel problems. Though most fruits, vegetables, and grain products contain both kinds of fiber, some do not. Among the sources of soluble fiber are barley bran, oat bran, dried beans, and legumes; among the sources of insoluble fiber are wheat bran, corn bran, and nuts.

There are many delicious high-fiber foods and new sources of fiber on the market. To increase your fiber intake, why not try eating more popcorn, dried fruit, nuts, or beans?

THE DIGESTIVE SYSTEM **279**

Overcoming Misconceptions

Myth. An individual cannot live without all of the parts of the digestive system. **Fact.** An individual can live a healthy life if some part has to be removed surgically. For example, a person can digest food even if the stomach has been removed, because most of the digestive process occurs after food leaves the stomach area. Individuals can live with up to two-thirds of their small intestine removed. Following an operation in which a section of the colon is removed, solid wastes are eliminated into a bag attached to the individual in the lower abdominal area. The gallbladder's removal usually causes no health complications. Individuals in each of these cases usually have to make adjustments in their eating habits, but they can live a healthy life.

L2 CLASS ACTIVITY. Explain to students that they have eaten a hamburger for lunch. Ask them to complete the following statements describing the parts of the digestive system that take the nutrients of the hamburger from the mouth into the body: After the hamburger is chewed and mixed with saliva, the (tongue) moves the food to the (esophagus). Muscles here force the food into the (stomach) where gastric juices mix with the food to form chyme. The food is then pushed by muscles into the (duodenum) where enzymes from the liver and pancreas break down sugars and fats. The food then enters the (small intestine). Here little structures called (villi) absorb the nutrients into the (bloodstream). The wastes not needed by the body are passed into the (large intestine or colon) and excreted from the body.

Independent Practice

L2 RESEARCH. Ask students to research the number of teeth and the types of salivary glands found in animals. Do these differ from humans in number and function?

L2 WRITING. Ask students to write a paragraph explaining what the following statement means: *If all the tiny tubes in the liver were laid end to end, they would cover 60 miles.*

L3 WRITING. Have students select one organ involved in the digestive process and write a paper on it, including the organ's function, importance, maintenance, and relation with other body organs. Have students conclude the paper with an analogy about the particular organ. (Name of organ) is like ( ) because. . . .

L2 PARENTAL INVOLVEMENT. Have students ask their parents to explain why doctors will not allow a patient undergoing surgery to have food or water after 10:00 P.M. the night before the surgery. Have students ask their parents to discuss any surgery they have had or the student has had that required anesthesia. Discuss the precautions used by a doctor or nurse to ensure that a patient follows these instructions prior to surgery. What could happen if the patient did not follow these instructions?

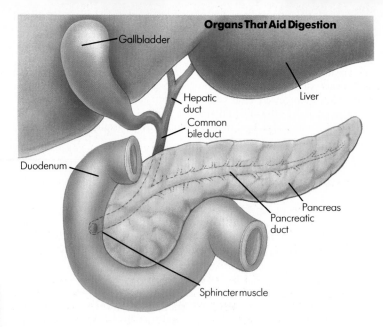

When chyme enters the duodenum, the sphincter muscle relaxes and allows bile and pancreatic enzymes to enter the duodenum.

Organs That Aid Digestion

Gallbladder
Hepatic duct
Common bile duct
Liver
Duodenum
Pancreas
Pancreatic duct
Sphincter muscle

DID YOU KNOW?

■ In 1989, the first U.S. liver transplant from a living donor took place. Twenty-one-month-old Alyssa Smith from Schertz, Texas, received a fist-sized portion of liver from her own mother's body. The removal of part of a living donor's liver for transplant purposes had been done in Brazil, Japan, and Australia, but this was the first time the procedure was performed in the United States.

Following are six major functions of the liver:

■ The liver produces **bile**, a yellowish-green, bitter fluid important in the breakdown of fats. The liver secretes up to 1 quart (0.9 l) of bile daily. Bile flows to the gallbladder through the hepatic duct where it is stored.
■ The liver converts the sugar glucose to glycogen, which is a form of starch, and stores it until needed.
■ The liver helps maintain the level of glucose in the blood. When the blood glucose level falls, glycogen is converted to glucose and released into the blood.
■ The liver removes worn-out red blood cells as blood circulates.
■ The liver changes toxic waste materials, such as ammonia, into a less toxic substance—urea, the chief substance in urine.
■ The liver stores a variety of substances including vitamins A, D, E, K, and B$_{12}$, and minerals such as iron.

KEEPING FIT

Medications and the Digestive Process

Americans spend millions of dollars a year for medications to aid in the digestive process. Much of this expenditure is a waste of money. Here is what you can do to help prevent problems and promote healthy digestion:

■ Chew your food thoroughly.
■ Eat slowly.
■ Eat a balanced diet.
■ Try to swallow your food without drinking liquids.
■ Drink five to six glasses of water daily.

■ Limit your intake of carbonated, acidic beverages.
■ Try not to eat too many fried or other greasy foods.
■ Avoid eating as a way of dealing with problems.
■ Stop eating before you feel full.

Additional Information

Evolution of Digestion. Ancient animals, like sponges, have no digestive cavity, so they can only digest minute particles of food through intracellular processes.

Next to evolve were animals with primitive digestive chambers, having just one opening through which both food and wastes pass. Only one meal at a time can be processed, and much digestion is still intracellular.

The complete digestive systems that evolved last include a more complex digestive cavity or tube, where food enters at one end, and wastes exit through the other. Animals with a digestive tube process food continuously. A complete digestive system is found in animals ranging from earthworms to humans.

The Gallbladder. The gallbladder is a small sac 3 to 4 inches (7 to 10 cm) long that stores bile. It is located on the undersurface of the liver. The neck of the gallbladder forms a duct leading to the duodenum, the first section of the small intestine. The gallbladder stores bile until food moves into the duodenum from the stomach. A hormone produced in the small intestine stimulates the release of bile through the bile duct into the duodenum.

The Pancreas. Recall that the pancreas produces the hormone insulin as part of the endocrine system. As part of the digestive system, the pancreas produces three digestive enzymes: trypsin, which digests proteins; amylase, which digests carbohydrates; and lipase, which digests fats. These enzymes are released into the small intestine through a series of ducts.

HOW DO YOU KNOW WHEN TO EAT?

You have read about how food is digested in your body, but what signals you to put food into your body? This is regulated by two sensations— hunger, a craving for food, and appetite, a desire for a certain kind of food. The hypothalamus, which is a small area of the brain, is the control center for hunger.

One theory is that the hypothalamus is stimulated by the glucose level in your blood. Glucose is a kind of sugar. When the glucose level is low, a cluster of nerve cells in the hypothalamus is stimulated and sends out nerve impulses. You respond by eating to satisfy that hungry feeling.

As your stomach fills with food, the glucose level rises and another area of the hypothalamus is stimulated. This time, nerve impulses give you a feeling of fullness. You stop eating.

LESSON 1 REVIEW

Reviewing Facts and Vocabulary

1. Trace the path a bite of pizza follows until it is absorbed into the bloodstream.
2. Describe the three different functions of the digestive system.
3. Define the following terms and use each in a sentence: *digestive enzyme, papillae, saliva, peristalsis*.

Thinking Critically

4. **Analysis.** Support the following statement: "The real work of the digestive system is done in the small intestine."

5. **Synthesis.** Change the names of the different parts of the digestive system to parts of mechanical instruments or machines based on their actions.

Applying Health Knowledge

6. Prepare a chart that shows what happens to food once it leaves the stomach. Describe the function of each organ involved in the digestive process.
7. Select three organs in the digestive system and make a life-size model of each. Make a poster that describes each organ's function in the digestive process.

THE DIGESTIVE SYSTEM   **281**

Answers to Lesson 1 Review

1. Mouth, esophagus, stomach, small intestine, bloodstream.
2. Descriptions for digestion, absorption, and elimination are on page 275.
3. Definitions can be found on pages 275 to 277. Sentences will vary.
4. The major part of digestion and absorption occurs here.
5. Answers will vary.

6. Descriptions should reflect a summary of this lesson.
7. Answers will vary but should reflect an understanding of the functions of three of the following: Salivary glands, tongue, esophagus, stomach, small intestine, large intestine, liver, gallbladder, or pancreas.

Assess

Check for Understanding

- Assign and discuss the lesson review. Encourage LD students to focus on question 1.

Evaluate

- Administer, grade, and discuss the *Lesson 1 Quiz*.

Reteach

- Have students make a chart of the parts of the digestive system, indicating what each part does.
- Ask students to complete *Reteaching Activity 37*.

Enrich

- Have students find out about the digestive systems of cows, chickens, and other animals. What foods do these animals eat? How are their digestive systems designed to digest those particular foods?

Close

Ask students to state the most important concepts studied in the lesson.

DID YOU KNOW?

- Species of animals, like cows and sheep, that eat a lot of hard-to-digest plant cellulose may have up to four stomachs to aid in its digestion.
- Obese people don't have unusually large stomachs, but fat deposits on the trunk may give them a "big belly" appearance.

Focus

Lesson Objective

After studying this lesson, students should be able to:

- explain the causes of, and preventive measures for, digestive disorders

Bellringer

Write the following on the chalkboard for students to work on while attendance is being taken: *List as many minor disorders of the digestive system as you can.* (Halitosis, indigestion, heartburn, flatulence, nausea, diarrhea, dehydration, constipation.)

Introducing the Lesson

Refer to the Bellringer. Ask volunteers to share their responses. Tell students they will learn more about digestive disorders and diseases as well as how to prevent them as they study this lesson.

Building Vocabulary

- Copy each of the vocabulary terms on a 3-by-5 inch index card. On the appropriate cards, write the definition of each term as it appears in the lesson. Place the cards face down on a table and invite students to get in groups of four to play "Password." Have students take turns giving one-word clues describing the vocabulary term to a partner. The partner should guess the digestive disorder being described.
- Ask students to complete *Workbook Vocabulary Activity 38.*

PROBLEMS AND CARE OF THE DIGESTIVE SYSTEM

LESSON 2 FOCUS

TERMS TO USE
- Indigestion
- Hiatal hernia
- Gallstones
- Peptic ulcers
- Gastritis
- Appendicitis
- Hepatitis

CONCEPTS TO LEARN
- Some digestive disorders are functional and can be prevented by avoiding certain situations or foods.
- A healthy digestive system is related to the practice of good eating habits.

ATTITUDES AND BEHAVIORS TO EVALUATE
- Self-Inventory, page 292.
- Building Decision-Making Skills, page 293.

The complex digestive system usually functions normally, digesting and absorbing food and eliminating undigested material. However, there are problems that are common to many people.

Common Functional Problems

Many digestive problems are related to eating habits and to the kinds of food eaten.

Halitosis

Halitosis, or bad breath, can result from disorders of the teeth or gums, from eating certain foods, and from using tobacco. The most frequent cause is poor oral health care. If daily brushing and flossing do not take care of halitosis, the cause may be a tooth or gum infection. A dentist can check that possible cause. Bad breath can also be the result of poor nutrition or of problems in the stomach or intestines. Contrary to the message given in advertisements, mints and mouthwashes do not prevent or cure halitosis, although they may cover up the odor.

Indigestion

Indigestion occurs when your body does not properly break down foods. It can be caused by stomach disorders, by eating too fast or too much, by eating certain foods, or by indulging in an excess of alcohol. Indigestion can also be caused by stress or can be a result of lactose intolerance. People with lactose intolerance do not have the enzyme that is needed to digest milk sugar, or lactose. Some symptoms of indigestion are cramps in the abdomen, a buildup of gas, and nausea.

Heartburn

Heartburn occurs when acid content from the stomach backs up into the esophagus. This backup can occur if the sphincter muscle between the esophagus and stomach does not close tightly. If a person has a **hiatal hernia,** a condition in which the upper part of the stomach pushes through the diaphragm, he or she may experience heartburn. If heartburn recurs or continues, a medical examination is necessary.

Gas

A certain amount of gas in the stomach or the intestines is normal. When a person has an excess amount of gas, it can be very uncom-

282 CHAPTER 14 DIGESTIVE AND URINARY SYSTEMS

Resources for Lesson 2

- **Guided Reading** Activity 38
- **Workbook** Vocabulary Activity 38
- **Reteaching** Activity 38
- **Lesson 2 Quiz**

Science and Technology Videodisc
Human Biology, Side 2
Ch 8 Treating Motion Sickness

fortable. Certain foods seem to be gas-forming for some people and not for others.

Nausea and Vomiting

Nausea and vomiting can be caused by motion (such as the rocking motion of a car, boat, or plane), pathogens, medicines, drugs, or other substances in the stomach. Nausea is a feeling of distress, fullness, and weakness. Nausea often precedes vomiting. Vomiting is a reflex response that can be a protection if you swallow a foreign substance. Vomiting is the result of reverse peristalsis, or waves of muscular contractions, in the stomach and esophagus. It is usually accompanied by strong muscular contractions in the chest and abdomen.

Diarrhea

Diarrhea is a condition in which the feces are watery and are expelled frequently. It can occur when food moves through the large intestine too rapidly. Numerous conditions can cause diarrhea, including a change in diet, food poisoning, overeating, emotional turmoil, and nutritional deficiencies. Diarrhea can also be caused by viral and bacterial infections. If water is not being reabsorbed into the bloodstream, dehydration or an excessive loss of body fluids can result. To prevent dehydration, a person should drink plenty of liquids, especially water. Diarrhea usually clears up when the cause of it is eliminated. Medical help is often necessary.

Constipation

Constipation is a condition in which feces become dry and hard and bowel movements are difficult. If feces stay in the large intestine too long, too much water is absorbed out of them. Constipation can be caused by a lack of fiber in the diet, erratic eating habits, drinking too little water, a lack of exercise, or constant use of laxatives. Eating a well-balanced diet, drinking plenty of water, and exercising regularly are the best ways to avoid constipation.

Common Structural Problems

Most digestive problems are temporary and not serious. However, if any problem continues for a long period of time or is accompanied by fever or other symptoms of illness, a medical checkup may be necessary.

Doctors have a variety of instruments and tests that allow them to view the gastrointestinal tract and detect problems.

Gallstones

Gallstones are small crystals formed from bile that can block the bile duct between the gallbladder and the duodenum, which is the first section of the small intestine. Gallstones can be treated either with medicines to dissolve them or by surgical removal of the gallbladder. Some gallstones can be shattered by ultrasound-guided shock waves.

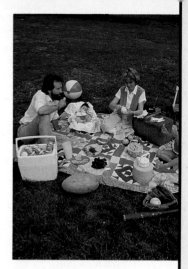

Good company and pleasant surroundings can help the digestive process.

PROBLEMS AND CARE OF THE DIGESTIVE SYSTEM **283**

Guided Practice

L2 DISCUSSION. Drinking at least 2 quarts of fluids, including water, each day helps prevent dehydration and constipation. Ask students to develop a list of things that can be done to promote the intake of water and juices. What tricks do class members use to assure their own consumption of adequate fluids?

L2 DISCUSSION. Binge-purge eating cycles (as in bulimia) have become a problem in our weight-conscious society. Discuss the health hazards of this practice. (Malnutrition, psychological trauma, severe intestinal disorders, and death.) What are the resources in your community for treatment of eating disorders?

L2 CLASS ACTIVITY. Abdominal pain may have many causes. (Gallstones, ulcers, constipation, appendicitis.) Ask students to role-play calling a doctor to describe abdominal discomfort. What should be reported? (Nausea, pain location, temperature, diarrhea.) Why is it important to heed the signs of abdominal distress and seek prompt treatment?

L1 EXPLANATION. Explain that cancer of the stomach and intestines frequently goes undetected for a long period of time. Explain the warning signs of cancer. Ask students to explain the relationship of diet to cancer development. (Increase fiber and reduce fats.)

L2 DISCUSSION. Ask if any students have had appendectomies. What were their symptoms? What tests were done to determine their condition? Review with the class the role of white blood cells in fighting infections.

L2 CLASS ACTIVITY. The suffix *-itis* means inflammation. Ask students to recall and write down five *-itis* diseases they have studied. What organ is inflamed? What are the symptoms of the inflammation?

Across the Curriculum

History. The ancient Sumerians were the first to discover that alkaline substances help neutralize irritating stomach acids. They often prescribed baking soda for people with upset stomachs.

Other prescriptions for indigestion included milk and peppermint leaves. Laxatives were used as long ago as 2500 B.C. in the Near East. Castor oil, extracted from the castor bean, was used for its laxative effects. By 1500 B.C., the Assyrians were suggesting the use of bran as a bulk-producing laxative.

Have students research other remedies that were discovered and used by people in other countries and cultures to treat digestive disorders.

Using Overcoming the Odds

■ **Speaker.** Invite a diabetic to speak to the class about limitations the disease imposes and how he or she has coped with them. Are there any ways in which the disease has changed the person's life for the better?

■ **Discussion.** Why did Corey need both a new kidney and a new pancreas? (Corey needed a new pancreas because diabetes is a disease caused by a defective pancreas. He needed a new kidney because fluctuating blood sugar levels led to kidney damage.)

■ **Answers**

1. The restrictions led to Corey's interest in food and cooking and to a desire to become a chef.

2. Answers will vary; students should consider their strengths to find ways to compensate.

3. You must like yourself to be your own best friend, and that depends on self-esteem.

L2 LAB. Using an anatomical model or chart, ask students to compare the size of the bile duct to a drinking straw. What size or type of objects can they visualize that would cause obstructions? Bring a piece of uncooked liver into the classroom to examine. Have students examine where the bile ducts would be located in the liver. Examine the size of the hole in the liver for an actual size of the bile duct.

L2 DISCUSSION. Almost everyone experiences disorders of the digestive system. Ask students to list some of the digestive disorders they have experienced and answer the following questions: What caused the disorder? How did you treat the disorder? Did you have to use medicine for the disorder? Discuss responses with the class.

L2 LAB. Bring to class X rays of the digestive system indicating an ulcer or other digestive disorder. Explain to the class the procedures involved in preparing for an X ray of the digestive system. Discuss the instructions doctors give to patients prior to getting an X ray and why it is necessary to follow these instructions for effective results.

Overcoming The Odds

Corey McManus is 18. He has big plans. Right now he is taking courses at a community college. In the future, he hopes to attend a culinary institute, study in France, and become a chef.

Corey recently graduated from the First State School at the Medical Center of Delaware, the nation's only outpatient school for chronically ill children. He attended the school for four years, taking regular academic courses in a hospital where doctors and nurses are available to give medical care when necessary.

Corey says, "I was born a diabetic. I grew up on fruits, nuts, and juices and no candy. I started giving myself insulin shots when I was 8 or 10 years old. Then, around the age of 14, I got really sick. I spent 5 months in a hospital. I have rapid progressive diabetes, and it started progressing. Besides having high blood pressure, I was diagnosed as having renal failure. I had what is called a kidney biopsy, and was told that I would need a kidney transplant." In the meanwhile, Corey went on CAPD, a portable system that acts as an artificial kidney, cleaning impurities from the blood. "To get a kidney," he says, "you have to get on a list, and it sometimes takes a long time. I was on the list for three years."

Because of his health problems Corey was a particularly hard match. He not only needed a kidney, he also needed a pancreas. A perfect match was found, and Corey received a new kidney and pancreas. However, after the operation, there were serious complications. He was in a coma for nearly a month, and his medical bill reached a quarter of a million dollars.

Because Corey had such difficulty digesting food, he was restricted from food with salt because of his high blood pressure and because foods high in salt can clog the kidneys. But the outcome of these restrictions hasn't all been bad. It is partly because of them that Corey's love of food and creative cooking has emerged. Now he has turned those restrictions into a promising career.

He continues, "I have side effects from medicines, and I still take insulin. But I feel great about myself. My best friend is me," he says with great energy. "My favorite person is me."

1. How have the restrictions of Corey's medical condition and diet inspired him to move forward and plan his future?
2. What restrictions are present in your life? What creative solutions might you use to work with these restrictions?
3. Corey says that he is his own best friend. If you are your own best friend, how do you think you got that way? If you are not, what can you do to become a better friend to yourself?

Meeting Special Needs

Diabetics. Individuals with diabetes have special needs in order for their digestive systems to function properly. They may need to take daily doses of insulin, usually by injection, to lead healthy lives. Modern technology has now produced an "artificial pancreas" in the form of an insulin pump for these individuals. The pump supplies insulin to their bodies continuously, eliminating the need for daily injections. The insulin pump is a small device that is embedded beneath the skin. A tube connects the pump to a large vein, where the insulin is injected into the bloodstream. Every two weeks the patient returns to the hospital to have the pump refilled with insulin.

Ulcers

An ulcer is an open sore on the skin or in the mucous membrane. As the surface tissue breaks down and dies, it leaves a raw, inflamed area. Ulcers that develop in the digestive system are called **peptic ulcers.** There are two main types of peptic ulcers. Gastric ulcers develop in the stomach, and are caused by an overproduction of hydrochloric acid and pepsin. Pepsin is a digestive enzyme in gastric juice. Duodenal ulcers develop in the duodenum and also result from too much gastric acid secretion.

Peptic ulcers are aggravated by stress and the use of tobacco. Doctors think some people may have a hereditary tendency to develop ulcers. We also know that overuse of aspirin irritates the stomach lining and can promote the formation of ulcers.

A person who has a peptic ulcer will usually experience pain in the upper part of the stomach, usually when the stomach is empty. Peptic ulcers may be treated with medicines that neutralize or reduce stomach acid or with antibiotics. In some cases surgery may be necessary, but because of the development of new medicines, surgery can frequently be avoided.

Gastritis

One of the most common disorders of the stomach is **gastritis,** which is an inflammation of the mucous membrane that lines the stomach. Gastritis can result from the presence of irritant foods, alcohol, or bacteria or viruses. A person suffering from gastritis usually experiences stomach cramps and pain in the upper abdomen. Vomiting usually occurs. Antibiotics cure the condition if bacteria are the cause.

Appendicitis

Appendicitis is the inflammation of the appendix, which is a 3- to 4-inch (8- to 10-cm) extension at one end of the large intestine. As a result of bacteria or foreign matter that gets lodged in it, the appendix becomes swollen and fills with pus. If it bursts, the pus spreads to other body organs, poisoning them.

The symptoms of appendicitis are usually pain and cramps in the lower right portion of the abdomen. These symptoms may be accompanied by fever and vomiting. Under no condition should laxatives be

---

K E E P I N G   F I T

Lactose Intolerance

When people say they are allergic to milk they may mean they are unable to digest lactose, or milk sugar. To digest milk sugar requires the enzyme lactase, and people who cannot digest lactose usually have low levels of the

enzyme. When a person's body cannot correctly digest lactose, drinking milk may result in gas, bloating, pain, or diarrhea.

About 70 percent of the world's population is lactose intolerant to some degree. However,

Caucasians from northern and western Europe tend to be lactose tolerant. Among the groups with lesser abilities to tolerate lactose are those of Mediterranean, African, and Asian roots.

PROBLEMS AND CARE OF THE DIGESTIVE SYSTEM **285**

---

286 CHAPTER 14 DIGESTIVE AND URINARY SYSTEMS

L3 RESEARCH. Ask a volunteer to prepare a report describing the differences in color and structure of kidney stones and gallstones. Ask the student to share the information with the class. Pictures or actual stones would enhance the report.

L2 PARENTAL INVOLVEMENT. Explain that diarrhea can be serious if it is not treated properly. Have students ask their parents what steps were taken when they were infants or small children to control diarrhea. Why is diarrhea more serious in an infant than in an adult?

L2 COMMUNITY INVOLVE-MENT. Have a student contact the local health department to acquire information about techniques to prevent transmission of hepatitis. Ask the student to share the information with the class. During the presentation, determine which practices are followed at home and school by students.

L2 WRITING. Ask each student to prepare a report about the use of fluoride to prevent tooth decay. What are the pros and cons? Is your local water supply fluoridated?

L1 USING THE LESSON RESOURCES. For additional student activities, refer to the lesson resources on page 282.

DID YOU KNOW?

■ Hepatitis B infection is a vaccine-preventable disease—yet an estimated 12,000 health-care workers become infected with it each year, mostly through needle-stick accidents.

Culturally Speaking

Cross-cultural Cancer

Researchers from China, Canada, and the United States have been studying why Chinese-Americans have four to seven times more colon and rectal cancer than Chinese who live in China. In fact, the colon cancer risks increase the longer a Chinese immigrant lives in North America.

The study concludes that saturated fats in the Western diet may be the single greatest factor in the high colo-rectal cancer rates here. Also cited as a cause for higher cancer rates is the sedentary life-style of many Americans—particularly the amount of time they spend sitting.

---

given to a person with these symptoms. Such substances can cause the appendix to burst. A doctor's care is essential. Surgical removal of the appendix may be necessary.

Hepatitis

Hepatitis is a serious inflammation of the liver that is most often caused by a viral infection. The severity of the infection depends on the type of virus involved. The two most common types are hepatitis A, which is sometimes called infectious hepatitis; and hepatitis B, which is sometimes called serum hepatitis. One symptom of hepatitis is jaundice, which is characterized by a yellow discoloration of the skin. The yellow color is the result of a malfunction of the liver.

Hepatitis A is transmitted by direct contact with an infected person or by contact with polluted water. Recovery is slow. Bed rest and a balanced diet are essential.

Hepatitis B results when the virus enters the bloodstream from a transfusion of contaminated human blood, from unclean needles used to administer medicines or drugs, or from surgical or dental instruments that have not been sterilized. Hepatitis B has also been known to be transmitted through sexual contact with an infected person.

Tooth Decay

It may surprise you to see tooth decay listed as a disease of the digestive tract. Teeth help prepare food for proper digestion. Tooth decay weakens a tooth and affects the way a person can bite and chew food. Tooth decay is also perhaps the most preventable disease of the digestive tract. Regular brushing, flossing, and dental checkups are the keys to preventing tooth decay.

Crohn's Disease

Crohn's disease is a chronic disease of the digestive tract. The cause of the disease is not known, but it may be influenced by heredity and environment. As the mucous lining of the digestive tract becomes inflamed, absorption of digested food from the small intestine is severely affected. Symptoms include cramps, diarrhea, and weight loss. Treatment depends on the severity of the symptoms. A diet that avoids raw fruits and vegetables is important. Medical help is essential.

Hemorrhoids

Hemorrhoids are a result of swelling of the veins in the lower rectum and anus. Internal hemorrhoids stay within the rectum. Swellings that push through the anus, however, produce external hemorrhoids. People who sit a lot or suffer from constipation are more susceptible to hemorrhoids. The signs of hemorrhoids includes itching, pain, and bleeding. Sitting in hot baths and using ointment may relieve the discomfort. If the pain and bleeding are severe, the hemorrhoids may need to be surgically removed. Regular exercise and a diet high in fiber can help prevent hemorrhoids.

286 CHAPTER 14 DIGESTIVE AND URINARY SYSTEMS

Across the Curriculum

Home Economics. A well-balanced diet is important in maintaining a healthy digestive system. For instance, a high-fiber diet enables the colon to retain water. This roughage is very important in the elimination of waste from the body and is recommended by the American Cancer Society to prevent bowel or colon cancer. In order to have a diet that is high in fiber, an individual must eat vegetables, fruits, and whole-grain foods. Ask a home economics teacher to visit the class and discuss examples of high-fiber foods and diets necessary for a well-balanced diet.

Have students determine how often they eat high-fiber foods and determine some steps that they can take to improve their diets.

By choosing a variety of foods, you will promote the health of your digestive system.

Care of the Digestive System

The main way to care for the digestive system is to practice good eating habits.

- Eat a variety of foods. Make sure your diet is low in fat and high in fiber.
- Eat regular meals. Eat complete meals at regular intervals during the day.
- Make meals a relaxing time. Do not hurry through your meals. Relax and enjoy them.
- Eat enough but not too much. Eat enough food to satisfy your hunger, but not so much as to stuff yourself.
- Drink plenty of water. Your digestive system needs a lot of water to do its job properly.

DID YOU KNOW?

- You can digest food even if your stomach has been removed. This is because most of the digestive process occurs in the small intestine.
- No gastrointestinal problem is listed among the ten leading causes of death among children and adolescents.

LESSON 2 REVIEW

Reviewing Facts and Vocabulary

1. What are two causes of halitosis?
2. What is lactose intolerance?

Thinking Critically

3. **Analysis.** How do diet and exercise contribute to the prevention of many common digestive disorders?

4. **Synthesis.** Develop a plan for an individual who eats too much and eats too fast.

Applying Health Knowledge

5. Make a list of over-the-counter medicines you have heard about for common digestive disorders. Tell what each can be used for. Then suggest a behavior that might eliminate the problem without the need for medicine.

Check for Understanding

- Assign and discuss the lesson review. Have LD students instead name three digestive disorders and two ways to care for the digestive tract.

Evaluate

- Administer, grade, and discuss the *Lesson 2 Quiz.*

Reteach

- Ask students to list the types of digestive disorders discussed in this lesson. Have them describe how these disorders can be avoided or eliminated.
- Ask students to complete *Reteaching Activity 38.*

Enrich

- Ask students to further investigate digestive disorders. Have them ask the school dietician about disorders that are caused by food contamination.

Close

Ask students to discuss the most important concepts studied in this lesson. Have them write a plan of action on behaviors they will change to prevent digestive disorders.

DID YOU KNOW?

- "To have a lot of gall" means to have a lot of nerve or a kind of distasteful boldness. Literally, the expression means that your gallbladder is overloaded with bile.

Answers to Lesson 2 Review

1. Answers will vary. Accept three of the following: Disorders of the teeth or gums; poor nutrition; problems in the stomach or intestines.
2. An inability to digest lactose due to low levels of the enzyme lactase.
3. A diet that is low in fat, high in fiber, and that includes plenty of water helps move food through the digestive system. Exercise promotes overall digestive health.
4. Plans will vary but might include suggestions for adding fiber to diet; eating more slowly; daily dietary requirements advice; regular exercise programs.
5. Answers will vary.

THE URINARY SYSTEM

LESSON 3 FOCUS

TERMS TO USE

- Kidneys
- Ureters
- Bladder
- Urethra
- Nephrons (NEF•rahnz)
- Urine
- Hemodialysis (hee•moh•dy•AL•uh•suhs)

CONCEPTS TO LEARN

- Filtering wastes from the circulatory system is essential to maintain life.
- Any persistent change in the normal function of the urinary system should receive medical attention.

ATTITUDES AND BEHAVIORS TO EVALUATE

- Self-Inventory, page 292.
- Building Decision-Making Skills, page 293.

T hree systems work together to regulate and control internal body conditions. The urinary system filters wastes from the circulatory system and eliminates the wastes from the body in the form of urine. The respiratory system removes the waste product carbon dioxide. The digestive system removes solid wastes.

Functions of the Urinary System

Water-soluble waste products are the result of all the chemical changes in the cells. Some of the wastes contain nitrogen and would become toxic if they remained in the body. As blood flows through the kidneys, extra salts, water, and nitrogenous wastes are filtered out into small tubules. The liquid wastes are stored temporarily in the bladder.

Structure of the Urinary System

The urinary system consists of two **kidneys;** the **ureters,** which are tubes that lead from the two kidneys to the bladder; the **bladder,** which stores the wastes in the form of urine; and the **urethra,** the tube that leads from the bladder to the outside of the body.

The Kidneys

The two kidneys are bean-shaped and are about the size of a fist. They lie on either side of the spine in the small of the back. The kidneys are embedded in a mass of fatty tissue that protects them. Within each kidney are as many as one million highly specialized tubules called nephrons. **Nephrons** are the functional units of the kidneys. Each nephron involves a tubule and a cluster of capillaries, called a glomerulus. The section of each nephron that surrounds the glomerulus is called Bowman's capsule.

Blood flows into each kidney through a renal artery that immediately branches into much smaller arterioles. Each glomerulus is an extension of the arterioles.

Because of the sudden change in the size of the blood vessels from arterioles to capillaries, pressure is built up as the blood flows through the glomerulus. Nephrons remove these substances from the blood, return the substances the body needs to the blood, and eliminates the remainder as urine. Urine is constantly being formed and collected in the bladder.

Although they are small, the kidneys do a tremendous amount of work. The kidneys filter every drop of blood in your body about once every hour. They are constantly separating harmful substances from the substances your body can use.

288 CHAPTER 14 DIGESTIVE AND URINARY SYSTEMS

Resources for Lesson 3

- **Transparency** 55
- **Guided Reading** Activity 39
- **Decision-Making** Activity 14
- **Workbook** Vocabulary Activity 39
- **Workbook** Application Activity 14
- **Reteaching** Activity 39
- **Enrichment** Activity 14
- **Health Labs** Activity 14

- **Cooperative Learning** Activity 14
- **Lesson 3 Quiz**
- **Chapter 14 Test**
- Science and Technology Videodisc
- **Human Biology, Side 2**
- Ch 18 Laser Treatment of Bladder Cancer

The fluid that passed through the filtering part of the kidney is called filtrate. Your kidneys process about 40 to 50 gallons (152 to 189 l) of filtrate each day. Of this, less than ½ gallon (2 l) is expelled as urine.

The Bladder and Urethra

The bladder is a muscular organ that stores urine. **Urine,** the liquid waste material, collects in the bladder until it is ready to be passed out of the body. The bladder may hold as much as a pint (500–600 ml) of urine. The need to urinate is stimulated as the bladder becomes full. Sphincter, or circular, muscles relax and allow urine to flow through the urethra. Control of the sphincter muscles is voluntary. In babies, lack of control is normal. An infant urinates when the bladder is full enough to cause a reflex stimulus.

Problems of the Urinary System

Because the function of the kidneys is so essential to maintaining the balance of fluids in the body any disruption of this function is potentially serious. Some of the more common disorders are described here.

- Incontinence is the inability of the body to control the bladder and the elimination of waste. Bladder incontinence may occur if the sphincter muscle that closes the urethra is torn, weak, or damaged. This condition is more common in older adults.
- Cystitis is a bacterial infection of the bladder that occurs most frequently in females. Symptoms include a burning sensation and a high frequency of urination. Fever and blood in the urine may be present.

The Urinary System

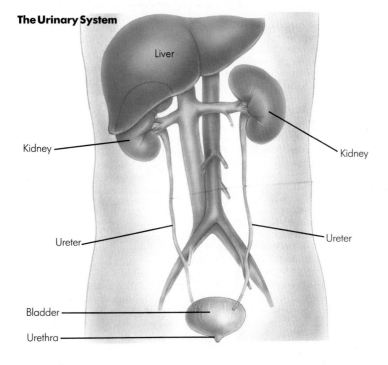

Liver

Kidney

Kidney

Ureter

Ureter

Bladder

Urethra

The urinary system functions in maintaining constant conditions in the body's internal environment.

THE URINARY SYSTEM **289**

Teach

Guided Practice

L2 CLASS ACTIVITY. Using a body systems model, ask students to compare the size of the bile duct to the size of the aorta and the size of the urethra. How are these vessels similar?

L1 DISCUSSION. Ask students to describe how the kidneys act as a filter to remove waste from the body. Have students list other filters used to clean, such as air-conditioner filters, filters used in automobiles, etc. How do these filters work compared to the kidneys?

L1 USING BODY SYSTEMS TRANSPARENCY 55. Refer to the Teaching Transparencies Binder.

L2 SPEAKER. If possible, invite as a speaker someone who is a candidate for or a recipient of a kidney, liver, or pancreatic transplant. Ask the speaker to answer questions such as these: What advantages do you see in the transplant? disadvantages? Why are (or were) you a candidate for this treatment? Are there emotional costs to this treatment?

L2 CLASS ACTIVITY. Using a torso model or chart, trace the flow of fluid wastes from the kidneys. Ask the class to identify areas in which stones might get lodged. Why can infections easily travel to the kidney from the bladder? Does the size of the urethra vary with age or sex? How are kidney stones treated? (Surgery, diet, exercise, laser, X rays.)

L2 CLASS ACTIVITY. Using a pictorial model, show students the structure of a nephron. Ask students to make a drawing of the nephron and label its parts.

L2 DISCUSSION. Kidneys can sustain damage both before birth and after birth. Discuss with the class some of the causes of kidney problems. (Examples: diet, drugs, hypertension, diabetes, heredity, genetic disorders.) What can students do to protect their kidney function?

Additional Information

The Kidneys. Kidney stones range in size from very tiny (and passable) to an inch (2.5 centimeters) or more in diameter. Pain is caused when a large stone gets caught in the bladder, ureter, or renal pelvis.

Kidney stones can sometimes be dissolved by a machine that uses shock waves to break large stones into smaller, sand-sized particles.

An adult's kidney weighs about 5 ounces. In an adult, the two kidneys filter about 425 gallons of blood each day, most of which is recycled.

L2 **EXPLANATION.** Explain
that a urinalysis is an important
part of a physical examination.
Analysis of the urine can help a
doctor diagnose certain diseases.

L2 **CLASS ACTIVITY.** Ask students to write paragraphs explaining why a person can survive with
a single functioning kidney.

Independent Practice

L3 **RESEARCH.** Ask a volunteer
to calculate the cost of kidney
dialysis for an individual for 1
year. A hospital billing office or
insurance agency can assist by
providing current figures. Ask the
volunteer to share his or her
findings with the class.

L2 **RESEARCH.** Ask a volunteer
to determine when in prenatal
development the kidneys are
developed. (First trimester.) What
prudent measures should be taken
by a pregnant woman to assure
proper development of the kidneys? Have the student report
back to the class.

L2 **RESEARCH.** Explain to students that a lithotripter is a device
that crumbles kidney stones so
that the individual is not required
to undergo surgery to remove kidney stones. Ask students to
research a lithotripter and write a
report on this modern procedure
to remove kidney stones.

L3 **RESEARCH.** Ask volunteers
to investigate the complications of
transplants and dialysis and prepare a table comparing these
treatments. Are there side effects
to both therapies? Are costs comparable?

L1 **USING THE LESSON
RESOURCES.** For additional student activities, refer to the lesson
resources on page 288.

DID YOU KNOW?

- Your kidney is about
  the size of your fist.
- Your right kidney is
  probably slightly
  lower than your left
  one.
- You can survive with
  just one kidney.
- Two kidneys filter
  about 50 gallons (190
  liters) of blood each
  day.
- Each day in the
  United States,
  Americans' kidneys
  filter about 10 billion
  gallons of liquid.

It is important to seek medical attention. If left untreated, the infection can move to the ureter and kidneys.
- Nephritis occurs when the nephrons of the kidneys become inflamed
  or infected. Symptoms may include high blood pressure, weakness,
  fatigue, and swelling of body tissues. Treatment usually involves
  relieving the symptoms.
- Urethritis is an inflammation of the urethra, the tube leading from the
  bladder to the outside of the body. The passage of urine becomes
  painful and difficult.
- When the kidneys are unable to rid wastes from the body, poisonous
  substances build and the normal function is seriously affected. The
  result is a series of symptoms called uremia. Dialysis, a treatment that
  literally cleans a person's blood, is usually required for uremia.
- Kidney stones are stonelike crystals that sometimes form from
  mineral salts and urea. Small stones may pass out of the body in

---

CONFLICT RESOLUTION

Carrie's younger sister,
Sue, has a serious kidney
disorder that requires frequent hemodialysis. The
expense of the procedure
and the need for the family to stay close to the hospital have put severe limits
on everyone in the family.
Carrie is starting to feel
that she's as restricted by
Sue's disease as Sue is.
However, whenever Carrie
complains, her parents say
she should be thankful
that she's healthy. Carrie
feels more and more
resentful toward her sister
and can't help feeling
guilty about it.

*How can Carrie resolve her
feelings?*

HEALTH UPDATE

LOOKING AT THE ISSUES

How to Get Enough Organs for Transplants

The number of organ transplants is on the rise. For
example, between 1983 and
1987, the number of kidney
transplants in the United
States went from 6,112 to
8,967; the number of heart
transplants from 172 to 1,512.
Technological advances have
made these procedures safer
than ever before. However,
the problem is that there are
many more people in need of
new organs than there are
organs being donated.

Analyzing Different Viewpoints

ONE VIEW. Some people propose paying donors for their
organs. They believe that
there is such a need for these
organs that payment would
provide the necessary incen-
tive for more people to donate.
(Presently, in the U.S., it is a
felony—a major federal
crime—to buy or sell a major
body part, so the laws would
first have to be changed.)

A SECOND VIEW. Others are
horrified by the idea of selling
organs. Some state religious

or ethical objections. Others
point out what has happened
in countries like India where
the poor often sell their kidneys for small amounts of
money and where black market sales of organs flourish.
Some people fear that selling
organs in the U.S. might
result in abuses of the poor or
elderly—or even in murder to
get organs for profit.

A THIRD VIEW. Another view
is to let people with such
problems die, unless they
can pay for the cost of this
procedure.

Exploring Your Views

1. How do you feel about
   being a living donor—
   donating a kidney, for
   example, if someone close
   to you needed it? What
   about for a stranger?
2. How do you feel about
   signing a donor card,
   requesting that, upon your
   death, your organs be
   donated?
3. How do you feel about
   people being allowed to
   sell their organs?

Additional Information

Urinary Problems. There are many types
of urinary problems that affect individuals
of all ages, ranging from urinary infections
and painful kidney stones to urinary
incontinence. The most debilitating urinary problem, however, is for those individuals whose kidneys are not functioning
properly and must depend on kidney dialysis to remove harmful waste from the

body. These individuals must receive treatments in order to survive until a kidney is
available for transplant. They may experience depression and frustration from having to undergo these uncomfortable and
expensive treatments. Though modern
technology has given hope to these individuals, they still need special support and
understanding to cope.

urine. Large stones can cause great pain. If a stone blocks the flow of urine, an infection often results. In the past surgery was necessary to remove a kidney stone. Now, however, a procedure called lithotripsy is frequently used. High-intensity sound waves are focused on the area where the stones are located. The sound waves pass through the body and literally crumble the stones. The technique is painless, and the resulting pieces pass out of the body in urine.

- Kidney failure may be caused by a blockage of urine, a very serious case of nephritis, or loss of blood. Normally a person can survive with one kidney, but if both kidneys fail or have to be removed, the person will die. Three techniques are in use today to help people who suffer from kidney failure.

Hemodialysis is a technique in which a person is connected to an artificial kidney machine. The machine, which is about the size of a washing machine, filters wastes from the blood. Dialysis must take place three times a week for approximately four hours each time. This kind of dialysis usually takes place in a hospital or clinical setting.

Peritoneal dialysis is a technique that uses the peritoneum, a thin membrane that surrounds the digestive organs inside the abdomen, to filter the blood and remove waste products through the use of a catheter, a tube that provides a passageway for fluids. Peritoneal dialysis allows the patient to be treated at home.

Another technique is a kidney transplant. A donated kidney is surgically placed within a person's body and functions just as the original kidney did.

An artery in the patient's arm is connected by tubing to the machine. Her blood flows through an artificial membrane that acts as a kidney and filters out waste materials. The cleansed blood then flows back into the patient's circulatory system. This procedure is hemodialysis.

Care of the Urinary System

The main way to care for your urinary system is to drink plenty of fluids. This should include six to eight glasses of water every day. A nutritionally balanced diet also plays a part in the care of the urinary system. Practicing good personal health care will help prevent the risk of infection to urinary organs. Any changes in urine color, odor, or frequency should be discussed with a doctor. Regular physical checkups are necessary to detect changes in urine content.

LESSON 3 REVIEW

Reviewing Facts and Vocabulary

1. Describe the function of the kidneys.
2. Describe the function of two systems, apart from the urinary system, that have a role in ridding the body of waste material.
3. Define the terms *urine, nephrons,* and *hemodialysis.*

Thinking Critically

4. **Analysis.** How does drinking plenty of fluids each day promote a healthy urinary system?

5. **Analysis.** How might kidney dialysis affect a person's life-style?

Applying Health Knowledge

6. Find out what is involved in kidney transplants. How do doctors match a donor and recipient? How long is the wait for a donor? What advancements have been made in the procedure? What is the success rate for this type of surgery?

THE URINARY SYSTEM **291**

Helping Students Improve Their Health

Reinforcing Vocabulary

- **Fiber.** Part of a plant that when eaten is undigestible.
- **Laxatives.** A product taken to relieve constipation.
- **Carbonated beverages.** Beverages that contain carbon dioxide.

Teaching Strategies

L1 EXPLANATION. Question 17 could be misinterpreted by parents and students. Many individuals believe that a drinking fountain is a breeding ground that will allow germs to be passed from one person to another. Many individuals deliberately do not drink from drinking fountains for this very reason.

L2 DISCUSSION. Have students discuss physiological problems that are associated with eating disorders and the specific anatomical structures of the digestive system. What dangers exist from the constant purging of a person living with the eating disorder bulimia?

L1 DISCUSSION. Have students discuss the signs and symptoms of an ulcer. What is an ulcer? What causes an ulcer to occur? How can teenagers help prevent getting an ulcer? What treatments do doctors use to help an individual who is diagnosed as having an ulcer?

DID YOU KNOW?

- If you gradually reduce the salt in your diet, you'll also gradually lose your taste for it. Give yourself 5 weeks to lose your sodium cravings.

Self-Inventory

Care of the Digestive and Urinary Systems

HOW DO YOU RATE?

There are many things you can do to promote healthy digestive and urinary systems. Number a sheet of paper from 1 through 25. Read each item below, and respond by writing *always or most of the time, sometimes,* or *seldom or never* for each item. Total the number of each type of response. Then proceed to the next section.

1. I eat a variety of healthy foods every day.
2. I do aerobic exercises for 20 minutes at least three times a week.
3. To reduce stress, I engage in activities that I like.
4. I drink at least six to eight glasses of water a day.
5. I chew each bite of food thoroughly before swallowing.
6. I eat two or more servings of fruit each day.
7. I eat foods that are high in fiber every day.
8. I eat three or more servings of vegetables each day.
9. I avoid overeating.
10. I stop eating before I am full.
11. I have a dental checkup every year.
12. I avoid eating when I am under stress or emotionally upset.
13. I regularly engage in activities that reduce my stress.

14. I brush my teeth after every meal.
15. I floss my teeth daily.
16. I eat foods that have a high water content such as celery, soup, and apples.
17. I take a drink whenever I pass a water fountain.
18. I limit the amount of salt in my diet.
19. I have regular bowel movements.
20. I look for changes in urine color, odor, or frequency.
21. I avoid salty snacks, such as chips, crackers, and pretzels.
22. I use laxatives only when recommended by a doctor.
23. I choose to drink fruit juices instead of soft drinks.
24. I seek medical attention when diarrhea persists for more than 48 hours.
25. I limit the amount of foods that might cause gas, such as carbonated beverages.

HOW DID YOU SCORE?

Give yourself 3 points for every *always or most of the time* answer, 1 point for every *sometimes* answer, and 0 points for every *seldom or never* answer. Find your total, and read below to see how you scored. Then proceed to the next section.

55 to 75
Excellent. Your health choices show you are taking care of your digestive and urinary systems.

35 to 54
Good. Your healthy choices are good but there are some things you could do to promote a healthier digestive or urinary system.

15 to 34
Fair. While you are doing some things to protect yourself from digestive and urinary problems, much improvement is still needed.

Below 15
Poor. You are taking unnecessary risks that could affect the health of your digestive and urinary systems both now and in the future.

WHAT ARE YOUR GOALS?

Identify an area in which your score was low, and use the goal-setting process to begin making a change.

1. The behavior I would like to change is ____.
2. If this behavior were completely changed, I would look, feel, or act differently in the following ways: ____.
3. The steps involved in making this change are ____.
4. My timetable for accomplishing this is ____.
5. People I will ask for help or assistance are ____.
6. The benefits I will receive as a result of making this change are ____.
7. My reward at the end of each week will be ____.

Meeting Students' Needs

For students who score *Excellent*. Suggest that students consider working summer intern positions at a hospital or health-care facility. Students may want to consider a career in medicine.

For students who score *Good*. Suggest that students conduct a health fair that stresses the health of the digestive and urinary systems.

For students who score *Fair*. Suggest that students analyze their behavior and make short-term goals for improving the care of their digestive and urinary systems.

For students who score *Poor*. Suggest that students discuss how habits are formed and how habits may be reshaped for the better.

Building Decision-Making Skills

Matt is a junior in high school. His little brother with whom he has a very close relationship has been diagnosed as having kidney damage that can be corrected only by a transplant. Matt has been identified as being the best donor. His parents have already asked him if he is willing to donate one of his kidneys. He is frightened and feels that he has no choice in this situation.

WHAT DO YOU THINK?

1. **Situation.** What do you think Matt is afraid of?
2. **Situation.** What risks are involved in this situation? To Matt? To his brother? To his parents?
3. **Choices.** What choices do you think Matt has?
4. **Choices.** Where might Matt go for more information? Whom might he talk to about this situation?
5. **Consequences.** How might Matt deal with his fears?
6. **Consequences.** How might Matt's health triangle be affected by this decision?
7. **Consequences.** How might his self-esteem be affected by this decision?
8. **Decision.** What do you think Matt should do?
9. **Evaluation.** Have you ever known anyone who faced a decision involving life and death? Describe the situation and your feelings about the courage involved in making that decision.

Jan and Angela, both sophomores in high school, have been best friends since third grade when Jan moved to town. Their families are good friends and periodically join together for an outing or a special occasion. Last spring Angela started being concerned about her weight. She told Jan she was going to lose 15 pounds—for sure this time. When she started eating less and exercising more she began to lose, slowly at first. She was very excited about her progress and Jan was happy for her. However, as time went on, it seemed that all Angela ever talked about was food. She even started showing some interest in cooking and often brought "treats" to school. By fall Angela had lost a lot of weight. In fact, her friends started asking Jan why Angela was still trying to lose more weight when she was already so thin. Jan is beginning to worry about her friend. What should she do?

WHAT DO YOU THINK?

10. **Situation.** What reasons might Jan have for being concerned?
11. **Choices.** What choices do you think Jan has?
12. **Consequences.** What are the advantages of each of the possible choices?
13. **Consequences.** What are the disadvantages of each of the possible choices?
14. **Consequences.** How might Angela's health triangle be affected by Jan's decision?
15. **Consequences.** How might Angela's family react to each of the possible choices?
16. **Consequences.** How might Jan's family react to each of the possible choices?
17. **Consequences.** What risks are involved in this situation?
18. **Decision.** What do you think Jan should do? Why do you think so?
19. **Decision.** How might Jan implement, or accomplish, her decision?
20. **Evaluation.** Have you ever known anyone with an eating disorder? If so, describe what the situation was like and what you learned from it.

THE URINARY SYSTEM **293**

Discussing the Answers

Situation 1. Matt has the opportunity to offer a special gift to his brother—the gift of life. Every person in Matt's place would be scared. Perhaps the best possible resolve in this situation would be to have Matt discuss this situation with his doctor. Once Matt is aware of the risks and alternatives, Matt can make an informed decision.

Situation 2. Jan must suspect that her friend Angela may be developing the psychological disorder, anorexia nervosa. It is important that Jan speak to a responsible adult immediately about her suspicions concerning Angela.

Building Decision-Making Skills

Teaching Strategies

L2 CLASS ACTIVITY. Have the class form two groups. Have one group support the idea of Matt donating a kidney to his younger brother. Have the other group provide reasons why Matt may not want to donate a kidney to his brother. Who is permitted to make such a decision? Can a parent require a child to involuntarily donate an organ, such as a kidney, for a family member? At what age should this decision be the adolescent's choice? What would be required if Matt donated one kidney and his remaining kidney began to malfunction?

L1 CLASS ACTIVITY. Have students role-play the part of Jan as she discusses her concerns regarding Angela with (a) her school counselor (b) a friend (c) Jan's parents (d) Angela's parents. How might these individuals vary in their response to Jan's concern? How might these individuals respond the same?

L1 CLASS ACTIVITY. Another possible role-play situation pertaining to the digestive system is: Your father smokes, drinks, eats foods high in fat, and works a job that is very stressful. Recently your father's doctor diagnosed that your father has an ulcer. Your father was told that he must quit smoking, avoid alcoholic beverages, eat a bland diet, and reduce his level of stress. It does not appear that your father is taking the suggestions of his doctor very seriously. You wonder if you should interfere.

DID YOU KNOW?

■ Tissue matching for organ donation depends on one of the most complicated genetic systems known in humans: the gene code for antigens and thus the acceptance or rejection of tissue transplants between different people.

Answers to Chapter 14 Review

REVIEW

Using Health Terms

1. Digestion
2. Absorption
3. Esophagus
4. Bile
5. Liver
6. Halitosis
7. Hemorrhoid
8. Heartburn
9. Vomiting
10. Ulcer
11. Gastritis
12. Kidneys

Building Academic Skills

13. Digestion, absorption, elimination.
14. About 4,500.
15. Mouth, esophagus, stomach, duodenum, jejunum, ileum, large intestine.

Recalling the Facts

16. Chewing, mashing, breaking food into smaller pieces.
17. Those that change food into simpler substances through the action of digestive enzymes.
18. They respond to heat, cold, pain, and pressure.
19. It stops.
20. They prevent food from backing up as it moves through the digestive process.
21. Aspirin, alcohol.
22. The small intestine.
23. Trypsin digests protein. Amylase digests carbohydrates. Lipase digests fats.
24. To absorb water and eliminate undigested food.
25. Answers will vary. Accept three of the following: Produces bile; converts glucose to glycogen; helps maintain level of glucose in the blood; removes worn-out red blood cells; changes toxic waste material into less toxic substance; stores vitamins and minerals.
26. It stores bile and releases it into the small intestine.
27. Acid content from the stomach backs up into the esophagus.
28. A condition in which the upper part of the stomach pushes through the diaphragm.

29. Certain foods seem to be gas-forming for some people but not for others.
30. Pain and cramps in the lower right portion of the abdomen; fever; vomiting.
31. Laxatives.
32. The liver.
33. Bed rest and a balanced diet.
34. Answers will vary. Accept three of the following:

Using Health Terms

On a separate sheet of paper, write the term that best matches each definition given below.

LESSON 1

1. The chemical and physical breakdown of food into smaller pieces.
2. The passage of digested food from the digestive tract into the circulatory system.
3. A tube that extends from the pharynx to the stomach.
4. A digestive juice produced in the liver that helps break down fats.
5. The largest gland in the body.

LESSON 2

6. Bad breath.
7. A swelling of the veins in the lower rectum and anus.
8. A condition caused when the stomach's acid backs up into the esophagus.
9. A strong result of reverse peristalsis.
10. An open sore on the skin or in the mucous membrane.
11. An inflammation of the mucous membrane that lines the stomach.

LESSON 3

12. Two bean-shaped organs that excrete the waste products of metabolism.

Building Academic Skills

LESSON 1

13. **Reading.** List the following processes in the order in which they take place in the body: absorption, elimination, digestion.
14. **Math.** If your dentist gives you a shot of a local anesthetic that numbs the lower right half of the mouth, about how many of your taste buds will be "out of order" until the anesthetic wears off?
15. **Reading.** Arrange the following organs of the digestive system in the order in which food passes through them: stomach, esophagus, duodenum, large intestine, ileum, mouth, jejunum.

Recalling the Facts

LESSON 1

16. What are the mechanical processes that take place during digestion?
17. What are the chemical processes that take place during digestion?
18. What functions do the nerve endings in the mouth serve?
19. During swallowing, what happens to breathing activity?
20. What is the role of the sphincter muscles located along the digestive tract?
21. Name two drugs that are absorbed directly into the blood from the stomach.
22. In what part of the digestive system does most of the chemical breakdown of food take place?
23. List three enzymes produced by the pancreas and describe the function of each.
24. What are the two main functions of the large intestine?
25. List three major functions of the liver.
26. What is the function of the gallbladder?

LESSON 2

27. What causes heartburn?
28. What is a hiatal hernia?
29. What can cause gas?
30. List three symptoms that may be present in a person suffering from appendicitis.
31. What medication should never be given to people who may have appendicitis?
32. What body organ is affected by hepatitis?
33. What is the usual treatment for hepatitis?
34. List three ways to prevent tooth decay.

LESSON 3

35. Name the four parts of the urinary system.
36. What is the difference between the ureters and the urethra?
37. In what body organ is urine stored?
38. Why are the kidneys important?
39. Why is it important to seek medical attention if you believe you have cystitis?
40. Name and define four problems that may be associated with the urinary system.
41. Describe the process of hemodialysis.

Brushing, flossing, getting regular dental check-ups.
35. Kidneys, ureters, bladder, urethra.
36. The ureters are tubes that connect each kidney to the bladder; the urethra is a tube that leads from the bladder to the outside of the body.
37. The bladder.

REVIEW

Thinking Critically

LESSON 1

42. Synthesis. Write a one-page composition that would explain why many gastrointestinal illnesses are stress-related.

43. Analysis. Summarize the work of gastric juices.

44. Synthesis. Develop a plan that would help young people prevent gastrointestinal problems.

45. Analysis. What evidence can you find that might indicate that gastrointestinal problems will increase in the years ahead?

LESSON 2

46. Synthesis. Explain what a person should do if she or he experiences heartburn regularly.

47. Analysis. Compare the conditions known as diarrhea and constipation.

48. Analysis. In what ways are smoking, stress, and digestive problems related?

49. Analysis. What causes appendicitis, and what can be its result?

LESSON 3

50. Synthesis. If you could do so, how would you redesign the urinary system of the human body? Make a drawing or diagram to show how this system would work. Name and label the parts of the system.

51. Evaluation. What are the three most important things you can do to keep your urinary system running smoothly?

52. Synthesis. What ideas can you add to those in the text that might help to keep your urinary system in good working order?

Making the Connection

LESSON 3

53. Math. Calculate the cost to an individual of kidney dialysis for one year based on average costs of treatment in your local area. A hospital billing office or an insurance agency can assist by providing current figures. Share your findings with the class.

Applying Health Knowledge

LESSON 1

54. You may have experienced the sensation of eating something and having it "go down the wrong way," making you choke. What causes this? What usually prevents this?

LESSON 2

55. Derek brushes his teeth after every meal and before he goes to bed, but his brother is always telling him he has bad breath. Which of the following should Derek do?
a. Start using a mouthwash every morning.
b. Visit a dentist.
c. Eat a breath mint every hour.

56. Amanda's parents have recently divorced, and she must decide which one of them she wants to live with. She also broke up with her boyfriend a month ago. These problems have been making her very unhappy and causing her to lose sleep and overeat. Is Amanda more likely to experience diarrhea or constipation? Why?

LESSON 3

57. You notice that your sister has gone to the bathroom six times in the last three hours. She tells you she has found blood in her urine and is experiencing a burning sensation whenever she urinates. You feel her forehead, and it is hot. What urinary infection might your sister be suffering from?

Beyond the Classroom

LESSON 2

58. Parental Involvement. Ask your parents to tell you about any problems with the digestive or urinary system they have experienced. Find out what their symptoms were, what actions they took to correct the problem, and how they evaluated the effectiveness of their actions.

59. Further Study. Research a digestive problem described in Lesson 2. Write a short paper on its causes, symptoms, and cures.

38. They continuously filter blood, removing harmful substances.

39. If untreated, the infection can spread to the ureters and kidneys.

40. Answers will vary. Accept definitions for four of the following: Incontinence, cystitis, nephritis, urethritis, uremia, kidney stones, kidney failure. Definitions can be found on pages 289 to 291.

41. A person is connected to an artificial kidney machine that filters wastes from the blood.

Thinking Critically

42. Compositions will vary.

43. They contain hydrochloric acid, digestive enzymes, and mucus and mix with food in the stomach to start the digestion of proteins.

44. Plans will vary but might include: Eating a well-balanced diet, drinking plenty of water, exercising regularly, avoiding stress.

45. Answers will vary. Possible answer: Many of the conditions occur over a period of time and so as one ages problems can build.

46. See a doctor for a medical examination.

47. Answers will vary. Possible answer: Both are disorders of the digestive system. Diarrhea occurs when food moves through the large intestine too rapidly thus not enough water is removed, making feces watery. Constipation occurs when food moves too slowly through the large intestine thus too much water is removed, making feces hard and dry.

48. Smoking and stress can interfere with the digestive process and result in digestive problems.

49. It is caused by bacteria or foreign matter that becomes lodged in the appendix. The appendix may burst, spreading poisons to other body organs.

50. Drawings will vary.

51. Drink plenty of fluids; eat a balanced diet; practice good personal health habits.

52. Answers will vary. Possible answers: Exercise; avoid certain foods and beverages; see a doctor for regular checkups.

Making the Connection

53. Answers will vary.

Applying Health Knowledge

54. Answers will vary. Possible answer: It may be caused by talking or laughing with food in one's mouth, thus opening the epiglottis; swallowing one's food before talking or laughing.

55. B.

56. Diarrhea—it is often associated with emotional turmoil.

57. Cystitis.

Beyond the Classroom

58. Answers will vary.

59. Answers will vary.

Lesson Summaries

LESSON 1. When a male reaches puberty, hormones stimulate the production of testosterone—initiating sperm production and the development of secondary sex characteristics. The structure, function, problems associated with the male reproductive system, and ways to care for the system are presented.

LESSON 2. When a female reaches puberty, hormones stimulate the production of estrogen and progesterone. Secondary sex characteristics result. During the reproductive years, one ovum a month matures, allowing an opportunity for fertilization. The structure, function, problems associated with the female reproductive system, and ways to care for the system are presented.

Introducing the Chapter

Provide on the chalkboard a typical "life plan" on a time line. Include time spent as a student, single worker, married person, parent, grandparent, retiree, etc. Relate one's personal health to each time period, giving examples of ways to maintain one's health to achieve quality life. Highlight possible childbearing years. Discuss the importance of maintaining the health of one's reproductive system. Point out the necessity of knowing the basics of both reproductive systems to maintain positive health over one's entire life span.

Encourage students to continue to fill in the body systems study chart that was introduced in Chapter 11, filling in the structure, function, problems, and care for each system presented in this chapter.

Performance Assessment ✓

Refer to pages T 23 to T 25 for a Performance Assessment strategy for this chapter. See the *Performance Assessment Activities* booklet for additional suggestions.

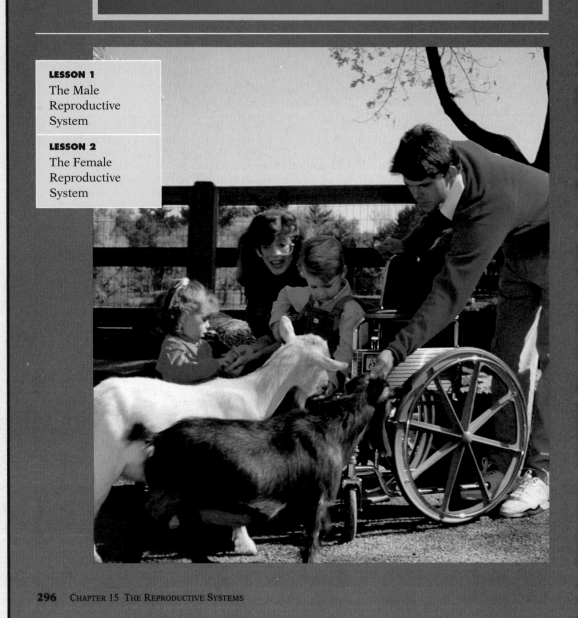

CHAPTER
15

THE REPRODUCTIVE SYSTEMS

LESSON 1
The Male Reproductive System

LESSON 2
The Female Reproductive System

Key to Ability Levels

Teaching strategies have been coded for varying learning styles and abilities.

L1 Level 1 activities are basic activities and should be within the ability range of all students.

L2 Level 2 activities are average activities and should be within the ability range of average to above-average students.

L3 Level 3 activities are challenging activities designed for the ability range of above-average students.

LD LD activities should be within the ability range of learning-disabled students.

LEP LEP activities should be within the ability range of Limited English Proficiency students.

THE MALE REPRODUCTIVE SYSTEM

W hen a male reaches puberty, hormones released by the pituitary gland stimulate the testes to begin producing testosterone. **Testosterone** is a male hormone that causes the testes to produce sperm. Testosterone is also responsible for other physical changes, such as the enlargement of the external reproductive organs that take place during puberty. In addition, testosterone is responsible for the development of secondary sex characteristics. These include broadened shoulders; facial, pubic, and underarm hair; a deepened voice; and muscular development.

The Function and Structure of the Male Reproductive System

The functions of the male reproductive system are the production of sperm and the transfer of sperm to a female's body during intercourse. As a result of intercourse, a sperm may unite with an egg cell, or ovum. If this occurs, the female is pregnant.

Male Reproductive Organs

The male reproductive system includes the testes, epididymis, vas deferens, seminal vesicles, prostate gland, Cowper's glands, urethra, and penis.

The Testes. The **testes,** or testicles, are two small glands that produce sperm. Both the production and survival of sperm require a temperature that is lower than body temperature. The testes hang outside the male's body in a sac called the scrotum. The **scrotum** protects sperm by keeping the testes at a temperature slightly below the normal body temperature of 98.6°F (37°C). If body temperature rises, the muscles of the scrotum relax, lowering the testes away from the body. If body temperature drops, the muscles contract, pulling the testes closer to the body. If the testes are too warm or too cold, the normal production of sperm does not occur.

Each testis contains several hundred yards of coiled tube that produce sperm and provide a passageway in which sperm move. Each sperm is shaped somewhat like a tadpole, the head containing the nucleus and the tail being the means of movement. Sperm cells are so tiny that 500 of them lined up end to end would measure only 1 inch (2.5 cm). Once a male reaches puberty, he is capable of producing sperm for the rest of his life.

The Epididymis. The tubes in each testis join a larger coiled tube, called the epididymis. The epididymis, located at the outer surface of each testis, stores sperm temporarily. Sperm mature in the epididymis.

THE MALE REPRODUCTIVE SYSTEM **297**

LESSON 1 FOCUS

TERMS TO USE
- Testosterone (te•STAHS•tuh•rohn)
- Testes
- Scrotum (SKROHT•uhm)
- Semen
- Urethra (yu•REE•thruh)
- Penis
- Sterility

CONCEPTS TO LEARN
- The male reproductive system consists of the penis and scrotum, the epididymis, vas deferens, seminal vesicles, prostate gland, Cowper's glands, and urethra.

ATTITUDES AND BEHAVIORS TO EVALUATE
- Self-Inventory, page 310.
- Building Decision-Making Skills, page 311.

Focus

Lesson Objectives

After studying this lesson, students should be able to:
- identify the structure and function of the male reproductive system
- identify some disorders of the male reproductive system

Bellringer

Write the following on the chalkboard for students to work on while attendance is being taken: *List three traits that you share with someone in your family and two traits that you have in common with no one in your family.*

Introducing the Lesson

Have students share their responses to the Bellringer. Help students understand that they inherited many of their characteristics from their parents, but that each of them is a unique individual. Students should understand that the reproductive system is the system that produces offspring and that their own characteristics were passed to them through their parents' reproductive systems. Tell students that this lesson details how to protect this very important system.

DID YOU KNOW?

- Each year, about 122,000 cases of prostate cancer are diagnosed in the U.S.
- Approximately 30,000 men die from prostate cancer annually.
- Until recently a standard rectal exam was recommended to detect prostate cancer in its early and treatable stages. Now, a new study recommends a blood test, called the prostatic specific antigen blood test, which can detect abnormalities in the amount of protein produced by the prostate gland. High levels of the protein can be a sign of prostate cancer.

Resources for Lesson 1

- **Transparencies** 20 and 56
- **Guided Reading** Activity 40
- **Workbook** Vocabulary Activity 40
- **Reteaching** Activity 40
- **Lesson 1 Quiz**
- **BARN Software,** Human Sexuality

- **Education in Sexuality**
- **Performance Assessment** Activity 15
- **ABC News InterActive Videodiscs**
- **Teenage Sexuality, Side 1**
- Ch 5 The Male Body

Building Vocabulary

- Ask students to read through the lesson and list all the unfamiliar words they find. Compare lists and create a final list on the chalkboard. Divide students into four groups and ask each group to work cooperatively to define each of the unfamiliar words. Add key vocabulary terms that students may not have selected. Once the terms are defined, have them create a crossword puzzle using the vocabulary terms and their definitions.
- Ask students to complete *Workbook Vocabulary Activity 40*.

Teach

Guided Practice

LD EXPLANATION. LD students may rely on class discussions for comprehension of the lesson's content due to high-level vocabulary. Assignment of independent reading is not recommended.

LEP CLASS ACTIVITY. Use charts or models to review the names and locations of the male reproductive system. Provide students with a drawing of the male reproductive anatomy and have students fill in the names of each of the parts as you explain them.

L1 USING BODY SYSTEMS TRANSPARENCY 56. Refer to the Teaching Transparencies Binder.

L2 DISCUSSION. Ask students to recall when they were very young and learned the names of the male reproductive body parts. Some of these names were not the scientific terms, but slang or baby terms. Discuss why families tell children incorrect names of body parts and what they think would be another approach to this topic.

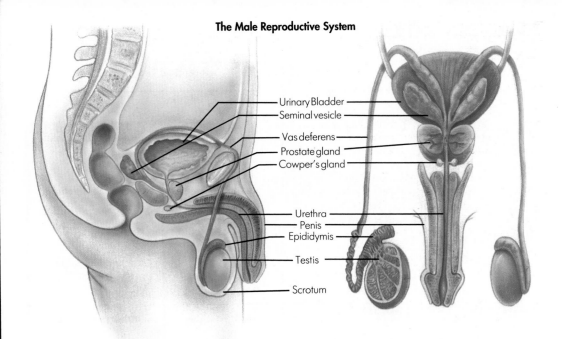

The Male Reproductive System

- Urinary Bladder
- Seminal vesicle
- Vas deferens
- Prostate gland
- Cowper's gland
- Urethra
- Penis
- Epididymis
- Testis
- Scrotum

DID YOU KNOW?

- There are 300 to 400 million sperm in each ejaculation, but only one can fertilize an ovum.
- One spoonful of semen contains between 100 to 500 million sperm.
- Some men choose to be sterilized by having an operation called a vasectomy. This operation is performed inside the scrotum. The vas deferens is cut and sealed so that sperm cannot travel to the penis.

The Vas Deferens and the Urethra. The vas deferens is a tube that extends from the lower end of each epididymis and connects with the urethra. Each vas deferens is about 18 inches (46 cm) long. As sperm move through the vas deferens, they are mixed in a fluid produced by the seminal vesicles.

The seminal vesicles are glands about 2 inches (5 cm) long and are attached to the vas deferens near the base of the bladder. These glands secrete a fluid that mixes with sperm to make them more mobile and to provide nourishment. The secretion of the seminal vesicles contains nutrients and is rich in fructose, a form of sugar. The seminal vesicles and vas deferens meet to form the ejaculatory duct, which opens into the urethra.

Sperm are then mixed with fluids secreted from the prostate gland, a small gland that surrounds the urethra, and from Cowper's glands, which are located below the prostate gland. The mixture of the fluids from the seminal vesicles, the prostate gland, and Cowper's glands with sperm forms **semen,** or seminal fluid. When a male ejaculates, he releases semen.

The **urethra** is a small tube that extends from the bladder as well as from each vas deferens through the penis to the outside of the body. The bladder stores urine, which leaves the body through the urethra. Both semen and urine leave the body through the urethra. However, they do not pass through the urethra at the same time. A muscle near the bladder contracts, preventing urine from entering the urethra when semen is present. Because urine is very high in acid, the lining of the urethra tends to be acidic. The secretion from the Cowper's glands (also called bulbourethral glands) lubricates the urethra and neutralizes the acid content before semen is ejaculated. This secretion also causes a small drop of clear fluid to leave the penis before the semen comes out. This fluid is called preejaculatory fluid.

298 CHAPTER 15 THE REPRODUCTIVE SYSTEMS

Additional Information

Circumcision. Until recently, nearly all newborn males were routinely circumcised at birth. Today, doctors and parents are questioning the need for the procedure.

Even a decade ago, most doctors believed that circumcision reduced infections caused by the accumulation of secretions and dirt under the foreskin. They also believed that circumcision in newborns was a nearly painless procedure—in fact, it was often done without anesthesia.

Epidemiological studies now have convinced many doctors that uncircumcised males who practice good health habits aren't at any major health disadvantage. Many also believe that the procedure is a painful and traumatic one for the newborn infant, so it should not be done routinely.

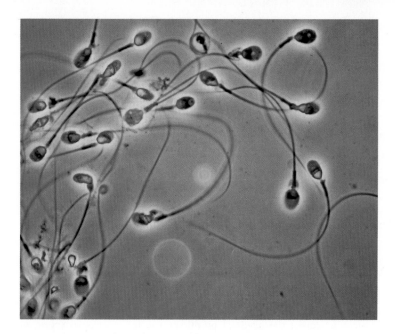

Sperm shown here are magnified 300 times.

The Penis. The **penis** is the external reproductive organ composed of spongy tissue that contains many blood vessels. As a result of increased blood flow, the penis becomes enlarged and erect. When the penis is erect, ejection or ejaculation of semen can occur through the urethra. Sometimes an erection results from the friction of clothing.

Males of every age experience erections. When a male enters puberty, he may experience an erection during the day. The erection may occur for no reason at all. Erections also occur as the result of being sexually aroused. Ejaculation does not always follow an erection.

When a male begins to produce sperm, he may experience a nocturnal emission, or "wet dream," which is an erection and an ejaculation during sleep. This is a normal occurrence.

At birth, the tip of the penis is covered with a fold of skin called foreskin. Some parents choose to have the foreskin surgically removed when the baby is born. This procedure is known as circumcision. It is important to know that it is normal if a male child is circumcised and it is normal if he is not.

K E E P I N G   F I T

Examination for Testicular Cancer

Testicular cancer occurs most frequently in males between the ages of 15 and 34. Males should perform regular testicular self-exams for cancer. While shower-ing, feel each testicle using a thumb and forefinger to see if there are hard lumps or notice-able swelling. Be aware of any ache in the groin area. See a doc-tor if any of these signs occur. Self-examination for testicular cancer should be carried out at least once a month for life.

Additional Information

Prenatal Sex Differentiation. It appears that the female is the "basic" sex into which embryos develop if not stimulated to do otherwise. When the gonads first appear in a developing embryo, they look the same in both sexes. But by 8 weeks after fertiliza-tion, they become recognizable as testes in male embryos, presumably due to genes on the Y chromosome. For female embryos, the gonads develop into ovaries by week 9 without any stimulation.

Shortly after the male embryo's testes develop, they start secreting testosterone, which causes the previously undifferentiat-ed external genitalia to form the penis and scrotum. In the absence of testosterone, the external genitalia develop into those of the female.

L3 CLASS ACTIVITY. Ask students to write a story for young boys aged 8 to 10 about growing into a man. The story should provide the facts that are important for them to know to assist them in understanding their body functions and what to expect as changes occur at puberty.

L2 DISCUSSION. Key male reproductive sex organs are on the exterior of the body. What means of protection for these organs should be considered when participating in sports? What could happen to a male if he received a hit in the groin area? Why is a kick to the groin suggested as a means of self-defense to use against an attack by a male?

L2 DISCUSSION. Ask the class to discuss the characteristics of being male. What is masculinity? At what age do children realize their sexual identity? How do males learn to be masculine? Are male babies treated differently than female babies?

L2 CLASS ACTIVITY. (Note: this is more effective presented to males only.) Using a model of testicles designed for instruction in testicular self-examination, have students identify typical changes signaling cancer. Following the examination of the model, explain the probability of having testicular cancer. What age groups are vulnerable? What appearance is normal and what is abnormal for the testes? Tell students that the difference in sizes of each testicle is normal. Enlargement, lumps, or any change from what was usual for the individual should be reported to a doctor.

L2 DISCUSSION. Ask students why they think many males do not regularly examine themselves for testicular abnormalities, such as nodules or lumps.

L1 USING LIFE MANAGEMENT SKILLS TRANSPARENCY 20. Refer to the Teaching Transparencies Binder.

DID YOU KNOW?

- Impotence, the inability to maintain an erection in order to have intercourse, is a common occurrence. Probably every man has suffered some temporary impotence, especially during periods of extreme stress, tiredness, or illness.
- Sexual potency and functioning do not rely just on the reproductive system but also on the vascular system, brain, nerves, and spinal cord. In addition, the pituitary, thyroid, and adrenal glands play a part in reproductive health.

L2 DISCUSSION. Ask students to think of all the problems that could cause sterility in males. What could cause temporary sterility? (Tight clothing, extreme cold, illness.) What could cause permanent sterility? (Chemical exposure, faulty functioning of separate parts, mumps as an older child.) Your class may find other causes. Explain that a sterile male can function sexually, however, he is not able to impregnate a female.

L2 EXPLANATION. Prostate cancer may be treated by hormones, radiation, or surgery. Explain that prostate cancer is usually not termed an aggressive cancer and many older men who develop prostate cancer do not die from it.

Independent Practice

L2 RESEARCH. Have students research the treatment for testicular cancer. What are the implications for a young man who is found to have this condition? Will he have normal sexual function? Can he father children?

L2 RESEARCH. Have students research the incidence of undescended testicles. When do the testicles normally descend into the scrotum? What happens if one testicle does not descend? Why may surgery be advisable? If it does not descend, will it impede normal sexual functioning? How common is this occurrence?

L2 WRITING. Have students read about circumcision, looking for information that answers the following questions: What is circumcision? When is it usually performed? How is it done? What cultural, physical, health, social, and psychological reasons are given in defending the procedure? What arguments are used against it? Ask students to summarize their findings in well-developed paragraphs.

L1 USING THE LESSON RESOURCES. For additional student activities, refer to the lesson resources on page 297.

Problems of the Male Reproductive System

The organs of the male reproductive system can be affected by both functional and structural problems. The effect of sexually transmitted diseases (STDs) on these organs will be discussed in Chapter 27.

Hernia

A hernia occurs when part of an organ pushes through an opening of a membrane or muscle that usually contains the organ. Hernias occur in various parts of the body. A common hernia of the male reproductive system is an inguinal hernia. This is a weak spot in the abdominal wall near the top of the scrotum. Sometimes straining the abdominal muscles can cause a tear in this spot. A part of the intestine can then push through into the scrotum. Sometimes surgery is necessary to correct such a hernia.

Sterility

Sterility is a condition in which a person is unable to reproduce. In a male this can be the result of producing too few sperm, or sperm of poor quality. Temperature changes, exposure to certain chemicals, smoking, contracting mumps as an adult, complications from an STD, or malfunction of the epididymis, vas deferens, Cowper's glands, or the prostate gland can all result in sterility.

Enlarged Prostate Gland

The prostate gland does not usually change in size until after about 50 years of age. It can enlarge for reasons such as infection, or a tumor, or old age. When the gland enlarges, it tends to squeeze the urethra and this affects urination. The treatment is most often a surgical procedure.

Cancer of the Prostate Gland

A cancer is an uncontrolled growth of cells. The prostate gland is often a cancer site in older males. Prostate cancer is the second highest incidence of cancer in males. Only a doctor can diagnose prostate cancer. Early detection is important because prostate cancer can be treated if it is localized in the gland. Radiation therapy and surgical removal of the prostate gland and surrounding tissue are the current treatments.

Cancer of the Testes

Cancer of the testes, or testicular cancer, occurs most frequently in males who are between the ages of 15 and 34. The first sign of testicular cancer is usually a slight enlargement of one of the testes. The male may not experience any pain at all, or he might have a dull ache in the lower abdomen and groin. Hard lumps, or nodules, on the testes may be a sign of this cancer. If discovered early, the condition can be treated effectively. Treatment involves surgery and radiation.

Additional Information

Male Sterility. Mumps, a once-common contagious viral infection characterized by a swelling of the salivary glands, has been nearly obliterated in the United States now that childhood immunization is commonplace. The blessing, however, is mixed for unimmunized adolescents and men who unwittingly have been exposed to the mumps virus. Mumps, when contracted after childhood, can cause inflammation of the testicles—a condition known as orchitis. This, in turn, can cause atrophy of the testicle, ultimately ending in sterility.

Care of the Male Reproductive System

Caring for the male reproductive system involves cleanliness, protection, and self-examination. Each of these factors plays a key role in maintaining good health.

A daily shower to clean the external organs—the penis and the scrotum—is essential. Avoiding clothing that is too tight and wearing a protector or supporter during strenuous activity will help protect the groin area and the external reproductive organs.

A male who is uncircumcised must practice extra hygiene. It is important that he wash underneath the foreskin daily.

In addition, once a male reaches puberty, he should perform a monthly self-examination of his testes for signs of cancer. Any lumps, thickenings, or change in texture or size of the testes should be reported to a doctor, even though such signs do not always mean there is cancer. If cancer is present, however, early detection usually means successful treatment.

LESSON 1 REVIEW

Reviewing Facts and Vocabulary

1. What is the function of the scrotum?

2. Trace the path that sperm follow from the testes to the urethra.

3. Why is the secretion from Cowper's glands so important?

4. Name two problems that can affect the male reproductive system, and describe them.

Thinking Critically

5. **Analysis.** Classify the organs and glands in the male reproductive system according to function in regard to sperm.
6. **Analysis.** How do Cowper's glands compare with the seminal vesicles?

Applying Health Knowledge

7. Your 11-year-old brother asks you what a "wet dream" is. What would you tell him?

Answers to Lesson 1 Review

1. Protects sperm by keeping the testes at a temperature slightly below normal body temperature.
2. Testes, epididymis, vas deferens, urethra.
3. It lubricates the urethra and neutralizes acid before ejaculation.
4. Answers will vary. See "Problems of the Male Reproductive System" on page 300.
5. Production—testes; protection—scrotum; storage—epididymis; transportation—vas deferens; fluid secretion—prostate, Cowper's, seminal vesicles.
6. Both secrete fluids that make up semen.
7. Answers will vary but might include that an erection and ejaculation is a normal occurrence during sleep.

Check for Understanding

- Assign and discuss the lesson review. Encourage LD students to focus on questions 1, 2, 3, and 4.

Evaluate

- Administer, grade, and discuss the *Lesson 1 Quiz.*

Reteach

- Ask each student to develop a summary outline for teaching a short course on male reproduction. Have them outline the topics, vocabulary terms, definitions, and major facts that they would cover in teaching such a course.
- Ask students to complete *Reteaching Activity 40.*

Enrich

- Have students explore the relationship between tobacco, alcohol, drugs, and the reproductive system. How do these substances affect the male reproductive system? Encourage students to use the text plus additional references.

Close

Ask students to state the most important concepts studied in the lesson.

DID YOU KNOW?

- Production of mature sperm declines with age, yet many elderly men have fathered children, including the artist Pablo Picasso, who had his last child at age 84.
- Some early scientists believed that each sperm contained a miniature human, called a homunculus.

Focus

Lesson Objectives

After studying this lesson, students should be able to:
- identify the structure and function of the female reproductive system
- identify some disorders of the female reproductive system

Bellringer

Write the following on the chalkboard for students to work on while attendance is being taken: *Complete the following statement: Becoming a woman means. . . .*

Introducing the Lesson

Refer to the Bellringer. Write some of the student responses on the chalkboard. If there are differences between male and female responses, discuss why these occurred. Discuss the following questions with your students: Is being a woman a matter of physical body parts? Are girls women when they begin to menstruate or before that point in life? What is the difference between a woman and a girl?

DID YOU KNOW?

- One study of over 100 women conducted at the National Institute of Environmental Health Sciences suggests that women who consumed more than 1 cup of brewed coffee each day were half as likely to get pregnant as women who drank less or no coffee.
- A 42-year-old South Dakota woman acting as a surrogate mother for her own daughter, who was born without a uterus, gave birth to twins in 1991. She is the first woman in the U.S. to give birth to her own grandchildren.
- In 1990, a Maryland woman pregnant with triplets gave birth to one of her babies 13 weeks early. The other two babies remained growing in utero.

THE FEMALE REPRODUCTIVE SYSTEM

LESSON 2 FOCUS

TERMS TO USE
- Ovaries
- Ovulation (ahv•you•LAY•shun)
- Fallopian tubes
- Fertilization
- Uterus
- Cervix
- Menstrual cycle

CONCEPTS TO LEARN
- Major organs of the female reproductive system are the labia majora, labia minora, the ovaries, Fallopian tubes, uterus, and vagina.

ATTITUDES AND BEHAVIORS TO EVALUATE
- Self-Inventory, page 310.
- Building Decision-Making Skills, page 311.

When a female reaches puberty, hormones released by the pituitary gland stimulate the ovaries to produce the hormones estrogen and progesterone. These hormones are responsible for secondary sex characteristics: breasts develop, hips widen, and pubic and underarm hair appear.

The Function and Structure of the Female Reproductive System

The female reproductive system serves three important functions:
- the production of egg cells, or ova
- the reception of sperm for fertilization to occur
- the nourishment and protection necessary for a fertilized ovum to develop until ready to live outside the female body

Female Reproductive Organs

The external parts of the female reproductive system are known as the vulva, which includes the mons pubis, soft tissue that covers the pubic bone; labia majora, the outer folds of skin that surround the opening of the vagina; and labia minora, the inner folds of skin. Internal reproductive organs include the ovaries, Fallopian tubes, uterus, and vagina.

The Ovaries. The **ovaries** are female sex glands that house the ova and produce female sex hormones. They are almond-shaped and located on each side of the body in the lower abdominal area. At birth, a female has over 1 million immature ova in her ovaries.

As a female reaches puberty, hormones cause the immature ova to mature. The ovaries begin to release one mature ovum each month. This process is called **ovulation.** Usually one ovary releases a mature ovum one month and the other ovary releases a mature ovum the next month. As endocrine glands, ovaries also produce hormones that are involved in the female reproductive cycle.

The Fallopian Tubes. When a mature ovum is released from an ovary, it moves into one of a pair of tubes called **Fallopian tubes.** An ovum moves through a Fallopian tube to the uterus. These tiny, muscular tubes lie close to each ovary and have fingerlike projections that, with a waving motion, draw the ovum into the tube. Each tube is about 4 inches (10 cm) long and about ¹/₃ inch (0.8 cm) in diameter. Tiny hairlike structures and muscular contractions move the ovum along.

Fertilization can occur if sperm cells are present while the ovum is in the Fallopian tube. One sperm cell unites with the ovum usually in the

302   Chapter 15 The Reproductive Systems

- **Transparencies** 21 and 57
- **Guided Reading** Activity 41
- **Decision-Making** Activity 15
- **Workbook** Voc Act 41, Appl Act 15
- **Reteaching** Activity 41
- **Enrichment** Activity 15
- **Health Labs** Activity 15

- **Cooperative Learning** Activity 15
- **Lesson 2 Quiz**
- **Chapter 15 Test**
- ABC News InterActive Videodiscs
- **Teenage Sexuality, Side 1**
- Ch 4 The Female Body

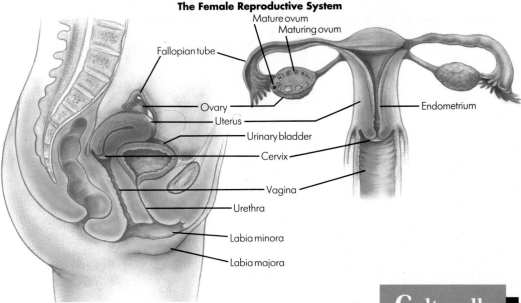

The Female Reproductive System

- Mature ovum
- Maturing ovum
- Fallopian tube
- Ovary
- Uterus
- Urinary bladder
- Cervix
- Vagina
- Urethra
- Labia minora
- Labia majora
- Endometrium

upper third of the Fallopian tube. Once fertilization occurs, the female is pregnant, and cell division begins. At the instant of fertilization, a membrane forms around the ovum to prevent any other sperm from penetrating it. The fertilized ovum, or zygote, continues moving through the Fallopian tube to the uterus, where it attaches to the uterine wall and begins to grow and develop.

The Uterus. The **uterus** is a small, muscular, pear-shaped organ, about the size of a fist. The lining of the uterus has several layers and a rich supply of capillaries.

When an ovary releases an ovum, the hormone estrogen causes the lining of the uterus to thicken in preparation to support a fertilized ovum. If fertilization has taken place, the zygote attaches to the wall of the uterus, where it is nourished for the next nine months of growth.

If fertilization has not occurred, the ovum disintegrates and the thickened lining of the uterus is not needed. As a result of the action of hormones, the lining breaks down and passes through the **cervix,** or neck of the uterus, and the vagina.

The Vagina. The vagina, also called the birth canal, is a muscular, very elastic tube that is a passageway from the uterus to the outside of the body. It is about 3½ inches (9 cm) long. During intercourse, semen is deposited in the vagina.

Menstruation

The process of shedding the lining of the uterus is called menstruation. The name comes from the Latin word *mensis,* meaning "month."

During menstruation about 2 to 3 fluid ounces (60 to 90 ml) of blood and other tissue leave the body. The menstrual flow usually lasts about 3 to 5 days. After the menstrual period ends, the entire cycle begins again.

THE FEMALE REPRODUCTIVE SYSTEM **303**

Culturally Speaking

Sharing Pregnancy

Distinct rituals are associated with pregnancy and childbirth in many cultures. One interesting practice is the couvade, where the father ritually shares the pregnancy and the pains of childbirth with the mother. In some California Indian groups, the father and mother traditionally avoided certain foods such as salt and meat, ate alone, and limited their activities. Neither would cook or touch tools. Couvade is still practiced in some form by groups in Basque country (Spain), and in the tropical forest cultures of Brazil. Many other cultures also put restrictions on the father-to-be. What ones do you know about?

Building Vocabulary

■ Write on the chalkboard a list of terms that you feel students need to understand in order to make this lesson meaningful. Starting at the beginning of a row and going down the list, ask students to make a statement that uses their assigned terms correctly, either by definition or explanation. If a student doesn't know the term, he or she can pass. Circle the terms that students were unable to use. Ask volunteers to use these terms correctly. Following this exercise, have each student write definitions of the lesson's vocabulary terms. Suggest that students take notes on the responses shared in the first exercise to help them with this part. They may use the text, but in all cases, their definitions should be in their own words.

■ Ask students to complete *Workbook Vocabulary Activity 41.*

Teach

Guided Practice

LD EXPLANATION. LD students may rely on class discussion for comprehension of the lesson's content due to high-level vocabulary. Assignment of independent reading is not recommended.

L1 EXPLANATION. Use a model or chart to show students where the female body parts are located, naming them correctly as they are identified. Provide students with a diagram of the female body genitalia and have them write in the names for the female reproductive body parts.

L1 USING BODY SYSTEMS TRANSPARENCY 57. Refer to the Teaching Transparencies Binder.

Additional Information

Menarche. Menarche refers to the first menstrual period, an event that occurs relatively late in puberty. In virtually all females the adolescent growth spurt peaks before menarche arrives. For most girls breasts and pubic hair also start to develop before they have their first period.

Although menarche signifies that the uterus is mature, it doesn't necessarily reflect the attainment of full reproductive function. Early menstrual cycles are often anovulatory—that is, bleeding occurs even though an egg hasn't been released from the ovary. As a consequence, there's often a period of adolescent sterility or partial sterility after menarche occurs, usually lasting from 12 to 18 months.

DID YOU KNOW?

- Some early scholars believed that ova held preformed humans, and that Eve's eggs contained all future generations wrapped one within the other like Russian dolls-within-dolls.

On average, the menstrual cycle is a 28-day cycle. Ovulation occurs approximately 14 days after Day 1 of the cycle.

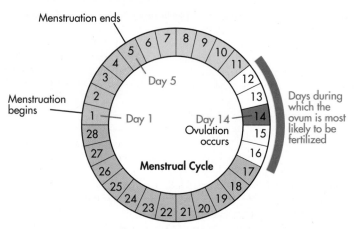

Menstruation ends

Menstruation begins

Day 5

Day 1

Day 14
Ovulation occurs

Menstrual Cycle

Days during which the ovum is most likely to be fertilized

The lining of the uterus thickens again, preparing for the possibility of a fertilized egg. Although there can be great variations, the **menstrual cycle**—the time from the beginning of one menstrual period to the onset of the next—is usually 28 days. The menstrual cycle is regulated by endocrine hormones.

Almost all females begin menstruating between the ages of 10 and 15. The menstrual cycle may be irregular at first. Although hormones control the menstrual cycle, poor nutrition, stress, and illness can influence the cycle.

Problems of the Female Reproductive System

The female reproductive system can be affected both structurally and functionally. The effects of sexually transmitted diseases, STDs, will be discussed in Chapter 27.

Menstrual Cramps

A female may experience abdominal cramps at the beginning of the menstrual period. Menstrual cramps are usually mild, lasting several hours. Light exercise can help relieve cramps. A warm bath or heating pad might also help relax the muscles. However, severe or persistent cramping may be an indication that medical attention is necessary.

Premenstrual Syndrome

Premenstrual syndrome (PMS) refers to a variety of symptoms that some females experience before each menstrual period. Symptoms vary and may be experienced several days to two weeks before the menstrual period. Many females never experience PMS.

The symptoms of PMS include nervous tension, anxiety, irritability, bloating, weight gain, depression, mood swings, and fatigue. The causes of PMS are not completely understood, but it seems to be more common in females in their 30s. Some doctors believe that PMS is related to a hormonal imbalance. Others attribute the cause to a nutritional deficiency.

304 CHAPTER 15 THE REPRODUCTIVE SYSTEMS

Additional Information

Conception. Despite all the unwanted and unplanned pregnancies, conception is still a matter of odds. A married couple can go through their lives without ever having a baby due to the odds working against them.

Fertilization of the ovum can only occur during a 2- to 3-day time period, when the cervical mucus forms small channels that allow sperm cells to enter the uterus. Once in the mucus, the sperm can live up to 48 hours. So, fertilization could theoretically occur 2 days after sexual intercourse. Females of fertile couples in their 20s have a 20 percent chance each month of conceiving. Females of couples in their late 30s have about an 8 percent chance per month of getting pregnant.

Most doctors recommend diet and life-style changes as the first treatment of PMS. They also encourage females to find ways to reduce stress. Some PMS sufferers find that reducing their intake of sugar, salt, and caffeine can help alleviate PMS symptoms. An increase in their intake of B vitamins, magnesium, leafy green vegetables, whole grains, and fruit can also help. Finally, a regular exercise program should be followed.

Toxic Shock Syndrome

Toxic shock syndrome (TSS) is a bacterial disease usually found in menstruating females who use tampons. Although the connection between TSS and tampons is unclear, the improper use of tampons increases the risks of developing TSS. Changing tampons regularly every 3 to 4 hours during menstruation is very important to reduce the growth of bacteria already present in the vagina.

The symptoms of TSS are similar to flu symptoms: sudden high fever, vomiting, diarrhea, and dizziness. Any female suffering these symptoms during a menstrual period should seek medical care immediately.

Vaginitis

Vaginitis, or vaginal infection, is a very common condition in females. Nonspecific vaginitis is caused by an excess of normal vaginal secretions and bacteria. This excess can irritate the genital tissue. Symptoms include itching, discharge, and a burning sensation during urination.

Another common vaginal infection is a yeast infection, which is caused by a fungus. The signs of yeast infection are a thick, white discharge and itching in the genital area.

Trichomoniasis often occurs at the end of a menstrual period and is caused by a protozoan, a small microscopic organism. The symptoms include an odorous discharge, genital itching, and occasionally, a burning sensation during urination.

Sterility

Sterility in a female can be the result of a blocked Fallopian tube, the failure of the ovaries to produce ova that can be fertilized, or a sexually transmitted disease that has not been treated.

KEEPING FIT

Getting a Routine Pelvic Exam

A pelvic exam is one in which a gynecologist checks a female's pelvic area, first with an instrument called a speculum and then by hand. This is done to check the shape, size, and position of pelvic organs and to check for any tumors or cysts.

The American College of Obstetricians and Gynecologists (ACOG) recommends that young females have pelvic exams by the time they are 18, or earlier if they are sexually active. These exams should occur yearly, even when there are no problems. In addition, females should have pelvic exams if they have menstrual problems, unusual vaginal discharge, or if they are planning to get pregnant.

THE FEMALE REPRODUCTIVE SYSTEM **305**

L2 DEMONSTRATION. The uterus is a most amazing organ. It is normally the size of a fist but stretches to accommodate a full-grown baby—some weighing over 10 pounds. Draw ovals on the chalkboard illustrating the ability of the uterus to stretch to meet the baby's needs and then shrink to normal size within 3 to 6 weeks.

L2 DISCUSSION. Ask students what is required to maintain female reproductive health. The discussion should include annual physical, pelvic exam, breast exam, reporting of problems, irregularities, and pain. Menstruation records should also be kept. If a person is sexually active, health maintenance should include an annual Pap smear. Discuss how each of these help a female maintain good health. What is the potential impact on having children if reproductive health is not maintained?

L2 COOPERATIVE LEARNING. Divide the class into four groups. Ask each group to develop a "documentary" on what it means to be female in our society. Have each approach the documentary from a different perspective. One group could be featuring a specific location and how the role of females has been traditionally handled there. Another could present the feminist point of view. The third could be from a minority American perspective, and the fourth, an urban versus rural perspective. Have students share their reports with the class.

L3 CLASS ACTIVITY. Have students write a story for a young child, 8 to 10 years of age, explaining growing up into womanhood. Drawings can be included. The story should explain not only what physical changes a female should expect, but why these changes occur.

Additional Information

The Rites of Menstruation. A natural part of the life of a female of the species, menstruation has historically been cloaked in myth and superstition.

Some African tribes believe that eating food prepared by a menstruating woman will lead to illness.

It is standard practice among the Naskapis of Canada that females wear a veil fashioned of caribou hide during their first menses.

To the Apaches, kneeling on a sacred deer-skin purportedly provides relief from menstrual cramps.

The word *taboo* may have roots in the Polynesian word meaning *menstruation*.

Yearly physical checkups will help detect any problems at an early stage.

Endometriosis

The endometrium, which is the inner lining of the uterus, sometimes is present abnormally in the abdominal cavity. This condition, endometriosis, usually causes sterility. Treatment involves hormone therapy and surgery.

Breast Cancer

About 1 out of 9 females develop breast cancer at some time in their lives. Most breast lumps are found by the females themselves. About 80 percent of these lumps are benign, which means they are noncancerous. Females with a family history of breast cancer are at a greater risk of developing a cancerous condition.

Ovarian Cysts

An ovarian cyst is a growth on the outside of an ovary. Small, noncancerous cysts can develop often but usually dissolve on their own. Large cysts may have to be surgically removed.

Cancer of the Cervix, Uterus, and Ovaries

The cervix, uterus, and ovaries are common sites of cancer in females. Cervical cancer is detected through a Pap smear, a test in which samples of cells are taken from the cervix by a doctor and viewed under a microscope. Early detection contributes to successful treatment. Early sexual activity, and a family history of cervical cancer and other factors, is related to an increased incidence of cervical cancer.

Doctors may also sample tissue from the lining of the uterus to check for cancerous cells. Uterine cancer is most common in females between the ages of 60 and 75. However, it can occur at any age. As with cervical cancer, early detection may bring greater success in treatment. The Pap smear is not as accurate in detecting cancer of the uterus as it is for cervical cancer. The American Cancer Society recommends that once a female reaches the age of 18, she begin having a yearly Pap smear.

DID YOU KNOW?

■ Multiple births involving four or more babies do not usually occur unless fertility drugs have been used.
■ The woman who gave birth to the most children on record gave birth to multiples twenty-seven times. She did this in the 1700s—long before the use of fertility drugs.
■ The two heaviest babies on record were born weighing 22 pounds, 8 ounces each. One was born in 1955; the other in 1982.

306 CHAPTER 15 THE REPRODUCTIVE SYSTEMS

Additional Information

Menstruation. When a female stops menstruating during her normally reproductive years, it is not considered healthy and the person should be examined by a doctor. Women who have lost an extreme amount of weight through dieting, bulimia, or anorexia often stop menstruating. The extreme loss of body weight causes the body to go into a conservation of energy mode and therefore menstruation may be interrupted.

Females who are extremely physically active, such as competitive long-distance runners or those who perform exercise compulsively, maintain low body weight, and may stop menstruating. Some females will temporarily stop menstruating for a month or two when they have been under mental stress.

Overcoming The Odds

Frances Hamilton is 44. She is an artist who lives in Boston, Massachusetts, with her artist husband, Peter Thibeault. Together, they not only share an interest in the arts but also a reproductive history that has brought them both pain and joy.

Frances Hamilton says, "I wasn't very interested in having children when I was younger. But then, when I was 35, that changed. It suddenly dawned on me that I really was going to get older. Then I developed a deep interest in becoming a mother."

But becoming a mother was not easy for Hamilton. She had three unsuccessful pregnancies.

But the fourth pregnancy did not fail. It resulted in the birth of Dinah Kate, now 5. "Having gone through the three losses," Hamilton continues, "there wasn't a moment during my pregnancy that I was relaxed. I kept waiting to hear bad news. It wasn't until Dinah was born and in my arms that I could believe she was okay."

Hamilton's fifth and sixth pregnancies again were unsuccessful. But her seventh pregnancy was Anna, her 8-month-old daughter.

For a time, the many losses Hamilton suffered affected her art work. "Because in a mis-carriage a woman bears so much of the responsibility—because it is her body that 'fails'—the losses really affected my self-esteem and my ability to complete projects. The process of creating and bearing a child is not unlike the

process of creating art. You bring something out of nothing, nurture it, and make it grow. Because of that parallel, in my work, too, I began starting things and losing the thread. I became discouraged very easily in the work.

"I've since made some images about the losses, but I found them so painful that I can't even look at them. I started to focus on images of mothers. I used my own mother and sought magazine images from the '50s, which is when I was growing up. And by identifying with my mother and the mothers of the '50s, I was able to keep working."

These days, Hamilton and Thibeault are very caught up in the lives of their two young daughters. "Every day Peter and I watch them playing together. And when the 5-year-old is making the baby laugh, it just goes through us like music. It's not just their individual presence but their connection with each other that gives us delight. A baby that you've waited for is a source of never-ending pleasure. We're so grateful."

About the experiences she and her husband have gone through in trying to have a family, she concludes, "I think you have to understand that adversity builds a stronger person. When things are difficult, it challenges you to develop your inner resources. In our case, it has made us better parents."

1. How did the repeated loss of her pregnancies affect Hamilton's self-esteem?
2. How did her art struggles parallel those in her reproductive life?
3. What struggles are you facing right now that may be chipping away at your self-esteem? How are they reflected in other areas of your life?

investigate the process of mammography. How is it done? What new technology is available to reduce the radiation exposure during this procedure? How early can a malignancy be detected? When should a woman begin regular mammography? Are more lumps malignant than benign? Can lumps be detected earlier by breast self-examination than by mammography? Ask students to report their findings to the class.

L3 **RESEARCH.** Have interested students research problems associated with a tubal pregnancy. How frequently do they occur? How does the female know there is a problem? What is the treatment?

L2 **PARENTAL INVOLVEMENT.** Have students ask their parents how the roles of males and females have changed since they were in their teens. Ask how they feel about the changes. Are there differences in what changes are good or not so good according to the sex of the person being interviewed? What does that say about societal acceptance of role changes? Have them report their findings to the class. Compare the findings.

L1 **USING THE LESSON RESOURCES.** For additional student activities, refer to the lesson resources on page 302.

Assess

Check for Understanding

- Assign and discuss the lesson review. Encourage LD students to focus on questions 1, 2, 3, and 4.
- Assign and discuss the chapter review.

Evaluate

- Administer, grade, and discuss the *Lesson 2 Quiz.*
- Administer, grade, and discuss the *Chapter 15 Test.*
- Refer to the Performance Assessment strategy for this chapter. See pages T 23 to T 25.

HEALTH UPDATE

LOOKING AT TECHNOLOGY

Laparoscopy

Surgery used to mean large incisions and lots of recovery time. Today, through the use of laparoscopes, incision size and recovery time are now being greatly reduced.

Laparoscopy is a technique that allows the doctor to look into the body with a miniature telescope called a laparoscope. The laparoscope is inserted through a small incision at the lower edge of the navel. It has a lens that allows for a clear view. A special attachment sends light down through the tube into the abdomen so that a doctor can look closely at the ovaries, Fallopian tubes, uterus, and other organs. If problems are detected, the doctor can then insert tiny surgical instruments through the laparoscope and use laser "knives" if necessary. With a video hookup, the surgeon can move the tiny instruments inside the patient's body while watching the movements on a large video monitor. Such techniques allow doctors to perform major surgery through incisions no larger than the size of a quarter.

Laparoscopy is used to diagnose and treat gynecological problems and many types of digestive problems. In particular, it is being used to identify the causes of infertility, and as an alternative to hysterectomies—the surgical removal of the uterus.

Laparoscopy can be done on an outpatient basis, meaning that the patient does not have to stay in the hospital overnight.

DID YOU KNOW?

- Each female is born with more than 500,000 ova in each of her ovaries. Only about 400 of these will mature and be able to be fertilized.
- Females in their early 40s can get pregnant and bear healthy babies. However, the ability to become pregnant decreases and chances of fetal abnormalities increase after age 40.
- The oldest mother on record was Ruth Alice Kistler, who, in 1956, gave birth at the age of 57.

For unknown reasons there has been an increase in the number of cases of ovarian cancer in recent years. There are often no signs of ovarian cancer until late in its development. It is most common in older females, but can affect anyone. Three important ways to detect ovarian cancer include a pelvic examination given by a doctor; a look at a female's family history, since females with a family history of ovarian cancer are at a greater risk of developing the disease; and a blood test called CA 125, which can detect this type of cancer. As with other forms of cancer, the earlier the disease is detected the more successful the treatment can be.

Care of the Female Reproductive System

Cleanliness is an important part of keeping the reproductive system healthy. The vagina is a self-cleansing organ. Once a female goes through puberty, the cells in the lining of the vagina are constantly being shed, causing a slight vaginal discharge. This is normal. Cleanliness is especially important during the menstrual period when menstrual flow may cause a slight odor. Sanitary napkins and tampons should be changed every few hours. Feminine hygiene products such as deodorant sprays and douches should not be necessary and may, in fact, cause irritation to the sensitive tissues around the vagina.

308 CHAPTER 15 THE REPRODUCTIVE SYSTEMS

Additional Information

Cervical Cancer. Cervical cancer occurs in about 2 percent of American women. It may develop at any age, but the peak incidence is between the ages of 35 and 45. It develops most often in women in poor health, those who have had many children, those with chronic cervical irritations or infections, and those with multiple sexual partners. Virgins rarely develop cervical cancer.

The cure rate for cervical cancer is high if it's detected early. However, chances of survival decrease dramatically as the cancer passes into the more advanced stages. Therefore, regular Pap smears to detect it early are recommended for all females over the age of 18.

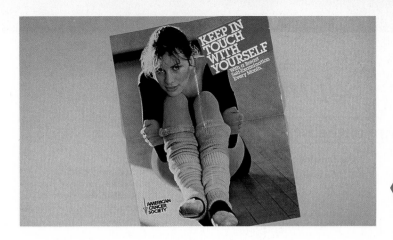

Early detection of breast cancer is still the best preventive health practice. The American Cancer Society recommends the monthly practice of breast self-examination (BSE). The best time to perform it is about one week after the menstrual period—the breasts are then least likely to be tender.

There are three ways to examine the breasts: in the shower, before a mirror, and lying down. Self-examination is most convenient in the shower because hands glide easier over wet skin. Follow this procedure during a bath or shower: With one hand raised over the head and the fingers of the other hand flat, move your hand over every part of each breast. Use the left hand to inspect the right breast and the right hand to inspect the left breast. Pay special attention to the area between the armpit and the breast, checking for any lump, hard knot, or tissue thickening. If you find anything unusual, contact your doctor at once. Only a doctor can make a diagnosis.

Once a female reaches her late 30s, the American Cancer Society recommends that she have a mammogram. This is an X ray of the breasts that detects the presence of abnormal tissue. For more information or to obtain a pamphlet on breast self-examination, contact your local American Cancer Society.

CONFLICT RESOLUTION

Carmina's mother was recently diagnosed with cancer. Her mother's sister Maria is 37 and considered to be at high risk for breast cancer because of family history. However, Maria refuses to get a mammogram. She has all kinds of excuses—she doesn't have time, she doesn't want to be exposed to unnecessary radiation, and she believes the test will hurt. Carmina thinks the real reason is Maria's fear of being diagnosed with cancer.

Help Carmina convince her aunt to get a mammogram.

LESSON 2 REVIEW

Reviewing Facts and Vocabulary

1. What is menstruation?
2. What is PMS?
3. Name two causes of sterility in females.
4. What are two types of vaginal infections?

Thinking Critically

5. **Analysis.** What is the relationship between ovulation, fertilization, and menstruation?

6. **Analysis.** How does the female reproductive system compare with the male reproductive system?

Applying Health Knowledge

7. Make a list of some of the myths you have heard about menstruation. Why do you think there is so much misinformation? Suggest some ways to clear up these types of myths.

THE FEMALE REPRODUCTIVE SYSTEM **309**

Answers to Lesson 2 Review

1. A monthly process of shedding the lining of the uterus.
2. Premenstrual syndrome refers to a variety of symptoms experienced by some females before each menstrual period.
3. Answers will vary. See "Sterility" on page 305 and "Endometriosis" on page 306 for possible causes.
4. Answers will vary. Accept two of the following: Nonspecific vaginitis, yeast infection, trichomoniasis.
5. Ovulation must occur before fertilization can take place. Menstruation usually does not occur if fertilization has taken place.
6. Both secrete hormones and produce reproductive cells.
7. Answers will vary.

Reteach

- Ask students to trace the pathways of a sperm cell and an ovum that unite during fertilization. Have students label the female parts and be able to explain the function of each.
- Ask students to complete *Reteaching Activity 41.*

Enrich

- Ask students to research menopause. What is the usual time of onset? How does it affect women physically and emotionally? What hormones change in the female body during menopause? What types of treatment do doctors often recommend to females at this stage of their lives? Does this mean the end of sexual activity for a healthy, normal person? Why would hormone therapy be advisable for some females?
- Ask students to consider the options currently available to females who have breast cancer. One is to have a complete mastectomy. The second is to have a lumpectomy and radiation. Another is to have a mastectomy, but delay reconstruction until a later date. Some patients may need chemotherapy in addition to the other procedures. The lumpectomy and the mastectomy are both rated with a 50 percent chance of survival. What considerations would a female have to think about to choose between the procedures?
- Ask students to complete *Enrichment Activity 15.*

Close

Ask students to state the most important concepts studied in the lesson.

DID YOU KNOW?

- All ova are in place at the time of a female's birth.
- Tubal pregnancy is unusual and cannot go to full term because the Fallopian tube does not expand. This life-threatening condition is sometimes mistaken for appendicitis or ovarian cysts.

Helping Students Improve Their Health

Using the Self-Inventory

Reinforcing Vocabulary

- **Hygiene.** Practices of cleanliness conducive to health.
- **Contracting.** Acquiring.

Teaching Strategies

L1 EXPLANATION. Occasionally students may try to hide their true hygienic practices. This inventory can be a good starting point to initiate good hygiene. Be aware of students who may express disgust at examining themselves. Explain that body awareness is important in maintaining health.

L1 EXPLANATION. Some parents, due to upbringing, may encourage their daughters to use feminine hygiene products. Stress that under most conditions these are not necessary and in some cases may create health problems.

L1 DISCUSSION. List and discuss high-risk behaviors in contracting an STD. What might be some alternatives to these behaviors?

L2 DISCUSSION. Ask students why the inventory would question the management of stress in relationship to the reproductive system. Is there a connection between the two? If so, what is it?

L1 SELF-ESTEEM. How would the fear of having a problem with one's reproductive system affect self-esteem? How is self-esteem affected when a person makes a decision to keep his or her reproductive system as healthy as possible?

Self-Inventory

Care of the Reproductive System

HOW DO YOU RATE?

Number a sheet of paper from 1 through 8. Read each item below, and respond by writing *always*, *sometimes*, or *never* for each item. Total the number of each type of response. Then proceed to the next section.

1. I eat a well-balanced diet.
2. I exercise regularly.
3. I manage the stress in my life.
4. I practice daily health care.
5. I avoid situations that might put me at risk of contracting an STD.
6. I have regular physical checkups.

For males only:

7. I do a monthly testicular self-exam.
8. I wear a protector or supporter if I am participating in strenuous activity.

For females only:

7. I do a monthly breast self-exam.
8. I avoid the use of feminine hygiene products, such as sprays or douches.

HOW DID YOU SCORE?

Give yourself 3 points for each *always* response, 1 point for each *sometimes* response, and 0 points for each *never* response. Find your total, and read below to see how you scored. Then proceed to the next section.

15 to 24
Excellent. Your health choices show you are taking care of your reproductive system. Keep up the good work!

8 to 14
Good, but there are some things you could do to promote a healthier reproductive system.

Below 8
Look out! You may be taking unnecessary risks that could affect the health of your reproductive system.

WHAT ARE YOUR GOALS?

Complete each statement below.

1. The behavior I would like to change or improve is ____.
2. If this behavior were completely changed, I would look, feel, or act differently in the following ways: ____.
3. The steps involved in making this change are ____.
4. My timetable is ____.
5. People I will ask for support or assistance are ____.
6. The benefits I will receive are ____.
7. My reward at the end of each week will be ____.

Meeting Students' Needs

For students who score *Excellent*. Have students consult your media specialist for more information on problems with the reproductive system. Ask them to pick three of these and do an extra-credit report on them.

For students who score *Good*. (1) Ask students to do an extra-credit report on the reasons for doing regular self-exams, and having regular physical checkups. (2) Discuss how high-risk behaviors increase the likelihood of contracting an STD.

For students who need to *Look Out*. Have students identify and list the items they did not score well on. From that list, ask them to make and work to achieve some behavior change goals. Have them retake the inventory in 1 month.

Building Decision-Making Skills

S everal of Shana's girlfriends are at her house for a sleepover to celebrate her 16th birthday. The topic of conversation becomes the girls' sexual experiences. Shana is still a virgin, but it seems that she is in the minority. Her boyfriend, whom she has been dating for several months, has been trying to talk her into "filling in the last piece of the puzzle of their relationship." The idea is admittedly exciting, but she has decided to wait to have sex until marriage. Shana is worried about what to tell the girls. What should she do?

WHAT DO YOU THINK?

1. **Situation.** Why does a decision need to be made?

2. **Choices.** List as many possible ways to handle this situation as you can.

3. **Consequences.** What are the advantages of each possibility?

4. **Consequences.** What are the disadvantages of each possibility?

5. **Situation.** What other decisions will Shana need to make soon?

6. **Situation.** Why should Shana deal with this situation one decision at a time?

7. **Consequences.** What risks are involved in the decision about what to tell her friends?

8. **Consequences.** How might her parents be affected by this decision?

9. **Consequences.** How might Shana's self-esteem be affected?

10. **Consequences.** How might her reputation be affected?

11. **Consequences.** What peer pressure is likely to be used in this situation?

12. **Decision.** What do you think Shana should say to her friends?

13. **Evaluation.** Do you think most teens are truthful when discussing their sexual experiences? Why or why not?

T he guys in the locker room are discussing their sexual exploits and have mentioned several girls Gino has dated as being "easy." The guys have tried to get him to reinforce their comments, but he has never "scored" with any of the girls. In fact he has not had sex with any girl and does not plan to until he is married. How should he handle the pressure from the guys?

WHAT DO YOU THINK?

14. **Choices.** What are Gino's choices?

15. **Consequences.** What are the advantages of each choice?

16. **Consequences.** What are the disadvantages of each choice?

17. **Consequences.** What risks are involved in this decision?

18. **Consequences.** How might Gino's health triangle be affected by this decision?

19. **Consequences.** How might Gino's current girlfriend be affected by this decision?

20. **Consequences.** How might his friends be affected by this decision?

21. **Consequences.** How might his parents be affected by this decision?

22. **Consequences.** How might younger brothers and sisters be affected by this decision?

23. **Decision.** How do you think Gino should handle this situation? Why?

Helping Students Improve Their Health

Building Decision-Making Skills

Teaching Strategies

L1 CLASS ACTIVITY. Create a role-play with Shana and her girlfriends discussing their sexual experiences. Have Shana express her desire to remain a virgin. Have some of the girls try to talk her into an experience, while others express their support for her decision.

L1 CLASS ACTIVITY. Have students participate in a role-play with Shana discussing her decision with her mother. Have her mother try to lend emotional support as well as inform Shana of the benefits of her decision.

L1 CLASS ACTIVITY. Create a role-play with Gino discussing this situation with his best friend. Have the friend be supportive, yet questioning how he can wait. Gino must have some well thought-out answers.

L2 DISCUSSION. Tell students that a friend of theirs is very promiscuous. This person thinks that he or she may have contracted an STD, but is afraid to seek help. What would they advise? Should the person reveal his or her sexual contacts? Why or why not?

Discussing the Answers

Situation 1. Part of any decision-making process has to be a willingness to deal with pressure to change your decision. Stress that a decision made by one person may not be to the liking of everyone, but the individual should be allowed to make his or her own decisions without undo pressure.

Situation 2. This situation is very similar to the first, though the gender has been changed. That change enlists new problems and pressures, because in our society males have been expected to "sow a few wild oats." It is important to stress we must let people know of our decisions. By letting people think or assume that we are sexually active, we may ruin the reputation of another individual.

Answers to Chapter 15 Review

Using Health Terms

1. Testes or testicles
2. Epididymis
3. Scrotum
4. Sterility
5. Semen
6. Immature ova
7. Vagina
8. Zygote
9. Ovulation
10. Menstruation
11. Fertilization
12. Fallopian tube
13. Endometriosis
14. Uterus
15. Benign

Building Academic Skills

16. Answers will vary.
17. Answers will vary.

Recalling the Facts

18. It stimulates the testes to produce sperm and is responsible for the development of secondary sex characteristics.
19. Facial, pubic, and underarm hair; broadened shoulders; a deepened voice; muscular development.
20. The production of sperm and the transfer of sperm to a female's body during intercourse.
21. A muscle near the bladder contracts, preventing urine from entering the urethra during ejaculation.
22. The Cowper's glands release fluid preceding ejaculation that neutralizes acid in the urethra.
23. See page 301.
24. If body temperature rises, the muscles of the scrotum relax, lowering the testes away from the body; if body temperature drops, the muscles contract, pulling the testes closer to the body.
25. Early cancer can be treated and cured in many cases. Monthly.
26. The production of ova; receives sperm as a result of intercourse; provides nourishment and protection to a developing fetus.

Using Health Terms

On a separate sheet of paper, write the term that best matches each definition given below.

LESSON 1
1. Glands that produce sperm.
2. Tube in which sperm are stored.
3. Sac that protects testes.
4. A disorder of the male reproductive system in which a male is unable to reproduce.
5. A mixture of fluids from glands with sperm; the fluids provide nourishment for sperm and help with their movement.

LESSON 2
6. Cells present in a female ovary from birth.
7. The birth canal.
8. A fertilized ovum.
9. The process in which an ovum is released from the ovaries.
10. The process by which the uterus sheds its lining.
11. The union of a sperm and an ovum.
12. Usual site of fertilization.
13. One possible cause of female sterility characterized by the inner lining of the uterus being present in the abdominal cavity.
14. Site of the development of the ovum if it is fertilized.
15. Lumps that are noncancerous.

Building Academic Skills

LESSON 1 AND LESSON 2
16. **Writing.** The changes one goes through during puberty can be awkward, embarrassing, and difficult. Write a two-page paper describing what it was like for an imaginary friend.

LESSON 2
17. **Reading.** Read Gilda Radner's autobiography, *It's Always Something*, about her struggle with ovarian cancer. Make a list of major events discussed in this book.

Recalling the Facts

LESSON 1
18. What is the function of testosterone?
19. What are the secondary sex characteristics for males?
20. What are the functions of the male reproductive system?
21. What prevents urine and semen from passing through the urethra at the same time?
22. How is acidity neutralized in the urethra thus ensuring that sperm are not killed?
23. Explain what is involved in caring for the male reproductive system.
24. How does the scrotum keep the testes at a temperature that is slightly below normal body temperature?
25. Why is it important for a male to examine his testes regularly? How often should it be done?

LESSON 2
26. What functions does the female reproductive system serve?
27. What causes menstrual cramps in females?
28. What are the secondary sex characteristics for females?
29. What functions do ovaries serve?
30. What are the internal reproductive organs in females?
31. Where does fertilization usually occur?
32. How does a mature ovum travel through the Fallopian tube?
33. What are two suspected causes of PMS?
34. What percentage of females are likely to develop breast cancer?
35. What is the purpose of doing a breast self-examination? How often should it be done? What is the best time to do it and why?
36. How are cervical, uterine, and ovarian cancers detected?
37. What is a Pap smear test?
38. How often should a female get a Pap smear?
39. What is toxic shock syndrome?

27. Contractions of the uterus.
28. Developing breasts; widening hips; pubic and underarm hair.
29. Produce and store ova; produce hormones that are involved in the female reproductive cycle.
30. Ovaries, Fallopian tubes, uterus, vagina.
31. In the Fallopian tubes.
32. Tiny hairlike structures and muscular contractions.
33. Hormonal imbalance; nutritional deficiency.
34. About 11 percent.
35. See page 309.
36. See pages 306 and 308.
37. A test in which samples of cells are taken from the cervix by a doctor and viewed under a microscope.
38. Once a year after turning 18.
39. A serious bacterial infection associated with the improper use of tampons.

Thinking Critically

40. Both are cancers of the male reproductive system,

REVIEW

Thinking Critically

LESSON 1

40. Analysis. Compare testicular to prostate cancer.

41. Evaluation. When a male is born, a decision needs to be made whether or not to have him circumcised. Research the procedure of this operation and discuss cultural and religious issues regarding circumcision. If you had an infant son, would you choose to have him circumcised? Why or why not?

LESSON 2

42. Synthesis. Ann is 14 years old. She still has not started menstruating, and her breasts have not developed. Some of her friends have started making fun of her. What advice or comfort would you offer to Ann?

43. Synthesis. PMS is still a relatively mysterious ailment. The causes are not yet fully understood. Some medicine companies are producing over-the-counter medications to treat PMS. From what you have learned, how effective do you think the medicines might be? What symptoms do you think the medicines help alleviate?

44. Analysis. Compare the male and female reproductive systems. Highlight similarities and differences.

45. Synthesis. Vaginal infections were once treated with a prescription medicine that is now available over-the-counter. What might the positive aspects of this change be? What might be negative about this?

Making the Connection

LESSON 2

46. Business Education. View ten different television commercials. For each, note the product, the intended customer, the stated message, and the implied message. How many of these commercials used sexual messages? Do you think sexual messages in advertising are appropriate? Explain your reasoning.

Applying Health Knowledge

LESSON 1

47. What would happen if Cowper's glands were not functioning properly?

48. How can a male increase his chances of surviving testicular cancer? Prostate cancer?

49. What do you think might be the result of a male wearing pants that are too tight?

50. Trace the path of sperm through the male reproductive system.

51. Why would it be important for a male to get a medical checkup if he experienced difficulty when urinating?

LESSON 2

52. The ovaries alternately release a mature ovum each month. What might happen if one ovary had to be removed?

53. When a fertilized ovum attaches to the uterine wall, it begins to grow and develop. What happens if the ovum is not fertilized?

54. Why does menstruation take place?

55. When in a female's menstrual cycle is she most likely to become pregnant?

56. Why would it be important for you to be aware of a history of cancer in your family?

57. Sometimes a fertilized ovum fails to move through the Fallopian tube to the uterus. Instead, the zygote continues to grow in the Fallopian tube. Why would it be impossible for this to be a normal pregnancy?

Beyond the Classroom

LESSON 2

58. Parental Involvement. Discuss with your parents feminine health-care ads found on television and in magazines. Discuss what these ads are designed to do. What merits or drawbacks do you and your parents see in them?

59. Community Involvement. Call or write your local American Cancer Society unit for pamphlets describing the correct procedure for breast and testicular self-examination.

THE FEMALE REPRODUCTIVE SYSTEM   **313**

---

are treated with radiation and/or surgery, and are more easily treated in early stages.

41. Answers will vary but should be supported logically.

42. Answers will vary. Possible answers: Listen to her concerns and feelings; help her find factual information about puberty.

43. Answers will vary. Possible answers: These drugs are probably best at treating bloating, fatigue, and cramping. These drugs are best for making one believe she feels better. Drugs may relieve feelings of general discomfort.

44. Answers will vary but should reflect an understanding of information regarding the male reproductive system in Lesson 1 and the female reproductive system in Lesson 2.

45. Answers will vary. Possible answers: This is good because one can get relief faster, save money in doctor's fees and on the medication. This is bad because one may spend time treating a problem incorrectly, thus losing valuable treatment time or may spend money on medication unnecessarily.

Making the Connection

46. Answers will vary but should be supported logically.

Applying Health Knowledge

47. The urethra would not be lubricated or neutralized of its acid residue from urine and some sperm would not survive the acid condition during ejaculation.

48. By doing a monthly testicular self-examination. By getting a yearly checkup from a doctor.

49. The testicles might be pushed up into the body, become too warm, and the production of sperm would be affected.

50. Sperm are produced in the testes, mature and are stored in the epididymis, travel through the vas deferens to the seminal vesicles, leave the body through the urethra.

51. He may have an enlarged prostate gland and may need surgery.

---

52. A female would have an ovum capable of being fertilized only every other month.

53. It disintegrates.

54. No fertilized ovum has attached itself to the uterine wall. Since it is not needed for pregnancy, the lining is shed.

55. When an ovum is moving through a Fallopian tube and sperm is present.

56. With some kinds of cancer, there seems to be a greater risk of developing cancer if there is a family history of it.

57. A fertilized ovum needs certain conditions to grow, which would not be present in the Fallopian tube.

Beyond the Classroom

58. Answers will vary.

59. Answers will vary.

Lesson Summaries

LESSON 1. The structure of teeth, their function, problems associated with teeth and gums, and oral hygiene are presented in this lesson.

LESSON 2. Of the special sense organs, our eyes provide us with the greatest amount of information about our environment. Their structure, functions, associated problems, and ways to care for them are discussed in this lesson.

LESSON 3. The structure of ears, their functions, problems associated with ears, and caring for the ears are presented in this lesson.

Introducing the Chapter

Tell students that we often take for granted the abilities of our body. Our teeth allow us to eat a variety of foods and even help us enunciate many words. Our eyes allow us to perceive our surroundings in color and depth. Our ears allow us to differentiate a wide range of sounds that hold meaning for us. These abilities are not only basic to our everyday functioning, they enable us to experience the variety in our environment. Ask students to consider how missing just one of these abilities would affect their lives. What special things would they miss? Tell them this chapter will present the structure, function, and care of the teeth, eyes, and ears.

Performance Assessment ✓

Refer to pages T 23 to T 25 for a Performance Assessment strategy for this chapter. See the *Performance Assessment Activities* booklet for additional suggestions.

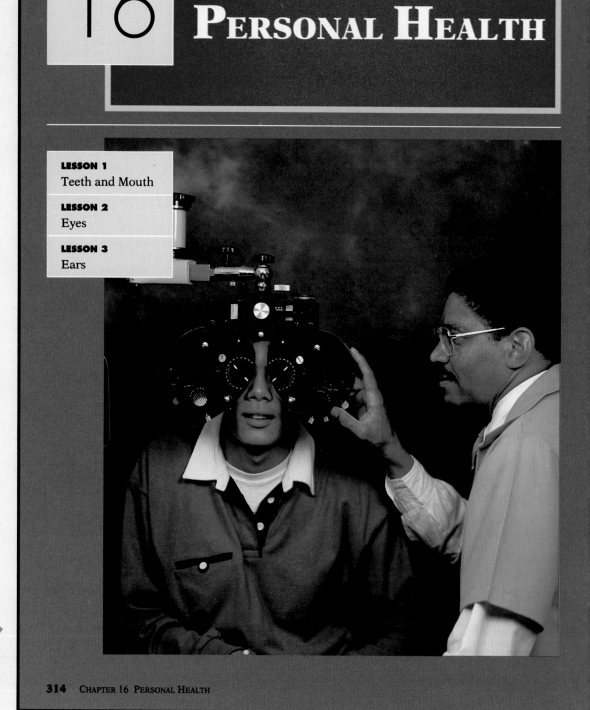

CHAPTER

16 PERSONAL HEALTH

LESSON 1
Teeth and Mouth

LESSON 2
Eyes

LESSON 3
Ears

Key to Ability Levels

Teaching strategies have been coded for varying learning styles and abilities.

L1 Level 1 activities are basic activities and should be within the ability range of all students.

L2 Level 2 activities are average activities and should be within the ability range of average to above-average students.

L3 Level 3 activities are challenging activities designed for the ability range of above-average students.

LD LD activities should be within the ability range of learning-disabled students.

LEP LEP activities should be within the ability range of Limited English Proficiency students.

TEETH AND MOUTH

What is the most common noncommunicable disease in the United States? If you guessed tooth decay, you are right. Most Americans have or have had tooth decay. Yet it is one of the most preventable diseases. Before learning more about good oral health, let us first look at the functions and structure of the teeth.

Functions and Structure of the Teeth

Within your mouth, your teeth are the most vital structures and perhaps the single most noticeable contributor to the appearance of your mouth and face. Your teeth not only allow you to chew food, they also form the shape and structure of your mouth.

The Periodontium

The area immediately around the teeth is called the **periodontium.** It is made up of the gums, periodontal ligament, and the jawbone. Together these structures support the teeth.

The Tooth

The tooth itself is divided into three major parts: the root, the neck, and the crown. The crown is the visible part of the tooth.

The **pulp** is the very sensitive, living tissue inside the tooth. The pulp is entirely enclosed by the hard inner walls of the tooth in the root canal. Blood vessels and nerves are also contained in the pulp cavity.

You experience a toothache when the pulp becomes inflamed because of a cavity or disease. Because the inflamed pulp cannot expand within the inflexible walls of the tooth, pressure builds within the tooth and results in pain.

The pulp is surrounded by a material called dentin. The dentin is covered in the root area of the tooth by a substance called cementum. The crown of the tooth is covered with a hard material called enamel.

Enamel is the hardest material in the body. It is the second hardest naturally occurring substance in nature, diamonds being the hardest. However, it is this hard substance, the enamel, that can be the victim of tooth decay.

Problems of the Teeth and Mouth

Good, regular oral health care is necessary for healthy, clean teeth. Oral health care is also an important factor in preventing periodontal disease and other tooth disorders. Let us look at what can happen when teeth and gums are not cared for properly.

TEETH AND MOUTH   **315**

LESSON 1 FOCUS

TERMS TO USE

- Periodontium (per•ee•oh•DAHN•tee•uhm)
- Pulp
- Periodontal (per•ee•oh•DAHN•tuhl) disease
- Plaque
- Tartar

CONCEPTS TO LEARN

- Regular oral health care is necessary for healthy, clean teeth.
- Oral health care is an important factor in preventing periodontal disease.

ATTITUDES AND BEHAVIORS TO EVALUATE

- Self-Inventory, page 332.
- Building Decision-Making Skills, page 333.

Focus

Lesson Objectives

After studying this lesson, students should be able to:
- describe the structure and function of the teeth and mouth
- define periodontal disease and explain its causes and prevention

Bellringer

Make a "Q-sort" by dividing an 8 1/2 by 11 inch sheet of paper into 5 sections. Write one term pertaining to the mouth and teeth found in the vocabulary terms in each section. Make enough copies to give each student one sheet. Write the following on the chalkboard for students to work on while attendance is being taken: *Tear the sheets into five sections. Then sort the terms into the following categories: parts of the tooth, parts of the mouth, mouth and tooth disorders.*

Introducing the Lesson

Refer to the Bellringer. Have volunteers share their categorized terms with the class. Discuss reasons for any differences. Explain to students that this lesson will contain information on the mouth and teeth.

DID YOU KNOW?

- On average, the number of teeth in an 18-year-old's mouth is 27. The average number of teeth in the mouth of a person aged 65 or older is 14.
- The average American adult has 23 filled cavities in his or her mouth.
- In one recent year, Americans made 466 million visits to their dentists.
- Forty-two percent of Americans did not visit the dentist in the past year.
- There are an estimated 135,000 dentists in the U.S.
- Every day, dentists in the U.S. fill about half a million cavities.

Resources for Lesson 1

- **Transparency** 58
- **Guided Reading** Activity 42
- **Workbook** Vocabulary Activity 42
- **Reteaching** Activity 42
- **Lesson 1 Quiz**
- **Performance Assessment** Activity 16

Science and Technology Videodisc
Human Biology, Side 2
Ch 7 Teeth Rings and Hearing Problems

A tooth is a living structure made up of many parts.

Labels on diagram: Enamel, Cusp, Gum, Gingiva, Dentin, Cementum, Pulp cavity with nerves and vessels, Periodontal ligaments, Periodontal membrane, Root canal, Bone, Crown, Neck, Root

Building Vocabulary

- Conduct a spelling bee with the vocabulary terms for the chapter. Have each student stand. After you pronounce a term, have the student repeat it and then attempt to spell it. If the student fails to spell the word correctly, he or she should sit down. Those students remaining on their feet at the end of the bee are the winners.
- Ask students to complete *Workbook Vocabulary Activity 42.*

Teach

Guided Practice

LD EXPLANATION. LD students may rely on class discussion for comprehension of the lesson's content due to high-level vocabulary. Assignment of independent reading is not recommended.

L2 DISCUSSION. Discuss why some teens need to have their wisdom teeth removed. Discuss the difference between impacted wisdom teeth and ones that have broken through the gum line.

L2 DEMONSTRATION. Bring an anatomical model of the teeth to class. Explain and point out to the class the 8 incisors, 20 molars, and 4 canine teeth on the model. Also, bring in dental X rays for the class to see cavities or fillings.

L1 USING BODY SYSTEMS TRANSPARENCY 58. Refer to the Teaching Transparencies Binder.

L2 COOPERATIVE LEARNING. Divide the class into small groups. Assign each group the name of an animal. Have that group find out how many teeth and what kinds of teeth that animal has. Talk about the reasons for the differences.

LEP CLASS ACTIVITY. Ask some students to make a collage with pictures of things important for good dental health. Others can make one with less than perfect smiles.

DID YOU KNOW?

- About 90 percent of teens covered by dental insurance have their wisdom teeth surgically removed. This is often a preventive measure, meant to prevent impacted teeth and other problems.
- Since only 28 percent of wisdom teeth are impacted, new studies suggest that having wisdom teeth removed as a matter of routine is unnecessary.

Periodontal Disease

Susan has bad breath. Larry's gums often bleed when he brushes his teeth. Michelle's front teeth have begun to spread. All three of these people have periodontal disease—the most common cause of tooth loss.

Periodontal disease is an inflammation of the periodontal structures. It is almost entirely preventable. Periodontal disease is primarily the result of the destructive action of bacteria in your mouth. Bacteria form plaque. **Plaque** is a sticky, colorless film that acts on sugar to form acids that destroy tooth enamel and irritate gums.

Unless plaque is removed once every 24 to 36 hours, it can harden into tartar. **Tartar,** or calculus, as it is sometimes called, is a very hard substance that irritates the underlying bone as well as the surrounding gums of your teeth.

Decay begins as the plaque eats into the enamel and then spreads to the dentin. Your tooth will become more sensitive as the decay reaches the pulp. You will experience a toothache when the decay reaches the pulp and exposes the nerve. If it is not treated, the bacterial infection can spread.

A tooth becomes abscessed when decay progresses to the stage where pus collects in and tissue becomes inflamed around the bone sockets of a tooth. An abscessed or badly decayed tooth in the upper jaw can spread infection into the sinuses.

KEEPING FIT

Knowing the Signs of Gum Disease

Periodontal disease can develop at any age. If you develop any of the following symptoms, see your dentist right away:

- gums that bleed very easily
- chronic bad breath or bad taste in the mouth
- loose or separating permanent teeth
- changes in your bite
- red, swollen, or painful gums sensitive to the touch
- pus between the teeth
- gums that seem to be pulling away from the teeth

316 CHAPTER 16 PERSONAL HEALTH

Additional Information

Mercury Fillings. Recently a panel of experts concluded that the mercury escaping from tooth fillings is of little danger to people who have the metal fillings in their mouths. Though silver amalgam does release mercury vapors into the mouth, the amount is so small that people are at little risk. The panel concluded that it is unnecessary to have silver amalgam fillings replaced with other materials, though a few isolated cases of reactions to the mercury in the fillings have been reported.

Technology. A new ultrasonic tool can do a root canal with twice the speed as the usual procedure and with far less pain. The high-frequency sound waves both clear away diseased portions of teeth and kill bacteria in the process.

Other Tooth and Mouth Disorders

In addition to periodontal disease, several other tooth and mouth disorders can occur. Sometimes they appear as a result of poor oral health, but just as often they develop because of poorly aligned teeth.

Halitosis. Halitosis is bad breath, a condition that can be caused by such factors as decayed teeth, eating certain foods, indigestion, and mouth infections. Mouthwashes and mints may temporarily cover up the odor. However, these breath fresheners do not cure halitosis. Good oral health care can control halitosis. If halitosis is caused by tooth decay or other infections, the only way to cure it is to treat the underlying cause of the problem.

Malocclusion. Malocclusion is a condition in which the teeth of the upper and lower jaws do not align properly. Malocclusion is often hereditary. If the teeth are too large for the jaw to accommodate them, or if a person has an extra tooth, the teeth are pushed out of alignment. Other factors that might cause malocclusion are thumb sucking or tooth loss. Malocclusion can lead to decay and disease and can also affect a person's speech and ability to chew. If malocclusion is severe, a person's appearance and self-esteem can be negatively affected.

Orthodontics is the specialty of dentistry that corrects malocclusion. Orthodontists may recommend the use of braces or other dental appliances to help align the teeth.

Gingivitis. Gingivitis is a disorder in which the gums become red and swollen and bleed easily. The inflammation may be caused by dental plaque, misaligned teeth, or deposits of decaying food. A dentist must determine the cause of the inflammation in order to treat gingivitis.

Braces are one orthodontic appliance used to correct misalignment of teeth.

A retainer is another orthodontic appliance used to straighten teeth.

HEALTH UPDATE

LOOKING AT TECHNOLOGY

Lasers: New Light on the Subject

Lasers are now being used in the dentist's office. Dental lasers are being used to vaporize cavities without harming healthy enamel on the patient's teeth. Experimenting with an ophthalmologist's laser, a Michigan dentist found that using a pulsating laser on cavities rather than a continuous beam could zap away cavities without overheating the surrounding gums. In addition to being used for cavities, dental lasers are now also being used to remove and shape gum tissue. This laser use has been found to be as effective as the scalpel usually used in routine gum surgeries. In addition, while 95 percent of people getting scalpel surgery on the gums required some anesthesia, the laser surgery method requires only 20 percent of patients to be anesthetized. The laser, unlike the scalpel, can also get at gum disease in its very earliest stages and in locations that a scalpel may not be able to reach easily.

Additional Information

Orthodontic Care. Millions of adults and children receive orthodontic treatment each year. More than 80 percent of young people aged 12 to 17 have some malocclusions. About 25 percent of those need treatment.

Today's braces have changed from the old wire, or "metal-mouth," type. They are smaller, lighter, and show far less metal than before. Mini-brackets that bond to the teeth eliminate the need for bands. Some braces have plastic coated wires in white or ivory and others are transparent or tooth-colored with thinner wires. Some braces come in colors of hot pink, grape, and blue.

Check for Understanding

■ Assign and discuss the lesson review. Encourage LD students to focus on questions 1 and 2.

Evaluate

■ Administer, grade, and discuss the *Lesson 1 Quiz*.

Reteach

■ Ask students to make a poster showing the progression of periodontal disease and how to prevent it.
■ Ask students to complete *Reteaching Activity 42*.

Enrich

■ Ask student volunteers to interview a dentist to find out the most common dental problems he or she sees in the teenage population. What are the primary causes of these problems? How might they be prevented? How can they be treated once they occur? Have the volunteers summarize their findings and share them with the class.

Close

Summarize the most important concepts in this lesson. Explain that responsible health habits such as brushing, flossing, and visiting the dentist annually will prevent dental complications later in life.

DID YOU KNOW?

■ The word *periodontal* comes from the Greek word meaning "around the tooth."
■ More than 50 percent of people over the age of 18 have at least early stages of periodontal disease.

HELP WANTED

Dental Hygienist

Successful and growing dental practice needs hygienist with knowledge, people skills, professional attitude and, of course, good hands. Your associate's degree from an accredited program qualifies you for a place on our team. If you have a bachelor's degree, we also can use those advanced skills. Excellent working conditions include friendly people and the latest equipment.

For more information, contact:
American Dental Hygienists Association
444 N. Michigan Ave.
Suite 3400
Chicago, IL 60611

Periodontitis. If gingivitis is untreated, a more serious form of gum disease, called periodontitis, can develop. This disease results in swollen, tender, and/or bleeding gums. Since bone surrounding the teeth is gradually destroyed, teeth can become loose and may fall out. As with gingivitis, good oral health care, including dental care, prevents this disease.

Care of the Teeth

More than 20 million Americans have already lost most or all of their teeth. This does not have to happen to you. With good care your teeth should last a lifetime. The choice is yours. If you spend 10 to 15 minutes a day cleaning and flossing your teeth, and if you limit foods high in sugar, you will probably be able to keep your teeth your entire life.

Regular brushing after eating and before bedtime is essential. Because a toothbrush often misses hard-to-reach spots, flossing is important. Flossing removes plaque and food particles that are stuck between teeth and between teeth and gums.

Periodontal disease, the most common cause of tooth loss, is almost entirely preventable. By age 15, four out of every five Americans have the beginnings of periodontal disease. In the early stages, the disease can be checked. Checking the progress of the disease requires preventive oral health and periodic visits to a dentist.

Your diet is a major contributor to the presence of plaque on your teeth. Frequent consumption of sugary foods promotes the formation of plaque. If you eat sweets, it is best to brush your teeth as soon as possible. Even if you do not eat sweets you still have to be concerned with plaque removal. Plaque is continually forming. It will form even if you eat nothing at all, so daily plaque removal is essential.

LESSON 1 REVIEW

Reviewing Facts and Vocabulary

1. How can you protect and maintain your teeth?
2. Describe the process of tooth decay.

Thinking Critically

3. **Synthesis.** Develop a message that would be appropriate for people who do not regularly brush or floss their teeth.
4. **Evaluation.** How would you be able to distinguish between a person who practices good oral health and one who doesn't?

Applying Health Knowledge

5. Make a report on the use of fluoride to prevent tooth decay. Is it added to the water in your community? If so, how has the rate of tooth decay changed since the introduction of fluoride?
6. Identify three ads for oral dental health. What do the ads claim? Make up your own ad for oral or dental health. Share it with the class.

Answers to Lesson 1 Review

1. Floss and brush daily, visit the dentist periodically, avoid sweets.
2. The description of the process of tooth decay can be found on page 316.
3. Answers will vary.
4. Answers will vary. Possible answers:

Good oral hygiene contributes to the prevention of halitosis, tooth decay, and red, swollen gums.
5. Answers will vary.
6. Answers will vary.

EYES

Your eyes have over a million electrical connections and are responsible for about 80 percent of the knowledge you acquire. They can distinguish nearly 8 million differences in color! Of the sense organs, the eyes provide the greatest knowledge of the environment. However, individuals who do not have full use of their sight can and do develop their other senses to a much higher degree.

The Eyes' Built-In Protection

The eyes are situated in orbits protected by the bony sockets of the skull. The general area around the eyes consists of the lacrimal glands, the eyebrows and eyelids, the conjunctiva, and the eyelashes.

The Lacrimal Glands

The **lacrimal gland,** located above each eye, is responsible for producing tears. Tears are made mostly of water and a small amount of salt and mucus. The salt gives the tears an antiseptic effect, which helps them fight pathogens. Tears keep the eyeballs moist and help remove foreign objects from the eyes.

Tears reach the surface of the eye through tiny ducts. Some of the tears evaporate from the eye's surface. Those that do not evaporate are drained into the nasal cavity by two tear ducts located at the inner corner of the eye. These ducts open into larger ducts that run down the nose. When the production of tears increases, the tear ducts are not able to carry away the extra quantity, and tears flow over the lower lid.

Eyebrows, Eyelids, and Eyelashes

Eyebrows are growths of hair that protect the eyes from foreign particles, perspiration, and direct rays of light.

Eyelids are folds of skin that protect the eye by covering its surface. The eyelids are controlled by an automatic reflex action that causes you to blink to protect the eyes. Your eyes are closed a total of about 30 minutes a day because of blinking!

Eyelashes help keep foreign particles out of the eyes. The eyelashes receive a lubricating secretion from oil glands. This oily secretion prevents the eyelids from sticking together.

Conjunctiva

Conjunctiva is a protective mucous membrane attached to the inner surface of the eyelids that continues over the outer surface of the eyeball. Several different conditions, including lack of sleep, can irritate this membrane, causing inflammation.

EYES **319**

> **LESSON 2 FOCUS**

> **TERMS TO USE**
> - Lacrimal (LAK•ree•mul) gland
> - Conjunctiva
> - Sclera (SKLER•uh)
> - Cornea
> - Choroid (KOHR•oid)
> - Aqueous humor (A•kwee•uhs HU•mer)
> - Vitreous humor (VIT•ree•uhs HU•mer)
> - Retina

> **CONCEPTS TO LEARN**
> - The parts around the eye provide protection to the eye.
> - Your eye adjusts to different intensities of light.
> - Many vision problems can be corrected with professional help.

> **ATTITUDES AND BEHAVIORS TO EVALUATE**
> - Self-Inventory, page 332.
> - Building Decision-Making Skills, page 333.

Focus

Lesson Objectives

After studying this lesson, students should be able to:
- label the parts of the eye
- explain the process of seeing
- describe common vision problems
- discuss eye care

Bellringer

Write the following on the chalkboard for students to complete while attendance is being taken: *Why do people wear glasses? Write a list of all the reasons you can think of.*

Introducing the Lesson

Refer to the Bellringer. As students share items from their lists, write a composite list on the chalkboard. Have students categorize the reasons as either medical or fashion.

Building Vocabulary

- Have students look at the illustration of the eye. Distribute several colors of clay. Direct students to create a model of the eye using different colors to represent the different structures. Upon completion, have students share their models and discuss the structures included as well as the functions.
- Ask students to complete *Workbook Vocabulary Activity 43.*

DID YOU KNOW?

- *Being the apple of one's eye* means being the object of one's affections. This expression comes from the ninth-century Anglo-Saxon word *aeppel,* which meant both apple and eye. Since then, scientists have determined that when you stare at something for which you have special feeling, your pupils dilate.

Resources for Lesson 2

- **Transparency** 59
- **Guided Reading** Act 43
- **Workbook** Voc Act 43
- **Reteaching** Activity 43
- **Lesson 2 Quiz**

Science and Technology Videodisc
Human Biology, Side 1
Ch 22 Vision Diagnosis

Human Biology, Side 2
Ch 2 Low Vision Clinic

Ch 3 Nearsightedness Surgery

Guided Practice

L1 LAB. Prepare your classroom by blocking out all window and door light with black construction paper or heavy cloth. Tell students that you are going to turn off the lights for 5 minutes. Also tell them you will begin counting off each second once the lights are turned off. Ask them to record the number of seconds that elapse until they begin to see objects in the room and until they see clearly.

Conclude this activity by discussing students' reactions. When the lights were first turned off, could they see at all? What was happening inside students' eyes to gradually allow them to see in the dark? (Pupils enlarge to admit light; explain to students that another reason is the gradual use of visual purple, a chemical in the rods that allows the eye to make out shapes in low light.) Why could students see better the longer they sat in the darkened room? (More time for the development of visual purple and for adjustment.)

L2 LAB. This experiment will show if students are right- or left-eye dominant. Give students the following directions.

1. Hold your finger out in front of you.
2. Line it up with some object across the room.
3. Close your left eye. Now open your left eye and close your right.
4. At which time did it appear that your finger jumped to the side? If the finger stays lined up with the object when your right eye is open, you are right-eye dominant.

L1 USING BODY SYSTEMS TRANSPARENCY 59. Refer to the Teaching Transparencies Binder.

L2 DISCUSSION. Have students find optical illusions and bring them to class to test other students. Discuss how our brain interprets what we see.

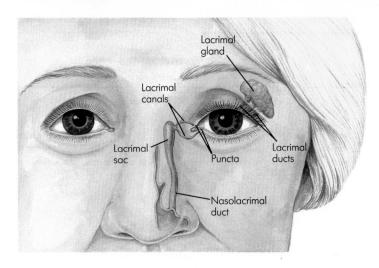

By producing tears, the lacrimal gland helps keep foreign objects out of the eye.

Structure of the Eye

The eyeball is about 1 inch (2.5 cm) in diameter. The eyeball is slightly longer than it is wide. This shape results from the bulge caused by the cornea, known as the window of the eye.

The Eyeball Wall

The wall of the eyeball is made up of three layers: the sclera, the choroid, and the retina.

The Sclera. The **sclera** is a white, tough membrane that helps the eye keep its spherical shape. This is the white part of your eye, and it helps protect the eye's delicate inner structure. In the front part of the eye, the sclera forms the colorless, transparent **cornea,** which is like a round clear dish supplied with many free nerve endings. Thus, the cornea is extremely sensitive to particles that come in contact with its surface.

The Choroid. The middle layer of the eyeball wall, the **choroid,** contains

- the iris, seen from the outside as the color of the eye;
- the suspensory ligaments, which blend with and hold the lens;
- the ciliary muscles, to which suspensory ligaments and the sclera are attached.

The iris is situated at the front of the eye. *Iris,* a Greek word meaning "rainbow," gives the eye its color. The iris is located in front of the lens. The black circle in the center of the iris is the pupil, which actually is a round hole, through which light passes.

Two sets of muscles in the iris change the size of the pupil, thus controlling the amount of light that enters the eye. In dim light one set of muscles, controlled by the sympathetic nervous system, pulls away from the iris, making it larger. This is called dilation.

In bright light the other set of muscles, controlled by the parasympathetic system, makes the pupil smaller. This is called contraction.

Additional Information

Eye Transplants. The transplantation of the whole eye is scientifically impossible. The reason—everyone's eyes are connected to the brain by the optic nerve, which is vital for sight. The optic nerve is a delicate thread and this nerve cannot be reconnected once it has been disconnected.

Therefore, the eye is never removed from its socket during surgery. The cornea, which is the clear part of the eye, has been successfully transplanted for years. A corneal transplant should not be confused with an eye transplant.

Behind the pupil is the lens, held by the suspensory ligaments. These ligaments, in turn, are connected to the ciliary muscles. The lens projects onto the retina an image of what is before it. The lens is curved, and the ciliary muscles help change its shape as the eye focuses on an object.

The cavity between the cornea and the lens is filled with a watery fluid called the **aqueous humor.** The words come from Latin; *aqueous* means "water," and *humor* means "fluid." The aqueous humor is continuously formed and drained off. This helps maintain pressure within the eye. The aqueous humor is a source of nutrients for structures, such as the cornea.

The **vitreous humor,** a thicker fluid, is found behind the lens and keeps the eyeball firm. *Vitreous* means "glasslike."

There are no blood vessels in the sclera, cornea, lens, aqueous humor, or vitreous humor. The choroid, the middle layer, contains the blood vessels that nourish the eyes.

The Retina.   The **retina** makes up the third layer of the eyeball wall. It contains the nerve cells and controls the processes responsible for vision. The retina contains millions of light-sensitive receptors that are classified as either rods or cones. Rods and cones bear names that describe their appearance.

The rods, which are cylindrical, register light and darkness and are used in dim light. They contain a photosensitive chemical called visual purple, which makes it possible to see in dim light. Light breaks down this visual purple so that when you go from a light room to a dark room at first, you cannot see. As the rods re-form the visual purple, you begin to see objects in shades of black, white, and gray. People who do not have enough visual purple experience night blindness. Rods lie toward the edge of the retina. An estimated 125 million rods are in a retina.

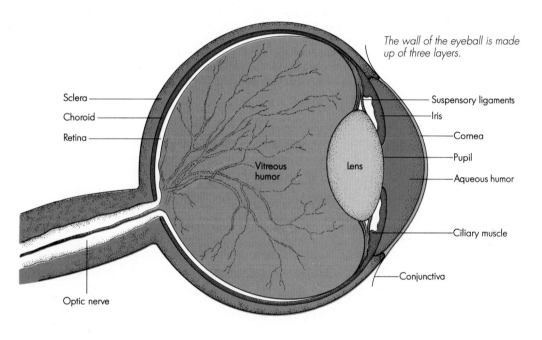

The wall of the eyeball is made up of three layers.

Sclera
Choroid
Retina
Vitreous humor
Lens
Optic nerve
Suspensory ligaments
Iris
Cornea
Pupil
Aqueous humor
Ciliary muscle
Conjunctiva

Additional Information

The Eye as a Camera. Similarities are often noted between a vertebrate's eyes, such as ours, and cameras. For example, both have a lens that can be focused for different distances, a mechanism for controlling the amount of entering light (the eye's iris), a light-sensitive material (the eye's retina and the camera's film), and a light-tight container. Both also form upside-down images and require special care and occasional repair.

There are, however, some important differences between eyes and cameras, one of the most prominent being the focusing mechanism. We focus by changing the shape of our lens, not the distance between the lens and the object being viewed as most modern cameras do.

L1 **CLASS ACTIVITY.** Distribute pre-cut strips of waxed paper (approximately 10 inches long by 3 inches wide). Then direct students to perform various activities of daily living—such as walking across the room, pouring a glass of water, or signing their names—with the strip of waxed paper held by its edge over their eyes. Vision will blur and resemble that of people who suffer from cataracts. Discuss what students experienced during this blurring.

L1 **CLASS ACTIVITY.** Perform the activity above, but use blindfolds so students will realize what it is like to be blind. Ask them to perform a simple task like tying shoes. Have them take turns with a partner and spend the class period experiencing blindness in several situations. Ask students to share what it was like to be blind. Ask how blindness could change their lives and goals.

L2 **CLASS ACTIVITY.** Have students pair off to act out the following situation: Your friend has just found out that he or she needs glasses and cannot wear contact lenses. He or she is very upset. Discuss the advice you would give. How would you try to help your friend feel better? Have pairs of students act out situations for the whole class.

L2 **DISCUSSION.** Discuss how sight develops and how we learn to use our eyes.

L2 **DISCUSSION.** What should you do if you get something in your eye? Discuss recommended techniques for removing foreign objects from the eye. Demonstrate first-aid techniques for eye injuries, including chemical burns.

L2 **DEMONSTRATION.** Use an anatomical model of the eye to differentiate the parts of the eye. Explain how light enters the eye and signals what one actually sees.

L1 **DISCUSSION.** Discuss adjustments a person would have to make if losing his or her sight. Explain the difference between being blind and having a visual impairment.

The cones, which are cone-shaped, are situated with their pointed end nearer the choroid layer. Cones give you vision in bright light and are able to detect differences in color. About 7 million cones are in a retina, concentrated in its back part.

Some people have a deficiency in perceiving colors, which is called color blindness. Almost all color blindness is mild. Color-blind people have trouble seeing shades of red or green. It is rare that a person has complete color blindness—a condition in which the person sees only shades of black, white, and gray.

The Optic Nerve

At the back of the eye is a large nerve cable that connects the eye with the brain. This is known as the optic nerve. At the point where this optic nerve connects with the eye, the nerve spreads and becomes part of the inner surface of the retina.

The point at which the optic nerve enters the eye is called the blind spot. Since there are no cones or rods in this area, vision in this spot is not possible.

Vision

As light rays pass through the cornea and aqueous humor, they are bent and directed through the pupil. The light rays then penetrate the lens, which adjusts to focus the light on the retina. This adjustment is called accommodation. The lens bulges to accommodate near objects and flattens to accommodate faraway objects.

The light-sensitive retina sends impulses along the optic nerve to the occipital lobe of the brain. The brain interprets the light rays as an image.

In normal vision a sharp image is produced. If you stand 20 feet (6 m) from an eye chart and can read the top eight lines, you have 20/20 vision. If you can read at 20 feet (6 m) what a person with normal vision can read at 40 feet (12 m) you have 20/40 vision. A person who has less than 20/200 vision and who cannot see the letter at the top of the chart is considered to be legally blind.

In A-1 the eyeball is too long from front to back, and the image is formed in front of the retina. As a result, distant objects are unclear. In B-1 the eyeball is too short from front to back, and the image is formed behind the retina. In this case, objects that are close are unclear. Corrective lenses in A-2 and B-2 help the image form where it should, on the retina, so objects can be seen clearly.

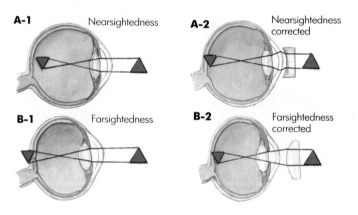

A-1 Nearsightedness
A-2 Nearsightedness corrected
B-1 Farsightedness
B-2 Farsightedness corrected

Additional Information

Sunglasses. Most sunglasses we buy do not indicate on their labels whether or not they are safe for exposure to UV radiation. UV radiation is a part of sunlight. It can damage the eyes if they are not protected by sunglasses that block or absorb the full range of UV-B and UV-A (290-380 nm). Such protective sunglasses should be worn in bright sunlight to prevent radiation damage. Prescription sunglasses will provide the necessary lens to block or absorb the UV radiation. However, it can be difficult to determine which nonprescription sunglasses have adequate UV protection.

Overcoming The Odds

Dr. David Hartman is a psychiatrist in private practice in Roanoke, Virginia. He is married and has three children. Dr. Hartman is also blind.

"I lost my sight when I was eight," he says. "I had a congenital eye disease that couldn't be corrected."

When Hartman was 9, he went to a school for the blind, which he attended for about 5 years. He continues, "The school helped me to reorient my thinking and I learned to be treated like everyone else. Even though I lived only 15 minutes from the school, I stayed there from Monday to Friday." Still, despite these separations, Hartman had great family support. "My mom read to me a lot," he says. "My dad figured out creative ways that I could do things. And my sister confronted me with reality.

"In eighth grade, I began public school," he continues. "It was easy for me to adapt to the academics. But the real challenge was to fit in socially. I'd wrestled at the school for the blind from third grade on, so when I wrestled in eighth grade, I was a little better than the other kids. That helped me to be seen by the other students as normal."

Hartman then went on to Gettysburg College where he was active in campus activities, including giving campus tours. With the help of two professors/mentors, Hartman did very well in college and applied to nine medical schools. One by one, eight of the schools rejected him. "At

the same time, I was reading The Old Man and the Sea," he says, "and that book helped me more than anything to see that often it's not the goal we are trying to achieve but the process that is most important."

Finally, Hartman was accepted at Temple University School of Medicine. After graduation, he went on to an internship at Temple and then to a psychiatric residency at the University of Pennsylvania. In 1975, a made-for-TV movie called Journey from Darkness about his quest to become a doctor was aired on national TV. Later, he wrote about his life in a book entitled White Coat, White Cane.

Today, Dr. Hartman thinks that his blindness is sometimes an asset. He says, "It allows me to have a different point of view. Some patients say they feel more comfortable because they don't feel I'm peering at them or scrutinizing them." He concludes, "We all have our disabilities. We all have our strengths, too. We need to explore and discover our strengths. We need to recognize that we each have our own uniqueness."

1. Hartman had lots of support along the way—from family, professors, and friends. How can support from caring people motivate someone to achieve goals and develop self-esteem?
2. Hartman says, "We all have our disabilities. We all have our strengths, too." What do you consider your disabilities? Your strengths? How can you accept and/or improve your weaknesses and more fully use and develop your strengths?

EYES **323**

Additional Information

Eye Care. "Pinkeye," or conjunctivitis, may result from allergic reactions, from exposure to cosmetics or chlorinated water, or from a bacterial infection or virus. Should a student get pinkeye, he or she should follow these steps:

- Don't touch the eye.
- Use tissues when wiping away pus and crust.

- Don't wear eye makeup.
- Don't wear contact lenses until the condition has cleared up.
- Don't use other people's washcloths and towels and warn them not to use yours.
- Use warm washcloth compresses on your eyes.
- If your eyes are light-sensitive or painful, call your doctor.

L2 **CLASS ACTIVITY.** Have students look at books printed in large print and Braille. Have a class representative talk with a local printer about the differences in cost for printing a page in large print and in regular print. Can the printer have copies made in Braille?

L1 **DISCUSSION.** Discuss what eye safety practices may be suggested or required on some jobs. Also relate the prevention of injury to the eyes in sports or recreation and around the home. Why are these safety practices necessary?

L2 **COOPERATIVE LEARNING.** Ask students to get into groups of five. Give each group a poster. Have the students divide the poster into three sections and label the first section "Eye Disease, Injury, or Disorder." Have them label the second section "Prevention" and the third section, "Treatment or First Aid." Ask them to fill in the poster with several examples and share it with the class.

Independent Practice

L3 **RESEARCH.** Have students look up information about the eyes of cats. What is it about the structure of cats' eyes that enable them to see in the dark? Are there other animals that see well at night? Compare the vision of these animals with the vision of humans.

L2 **RESEARCH.** Have students visit a local library to find out what services are available for people with visual impairments. Does the school library have any special resources for those with limited sight?

L1 **PARENTAL INVOLVEMENT.** Have students discuss with their parents any relatives who have suffered an eye injury or experienced other eye diseases or disorders. Have them ask about the treatment used. Also, have them check to see what eye products are used in their homes. Have volunteers share their findings with the class.

L1 **USING THE LESSON RESOURCES.** For additional student activities, refer to the lesson resources on page 319.

Culturally Speaking

Mixed Signals

Raising your eyebrows briefly, "the eyebrow flash," indicates friendliness if you are Balinese, Papuan, Samoan, or American. In Japan, however, it is regarded as an indecent gesture and is avoided. Your culture also influences whether or not to maintain eye contact. Many Americans have learned to make eye contact to show attention, but not to make constant contact, or stare, because it is considered rude. In Japan, eyes are to be lowered as a sign of respect when listening. In Bolivia, constant eye contact is expected.

Eye Problems

Nearsightedness (myopia) is a condition in which light rays are focused in front of the retina. A person who is nearsighted can see clearly when things are close, but distant objects are blurred. Concave corrective lenses in eyeglasses make the rays focus farther back.

Farsightedness (hyperopia) occurs when the light rays are focused behind the retina. Someone who is farsighted can see distant objects clearly, but things close up are blurred. This condition is corrected by convex lenses in eyeglasses.

Astigmatism occurs when the curvature of the lens is uneven. Light rays focus at different points, causing the image to be blurred. This condition is corrected with specially ground lenses for eyeglasses.

A cataract is a clouding of the lens, which causes blurring or hazy vision and problems with night vision. The clouded lens may be surgically removed and vision restored with corrective glasses. A cataract is the most frequent single cause of blindness among adults.

Crossed eyes (strabismus) might occur when the eye muscles of both eyes do not work together, causing one or both eyes to turn inward or outward. A person with crossed eyes may then see two images because the brain, even though it can interpret the images, cannot fuse the input from each eye.

Amblyopia is a condition of reduced or dim vision in an eye that otherwise appears to be normal. This condition occurs when a child with strabismus favors one eye and the unused eye loses some ability to see. Amblyopia is a major cause of partial vision loss in children. Prevention depends on early diagnosis. Treatment of amblyopia includes wearing corrective lenses, wearing an eye patch on the weaker eye, or possible surgery to correct the eye muscle.

Glaucoma is caused by increased fluid pressure in the eyeball, either because too much aqueous humor is produced or because it drains inadequately. Glaucoma may cause damage to the optic nerve and result in blindness. Glaucoma usually develops slowly and painlessly, and can be diagnosed during an eye examination. If glaucoma is detected early, it can be treated with medication or surgery.

A sty is an eye infection caused by bacteria that lodge in the glands of the eyelids. A physician can prescribe treatment or antibiotic drops for a sty.

Conjunctivitis is an eye infection that affects the sclera and the conjunctiva and causes reddening. It is sometimes called pinkeye when it affects children. A doctor can treat this condition with antibiotics.

KEEPING FIT

Preventing Computer Eyestrain

To prevent or decrease the problem of computer eyestrain, remember to
- place your screen so your line of vision is just below eye-level.
- place the screen 20 to 24 inches from your face.
- place the screen away from a window.
- use a glare-filtering cover over the screen.
- look away from the screen, focusing on a distant object, about every 15 minutes.
- remove dust from the screen on a regular basis.
- take breaks.
- adjust the brightness of the letters on the screen so that they are neither too bright nor too faint.

324 CHAPTER 16 PERSONAL HEALTH

Additional Information

Effects of Diabetes. Diabetic retinopathy is a condition that damages the small blood vessels nourishing the retina and occurs as a result of the inadequate or faulty insulin production caused by diabetes. It is essential for all persons with diabetes to pay attention to any of the following warning signs that are possible indicators of vision loss: loss, distortion, or dimness of vision; pain in or around the eyes; excessive tearing or discharge from the eye; swelling of the eyelids or protrusion of the eye; double vision; flashes of light, halos around lights, or floating spots; a sudden crossing or deviation of one eye; a change in color of an eye.

Goggles or protective glasses are worn in technical education classes to protect the eyes.

A detached retina is the separation of the retina from underlying tissue. This condition can sometimes be treated and corrected with laser surgery.

Care of the Eyes

Often we take our sight for granted. Yet reports from the National Society to Prevent Blindness indicate that we could do much more to protect and promote healthy eyes. It is important to read and to watch television in a well-lighted room. When viewing television, sit at a comfortable distance from the set. Take breaks from using your eyes for long periods of time by closing your eyes. Avoid rubbing your eyes, and avoid direct sun or bright light. Wear protective goggles or glasses when engaging in an activity or sport that could cause an eye injury. Finally, have regular eye checkups by a trained professional.

LESSON 2 REVIEW

Reviewing Facts and Vocabulary

1. How do lacrimal glands protect the eyes?
2. Describe the main functions of the three layers of the eyeball.
3. How does the eye receive its nourishment?
4. Explain the role of the rods and cones in vision.
5. What is a detached retina?

Thinking Critically

6. **Analysis.** Compare farsightedness and nearsightedness.

7. **Evaluation.** Do you think it is important for school-aged children to have their vision tested on a regular basis? Why or why not?

Applying Health Knowledge

8. Interview someone who is blind or visually impaired, or visit a center for the blind. What special problems do people with visual impairments have? How have their other senses accommodated for their lack of vision?

- Assign and discuss the lesson review. Encourage LD students to focus on questions 1, 5, and 7.

Evaluate

- Administer, grade, and discuss the *Lesson 2 Quiz.*

Reteach

- Have students make posters of eye charts and eye tests. Under each, have them describe in their own words the purpose of the chart or test as it relates to eye health.
- Ask students to complete *Reteaching Activity 43.*

Enrich

- Have students write a children's book for grade school children that creatively presents some basic information about eye structure and eye care. For example, students might make the main character of the book a private eye named Investigator Sight, who is better known as I. Sight. This character might take the readers on a secret journey through a giant eyeball to uncover the many mysteries of vision.

Close

Summarize the most important concepts in this lesson. Ask the students what health behaviors they will adopt to take care of their eyes.

Answers to Lesson 2 Review

1. They produce tears that constantly cleanse the eyes.
2. Functions of the sclera, choroid, and retina are on pages 320 to 322.
3. Through blood vessels in the choroid.
4. Rods register light and darkness and contain a photosensitive material that makes it possible to see in dim light. Cones give one vision in bright light and detect differences in colors.
5. The separation of the retina from underlying tissue.
6. With farsightedness, distant objects are clear. Close objects are clear with nearsightedness.
7. Answers will vary but should be supported logically.
8. Answers will vary.

DID YOU KNOW?

- A new study in the *Journal of the American Optometric Association* indicates that inner-city teens with vision problems are often misdiagnosed as having learning disabilities.
- The muscles that move the lens of the eye and help it to change shape move about 17,000 times each day.

EARS

Focus

Focus

Lesson Objectives

After studying this lesson, students should be able to:
- label the parts of the ear
- explain the process of hearing
- describe common hearing problems
- discuss ear care

Bellringer

Write the following on the chalkboard for students to work on while attendance is being taken:
Explain the difference between being partially hearing impaired and being totally hearing impaired.

Introducing the Lesson

Ask students to share their responses to the Bellringer. Explain the difference between hearing loss for the partially hearing impaired and the totally hearing impaired. Explain that many factors, including loud noises, can cause vibrations in the inner ear and damage hearing. Some individuals are born with a total hearing impairment and are deaf. Others develop a partial or total hearing impairment from external factors, including noises or diseases, that affect hearing. This lesson will provide information on how the sounds or messages are transmitted through the ear to the brain and how external factors can determine the extent of hearing loss.

DID YOU KNOW?

- If someone says his or her *ears are burning,* it means he or she senses being the subject of a conversation. Ancient Roman author Pliny maintained that guardian angels touched one's right ear if the talk was favorable, but touched the left if it was not.
- "The walls have ears" means that what one says can be overheard when one least expects it. It refers to ancient Greek tyrant Dionysius's cave in which he held prisoners. With its ear-shaped entrance and tendency to carry sound, the cave allowed him to eavesdrop on far-off prisoners.

LESSON 3 FOCUS

TERMS TO USE
- External auditory canal
- Ossicles (AH•si•kuhlz)
- Labyrinth (LAB•uh•rinth)
- Binaural (by•NAWR•uhl) hearing
- Sensory deafness
- Otosclerosis (OHT•oh•skluh•ROH•suhs)
- Tinnitus (TIN•uht•uhs)

CONCEPTS TO LEARN
- Hearing is the result of sound waves moving through the structures of the ear.
- Hearing loss is one of the potential hazards of being around noise.

ATTITUDES AND BEHAVIORS TO EVALUATE
- Self-Inventory, page 332.
- Building Decision-Making Skills, page 333.

J ulie, a tenth grader, spends two afternoons a week teaching sign language to children who are deaf. Julie lost her hearing as a young child, but she has not let that slow her down. Julie communicates not only through sign language but also by reading lips.

Julie is among thousands of people who are deaf or hearing impaired. Disorders of the ear may result in a loss of hearing and may affect the sense of balance. Birth defects, injuries, and disease are three causes of hearing loss. Many times the cause is unknown. Before learning how these causes affect hearing, let us learn how the complicated process of hearing takes place.

Structure of the Ear

The ear extends deep into the skull and has three main parts: the outer ear, the middle ear, and the inner ear.

The Outer Ear

The outer ear consists of a fleshy curved part that is attached to each side of the head and is called the auricle. Composed of fatty tissue and cartilage, the cup-shaped auricle collects sound waves and directs them into the ear. Looking directly into the ear, you can see the **external auditory canal.** It is a passageway about 1 inch (2.5 cm) long. The outer part is lined with fine hairs and tiny wax-producing glands. The wax and tiny hairs protect the ear by keeping out foreign substances. The inner two-thirds of the auditory canal is surrounded by the temporal bone, one of the hardest bones in the body. The auditory canal leads to the eardrum, which is a thin sheet of tissue that separates the outer ear from the middle ear.

The Middle Ear

Behind the eardrum are three small bones called the **ossicles,** which are linked together and connect the eardrum with the inner ear:

- The malleus is the first bone. It is attached to the eardrum and is the largest of the three bones.
- The incus is the middle bone. It connects the malleus and the innermost bone, the stapes.
- The stapes is stirrup-shaped and attaches to the inner ear. It is the smallest bone in the body. The ends of the stapes are attached by ligaments to a membrane called the oval window, which leads to the inner ear.

Two other parts of the head connect to the middle ear. Although these parts are not actually a part of the middle ear, they can affect your hearing:

Resources for Lesson 3

- **Transparency** 60
- **Guided Reading** Act 44
- **Decision-Making** Act 16
- **Workbook** Voc Act 44, Appl Act 16
- **Reteaching** Activity 44
- **Enrichment** Activity 16
- **Health Labs** Activity 16
- **Cooperative Learning** Activity 16

- **Lesson 3 Quiz, Chapter 16 Test**
Science and Technology Videodisc
Human Biology, Side 2
Ch 4 Sounds Made by the Ear

Ch 5 Ear Implants

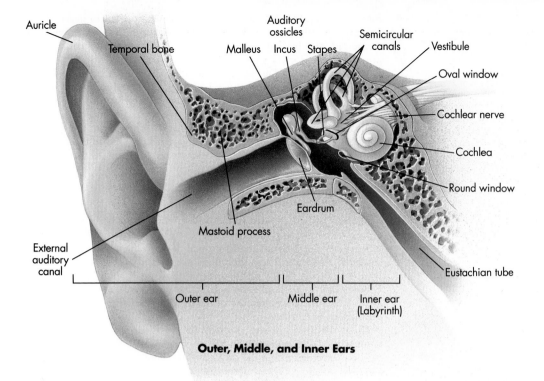

Auricle
Temporal bone
Malleus
Incus
Stapes
Auditory ossicles
Semicircular canals
Vestibule
Oval window
Cochlear nerve
Cochlea
Round window
External auditory canal
Mastoid process
Eardrum
Eustachian tube
Outer ear
Middle ear
Inner ear (Labyrinth)

Outer, Middle, and Inner Ears

Your ear has three main parts.

- The mastoid process is a series of small air-filled spaces in the bones that lie behind the middle ear. These spaces connect with the middle ear.
- The eustachian tube is about 1½ inches (4 cm) long and connects the nasal cavity in the back of the throat with the middle ear.

Have your ears ever popped as you rode in an elevator? That sensation was your eustachian tube opening to let air pass between your throat and middle ear. The eustachian tube opens when you swallow, blow your nose, or yawn, thus equalizing the pressure on either side of the eardrum. If the eustachian tube did not open, the eardrum would rupture with a sudden change in pressure like the one that occurs when riding in an elevator or an airplane.

The Inner Ear

The inner ear, also called the **labyrinth,** consists of three delicate parts: the vestibule, the semicircular canals, and the cochlea.

The vestibule, which forms the central part of the inner ear, contains the utricle and saccule. These tiny baglike structures are lined with hair cells. These hair cells are specialized sense cells with tiny, hairlike projections. They play an important role in balance.

The semicircular canals consist of three canals set at right angles to one another. Each contains a fluid-filled duct that widens at one end to

EARS **327**

Building Vocabulary

- Distribute copies of the vocabulary terms to students. Ask students to divide a sheet of paper into two categories. Label one "Terms that Name Parts of the Ear" and the other "Terms that Do Not." Have students place each term into the category where it belongs. Have students verify their hunches by looking in the Glossary. Ask them to use each term in an original sentence.
- Ask students to complete *Workbook Vocabulary Activity 44.*

Teach

Guided Practice

L1 USING BODY SYSTEMS TRANSPARENCY 60. Refer to the Teaching Transparencies Binder.

LD CLASS ACTIVITY. Provide LD students with a drawing of the outer, middle, and inner ear. Have students label and briefly describe each structure.

L2 DISCUSSION. How do closed-captioned TV programs for the hearing impaired work? Have students develop a list of TV programs they watch that are closed-captioned. What conclusions can students draw from this quick research about the variety of TV programs available for those with a hearing impairment?

L1 DISCUSSION. Talk about how your ears pop in elevators or on planes. (This is due to a change in air pressure in the eustachian tube.) What are some common remedies for dealing with discomforts caused by this type of pressure in the ears? (Swallowing, yawning, chewing gum.) Why do these methods work? (They force the valve at the throat end of the eustachian tube to open and release or admit air as needed.)

Additional Information

Acuity and Range of Human Hearing. Human hearing is about 10 times more sensitive than human vision when the energy of audible sound waves is compared with the energy of visible light waves. In fact, if our hearing were much more acute, it would result in our experiencing a constant buzzing or hissing sensation.

Human ears can detect sound waves from about 20 to 20,000 cycles per second (or hertz), which is a range of over 10 octaves. Human voices range from about 500 to 4,000 hertz, so it's not surprising that our greatest acuity falls within that range, occurring between about 1,000 and 2,000 hertz.

form a pouch. This pouch contains hair cells attached to nerve fibers. The ducts of the semicircular canals connect with the utricle, which is connected, also by a duct, to the saccule. The three semicircular canals are responsible for your sense of balance.

The cochlea resembles a snail shell. It is made up of three fluid-filled ducts. Within one of these ducts is the basilar membrane, which consists of over 15,000 hair cells. These hair cells make up the organ of Corti, which contains the hearing receptors.

Also in the inner ear is the auditory nerve. Fibers from the auditory nerve extend to each hair cell in the organ of Corti and to the hair cells of the saccule, utricle, and semicircular canals.

The Path of Sound Waves

In order for you to hear, sound waves, which are vibrations in the air caused by anything that moves, must reach the organ of Corti. Sound waves enter the external auditory canal through the auricle, causing the eardrum to vibrate. These vibrations are carried across the middle ear by the malleus, incus, and stapes to the oval window, the opening between the middle and inner ear. Sound vibrations cause the stapes to move like a plunger in and out of the oval window, thus causing fluid in the cochlea to vibrate.

These vibrations travel through the vestibule and along the two strands of tissue coiled up in the cochlea. Hair cells of the organ of Corti, a structure within the cochlear duct, bend, stimulating the nerves attached to them. These nerves send messages through the auditory nerve to the temporal lobe, which is the center of hearing in the brain. It is here that sounds are classified and interpreted.

Binaural Hearing

Binaural hearing is the ability to determine the direction a sound comes from by being able to hear it with both ears. A sound coming from the right is slightly louder in the right ear. It also reaches your

Sounds travel through your ear to be interpreted in your brain.

Overcoming Misconceptions

Myth. All hearing losses are the same. **Fact.** The term *deafness* includes a wide range of hearing losses that have different effects on the ability to process sound and understand speech. **Myth.** All deaf people are mute. **Fact.** Some deaf people speak very well and clearly. The inability to hear does not affect physical ability to produce sounds, though a challenge lies in their matching sounds exactly. **Myth.** All deaf people can read lips. **Fact.** Some are very skilled lip-readers, but many are not. **Myth.** Hearing impaired individuals are not sensitive to noise. **Fact.** Some hearing problems accentuate sensitivity to noise.

right ear a fraction of a second sooner than it reaches your left ear. Your brain, picking up on this difference in time and loudness, determines the direction from which the sound comes.

The Sense of Balance

You may not think of balance when you are identifying your senses. How does your body maintain its balance? Your brain receives information from various sense organs about your body's balance. Your eyes and certain pressure-sensitive cells in your arms and legs send messages to your brain about changes in body positions. However, it is the semicircular canals in the ears that provide much of the brain's information about balance.

The Crista

Movement of your head causes the fluid in the semicircular canals to move in a certain direction. At one end of each canal is an organ called a crista. Each crista consists of tiny hairs covered by a dome-shaped, jellylike mass called the cupula. Nerves connect the crista to the brain.

Movements of the head cause fluid to press against a crista, bending the tiny, sensitive hairs. Nerve endings send a message to the brain about these bent hairs. The brain sends a message back, directing the muscles to make the necessary adjustments to maintain balance.

The semicircular canals also enable you to recognize the direction in which your body is moving when you have your eyes closed. The three canals are at right angles to each other. When the head or body moves up or down, forward or backward, or from side to side, the fluid in the canals moves, affecting the delicate hairs in the crista. Again, the nerve endings are stimulated, sending an impulse to the brain.

The movement of your head affects the hairs in the crista in the ear to help you maintain balance.

SENSORINEURAL DEAFNESS

Very loud noises that leave your ears ringing can cause permanent damage through accumulative hearing loss. It is usually not noticeable until one reaches the age of 40 or 50.

Sensorineural deafness is hearing loss caused by excessive noise over a long time. Such noise affects the sensitive sensory hair cells in the inner ear. Unfortunately, this type of deafness cannot be corrected. Its cause is all around us—noise. Constant exposure to 90 decibels or above can cause permanent damage to hearing. This type of deafness is gradual. At first, only the high-frequency sounds are lost. Gradually, the nerve cells that transmit lower tones become damaged, and a person cannot hear voices. Whether the sound is rock music or a motorcycle's engine, the damage is caused by the volume of the sound, not the quality.

The prevention of sensory deafness is simple. The first step is to turn down the volume on the stereo, television, radio, or electric guitar to below 65 decibels. (Ordinary conversation is about 60 decibels.) If you work with an object that causes noise of 85 decibels or more—such as a lawn mower, a motorcycle, a vacuum cleaner, factory machinery, trucks, or planes—wear hearing protection.

DID YOU KNOW?

- Rhulin Thomas could not hear when he flew alone across the United States.
- Bonnie Sloan could not hear when she became a psychiatrist.
- Ron Smith could not hear when he bowled a perfect game of 300.
- Walter Wettschreck could not hear when he became Captain of a Civil Air Patrol Squadron.
- Albert Berg could not hear when he coached football at Purdue University.
- Robert Mather could not hear when he passed the bar exam.

EARS **329**

L1 DEMONSTRATION. Have a school nurse demonstrate the audiometer for the class. Ask students to discuss hearing devices that are available for the hearing impaired.

L1 COOPERATIVE LEARNING. Pair students for this experiment, but have only one pair perform it at a time. Have one student stand in one place and close his or her eyes so he or she is unable to tell where his or her partner is in the room. Have the first student hold a hand tightly over one ear. The partner should make noises on different sides of the student, in front, back, above, and below head level. Ask if the student can tell from which direction the sound is coming. (Probably not.) Repeat the experiment again while listening with both ears. Have the students switch positions.

LEP DEMONSTRATION. Use an anatomical model of the ear to explain the path of sound to the brain where the message is interpreted. Ask students to form groups of five and make a collage of external factors that affect hearing.

L1 CLASS ACITVITY. Bring a level to class. Point out how the level is used to determine the horizontal angle of a surface. Have students use the level on different objects to see if each one is balanced. Explain how the small bulb, which is partially filled with water, works. (The slightest change causes the bubble to shift.) Demonstrate to the class the similarities of the level to the ear in maintaining balance. Explain with charts or drawings how the liquid in the semicircular canals constantly shifts to compensate for movement.

Meeting Special Needs

The Hearing Impaired. The following are communication tips for communicating with the hearing impaired: Don't assume a hearing aid corrects a hearing loss; get the attention of the deaf person before you begin speaking; face the deaf person and maintain eye contact; stand close to the deaf person; make sure the deaf person can clearly see your mouth and face; stand in a well-lighted place; speak and enunciate clearly and don't exaggerate your lip movements; use your voice but don't shout; use facial expressions and body language to make the message clear; be sensitive as to whether the deaf person understands or is just being polite; write technical or difficult vocabulary on the chalkboard.

L2 PARENTAL INVOLVEMENT.
Ask students to develop case histories of any family members who have had hearing problems. Did anyone wear a hearing aid? Identify any sources of noise pollution in your home. Ask family members to list ways they can reduce noise pollution in the home.

L2 RESEARCH. Have each student watch five television commercials. What impact does the auditory part of the commercial have in selling the product? Is what is seen more or less important in the commercial than what is heard?

L3 RESEARCH. Ask students to research and report on one of the following: Francisco Goya, Ludwig van Beethoven, Thomas Alva Edison, Alexander Graham Bell, or Lou Ferrigno.

L3 RESEARCH. Have students research advances in modern recording technology for the deaf. What is the TDD? (Telecommunications Devices for the Deaf.)

L2 PERSONAL INVOLVEMENT.
Have students keep an inventory of loud sounds they hear outside the classroom. Which are potentially detrimental to hearing? What can be done to reduce this problem?

L1 USING THE LESSON RESOURCES. For additional student activities, refer to the lesson resources on page 326.

DID YOU KNOW?

■ About 10 million Americans are regularly exposed at work to noises loud enough to cause permanent hearing damage.
■ Some cities are now issuing anti-noise citations to enforce anti-noise ordinances meant to curb deafening noises that may affect the public.

A closed-caption decoder box helps the hearing impaired enjoy television.

CONFLICT RESOLUTION

Robert's been hearing impaired since birth. For as long as he can remember, he has suffered discrimination from many hearing people who don't know him. Because his speech is distinctive, since he's never heard spoken language clearly, others have difficulty understanding him. Some people think he is "dumb" in addition to being deaf. Ironically, Robert's IQ is above average, and he gets straight A's in school.

Research the achievements of some famous deaf people. Prepare a poster that would educate hearing people about the capabilities of hearing-impaired persons.

Problems of the Ear

Deafness is defined as the loss of the ability to hear, which may be partial or complete. When a hearing problem is associated with the outer or middle ear, it is called conduction deafness. Conduction deafness means that sound waves are prevented from reaching the eardrum or that sound waves are not being transmitted to the cochlea. A buildup of wax or some other form of blockage can prevent sound waves from reaching the eardrum. Middle ear infections or diseases involving the ossicles can result in this type of deafness.

Otosclerosis is a hereditary disease that is a common cause of partial deafness. Otosclerosis occurs when an overgrowth of bone causes the ossicles to lose their ability to move. Thus, sound waves never reach the inner ear. Otosclerosis is usually progressive, meaning that its severity increases with time. Surgical procedures can help people with otosclerosis to regain their hearing.

When hearing loss is associated with the inner ear, this is called sensorineural deafness or nerve deafness. There is damage to the cochlea, auditory nerve, or part of the brain. Nerve deafness can result from continued exposure to high-intensity noise and from tumors.

KEEPING FIT

Communicating With Someone Who Is Hearing Impaired

Follow these guidelines when you are communicating with someone who is hearing impaired:
■ Face the person and speak clearly.
■ Speak loudly, but do not shout.

■ Speak more slowly.
■ Don't overly exaggerate your lip movements or facial gestures.
■ Don't cover your mouth when you speak.
■ Don't chew food or gum.

■ Avoid talking from another room or over avoidable background noise, such as running water.
■ Don't expect everyone who is hearing impaired to read lips.

Additional Information

Effects of Noise. Several studies have been done on the effect of noise on our health. Scientists agree that noise causes stress and can raise blood pressure. A study by Dr. Ernest A. Peterson and colleagues at the University of Miami School of Medicine showed that monkeys developed sustained high blood pressure after being exposed for 9 months to patterns and levels of noise that are frequently encountered by people. The noise levels used in the study were below those that can damage hearing.

Studies at the University of Oregon showed that children who attended school along a flight path of Los Angeles International Airport had higher blood pressure than children attending schools in quiet areas.

Some medicines can damage the hair cells in the cochlea or the auditory nerve, causing a hearing loss. Certain medicines taken by a female during pregnancy can prevent the normal development of the baby's cochlea.

Have you ever experienced a ringing noise in your ears? This common condition is called **tinnitus,** and it can be irritating. Tinnitus can be caused by several conditions, including a buildup of ear wax, fluid in the middle ear, a change in pressure in the inner ear, or an ear infection. Tinnitus itself is not an ear disease. It is usually a symptom of some other problem. Once that problem is identified and corrected, the tinnitus may go away.

Care of the Ears

The ears are a delicate instrument that must be carefully maintained. It is important to clean them regularly and to protect them against weather, especially the cold.

Cleaning the outer ears should always be done with a cotton swab. Use the soft head of the swab to take out dirt and ear wax, but do not push the swab into the ear. Never use pencils or other sharp items to clean ears.

Sometimes, because of vibrations or a buildup of ear wax, the inside of the ear may feel ticklish. When this happens, gently use your thumb to wiggle the outer ear passage. Do not use swabs or sharp items to stop the tickling.

Cold weather, drafts, and sudden changes of temperature can prepare the way for ear infections. These infections can be very painful. Use ear muffs or a hat that covers the ears in the cold weather to prevent infection in the inner ear and frostbite of the earlobes. If there are bad drafts, you may want to put a piece of cotton in the outer ear passage to stop wind from entering the inner ear.

Protecting your ears from loud noise will protect your hearing.

LESSON 3 REVIEW

Reviewing Facts and Vocabulary

1. What is the function of the auditory canal?
2. How is the ear protected from foreign substances?
3. Describe what makes up the labyrinth of the ear.
4. How should the ears be cleaned?

Thinking Critically

5. **Analysis.** What is the relationship between your sense of hearing and your sense of balance?

6. **Synthesis.** Summarize the kinds of things that one can do to prevent ear problems.

Applying Health Knowledge

7. Make a diagram showing the path of a sound wave from the outside environment to its interpretation in the brain.

EARS **331**

Answers to Lesson 3 Review

1. It allows sound waves to reach the eardrum.
2. Wax and tiny hairs keep out foreign substances.
3. It consists of three delicate parts: vestibule, semicircular canals, cochlea.
4. Clean outer ears with cotton swab.
5. The semicircular canals in the ears pro- vide much of the brain's information about balance.
6. Protect ears from excessive noise; keep ears clean; do not push swabs, pencils, or other sharp objects in the ears; pro- tect ears from cold weather.
7. Diagrams should reflect the path as described on page 328.

Helping Students Improve Their Health

Using the Self-Inventory

Reinforcing Vocabulary

- **Periodically.** Occurring or recurring at regular intervals.
- **Goggles.** Protective eyewear.
- **Ultraviolet rays.** Harmful rays of light that the sun produces.
- **Decibels.** A unit of measurement for sound.

Teaching Strategies

L1 **EXPLANATION.** Question 20 may be misinterpreted by parents and students. It is never appropriate to hit anyone in any location of the body. This question may require further clarification.

L1 **DISCUSSION.** Have students discuss how good personal health practices are formulated. Is it possible to change bad habits of a lifetime into good personal health habits? Have students design a personal health plan for improvement.

L2 **DISCUSSION.** Have students debate the pros and cons, from a health standpoint, of attending a loud rock concert. What can students do to protect their ears when attending such a concert?

L2 **DISCUSSION.** Have students discuss the special care necessary to take care of wearing braces on one's teeth. Invite an orthodontist to speak on special health-care issues that are specific to wearing braces.

L1 **CLASS ACTIVITY.** Have students role-play a personal health dilemma. Have one student confront a friend about a personal hygiene problem, such as not brushing one's teeth. How should this friend handle this situation?

DID YOU KNOW?

- Experts estimate that some 28 million Americans now suffer from significant hearing problems—10 million due to excessive noise.

Self-Inventory

Your Personal Health

HOW DO YOU RATE?

Number a sheet of paper from 1 through 20. Read each item below, and respond by writing *MT* if the statement describes you all or most of the time, *ST* if the statement describes you some of the time, and *N* if the statement seldom or never applies to you. Total the number of each type of response. Then proceed to the next section.

1. I brush my teeth every day.
2. I brush my teeth more than once a day.
3. I use a soft toothbrush.
4. I brush my tongue when I brush my teeth.
5. I floss my teeth.
6. I floss my teeth every day.
7. I have regular dental check-ups.
8. I am careful not to bump someone who is drinking from a water fountain.
9. I avoid reading in poorly lighted areas.
10. When reading or studying for long periods of time, I rest my eyes periodically by looking at a distant object.
11. I use safety glasses or goggles when involved in activities or sports that could cause an eye injury.
12. I avoid rubbing my eyes.
13. When in bright outdoor light, I wear sunglasses that filter ultraviolet rays.
14. I have my eyes checked by a professional on a regular basis.
15. I wear glasses or contacts when prescribed for me.

16. I clean my ears every day.
17. I protect my ears in very cold temperatures.
18. I avoid extremely loud noise (85 decibels or more).
19. I wear ear protection when I know I will be around loud noises.
20. I am careful to never hit someone in the ears.

HOW DID YOU SCORE?

Give yourself 2 points for each statement that describes you *all* or *most of the time*, 1 point for each statement that describes you *some of the time*, and 0 points for each *seldom* or *never* response. Find your total, and read below to see how you scored. Then proceed to the next section.

36 to 40
Excellent. You are practicing excellent habits.

31 to 35
Good. Although your personal health habits are good, you could improve in some areas.

25 to 30
Fair. Be careful. Your personal habits may be putting some aspects of your total health in danger.

Below 25
Look out! You are not taking a very responsible approach to your own health. More importantly, you may be taking unnecessary health risks.

WHAT ARE YOUR GOALS?

If you received an *excellent* or *good* score, complete the statements in Part A. If your score

was rated *fair* or *look out*, complete Parts A and B.

Part A

1. I plan to learn more about personal health habits for my teeth, eyes, and ears by ____.
2. My timetable for accomplishing this is ____.
3. I plan to share my information with others by ____.

Part B

4. The behavior or attitude toward the health of my teeth, eyes, and ears I would most like to change is ____.
5. The steps involved in making this change are ____.
6. My rewards for making this change will be ____.

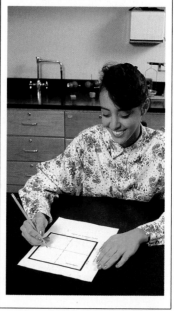

Meeting Students' Needs

For students who score *Excellent*. Show students a correlation between good health practices and the positive things that result, such as lower health insurance premiums and a more attractive appearance.

For students who score *Good* or *Fair*. Suggest that students attend a health fair in which they will have various aspects of their personal health evaluated and sug-

gestions given on ways to improve their health.

For students who need to *Look Out!* Show students the results from lacking good personal health practices. Demonstrate to students that one may change poor health habits with determination and a commitment to good health. Have them establish several behavior-change goals.

Building Decision-Making Skills

Building Decision-Making Skills

C asey, the class clown, is a great guy with good looks, a super sense of humor, and a very pleasant personality. Unfortunately he also has poor personal health habits that lead to bad breath. He wrote Colleen a clever note asking her out. Colleen likes Casey, but not his breath. She has asked you, a mutual friend, for advice on how to handle the situation. What should Colleen do? Her choices might include:

A. Write a clever note saying she'd love to go, but only if he used toothpaste.

B. Agree to go, but let you or another friend, counselor, or coach talk to him about oral health care.

C. Make up an excuse for not going.

D. Say she is sorry she can't go and honestly explain why.

E. Go with him but wait until she gets to know him better before telling him that his breath is a real turnoff.

WHAT DO YOU THINK?

1. **Choices.** What other options does Colleen have?

2. **Consequences.** What are the pros and cons of each choice?

3. **Consequences.** If Colleen decides to tell Casey he needs to improve his oral health, how may his self-esteem be affected?

4. **Consequences.** If Colleen decides to talk to Casey about this problem, how could she go about it in a caring, thoughtful way?

5. **Decision.** What choice would you recommend to Colleen? Why?

6. **Evaluation.** Have you ever found yourself torn between telling someone something that might be embarrassing or hurtful, but that is offensive to others? Describe the situation, how you handled it, and what you learned from it.

C harmaine is a smart, personable teen and one of Tricia's best friends. Charmaine has long, wavy hair, great eyes, and a clear complexion. She is popular with her classmates, many of whom think she is beautiful. But Charmaine is very self-conscious about her crooked teeth. She would like to have braces, but the cost is quite high. Tricia is finding it harder and harder to be with Charmaine because she keeps calling herself ugly. She's also started refusing to go out with Tricia and her other friends because, although it's untrue, she's convinced that everyone is staring at her crooked teeth. What should Tricia do? Some of her choices might include:

A. Stop including Charmaine in activities until she stops putting herself down.

B. Explain to Charmaine that no one is perfect. Since she has so many other great qualities, she should stop complaining about one little imperfection.

C. Try to support Charmaine by listing her other positive qualities that have nothing to do with physical appearance.

D. Suggest that Charmaine talk with a school counselor who can help her see that looks aren't the only thing in life that's important.

WHAT DO YOU THINK?

7. **Situation.** Why does a decision need to be made?

8. **Choices.** What other choices does Tricia have?

9. **Consequences.** What are the positive and negative aspects of each choice?

10. **Decision.** Which choice do you think is best for Tricia? Explain your answer.

11. **Evaluation.** In our beauty-conscious society, how much do people pay attention to artificial beauty? Name ways people do this. How would you handle a situation in which someone shows favor to another person because he or she is attractive?

Teaching Strategies

L1 CLASS ACTIVITY. Have the class divide into groups of four. Have students brainstorm ways in which Colleen could talk to Casey about his bad breath.

L1 CLASS ACTIVITY. Have students role-play Colleen's situation. Discuss the consequences of each way of addressing Casey's problem of bad breath.

L1 DISCUSSION. How might Casey respond to being informed that his breath puts people off? Have students determine the manner in which they would choose to have someone talk to them if it were they who had the bad breath.

L1 CLASS ACTIVITY. Have students role-play the part of Tricia as she talks to Charmaine about Charmaine's crooked teeth.

L1 CLASS ACTIVITY. Another possible role-play situation includes: Your friend needs to wear glasses, but is too self-conscious when wearing them. Recently, your friend's grades have dropped because of not being able to see. To make matters worse, your friend is driving her younger brothers and sisters to school without her glasses. You fear that someone may get seriously injured. You know that you should do something, but what?

L2 DISCUSSION. Have students debate the pros and cons of temporary attractiveness, such as tanning booths, use of steroids, and the eating disorder, bulimia, against long-term health risks. Why do some students choose to take such risks?

L1 CLASS ACTIVITY. Have students present demonstrations on the proper care of teeth, eyes, and ears to a local elementary school. Have students develop short skits that will teach younger students the value of good personal health.

Discussing the Answers

Situation 1. We do not know whether Casey may have a health problem or poor hygiene. Nor do we know whether or not Casey is aware of the problem. Perhaps Colleen could ask the school nurse to speak to Casey about his bad breath.

Situation 2. In this day and age, one does have the capability to change some things and if someone would feel better about him- or herself, one might as well make the change if there are no negative health repercussions. Perhaps the best resolve would be for Tricia to suggest that Charmaine save her money to have her teeth straightened. Perhaps Charmaine could share the cost with her parents. Regardless, Tricia should support her friend.

Answers to Chapter 1 Review

Using Health Terms

1. Enamel
2. Tartar or calculus
3. Halitosis
4. Periodontium
5. Abscessed
6. Pulp
7. Plaque
8. Lacrimal gland
9. Cornea
10. Visual purple
11. Blind spot
12. Dilation
13. Astigmatism
14. Binaural hearing
15. Otosclerosis
16. Ossicles
17. Labyrinth
18. Tinnitus

Building Academic Skills

19. Answers will vary.

Recalling the Facts

20. The pulp becomes inflamed but can't expand within the inflexible walls of the tooth.
21. With preventive oral health care and regular visits to the dentist.
22. By treating the underlying cause, such as tooth decay or infections.
23. They allow one to chew food and form the shape and structure of the mouth.
24. Gums, periodontal ligament, jawbone. They support the teeth.
25. It is the result of the destructive action of bacteria in one's mouth.
26. Floss and brush daily, reduce intake of sugary foods, regular dental checkups.
27. Occipital lobe.
28. See "Eye Problems" on pages 324-325.
29. Lacrimal glands—produce tears; eyebrows—protect the eyes from foreign particles, perspiration, and direct rays of light; eyelids—protect by covering eyes; eyelashes—keep out foreign particles; conjunctiva—protective mucous membrane.
30. That person can stand 20 feet away from the eye chart and

334 CHAPTER 16 PERSONAL HEALTH

REVIEW

Using Health Terms

On a separate sheet of paper, write the term that best matches each definition given below.

LESSON 1

1. The second hardest naturally occurring substance in nature.
2. Hard substance that builds on plaque.
3. Bad breath.
4. The area immediately around the teeth.
5. Swollen and inflamed with pus gathering.
6. Living tissue inside the tooth.
7. Sticky, colorless film that forms on teeth and promotes tooth decay.

LESSON 2

8. Responsible for producing tears.
9. The window of the eye.
10. Photosensitive chemical in rods that enables one to see in dim light.
11. The point where the optic nerve enters the eye.
12. The process in which the pupil of the eye gets larger.
13. A condition in which the eye lens has an uneven curvature.

LESSON 3

14. The ability to determine the direction a sound comes from.
15. A hereditary disease in which an overgrowth of bone causes the ossicles to lose their ability to move.
16. Three small bones that connect the eardrum with the inner ear.
17. The inner ear.
18. Ringing in the ear.

Building Academic Skills

LESSON 1

19. **Writing.** Write a set of directions for third graders describing the best procedures to use when brushing and flossing one's teeth. Make sure your steps are in logical order.

Recalling the Facts

LESSON 1

20. What is the actual physical cause for the pain of a toothache?
21. How can periodontal disease be stopped in its early stages?
22. How can halitosis be cured?
23. What functions do teeth serve?
24. What are the parts of the periodontium and what function do they serve together?
25. What causes periodontal disease?
26. What is good oral hygiene?

LESSON 2

27. What part of the brain is responsible for vision?
28. Name and describe three vision problems that can be corrected.
29. Name and tell the function of the general area around the eyes.
30. What does it mean when someone has 20/20 vision?
31. Why is contraction and dilation of the pupil important?
32. What is the white part of one's eye called and what does it do?
33. Name three things that you can do to protect your eyes.
34. What is behind the pupil and what function does that part serve?
35. What in the retina enables people to see color?
36. How does the lens change and for what purpose does it change?

LESSON 3

37. What is the significance of the semicircular canals?
38. What is binaural hearing?
39. What are some objects that create noises louder than 65 decibels?
40. What is the oval window and what is its significance?
41. What role does the temporal lobe play in the hearing process?
42. What might contribute to ear infections?

read the top 8 lines.
31. This action controls the amount of light that enters the eyes.
32. The sclera. It helps the eye keep its spherical shape and protects the eye's delicate inner structure.
33. Answers will vary. Accept three of the suggestions on page 325.
34. The lens—forms an image

on the retina of what is before it.
35. Cones.
36. It bulges to accommodate near objects and flattens to accommodate distant objects.
37. They are responsible for one's sense of balance.
38. The ability to determine from which direction a sound comes.

39. Answers may include but are not limited to: stereos, televisions, radios, electric guitars, lawn mowers, motorcycles, vacuum cleaners, factory machinery, trucks, jets.
40. It is a membrane between the middle and inner ear. The stapes move like a plunger in and out of the oval window, caus-

REVIEW

Thinking Critically

LESSON 1

43. Synthesis. What problems might occur if a person lost all his or her teeth? How might this affect this person's life and/or attitude?

44. Analysis. Compare gingivitis and periodontitis.

45. Synthesis. Conduct a survey of how many people in your class wear braces. What might these numbers indicate?

LESSON 2

46. Analysis. What activities would require protective eyewear? What rule could you give for when to wear protective eyewear?

47. Evaluation. Some people overcompensate when they encounter someone with a disability. For example, they may talk louder than normal when speaking to someone who is visually impaired. Why do you suppose people do this? Is it necessary? Support your answer.

LESSON 3

48. Synthesis. Why do you suppose the inner ear is also known as the labyrinth?

Making the Connection

LESSON 2

49. Home Economics. Research different prices for eyewear. Identify factors that are responsible for price differences.

LESSON 3

50. Science. Measure the decibels of sound at a school dance, athletic event, in the cafeteria, or in the parking lot. Compare readings to safety levels. This is also a good way to measure which class can yell the loudest at pep rallies.

51. Language Arts. Watch five television commercials. What impact does the auditory part have in selling the product? Is what is seen more or less important in these commercials than what is heard?

Applying Health Knowledge

LESSON 1

52. If your best friend had halitosis, how might you tell him or her?

53. Talk to a person who wears orthodontic braces. Find out how the braces have affected that person's life. How did the person feel before the braces were put on? How does he or she feel now?

54. You may not be aware of how much high-sugar food you ingest in a day. Keep a journal of your daily food intake for one week. Evaluate it. Were the results what you expected? Is there anything in your diet that should be adjusted? Explain.

LESSON 2

55. How might a blind spot affect one's daily life in terms of transportation safety?

LESSON 3

56. An old expression you may have heard is "Never stick anything smaller than your elbow in your ear." What does this mean?

57. Find out about the outer ear ailment known as cauliflower ear. What is it? What causes it? What effect does it have on hearing?

58. Whenever you warn your friends that loud music will damage their hearing, they say it won't happen to them, but if it does they can always get hearing aids. How would you respond? Support your answer.

Beyond the Classroom

LESSON 2

59. Further Study. Research the Braille alphabet. Find out all you can about it.

LESSON 3

60. Further Study. Take a sign language class or borrow a book on signing from your local library. Practice with a friend. Perhaps you could become proficient enough to volunteer in a community center or a school for the hearing impaired.

ing fluid in the cochlea to move.

41. It is the part of the brain in which sounds are classified and interpreted.

42. Cold weather, drafts, and sudden changes of temperature.

Thinking Critically

43. Answers will vary. Possible answers: The person would need to get dentures, which would be expensive. Having dentures may cause one to modify his or her eating habits. Poorly fitting dentures would be painful and may require an investment of time to get them adjusted. Without dentures, one may have trouble getting enough variety in what he or she eats. The person may get angry or frustrated with the dentures and/or feel self-conscious.

44. Both are mouth disorders that cause bleeding gums and must be treated by a dentist. Gingivitis is an inflammation of the gums. Periodontitis also affects the gums but is more serious. Periodontitis also affects bone surrounding the teeth.

45. Answers will vary.

46. Answers will vary. Possible answers: Skiing, racquetball, chemical experiments, woodworking, welding, etc. Rule of thumb—any harsh light, hazardous fumes, or flying objects dictate wearing protective lenses.

47. Answers will vary.

48. Answers will vary. Possible answer: A labyrinth is a maze or complex arrangement. The inner ear is a very intricate part of the body which may resemble a maze.

Making the Connection

49. Answers will vary.
50. Answers will vary.
51. Answers will vary.

Applying Health Knowledge

52. Answers will vary. Possible answer: Kindly, compassionately, and honestly tell the friend what you have noticed and suggest ways to take care of it.

53. Answers will vary.
54. Answers will vary.
55. Answers will vary. Possible

answer: One needs to be aware of his or her blind spot and look over his or her shoulder when changing lanes.

56. One should not put small objects in one's ear because the objects might go down the auditory canal or push wax down into the auditory canal and damage the middle or inner ear.

57. It is damage to the skin and cartilage of the outer ear and is usually caused by repeated blows or twisting of the ear. It does not adversely affect hearing.

58. Answers will vary. Possible answer: Inform them that constant exposure to 85 decibels or above can cause permanent damage and that it happens gradually

so they might not even notice until it is too late. Hearing aids cannot help this type of deafness.

Beyond the Classroom

59. Answers will vary.
60. Answers will vary.

Lesson Summaries

LESSON 1. In the past, fitness and exercise were a part of every-day life. With the age of labor-saving devices came a more sedentary life-style, which has had a negative impact on health. Specifically, immobility affects the circulatory, digestive, and nervous systems. To counteract these life-style induced health consequences, regular exercise is necessary. Regular exercise contributes to physical health by building a strong, durable body. It helps control body weight by burning calories while increasing the body's rate of metabolism. Exercise can also improve aspects of mental and social health.

LESSON 2. Physical fitness includes body composition, flexibility, muscle strength, muscle endurance, and heart and lung endurance. Each component of physical fitness can be measured to determine fitness in that area. The results can be used to establish an exercise program that is safe and effective.

Introducing the Chapter

Tell students that physical fitness plays an important role toward achieving and maintaining total fitness or overall health. Exercise is the primary contributor to good physical fitness. It also contributes to mental and social health. Tell them this chapter will present the benefits of exercise and ways to evaluate an individual's level of physical fitness. Types of exercise to achieve fitness for each of the components of physical fitness are discussed as well.

Performance Assessment ✓

Refer to pages T 23 to T 25 for a Performance Assessment strategy for this chapter. See the *Performance Assessment Activities* booklet for additional suggestions.

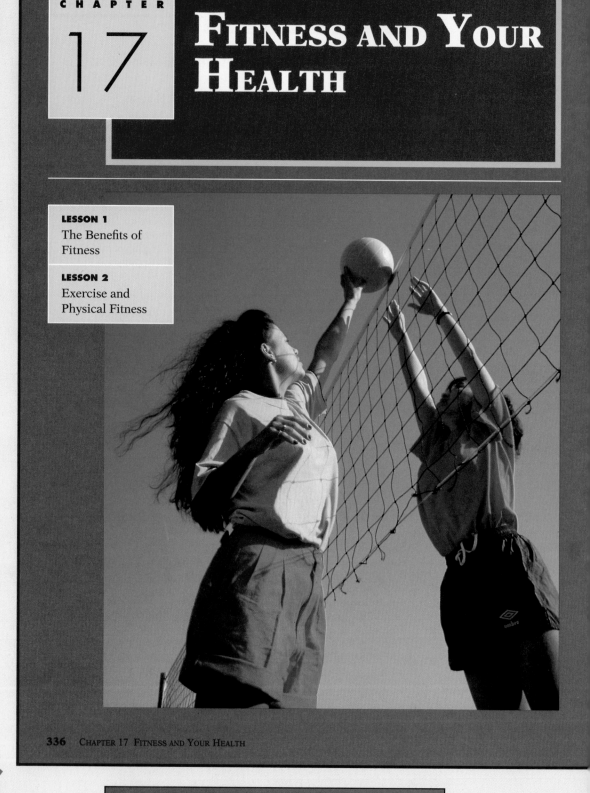

CHAPTER 17 FITNESS AND YOUR HEALTH

LESSON 1
The Benefits of Fitness

LESSON 2
Exercise and Physical Fitness

336   CHAPTER 17 FITNESS AND YOUR HEALTH

Key to Ability Levels

Teaching strategies have been coded for varying learning styles and abilities.

L1 Level 1 activities are basic activities and should be within the ability range of all students.

L2 Level 2 activities are average activities and should be within the ability range of average to above-average students.

L3 Level 3 activities are challenging activities designed for the ability range of above-average students.

LD LD activities should be within the ability range of learning-disabled students.

LEP LEP activities should be within the ability range of Limited English Proficiency students.

THE BENEFITS OF FITNESS

The word *health* is often associated only with physical fitness, though you know there are other components of health. **Fitness** means "readiness." Fit people are better equipped than nonfit people to handle day-to-day situations.

Your level of fitness includes all aspects of your health and life. It affects your physical, mental, and social health. Your level of fitness affects how you sleep, eat, and learn. If you are fit, you look good, you have energy, and you generally feel good about yourself. Maintaining a high level of fitness is a lifelong challenge.

Fitness in the Past

During the period of growth and frontier settlement in the United States, most people were very active. Fitness and exercise were a part of everyday life. In fact, being fit was necessary for survival. Because people had so much activity during their workday, they looked for ways to make their lives easier.

Soon came the age of labor-saving devices—inventions that ranged from automobiles and dishwashers to electric shavers and hair dryers. Thousands of mechanical and electronic inventions made life so easy for many Americans that they adopted sedentary life-styles. Sedentary living is inactive living, a way of life that is devoid of daily physical activity beyond that required for attending school or going to work.

Medical researchers and scientists have found that a sedentary way of life is not good for one's health. In fact, some consider it to be a health hazard. Muscle strength is lost as a result of an inactive life-style. It has become evident that the lack of regular activity contributes to the risk of cardiovascular diseases.

In addition, immobility negatively affects the respiratory, digestive, and nervous systems. These findings, along with the abundance of new information about disease prevention, have begun to change our attitudes toward fitness.

Fitness Today

The United States experienced a fitness boom during the 1970s that is still growing today. Walking and jogging trails and bicycle paths have been developed in neighborhoods all over the country. At almost any time of day, you can see people of all ages exercising. In fact, millions of Americans make exercise a part of their regular schedule.

Aerobic exercise, dance classes, and weight-training programs have become very popular. More and more people are participating in lifetime sports, such as tennis, swimming, softball, race walking, or jogging. These sports are ones that can be enjoyed and participated in throughout life.

LESSON 1 FOCUS

TERMS TO USE
- Fitness
- Basal metabolism

CONCEPTS TO LEARN
- Exercise improves your physical health.
- Exercise contributes to your social and mental health.

ATTITUDES AND BEHAVIORS TO EVALUATE
- Self-Inventory, page 348.
- Building Decision-Making Skills, page 349.

It's important to plan time for exercise.

THE BENEFITS OF FITNESS **337**

Focus

Lesson Objectives
After studying this lesson, students should be able to:
- explain how the invention of labor-saving devices has contributed to a sedentary way of life
- identify ways to build more physical activity into their daily routine
- describe ways in which exercise affects the body's circulatory, digestive, and nervous systems
- explain some of the benefits of exercise to their mental and social health

Bellringer
Write the following on the chalkboard for students to work on while attendance is being taken: *Write your own definitions of fitness, exercise, and metabolism. Be prepared to discuss your definitions.*

Introducing the Lesson
Have students share their responses to the Bellringer. Ask them to list the benefits of exercise. Point out that exercise is a major factor in total fitness, and that this lesson will focus on the role that exercise plays in physical, mental, and social health.

Building Vocabulary
- Have students use the terms *fit* or *fitness* and *basal metabolism* in a paragraph. Ask them to read their paragraphs to the class.
- Ask students to complete *Workbook Vocabulary Activity 45.*

Resources for Lesson 1

- **Guided Reading** Act 45
- **Workbook** Voc Act 45
- **Reteaching** Activity 45
- **Lesson 1 Quiz**
- **BARN Software,** Body Management
- **Posters** 5 and 6
- **Performance Assessment** Activity 17

Science and Technology Videodisc
Human Biology, Side 1
Ch 12 Heart Rehabilitation

Human Biology, Side 2
Ch 11 Obesity and Heredity

Guided Practice

L1 EXPLANATION. Stress the fact that being a "couch potato" can be hazardous to one's health. Excessive TV viewing and a reliance on too many labor-saving devices can lead to a sedentary, rather than a healthy, life-style.

L1 DISCUSSION. Ask students to list their physical activities during the past week. Talk about the benefits of such activities. Ask them if they think they are getting enough exercise. Request that they try to agree on a single definition of enough exercise. Afterwards, discuss the reasons that prevented them from reaching a consensus. (Many factors are involved, such as age, weight, general health, family history, etc.)

L1 SPEAKER. Invite an aerobic dance instructor to demonstrate dance movements and speak to the students about his or her classes. Ask him or her to lead the class in some exercise routines.

L1 CLASS ACTIVITY. Collect brochures, flyers, and other information about school and community exercise programs. Ask for volunteers to make a display of the materials and to discuss some of the information contained in them.

L1 CLASS ACTIVITY. Have students brainstorm ways they can add more physical activity to their daily lives. Next, ask students to choose at least one suggestion they would be willing to implement in their daily routines. Have them keep a simple log of times they chose to increase their physical activity by following the suggestions. In a later class, ask students to discuss the experience and ways to continue to increase physical activity throughout each day.

DID YOU KNOW?

- In an ongoing study of 57,000 people, it has been shown that regular exercise reduces the risks of both colon cancer and cardiovascular disease.
- People who do not exercise are twice as likely to develop cardiovascular disease as people who exercise.
- One study showed that men who exercise regularly live an average of 2 years longer than men who do not.

As you use many labor-saving devices, exercise may become less a part of your routine. For this reason, it is important to plan times for regular exercise or leisure physical activity. In addition, you need to look for opportunities during the day that help build physical activity into your routine.

Exercise and Your Physical Health

Exercise, the primary contributor to good physical fitness, also contributes to mental and social health. Exercise improves the physical part of your health by building a strong body. Exercise can also help reduce the feeling of chronic fatigue, stiffness, and lack of coordination. It can help improve the sense organ functions and motor responses. Sense organ functions refers to your ability to use your senses to their optimal levels.

EXERCISING THROUGHOUT THE DAY

Think about your activity during the day. Whenever possible do you

- stand rather than sit,
- sit up rather than lie down,
- walk rather than ride in a car,
- ride a bike rather than ride in a car,
- use stairs rather than an elevator or an escalator,
- walk around (pace) rather than stand still,
- run or jog rather than walk,
- walk briskly rather than walk slowly,
- use body power rather than a machine?

These behaviors sound simple, but they all add up to an increase in physical activity. Be aware of times throughout your day when you could choose a more active routine.

Exercise for Your Nervous System

Exercise contributes to the functioning of your nervous system by tuning it to a high level, allowing for more skillful body movements. Exercise can improve your reaction time by helping you respond more quickly to stimuli. Your overall mental performance improves too.

KEEPING FIT

Fifteen Great Reasons to Work Out

A regular exercise regimen can bring many benefits to many areas of your life. These include:
- improved cardiovascular health
- better weight control
- improved metabolism
- improved breathing capacity

- improved flexibility
- improved endurance
- improved strength
- improved appearance
- improved self-esteem
- a chance to socialize

- increased mental alertness
- increased ability to handle stress
- less fatigue and more energy
- improved sleep
- a more positive attitude

338 CHAPTER 17 FITNESS AND YOUR HEALTH

Across the Curriculum

Home Economics. Labor-saving inventions can be found in almost every home. Although they are promoted as saving time and energy, they also contribute to a sedentary way of living. Have students inventory their homes, making lists of these devices. Have them list them in four columns: used every day, used frequently, seldom used, never used. With their par- ents' assistance, ask them to write a note beside each item in the "seldom used" and "never used" column, explaining why the item was purchased (or if it was received as a gift) and why it is seldom or never used. Afterwards, ask students to find the current price of each of the seldom- or never-used items.

Overcoming The Odds

Pratima Chaterjee is 17. "Tima," as she is called by her friends, likes to hike and play piano. She has been studying ballet for eight years. Her dream is to dance with a major ballet company. She commutes to the city on weekends to participate in workshops and a performing arts program. With all that she has to do, she sometimes feels very pressured. That's why she says that balance—not just on her toes but in her life—is so important.

Tima says, "This is a very busy time in my life. I work out at the barre every day, and I take dance classes. At school I take Advanced Placement courses. I also have a strong family with lots of time commitments. Sometimes, I feel overwhelmed. That's why I guess I'm grateful for the many perspectives of my grandparents. Because of them I can see different life-styles and pick and choose what will work for me.

"Sometimes it feels as if there's a culture collision in my own living room," she says, laughing. "My American grandmother belongs to a fitness club and a race-walking group. I admire that. She has a great sense of humor, too. However, she eats a lot of

high-fat foods. My grandmother from India doesn't exercise at all, but she is a vegetarian, which I admire. I tried the no meat, no eggs, no milk route, but I got weak. I need a lot of good food for the kind of

dance training that I do, so now I eat chicken and fish in moderation. My Scottish grandfather has tons of hobbies and knows how to have fun. I'd like to be like that when I'm older; I'd even like to be more like that now. My other grandfather always talks to me about the importance of balance and keeping things in perspective. I try to follow his advice and example, too."

Tima continues, "I don't want to wake up when I'm 40

and realize I have to do radical things all of a sudden just to stay alive because I've abused myself along the way. I want to dance well, but I don't want to starve. I want to be in top shape, but I don't want to ruin my body in the process. I've had too many friends with stress fractures, eating disorders, wrecked knees, and worse—and all in the name of being fit. I want to be a choreographer when I'm older, so I've got to take steps now to make sure my body will work well and work gracefully for a long, long time. I keep hearing my grandfather's words about keeping it all in balance, and I try."

1. Pratima has many examples of different life-styles in her own family. What are the pluses and minuses of having such a variety of life-style models?

2. What are the many kinds of life-styles represented in your extended family? Which do you think are healthiest? Are these the ones you try to follow? Why or why not?

3. Do you ever feel burned out? What do you think causes you to feel this way? What steps can you take to get your life in better balance?

■ **Discussion.** What does Tima see as the positive aspects of the life-style of each of her grandparents? (Positive aspects of life-style of Tima's American grandmother include a commitment to exercise and a sense of humor; of her Indian grandmother, a healthful diet; of her Scottish grandfather, a commitment to stimulating activities; and of her Indian grandfather, a sense of balance and perspective in life.)

■ **Discussion.** Which aspects of Tima's life-style are healthful? Which aspects are not? (Most aspects of Tima's life-style are healthful—she pays attention to her diet, gets lots of exercise, and is very busy and involved with life. However, her commitment to dance, school, and family is also very time-consuming, so her life is relatively stressful.)

■ **Answers**
1. Pluses include a richly textured life and lots of alternatives; minuses include conflicting beliefs and customs.
2. Answers will vary. Are their reasons for not following healthy practices valid?
3. Students must list their priorities and cut down on low-priority time commitments.

LEP **CLASS ACTIVITY.** Have students find cartoons and comic strips about fitness, exercise, and weight control. Choose some of the examples to use in a discussion of these concepts.

L1 **EXPLANATION.** Emphasize that the rate of basal metabolism depends on such factors as age, sex (with males slightly higher than females), weight, body fat, amount of sleep (about 10 percent lower during sleep), and surrounding temperature.

L2 **CLASS ACTIVITY.** Ask for volunteers to create a bulletin board titled "You Can't Be the Picture of Health if You Don't Have All of the Pieces!" Label large jigsaw puzzle pieces with the key concepts from this lesson. Discuss what happens if a piece is missing.

Meeting Special Needs

The Physically and Mentally Challenged. Many individuals who are physically or mentally challenged participate in and enjoy physical activities. Have students research Special Olympics. Ask for volunteers to interview young people who participate in Special Olympics and people who volunteer their assistance dur-

ing the events. Also, ask students to find articles in newspapers and magazines about athletic accomplishments of individuals who are physically challenged. Survey the community for such individuals, and ask if they would be willing to be interviewed by one or two students.

L1 PARENTAL INVOLVEMENT. Have students ask their parents about the kinds of exercise they and the students' grandparents were involved in when they were younger. Ask the parents to discuss how physical activity in the grandparents' early adult years differed from today's sedentary life-style. How have the parents' and grandparents' activity levels changed throughout the years?

L1 PARENTAL INVOLVEMENT. Ask for volunteers to enlist their parents in a joint exercise program. Have students write short reports of their progress to turn in each week.

L2 COMMUNITY INVOLVE-MENT. Select students to interview community members about the kinds of physical exercise activities available to teens and their family members. Have students find out about location, fees, equipment needed, date and time of activity, etc. Ask them to share their information (including any brochures or flyers) with the class.

L3 RESEARCH. Assign students to design and administer a campus survey of students' total fitness. Have them include in the survey questions about sedentary versus active life-styles, types and amounts of exercise students and their families participate in, whether they prefer (and choose) group or solo exercising, attitudes toward exercise and fitness, benefits they have experienced from exercise, etc. Stress that students' responses will be anonymous. Afterwards, ask students to tally the results and present their findings to the class.

L1 SELF-ESTEEM. Establish a contract with each student, stating specific fitness goals to achieve by the end of the course. Determine what level of performance will be acceptable for that portion of the student's grade, and discuss this in advance with each student. Discuss how achieving a fitness goal might affect a person's self-esteem.

L1 USING THE LESSON RESOURCES For additional student activities, refer to the lesson resources on page 337.

Culturally Speaking

Association Football

Soccer, known everywhere but the U.S. as "football," is a truly international sport. A Chinese military text from the 3rd or 4th century B.C. mentions a football game, and Roman soldiers also played a variety of the game. Archaeologists have found large "ball courts" in Mexico, and there is evidence that Greece and Japan have a long football history as well. England formalized the sport, with the first competition held with Scotland in 1872. The governing body of soccer, the Federacion Internationale de Football Asociación (FIFA), today has more member countries than does the United Nations.

Exercise for Your Respiratory System

With regular exercise, your respiratory system begins to work slower and more efficiently so that you take fewer but deeper breaths. Your lung capacity, the amount of air that you can take in with a single breath, increases. Your body uses oxygen more efficiently as your fitness level improves.

Exercise for Your Cardiovascular System

Regular exercise is a great help to the heart. The heart is a muscle, and like any muscle, the more it is used, the stronger it gets. A strong heart can pump blood more efficiently than a weak one, so more work is done with less effort.

Exercise and Weight Control

One out of every three Americans is overweight. Sedentary living is as much to blame for this situation as is overeating.

Your Metabolism. The absolute minimum amount of energy required to maintain the life processes in your body is called **basal metabolism.** We get our energy from food, and the energy value of food is measured in units of heat called calories. Your body requires a minimum number of calories each day in order to maintain itself. Additional calories must be used, or they will be stored as fat.

Your metabolic rate increases during exercise—during exercise you burn up more calories than when you are at rest. The number of calories you burn depends on the nature of the activity. The benefit of physical activity remains for a short while even after you stop exercising. Your metabolic rate takes some time to return to normal, so during that time you are still burning more calories than before you began exercising.

Your Weight. Much has been written about dieting, weight reduction, obesity, and exercise. There is more information about weight control in Chapter 20. However, the following statements provide an overview.

- If you take in fewer calories than you burn, you lose weight.
- If you take in more calories than you burn, you gain weight.

If you take in more calories than you can use, the excess calories are stored in the body as fat. One pound (0.5 kg) of fat is equal to about 3,500 calories. A person must control calories to control weight.

Exercise is helpful in the prevention of becoming overfat. Overfat is an excessive amount of fat in the body. Being overfat and 20 to 30 percent above recommended weight results in obesity. Both of these conditions have been associated with heart disease and can be a problem among people in all age groups. Vigorous or moderate exercise can help reduce body fat and contribute to weight reduction.

Your Ability to Recuperate. Exercise can help the body's protection against disease by building resistance through improved fitness. A strong, toned body is capable of recuperation, or restoring itself, at a faster rate than a body that is overweight or in poor condition.

340 CHAPTER 17 FITNESS AND YOUR HEALTH

Additional Information

Weight Loss and Exercise. The expression "burning off calories" is often used, but what does it mean? The process of burning, or combustion, is one form of a reaction called oxidation. This means the uniting of oxygen with other substances. Food that is used by your body for fuel combines with oxygen. This type of oxida-tion reaction is not as rapid as burning, but it still releases energy. Your body uses this energy for body heat, for automatic processes, and for physical activities. So when you run down the basketball court, dance, go up the stairs, or pound a nail with a hammer, you really are "burning" off calories.

Exercise and Your Mental and Social Health

Some people who do sedentary work for long periods of time find that an exercise break refreshes them and leads to more productive work time. Many people have found that after a long day of school or work, exercise gives them an energy boost. They are less fatigued during the evening hours. Feeling better physically has a positive effect on mental and social health.

Mental Benefits

Exercise contributes to mental health in a number of ways:

- Being physically fit gives you a sense of pride and accomplishment for taking care of yourself.
- Getting fit and staying fit contributes to positive self-esteem because you will look better and feel better about yourself.
- Physical fitness helps you deal with strong emotions, stress, and times when you feel down.
- Exercise can be a healthy outlet for tension, anger, or frustration.
- Exercise offers a form of relaxation.

Social Benefits

Some exercise programs can benefit the social side of your health. Through participation in organized exercise activities, you have an opportunity to meet new people. Many people find that exercising with a friend or in a group makes the workout more enjoyable. Working out with someone else can also help motivate a person to continue with an exercise program.

Exercising in organized activities helps you get to know and get along with others.

Assess

Check for Understanding

- Assign and discuss the lesson review.

Evaluate

- Administer, grade, and discuss the *Lesson 1 Quiz.*

Reteach

- Have students pair up. Give each pair of students large jig-saw puzzle pieces labeled with the main concepts from the lesson. Assign them to put the pieces together and to explain and discuss each of the concepts with each other.
- Ask students to complete *Reteaching Activity 45.*

Enrich

- Ask students to design a model showing the heart and ways in which it is strengthened by physical exercise.

Close

Remove the label and top lid from five empty food cans. Write one of the following concepts on each can: *fitness, exercise, weight control, mental health,* and *social health.* Divide students into five groups, and give each group one of the cans. Give slips of paper to each student. Ask them to see how quickly they can fill their assigned can with slips of paper that review related concepts.

DID YOU KNOW?

- The Tarahumara Indian tribe of Mexico is known for its great long-distance runners. Tarahumara hunters have been known to chase deer until the animals drop from exhaustion. Sometimes, that's a 200-mile run over 2 or 3 days.

LESSON 1 REVIEW

Reviewing Facts and Vocabulary

1. How does physical fitness relate to health?
2. What are the health implications of a sedentary life-style?
3. What is basal metabolism?
4. What are three ways in which exercise contributes to your physical health?

Thinking Critically

5. **Synthesis.** Suggest ways that people who need regular exercise and are opposed to it can be encouraged to participate.

6. **Evaluation.** Discuss the accuracy of this statement: *He is overweight because he eats too much.*

Applying Health Knowledge

7. Make a list of 10 activities you do almost every day. Next to each, write a statement indicating how a higher level of fitness would help you in each of the activities. Compare your list of statements with those of other class members.

THE BENEFITS OF FITNESS **341**

Answers to Lesson 1 Review

1. It is only one aspect of health.
2. Loss of muscular strength; negatively affects cardiovascular, respiratory, digestive, and nervous systems.
3. The absolute minimum amount of energy required to maintain life processes.
4. Answers will vary. Possible answers include the following: strengthens body, reduces fatigue, improves mental performance, increases lung capacity and metabolic rate, strengthens heart, builds resistance against disease.
5. Answers will vary.
6. The statement should say that he eats too much and exercises too little.
7. Answers will vary.

Focus

Lesson Objectives

After studying this lesson, students should be able to:
- explain the basic components of physical fitness
- assess their personal level of fitness
- distinguish among isometric, isotonic, and isokinetic exercises
- explain the difference between anaerobic and aerobic exercises
- describe benefits of aerobic exercise

Bellringer

Write the following on the chalkboard for students to work on while attendance is being taken: *Physical fitness consists of five components: body composition, flexibility, muscular strength, muscular endurance, and cardiorespiratory (heart and lung) endurance. Write your own definitions of these five components, and circle the component you think is the most important. Be prepared to discuss the reason for your choice.*

Introducing the Lesson

Have students share their responses to the Bellringer. Point out the role that the components play in physical fitness. Explain that each is important in becoming physically fit.

DID YOU KNOW?

- In one recent year, about 300,000 Americans took part in middle-distance triathalons, three-part races in which they biked for 25 miles, ran 6.2 miles, and swam 1 mile.
- In the same year, about 250,000 Americans ran in marathons, which are 26.2 miles long.
- The maximum distance you should be able to run in a race is approximately 3 times the average distance you run each day.

EXERCISE AND PHYSICAL FITNESS

LESSON 2 FOCUS

TERMS TO USE
- Physical fitness
- Body composition
- Flexibility
- Muscular strength
- Muscular endurance
- Cardiorespiratory endurance
- Anaerobic exercise
- Aerobic exercise

CONCEPTS TO LEARN
- Physical fitness includes many components.
- There are benefits to both anaerobic and aerobic exercise.
- Weight training contributes to muscular strength and endurance.

ATTITUDES AND BEHAVIORS TO EVALUATE
- Self-Inventory, page 348.
- Building Decision-Making Skills, page 349.

P attyann is the school's star soccer player. She moves up and down the field with speed and grace. Pattyann can outmaneuver almost any other player. Yet she cannot touch her toes or reach her hands to the ground.

Karen has competed on the balance beam since she was 8 years old. Last year she won the city title for her event. Yet when Karen is late for the bus, she gets completely out of breath after running half a block.

Jerry runs 4 miles every day. He also runs in races all over the state. Yet Jerry cannot do 25 sit-ups or push-ups.

Would it surprise you to know that the physical fitness program of each of these students is lacking?

Basic Components of Physical Fitness

Physical fitness can be defined as the ability to carry out daily tasks easily and have enough reserve energy to respond to unexpected demands. Physical fitness includes these components:

- **Body composition** refers to the percent of fat, lean muscle, bone, connective tissue, water, and so forth in the body. The term *percent body fat* refers to the amount of fat in the body in relation to total body weight.
- **Flexibility** is the ability to move a body part through a full range of motion.
- **Muscular strength** is the ability to exert force against resistance.
- **Muscular endurance** is the ability of muscles to keep working over a period of time without causing fatigue.
- **Cardiorespiratory endurance** is the ability of the heart, lungs, and blood vessels to send fuel and oxygen to the body's tissues during long periods of vigorous activity.

Measuring Body Composition

Appearance is probably one of the biggest reasons people exercise and watch what they eat. A combination of diet and physical activity is essential for weight control. One way to improve physical fitness is to control the percentage of body fat to total body weight. Two ways to determine percent body fat include underwater weighing and skinfold measurements done with calipers.

Using calipers is easy and inexpensive. Underneath your skin is a layer of fat. By having the thickness of skinfolds in specific areas of your body measured with calipers, a percentage of body fat can be determined. There is a high relationship between the measure of this fat and the fat inside your body. The measurements taken are compared to those on a chart for an estimated percent body fat.

342 CHAPTER 17 FITNESS AND YOUR HEALTH

Resources for Lesson 2

- **Transparencies** 6 and 7
- **Guided Reading** Activity 46
- **Decision-Making** Activity 17
- **Workbook** Vocabulary Activity 46
- **Workbook** Application Activity 17
- **Reteaching** Activity 46
- **Enrichment** Activity 17
- **Health Labs** Activity 17

- **Cooperative Learning** Activity 17
- **Lesson 2 Quiz**
- **Chapter 17 Test**
- Science and Technology Videodisc
- **Human Biology, Side 2**
- Ch 12 Measuring Body Fat

Exercising is an effective way to control body fat. Exercise that is aerobic, continued for a fairly long period of time, and done regularly is most effective for losing body fat. The key is to expend as many calories as possible during each regular exercise period.

Measuring Flexibility

Flexibility is specific to each moving joint. For this reason, it is difficult to measure total body flexibility. However, the following test will give you a general measure of your level of fitness in this area. You should remember two important points when taking this flexibility test. First, do some light stretching to warm up your muscles. This will help prevent injury from too vigorous a movement. Second, avoid quick, jerking movements. Your reach should be gradual and slow.

Now follow these directions to measure your flexibility.

- Sit on the floor with your legs straight in front of you with your shoes off. Your heels should touch a piece of tape on the floor and be about 5 inches (13 cm) apart.
- Place a yardstick or meter stick between your legs so that it rests on the floor with the 36-inch (or 1 meter) end pointing away from your body. The 15-inch (38 cm) mark on the stick is to be even with your heels. (It is best to tape the measuring stick in place so that it does not move.)
- Slowly reach with both hands as far forward as possible and hold this position. Practice three times and measure the fourth.
- The score is the most distant point the fingertips reach on the measuring stick.

BODY FLEXIBILITY

Scoring		Rating
Male	**Female**	
22 inches (56 cm) or more	23 inches (58 cm) or more	Excellent
17–21 inches (43–53 cm)	20–22 inches (51–56 cm)	Good
13–16 inches (33–41 cm)	17–19 inches (43–48 cm)	Average
9–12 inches (23–30 cm)	14–16 inches (36–41 cm)	Fair
8 inches (20 cm) or less	13 inches (33 cm) or less	Poor

Measuring Upper Body Strength and Endurance

Pull-ups can measure upper body strength and endurance. Follow these directions:

- Hang from a horizontal bar with your palms facing away from your body. Arms and legs should be fully extended.
- Raise your body, keeping your legs still, until your chin clears the bar.
- Lower your body to the starting position. Repeat as many times as you can with no time limit.

CONFLICT RESOLUTION

Ana and Luis are having an argument about whose exercise program is better. Ana works out on a weight machine for an hour after school each day and does calisthenics at home on weekends. She always works up a sweat, so she feels she must be giving her heart a good workout. Luis walks three miles every day and goes swimming or cross-country skiing just about every weekend. Luis assumes that if his heart is healthy, he's physically fit. Ana and Luis have asked you to help them resolve their disagreement.

Assess their programs, suggest improvements, and explain the merits of both anaerobic and aerobic exercise.

Building Vocabulary

- Have each student create a simple crossword puzzle using each of the vocabulary terms and words they learned in the lesson. Afterwards, ask them to exchange their puzzle with another student. Provide several minutes for them to complete each other's puzzle.
- Ask students to complete *Workbook Vocabulary Activity 46*.

Teach

Guided Practice

L1 EXPLANATION. Talk about the importance of exercise in weight loss and weight control. Stress that overweight, which is in most cases caused by eating too much food and not getting enough exercise, can create health problems. Emphasize that "miracle" diets usually promise quick weight loss, but they are nutritionally unsound and some may endanger health. The key to weight control is balance—the amount of food energy eaten balanced by the amount of energy the body uses.

L2 CLASS ACTIVITY. Have students write and present a skit about teens trying to improve their appearance by controlling the ratio of body fat to total body weight. Have them feature healthy ways to achieve this goal.

L1 SPEAKER. Invite a doctor or dietician to speak to the class about various types of diets and their health consequences.

L1 DISCUSSION. Ask why dieting alone is not enough to lose weight or reduce body fat.

L1 CLASS ACTIVITY. Pair students and have them assess each other's flexibility as described on this page. (You will need tape on the floor and a yardstick.) Use the scoring guide to establish a baseline score. Discuss some exercises or fitness activities that will help students improve their score.

L1 USING HEALTH AWARENESS TRANSPARENCIES 6 AND 7. Refer to the Teaching Transparencies Binder.

Across the Curriculum

Home Economics. Have students compute the costs associated with various types of exercise. Ask them to include such expenses as equipment, use of facilities, clothing, and transportation.

Math. During exercise, the output of blood may be more than 21 quarts a minute. Compute the output of blood in 1, 3, and 5 hours based on this figure. Draw conclusions about the role of exercise in maintaining a strong heart.

Music. Ask for volunteers to identify songs that are about (or that mention) fitness and exercise. Have them share the recordings or written lyrics with the class.

L1 DEMONSTRATION. Invite a practitioner to demonstrate yoga, a form of exercise that helps keep the body flexible and strengthens the muscles. Before the class, have students read library information about yoga and other forms of exercise that include relaxation methods.

L1 CLASS ACTIVITY. Find an appropriate place outdoors or in the gym to assess students' upper body strength and endurance as discussed on this page. (You will need a horizontal bar.) Record and save each student's score. Discuss exercises or activities that will help improve this score. Later in the year, repeat the exercise, and compare each student's previous score.

L1 CLASS ACTIVITY. Divide the class into pairs to determine each other's abdominal strength and endurance. Ask them to refer to the instructions and scoring on this page.

L1 CLASS ACTIVITY. Divide the class into pairs. Have students assess cardiorespiratory (heart and lung) endurance using the 3-minute step test on page 345. (You will need a sturdy bench and a stopwatch.)

L3 CLASS ACTIVITY. Have students write articles to submit to the campus newspaper. Have them feature classroom activities involving assessment of flexibility, upper body strength and muscle endurance, abdominal strength and endurance, and cardiorespiratory endurance. Provide a camera and film for taking photographs of the activities to submit with the articles.

L2 CLASS ACTIVITY. Select a small group of students to design and create a bulletin board titled "Don't Be Confused About the Basic Components of Physical Fitness." Ask them to include major ideas in the lesson. Inform them that the bulletin board will be used to summarize the main ideas for the entire class at the end of the lesson.

L1 DEMONSTRATION. Ask a weight trainer to come to class and discuss his or her weight-training program and goals. Request that the speaker demonstrate some weight-training exercises.

Doing modified sit-ups tests abdominal muscular strength and endurance.

UPPER BODY STRENGTH AND ENDURANCE

Scoring (number of pull-ups)		Rating
Males	Females	
ages 13-14	ages 13-14	Excellent
7-10 times	2 times	
ages 15-16	ages 15-16	Excellent
11 times	2 times	
ages 13-14	ages 13-14	Good
5-6 times	1 time	
ages 15-16	ages 15-16	Good
9-10 times	1 time	

Abdominal Strength and Endurance. Test your abdominal strength and endurance with a one-minute modified sit-up test. You will need a stopwatch and a partner.

- Start by lying on your back with your knees slightly bent. Your partner should hold your ankles for support. Your heels should be 1 to 1½ feet from your buttocks.
- With your arms crossed on your chest, do as many modified sit-ups as you can in one minute. Your elbows should touch your thighs each time.
- Return to full starting position with your back to the floor in between each sit-up.
- Be sure you do not hold your breath during the test. Breathe freely.
- Your partner should keep the time and your sit-up count.

ABDOMINAL STRENGTH AND ENDURANCE

Scoring (number of sit-ups in 1 minute)		Rating
Male	Female	
40 or more	30 or more	Excellent
33–39	24–29	Good
29–32	18–23	Average
21–28	11–17	Fair
Less than 21	Less than 11	Poor

K E E P I N G   F I T

Exercise Programs

Dr. Kenneth Cooper, the "father of aerobics," recommends that 14- to 18-year-olds try some of these regular exercise programs to increase their levels of fitness:

- walking 3 miles, 4 times per week, in less than 45 minutes for girls and less than 43 minutes for boys;
- swimming 1,000 yards, 4 times a week, in less than 25 minutes for girls and less than 24 minutes for boys;
- running or jogging 3 miles, 4 times a week, in less than 27 minutes for girls and 24 minutes for boys;
- cycling 8 miles in less than 40 minutes for girls and less than 32 minutes for boys.

Across the Curriculum

Social Studies. The popularity of some types of physical exercise differs in various parts of the United States. This is due to differences in temperature, terrain, natural resources, local customs, economic resources, etc. Have students use library resources to identify types of physical exercise commonly enjoyed in various geographical areas of the country (such as snow skiing in the northwest and water skiing in the south). For additional information, students may call toll-free numbers to reach states' departments of tourism.

Measuring Cardiorespiratory Endurance

One way to measure cardiorespiratory endurance is the 1-mile (1.6 km) run/walk. On a measured course, cover the distances as fast as you can. If you need to walk some of the distance, walk as fast as you can.

CARDIORESPIRATORY ENDURANCE

Scoring		Rating
Male	**Female**	
Under 7 minutes	Under 8 minutes	Excellent
7:01–7:30	8:01–8:30	Good
7:31–8:00	8:31–9:00	Average
8:01–8:30	9:01–9:30	Fair
8:31–9:00	9:31–10:00	Low
9:01 or longer	10:01 or longer	Poor

This 3-minute step test also will measure your cardiorespiratory fitness:

- Using a sturdy bench about 8 inches (20 cm) high, step up and down every 2 seconds for 3 minutes.
- Fully extend each leg as you step. Step up with your right foot, then your left. Step down with your right foot first. Stepping should be continuous.
- Step at the rate of 24 steps per minute for 3 minutes.
- After 30 seconds, count your pulse for 1 minute.
- Find your pulse either on your wrist or on the side of your neck. This count gives you your pulse recovery rate, which is the rate at which your heart beats following activity.

PULSE RECOVERY RATE

Scoring (number of heartbeats)	Rating
70–80	Excellent
81–105	Good
106–119	Average
120–130	Fair
131 or more	Poor

Types of Exercise

Sensible exercise is good for you. The more muscles and joints you use, the greater the health gain. Exercise is generally one of two types, anaerobic or aerobic.

Anaerobic exercise is intense physical activity in which the body's supply of oxygen to produce energy does not meet the demand. Running a 100-meter dash is an anaerobic activity. **Aerobic exercise** is vigorous activity that uses continuous oxygen. This activity usually needs to last at least 20 minutes. During this time heart rate increases and oxygen is transported to the muscles to be used as energy to do more work. Running for a couple of miles is an example of an aerobic exercise.

A step test measures your cardiorespiratory fitness.

DID YOU KNOW?

- The Centers for Disease Control and Prevention reported in January 1992 that fewer than 40 percent of high school students get enough vigorous exercise each week.
- The average 14- to 17-year-old American is now 5 to 7 pounds heavier than in 1980.
- Many health clubs, once centered only on exercise, have expanded their offering to include seminars in nutrition, stress management, smoking cessation, weight loss, and even attitude-enhancement and self-esteem.

EXERCISE AND PHYSICAL FITNESS **345**

LEP CLASS ACTIVITY. Set up an ongoing tournament of arm wrestling for students to participate in just before the bell rings at the beginning or end of class. Point out that to some extent this exercise is isometric. Have students explain why this is so.

LEP CLASS ACTIVITY. Lead students in brainstorming a list of exercises. Next, have them categorize and list the anaerobic and aerobic exercises. Discuss the differences between aerobic and anaerobic exercises.

L2 CLASS ACTIVITY. Choose students to debate the topic: *Everyone should participate in aerobic exercise.*

L1 DEMONSTRATION. Invite a physical education teacher or coach to demonstrate exercises that reduce body fat, improve flexibility, condition muscles, and strengthen the heart and lungs. Discuss how a person can judge the potential value of specific exercises. What health and safety considerations should people make in selecting an exercise program?

L1 DISCUSSION. Talk about why regular exercise is necessary for the body.

L2 CLASS ACTIVITY. Have students write public service announcements promoting aerobic exercise. Ask for volunteers to share some of the announcements with the class.

L3 CLASS ACTIVITY. Provide basic art supplies, and have students design logos for T-shirts promoting their favorite kind of aerobic exercise. Choose some of the designs to feature in a display titled "These Aerobic Exercises Rate an A+!"

L1 DEMONSTRATION. Invite a physical therapist to demonstrate heart, lung, and muscle-strengthening programs for people who are physically impaired or for the elderly. Also, ask the therapist to demonstrate some flexibility exercises for these individuals.

L2 CLASS ACTIVITY. Ask for volunteers to write the lyrics to a rap or other kind of song about physical fitness and exercise. Have them present their music to the class.

Additional Information

Body Weight. Because the slim, trim look is often considered an ideal, underweight people are usually envied. If underweight people are in good health, a thin body should be of no concern. However, the person who is extremely underweight can have as many health problems as one who is overweight. Underweight people may have poorly developed muscles and poor posture. They lack fat layers, which means they have little insulation. Thus they tire easily and are more sensitive to cold temperatures. Being underweight has many causes. Frustration and tension can affect the appetite. Some may be so involved in activities that they find little time to eat. Being underweight can be caused by physical or medical problems.

Independent Practice

L2 **WRITING.** Ask students to write a short story in which two people make different decisions about physical fitness and exercise. Ask them to show how the decisions affect the rest of their lives. Afterwards, select some of the stories to read to the class.

L2 **COMMUNITY INVOLVEMENT.** Choose students to investigate whether or not there are community sources for determining body fatness by underwater weighing or use of skinfold calipers. If so, assist the students in making an appointment to find out more about measuring body composition. Before the appointment, have students use the library to locate and read current information on the subject.

L2 **COMMUNITY INVOLVEMENT.** Ask for volunteers to interview someone they know who has had a broken arm or leg in a cast for a number of weeks. Have them find out how the inactivity caused by the cast affected the muscles and previous degree of conditioning. Have students share what they learn with the class.

L2 **COMMUNITY INVOLVEMENT.** Ask for volunteers to interview an elderly person in their family, extended family, or neighborhood. Have them ask questions such as: How important has exercise been to you in your life? Why? Do you still exercise? If so, what kinds of exercise do you engage in now? What kinds of obstacles to exercising do you encounter? How do you deal with the obstacles? What would you do differently in the area of physical fitness if you had life to live over? Request that students share the results of the interview with the class.

L1 **USING THE LESSON RESOURCES.** For additional student activities, refer to the lesson resources on page 342.

Anaerobic Exercise

Anaerobic exercises improve muscular strength, muscular endurance, and flexibility. Anaerobic exercises may not raise your general level of fitness because they do not require the body to increase its use of oxygen. Weight training is considered an anaerobic exercise.

WEIGHT TRAINING

Weight-training programs are designed to build muscular strength and endurance. Weight training is a good way to tone muscles. However, you may not lose weight. Muscle tissue weighs more than fat tissue.

There are three types of weight-training programs:

- Isometric. This type of exercise involves muscular strength with little or no movement of the body part. With this type of exercise, you use muscle tension to build strength. Putting the palms of your hands together in front of you and pushing is an example of an isometric exercise. Pushing against a wall is another example.
- Isotonic. This type of exercise involves muscular contraction with movement. You develop muscular strength and flexibility with repeated movements using weights. Push-ups, pull-ups, and modified sit-ups are isotonic exercises. Lifting weights also is isotonic exercise.
- Isokinetic. This type of exercise involves muscular strength and endurance, and flexibility. With this type of exercise, resistance is moved through an entire range of motion, such as pushing or pulling against a hydraulic lever of certain exercise equipment.

During exercise muscle fibers become thicker and are able to do more work. Eventually, repeating the same amount of exercise causes muscles

HEALTH UPDATE

LOOKING AT TECHNOLOGY

Biomechanics: Sports on a Screen

Training for athletic performance and fitness is no longer just limited to the playing field. Advanced technology is now being used to measure and analyze athletes' motions and body functions. This science, called *biomechanics*, involves using computers to measure those forces that act both within and upon the athlete's body. Computers also monitor such things as breathing, heart rate, muscular contractions, pressure changes, and calories consumed. Using high-speed film or videotapes of athletes performing, it can provide mathematical analysis of both the athlete's motion and his or her energy consumption. Using such high-tech statistics can help athletes in training develop specific ways to perform at their best levels of athletic achievement, minimize fatigue, and avoid injuries.

In addition to helping athletes, biomechanics is now also being used to help people with various skeletal or muscular diseases, conditions, or injuries.

Across the Curriculum

Science. Have students find their weight in kilograms (weight in pounds ÷ 2.2 = weight in kilograms). Next, have them determine their basal energy needs by applying the following equation: weight in kilograms × 22 (for females) or 24 (for males) = basal calories needed. Then, estimate the percent of basal calories required for their usual activity level (very sedentary, 20 percent; sedentary, 30 percent; moderately active, 40 percent; very active, 50 percent). Total the calories needed for basal metabolism and activities, then add 10 percent for specific dynamic effect (energy expended to digest and absorb nutrients from food) to find total daily energy needs.

to reach a limit. For muscles to keep getting stronger, it is necessary that you gradually increase how often, how hard, or how long you use a particular muscle group.

Conditioning programs are reversible. A person in good physical condition can lose much strength and endurance in just two or three weeks of inactivity.

Aerobic Exercise

Brisk walking, jogging, swimming, dancing, cycling, and any other nonstop vigorous exercises are aerobic activities. During aerobic exercise the body has a greater demand for oxygen to provide the muscles with the energy they need to carry out the activity. This kind of exercise increases the lungs' capacity to hold air.

Aerobic exercises are rhythmic and sustained and use the large muscle groups, particularly those in the hips and legs.

Aerobic exercise causes the arteries to enlarge and increases the dilation of capillaries that take blood to the muscles. Blood flow increases to the skeletal muscles.

As these large muscles contract, they press against the blood vessels, sending increased amounts of blood to the heart. The heart becomes a stronger and more efficient pump, so it beats slower during exercising and at rest. The slower the heart rate the longer the heart can rest between beats.

Exercises that improve the condition of the heart and lungs have three essential characteristics:

- They must be brisk. They should raise the heart rate and breathing rate.
- They must be continuous. They should be done for 20 to 30 minutes without stopping.
- They must be regular. They should be repeated at least three times a week to maintain one's fitness level.

Aerobic exercise is important in maintaining and improving one's fitness level.

Assess

Check for Understanding

- Assign and discuss the lesson review.
- Assign and discuss the chapter review.

Evaluate

- Administer, grade, and discuss the *Lesson 2 Quiz.*
- Administer, grade, and discuss the *Chapter 17 Test.*
- Refer to the Performance Assessment strategy for this chapter. See pages T 23 to T 25.

Reteach

- Have students list the ways they get exercise in a typical week. Then ask them to decide which characteristics each form of exercise has. Does it improve flexibility? improve muscular strength and endurance? increase cardiorespiratory endurance?
- Ask students to complete *Reteaching Activity 46.*

Enrich

- Choose students to investigate the use of new high-tech methods to evaluate athletes and their performance.
- Ask students to complete *Enrichment Activity 17.*

Close

Ask students to state the most important concepts they learned from the lesson.

LESSON 2 REVIEW

Reviewing Facts and Vocabulary

1. Define the term *physical fitness.*
2. What two important points should you remember before taking a body flexibility test?
3. Define the term *pulse recovery rate.*

Thinking Critically

4. **Analysis.** Compare muscular strength to muscular endurance.
5. **Evaluation.** Discuss the accuracy of this statement: *Aerobic exercise is better for you than anaerobic exercise.*

Applying Health Knowledge

6. Interview a person who exercises regularly. What motivates that person to exercise? What benefits does he or she receive? Then interview one who does not exercise regularly. What conclusions can you draw?
7. Write an advertisement to promote physical fitness. Include at least five selling points.
8. Find advertisements in magazines or newspapers for equipment that claims to increase physical fitness and well-being. Discuss the claims in class. Evaluate the accuracy of the advertisements.

EXERCISE AND PHYSICAL FITNESS **347**

Answers to Lesson 2 Review

1. The ability to carry out daily tasks easily and have enough reserve energy to respond to unexpected demands.
2. Stretch before taking the test; avoid quick, jerking movements.
3. The rate at which one's heart beats following activity.
4. Muscular strength is the ability to exert force against resistance. Muscular endurance is the ability of the muscles to work over a period of time. A person could have strength without endurance or endurance without strength.
5. Answers will vary.
6. Answers will vary.
7. Answers will vary.
8. Answers will vary.

DID YOU KNOW?

- If you put 10 people in an average-size room, they will raise the room's temperature 1 degree per hour. A person usually produces about 11 BTUs, or British Thermal Units, per day; but during excercise, 3 or 4 times as much heat may be produced.
- Just by breathing and sweating, each American gives off about a quart (1 l) of moisture per day.

Helping Students Improve Their Health

Using the Self-Inventory

Reinforcing Vocabulary

- **Sedentary.** Mostly sitting, rather than moving.
- **Lifetime sports.** Activities that one can participate in throughout the years.
- **Ideal weight.** Weighing the amount that is appropriate for one's age, height, gender, and bone structure.

Teaching Strategies

L1 EXPLANATION. Students are generally more sedentary today than they were a decade ago. TV, VCRs, and computer games require very little physical activity. Encourage students to keep a daily log that calculates the amount of TV they watch during a week. Help students to replace sedentary activities with activities that build cardiorespiratory fitness.

L2 CLASS ACTIVITY. Have students calculate their resting heart rate, maximum heart rate, training heart rate, and recovery heart rate. Have students participate in an aerobic activity that will allow them to monitor their training heart rate and calculate their recovery heart rate. After a period of weeks of aerobic activity, compare one's former resting heart rate with the current resting heart rate. The slower the heartbeat, the more efficiently the heart does its job.

L1 CLASS ACTIVITY. Have students record their daily caloric intake versus their energy expenditure for a week. Have students determine whether or not this will lead to weight gain or loss.

Self-Inventory

Figuring Out Your Fitness

HOW DO YOU RATE?

Number a sheet of paper from 1 through 30. Read each item below, and respond by writing *yes* or *no* for each item. Total the number of *yes* and *no* responses. Then proceed to the next section.

1. I exercise because I enjoy it.
2. I am more active than I am sedentary.
3. I do at least 20 minutes of aerobic exercise at least three times a week.
4. I keep an activity log or journal of my daily exercise workouts.
5. I use the stairs instead of escalators or elevators whenever possible.
6. I do not use tobacco.
7. I do not use alcohol or illegal drugs.
8. I regularly participate in lifetime sports, such as tennis, swimming, and softball.
9. I walk or ride a bike when possible, rather than take a car.
10. I take in about the same number of calories that I burn.
11. I often use exercise to deal with tension, anger, or frustration.
12. I keep within 5 pounds (2 kg) of my ideal weight.
13. I seldom feel tired or run-down.
14. I get at least 8 hours of sleep each night.
15. I plan regular times for exercise.

16. I stand rather than sit whenever possible.
17. I make daily, personal decisions to be fit.
18. I avoid consuming high-fat foods and snacks.
19. I usually follow through with my exercise plans.
20. I tend to eat nutritious meals and snacks.
21. I usually warm up before starting an exercise session.
22. I usually cool down after an exercise session.
23. Stretching is a part of my warm-up.
24. Stretching is a part of my cool down.
25. I enjoy a variety of physical activities.
26. I feel better after I exercise.
27. I motivate myself to exercise regularly.
28. I vary my exercise activities.
29. I encourage my friends to exercise.
30. I encourage family members to exercise.

HOW DID YOU SCORE?

Give yourself 1 point for every *yes* answer. Read below to see how you scored. Then proceed to the next section.

21 to 30
Excellent. Fitness is a part of your daily life. Keep up the good work.

11 to 20
Good. Your fitness behavior is positive, but limited in scope. Ask your family and friends to

support and encourage you in making fitness a part of each day.

5 to 10
Fair. You need to increase your activity level in order to get more benefits.

Below 5
Poor. You're missing out on a lot of fun that comes with exercise. Get off the couch and move your body! No one else can do it for you.

WHAT ARE YOUR GOALS?

If you received an *excellent* or *good* score, complete the statements in Part A. If your score was *fair* or *poor,* complete the statements in Parts A and B.

Part A

1. I plan to learn more about fitness and health by ____.
2. My timetable for accomplishing this is ____.
3. I plan to share my information with others by ____.

Part B

4. The behavior or attitude toward fitness that I would most like to change is ____.
5. The steps involved in making this change are ____.
6. My rewards for making this change will be ____.
7. My timetable for making this change is ____.
8. The people or groups I will ask for help are ____.

Meeting Students' Needs

For students who score *Excellent* or *Good*. Have students evaluate the physical fitness level of the entire school population. Have students determine a course of action that will improve the fitness level of students and teachers.

For students who score *Fair*. Have students determine ways in which they can

increase their activity level, such as by walking more, taking the stairs instead of the elevator, etc.

For students who score *Poor*. Have students set short- and long-term goals for improving fitness. Monitor students' improvement on a weekly basis.

Building Decision-Making Skills

Andrew is quite overweight and is constantly making fun of his physique and his lack of activity. Kevin believes that Andrew really would like to do something about his problem, but that he doesn't know how to go about it. Kevin works out regularly and would like to invite Andrew to join him, but he doesn't know if he should.

WHAT DO YOU THINK?

1. **Situation.** What might be holding Andrew back from regular workouts and becoming fit? Is it possible that there are health issues that Kevin doesn't know about?

2. **Situation.** What decision does Kevin need to make?

3. **Choices.** Assuming he decides to ask Andrew, what are some possible approaches Kevin could use?

4. **Consequences.** What are the advantages and disadvantages of each approach?

5. **Consequences.** How might Kevin's asking Andrew to work out affect Andrew's self-esteem? How might it affect Kevin's self-esteem?

6. **Consequences.** What's the worst thing that might happen if Kevin asks Andrew to join him in a workout? What's the best thing that might happen? What would probably happen? Do you think the risks are worth it?

7. **Decision.** What do you think Kevin should do? How should he go about it?

8. **Evaluation.** Have you ever been in a situation where you wanted to help someone but didn't because you were afraid of what others would think? How did you handle the situation? How would you handle it now?

Byron's father is very athletic. He pushed Byron into a lot of sports when Byron was young and today Byron is really turned off by any mention of sports. He knows it's important to be active but he also knows that sports are not for him. What should Byron do?

WHAT DO YOU THINK?

9. **Situation.** What reasons might Byron have for being turned off by sports?

10. **Choices.** If sports are out, what other choices does Byron have?

11. **Consequences.** What are the advantages of each choice?

12. **Consequences.** What are the disadvantages of each choice?

13. **Consequences.** Who will be affected by Byron's decision?

14. **Consequences.** How might Byron's self-esteem be affected by this decision?

15. **Consequences.** What risks are involved in this decision?

16. **Consequences.** How might Byron's health triangle be affected by this decision?

17. **Decision.** What should Byron do? Explain your answer.

Building Decision-Making Skills

Teaching Strategies

L1 CLASS ACTIVITY. Frequently, people use humor to make light of a serious subject. People also sometimes ridicule themselves before others may. This appears to be the case with Andrew. Have students role-play Kevin inviting Andrew to work out with him. What might be Andrew's initial reaction? How can Kevin prepare himself for Andrew's possible reaction? How can Kevin guarantee himself the best possible chance for success?

L1 CLASS ACTIVITY. Other possible role-plays pertaining to fitness include: (1) Your father is recovering from bypass surgery. You are concerned with his stressful job and sedentary life-style. (2) Your grandmother has just been diagnosed as having diabetes. Your grandmother loves chocolate but is not allowed to have any. Your grandfather continues to buy your grandmother chocolate. (3) You have been trying to lose a couple of pounds sensibly. Your mother continues to cook your favorite, fattening foods for dinner and seems to be hurt when you do not eat the food.

L2 CLASS ACTIVITY. Have students prepare a smorgasbord of healthful treats for all to enjoy. Have students tell the nutritional value of each food and how much exercise it would take to burn off the calories of healthful treats versus junk food.

Discussing the Answers

Situation 1. Perhaps a way to handle this situation would be to have Kevin tell Andrew the truth—that he cares about Andrew's health and well-being and wants to help him lose weight if Andrew wants to lose weight. Generally, most people would welcome honest, caring, uncriticizing concern. As another alternative, Kevin could just invite Andrew to do things with him without mentioning why he's being invited to work out—just to get him on track.

Situation 2. Discussion should center around the fact that activity does not have to be sports oriented.

REVIEW

Answers to Chapter 17 Review

Using Health Terms

1. Overfat
2. Basal metabolism
3. Percent body fat
4. Anaerobic exercise
5. Aerobic exercise
6. Isometric
7. Isotonic

Building Academic Skills

8. Being inactive or sitting for long periods of time.
9. One thousand calories.
10. C.

Recalling the Facts

11. Physical, mental, and social health.
12. The cardiovascular, respiratory, digestive, and nervous systems.
13. Slow.
14. High.
15. The more a muscle is used the stronger it becomes.
16. In calories.
17. They are stored as fat.
18. Gain weight.
19. About 3,500.
20. By having the thickness of skinfolds in specific areas of the body measured with calipers, a percentage of body fat can be determined.
21. Answers will vary. Accept one of the following: the 1-mile run/walk—cover the distance as fast as possible, the less time it takes the better your cardiorespiratory endurance is; the 3-minute step test—for 3 minutes, step up and down a height of 8 inches at a rate of 24 steps per minute and count your pulse when you have finished for 1 minute.
22. They do not require the body to increase its use of oxygen.
23. It builds muscular strength and endurance and is a good way to tone muscles.

Using Health Terms

On a separate sheet of paper, write the term that best matches each definition given below.

LESSON 1

1. An excessive amount of fat in the body, often associated with heart disease.
2. The minimum amount of energy required to maintain the life processes in your body.

LESSON 2

3. The amount of fat in the body in relation to total body weight.
4. Intense physical activity lasting a few seconds to a few minutes.
5. Continuous vigorous activity lasting at least 20 minutes, during which the heart rate increases.
6. A type of weight-training exercise that involves muscular contraction but little or no movement of the body part stressed.
7. A type of exercise that involves repeated movements using weights.

Building Academic Skills

LESSON 1

8. **Reading.** Use the context clues below to define the term *sedentary:*
   As a receptionist, Claudia sits at a desk for eight hours a day answering the telephone. She has a sedentary job.
9. **Math.** One pound of fat is equal to about 3,500 calories. How many calories must be eliminated from the diet each day in order to lose 2 pounds in a 1-week period?

LESSON 2

10. **Reading.** Which of the following statements is the best summary of Lesson 2?
    a. Physical fitness is the ability to carry out daily tasks easily and to respond to unexpected demands.
    b. Sensible exercise is good for you.
    c. Physical fitness can be achieved through weight control and a variety of exercises.

Recalling the Facts

LESSON 1

11. What aspects of your overall health does fitness affect?
12. What body systems are negatively affected by immobility?
13. Is it better for your respiratory system to work slow or fast?
14. Is it better for your lung capacity to be high or low?
15. What makes a muscle grow stronger?
16. How is the energy value of food measured?
17. What happens to calories your body takes in but does not use?
18. If you take in more calories than you burn, do you lose or gain weight?
19. How many calories equal one pound of fat?

LESSON 2

20. Explain how calipers measure percent body fat.
21. Describe one way to measure cardiorespiratory endurance.
22. Why do anaerobic exercises generally not raise a person's level of fitness?
23. What are the benefits of including weight training in an exercise program?
24. Which kind of weight training would you use to build muscular strength with little or no body movement?
25. Which kind of weight training would you use to increase muscular strength and endurance, and flexibility?
26. Which weighs more, muscle tissue or fat tissue?
27. What kind of weight training builds muscular strength and flexibility with repeated movements using weights?
28. What are three requirements for exercises to improve the condition of the heart and lungs?
29. Give three examples of aerobic exercises.
30. Is weight training an aerobic or an anaerobic exercise?
31. What benefits can a person gain from anaerobic exercise?

REVIEW

Thinking Critically

LESSON 1

32. Analysis. What advantage does a totally fit person have over an unfit person on a day-to-day basis?

33. Synthesis. What are two possible social benefits of an exercise program? Explain your answer.

LESSON 2

34. Synthesis. Participating in an aerobics class three times a week will contribute to cardiovascular fitness. Some people cannot afford this, or do not want to exercise in front of a group. What would accomplish the same goal and be more private—as well as less expensive?

35. Evaluation. The following students participated in the school's annual assessment of upper body strength and endurance. Rate each student's performance based on the information provided in your text. All students were age 13 or 14.
  a. Jerry Ono: 7-10
  b. Sheila Gordon: 2
  c. Sam Miller: 5-6
  d. Shirley Obetz: 1

36. Evaluation. During a 1-mile run/walk cardiorespiratory endurance test, what would be the rating for each of the following persons?
  a. Frank Deerwater: 9 minutes
  b. Juanita Gonzalez: 8 minutes, 15 seconds
  c. Jake Karpels: 7 minutes, 2 seconds
  d. Shelley Jones: 8 minutes, 12 seconds

37. Synthesis. What factors should you consider in selecting exercises for your total fitness program?

Making the Connection

LESSON 1

38. Art. Design a poster with a slogan that illustrates the benefits of being physically fit. Display the posters throughout your school.

Applying Health Knowledge

LESSON 1

39. For each pair described below, which individuals are choosing the more physically fit way of living?
  a. Dave and Donna both work for Fidelity Insurance, which is located on the third floor of the Grover Building. Dave always takes the elevator to the third floor; Donna always uses the stairs.
  b. The Jacksons and the Smiths live next door to each other. Their lawns are identical in size. The Jacksons use a hand mower to keep their lawn trim; the Smiths use a riding mower.

LESSON 2

40. Label each type of exercise described below as *isometric, isotonic,* or *isokinetic.*
  a. using a rowing machine
  b. doing push-ups
  c. pushing against a wall

Beyond the Classroom

LESSON 1

41. Community Involvement. Interview five working adults. Ask each what kind of exercise they get on their jobs and what kinds of exercise they get outside their jobs.

LESSON 2

42. Community Involvement. Call or visit a health spa, physical fitness center, or your local YMCA or YWCA. Find out what kinds of fitness exercises they recommend for teenagers. Discover what types of equipment and facilities they have. Also find out what other services they provide. Report to your class on the services and equipment offered and the fees charged.

43. Parental Involvement. Talk to your parents and siblings about a family exercise program. Work together to set up a regular plan of family fitness and exercise.

24. Isometric.
25. Isokinetic.
26. Muscle tissue.
27. Isotonic.
28. They must be brisk—raise heart and breathing rate, continuous—for 20 to 30 minutes without stopping, and regular—at least 3 times a week.
29. Answers may include but are not limited to three of the following: brisk walking, jogging, swimming, dancing, cycling.
30. Anaerobic exercise.
31. Muscular strength, muscular endurance, and flexibility.

Thinking Critically
32. A fit person is better able to handle what he or she is faced with every day.
33. Answers will vary. Possible answers: One can meet new people by taking an exercise class; one can exercise with a friend and get to visit while being more motivated to continue exercising.
34. Answers will vary. Possible answers: Jogging, walking briskly, or using an exercise videotape at home.
35. A—excellent; B—excellent; C—good; D—good.
36. A—low; B—good; C—good; D—good.
37. Answers will vary. Possible answers: Age; weight; any hindering physical conditions, such as bad knees; previous level of activity; type of activity one enjoys.

Making the Connection
38. Posters will vary.

Applying Health Knowledge
39. A—Donna; B—the Jacksons.
40. A—isokinetic; B—isotonic; C—isometric.

Beyond the Classroom
41. Answers will vary.
42. Answers will vary.
43. Answers will vary.

Lesson Summaries

LESSON 1. To design an exercise program, students should decide upon goals for a program, select appropriate exercises to achieve the goals, and establish when and where to exercise. Each exercise session should include activities that warm up, work out, and cool down the body. Students should check their progress to monitor their exercise program's effectiveness.

LESSON 2. With any movement activity, there is risk of accident or injury. Risks of injury to the skeletal and muscular systems exist, due to the nature of the activities or not adequately warming up. Proper treatment can reduce the extent and duration of these injuries. Weather-related risks also exist. Problems associated with excessive heat or cold can generally be prevented.

Introducing the Chapter

Ask students to list their physical activities during the past week. Discuss the benefits of such activities. Do students think they are getting enough exercise? Ask them to try to agree on a single definition of enough exercise. Afterwards, discuss the reasons that prevented them from reaching a consensus. (Many factors are involved, such as age, weight, general health, etc.) Tell students this chapter will present factors that are important to consider when starting an exercise program. It will also discuss injuries that are associated with activity.

Performance Assessment ✓

Refer to pages T 23 to T 25 for a Performance Assessment strategy for this chapter. See the *Performance Assessment Activities* booklet for additional suggestions.

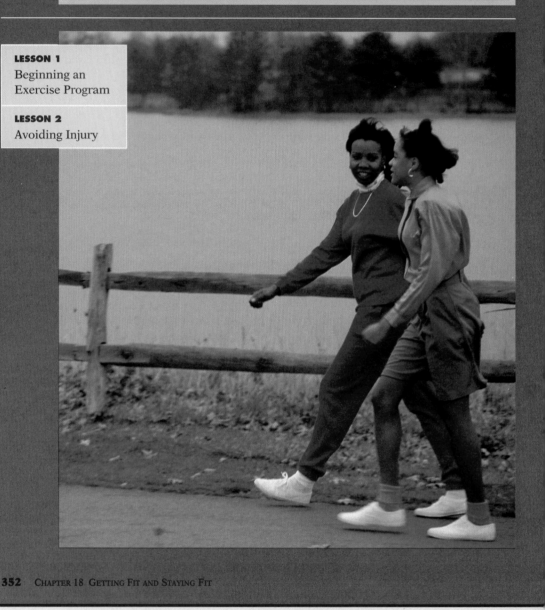

CHAPTER

18 GETTING FIT AND STAYING FIT

LESSON 1
Beginning an Exercise Program

LESSON 2
Avoiding Injury

Key to Ability Levels

Teaching strategies have been coded for varying learning styles and abilities.

L1 Level 1 activities are basic activities and should be within the ability range of all students.

L2 Level 2 activities are average activities and should be within the ability range of average to above-average students.

L3 Level 3 activities are challenging activities designed for the ability range of above-average students.

LD LD activities should be within the ability range of learning-disabled students.

LEP LEP activities should be within the ability range of Limited English Proficiency students.

BEGINNING AN EXERCISE PROGRAM

In the previous chapter you learned what exercise does for the body and how exercise influences your level of fitness. You also had an opportunity to determine your level of physical fitness. Now you are ready to plan an exercise program to improve or maintain your fitness level. To design an exercise program for yourself, you need to consider what you hope to accomplish and what you enjoy doing.

Setting Your Goals

If your goal is to strengthen muscles, you will probably choose an anaerobic exercise program, such as lifting weights or using a strength-training machine.

If your goal is to improve your endurance, you will probably develop a program of aerobic exercise, such as walking, jogging, cycling, or swimming. It could be that you have a combination of these goals in mind.

Finding the Right Exercise

Choose exercises that are appropriate for the location in which you live. The available facilities and weather are important considerations. You also need to consider any physical problems or limitations you may have. Seek medical advice, especially if you have not been exercising at all or if you have any health problems.

As you consider what exercise to do, it is important to pick something you enjoy. It is unlikely that you will continue an exercise activity if you do not enjoy it or cannot do it very well. In addition, consider exercise that you already do during a day. You may walk briskly to and from classes, so you might want to pick an exercise that does not involve walking.

By developing a regular plan of exercise, you prepare yourself for dealing more effectively with the problems and challenges of daily living. You will look and feel better. As you begin to improve your level of fitness, you may actually find you have more energy each day.

By developing these exercise habits now, you will find that they can become part of your life as an adult. You will continue to enjoy activities that others are not able to enjoy because you have chosen to take care of yourself. More than likely, you will live longer because people who take care of their bodies are less likely to develop poor health and disease.

When and Where to Exercise

It is best to find a regular time during the day to exercise so that exercise becomes a part of your routine. Try not to exercise after eating.

BEGINNING AN EXERCISE PROGRAM **353**

LESSON 1 FOCUS

TERMS TO USE
- Warming up
- Target heart rate
- Cooling down
- Resting heart rate

CONCEPTS TO LEARN
- To be successful, a personal exercise program must meet the needs of the individual.
- Regular exercise is a major part of a healthy life-style.
- Specific, realistic, attainable goals are essential to any personal exercise program.
- Every exercise session should include a warm-up, a workout, and a cool down.

ATTITUDES AND BEHAVIORS TO EVALUATE
- Self-Inventory, page 366.
- Building Decision-Making Skills, page 367.

Resources for Lesson 1

- **Guided Reading** Activity 47
- **Workbook** Vocabulary Activity 47
- **Reteaching** Activity 47
- **Lesson 1 Quiz**
- **BARN Software,** Body Management
- **Improving Physical Fitness**
- **Posters** 5 and 6
- **Performance Assessment** Activity 18

Focus

Lesson Objectives

After studying this lesson, students should be able to:
- develop a regular plan of exercise
- identify common myths about exercise
- explain the components of an exercise session, and discuss why each component is important to overall fitness
- describe ways to evaluate a personal fitness program
- contrast their resting heart rate with their target heart rate

Bellringer

Write the following on the chalkboard for students to work on while attendance is being taken: *Make a written list of the benefits of exercise. Next, illustrate and describe a safe warm-up or cool-down exercise. Be prepared to share your written list and your drawing with the class.*

Introducing the Lesson

Refer to the Bellringer. Ask volunteers to share their written lists and drawings of warm-up and cool-down exercises with the class. Discuss why the lists are different. Tell students that they will learn in this lesson how to design and begin a personal exercise program and ways to check their progress.

DID YOU KNOW?

- A new eight-year study shows that moderate exercise can greatly raise a person's chances of survival despite high blood pressure. In the study, the least fit males were five times more likely to have died than males who were physically active. In addition, those who exercised regularly were often able to lower their blood pressure, reducing their risk for heart attack and stroke.
- During periods of high physical activity, such as during training for various sports seasons, teen nutritional needs increase.

Building Vocabulary

- Ask students to work in pairs to write a short paper using each of the vocabulary terms. Afterwards, ask them to test each other's understanding of the terms' definitions.
- Write the following terms on the chalkboard: *warming up, target heart rate, cooling down,* and *resting heart rate.* Ask what these terms have in common. (They are all part of an exercise program.) Discuss the importance of warming up and cooling down. Ask students to explain the difference between the target heart rate and the resting heart rate.
- Ask students to complete *Workbook Vocabulary Activity 47.*

Teach

Guided Practice

L1 **SELF-ESTEEM.** Ask students to write a paragraph comparing a day in the life of a physically fit person and one who is not physically fit. Ask them to share their paragraphs. Next, describe in detail one individual, perhaps a weight lifter, who works out at a gym five nights a week. Ask the class if this individual is fit. Ask those who volunteer to explain their answers. Explain to the class that being fit means being physically, mentally, socially, and emotionally prepared for what lies ahead. Stress that fitness is more than muscle development. Ask how fitness is related to self-esteem.

LEP **CLASS ACTIVITY.** Ask students to raise their hands to indicate which of them exercises regularly. Then call upon those students to describe how they feel after a good workout. (Students probably will say they feel refreshed, exhilarated, and invigorated after a workout.) Tell students these are natural responses. Next, lead students in a discussion of the advantages of a regular plan of exercise, such as preparing themselves for dealing more effectively with daily life, looking and feeling better, having more energy, reducing body fat, etc.

CONFLICT RESOLUTION

Carla runs on her school's cross-country team and thinks she has a really good coach. The team recently placed in a regional meet and qualified to run in the state meet. To get more practice time in, the coach has extended the workout part of the practice the last couple of weeks. Consequently, some team members have skipped the usual cool down. Some say they cool down as they catch rides to go home. Carla thinks a cool down is important

What should Carla say to her teammates about this?

By joining a team or a league, you set up situations that will encourage you to participate in activities you want to do more often.

During exercise more blood is diverted to the skeletal muscles, depriving the stomach of oxygen, affecting the rate of digestion. Exercising on a full stomach can result in stomach cramps or nausea.

Consider safety in choosing when and where to exercise. If your program takes you outside at night, wear reflective clothing and practice good safety habits. Consider working out with a partner, and avoid unlighted streets, dark alleys, and remote areas.

DID YOU KNOW?

- Who says professional athletes have to burn out? In 1991, at age 44, record-holding baseball pitcher Nolan Ryan of Texas was still pitching in the big leagues—after 26 straight years.
- Edwin Robinson of Maine became blind and almost deaf after a truck crash. Ten years later, while outside during a storm, he was struck by lightning. When he regained consciousness, both his sight and his hearing had returned. At age 73, he still enjoys motorbiking.

COMMON MYTHS ABOUT EXERCISE

A myth is a belief or opinion based on false reasoning. There are many myths about fitness and exercise. Here are a few, with explanations of why they are false:
- Myth 1: Exercise makes you tired. As you get in better shape, you will find that exercising gives you more energy than you had before. Regular exercise can actually reduce stress and fatigue.
- Myth 2: Exercise takes too much time. Regular exercise does not have to take more than 25 to 40 minutes, three times a week.
- Myth 3: All exercise gives you the same benefits. All physical activities can give you enjoyment, but only frequent, continuous activity helps the heart and lungs, and burns off fat and calories.
- Myth 4: Exercise is expensive. Some of the most beneficial exercises are very inexpensive, such as walking or jogging. Swimming is another excellent activity that is reasonably priced.
- Myth 5: Exercise means playing a sport. While team sports are exercise, individual activities such as walking, running, biking, or swimming are excellent forms of exercise, too.
- Myth 6: You have to be athletic to exercise. Most aerobic activities, such as those mentioned above, do not require any special athletic abilities. In fact, many people who find school sports difficult have discovered that these other activities are easy to do and are enjoyable.

Across the Curriculum

Music. Play a variety of different types of music for the class. Have students discuss which music they would prefer to do exercises to and why.

Social Studies. Have students discuss dance as an important form of exercise. Next, encourage students to name folk dances and the country or ethnic group from which the dance originated. Ask for volunteers to prepare and present demonstrations of folk dances.

Math. Each excess pound of body fat requires extra miles of capillaries. If 20 miles of capillaries are needed to supply one pound of excess fat, have students calculate the extra miles needed for 10, 15, 20, and 35 pounds of excess fat.

Components of an Exercise Session

There are three components of an exercise session. They include

- the warm-up,
- the workout,
- the cool down.

The Warm-Up

Warming up is engaging in activity that prepares the muscles for the work that is to come. The first step in warming up is to stretch the large muscles. Stretches should be slow and smooth, not jerky. Stretching helps increase the elasticity of muscles and tendons. Stretching can prevent injury to the muscles and tissue surrounding the joints.

The second stage of the warm-up is to perform the activity slowly for about 5 minutes. So if you are going to jog 2 miles, you might walk briskly for about 5 minutes before you begin to jog. If you are going to bike 10 miles, you might ride at an easy pace for the first 5 minutes, then pick up the pace.

Warming up allows your pulse rate to increase gradually. A sudden increase in the pulse rate puts unnecessary strain on the heart and the blood vessels.

The Workout

This is the component of your exercise program in which you are actually performing the exercise at its highest intensity. The intensity depends on your current fitness level. Choose an activity that continually uses the large muscle groups. Biking, walking, swimming, and running are good examples. You should work hard, but not overdo it. Studies have shown that doubling the amount of exercise does not double its effectiveness. Overdoing exercise can cause sleeplessness or chronically sore muscles.

Frequency. To begin both anaerobic and aerobic programs, you should schedule workouts three times a week, with no less than one day and no more than two days between sessions.

Many people enjoy their aerobic exercise routine so much that they do it more often than three times a week. There is no real harm in doing aerobic exercise five times a week once one is physically fit.

Exercising more than three times a week for six months should help get you physically fit. You then must maintain your program at least three times a week to maintain your fitness level.

Intensity. It is very important not to overdo exercise. You must start slowly and build endurance. In weight training, start with a lighter weight and build to the heavier ones. In aerobic programs, work toward your target heart rate. Your **target heart rate** is 70 to 85 percent of your maximum heart rate. The target rate provides a range for exertion.

To find your target heart rate, first estimate your maximum heart rate by subtracting your age from 220. For example, if you are 15 years old, subtract 15 from 220 to get 205. Your maximum heart rate would be 205 beats per minute. Your target heart rate would be between 70 and

L2 CLASS ACTIVITY. Have students list a number of fitness activities that they like well enough to do throughout life. Ask them to develop a second list of activities they would like to try. Have them determine what resources would be needed to try these activities. Challenge students to try several of the new activities throughout the course and to share their reactions with the class.

L1 EXPLANATION. Although the chapter discusses fitness in terms of physical activity, stress the importance of a good diet and adequate rest as contributors to fitness.

L2 EXPLANATION. It has been estimated that people in North America carry around more than 200 million tons of excess fat. Discuss why there is more of a weight problem among people in North America than among people in other parts of the world.

L1 EXPLANATION. Talk about the benefits of exercise to bone formation. (Among many other benefits, regular weight-bearing exercise puts stress on bones, which, in turn, stimulates bone formation. Exercise protects from bone loss.)

L1 EXPLANATION. Talk to students about horse races or car races they may have seen. Ask if horses or race cars start cold. (Never. Horses walk, and cars take warm-up laps before racing.) The same is true of professional athletes. They never start a practice or game without a warm-up. The same applies for anyone who is beginning an exercise workout. The body needs time to adjust. Ask for volunteers to explain the difference between warming up and cooling down.

L1 DISCUSSION. Ask how many students have ever had a muscle cramp after a game or other vigorous activity. What did it feel like? Did you warm up before the game or exercise session? If so, what kind of warm-up exercises did you do? (Most students will acknowledge that they did little or no warming up.) Point out that warming up gets the muscles ready for action and that people who warm up prior to exercise suffer fewer cramps and fewer injuries.

Across the Curriculum

Reading. Have students read about various organizations that incorporate exercise as part of their fund-raising efforts. Afterwards, work with them in arranging with an organization (such as the March of Dimes) to organize a walk-a-thon for their class or school.

Industrial Arts. Many aerobic exercise programs use the "step bench" or "box step" as part of their routines. Assign students to research the kinds of step benches currently available and the pros and cons of each. Afterwards, ask for volunteers to construct some benches to use in classroom step-bench demonstrations.

LEP **CLASS ACTIVITY.** Ask students to search through books and current magazines for examples of activities that would be appropriate for warm-up and cool-down exercises. Have them sketch or cut out illustrations of favorite examples as reminders for their fitness journals. Ask for volunteers to demonstrate some of the exercises.

L3 **COOPERATIVE LEARNING.** Have groups of students design and complete a short newsletter for teens that describes anaerobic and aerobic exercises, warm-ups, and cool downs. Ask them to focus on the most important concepts in the lesson. Have students develop periodic newsletters as class projects to be distributed to other classes or posted at various locations in the school. As an alternate activity, students can develop a fitness newsletter to share with members of their families.

LEP **CLASS ACTIVITY.** Have students take their pulse and figure their target heart rate.

L1 **CLASS ACTIVITY.** Point out to students the list on page 357 (The Value of Various Activities for the Heart and Lungs). Ask them to rate the exercises/sports they have tried, from "10" for their favorite to "1" for least favorite. Next, have them write answers to the following questions for each exercise/sport they have tried: How often have you done this exercise/sport? When? Where? Would you make it part of a lasting exercise program? Why or why not? Lead the class in a discussion of some of the responses.

L2 **CLASS ACTIVITY.** Select students to plan a sporting activity for the class. Have students list what needs to be done in advance and what equipment will be needed. Will money be involved? If so, how will students get the money? What permissions may be necessary? Should other students and faculty members be invited to participate? When and where should the event be held? At what time? Assist students in finalizing plans for the event.

85 percent of 205, or between 144 and 174 beats per minute. You should never exercise to your maximum heart rate. Exercise at a level to stay within the range of your target heart rate.

You can learn to take your heart rate, but a general rule of thumb is that if you cannot talk while you are exercising, you are probably doing too much.

Duration. In weight training, do the exercises slowly, taking at least 2 seconds each time you lower a weight. Rest for 1 or 2 minutes between sets, and do a variety of exercises to strengthen your muscles in the full range of motion. A set consists of 10 to 14 repetitions.

The time spent doing aerobic exercises should be built up gradually. The goal in aerobics is to spend 20 to 30 minutes in your target heart rate.

The Cool Down

Just as your body needs to be readied for increased activity, it needs to be returned gradually to a less active state. During exercise an increased amount of blood is pumped to the heart with the help of contractions of large leg muscles that push against the veins. If the leg muscles relax suddenly, pooling may result. The blood will collect in your extremities instead of getting back to the heart. The heart is still pumping hard, but less blood is returning to it. Pooling can cause lightheadedness, even fainting.

When you are **cooling down,** you gradually decrease activity. Your muscles continue to assist in returning the blood to the heart until your pulse rate slows. During cool down, the metabolic processes can gradually return to resting levels.

The best way to cool down is simply to slow down activity. Slower activity should be done for about 5 minutes, followed by 5 minutes of stretching. You have cooled down adequately when your heart rate is within 20 to 30 beats of your regular heart rate.

Always warm up and cool down when you exercise.

356 CHAPTER 18 GETTING FIT AND STAYING FIT

Meeting Special Needs

The Physically Challenged. Ask students to research the history and activities of Special Olympics. Have them determine when it began. What was its purpose? Who can participate? What are some of the opportunities for volunteers? In what countries are Special Olympics held? What does it cost to participate? How are the events funded? When are they held? Request representatives and/or volunteers from the community to speak to the class about Special Olympics and ways for students to get involved.

THE VALUE OF VARIOUS ACTIVITIES FOR THE HEART AND LUNGS

Column A	Column B	Column C
High level of conditioning	Moderate level of conditioning	Low level of conditioning
Bicycling	Basketball	Baseball
Cross-country skiing	Calisthenics	Bowling
Uphill hiking	Field hockey	Downhill skiing
Ice hockey	Handball	Football
Jogging	Racquetball	Golf (on foot or by cart)
Jumping rope	Squash	Softball
Rowing	Tennis (singles)	Volleyball
Running in place	Walking	
Soccer		
Stationary cycling		
Swimming		

Column A
These exercises are naturally very vigorous. They need to be done for at least 20 minutes, three times a week. They maintain fitness and contribute to weight control.

Column B
These activities are moderately vigorous, but they can be excellent conditioners if done briskly for at least 30 minutes, three times a week. When done briskly, they offer benefits similar to those activities in column A.

Column C
These activities, though they may be vigorous, are usually not sustained long enough to provide conditioning benefits. They can improve coordination, flexibility, and muscle tone. However, they must be combined with activities in column A or B to improve total fitness.

Checking Your Progress

In planning your fitness program, you need to include an evaluation to see how well you are doing. You need to take time to think about your program. Do you feel better? Can you lift more weight and for a longer period of time? Are you walking farther in a shorter amount of time? The questions you ask yourself depend on the program you developed and the goals you set.

Many people like to keep a journal to track their progress. If you decide to do this, begin the journal the day you begin your exercise program, or as close to it as you can. In the journal list your goals and some information about yourself, such as weight, measurements, how you feel, how well you sleep, how long you sleep, and how energetic you feel. Keep track of the frequency, intensity, and duration of your workouts.

At the end of 6 weeks, check the same information about yourself that you checked when you started the journal. Compare the figures. Do not be discouraged if the change is not dramatic: it often takes 12 weeks to see any change. Check yourself every 6 weeks and compare your most recent figures with your initial figures. You will be living proof that exercise works!

BEGINNING AN EXERCISE PROGRAM **357**

L1 CLASS ACTIVITY. Choose students to create a bulletin board or other exhibit entitled "Inch Off Those Pounds Through Exercise." Have them feature major points in the lesson.

LEP CLASS ACTIVITY. Ask students to write the name of a sport or physical hobby in which they are skilled or would like to be skilled. Ask them to explain in one sentence why the sport or activity is important to them. Afterwards, write some of the sports and activities they name on the chalkboard, along with their reasons for preferring that sport or activity. Point out that an important part of being healthy is choosing what is right and best for them as individuals—not what is most popular among their peers.

L1 COOPERATIVE LEARNING. Have students form small groups, each having a leader. Ask the leader to guide the group in choosing an activity, acceptable to all, for a fitness program. Have group members decide on a realistic goal for a period of 2 weeks. Ask them to discuss ways they can motivate themselves to stick to the program. After 2 weeks, have group leaders present their group's results to the class.

Independent Practice

L3 COMMUNITY INVOLVEMENT. Ask students to observe people at a park or exercise course and record the following information: The number of people observed, what they did to warm up and cool down, in what physical shape they appeared to be, and how well they followed the exercise guidelines in the lesson. Ask students to draw conclusions based on their observations and to share them with the class.

Across the Curriculum

Language Arts. Ask students to write a short report addressing the following questions: What activity would you enjoy doing as a regular part of your life, now and in the future? How might your ability to perform this activity change as you grow older? How might your ability to continue this activity change as your responsibilities in life change? Would it be difficult to stick to this activity as time goes by? Ask for volunteers to read their reports to the class. Have students find newspaper and magazine examples of older adults who are physically active.

L2 COMMUNITY INVOLVE-MENT. Have students locate retail outlets that sell reflective clothing and other items for people who exercise at night. Assist students in getting permission to demonstrate the clothing and other items to the class.

L1 WRITING. Ask each student to choose a sporting activity from the list on page 357 (The Value of Various Activities for the Heart and Lungs), and write a two-page report about the activity. As part of the report, have them include information about amateur versus professional participation in the sport and/or a brief profile of a leader in the sport.

L2 WRITING. Have students write the President's Council on Physical Fitness for fitness norms for their age group. Select one of the letters to mail. When the information is received, make copies to share with the students.

L1 PERSONAL INVOLVEMENT. Ask students to write down a fitness goal they want to achieve in 4 to 6 weeks. Ask them to prepare a plan of action that will help them reach their goal. Have them think about what information they need to put their plan into action and decide where they can find the information needed. Have them start their plan and keep records of their progress.

L1 PARENTAL INVOLVEMENT. Ask for volunteers who are beginning (or continuing) a personal exercise program to keep a record of their resting heart rate at various times throughout the year. Have them make a graph of their readings and analyze improvements as they become more fit. Ask them to encourage their parents or other adults to participate in this project at the same time.

L1 USING THE LESSON RESOURCES. For additional student activities, refer to the lesson resources on page 353.

HEALTH UPDATE

LOOKING AT TECHNOLOGY

Magnetic Resonance Imaging

In the past, when people were injured while exercising or playing sports, diagnosing the injury was often guesswork. Now, with magnetic resonance imaging, or MRI, experts can evaluate neck, knee, shoulder, and other injuries in a painless way using a strong magnetic field. For example, they can tell how severely a ligament is torn and easily determine if an operation will be necessary. An MRI even allows physicians to see through both organs and bones.

How does MRI work? The patient lies on a table inside a giant magnet, and its magnetic field works on the patient's body. Instead of using X rays or contrast dyes, as many diagnostic tests do, the MRI uses radio waves and magnetism to make images. A computer analyzes the pattern of magnetic energy. It takes into account the length and strength of radio signals and makes the pattern into a picture. The radiologist then interprets the picture and can more clearly diagnose the problem. In addition to getting a three-dimensional image of inside the body, the physician can also get a two-dimensional "slice" of any body part and have that image displayed on a screen.

Your Resting Heart Rate

Your **resting heart rate** is found by taking your pulse at intervals when you are not active—perhaps while you are reading a good book. If you measure your pulse several times, the average is your resting heart rate. Your resting heart rate indicates your level of fitness. A person of average fitness has a resting heart rate between 72 and 84 beats a minute. After only 4 weeks of an exercise program, that rate can decrease by 5 to 10 beats a minute. A resting heart rate below 72 beats a minute indicates a good fitness level. A young athlete at the top of his or her form may have a resting rate as low as 40 beats a minute.

K E E P I N G   F I T

Exercising: Some Basic Principles

In *The Family Fitness Handbook*, authors Bob Glover and Jack Shepherd present these basic fitness principles:
- Exercise should be progressive. Never increase your exercise by more than 10 percent from one week to the next.
- Exercise with regularity.
- Use specific exercises to achieve specific fitness benefits.
- Vary the exercises you do.
- Make the exercises adaptable to your body and level of fitness, as well as to your schedule, fitness goals, environment, weather, and the seasons.
- Try to be patient. Fitness takes time.
- Exercise in moderation.

Additional Information

Fitness Equipment Alternative. Students do not need fancy athletic equipment to get physically fit. For example, they can get an excellent workout just by climbing stairs. Tell students the following: First, find a safe set of well-lighted stairs with limited traffic. Be sure to wear nonslip shoes. Start slowly, remembering to warm up and stretch first. Climb stairs several times a week, aiming to increase both the time you spend climbing and the speed at which you climb. Be certain to tell students that stair climbing is not recommended for people with heart or knee problems.

Reward yourself when you make progress toward your fitness goal.

Your Body Measurements

Many people begin an exercise program to lose weight and to improve muscle tone. If you are exercising and not eating any more calories than you need, you will lose weight and improve muscle tone.

It is possible to lose fat without losing weight, so do not be discouraged if the scale is not moving very much when you write your 6-week measurements in your journal. Muscle tissue is heavier than fat tissue. If you are building muscle, the scale may even go up a bit. That does not matter; getting rid of the fat and becoming fit is what matters. When you take your measurements, you will probably see a change there. Use a standard measuring tape and measure your waist, upper arm, upper leg, and hips. Record and date your measurements.

LESSON 1 REVIEW

Reviewing Facts and Vocabulary

1. What should you consider in selecting exercises for your fitness program?
2. Why should you exercise on an empty stomach?
3. Why is a warm-up an important part of your workout?
4. How does the warm-up contribute to physical fitness? How should warm-up exercises be done?
5. What is cooling down?

Thinking Critically

6. **Analysis.** What is the difference between aerobic and anaerobic exercise?

7. **Evaluation.** Are there any justifications for engaging in physical activity that is not aerobic?
8. **Analysis.** How is your resting heart rate an indicator of your fitness level?

Applying Health Knowledge

9. Keep a record of your pulse rate during different physical activities. Which activity makes your heart work the hardest? Compare your pulse rate record with your classmates' records.
10. Some people start an exercise program only to give it up, claiming that exercise is boring or too hard or that they just do not have time. What suggestions can you give to help them stay with their exercise programs?

Answers to Lesson 1 Review

1. Available facilities, weather, physical limitations, activities one enjoys.
2. To avoid stomach cramps and nausea.
3. See "The Warm-Up" on page 355.
4. It improves flexibility. Slowly and smoothly.
5. Gradually decreasing activity.
6. Aerobic exercise conditions the heart and lungs. Anaerobic exercise improves body movement and muscle strength.
7. Answers will vary.
8. The slower one's resting heart rate is, the less one's heart must work.
9. Answers will vary.
10. Answers will vary.

Assess

Check for Understanding
- Assign and discuss the lesson review. Encourage LD students to focus on questions 1, 2, 3, and 5.

Evaluate
- Administer, grade, and discuss the *Lesson 1 Quiz.*

Reteach
- Have students make a short videotape demonstrating correct and incorrect ways to warm up before and cool down after a workout. Ask them to provide commentary on the videotape about what happens to the body during these basic before- and after-exercise techniques as well as what might happen if they are omitted or done improperly.
- Ask students to complete *Reteaching Activity 47.*

Enrich
- Ask for volunteers to write a short puppet show. Have them make two puppets named A. Robic and Anna Robic. Ask them to create a short script in which the puppet pair define, describe, and demonstrate respectively the basics of aerobic and anaerobic exercise. Have students perform their puppet shows.

Close

Ask students to state the most important concepts learned in the lesson. Have students work in pairs to construct a mobile that illustrates major ideas in the lesson. When completed, have pairs define and explain one concept they have illustrated.

Focus

Lesson Objectives

After studying this lesson, students should be able to:

- describe the most common injuries that occur during exercise
- differentiate between heat cramps, heat exhaustion, and heatstroke
- identify the negative effects of using steroids
- list points to consider when choosing clothing and equipment for exercise
- explain ways to avoid risk and injury during exercise

Bellringer

Write the following on the chalkboard for students to work on while attendance is being taken: *Write a paragraph describing a recent injury that you or someone else suffered as a result of exercise.*

Introducing the Lesson

Have students share their responses to the Bellringer. Discuss ways each of the injuries might have been avoided.

Building Vocabulary

- Have students write a definition of each of the vocabulary terms, and give an example of how each might occur.
- Ask students to complete *Workbook Vocabulary Activity 48.*

DID YOU KNOW?

- While more males than females exercise with equipment, run, and jog, more females than males walk, swim, bike, do aerobics, and do calisthenics.
- About 80 percent of all back problems are directly caused by muscle weakness. Simple strengthening exercises with weights could make a large difference in your back health in the years to come.

AVOIDING INJURY

LESSON 2 FOCUS

TERMS TO USE

- Sprain
- Bruise
- Strain
- Tendinitis (ten•duh•NYT•uhs)
- Hernias
- Frostbite

CONCEPTS TO LEARN

- There is always a risk of injury during exercise.
- Most injuries or conditions can often be prevented by taking adequate precautions, including a good warm-up and the use of good equipment and proper technique.

ATTITUDES AND BEHAVIORS TO EVALUATE

- Self-Inventory, page 366.
- Building Decision-Making Skills, page 367.

With any movement activity, there is always a risk of accident or injury. There are many ways to prevent the more common injuries associated with exercise. The risk of injury during exercise increases when a person is not in good physical condition or has not sufficiently warmed up. To attempt activities beyond your level of ability also increases the risk of injury.

Injuries most often occur when the body is not prepared for the demands placed on it. Even when people are in good physical condition there is risk of injury based solely on the nature of the activity.

The most common injuries that occur from exercise are to the muscular and skeletal systems. This is because movement is fundamental to muscle and joint activity, as well as to exercise. Injury to these areas is likely when you exercise too long or too hard.

Injuries to the Skeletal System

Sprains and dislocations are the most common injuries of the skeletal system. They involve joints and result from too much stress being placed on a joint. If you experience a sudden blow or twist or stretch, the tissues that join the bones can strain, pull, or tear.

Have you ever stepped off a curb in the wrong way and twisted your ankle? Sprains can occur as easily as that! A **sprain** is an injury to tissues surrounding a joint. Ligaments may be stretched and torn. A sprain may be accompanied by severe pain, swelling, and difficulty in moving.

If you suffer a sprain, apply cold packs or ice to the sprained area. Elevate the area, if possible, to help control swelling. Also, apply an elastic wrap to the area. Wrapping and cold exposure cause the blood vessels to become narrower, lessening the internal bleeding. Elevating the injured area increases the flow of blood in the veins that lead away from the injury.

Stress on a joint can result in torn cartilage when the strong connective tissue has been pulled out from the bone. Surgery is usually required for this injury. Because it can be difficult to distinguish a sprain from a dislocation or a fracture, a health professional should check more serious sprains.

A dislocation is also a serious injury. A dislocation occurs when the end of a bone is pushed out of its joint. The ligaments holding the bones are severely stretched and may even be torn. Dislocations are usually quite painful. The joint must be set back into its normal position and held there while the surrounding tissue heals.

Never attempt to replace a dislocation yourself. Joints are surrounded by many tiny blood vessels and nerves. You risk further damage to them if you do not know what you are doing. Keep the injured area very still, apply cold packs or ice, and seek medical attention right away.

Resources for Lesson 2

- **Guided Reading** Activity 48
- **Decision-Making** Activity 18
- **Workbook** Vocabulary Activity 48
- **Workbook** Application Activity 18
- **Reteaching** Activity 48
- **Enrichment** Activity 18
- **Health Labs** Activity 18

- **Cooperative Learning** Activity 18
- **Lesson 2 Quiz**
- **Chapter 18 Test**
- ABC News InterActive Videodiscs **Drugs and Substance Abuse, Side 1** Ch 8 Steroids

Injuries to the skeletal system can occur during many activities.

Injuries to the Muscular System

Some of the most common injuries to muscles are bruises, strains, tendinitis, pulled and torn muscles, muscle cramps, and hernias.

A **bruise** is an injury to tissue under the skin. Bruises usually result from a blow to the muscle. Discoloration results when the capillaries break and ooze blood. If cold packs are applied immediately, swelling and discoloration will be reduced.

A muscle **strain** results when muscles are overworked. Have you ever participated in a strenuous activity you were not used to and then been sore the next day? You experienced muscle strain. Resting the muscles and applying ice for the first 24 hours are the best ways to treat muscle strains. You can prevent some strains by warming up properly and gradually building up your level of exertion. In other words, avoid going all out your first day of exercise.

Tendinitis occurs when a tendon—the connective tissue of the muscles and bones—is stretched or torn. The injured area becomes inflamed. A common example of tendinitis is tennis elbow. To treat tendinitis, first rest the injured area to decrease the inflammation, and then use prescribed medicines or physical therapy to help cure the injury.

A pulled or torn muscle can cause severe pain and require you to cease your activity. In a pulled or torn muscle, the large muscle is separated or torn from its point of attachment. This injury can damage the blood vessels that supply nourishment to that muscle. Immediate medical care may be necessary. Cold packs should be put on the muscle area right away.

As with other muscle injuries, lack of warm-up and overexertion of an unprepared muscle are the major causes of a pulled or torn muscle.

Muscle cramps occur when a muscle contracts tightly and will not relax. Cramps usually happen as the result of an irritation within the muscle. When a muscle cramp occurs, all fibers contract at the same time. This may be caused by temporary lack of food or oxygen to the muscle. Sometimes cramping occurs as a result of a person's losing

DID YOU KNOW?

- You can put unnecessary strain on your muscles if the heels of your athletic shoes wear down too far.
- Runners should not run in walking shoes because they do not have enough cushioning. Walkers should not walk in running shoes because they do not have much heel and the Achilles tendon is not supported.

AVOIDING INJURY **361**

Teach

Guided Practice

L1 CLASS ACTIVITY. Ask students to make a written list of 10 sports and exercises. Then have them rank each one as to its potential for injury, with "1" representing activities that have the greatest risk of causing injury and "10" as least likely. Lead them in a discussion of their lists and reasons for their rankings.

L1 SPEAKER. Invite an athletic trainer to class to discuss common sports injuries and what is being done to prevent and treat them. Have students make a list of questions to ask the speaker.

L1 DISCUSSION. Talk about the differences between a sprain and a strain and ways both might be treated.

L1 DISCUSSION. Have students bring to class articles from newspapers and magazines that describe sporting or athletic injuries. Discuss the consequences of the injuries and ways they might have been prevented.

L1 DISCUSSION. Have students talk about the short-term and possible long-term effects of heat cramps, heat exhaustion, heatstroke, and frostbite. Conclude the discussion by addressing prevention and treatments.

LD CLASS ACTIVITY. Have students verbalize symptoms of and care procedures for heatstroke and frostbite.

L3 COOPERATIVE LEARNING. Have pairs of students develop a case history of someone with a heat-related injury. Ask students to trade case histories with another pair and list ways to avoid the injury in the future.

L2 COOPERATIVE LEARNING. Divide the class into small groups. Have groups talk with coaches or physical education teachers in the school about ways sporting equipment can decrease injuries. Have each group present a report and demonstrate the use of some sporting equipment that helps prevent injuries.

This physical therapist is helping this teen regain the mobility in her arm.

Left column (teacher notes)

L2 CLASS ACTIVITY. Have each student develop a quiz about common sports injuries and how they can be prevented. Have students exchange their quizzes with each other.

L1 DISCUSSION. Ask students to identify and evaluate common myths related to the treatment of each injury discussed in the lesson. (Myths might include putting hot water on a frostbite, applying heat to sprains, working through the pain, etc.)

L2 DISCUSSION. Talk about reasons why cold packs are applied to sprains and muscle injuries.

L2 COOPERATIVE LEARNING. Divide the class into small groups. Give each group a slip of paper describing a common sports injury. Have each group develop a skit showing ways its assigned injury could occur and how it might be prevented.

L1 SPEAKER. Invite one or more cyclists to demonstrate and speak about recent equipment designed to promote safety. (Examples might include reflective clothing, rearview mirrors on helmets, high-impact helmets, etc.)

L1 CLASS ACTIVITY. Ask students to bring an item or illustration of a piece of sporting gear that they think offers good value, comfort, and protection from injury during exercise. Have them present the item to the class and discuss the reasons for their choice.

L1 CLASS ACTIVITY. Set up a panel of runners, marathoners, or others who jog regularly. Ask them to share their experiences while running. Have them talk about ways they avoid risk and injury during exercise.

L2 CLASS ACTIVITY. Display copies of magazines specializing in running, walking, weight lifting, and other activities. Let students use the magazines to find articles about avoiding risk and injury during exercise. Have them write a short summary of the articles. Close with a discussion comparing the information in the magazines with that in the lesson.

Right column (main text)

large amounts of salt and water through perspiration. Tired, overworked muscles sometimes cramp.

Massaging the muscle area firmly can help a cramp. Continuing to work the muscle lightly can help relieve the cramp. Heat can also help. You can help prevent cramps by warming up properly and by drinking enough fluids before and during exercise.

Cramps are dangerous if they occur while swimming. You could drown before you are able to relieve a severe cramp. The most important point to remember is to remain calm. Your body will float if you do not panic. It is best to take a deep breath, curl over, and massage the muscle. Although cramps are painful, they do not involve injury.

Hernias, or ruptures, are weak areas in the muscle supporting various organs. This usually occurs in the abdominal area. Part of an organ such as the intestine may push through this weak area. Hernias can be caused by a lack of warm-up exercises or by picking up heavy objects improperly. Surgery is usually necessary to correct a hernia.

Weather-Related Risks

Certain health problems can occur in hot and cold weather. The major ones are heat cramps, heat exhaustion, heatstroke, and frostbite.

Heat cramps can occur when a person loses a large amount of water and electrolytes—for example, body salt—through perspiration. Massaging and drinking small amounts of salt water every 15 to 20 minutes will usually relieve the condition.

Heat exhaustion usually results from exercise or overexertion in a hot, humid atmosphere. The body becomes overheated with the loss of a large amount of water and electrolytes. The skin becomes pale and moist. A person may also experience dizziness, headache, shortness of breath, and nausea. The person should be moved to a cool place and kept lying down, with the feet raised.

You can prevent heat exhaustion by drinking plenty of fluids before and during exercise. Activities on hot, humid days should be restricted, especially if you are not accustomed to the weather.

Heatstroke is a more serious condition. Heatstroke usually follows prolonged exposure to direct sun, dehydration, and profuse sweating. It may also be caused by obesity or the inability of the body to adapt to a weather situation. The body loses its ability to rid itself of the heat that has built up. The body retains the heat, the person does not perspire,

KEEPING FIT

Training

Here are some steps to follow before participating in any sport.
- Make sure you first get in good condition.
- Work to improve cardiopulmonary function, endurance, flexibility, and strength.

- Forget the no-pain-no-gain approach. Train slowly and progressively.
- Eat a variety of complex carbohydrates.
- Drink lots of liquids.

- Get regular, uninterrupted sleep.
- Wear proper equipment. Make sure it fits.
- If it is too stressful or too painful, stop.

362 CHAPTER 18 GETTING FIT AND STAYING FIT

Across the Curriculum

Physical Education. If your school has a swimming program, have students practice how to safely deal with a severe cramp while swimming in deep water.

Chemistry. Ask students to locate and read current research on physical and psychological effects of using steroids.

History. Ask students to find instances in history (such as mountain climbing expeditions) in which individuals experienced weather-related risks and injuries. Have them present an oral report of their findings.

and body temperature can get as high as 108 degrees. The person may collapse suddenly, have a rapid pulse, twitching muscles, and difficulty breathing. The skin will be dry and hot, and blood will rush to the head and face.

If you are present when someone experiences heatstroke, call for help right away. Heatstroke is a life-threatening situation. Serious organ damage can result from such a high body temperature. Move the person to a cool place, loosen the clothing, and spray or sponge the person with cold water. Monitor the person's breathing. It may be necessary to administer artificial respiration.

When there is prolonged exposure of a body part to a freezing or near-freezing temperature, **frostbite** occurs. In this situation, the exposed tissue freezes. The normal activity of the cells is stopped. When circulation of the blood stops, cells begin to die.

Frostbite occurs most often to the chin, cheeks, nose, ears, fingers, and toes. Dressing warmly, covering all exposed skin—especially the head, face, fingers, and toes—and avoiding fatigue and excessive exposure to cold while exercising helps prevent frostbite.

If frostbite does occur, apply blankets to warm the body. The frostbitten body part should never be rubbed or exposed to intense heat. This causes further damage. The body must be gradually warmed. If frostbite is severe, the person should be kept quiet and watched for signs of shock or difficult breathing. Because of tissue damage, medical care should be sought.

STEROIDS: TOO BIG A RISK

Weight lifters and shot-putters began using anabolic steroids more than 35 years ago to improve performance. Unfortunately, anabolic steroids are now used in junior and senior high schools around the United States.

Anabolic steroids are chemicals similar to the male hormone testosterone. They are taken by athletes and bodybuilders to increase muscle mass without increasing fat while doing weight training.

Many young people have not been warned of the dangerous physical and psychological effects of using these drugs. Some people think the drugs are only training aids. The short-term gain from anabolic steroids seems to motivate some people to use these drugs regardless of their long-term health risks.

The negative consequences of taking these drugs are enormous. Consider the health risks involved:
- increased risk of cancer and heart disease
- sterility
- skin problems
- unusual weight gain or loss
- sexual dysfunction
- suicidal or depressive tendencies

Consider also the following facts:
- Illegal distribution of steroids is a felony.
- Possession without a prescription is illegal.
- Athletes who test positive for steroids risk their careers.
- Purchasing "street steroids" adds risks because you do not know what you are getting.

Even when steroids do increase muscle mass, the effects are short-term. The conclusion: steroids mean trouble.

Applying heat can help relieve a cramp.

AVOIDING INJURY **363**

L1 SPEAKER. Invite a doctor or other medical worker to speak to the class about exercise and sports for people with medical disabilities. Ask the speaker to talk about fitness for persons who are orthopedically, hearing, or visually impaired. Also, request that they discuss ways in which persons with physical conditions such as arthritis, asthma, obesity, diabetes, and epilepsy can avoid risk and injury during exercise.

Independent Practice

L3 RESEARCH. Have students research the meaning of "the wall" that marathon runners sometimes experience. Ask them to find answers to questions such as: When and why do they usually "hit" the wall? What are the physiological explanations for this occurrence? What, in particular, happens to glucose during the process?

L2 READING. Have students use classroom and library resources, such as *Consumer Reports,* to read independent, unbiased evaluations of various kinds of sports and exercise equipment. Ask them to share their findings with the class.

L2 COMMUNITY INVOLVEMENT. Choose several students to develop a list of interview questions to ask a physical therapist. Next, assist them in making arrangements to visit a physical therapist to find answers to the questions. Request that they report their findings to the class.

L2 PARENTAL INVOLVEMENT. Ask for volunteers to talk with family members or friends who have used the services of physical therapists. Have them find out what kinds of treatment were used and how the injured people feel about physical therapy.

L2 COMMUNITY INVOLVEMENT. In groups of two or three, have students volunteer to help a physical therapy assistant, a social worker, or a nurse conduct exercise classes at a retirement center or nursing facility. Ask students to compare their experiences with a physical activity program for a healthy teenager. Have them share their experiences with the rest of the class.

Additional Information

Cross Training. Cross training means varying one's fitness program to include several kinds of exercise. For example, someone engaged in cross training might do an intense aerobic dance workout one day, bike the next day, swim the third day, and walk with hand weights the fourth day. As an alternative, he or she might combine within one workout session swimming for the upper body and aerobic dance for the lower body. Varying the kind of exercise one does not only provides a change of pace for the mind, but it also gives muscles and joints most stressed by a particular kind of exercise needed time to rest. In addition, cross training helps people achieve a higher level of total body fitness.

Overcoming
The Odds

Missy Meharg is 28. She has an advanced degree in psychophysiology of sports. She is a master field hockey player and head coach at the University of Maryland. She knows a lot about winning and physical fitness. But she also knows a lot about losing and injuries.

In college, she played both lacrosse and field hockey and was voted Most Valuable Player in both. Soon, however, she began to channel most of her athletic energies toward field hockey, an Olympic sport. As a member of the U.S. National Team, her new goal was to compete in the Pan American Games or an Olympic event, but she was cut from the team and became a first alternate in 1988. Not one to give up, Meharg tried out again for the U.S. National Team in 1989, made it, and went on tour in Russia and other countries. Two years later, again a member of the National Team, she competed in the Pan American Games and the Olympic Qualifying Tournament. Unfortunately, the team did not qualify for the Olympics in Barcelona in 1992, but Meharg is upbeat about the loss. "It's okay because I really did what I wanted to do, and I tried my best."

In her athletic career, Meharg has had three major injuries. The first was a really bad ankle injury in which she stretched the ligaments. So was the second. The last injury, however, was the most serious. She had just gotten a new pair of in-line skates and was using them as a form of aerobic training. "I was going down a hill a little fast, thinking I was a little better than I was, and I was not being safety conscious. I was flying. The next thing I knew, my feet were straight above my head. I came down backwards on both wrists. I broke my scaphoid bone in half in my left wrist. It's the slowest healing bone in your body." Meharg then had a difficult choice to make: have a long

arm cast for three months and not be able to play, or have an operation in which a screw would be put into the bone to keep it together. She opted for the latter. She was back playing — more cautiously —just one month later. She continues, "Ever since, I don't take the risks I used to."

What advice does Meharg give young athletes? "Know your limitations. Most athletic injuries are acquired because of lack of knowledge or lack of preparation. Every time I go out to play anything now I always do a small run—8 to 10 minutes to warm up, then a full stretch to take care of all the major muscle masses, and then I start the activity slowly and work up to 100 percent. I do the cool down the same way." She concludes, "When I was younger, I didn't realize how important total fitness was. I do now. I'd say that overall health is so dependent on your overall fitness level. I know that decision making and being mentally stable are closely related to being healthy and physically fit."

1. What advice does Meharg give about avoiding injury when exercising?
2. How does your level of fitness affect your mental and social health?

Additional Information

Heat Index. Heavy exercise on hot, humid days can be dangerous. Bioclimatologists have developed a heat index that combines heat and humidity values so one can assess the risks of prolonged activity in various conditions. For example, 90° + 60% humidity = a heat index of 100, the apparent temperature; 95° + 65% humidity = a heat index of 119; 100° + 60% humidity = a heat index of 132. What do these numbers mean? A heat index of 80 to 90 means fatigue is possible; 90 to 105, that heat cramps and heat exhaustion are possible; 105 to 130, that heat cramps and heat exhaustion are likely and heatstroke possible; 130 or above, that heatstroke is likely.

Dressing Properly and Choosing the Proper Equipment

Sports and exercise equipment are big business. Clothing, shoes, apparatus, and food supplements are all part of a multi-million dollar industry. How much money you spend on dress and equipment for an activity depends on you. It depends on your motives. Some people want to wear the highest-priced clothing, have the most expensive athletic shoes, or use some name-brand sports equipment endorsed by a major sports performer. These choices may have nothing to do with safety, comfort, or performance during your activity—factors that other people consider to be most important. Here are some tips for making wise buying decisions:

- Clothing should be comfortable and loose around the joints. Cotton or other porous materials are best because they absorb perspiration and allow air through.
- Footwear should have a cushioned heel, good arch support, and ample toe room.
- If you are starting a new sport, rent or borrow the equipment to see how you like the sport before spending a lot of money on equipment.

Avoiding Risk and Injury During Exercise

What can you think of that would help you avoid being injured during exercise? Think back to your own experiences during exercise or to the experiences of others you know who have been injured.

Why do people get hurt? As you begin your own exercise program, think carefully about safety and caring for your body. If you think of your body as a valuable resource, one that needs care and attention, then you will see that prevention is the best way to avoid injuries.

DID YOU KNOW?

- To emphasize total body stretching and strengthening, take ballet or modern dance classes. Both help alignment of head, arms, torso, legs, and feet.
- You can discover if you have any errors in your running form by having a friend video-tape you while you are running.

LESSON 2 REVIEW

Reviewing Facts and Vocabulary

1. Describe five injuries that can occur during exercise.
2. Name two injuries to the muscles and to the joints that may occur when the body is not in condition or when there is not sufficient warm-up.
3. What is tendinitis?

Thinking Critically

4. **Analysis.** Compare heatstroke and heat exhaustion.
5. **Analysis.** What is the difference between a sprain and a strain?

Applying Health Knowledge

6. Compile a list of at least 10 sports and recreational activities adults engage in as part of an exercise program. Evaluate the risk of injury in each.
7. Research the cost of dress and equipment for a particular exercise program. Make two detailed lists: one of what is necessary for the program; the other of what might be used in the program. Use newspapers, catalogs, and other means to compare prices. Show how little could be spent and how much could be spent for the exercise program chosen.

AVOIDING INJURY **365**

Answers to Lesson 2 Review

1. Answers will vary. Accept any five descriptions found on pages 360 to 362.
2. Answers will vary. Accept two of the following: Sprain, dislocation, pulled or torn muscle, strain, muscle cramp.
3. Inflammation that occurs when a tendon is torn.
4. Answers will vary but should reflect an understanding of the information on pages 362 to 363.
5. Answers will vary but should reflect an understanding of the information on pages 360 to 361.
6. Answers will vary.
7. Answers will vary.

Helping Students Improve Their Health

Teaching Strategies

L1 EXPLANATION. It is important that students recognize that cardiovascular fitness is improved only when one engages in aerobic activities, such as the activities listed in the self-inventory. It would also be important to stress to students that for true improvements in cardiovascular fitness, one would need to participate in these activities for a minimum of twenty minutes at the individual's training or target heart rate.

L1 DISCUSSION. Have students brainstorm a list of their favorite activities that they enjoy participating in after school. Create ideas on how to turn the most sedentary activities into physically active adventures.

L1 CLASS ACTIVITY. Have students take their resting heart rate in class and record this number on a sheet of paper. Have students contract to increase their aerobic activity level in order to improve their level of cardiovascular fitness. Have students keep a diary of their activity level. After 6 weeks, have students check their resting heart rate in order to determine if the number has decreased. If the number has decreased, it can be assumed that their level of cardiovascular fitness has improved.

DID YOU KNOW?

■ In 5 hours and 31 minutes, 81-year-old Mavis Lindgren ran a marathon (26.1 miles). It was her 52nd time to run a marathon. She ran her first race at age 70.

Self-Inventory

Aerobic Alternatives

HOW DO YOU RATE?

Number a sheet of paper from 1 through 12. Read each item below, and respond by writing *MT* for any activity you do more than three times a week. Write *TT* for any activity you do two or three times a week and *OW* for any activity you do once a week.

1. I walk continuously 20 minutes or more.
2. I walk continuously 20 minutes or more using hand weights.
3. I jog or run continuously 20 minutes or more.
4. I swim continuously 20 minutes or more.
5. I ride a bike continuously 20 minutes or more.
6. I dance continuously 20 minutes or more.
7. I roller-skate or use rollerblades continuously 20 minutes or more.
8. I play basketball continuously 20 minutes or more.
9. I play volleyball continuously 20 minutes or more.
10. I play tennis or badminton continuously 20 minutes or more.
11. I play football or soccer continuously 20 minutes or more.
12. I play softball or baseball continuously 20 minutes or more.

HOW DID YOU SCORE?

Give yourself 5 points for every *MT* response, 3 points for every *TT* response, and 1 point for every *OW* response. Find your total, and read below to see how you scored. Then proceed to the next section.

15 and above
Excellent. You are to be commended for promoting your health. Keep up the good work.

5 to 14
Good. It's great you are active. More activity will increase your fitness and health.

Below 5
Needs Improvement. Join in the fun and fitness. Feel good about yourself. Try some of the activities listed above. You are sure to find one you will enjoy.

WHAT ARE YOUR GOALS?

If you received an *excellent* or *good* score, complete the statements in Part A. If your score *needs improvement,* complete Parts A and B.

Part A

1. I plan to learn more about different types of aerobic exercise by ____.
2. My timetable for accomplishing this is ____.
3. I plan to share my information with others by ____.

Part B

4. The behavior or attitude toward aerobic exercise that I would most like to change is ____.
5. The steps involved in making this change are ____.
6. My rewards for making this change will be ____.
7. My timetable for making this change is ____.
8. The people or groups I will ask for help are ____.

Meeting Students' Needs

For students who score *Excellent*. Encourage students, as a group, to create an exercise video and market their product as a fund-raiser.

For students who score *Good*. Have students design an after-school exercise hour that will utilize available school facilities. Have them organize a peer-support structure to encourage others to improve their level of fitness.

For students who *Need Improvement*. Suggest that students pick a 20-minute time period after school when they could begin engaging in physical activity. Have students commit to giving up one-half hour of TV every other night for activity.

Building Decision-Making Skills

D an and his friend, Tony, have always shared a commitment to good health and fitness. Their fitness program includes eating nutritious foods, working out together, and avoiding alcohol and other drugs. The boys' workout program is varied. Some days they jog or cycle; other days they lift weights and do calisthenics. Recently Tony has had to cut back on his workout time with Dan

in order to study for final exams. Dan has noticed that sometimes Tony stays up all night studying. He seems to have unpredictable mood swings, and he's been seen in the company of some of the school's known drug users. Dan suspects that Tony is using steroids, but he doesn't know for sure. He wants to confront his friend, but if he is wrong, he could ruin a great friendship. What should Dan do?

A. Look for more evidence before confronting Tony. Then talk with him about his concern.

B. Forget it and do nothing. Final exams will be over in a few weeks and things will probably be back to normal.

C. Tell Tony's parents of his suspicions and let them handle it.

D. Stop being friends with Tony

since he no longer seems to share a commitment to good health and fitness.

WHAT DO YOU THINK?

1. **Choices.** What other choices does Dan have?

2. **Consequences.** What are the advantages of each choice?

3. **Consequences.** What are the disadvantages of each choice?

4. **Decision.** What do you think Dan should do?

5. **Evaluation.** Have you ever been in a situation where a friend appeared to be losing his or her energy and health? How did you handle the situation? Would you do the same thing now? Explain your answer.

D ana loves her part-time job at a local restaurant. She likes the people she works with and all the things she's been able to do with the money she's earned. The only bad part about the job is that she's gaining

weight and feeling sluggish, probably because of her love for the restaurant's famous double fudge sundaes and because she has quit running track in order to work more hours. What should Dana do?

A. Reduce her hours and rejoin the track team.

B. Control the number of sundaes she eats.

C. Get into some other kind of exercise program.

D. Get a different job—one that doesn't tempt her with food.

WHAT DO YOU THINK?

6. **Choices.** What other choices does Dana have?

7. **Consequences.** What are the advantages and disadvantages of each choice?

8. **Decision.** Which choice should Dana make?

9. **Evaluation.** Why might it be important for teens to have a job and be part of a school activity?

10. **Evaluation.** Staying active can be one of the most difficult things to do. How does one overcome this difficulty?

Discussing the Answers

Situation 1. If Dan's suspicions are correct, there is a strong possibility that the friendship may not survive Tony's continued use of steroids. Because Dan cares about his friend, he must do something. Perhaps the best resolve in this situation would be to talk to a trusted adult, such as a guidance counselor. The guidance counselor may be able to advise Dan

on whether or not something should be done.

Situation 2. Obviously, Dana cares about this weight gain and would like to do something about it. Dana needs to find the commitment to say no to the double fudge sundaes and yes to finding time in her schedule to maintain physical activity.

Helping Students Improve Their Health

Building Decision-Making Skills

Teaching Strategies

L1 CLASS ACTIVITY. Have students role-play Dan as he discusses his concern about Tony with (a) a guidance counselor, (b) another friend, (c) Dan's parents, (d) Tony's parents. How might these different support systems vary in their responses? How might these support systems react the same? Which support system, if any, should Dan try first?

L1 CLASS ACTIVITY. Have students discuss the issue of Dana gaining weight. How can Dana begin to lose this weight? Should Dana quit her job at the restaurant? Should Dana take diet pills or use other drastic methods to achieve weight loss?

L1 CLASS ACTIVITY. Other possible role-plays pertaining to teenagers getting fit and staying fit include: (1) A friend of yours has always had a weight problem. For years your friend has tried to lose weight desperately and has failed, while tolerating cruel jokes from classmates. Recently, your friend has begun to be successful in losing weight. Everyone is complimenting your friend on how good he or she looks. The problem now, you believe, is that your friend has become dependent upon diet pills. You do not want to ruin the happiness that your friend is experiencing, but you are concerned. (2) Your family never exercises together and now you would like everyone in your family to get involved in some kind of physical activity as a family. Your father is very resistant. You wonder how you can convince your father to become involved.

L2 DISCUSSION. Have students debate the pros and cons of professional athletic events advertising beer products through commercials. Is it appropriate that these two different images be presented together? What kind of mixed statement does this send to adolescents?

Answers to Chapter 18 Review

Using Health Terms

1. Anaerobic
2. Target heart rate
3. Frequency
4. Aerobic
5. Duration
6. Muscle cramps
7. Anabolic steroids
8. Hernias or ruptures
9. Bruise
10. Frostbite

Building Academic Skills

11. Answers will vary.
12. Stories will vary.

Recalling the Facts

13. Lightheadedness and possibly fainting.
14. The slower one's resting heart rate, the more physically fit he or she is.
15. Answers may include but are not limited to: Anaerobic—lifting weights or using weight-training machines; aerobic—walking, jogging, cycling, swimming.
16. During exercise the stomach is deprived of oxygen, so if it is full you might experience stomach cramps or nausea.
17. Warm-up, workout, cool down.
18. It allows the pulse rate to increase slowly.
19. If one can't talk while exercising, one is working too hard.
20. Exercise builds muscle tissue, which is heavier than fat.
21. Answers will vary. Accept answers from the chart on page 357.
22. The purpose is to record one's progress. It might include goals, weight, measurements, how one feels, how well and how long one sleeps, resting heart rate, target heart rate, frequency/intensity/duration of workouts.
23. Every six weeks.
24. Improve or maintain one's current level of fitness.
25. Six months of three times a week.
26. Poor physical condition, insufficient warm-up,

Using Health Terms

On a separate sheet of paper, write the term that best matches each definition given below.

LESSON 1

1. Type of activity that targets specific muscle groups, usually to strengthen them.
2. The optimum heart rate one should sustain during exercise.
3. How often something is done.
4. Type of exercise designed to improve one's endurance.
5. How long something is done.

LESSON 2

6. Occurs when a muscle contracts tightly and will not relax.
7. Chemicals used to increase muscle mass without increasing fat.
8. Weak area in a muscle through which part of another organ, such as the intestines, may push out.
9. Injury to tissue under the skin, resulting from a blow to the muscle.
10. Frozen tissue as a result of prolonged exposure to extreme cold.

Building Academic Skills

LESSON 1

11. **Reading.** Many people believe that exercise will help them live longer, healthier, happier lives. There are those who disagree, however. Read *The Exercise Myth* by Henry A. Solomon, M.D. Decide what the author's point of view is and what his purpose for writing is. Then decide if you think his point is valid or not. Support your opinion in writing.

LESSON 2

12. **Writing.** Many fiction writers research background to make their accounts more realistic. Using accurate facts, write a short fiction story in which the main character has chosen to use anabolic steroids.

Recalling the Facts

LESSON 1

13. What can happen as a result of pooling?
14. How does a person's resting heart rate indicate his or her level of fitness?
15. Give examples of anaerobic exercises and aerobic exercises.
16. Why should a person not exercise too soon after eating?
17. What three components should every exercise program consist of?
18. How is warming up beneficial to a person's pulse rate?
19. If someone does not know his or her target heart rate, what is a good rule of thumb to follow?
20. Why might a person weigh more instead of less after starting to exercise?
21. Give two examples of activities that promote a high level of conditioning, two that are moderate level, and two that are low level.
22. What is the purpose of an exercise journal and what might be included in it?
23. How often should someone check his or her improvement due to exercise?
24. What should an exercise program do?
25. How long will it likely take for a person to become physically fit?

LESSON 2

26. What are three factors that increase the risk of injury?
27. What should be done for a dislocation?
28. What causes and prevents muscle cramps?
29. What can be done to relieve a muscle cramp?
30. What is tennis elbow and how should it be treated?
31. What are two things one should never do to treat frostbite?
32. Which two body systems are most likely to be injured during exercise?
33. Why does a bruise become discolored?
34. What are the two most common injuries to the skeletal system?

attempting physical activities beyond one's level of ability.
27. Keep the injury as quiet as possible and seek medical attention.
28. Causes—temporary lack of food or oxygen to the muscle, overtiring and overworking muscles, strenuous exercise. Prevention—

warm up properly, drink plenty of fluids before and during exercise.
29. Massage the muscle, move or continue to work the muscle, apply heat.
30. A tendinitis injury. The injured area should be allowed to rest and then medicine or physical therapy to treat it.

Thinking Critically

LESSON 1

35. Synthesis. Explain the phrase "No pain, no gain," and tell why it is not true.

36. Synthesis. Outline an exercise program for yourself. Include alternative activities if poor weather should interfere with your program.

37. Evaluation. Interest in exercise is a fairly recent trend. Do you think it will continue? Support your answer.

38. Analysis. What types of safety equipment would be needed for the following activities? Explain.

a. bicycling   e. playing basketball
b. skateboarding   f. playing soccer
c. running at night   g. playing football
d. playing softball   h. playing ice hockey

LESSON 2

39. Analysis. For each of the following situations, tell what injury the victim has suffered and how you would help him or her.

a. Mr. Smythe had been working in his garden for 3 hours in the hot sun. Suddenly, he fell to the ground. He was not perspiring, and he felt very hot. His pulse was racing, breathing was difficult, and his face was very red.

b. After jogging 5 miles in 96-degree heat, Jenny felt she could not go on. She was perspiring a lot. She became pale, dizzy, nauseated, and had trouble breathing.

Making the Connection

LESSON 1

40. Language Arts. Prepare a short talk about physical fitness for an elementary school class. Present and define these components of physical fitness—flexibility, muscular strength, muscular endurance, and cardiorespiratory endurance. Demonstrate at least one fitness test that could be used to assess each component.

Applying Health Knowledge

LESSON 1

41. What exercise limitations might be posed by weather in the area where you live?

42. Give examples of physical limitations someone your age might have.

43. Which of the following schedules would be better for exercise? Explain why.
a. Monday, Tuesday, Wednesday
b. Monday, Friday, Sunday
c. Monday, Wednesday, Saturday

44. Plan a warm-up for an activity you enjoy.

45. What is a good cool-down activity for jogging?

LESSON 2

46. For treatment of a sprain, why should heat not be applied to the injured area?

47. According to Peter Francis, Ph.D., and Lorna Francis, Ph.D., authors of *If It Hurts, Don't Do It*, 40 percent of America's adult population does not exercise at all. Discuss why you think that is. What do you think you could say or do to convince these people to start exercising?

Beyond the Classroom

LESSON 1

48. Community Involvement. Research aerobic programs available in your community. Contact the instructor of each program to find out what type of warm-up, workout, and cool down is practiced. Publish your information in a directory or an article in the school newspaper.

49. Parental Involvement. Sometimes exercising with someone provides needed support and motivation. With a parent, develop an exercise program with activities appropriate and convenient for everyone in your family. Do your exercises together.

50. Further Study. Find out all you can about sports medicine and what types of careers this field might lead to.

31. Never rub the injured area or expose it to intense heat.

32. Skeletal and muscular systems.

33. Capillaries break and ooze blood under the skin.

34. Sprains and dislocations.

Thinking Critically

35. It means that if the exercise does not hurt one is not benefitting from it. Exercise should not hurt. If it does, one is either doing something incorrectly or doing too much.

36. Answers will vary but outlines should include activities for warm-up, workout, and cool down.

37. Answers will vary but should be supported logically.

38. Answers will vary. Possible answers: A—helmet; B—helmet, knee and elbow pads; C—reflective clothing; D—helmet when batting; E—mouth guards, athletic supporter for males; F—shin and mouth guards, cleats, athletic supporters for males; G—mouth guards, helmets, shoulder pads, cleats; H—helmet, mouth guard, shoulder pads, rib protector, hip pads, gloves, thigh and shin guards. Explanations will vary.

39. A—heatstroke. Call for an ambulance, then move victim to a cool place, loosen any restrictive clothing, and spray or sponge victim with cold water. Administer artificial respiration if necessary. B—heat exhaustion. Move victim to a cool place, keep him or her lying down with his or her head slightly lowered.

Making the Connection

40. Answers will vary.

Applying Health Knowledge

41. Answers will vary but accept any examples of inclement weather.

42. Answers will vary. Possible answers: Congenital heart problems, obesity, bone or muscle deformities.

43. C—there is at least one day between exercise days, but no more than two.

44. Answers will vary. Refer to page 355.

45. Answers will vary. Possible answer: Walking.

46. Heat would cause the blood vessels to expand and would increase internal bleeding, making the injury worse.

47. Answers will vary. Possible answers: Stress that exercise does not have to be overwhelming or painful to be beneficial, point out benefits of moderate exercise.

Beyond the Classroom

48. Answers will vary.

49. Answers will vary.

50. Answers will vary.

Lesson Summaries

LESSON 1. Food impacts life because it supplies nutrients the body needs to function properly. Food choices are linked to one's physical needs, social and cultural background, and emotions.

LESSON 2. During digestion, food breaks down, and simpler nutrients are released and absorbed to provide energy, build, repair, and maintain body tissues, and regulate body processes.

LESSON 3. Food selection guidelines, such as the Dietary Guidelines and Daily Food Guide, help one choose a healthful diet. A varied, moderate, and balanced diet forms the foundation of a healthy eating pattern.

LESSON 4. Information on food labels, on supermarket shelves, and even in restaurants can help consumers know what they are buying and eating.

Introducing the Chapter

Display a food that is probably unfamiliar to many of your students, such as fresh ginger, artichokes, or chutney. Ask for volunteers to taste the food. Then discuss why the volunteers were willing to try something new. Why were other people less willing to do so? What factors influenced their decision to try something new? (Peer pressure, smell, appearance, color, etc.) Tell students that they will learn about their reasons for making food choices and about the positive effects of good nutrition as they study this chapter.

Performance Assessment ✓

Refer to pages T 23 to T 25 for a Performance Assessment strategy for this chapter. See the *Performance Assessment Activities* booklet for additional suggestions.

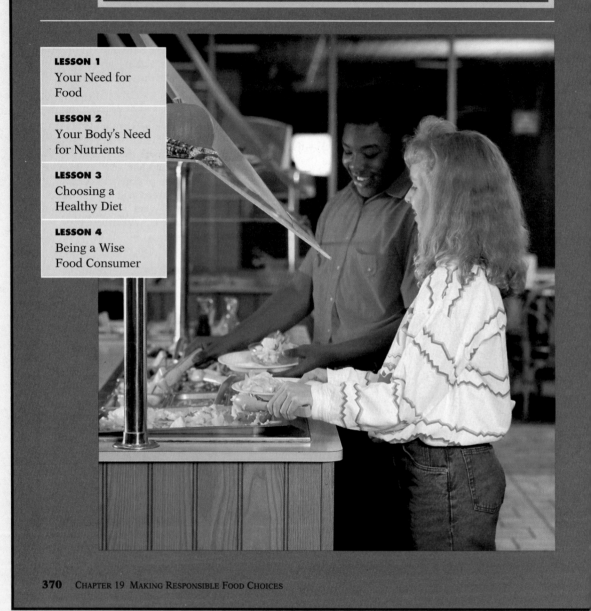

CHAPTER 19
MAKING RESPONSIBLE FOOD CHOICES

LESSON 1
Your Need for Food

LESSON 2
Your Body's Need for Nutrients

LESSON 3
Choosing a Healthy Diet

LESSON 4
Being a Wise Food Consumer

Key to Ability Levels

Teaching strategies have been coded for varying learning styles and abilities.

L1 Level 1 activities are basic activities and should be within the ability range of all students.

L2 Level 2 activities are average activities and should be within the ability range of average to above-average students.

L3 Level 3 activities are challenging activities designed for the ability range of above-average students.

LD LD activities should be within the ability range of learning-disabled students.

LEP LEP activities should be within the ability range of Limited English Proficiency students.

YOUR NEED FOR FOOD

In one way or another, food affects almost everything you do. It affects how you look, feel, and act. It affects how you grow. It even affects your abilities—how well you function each day. Conversely, how you look, feel, and act influences what you eat.

Food has an impact on life because it supplies nutrients. **Nutrients** are substances in food that the body needs to function properly such as in growing, in repairing itself, and in having a supply of energy.

Nutrition is both a pure science and a social science. As a pure science it looks at how the body uses nutrients. As a social science it looks at the relationship between food and human behavior and the environment, or how and why people eat.

Why Do You Eat?

Have you ever wondered why you eat and why you make certain food choices? The reasons may be more complex than you realize. Your choices about food are linked to your physical needs, your environment, and your emotions.

Your Physical Health

The most basic reason for eating is physical. Eating is a matter of survival, as well as growth, energy, and fitness.

Food, along with air and water, is one of life's basic needs. When you go without food for a long time, you feel hungry. This is your body's signal that it needs more food. After you eat, the feelings of hunger disappear. You have satisfied your physical need for food.

Eating the right amounts and kinds of food gives energy and stamina for active life-styles. A nutritious diet provides for growth and maintenance of a healthy body and helps keep you mentally alert.

If good food choices aid health and performance, then what you eat affects everyday living. In addition, six out of ten leading causes of death in the United States are linked in some way to food. Eating well not only reduces health risks, it also adds to the quality and the length of your life.

Your Environment

Your food choices are linked to many factors. Your cultural heritage, your family and social relationships, media messages, and life-style all influence the foods you like and choose.

Culture. What foods do you associate with picnics, baseball games, county fairs, holidays, and birthday parties? Your food choices reflect

---

LESSON 1 FOCUS

TERMS TO USE
- Nutrients (NOO•tree•uhnts)
- Nutrition

CONCEPTS TO LEARN
- Your body depends on you to provide nutrients that it needs to function.
- Food choices are linked to cultural heritage, family and social relationships, media messages, and life-style.
- At every stage of life, good nutrition is essential for health.

ATTITUDES AND BEHAVIORS TO EVALUATE
- Self-Inventory, page 398.
- Building Decision-Making Skills, page 399.

Focus

Lesson Objectives

After studying this lesson, students should be able to:
- describe factors that influence one's food choices
- explain how food choices reflect one's culture, ethnic background, and, perhaps, one's religious beliefs
- identify ways that family members and friends may affect one's food decisions and preferences
- point out how time and money influence food choices
- discuss how eating relates to a person's emotions

Bellringer

Write the following on the chalkboard for students to work on while attendance is being taken: *List five foods you like and five you dislike. Beside each food, write a reason why you like or dislike it.*

Introducing the Lesson

Have volunteers share their responses to the Bellringer. On the chalkboard, list foods that come up repeatedly. Students may change their minds as they hear others' responses. Ask students to name factors other than taste that influence their choice of foods. Tell them they will learn more about influences on food choices as they study this lesson.

DID YOU KNOW?

- The word *gourmet*, which means someone who is an expert on food and drink, originally meant wine taster.
- Why don't many of us eat enough vegetables? Typical excuses include not enough refrigerator space, disagreeable taste, and too difficult to prepare.

YOUR NEED FOR FOOD **371**

Resources for Lesson 1

- **Guided Reading** Activity 49
- **Workbook** Vocabulary Activity 49
- **Reteaching** Activity 49
- **Lesson 1 Quiz**
- **BARN Software,** Body Management
- **Performance Assessment** Activity 19

Building Vocabulary

- Have students use the terms *nutrients* and *nutrition* in a written paragraph. Ask them to read their paragraphs to the class.
- Ask students to complete *Workbook Vocabulary Activity 49.*

Teach

Guided Practice

L1 DISCUSSION. Talk about how food is related to common adolescent health concerns such as weight control, cavities, acne, etc. Point out the relationship of diet to overall well-being.

L1 CLASS ACTIVITY. Most newspapers have a food section one day each week. Ask students to begin reading that section to collect questions submitted and answered about nutrition. Use these as a point of discussion and for collecting additional information throughout the unit.

LD DISCUSSION. Ask students to describe one of their family's favorite foods and explain why it is special. (Examples might include an old family recipe, a food that is served on special occasions, or a food that is part of a cultural tradition.)

L1 CLASS ACTIVITY. Ask a representative of the Jewish (or other) faith to describe his or her food customs.

L1 CLASS ACTIVITY. Ask students who have lived in other regions of the United States to present a brief oral report describing the differences in food customs they have found among the various regions.

L1 CLASS ACTIVITY. Ask students to write and present a skit portraying the role of peer pressure on food choices. Afterwards, ask students to list foods they eat with friends that they might not eat at home.

the culture you live in, as well as your ethnic background and perhaps your religious beliefs. Teenagers have a culture of their own, too. What food practices seem to be part of teen culture?

Family and Friends. Children pattern their food habits after their role models, perhaps parents or older brothers and sisters. What you ate as a child, what you learned to like and dislike, and when you ate meals were all influenced by your family. These influences affect your food decisions and preferences now—and they will continue to influence you throughout your life.

As you have grown older, friends have influenced your food choices. Perhaps you tried new foods at their homes or tasted different foods at parties. Because eating can be a social experience, food is the focus of many gatherings. Many people use food as gifts. A gift of food may show someone you care.

Advertising. Food ads are everywhere—on television, in magazines, and on billboards. Food ads are created to make you aware of certain foods and, perhaps, of their benefits. Most importantly, they shape food decisions. Think of food ads you see and hear on television. Which foods have you bought or tried as a result of an ad?

Many people believe everything they read in newspapers and see and hear on television and radio. Yet, an ad may tell just part of the truth. For example, an ad may state that a food is low in fat without mentioning that it is high in calories. Advertisers spend millions of dollars on powerful persuasion techniques. Ads may try to persuade you that status, sex appeal, weight loss, or a terrific appearance will be yours if you buy the product.

To make informed food choices, you need to know about food and health. You need to listen and judge advertising messages carefully. That way, you—not advertisers—control what foods you buy and eat.

Time and Money. Cost, convenience, taste, nutrition, and food safety are the factors that influence food shopping most, according to consumer studies.

With today's busy life-styles, people rely more on foods they can cook and eat quickly, such as convenience foods and microwave meals. To stay healthy, choose nutritious foods that you can prepare and eat within the time you have available. Skipping meals is not the answer.

Cost also affects food choices. How has cost affected food decisions you have made?

KEEPING FIT

Your Family's Cooking Heritage

Many families have family recipes or foods that they serve only on special occasions. Sometimes these food choices stem from particular tastes of the individuals within that family. But often, specific ingredients, recipes, serving styles, or food lore hold valuable family history. A family's food choices often have strong ties to the culture of one's ancestors or relatives. Learning to grow, prepare, and cook these foods can become a hands-on way of learning about your cultural heritage. It can also be an effective way to preserve and pass on your family's history.

Across the Curriculum

Social Studies. Have students research foods that are popular in different countries. If possible, bring (or have students bring) to class produce (such as mangoes, pomegranates, etc.) and other foods, and discuss with students the source of these foods. Also, ask students to locate pictures of foreign foods or foreign recipes from cookbooks. Discuss how culture and ethnic background affect food traditions and choices.

Home Economics. Many students and their families fail to eat breakfast, citing lack of time to prepare it. Invite a home economics teacher to demonstrate and prepare quick-fix breakfast foods.

Nutritional needs are different at various stages of life. Which of these individuals probably need more calories than other individuals of the same age?

Your Emotions

Think about some of your eating habits. Have you ever headed to the refrigerator just because you had nothing else to do? Do you tend to eat more—or less—when you feel stressed, frustrated, or depressed? Do you tend to eat when you are watching an exciting game? What do you eat when you feel really good or when you want to celebrate? What foods do you think are just plain fun to eat?

Eating is closely tied to emotions. Eating to relieve tension or boredom can result in overeating. However, if you lose your appetite when you are upset or bored, you may miss out on getting essential nutrients. By understanding how eating relates to emotions, you can make more healthful food choices.

L1 DISCUSSION. Ask students to identify the leading factors that affect their food choices. Have them consider questions such as: Do they really love pizza or do they eat it because their friends do? Do they choose easy foods for breakfast when they prepare it themselves? How much do they consider the cost of foods when eating out?

L1 DISCUSSION. Is peer pressure a positive or negative influence on food choices? Why? (It can be both. For example, friends can encourage a sense of adventure by introducing peers to new foods, but they may pressure their friends into poor food choices.)

L1 DISCUSSION. Talk about why the majority of total advertising time (for food) on television is spent on desserts, snacks, and soft drinks. (Compared to the other foods advertised, these are probably bought by most of the television audience.)

LEP CLASS ACTIVITY. Give each student a food advertisement from a magazine or newspaper and ask them if the ad makes them want to eat the food. Have them give reasons for their answers.

DID YOU KNOW?

■ How far can the human body go in 20 minutes on 200 calories of "fuel"? It depends on how you travel—you can swim for 850 yards, bike for 5 miles, or run for 2 miles.

Independent Practice

L1 PARENTAL INVOLVEMENT. Ask for volunteers to interview older family members or neighbors about their food choices and reasons for those choices.

L1 COMMUNITY INVOLVEMENT. Ask for volunteers to visit an ethnic restaurant to try new foods. Afterwards, have them discuss their experience with the class.

Additional Information

Advertising. Advertising is regulated by federal and state laws and agencies. The Federal Trade Commission (FTC) oversees truth in advertising. The Food and Drug Administration (FDA) deals with the labeling and advertising of material shipped with packages or used as supplements to labels. Radio and television advertising are regulated by the Federal Communications Commission (FCC). State laws for advertising vary widely, although most states have truth-in-advertising laws prohibiting false and misleading advertisements.

■ **Discussion.** Why should Ray avoid eating processed foods? How could this be considered a health bonus? (They often contain "hidden" grain products as additives, thickeners, and emulsifiers—as well as fat, salt, and refined sugar.)

■ **Speaker.** Invite a nutrition expert to speak to the class about food allergies. (Check with a local university or hospital for speakers; ask the speaker to address which food allergies are most common, their usual symptoms, and the dietary restrictions associated with each.)

■ **Answers**

1. It lowered his self-esteem because he felt sorry for himself.

2. Learn about or devise alternatives—foods, activities, ways of doing things, whatever the restrictions are.

3. When you help others cope, you quit feeling sorry for yourself and improve your self-esteem.

L2 **SELF-ESTEEM.** Have students examine their present diet to understand factors that influence food choices. Ask them to list at least one food that they eat because of each of the following influences: childhood preference, family custom, ethnic background, teen culture, peer pressure, role models, advertising, time, money, and personal emotions. Ask them to think of times when they were feeling low and times when they were feeling good. Did their self-esteem influence their food choices at those times?

L1 **USING THE LESSON RESOURCES.** For additional student activities, refer to the lesson resources on page 371.

Overcoming The Odds

"My name is Ray Winne-mucca. I'm 16 years old. I've always been pretty healthy. My parents have always talked about respecting and nourishing our bodies. We've always had a garden. We don't buy much junk food. So when I started having a problem, food was the last thing anybody suspected."

The problem Ray is talking about is celiac sprue disease. It is a chronic disease caused by the body's inability to tolerate gluten, a protein found in wheat, rye, barley, and oats. It causes the body to have a hard time absorbing essential nutrients and digesting food properly. "I started having these awful stomach cramps. I was losing weight and feeling really tired all the time. My stomach was bloated. Our doctor gave me antibiotics in case I had an intestinal infection. Then my bones started to hurt. I even seemed to stop growing, and that's when they took me to the medical center for all kinds

of tests. For the first time, I was scared. I started to think all kinds of awful things. I even thought I might be dying.

"Then they diagnosed celiac sprue disease. They told me I'd just have to eat a gluten-free

diet, which sounded like no big deal. What I didn't realize at the time was that many foods I eat come from these grains. Many thickeners, additives, and emulsifiers used in processed foods are on my 'No' list, so chocolate milk, many salad dressings, canned

soups, and even ice cream are out.

"For a while I was really depressed and then I got angry. I felt bad about myself because I had to say no to foods my friends could eat. It was hard. Eventually, I got sick of feeling depressed and got motivated to learn all I could about food. Now, my friends ask me to cook for them sometimes because I'm really creative about it. My energy is back, and my size is normal for my age. Still, I wish I didn't have this problem. I'll be on this special diet for the rest of my life. So I have to make the best of it.

"Right now, I'm working on a gluten-free cook-book with recipes like gluten-free pizza for people my age that have celiac sprue disease. I feel good that out of this I'm learning new skills and reaching out."

1. How did Ray's health problem affect his self-esteem?
2. When faced with a health concern, what are some ways a person can, as Ray has, "make the best of it"?
3. How can learning new skills and reaching out help a person cope with dietary, health, or other problems?

374 Chapter 19 Making Responsible Food Choices

Additional Information

Feeding Strategies. Although humans and other animals do many things that plants cannot, plants do something extremely important that animals cannot—they can synthesize all the compounds they require from a few basic inorganic substances. They are therefore called autotrophs or "self-feeders."

Animals, on the other hand, including most bacteria, are called heterotrophs or "other-feeders," because there are usually many compounds they cannot synthesize, which therefore must be present in their food. Animals may eat plants (herbivores), other animals (carnivores), both plants and animals (omnivores), or the wastes or remains of other organisms (detrivores).

Nutrition Throughout Your Life

At every stage in life, good nutrition is essential for health. Even before you were born, then as an infant and a child, and now as a teen, nutrients in food have provided you with substances you needed to grow and develop. At each age you have needed the same nutrients. As you have grown and developed, however, you have needed them in increasing amounts.

Adults of all ages continue to need the same nutrients, though in slightly smaller amounts. As people become less active and as metabolic rate declines with age, caloric needs go down. However, the need for the right nutrients in the right amounts is still important. No matter what age a person is, choosing foods wisely is a major key to health.

Nutrition and Adolescence

Next to the first years of your life, adolescence is the period of the fastest and most growth you will experience. Adolescence is also a time when your life-style is probably a very active one. Good nutrition is important to both your growth and the energy you need to maintain an active life-style.

Many teenagers, however, skip meals or substitute high-fat or sugary foods for more nutritious choices. Why do you think this is true?

As you read about nutrition and its effect on your body and health, evaluate your own eating habits. Identify food choices you can control, changes you might need to make, and food choices that could affect your total health and level of performance. Then plan to promote your health by making wise food choices.

Culturally Speaking

Foods on the World's Table

As you learn about other cultures, you may also increase your knowledge about food and learn to like various foods or new ways to prepare foods. Consider these international food facts:

- In Israel, salad may be served for breakfast.
- Arab foods often include heavily spiced lamb and chicken mixed with rice.
- The national drink in Iran is tea.
- On holidays in India, sweetened milk is served.
- In Vietnam, fish is often served in the form of a sauce called nuoc mam. Buffalo is sometimes a main dish.

Assess

Check for Understanding
- Assign and discuss the lesson review. Encourage LD students to focus on questions 1, 2, 3, and 4.

Evaluate
- Administer, grade, and discuss the *Lesson 1 Quiz*.

Reteach
- Have students make a list of the factors that influence people's food choices. After each factor, ask them to write at least one sentence, summarizing what they learned about that factor in the lesson.
- Ask students to complete *Reteaching Activity 49*.

Enrich
- Ask for volunteers to videotape several television food commercials to present to the class. Have students critique the effectiveness of the ads.

Close

Place seven plates or soup bowls on a table with a label in front of each one with the following concepts: *physical health, culture, family and friends, advertising, time and money, emotions,* and *nutrition and adolescence.* Divide the class into seven groups, and assign each group one of the seven concepts. Have each group compose a paragraph summarizing its concept. Bring the class together, and select volunteers to read the paragraphs aloud. Briefly discuss whether the paragraphs accurately summarize the concepts.

LESSON 1 REVIEW

Reviewing Facts and Vocabulary

1. Define the terms *nutrients* and *nutrition*.
2. Describe factors that influence food choices, and give five examples.
3. Why is good nutrition so important during adolescence?
4. Describe how your nutritional needs will change between your teen years and adult years.

Thinking Critically

5. **Analysis.** How have your culture and family influenced your food habits?

6. **Analysis.** Compare your food habits with those of a friend. What might account for the differences?
7. **Synthesis.** Describe how emotions can affect food choices. Give two examples.

Applying Health Knowledge

8. Evaluate five food advertisements on radio or television. Discuss the approach each one uses to influence your food choices.
9. Read the newspaper for a week. Find five stories that show how the world around you influences food choices. Summarize your findings in writing.

Answers to Lesson 1 Review

1. Definitions are on page 371.
2. Cultural heritage, family and social relationships, media messages, life-style. Examples may include those found on pages 371 to 372.
3. Adolescence is the second fastest period of growth, and good nutrition is important for growth and energy.
4. The same nutrients will be needed, though in slightly smaller amounts.
5. Answers will vary.
6. Answers will vary.
7. Answers will vary. Possible answer: One may eat more or less because one is bored, happy, stressed, or depressed.
8. Answers will vary.
9. Answers will vary.

Focus

Lesson Objectives

After studying this lesson, students should be able to:

- define each of the six main categories of nutrients
- describe the role of each class of nutrient in maintaining good health
- identify food sources for each nutrient
- define cholesterol and explain its relationship to overall health
- contrast complete and incomplete proteins
- discuss properties of water-soluble vitamins and fat-soluble vitamins
- explain the meaning of Recommended Dietary Allowances and their role as guidelines for nutrient and caloric intake

Bellringer

Write the following on the chalkboard for students to work on while attendance is being taken: *List the following nutrients on a sheet of paper: carbohydrates, fats, proteins, vitamins, minerals, and water. For each nutrient, list as many foods as you can that are good sources of that nutrient.*

Introducing the Lesson

Have students share their responses to the Bellringer. Ask them to save their responses until the end of the lesson to check their accuracy.

DID YOU KNOW?

According to Tom Parker's book, *In One Day*, each day Americans consume:

- 170 million eggs
- 12 million chickens
- 1.2 million bushels of potatoes
- 200 million pounds of fresh fruit and vegetables
- 12.5 million pounds of cheese
- 3 million pounds of butter
- 7 million pounds of margarine
- 3 million gallons of ice cream and ice milk
- 50 million pounds of sugar
- 47 million hot dogs
- 75 acres of pizza.

LESSON 2

YOUR BODY'S NEED FOR NUTRIENTS

Nutrients in food perform life-sustaining functions in the body. During digestion, food is broken down into simpler forms of nutrients that are released and absorbed. Through the blood, nutrients are taken to body cells where nourishment takes place.

Nutrients nourish the body in three main ways. They provide energy; build, repair, and maintain body tissues; and regulate body processes.

Scientists have identified more than 40 different nutrients for good health. These nutrients can be grouped into six main categories: carbohydrates, fats, proteins, vitamins, minerals, and water. Each has a unique function in the normal growth and functioning of the body. As you will see, no one food provides all the nutrients your body needs.

Carbohydrates

For most body functions, **carbohydrates** are the body's preferred source of energy, or calories. There are several forms of carbohydrates, including sugars, starches, and fiber.

Many people think of sugar only as table sugar. However, sugars really are the simplest form of carbohydrate. They include fructose in fruit, lactose in milk, maltose in grain, and sucrose in table sugar.

Complex carbohydrates, such as starches, have a more complicated chemical structure. Digestion breaks them down into glucose, a simple sugar, which is absorbed in the blood.

Roles of Carbohydrates

Carbohydrates, found mainly in plant sources of food, are your body's most important sources of energy, or calories. Health experts recommend that 55 to 65 percent of your calories come from carbohydrates, mainly complex carbohydrates.

Eating enough carbohydrates allows protein to be used for building and repairing the body. When protein is used for energy, it cannot be used for other purposes.

Contrary to popular belief, carbohydrate-rich foods are not necessarily fattening. Ounce for ounce, carbohydrates have the same number of calories as proteins do, and fewer calories than fat.

Sources of Carbohydrates

Good sources of complex carbohydrates include vegetables and legumes (especially peas, beans, and potatoes), pasta, seeds, and nuts. Sugars, or simple carbohydrates, are present naturally in many foods, including

376 CHAPTER 19 MAKING RESPONSIBLE FOOD CHOICES

Resources for Lesson 2

- **Guided Reading** Act 50
- **Workbook** Voc Act 50

Science and Technology Videodisc
Human Biology, Side 2
Ch 14 Measuring Calcium Deficiency

- **Reteaching** Act 50
- **Lesson 2 Quiz**

ABC News InterActive Videodiscs
Drugs and Substance Abuse, Side 1
Ch 8 Steroids

---

fruits, some vegetables, and milk. Table sugar, syrups, and molasses are examples of processed sugars. Processed sugars are added to many foods, including sweet desserts, candies, and soft drinks.

Fiber

Dietary fiber is another form of complex carbohydrate, but it is not a nutrient in the true sense. Fiber is the tough, stringy part of vegetables, fruits, and grains. Because it cannot be digested, fiber serves other functions. It helps move waste through your digestive system and helps prevent constipation, appendicitis, and other intestinal problems. Eating enough fiber throughout your life may help protect you from some cancers and heart disease and can help you control diabetes. Just how fiber is involved is not yet clear, though some types of fiber are known to lower blood cholesterol and control blood sugar.

If you are watching your weight, fiber has other benefits. Fiber-rich foods are bulky, so they offer a feeling of fullness. They tend to be lower in fat and calories, and they may take longer to chew.

Most Americans may benefit from eating more high-fiber foods. To increase the amount of fiber in your diet, eat vegetables and fruits, especially those with edible skins and seeds; and whole-grain products, including whole wheat breads and pasta, whole rye bread, bran, brown rice, oatmeal, corn tortillas, and popcorn.

Fats

With all the talk about fat these days, some people wonder why they really need it. The nutrient fat has several important functions in health.

Fat is known by the scientific name *lipid*. **Lipids** are fatty substances that do not dissolve in water.

Fats are composed of the same three elements as carbohydrates—carbon, hydrogen, and oxygen. The chemical makeup of fats determines their type: saturated, or polyunsaturated. Fats are made up of fatty acids attached to a glycerol molecule. Each fatty acid is a long chain of carbon, hydrogen, and oxygen. A fatty acid is **saturated** when the carbon chain holds all the hydrogen it can. Polyunsaturated fatty acids have two or more missing hydrogen atoms on the carbon chain.

There are about 30 different fatty acids. Fats are neither totally saturated nor totally unsaturated. Instead, they are a mixture.

Animal fats and some vegetable oils (palm, palm kernel, and coconut) have a high proportion of saturated fats. Fats in beef, pork, egg yolks,

Eating foods high in fiber is one way to care for your digestive system.

Building Vocabulary

- Have each student create a crossword puzzle or sentence-completion activity using all the vocabulary terms. Afterwards, ask them to exchange their puzzle or activity with another student. Provide several minutes for them to complete each other's word challenge.
- Have students make sets of flash cards to review the definitions and functions of each of the vocabulary terms.
- Ask students to complete *Workbook Vocabulary Activity 50.*

Teach

Guided Practice

L1 DISCUSSION. Talk about why carbohydrate foods often are considered fattening. Describe a low-carbohydrate diet. Stress that while omitting or limiting simple carbohydrates can drastically reduce one's caloric intake, complex carbohydrates are essential to a well-balanced diet.

L1 CLASS ACTIVITY. Ask students to record what they eat for one day and to circle each food that contains fiber. If their fiber intake appears inadequate, work with them in making plans to improve their daily diets.

L1 CLASS ACTIVITY. Point out to students that they need 20-30 grams of fiber a day. Set up a collection of breakfast cereals, and have students check the nutritional label on each box to calculate how many servings of that cereal they would have to eat to meet the requirement. (Make sure students understand that breakfast cereal is only one source of their daily fiber. Have students list on the chalkboard other fiber sources.)

KEEPING FIT

Calculating Your Ideal Fat Intake

- According to Sushma Palmer, a nutritional biochemist, you can quickly become a fat calculator. To determine your daily fat allowance, she offers the following formula to calculate your ideal fat-gram number. Take your ideal weight and cut it in half. For someone whose ideal weight is 120 pounds, that would be 60 grams of daily fat, or 2.1 ounces.
- Sushma Palmer also says that only one-third of your daily allowance of fats should come from saturated fats. To calculate your recommended amount of daily saturated fats, she advises that you take your daily fat allowance (calculated above) and divide that by 3.

YOUR BODY'S NEED FOR NUTRIENTS **377**

Across the Curriculum

Math. On the chalkboard, write the information for calculating how much protein is needed for two age groups: *11- to 14-year-olds (.45 x ideal body weight)* and *15-to 18-year-olds (.39 x ideal body weight)*. Have students calculate their own protein needs. Emphasize that their answers are the recommended daily grams of protein their bodies need.

Home Economics. Have students weigh a raw potato. Next, ask them to puree the potato in a food processor and then drain and measure the liquid from the pureed potato. Then have students calculate the percent by weight of the water content. Ask for suggestions of other foods to test for water content.

dents find definitions of *whole
grain* and give examples. (Whole
grains consist of the endosperm,
germ, and bran. Whole wheat
bread contains a whole grain;
white bread has only the endosperm.) Discuss the health benefits
of whole grains. (They have more
fiber and more nutrients.)

L1 DISCUSSION. Talk about
why fats are important in the
body. Then ask students to identify the dangers of having too many
fats in their diets. (Diets high in
fat may be high in calories, which
can lead to obesity. For many people, high-fat diets increase the risk
of heart attacks and strokes.)

L1 DISCUSSION. Is it healthy
to cut fat out of their diet? If not,
why not? (Among other functions,
fat carries vitamins in the bloodstream, provides energy, and
becomes part of cell membranes.)

L2 COOPERATIVE LEARNING.
Divide the class into six groups.
Using food composition charts,
have students investigate differences in fat content among these
foods: (1) whole, 2 percent, and
skim milk; (2) cheddar and skim
milk mozzarella cheese; (3) ice
cream and ice milk; (4) chicken
with and without skin; (5) butter,
margarine, and lard; and (6)
bologna and lean meat.

L1 EXPLANATION. Stress that
it makes no difference if a vegetable oil is promoted as "low
cholesterol" or "no cholesterol."
Cholesterol only comes from
animal sources of food.

LEP CLASS ACTIVITY. Provide
various kinds of food for students
to identify hidden fats. Have students rub small amounts of food
(such as an apple, potato chips,
candy, a slice of luncheon meat,
cookies) on a brown paper bag.
Allow the paper to dry and see
what happens. Help them conclude that foods with fat leave a
spot; foods without fat will dry
without leaving a spot.

DID YOU KNOW?

- Too much saturated
  fat, as well as total fat,
  in the diet puts an
  individual at risk of
  heart disease.
- To reduce the amount
  of saturated fat in
  your diet, substitute
  nonmeat sources of
  protein for meat occa-
  sionally, substitute
  margarine for butter
  and skim milk or low-
  fat milk for whole
  milk, and substitute
  vegetable (unsaturat-
  ed) oils for solid (saturated) fats.
- To reduce total fat
  intake, substitute
  poultry and fish for
  beef, lamb, and pork
  frequently; use less
  margarine, butter,
  and oils; avoid fried
  foods and rich,
  creamy sauces; substi-
  tute low-fat and skim
  milk for whole milk;
  eat fewer pies, pas-
  tries, and cakes; and
  reduce the amount of
  ice cream, whipped
  cream, and cookies
  you eat.

and dairy foods are higher in saturated fats than fats in chicken and
fish. Fats high in saturated fatty acids are usually solid or semisolid at
room temperature.

Most vegetable fats, including soybean, corn, cottonseed, and olive
oils, have a higher proportion of unsaturated fatty acids. Fats high in
unsaturated fatty acids are liquids, or oils, at room temperature.

Processing can change the characteristics of fats. By adding missing
hydrogen to fatty acids, hydrogenation makes fats more saturated and
firmer in texture. For example, margarine is hydrogenated vegetable oil.
As a general rule, firmer fats are more saturated.

Roles of Fats

Fats are an important source of calories. Ounce for ounce, fats provide more than twice the energy of carbohydrates or proteins. For good
health, fats should supply no more than 30 percent of your daily calorie
intake.

Fats carry fat-soluble vitamins A, D, E, and K into your blood. Without
fats, our bodies could not use these nutrients.

Fats provide essential fatty acids. The body cannot make linoleic acid,
a fatty acid essential for growth and healthy skin. It must come from
your diet. Dietary fats offer other benefits, too. Fats add flavor, and they
help satisfy hunger because they take longer to digest than carbohydrates and proteins do.

Body fat, or adipose tissue, is a form of stored energy. It accumulates
when people consume excess calories from any source—carbohydrates,
fats, or proteins. Your body needs some body fat. It surrounds and cushions your vital organs, protecting them from injury. The fat layer under
your skin insulates your body from heat and cold.

Sources of Fats

Almost every food has some fat—at least in very small amounts. Some
have much more fat than others.

Visible fats—butter, margarine, vegetable oil, and the fat layer on
meat and poultry—account for about 40 percent of the fat in our diets.
Many fats also are hidden in foods, for example, fat marbled in meat.
Chocolate, seeds, nuts, egg yolks, ice cream, cheese, cream soups, crois-
sants, and doughnuts all have hidden fats. Some food preparation methods—frying and cooking with sauces—add fats to food, too.

Cholesterol

Cholesterol is a fatlike substance. In many ways cholesterol resembles fat, but its structure is quite different. Because the human liver can
make the cholesterol it needs, cholesterol is not considered a nutrient.

Cholesterol is an essential part of each cell membrane in the human
body. The body uses cholesterol to produce certain hormones, vitamin
D (in the presence of sunlight), and the protective sheath around nerve
fibers. The liver uses cholesterol to make bile acids that aid in digestion.

The terms *dietary cholesterol* and *serum cholesterol* often are confused.
Dietary cholesterol comes from food. Serum, or blood, cholesterol circulates in your blood.

Additional Information

Vegetarian Diets. Consuming enough
complete protein is a challenge for some
vegetarians. Lacto-ovo-vegetarians avoid
only meat, poultry, and fish. They get complete protein from eggs, milk, cheese, and
yogurt. *Lacto* means milk and *ovo* means
eggs. Other individuals, called *vegans*,
eliminate all animal sources of food.
Unless they combine foods carefully, their
meals will not have the protein they need.
Three equations help plan vegetarian
meals with complete protein:

- Legumes + Grains = Complete Protein
- Legumes + Nuts or Seeds = Complete
  Protein
- Any Plant Protein + Eggs or Dairy
  Products = Complete Protein

Dietary cholesterol is present only in foods of animal origin—meat, poultry, fish, eggs, and dairy products. Egg yolks and organ meats are especially high in cholesterol. Fruits, vegetables, grains, legumes, and other foods from plant sources are, by nature, cholesterol-free.

In some people, the body makes too much cholesterol. High blood cholesterol is a major risk factor for heart and other circulatory diseases. Consuming too much cholesterol may contribute to elevated serum cholesterol; limiting cholesterol intake may reduce the risk.

Proteins

Proteins are a vital part of every body cell. Muscle, bone, connective tissue, teeth, skin, blood, and vital organs all contain protein. The term *protein* comes from the Greek *proteios*, meaning "of prime importance." The name fits because without protein, life could not exist.

Proteins actually are made of chains of building blocks called **amino acids.** Just as letters of the alphabet are arranged to make different words, amino acids are arranged in countless ways to make different body proteins.

Your body can make all but 9 of the 20 different amino acids. These 9 are called essential amino acids, because they must come from foods you eat. The rest your body can make if you eat enough protein-rich foods.

These foods are all high in fat. They have been fried.

Roles of Proteins

Your body uses proteins mainly for building and maintaining all body tissues. During periods of growth—infancy, childhood, adolescence, and pregnancy—amino acids build new body tissues. Throughout life new proteins form constantly to replace damaged or worn-out body cells.

Proteins in enzymes, hormones, and antibodies also help regulate many body processes. Enzymes are substances that control the rate of thousands of biochemical reactions in your body cells. Hormones regulate reactions. Antibodies help identify and destroy bacteria and viruses that cause disease in the body.

If you do not get enough calories from carbohydrates and fats, proteins from food provide the necessary energy. However, proteins are a less efficient energy source than carbohydrates and fats. When proteins are used for energy, they are not available for building and repairing body tissue. Proteins should supply only 10 to 15 percent of the calories in your diet.

K E E P I N G   F I T

Pumping Iron—Nutritionally

Many teens consume amounts of iron that are below the RDA, or Recommended Dietary Allowance. Females who menstruate are particularly likely to be low in iron. Yet during the teen years, when growth is rapid, high iron levels are needed for increasing blood volume and muscle mass. Iron is needed for the hemoglobin in your blood, which carries oxygen throughout your body. Without it, you may feel tired and have little endurance when playing sports.

To make sure you get enough iron, eat foods that contain high levels of it. These include liver, clams, beef, black beans, chick peas, raw spinach, pumpkin seeds, shrimp, and navy beans.

YOUR BODY'S NEED FOR NUTRIENTS   **379**

L2 **CLASS ACTIVITY.** Using a food composition table, have students compare the fat content of one serving of each of the following: french fries, potato chips, and a plain baked potato. Ask students what accounts for the differences. What happens to the fat content of a baked potato when sour cream, butter, or gravy is added?

L1 **CLASS ACTIVITY.** Have students read current consumer health articles on fat and cholesterol from newspapers and news magazines. In class, ask them to share the main ideas with the class. Lead students in evaluating the reliability of the information.

L1 **DISCUSSION.** Present this case study to the class: Their friend Tim, a vegetarian, is coming for a two-day visit. He doesn't eat meat, poultry, or fish. What foods will they offer? Lead students in brainstorming a list of tasty, nutritious foods they could offer Tim and stay within the guidelines of his diet.

L2 **COOPERATIVE LEARNING.** Divide the class into small groups. Provide each group with several grocery advertisements from which to select complete and incomplete proteins. Have them compare the cost of these food items and draw conclusions about cost-effective protein sources.

L1 **CLASS ACTIVITY.** People need fruits and vegetables rich in vitamins C and A every day. Have students use classroom sources to find out what foods are good sources of these vitamins. Discuss their findings with the class.

L1 **SPEAKER.** Ask a home economics teacher to demonstrate and discuss ways to cut down on vitamin loss in food handling.

L1 **EXPLANATION.** Point out that taking extra fat-soluble vitamins may be dangerous. The vitamins can accumulate in the body's fat tissues, and excess buildup can be toxic.

Across the Curriculum

Home Economics. Using a home economics foods laboratory, have students compare the fat content in a quarter pound of three types of ground beef: chuck, round, and sirloin. Have them break the beef apart; and, without adding fat, brown it in a frying pan. Instruct them to pour off the fat and measure it in a measuring cup or with measuring spoons. Ask students to make a simple chart showing the results.

Science. Divide the class into small groups, and assign each group a vitamin. Have the groups investigate the benefits of that vitamin, the problems caused by a lack of it, and the foods rich in it. Have each group report back to class.

Sources of Proteins

Animal sources of foods, such as fish, meat, poultry, eggs, milk, cheese, and yogurt, contain all the essential amino acids. For this reason they are called complete protein sources.

Legumes, seeds, and nuts are the best source of plant proteins. However, no single plant protein has all essential amino acids in adequate amounts. For this reason they are called incomplete protein foods.

Plant proteins can be combined with either animal proteins or certain other plant foods to make complete protein foods. Following are some of these combinations:

- legumes + seeds or nuts (peanuts with mixed nuts)
- legumes + grains (beans and rice, peanut butter on bread, tortilla and refried beans, tofu-vegetable stir fry over noodles)
- any plant protein + dairy products or eggs (macaroni and cheese, rice pudding)

WATER-SOLUBLE VITAMINS

Vitamin	Role in Body	Food Source
C (ascorbic acid)	Protects against infection; helps with formation of connective tissue; helps wounds heal; maintains elasticity and strength of blood vessels.	Citrus fruits, tomatoes, cabbage, broccoli, potatoes, peppers
B_1 (thiamine)	Changes glucose into energy or fat; helps prevent nervous irritability; necessary for good appetite.	Whole-grain or enriched cereals, liver, yeast, nuts, legumes, wheat germ
B_2 (riboflavin)	Transports hydrogen; is essential in the metabolism of carbohydrates, fats, and proteins; helps keep skin in healthy condition.	Liver, green leafy vegetables, milk, cheese, eggs, fish, whole-grain or enriched cereals
Niacin	Hydrogen transport; important to maintenance of all body tissues; energy production; needed by body to utilize carbohydrates, to synthesize human fat, and for tissue respiration.	Yeast, liver, wheat germ, kidney, eggs, fish
B_6	Essential to amino-acid and carbohydrate metabolism.	Yeast, wheat bran and germ, liver, kidneys, meat, whole grains, fish, vegetables
Pantothenic acid	Functions in the breakdown and synthesis of carbohydrates, fats, and proteins; necessary for synthesis of some of the adrenal hormones.	Liver, kidney, milk, yeast, wheat germ, whole-grain cereals and breads, green vegetables
Folacin (folic acid)	Necessary for the production of RNA and DNA and normal red blood cells.	Liver, nuts, green vegetables, orange juice
B_{12} (cyanocobalamin)	Necessary for production of red blood cells and normal growth.	Meat, liver, eggs, milk

380 CHAPTER 19 MAKING RESPONSIBLE FOOD CHOICES

Vitamins

Vitamins are known as micronutrients because they are needed in small amounts. Vitamins help regulate many vital body processes. They work with enzymes by triggering specific chemical reactions that allow the digestion, absorption, metabolism, and use of other nutrients.

Contrary to popular belief, vitamins do not supply calories. Some, however, do speed up reactions that produce energy in body cells.

Vitamins are classified into two groups: water-soluble vitamins and fat-soluble vitamins. Their solubility determines certain characteristics: how they are absorbed and carried in the blood, whether they are stored in the body, and what may happen during food preparation.

Water-Soluble Vitamins

Vitamins B complex and C are water-soluble vitamins, meaning they dissolve in water. For this reason they pass easily into the blood in the process of digestion. However, water-soluble vitamins are not stored to any extent in the body tissue. Instead, any excess is excreted in urine. Since there are no reserves, your diet needs an adequate supply of foods that contain water-soluble vitamins every day.

Foods need to be cooked carefully so that water-soluble vitamins are not destroyed by heat or lost through steam or in cooking water. To retain water-soluble vitamins in fruits and vegetables, follow these tips:

- Cook fruits and vegetables quickly.
- Steam them, or use only small amounts of cooking water.
- Cover food during cooking.
- Use leftover liquid in soups and stews.

If the liquid from these potatoes is thrown away, many vitamins will be lost. It would be much better to cook vegetables in a small amount of water and use the liquid that is left in a soup or sauce.

FAT-SOLUBLE VITAMINS

Vitamin	Role in Body	Food Source
A	Maintenance of epithelial tissue; strengthens tooth enamel and favors utilization of calcium and phosphorus in bone formation; growth of body cells; keeps eyes moist.	Milk and other dairy products, green vegetables, carrots, animal liver
D	Promotes absorption and utilization of calcium and phosphorus; essential for normal bone and tooth development.	Fish oils, beef, butter, eggs, milk; produced in the skin upon exposure to ultraviolet rays in sunlight
E	May relate to oxidation and longevity; may be a protection against red blood cell destruction.	Widely distributed in foods; yellow vegetable oils, and wheat germ
K	Essential for blood clotting; assists in regulating blood calcium level.	Spinach, eggs, liver, cabbage, tomatoes; produced by intestinal bacteria

---

LD **EXPLANATION.** On the chalkboard, list the different nutrients. Next to each, write one source of the nutrient and, in one simplified sentence, describe the body's uses for it. Have LD students copy this information into their class notes for later review.

L1 **CLASS ACTIVITY.** Ask students to bring nutrition information labels (from cereal boxes, snack foods, and other processed foods) to class. Collect labels, read aloud the nutrient content from a label, and ask the class to guess the type of food by the nutrient composition. Discuss why many packaged foods are calorie-rich, but nutrient-poor.

LEP **CLASS ACTIVITY.** Provide basic art supplies, and have students create posters titled "You Are What You Eat." Display and discuss their completed posters. Ask them if they think food plays an important role in "who they are." Also, discuss how much control teens have over what they eat.

L3 **COOPERATIVE LEARNING.** Have students work in groups to develop a lesson for a grade school class on the importance of nutrients. Groups might write skits, design games, or produce a video. Arrange to have one or more lessons presented to a grade school class, Scout meeting, etc.

Independent Practice

L1 **PERSONAL INVOLVEMENT.** Have students list all the complex and simple carbohydrates they have eaten in the past 24 hours. Ask each student to compare the 2 lists and write a summary statement about his or her intake of carbohydrates.

L3 **RESEARCH.** Have students research the relationship between carbohydrates and tooth decay. (Bacteria in plaque acts on carbohydrates to form acids that destroy tooth enamel and irritate gums. Frequent consumption of sticky, sugary foods increases the risk.)

Overcoming Misconceptions

Myth. "Athletic" drinks are necessary for active teens and young adults. **Fact.** "Athletic" drinks designed to replace salts lost in perspiration are not necessary unless an individual loses more than 3 quarts of water (about 6 pounds of weight) during an activity. Sweat has a lower concentration of salts than blood, so people lose proportionately more water than salts when they perspire. The most pressing need is to replace the lost water. If someone exceeds 3 quarts of replacement fluid, they may add about 1/2 teaspoon of salt for each quart thereafter. Salt tablets are not recommended, and concentrated salt should not be consumed unless large quantities of water are drunk at the same time.

L1 PARENTAL INVOLVEMENT.
Ask for volunteers to investigate their family history of serum cholesterol levels and cardiovascular disease. Request that they find out whether or not family members changed their diets or life-styles to lower serum cholesterol, and if so, in what ways. Remind students that family history is one risk factor for them, and obesity and smoking are others.

L2 COMMUNITY INVOLVEMENT.
Have students interview three adults to find out what brand of margarine, butter, or oil they use and why. Have students ask the adults if they know the definition of *saturated*, *unsaturated*, and *polyunsaturated*. Request that students report their findings to the class. Follow up by having students analyze ways that advertisements are used to make people think they are buying something better for their health.

L2 PERSONAL INVOLVEMENT.
Ask students to record their diets for 24 hours and then calculate the amount of protein they ate. Have them determine how their diet compares with their protein recommendation.

L1 WRITING.
Have students choose a nutrient to research. Have them write a paper explaining the nutrient's function and discussing what happens if they get too much or not enough of the nutrient. Ask them to include recommendations on ways to get the appropriate amount of the nutrient. Have them cite sources of information that they used.

L2 COMMUNITY INVOLVEMENT.
Choose students to interview a social service agency representative. Have them ask about nutritional deficiency problems in the local community. Request that students find out what programs are available to alleviate nutritional deficiencies and what role is played by volunteers. Have students compile a list of qualifications for volunteers and share the list with the class.

L1 USING THE LESSON RESOURCES.
For additional student activities, refer to the lesson resources on page 376.

DID YOU KNOW?

- Fat makes up about 40 percent of the average American's diet.
- If you were to take away just one tablespoon of fat from your daily diet, you could lose as much as 10 pounds in a year.
- Low-fat lunches are beginning to be served in the nation's schools. Lower-fat school lunches should be the norm by 1994.
- Bananas are the most popular fruit in the U.S., followed by apples. Potatoes are the most popular vegetable, followed by one of the least nutritious–iceberg lettuce. Both bananas and potatoes are excellent sources of potassium.

Fat-Soluble Vitamins

Vitamins A, D, E, and K are fat-soluble vitamins, meaning they are absorbed and transported by fat. The body stores fat-soluble vitamins in fatty tissue. Excess buildup of these vitamins can have a dangerous toxic effect. People who take nutrient supplements with very large doses of fat-soluble vitamins are especially vulnerable to the toxic effects.

Minerals

Minerals are inorganic substances that the body cannot manufacture. Like vitamins, they are micronutrients and act as catalysts, regulating many vital body processes. Despite the small amounts our bodies need, each mineral has its own unique function in health.

ELECTROLYTES

Sodium, chlorine, and potassium are important minerals in the body. They are present in relatively large amounts when compared to many other minerals. They are unique among nutrients because they become electrically charged when in solution as they are in the body fluids. Because of their electrical charges they are called electrolytes.

Sodium and chlorine combine to form table salt. Potassium is found in most foods, particularly bananas, oranges, prunes, and meats. Electrolytes also are found in water and other liquids.

These and other electrolytes must be present in the body and must be present in certain concentrations. Electrolyte balance requires that the intake of water and electrolytes is equal to the amounts of water and electrolytes eliminated from the body in perspiration, feces, and urine.

Water

Water is your body's most essential nutrient. Only oxygen is more important to life. Flesh feels solid, but the human body actually is about two-thirds water.

Water is a regulator and is vital to every body function. Mainly through the plasma in your blood, water carries nutrients to and transports waste from your cells. Water lubricates your joints and mucous membranes. It enables you to swallow and digest foods, absorb nutrients, and eliminate wastes. Through perspiration, water helps your body cool down and prevents the buildup of internal heat.

Most people use about 10 cups (2.4 l) of water a day. If they sweat a lot from fever, hot weather, or strenuous exercise, they use more. Some water can be replaced by drinking fluids (juice, milk, water)—about 6 to 8 cups (1.4 to 1.9 l) daily.

Food also supplies water. On average, fruits, vegetables, and milk products contain about 75 percent water; poultry and meat, 50 to 60 percent; and grain products, between 5 and 35 percent.

Additional Information

Soft Drinks. According to research, the average American drinks more soft drinks than water, milk, or juice. This is especially true of teenagers!

In the past, soft drinks were snack beverages. Today they accompany many fast-food meals. Young people who drink large amounts of soft drinks typically have diets low in calcium, riboflavin, and vitamins A and C—just when their needs are highest. Unless they're sugar-free, soft drinks promote tooth decay. Each sip bathes teeth with sugar.

Phosphates in soft drinks provide phosphorus. But too much phosphorus without adequate calcium throws off the balance of these nutrients needed for bone health.

Mineral	Primary Function	Food Source
Calcium	Building material of bones and teeth (about 99 percent of body calcium is in your skeleton); regulation of body functions: heart muscle contraction, blood clotting.	Dairy products, leafy vegetables, apricots
Phosphorus	Combines with calcium to give rigidity to bones and teeth; essential in cell metabolism; helps to maintain proper acid-base balance of blood (calcium and phosphorus are the most abundant minerals in the body).	Peas, beans, milk, liver, meat, cottage cheese, broccoli, whole grains
Iron	Part of the red blood cell's oxygen and carbon dioxide transport system; necessary for cellular respiration; important for use of energy in cells and for resistance to infection.	Liver, meat, shellfish, peanuts, dried fruits, eggs
Iodine	Essential component of the thyroid hormone, thyroxine, which controls the rate of cell oxidation; helps maintain proper water balance.	Iodized salt, seafood
Manganese	Enzyme activator for carbohydrate, protein, and fat metabolism; also important in growth of cartilage and bone tissue.	Wheat germ, nuts, bran, green leafy vegetables, cereal grains
Copper	An essential ingredient in several respiratory enzymes; needed for development of young red blood cells.	Kidney, liver, beans, Brazil nuts, whole meal flour, lentils, parsley
Zinc	The function is unknown, although it is a component of many enzyme systems and is an essential component of the pancreatic hormone insulin.	Shellfish, meat, milk, eggs
Cobalt	An essential part of Vitamin B_{12}.	Sources of Vitamin B_{12}, such as meats, milk, and milk products
Fluorine	Essential to normal tooth and bone development and maintenance; excesses are undesirable.	Drinking water in some areas
Molybdenum	Essential for enzymes that make uric acid.	Legumes, meat products, some cereal grains
Sodium	Regulates the fluid and acid-base balance in the body.	Table salt, milk, meat, fish, poultry, egg whites
Chloride	Associated with sodium and its functions; a part of the gastric juice, hydrochloric acid; the chloride ion also functions in the starch-splitting system of saliva.	Same as sodium
Potassium	Part of the system that controls the acid-base and liquid balances; thought to be an important enzyme activator in the use of amino acids.	Readily available in most foods
Magnesium	Enzyme activator related to carbohydrate metabolism.	Readily available in most foods
Sulfur	Component of the hormone insulin and the sulfur amino acids; builds hair, nails, skin.	Nuts, dried fruits, barley and oatmeal, eggs, beans, cheese, and brown sugar

YOUR BODY'S NEED FOR NUTRIENTS **383**

Assess

Check for Understanding
- Assign and discuss the lesson review. Encourage LD students to focus on questions 1, 2, 3, 4, 5, and 6.

Evaluate
- Administer, grade, and discuss the *Lesson 2 Quiz*.

Reteach
- Have students list the six main categories of nutrients. After each nutrient, ask them to write at least one sentence, summarizing what they learned about the nutrient from the lesson.
- Have students copy the section headings (written in bold print in the textbook) into their notebooks. Ask them to leave two to three lines after each heading. Instruct students to write an original summary sentence for each heading in the appropriate space.
- Make up some advice-column type questions that can be answered at least partially with information from the lesson. Have students work individually to compose response letters.
- Ask students to complete *Reteaching Activity 50*.

Enrich
- Ask for volunteers to visit local supermarkets and read the labels on a variety of bread packages. Have one group compile a list of the names of whole-grain breads, the breads' weights, and their prices. Have the second group make a list of non-whole-grain breads and the breads' weights and prices. Tell students to make their selections as to whether or not each bread is whole-grain according to the first ingredient listed on the label. Have them discuss their findings with the class.

Across the Curriculum

Social Studies. Invite several adults who follow vegetarian diets to come to class and describe what they eat and discuss reasons for their food choices. Follow up by asking for volunteers to try a vegetarian diet for several days. Have them report to the class their reactions to the experience. Ask the students if it was difficult to avoid meat. Were they hungrier than usual? How did their family and friends react? Would they consider being vegetarians?

Home Economics. Have students gather recipes for vegetarian sandwiches and meals. Prepare some of the foods, and have a food-tasting session.

- Have students find out the recommended serum cholesterol levels and the average serum cholesterol levels by age and sex. Have them find answers to the following questions: What levels are considered high-risk, moderate-risk, normal, and low-risk for cardiovascular disease and heart attacks? What is the importance of the relationship of HDL levels to LDL levels? What ratio is considered healthy?
- Choose students to research the problems caused by deficiency or overconsumption of one of these minerals: calcium, phosphorus, magnesium, chlorine, potassium, sodium, iron, iodine, or zinc.

Close

Display numerous pictures of foods, including foods high in nutritional value and those with poor nutritional value such as highly processed foods, saturated fats, carbonated beverages, etc. Divide the class into small groups, and ask each group to select three pictures of foods with good nutritional value and three with poor nutritional value. Ask a student from each group to explain the group's choices. Summarize by reminding students to include all nutrients in their diets and to be selective about the quality of nutrients they eat.

DID YOU KNOW?

- Here's why you should eat your spinach. It's a good source of beta carotene, which helps prevent heart disease, cancer, and cataracts, and of magnesium, which helps keep blood cholesterol down. It's also rich in fiber.

Without water, our bodies could not survive.

Nutrients: How Much Do You Need?

No matter what age, everyone needs the same nutrients. The only significant difference is the amount needed. However, at your age, without the nutrients needed for growth and development, your body will not reach its full potential.

Age and sex are two factors that determine how many nutrients you need. Teenagers, who are growing rapidly, have the highest nutrient need. Compared to females, males tend to be bigger, and their body composition is different, so they usually need more nutrients. For females, pregnancy and lactation or nursing require extra calories and nutrients to support the needs of both mother and baby.

Recommended Dietary Allowances

How much of each nutrient does your body need every day? The Food and Nutrition Board of the National Research Council, the National Academy of Sciences, has developed nutrient guidelines for people in the United States. The recommendations are listed by age and sex, and for females during pregnancy and lactation. The amounts recommended are considered to be adequate to maintain health for everyone, from infancy through adulthood.

The **Recommended Dietary Allowances (RDA)** suggest the amounts of 19 essential nutrients that most people need daily to stay healthy. The RDA also include guidelines for calories and estimated intake for vitamins and minerals. Your own nutritional and caloric needs may be slightly more or slightly less.

Every few years scientists update the Recommended Dietary Allowances. Each new edition reflects the latest research on nutrition and health. RDA were first published in 1943.

LESSON 2 REVIEW

Reviewing Facts and Vocabulary

1. Name the six classes of nutrients.
2. What three nutrients provide energy?
3. Describe the importance of dietary fiber, and list three sources.
4. Name three functions of fats.
5. What is cholesterol? What does it do?
6. What is protein? What does it do?

Thinking Critically

7. **Analysis.** Compare fat- and water-soluble vitamins.

8. **Evaluation.** Why do you think water is considered a nutrient?

Applying Health Knowledge

9. Is a bean burrito a complete or incomplete protein food? Explain your answer.

Answers to Lesson 2 Review

1. Carbohydrates, fats, proteins, vitamins, minerals, and water.
2. Sugars, starches, and fiber.
3. See page 377.
4. Fats are an important source of calories, carry fat-soluble vitamins into the blood, provide essential fatty acids.
5. A fatlike substance. See page 378.

6. A vital part of every body cell. See page 379.
7. Answers will vary but should reflect an understanding of the information on pages 380 to 382.
8. Answers will vary. Possible answer: It is essential to life.
9. Complete. It contains legumes + grains.

CHOOSING A HEALTHY DIET

What should you eat to stay healthy, to grow, and to have the energy you need? Along with exercise, eating a varied, moderate, and balanced diet is an important strategy for fitness. Your **diet** is everything you eat and drink.

Many Americans feel bombarded with information linking food, nutrition, and health. Food selection guides, such as the Dietary Guidelines and Daily Food Guide, help you choose a healthy diet that is right for you.

Dietary Guidelines for Americans

To help you sift through thousands of foods on store shelves and restaurant menus, the U.S. Department of Agriculture has published nutritional advice on how to eat to stay healthy. The Dietary Guidelines are meant for healthy Americans aged 2 years and over. Following the Dietary Guidelines will decrease your risk of diet-related problems now and in the future.

Eat a Variety of Foods

Your body needs about 40 nutrients. However, no one food has all the nutrients—in adequate amounts—that you need for growth, energy, and health. By eating a variety of foods daily, your body can get the many nutrients it needs. The **Daily Food Guide** offers an easy way to choose a varied, balanced, and moderate diet. Just eat adequate amounts from the following five food groups daily:

- bread, cereal, rice, and pasta
- fruit
- vegetable
- meat, poultry, fish, dry beans, eggs, and nuts
- milk, yogurt, and cheese

Combination foods, such as pizza or burritos, contain ingredients from more than one food group and supply the same nutrients as the foods they contain.

Foods in a particular food group supply similar amounts of key nutrients. However, the nutrient value of foods within a group differs, so eating a variety within each food group is important, too.

How many servings from each food group do you need? That depends on your age, sex, physical condition, body size, and activity level. Most people need at least the minimum servings daily. Teenage boys and active men usually need the most. Young children may need fewer servings. Except for additional iron and calcium needed by females, eating the recommended number of servings should supply all the nutrients most people need.

CHOOSING A HEALTHY DIET **385**

LESSON 3 FOCUS

TERMS TO USE
- Diet
- Daily Food Guide
- Empty-calorie foods

CONCEPTS TO LEARN
- Your diet is everything you eat and drink.
- You should eat adequate amounts from the five food groups daily.
- A varied, moderate, and balanced diet is the basis of a healthy eating pattern.
- Applying principles of good nutrition is important when eating out.

ATTITUDES AND BEHAVIORS TO EVALUATE
- Self-Inventory, page 398.
- Building Decision-Making Skills, page 399.

Lesson Objectives

After studying this lesson, students should be able to:
- name the five food groups and the recommended range of servings for each
- describe tips to control fat, sugars, and sodium in foods
- explain how to use the food groups and nutrients to develop healthy eating patterns
- list ways to make healthy fast-food choices

Bellringer

Write the following on the chalkboard for students to work on while attendance is being taken: *Divide a sheet of paper into three lengthwise columns. In the left column, list the five food groups. In the center column, name at least three foods that belong in each group. In the right column, rank the five groups according to how much you eat the foods, with "1" for most-eaten group to "5" for least-eaten group.*

Introducing the Lesson

Have students share their responses to the Bellringer. List the five groups on the chalkboard, and tally student intake of each of the groups. Talk about the importance of each group and the need to eat a variety of foods from each group.

DID YOU KNOW?

- In 1988, San Francisco Giants president and general manager Al Rosen suffered a heart attack. Afterwards, he asked that Candlestick Park offer fans healthier snack foods at the concession stands. Rather than the usual high-fat hot dogs, peanuts, and popcorn, the ballpark now also sells bottled water, fresh fruit, yogurt, and even tofu (soy) hot dogs.

Resources for Lesson 3

- **Transparencies** 8, 9, and 23
- **Guided Reading** Act 51
- **Workbook** Voc Act 51
- **Reteaching** Act 51
- **Lesson 3 Quiz**
- **Poster** 11

Science and Technology Videodisc
Human Biology, Side 1
Ch 11 Through-the-Skin Heart Drug

Human Biology, Side 2
Ch 11 Obesity and Heredity

Building Vocabulary

- Have students use the vocabulary terms in a written paragraph. Ask them to read their paragraphs to the class.
- Provide newspapers and magazines, and have students locate articles using each of the vocabulary terms. Select some of the articles to discuss with the class.
- Ask students to complete *Workbook Vocabulary Activity 51.*

Teach

Guided Practice

L1 USING HEALTH AWARENESS TRANSPARENCIES 8 AND 9. Refer to the Teaching Transparencies Binder.

L1 USING LIFE MANAGEMENT SKILLS TRANSPARENCY 23. Refer to the Teaching Transparencies Binder.

L1 CLASS ACTIVITY. Use photographs of actual examples to illustrate serving sizes of various foods.

L1 COOPERATIVE LEARNING. Divide the class into five groups, and assign each one a food group. Have students compete to see which group can list the most examples of foods in their food group. Give students 2 minutes to complete the lists. At the end of the 2 minutes, have each group share its list. Ask the rest of the class to add to each list and give the recommended number of servings per day for a teen.

L1 DISCUSSION. Have students brainstorm a list of sources of dietary fat. Talk about ways to control fat in foods.

The Food Guide Pyramid focuses on fat because most American diets are too high in fat. Note that some fat and sugar symbols are shown in all the food groups. This is to remind you that even foods that are naturally low in fat may be prepared in ways that add to their fat or sugar content.

Food Guide Pyramid
A Guide to Daily Food Choices

Food Groups

Bread, Cereal, Rice, and Pasta.   Enriched and whole-grain products are good sources of complex carbohydrates, iron, and B vitamins. Whole-grain foods are also good fiber sources. You need 6 to 11 servings daily.

Fruits.   Fruit and fruit juices (as long as the juice is 100 percent juice) can be good sources of vitamins A and C and carbohydrates. Some fruits provide more vitamins than others, so eat a variety. Fruits with edible skins are good fiber sources, if you eat the skin. You need 2 to 4 servings of fruit daily.

Vegetables.   Many vegetables and vegetable juices are good sources of vitamins A or C. Starchy vegetables, such as potatoes and squash, also supply complex carbohydrates—starch and fiber. Each day eat at least 3 to 5 servings. Eat dark green leafy vegetables several times a week.

Meat, Poultry, Fish, Dry Beans, Eggs, and Nuts.   Eggs, dry beans, nuts, and seeds are alternates. These foods along with meat, poultry, and fish are good sources of protein, iron, and B vitamins. At least 2 to 3 servings equal the recommended 5 to 7 ounces (142 to 198 g) daily.

Milk, Yogurt, and Cheese.   These foods are good sources of protein, calcium, and riboflavin, a B vitamin. You need at least 2 to 3 servings daily.

Fats, Oils, and Sweets.   Some foods do not belong in the five food groups: for example, cakes, cookies, doughnuts, soft drinks, candy, jam, salad dressing, chips, condiments, gravy, mayonnaise, margarine, butter, coffee, and tea. Many provide carbohydrates (mainly sugars) or fats, but few other nutrients, so they are often called **empty-calorie foods.**

386   CHAPTER 19 MAKING RESPONSIBLE FOOD CHOICES

Additional Information

How Many Calories Do You Need in a Day? Here's one way to get a rough idea of your daily calorie needs. If you are extremely inactive, you need about 12 calories per pound to stay at your current weight. If you are involved in light activity, you need 15 calories per pound. When you're moderately active, go up to 20 calories per pound. So if you are a moderately active person weighing 140 pounds, your calorie needs work out to 140 × 20 = 2,800 calories a day.

Fatty and sugary foods provide taste and interest to meals and snacks. Because they supply mainly calories but few nutrients, health experts recommend using these foods sparingly.

Maintain Healthy Weight

According to nutrition experts, being too fat or too thin increases the chance of health problems. In the next chapter, you will learn more about managing weight. The following principles apply to everyone—whether the goal is to lose, gain, or maintain weight:

- Controlling body fat is more important to health than controlling body weight.
- Smart eating and regular exercise are the best ways to keep a healthful weight.
- No matter what their source, all calories add up the same way.
- Watching your diet and exercising is more important than watching the scale.

Choose a Diet Low in Fat, Saturated Fat, and Cholesterol

Too much fat in your diet is not healthy; neither is too much fat on the body. Diets high in fat, saturated fat, and cholesterol increase the risk of heart disease. A buildup of cholesterol and fat on arterial walls can lead to heart attacks. For some people, eating less fat, especially saturated fat, and cholesterol lessens the problem. High-fat diets are linked to obesity and some cancers.

Most Americans eat too much fat. Even after cutting back, many people still get 37 percent of their calories from fat. Health experts recommend getting 30 percent or less, including less than 10 percent from saturated fats.

Controlling dietary cholesterol can control blood cholesterol. That is why many experts recommend limiting cholesterol intake to 300 milligrams per day. Cutting back on fat, especially saturated fat, has an even greater effect on controlling blood cholesterol.

Controlling Fat in Foods. Follow these tips to help control the fat and cholesterol in your diet:

- Cut off the fat you see on meat. Remove skin from chicken and turkey; there is a fat layer under the skin.

K E E P I N G   F I T

Smart Snacking

- Snack mostly on foods from the five food groups. Limit fats and sweets!
- Plan your snacks when you can. Carry fresh fruit, such as grapes or a pear, instead of candy or chips.

- Help keep nutritious snacks on hand, such as plain popcorn, fruit, yogurt, fresh vegetables, cheese, and whole-grain crackers.

- Snack early, well before mealtime so that you do not spoil your appetite.
- Choose a substantial snack, if it must replace a meal.

CHOOSING A HEALTHY DIET **387**

Overcoming Misconceptions

Myth. Only older adults need to know their cholesterol level. **Fact.** Young people with a family history of cardiovascular disease are advised to know their serum cholesterol levels. (Serum cholesterol is found in blood; dietary cholesterol, in food.) Cholesterol screening is one way to identify people with an increased risk of cardiovascular disease. In fact, some doctors believe it is wise to get this baseline data while a person is young so doctors can monitor changes. Because the body makes cholesterol, elevated serum cholesterol is not necessarily associated with consuming large amounts of dietary cholesterol.

Asking for your salad dressing on the side is one way to control and reduce the quantity you use.

- Eat lean meat, fish, and poultry.
- Choose lower-fat milk, cheese, and yogurt.
- Eat less salad dressing. Spread only a little margarine, butter, or mayonnaise on bread. Use less gravy or sour cream on potatoes.
- Cut down on fried foods. Eat roasted, baked, broiled, or grilled meat, poultry, or fish instead.
- Eat vegetables that are steamed, boiled, or baked, rather than fried. (Limit the amount of french fries and fried onion rings in your diet.)
- Eat plenty of vegetables, fruits, and whole-grain foods.

Choose a Diet With Plenty of Vegetables, Fruits, and Grain Products

Why do vegetables, fruits, and grain products get special attention? They are excellent sources of complex carbohydrates and fiber, and are usually low in fats. Unlike many sugary foods, they provide essential vitamins and minerals. These foods are good choices and are low in calories.

From the viewpoint of disease prevention, a diet high in fiber and complex carbohydrates, yet low in fat, is advised. It seems to decrease the risk for heart disease, obesity, and some cancers. The National Cancer Institute recommends 20 to 35 milligrams of fiber a day. The average American eats only 10 to 15 milligrams daily.

To cut back on fat and reach the goal of 55 to 65 percent of calories from carbohydrates, eat plenty of vegetables, fruits, and grain products. Because they also are low in calories, these foods can help you control weight, too.

Use Sugars Only in Moderation

Sugars are carbohydrates; they taste good. Why limit them? On average, Americans eat a lot of sugar, up to 120 pounds (54 kg) yearly. Some sugars are present naturally in food, but much sugar is added during processing. Added sugars provide energy, but no other nutrients.

DID YOU KNOW?

Here are some one-serving portions of vegetables:
- ½ cup cooked or raw vegetables
- 1 cup leafy raw vegetables
- ¾ cup vegetable juice

One serving of meat, poultry, fish, or alternates equals:
- 2 ounces of lean meat
- 2 eggs
- 1 cup cooked dry beans
- 2 ounces peanut butter

One serving of milk, yogurt, or cheese is:
- 8 ounces of milk or yogurt
- 1½ ounces natural cheese
- 2 ounces processed cheese

388 CHAPTER 19 MAKING RESPONSIBLE FOOD CHOICES

Across the Curriculum

Home Economics. Have students prepare a dish that combines the vegetable and meat-poultry-fish-alternates groups. (Consider stew or a shish-kabob.) Ask students to identify the nutrients and servings provided by the food prepared.

Social Studies. Have students interview foreign students or use library resources to learn about eating patterns in different countries. Ask them to find answers to questions about a country such as: How many meals are eaten each day? What are some typical meals? Do foods tend to be high (or low) in fat, sugar, and salt? Are snacks an important part of the diet? What percentage of meals are eaten at home? Are fast foods popular?

Most people can eat moderate amounts of sugar unless they must limit caloric intake. However, there are health cautions for eating too much, too often.

Carbohydrates—sugars and starches—contribute to tooth decay if they are eaten frequently and if they stick to teeth. Sipping a soda for an hour causes more harm than drinking it all at once.

Between-meal sweet snacks can damage teeth more than sweets eaten with a meal. Other foods in the meal help neutralize damaging acids that result from carbohydrates. After eating sweets, brush your teeth to remove food debris.

Control your sweet tooth for other reasons. Too much added sugar may mean too many calories, which can lead to obesity. When sweet desserts, sugary snacks, and sodas replace nutritious foods, you may miss out on essential nutrients. Sodas will not replace the calcium you would get in milk.

Controlling Sugars in Foods. To control the added sugar in your food choices follow these tips:

■ Cut back on foods with added sugars, such as soda, candy, cakes, and fruits canned in syrup. A 12-ounce (355-ml) regular soda has 9 to 12 teaspoons (45 to 60 ml) of sugar.
■ Read food labels. Choose foods with less added sugar.

Use Salt and Sodium Only in Moderation

What is the salt-sodium connection? Salt is made from two essential nutrients, sodium and chloride. Both help maintain the body's fluid balance. In so doing, sodium helps transport nutrients into your cells and helps wastes move out. It helps maintain your normal blood pressure and nerve function.

Sodium comes from many foods. About 10 percent of the sodium we eat is naturally present in food. Celery, for example, is high in sodium. Salt is added to preserve and flavor food; 75 percent of the sodium we eat comes from processed foods. The rest comes from the salt shaker.

Most people consume more salt and sodium than they need. For some, a high-sodium diet increases the risk of hypertension.

Most Americans consume too much salt. Think about other options before you add salt to your food.

These foods are all high in sugar. Eat them sparingly for good health.

CHOOSING A HEALTHY DIET **389**

L2 CLASS ACTIVITY. Distribute restaurant menus to students. Have them practice selecting foods low in sugar, fat, and sodium. Ask them to point out foods high in sugar, fat, and sodium.

L2 CLASS ACTIVITY. Select students to try various salt substitutes and alternative sweeteners and decide which ones they might consider using on a regular basis. Ask them to consider taste, cost, relative nutritional value, and safety in making their decisions.

L1 CLASS ACTIVITY. Distribute at least seven index cards to each student, and ask them to keep the cards throughout the week. Have them label each card with their name and one of these food groups: Milk, Meat, Fruit, Vegetable, Bread, Combination, and Other. Ask them to write down everything they eat, listing each food on the appropriate card. Tell students that if the food contains partial servings from more than one group to list it on the "Combination" card. At the end of the week, have students deposit their cards in boxes labeled with the above seven groups. Select volunteers to count the cards in each box and record the results on the chalkboard. Next, ask students: Did you eat foods from each of the five main food groups? From which group did you eat the most foods? Why? The least? Why? Which foods were a combination of more than one group? What foods did you list on the "Other" card?

L1 SPEAKER. Invite a home economics teacher to discuss and illustrate examples of healthy snacks that students would enjoy.

L1 DISCUSSION. Snacking is a typical teenage eating pattern. Have students list on the chalkboard snack foods in each food group, including the "empty-calorie group." Ask them to identify which snacks are the most nutritious.

Additional Information

Grains. Grains figure prominently among the relatively few species of plants that furnish people with most of their food worldwide. The most important domesticated species include:

■ wheat—domesticated nearly 9,000 years ago in the Near East and today the world's most widely cultivated plant;

■ rice—domesticated in Southeast Asia and today the plant that feeds more people than any other;

■ maize—domesticated in the Americas and today used chiefly to feed livestock;

■ sorghum, barley, rye, oats, and millet—each less important than the first three but still significant food crops in various parts of the world today.

Controlling Sodium in Foods. Follow these tips to help control sodium and salt:

- Taste foods before you salt. If you must add salt, shake once, not twice.
- Limit salty snack foods, such as chips, crackers, pretzels, and nuts.
- Season foods with herbs and spices, and use less salt in cooking.
- Read food labels for sodium content. Buy lower-sodium foods when you can.
- Use catsup, mustard, other condiments, and foods in salt solutions (such as pickles) sparingly.

Healthful Eating Patterns

A varied, moderate, and balanced diet forms the foundation of a healthful eating pattern. Whether you eat three meals a day, or four, five, or six minimeals instead, follow Dietary Guidelines and the Daily Food Guide, and avoid overeating.

Meals and snacks that represent all five food groups provide nutrients you need. Variety is important within each meal because nutrients in one food affect how your body uses nutrients in another.

When planning menus, remember that there are no good or bad foods. Any food that supplies calories and nutrients can be part of a nutritious diet. Nutrition guidelines apply to all your food choices for a day or more, not for just a single meal or food. You can enjoy a soft drink or fries occasionally, as long as your total diet is healthy.

Meals

A healthy meal includes variety from the food groups. Calories and nutrient intake are also spread throughout the day.

Breakfast. Breakfast may be your most important meal. After 10 to 12 hours without food, your body needs to be refueled. According to breakfast studies, eating a nutritious morning meal is linked with better mental and physical performance in late morning. Those who ate breakfast also reacted faster and experienced less muscle fatigue than those who skipped breakfast.

Breakfast can include any foods you enjoy—pizza, a peanut butter sandwich, a salad. Just make it nutritious. To get enough vitamin C during the day, choose citrus juice or fruit for breakfast. Choose fiber-rich, whole-grain breads and cereals. Breakfast is also a good time to get one calcium-rich serving of milk, cheese, or yogurt.

Lunch and Dinner. Eating other nutritious meals is important for health and energy. Typically, Americans eat a midday and an evening meal. Other cultural groups may follow a different pattern.

For most lunches and dinners, plan around a high-protein main dish. Then balance your meal with foods from the other food groups. Add side dishes, such as salads, fruit, vegetables, pasta, rice, or bread; a beverage; and perhaps a dessert. Each meal should provide about one-third of your daily needs for nutrients and calories.

HELP WANTED

Dietician

You are what you eat! We want a healthy person to manage the food preparation department of a large nursing home. We prefer an ADA-registered dietician with a bachelor's or master's degree, who has served a 6- to 12-month internship. You must be knowledgeable of the special nutrition needs of senior citizens with a wide variety of medical conditions. You must also take pride in the preparation and presentation of outstanding meals. You will need to be a "people person," who can work with both our patients and our staff, as well as a business person, who can manage the ordering and record-keeping duties

For more information contact:
The American Dietetic Association
216 West Jackson Blvd.
Chicago, IL 60606-6995

L2 CLASS ACTIVITY.

L2 CLASS ACTIVITY. Have students plan a breakfast menu that includes at least one nontraditional breakfast food. Stress that the menu should be well-balanced and supply about one-third of the day's calories. Discuss the completed projects. Ask for volunteers to list nontraditional breakfast foods that they enjoy.

LD CLASS ACTIVITY. Have students choose a healthy meal plan for one day and discuss the role each food plays in the plan.

L2 CLASS ACTIVITY. Select students to create a bulletin board illustrating nutritious snacks. Title the board "Super Snack Selections."

L1 SPEAKER. Invite an owner or manager of a local fast-food business to speak to the class about current efforts to reduce sugar, fat, and/or sodium in the restaurant's food preparation. Ask the speaker to discuss the role of consumer concerns in bringing about these changes. Discuss improvements that still need to be made to improve nutrition and reduce dietary risk.

Independent Practice

L1 COMMUNITY INVOLVEMENT. By law, school lunch programs must serve meals representing the five food groups. Using the weekly school lunch menu, have students classify meals into the five food groups.

L1 PERSONAL INVOLVEMENT. Ask students to study the five food groups, and to write down at least one new food they would be willing to try in each group.

L1 PARENTAL INVOLVEMENT. Have students ask their parents to share a recipe for one of the family's favorite foods (based on one of the five food groups and relatively low in sugar, fat, and sodium). Make copies of the recipes to distribute to the class.

Across the Curriculum

Home Economics. Place 10 breakfast cereals with varying sugar contents in small cups—1 cup of each cereal for each student. Arrange each type on a separate tray. Number each tray and the corresponding cereal box. Remove the boxes. Ask students to taste each cereal and indicate their preferences, using a scale of 1 to 10 with 10 being the most favored. Then have them rate the sugar content. Ask if there is a correlation between perceived sweetness and tastiness. Was there general agreement among students? Did students' perceptions of sweetness correspond with label information?

Snacking

Many teenagers need snacks. Nutritional and caloric needs are at their highest level because adolescents are active and growing. It is important to choose snack foods that are high in nutrients, and not just high in calories.

Carefully chosen, snacks provide essential nutrients, but they should never replace meals. Snacks offer a chance to get nutrients you may miss at mealtime. For example, if you did not drink vitamin C-rich juice for breakfast, an orange or tangerine can be a great snack. Make milk a snack, too.

HEALTH UPDATE

LOOKING AT THE ISSUES

How Much Meat Should We Eat?

Because a high-fat diet has been linked to many diseases and other health problems, many Americans are listening and cutting their consumption of animal foods. Some people, however, claim that people should not only eat less animal food, they should eat none at all.

Analyzing Different Viewpoints

ONE VIEW. Many people who eat meat say they enjoy it, and as long as they eat it in moderation and cook it in healthful ways, there is no problem.

A SECOND VIEW. Some nutritionists claim that meat provides amino acids, the building blocks of protein, as well as important vitamins and minerals. They also point out that strict vegetarians may suffer ill health effects from deficiencies in minerals such as calcium, and vitamins such as B_{12}.

A THIRD VIEW. Some people choose to be vegetarians for health reasons. They cite studies linking animal products with heart disease, high cholesterol, and some cancers. In addition, they point out that meat eaters are more likely than vegetarians to ingest agricultural chemicals.

A FOURTH VIEW. Other people choose not to eat meat on moral grounds. They believe that animal life should not be sacrificed for human beings. They talk about the unnecessary pain, abuse, and slaughter of animals raised for human consumption.

A FIFTH VIEW. Still others refuse to eat meat because they claim the process of raising animals for food uses up resources that should instead be used to feed hungry humans. They point to the destruction of forests for grazing land and the huge amounts of water needed for cattle raising.

Exploring Your Views

1. If you are a meat and dairy consumer, what steps can you take to make sure you are not getting too much of your food from animal sources? If you are a vegetarian, what steps can you take to make sure you are getting enough protein, minerals, and vitamins?

L2 **PERSONAL INVOLVEMENT.** Have students plan a daily menu, including snacks, that appeals to them and that provides an adequate number of servings from the five food groups. Display and discuss some of the examples.

L2 **RESEARCH.** Have students identify fats on food labels and then classify them as saturated or unsaturated.

L2 **COMMUNITY INVOLVEMENT.** Select students to interview a dietician, nurse, or doctor to learn ways to modify the amount of saturated fat, sugars, and sodium in the diet. Have students write the recommendations in their own words and share them with the class.

L1 **PERSONAL INVOLVEMENT.** Have students select one area of their diet that needs improvement, and write down a goal to improve. Help students analyze their progress at the end of a week.

L3 **COMMUNITY INVOLVEMENT.** Select students to interview local restaurant owners about their efforts to control sugar, fat, and sodium in their food. Ask students to share their findings with the class.

L1 **USING THE LESSON RESOURCES.** For additional student activities, refer to the lesson resources on page 385.

Additional Information

Nutritious Snacks. To add protein to the diet, try hard-boiled eggs, pieces of cheese, chunks of tuna, or slices of leftover roast or steak.

To add vitamin C to the diet, try strawberries, other berries, melon, tomatoes, citrus fruits, raw pineapple, or nectarines.

To add vitamin A, eat carrot sticks, raw broccoli, green pepper rings, or dark green vegetables. Also try yellow fruits and vegetables.

To add calcium to the diet, try any dairy product, frozen yogurt, cheese chunks, custard, cottage cheese, or fruit.

To add B vitamins and minerals to the diet, use whole-grain or enriched breads and cereal, dairy products, nuts, or raisins.

Check for Understanding

- Assign and discuss the lesson review. Encourage LD students to focus on questions 1, 2, 3, 4, 6, and 7.

Evaluate

- Administer, grade, and discuss the *Lesson 3 Quiz.*

Reteach

- Ask for volunteers to bring a menu from their favorite restaurant. Have them identify the food groups represented by the various menu items, including food combinations.
- Ask students to complete *Reteaching Activity 51.*

Enrich

- Have students keep a 24-hour record of everything they eat and drink, including amounts. Then ask them to exchange their food records and pretend they are dieticians working with a client. Provide food composition tables, and ask them to calculate the nutrients and calories in their partners' food record. Next, ask them to compare these values to the RDA, and write a short paper, analyzing their "clients'" diet. Have them meet with each other, suggesting changes the other might make.

Close

Ask students to state the most important concepts learned in the lesson.

Eating Out

On average, people eat 30 percent of their calories and more than 20 percent of their meals away from home. Fast-food restaurants serve 40 percent of those meals. You need to apply principles of good nutrition to restaurant, cafeteria, vending machine, and fast-food eating.

Most restaurants offer enough variety for nutritional choices. To eat fewer calories, you might skip the appetizer, order a small portion (a cup instead of a bowl of soup), ask for salad dressing or butter on the side, split dessert with a friend, or order fruit rather than a sweet dessert.

Fast Foods. Fast foods are convenient, relatively low-cost, predictable, and quick. Carefully chosen, fast-food meals supply many essential nutrients. However, they tend to be high in calories, fat, and sodium.

Today, with more salad bars, vegetables, yogurt, and low-fat, low-sodium menu items, you can make healthy fast-food choices. Many restaurants provide free nutritional information on menu items, too. Consider these tips for healthy fast-food choices:

- Order the regular sandwich instead of the double or deluxe size.
- Enjoy salad bars. Go heavy on fresh fruits and vegetables, but light on creamed salads and dressings. One ladle often holds 2 tablespoons (30 ml) of dressing, which can be 150 calories.
- At potato and pasta bars, avoid overloading sauces, sour cream, and butter.
- Avoid breaded chicken and fish sandwiches. Order lean meats and grilled chicken and fish instead.
- Skip high-fat, high-sugar desserts.
- Choose milk instead of a soft drink for added nutrients.
- When fixing your sandwich, load up on lettuce, tomato, and onion.
- Skip the french fries or fried onion rings, especially if you order a fried poultry or fish sandwich. At the very least, order a small serving with no salt.

LESSON 3 REVIEW

Reviewing Facts and Vocabulary

1. Name the five food groups and the recommended range of servings for each.
2. What are four weight-control principles that apply to everyone?
3. Why should you limit the added sugar in your diet?
4. Why are people urged to control sodium and salt in their diets?

Thinking Critically

5. **Analysis.** What are some possible results of an unhealthy eating pattern?

6. **Evaluation.** What foods in your diet are empty-calorie foods? How often do you eat them?
7. **Evaluation.** What foods in your diet may be high in sodium or salt?

Applying Health Knowledge

8. Record your meals and snacks for a day. Evaluate them using the Daily Food Guide and Dietary Guidelines. Make recommendations for any improvements.
9. Go to a fast-food restaurant. Plan a nutritious, fat-controlled meal from the menu.

392 CHAPTER 19 MAKING RESPONSIBLE FOOD CHOICES

Answers to Lesson 3 Review

1. Breads, cereals, grain products; fruits; vegetables; meat, poultry, fish, and alternates; milk, cheese, and yogurt. See page 386 for recommended servings.
2. See page 387.
3. It only adds calories but no nutrients and contributes to tooth decay.
4. Too much salt and sodium may increase one's risk of hypertension.

5. Answers will vary. Possible answer: One may not get enough of all the nutrients one needs and growth, energy, and health will suffer.
6. Answers will vary.
7. Answers will vary. Possible answers: Potato chips, diet soda.
8. Answers will vary.
9. Answers will vary.

BEING A WISE FOOD CONSUMER

Now that you know the basics about nutrition, how can you be a wise consumer and make healthy food choices? Information on food labels, on supermarket shelves, and on restaurant menus can help you know what you are buying and eating.

Food Labeling

Food labels say more about food than you may realize. By knowing how to use them, you can be a smart consumer. All labels on processed foods must state the following information:

- name of the food, including the variety, style, packing medium, and special dietary properties
- net amount in weight or volume
- name and address of the manufacturer, packer, or distributor

In addition, labels must carry information about ingredients and nutrient and caloric content. Some labels also give nutritional or health claims and preparation instructions.

The Food and Drug Administration (FDA) and U.S. Department of Agriculture (USDA) regulate food labeling. Because labels have become confusing, Congress recently passed a law requiring the food industry to create straightforward, standardized labels for most foods. In 1993 the FDA released its new guidelines, to go into effect the following year.

Nutrition Labels

Nutrition labels indicate the nutritional and caloric content of foods. This information helps you find good sources of nutrients, compare nutrients and calories in various brands, and choose foods for special diets.

Under the new FDA guidelines, all foods require nutrition labels with the exception of the following:

- food served in restaurants
- plain coffee and tea
- some spices and other foods that contain no nutrients
- fresh meat, poultry, and fish; and fresh fruits and vegetables
- food produced by very small companies or offered in very small packages

What nutritional information goes on a food label?
- serving size
- servings per container
- calories per serving and calories per serving from fat
- grams of total fat, saturated fat, cholesterol, sodium, carbohydrates, dietary fiber, sugars, and protein per serving
- percentage of the recommended Daily Value (DV) the product supplies of the above nutrients plus some important minerals and vitamins

BEING A WISE FOOD CONSUMER **393**

LESSON 4 FOCUS

TERMS TO USE
- Food additives
- Enriched
- Fortification (fawrt•uh•fuh•KAY•shuhn)
- Unit pricing

CONCEPTS TO LEARN
- Knowing how to use food labels can make you a smart consumer.
- Governmental and private agencies exist to protect the consumer in various ways.
- The federal government maintains an ongoing program of enacting new regulations and providing important information to consumers.
- Unit pricing allows you to compare food prices.

ATTITUDES AND BEHAVIORS TO EVALUATE
- Self-Inventory, page 398.
- Building Decision-Making Skills, page 399.

Lesson Objectives

After studying this lesson, students should be able to:

- list the information required on a nutrition information label
- explain the difference between enriched and fortified foods
- name reasons why additives are used in food
- interpret open-dating information on food labels
- compare food prices by using unit pricing

Bellringer

Write the following on the chalkboard for students to work on while attendance is being taken: *In the grocery sack at the front of the class is an ordinary can of corn. List five items of information that are printed on the can's label.*

Introducing the Lesson

On the chalkboard, list students' responses to the Bellringer. Tell students they will learn about information that is required to be on food labels and how to use the information to make wise choices when selecting food.

Building Vocabulary

- Have students design a "Help Wanted" advertisement for a supermarket employee. Ask them to use as many vocabulary terms as possible in their ad.
- Ask students to complete *Workbook Vocabulary Activity 52.*

DID YOU KNOW?

- According to Jane Brody, nutritionist and columnist for *The New York Times*, you should eat breakfast like a king, lunch like a prince, and dinner like a pauper. Unfortunately, many Americans do just the opposite.
- In a lifetime, the average American eats about 50 tons (45.4 metric tons) of food.

Resources for Lesson 4

- **Transparency** 24
- **Guided Reading** Activity 52
- **Decision-Making** Activity 19
- **Workbook** Vocabulary Activity 52
- **Workbook** Application Activity 19
- **Reteaching** Activity 52

- **Enrichment** Activity 19
- **Health Labs** Activity 19
- **Cooperative Learning** Activity 19
- **Lesson 4 Quiz**
- **Chapter 19 Test**

Guided Practice

L1 CLASS ACTIVITY. Ask students to bring in empty food containers. Have them locate, read, and discuss any misleading nutrient or health claims printed on the labels.

L1 SPEAKER. Invite the county extension agent and a home economics teacher to talk to the class about current developments in food and shelf labeling.

L1 CLASS ACTIVITY. Either photocopy the content information or copy the ingredients from several food labels listing many additives. Distribute the information to the class and ask students to guess what type of food contains these ingredients. Ask them what purposes they think the additives serve.

L3 CLASS ACTIVITY. Point out that food additives, including artificial flavors, dyes, taste enhancers, and preservatives are very common. Then have students study labels on prepared foods (such as hot dogs, luncheon meats, cereals, ice cream, yogurt, powdered drinks, etc.) to compile lists of chemical additives to foods. Ask students to use library resources to research each of the additives and give a brief report to the class about their advantages and disadvantages.

L1 EXPLANATION. Point out that *fortified* and *enriched* are used interchangeably to mean that nutrients have been added to food.

L2 CLASS ACTIVITY. Select students to create a poster or bulletin board featuring foods that are fortified or enriched.

L2 DISCUSSION. Ask students which categories of additives they consider most and least important and why. (Many people believe that preservatives and nutrients are the most important, because it is more important to prevent spoilage and provide nutrition than to make food appealing by adding color and flavor.)

L1 USING LIFE MANAGEMENT SKILLS TRANSPARENCY 24. Refer to the Teaching Transparencies Binder.

Serving sizes are more consistent across product lines and reflect the amounts people actually eat.	**Nutrition Facts**		New title signals that the label contains the newly required information.

Nutrition Facts

Serving Size ½ cup (114g)   Servings Per Container 4

Amount Per Serving

Calories 90	Calories from Fat 30

	% Daily Value*
Total Fat 3g	5%
Saturated Fat 0g	0%
Cholesterol 0mg	0%
Sodium 300mg	13%
Total Carbohydrate 13g	4%
Dietary Fiber 3g	12%
Sugars 3g	
Protein 3g	

Vitamin A	80%	•	Vitamin C	60%
Calcium	4%	•	Iron	4%

* Percent Daily Values are based on a 2,000 calorie diet. Your daily values may be higher or lower depending on your calorie needs:

	Calories	2,000	2,500
Total Fat	Less than	65g	80g
Sat Fat	Less than	20g	25g
Cholesterol	Less than	300mg	300mg
Sodium	Less than	2,400mg	2,400mg
Total Carbohydrate		300g	375g
Fiber		25g	30g

Calories per gram: Fat 9   •   Carbohydrates 4   •   Protein 4

Source: Food and Drug Administration 1992

Side labels:
- List of nutrients covers those most important to the health of today's consumers.
- Daily values are based on a daily diet of 2,000 and 2,500 calories.
- Label shows **calories per gram** of fat, carbohydrates, and protein.
- **Calories from fat** help consumers meet dietary guidelines that recommend people get no more than 30 percent of their calories from fat.
- **% Daily Value** shows how a food fits into the overall daily diet.

As this sample shows, the new food label will provide easy-to-use nutrition information.

The new guidelines require that labels on beverages containing fruit juice specify the percentage of fruit juice they contain.

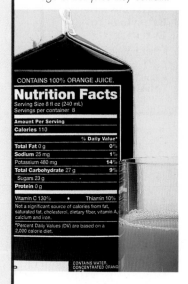

In addition to this information, the new labels contain guidelines on the amount of nutrients people need in their daily diets. For example, the FDA recommends 25 grams of dietary fiber and a maximum of 65 grams of fat each day for an average woman or child, slightly more for an adult man. The DV is the reference value for labeling food. Individual nutrient needs vary depending on age, sex, size, health, and activity level.

Some nutrient labels have two lists. If a food is eaten with another food, for example, cereal with milk, nutritional information is given for the product alone and with the other food.

Regulations now permit labels of certain foods to claim *possible* benefit in combatting a disease or condition. For example, labels on products that are high in calcium can claim to be a possible help in preventing osteoporosis. Labels on foods high in fiber, low in fat, or high in vitamins A and C can claim they "may help" to prevent cancer.

Ingredient Listing

Almost all food labels must have an ingredient list. The only exceptions are foods with one ingredient, such as some peanut butters and canned fruits and vegetables.

Labels list ingredients by weight, in descending order. The ingredient in greatest amount is first. Food labels with several similar ingredients are confusing. For example, when three sweeteners—corn syrup, sugar, and honey—are used, instead of just sugar, each is listed separately and lower on the list.

Food Additives. Additives must be listed on food labels. **Food additives** are substances added to food intentionally to produce a desired effect. They are used to:

394 CHAPTER 19 MAKING RESPONSIBLE FOOD CHOICES

Across the Curriculum

Home Economics. Divide the class into three groups. Have each group conduct one of the following demonstrations to explore the functions of food additives. Assign each group to compare the results and draw conclusions, to be discussed in class. 1) Flavor. Have students make oatmeal cookies with and without salt and vanilla. 2) Appearance. Have students cut an apple in half and brush one half with citric or ascorbic acid. Let both halves sit for several minutes. 3) Preservation. In separate plastic bags, store bakery bread without additives and supermarket bread with additives. Let the bread sit for several days at room temperature.

- add nutrients,
- lengthen storage life,
- give flavor or color,
- maintain texture,
- control food's acidity,
- help age foods, such as cheese.

Foods are enriched or fortified to improve nutrient value. In **enriched** foods, nutrients lost in processing are added back. Breads, pastas, and rice made of refined grains are enriched with B vitamins and iron. **Fortification** adds nutrients not naturally present. Because vitamin D helps deposit calcium in bones, milk is fortified with vitamin D.

The FDA and USDA regulate most foods that cross state lines. This includes foods with additives. If food manufacturers want to use regulated additives in their products, they must prove to the appropriate government agency that the additives are safe in the amounts used.

Some additives, such as sugar and salt, are termed *generally recognized as safe (GRAS)*. Because they have been used safely for years, these 700 or so additives can be used without permission. The GRAS list is constantly reviewed.

To avoid eating too much of any one additive, health experts recommend eating a variety of foods. People with allergies to certain additives must check food labels.

Milk is fortified with vitamin D.

MAKING SENSE OF LABEL TERMS

Terms such as *low-fat*, *low-calorie*, *low-cholesterol*, and *low-sodium* must now refer to foods that can be eaten frequently without a person exceeding dietary guidelines for the substance. For example, a low-fat food must contain 3 grams or less of fat per serving and a low-calorie food must contain 40 calories or less per serving. Low-calorie *meals*, such as frozen dinners, may contain no more than 120 calories.

- **Light:** This term now means that calories in an item have been reduced by at least a third, or the fat or sodium by at least a half.
- **Less and more:** A food must contain 25 percent less of a nutrient or of calories than a comparable food and 10 percent more than the regular food to be able to use these terms.
- **-free:** A product can contain no amount, or only a negligible amount, of the substance, such as fat, cholesterol, sodium, sugars, or calories.
- **High:** This term may be used if the food supplies 20 percent or more of the Daily Value of a particular nutrient in a serving. A good source must supply 10 to 19 percent of the nutrient.
- **Fresh:** Only foods that are raw, unprocessed, contain no preservatives, and have never been frozen or heated can be labeled fresh.
- **Natural:** This term is defined for meat and poultry only. According to the USDA, it means the food is minimally processed with no artificial or synthetic ingredients.

The FDA is also considering a definition for the term *healthy* based on a food's fat, cholesterol, and sodium content.

Sugar and Fat Substitutes. The food industry has responded to many consumer concerns about nutrition. In many cases, the industry has been very creative in substituting ingredients that lower either the calorie count or the fat content.

CONFLICT RESOLUTION

In 1986, California voters approved a toxic right-to-know law. Other states are considering similar legislation. Such laws require warning labels on foods and other products that contain chemicals known to cause cancer or birth defects. Consumer groups that support the legislation believe this law would eliminate the use of dangerous chemicals. Opponents, largely from business and industry, argue that the law would cost billions of dollars, lead to a loss of jobs and an increase in the number of lawsuits.

Explain how you would vote on a toxic right-to-know bill.

DID YOU KNOW?

- The worst high-salt offenders in the American diet are soups, sauces, ham, processed cheese, soy sauce, pickles, and frozen meals.
- Americans each ate 50 pounds of bread last year—a loaf or so a week. Unfortunately, 55 percent of it was white bread.

Overcoming Misconceptions

Myth. Food preservation is a relatively new procedure. **Fact.** During medieval times, meat and fish were preserved by heavy dry salting or by keeping them in brine. In dry salting, the food was buried in a bed of granular dry salt. The brine solution was a mixture of water and salt. Sometimes the food remained in the salt or brine for months, absorbing a great deal of flavor. Before cooking, the meat or fish was soaked in several changes of water to remove the salt. Cooks could use other methods to absorb excess salt. Sometimes a large bag of oatmeal was suspended in the cooking pot; or whole grains, breadcrumbs, or dried beans and peas were cooked with the food.

These containers of milk cannot be sold after the date shown on the labels.

Fructose, natural fruit sugar, is used as a caloric substitute. Because it is sweeter than table sugar, less is needed, so it supplies fewer calories.

Two noncaloric sweeteners are used in the United States—saccharin and aspartame. They are commonly added to soft drinks and frozen desserts, or you can buy them in powdered form. These sweeteners are considered safe when used in moderation.

With the public's recent concern about fat, the food industry has developed several types of fat substitutes. They have the potential for widespread use in processed foods, fried foods, and home cooking as a way to reduce fat intake.

Open-Dating

Many food products are open dated with a system that consumers can easily interpret. Look for these dates on labels:

- expiration date—last date you should use or consume the product
- freshness date—last date a food is thought to be fresh
- pack date—packaging date
- sell date—last date product (for example, milk) should be sold (although you can store it past this date).

Shelf Labeling

Shelf labeling helps consumers get the most nutrition for their food dollar. Unit pricing and, to a lesser extent, nutritional shelf labels are posted under food products. Many stores also display printed information about fresh products.

Unit Pricing

Unit pricing allows you to compare food prices. It shows the cost per unit of different-size packages. Suppose an 8-ounce can of Jiffy Beans cost 88¢; the unit price per ounce is 11¢. A 12-ounce can of the same brand costs $1.04, which is 8.7¢ per ounce. Instead of calculating these amounts, you can look at unit price labels on the shelf. Unit pricing also helps you compare different brands.

There is a caution. Before you buy the larger size, which may cost less per unit, decide whether you can use the extra amount.

KEEPING FIT

Preservative and Additive Alert

Some people have severe allergic reactions to some of the nearly 3,000 additives and preservatives in foods.

When you know you are allergic to a certain substance, learn its alternate names. For example, sulfites may be listed on labels as sodium sulfite, sodium bisulfite, sulfur dioxide, potassium metabisulfite, or sodium metabisulfite.

Otherwise, when you read labels, you may miss the fact that the very thing you are allergic to is in the food you are about to consume.

Across the Curriculum

Home Economics. Ask students to make a list of 5 to 10 of the additives found most commonly in foods in the food lab or at home. Have them write a letter to a consumer advocacy group, requesting information on the safety of these additives.

Science. Ask students to research and write about: (1) the chemical properties shared by pepper and mustard that make them useful in retarding food spoilage. (Have them explain the chemical nature of these preservatives); or (2) the chemical properties that make emulsifiers useful in preventing salad dressing and other oil mixtures from separating.

Good nutrition during adolescence is a vital link to total health.

Nutritional Shelf Labels

More and more stores have nutritional information on grocery shelves, next to the unit price. These labels might describe fat, sodium, or caloric content. Currently, no standard format exists for nutritional shelf labels. If your supermarket has them, ask the customer service staff how to use them.

LESSON 4 REVIEW

Reviewing Facts and Vocabulary

1. List the information required on a nutritional information label.
2. What do the terms *enriched* and *fortified* mean?
3. Describe the way ingredients are listed on food labels.
4. What are four reasons food additives are used in food?
5. What do *open dating* and *unit pricing* mean?

Thinking Critically

6. **Analysis.** How can food labels help you make smart food choices?
7. **Analysis.** Compare two similar food products using the information on their labels.

8. **Evaluation.** What information could you use to find hot dogs that had less fat and less sodium than the standard?

Applying Health Knowledge

9. Create a food label for a food of your choice. Include all the required information, including a nutritional information label. Support any nutrient claim with specific nutritional information.
10. Visit the grocery store, and compare the cost of several foods using unit pricing: two brands of the same size product and two sizes of the same product. Which would you buy? Why?

BEING A WISE FOOD CONSUMER **397**

Answers to Lesson 4 Review

1. See page 393.
2. Enriched—nutrients lost in processing are added back. Fortified—nutrients not naturally present are added.
3. By weight, in descending order.
4. Accept four of the bulleted items on page 394.
5. See page 396.

6. Answers will vary. Possible answers: One knows what one is getting in the product and for what price.
7. Answers will vary.
8. Nutritional information on the label, the Daily Food Guide, and Dietary Guidelines or nutritional shelf labels.
9. Answers will vary.
10. Answers will vary.

Check for Understanding
- Assign and discuss the lesson review.
- Assign and discuss the chapter review.

Evaluate
- Administer, grade, and discuss the *Lesson 4 Quiz*.
- Administer, grade, and discuss the *Chapter 19 Test*.
- Refer to the Performance Assessment strategy for this chapter. See pages T 23 to T 25.

Reteach
- Divide the class into five groups, and assign each group one of the main food groups. Have them design a food label for a food product from that group. Tell them to include required information, such as nutrients, calories, ingredients, and other facts to inform and assist the consumer. Display and discuss the completed labels.
- Ask students to complete *Reteaching Activity 52.*

Enrich
- Ask for volunteers to bring to class packaged food items from other countries. Display the items and have students compare the labels with those on products produced and packaged in the United States.
- Ask students to complete *Enrichment Activity 19.*

Close

Divide the class into groups of two, and give each group labels from cans, packages, or boxes of food. Briefly go through the lesson, having students identify required information on the labels, as well as any health claims or additional information. Also, ask them to identify and explain open-dating information.

Helping Students Improve Their Health

Reinforcing Vocabulary

- **Nutrient label.** A listing of the vitamins and minerals and other nutritious components of a particular food.
- **Ingredient list.** A listing of the ingredients found in a food in rank order of most to least.

Teaching Strategies

L1 EXPLANATION. Question 17 could be misinterpreted by parents and students. It is illegal for teenagers to purchase any alcoholic beverages. However, teenagers may be served alcoholic beverages by their parents.

L1 DISCUSSION. Have students bring in different food packaging labels. Have students analyze the terminology used in packaging. What do terms such as *low calorie, lite,* and *natural* really mean? Are there legal definitions that apply to the use of these words in advertising? Is this truthful advertising? Do consumers generally understand what these terms actually mean?

L1 CLASS ACTIVITY. Play a game of nutritional bingo. Using construction paper, create bingo cards. Construct 24 different nutrition-related questions and place questions on index cards. Have the middle spot of the bingo cards be a free space. Write the answers to the nutrition questions on the bingo cards in different orders. Allow students to use paper clips to mark the correct responses on their bingo cards as questions are read.

L3 CLASS ACTIVITY. Ask selected students to videotape a lunch period in your school cafeteria. Have them interview students and teachers as to their food choices. Play the video for the class. Ask whether or not students generally make sound nutritional choices. Do teachers eat differently than students? What can students do to eat more nutritiously at school?

Self-Inventory

Making Healthy Food Choices

HOW DO YOU RATE?

Number a sheet of paper from 1 through 25. Read each item below and respond by writing *almost always, sometimes, seldom,* or *never* for each item. Then proceed to the next section.

1. I eat foods from several food groups at each meal.
2. Each day I eat at least six servings from the breads, cereals, grains, and pasta group.
3. Each day I eat at least three servings from the vegetable group.
4. Each day I eat at least three servings from the fruit group.
5. Each day I eat at least two servings from the meat, poultry, fish, and alternates group.
6. Each day I eat at least two servings from the milk, yogurt, and cheese group.
7. I eat fried foods, such as french fries and fried onion rings sparingly.
8. I avoid high-fat desserts and baked foods.
9. I eat gravies and rich sauces sparingly.
10. I cut all visible fat off meat and remove the skin from chicken.
11. I reach for fresh fruit instead of a sweet dessert or snack.
12. I buy fruit packed in water or juice rather than heavy syrup.

13. I eat whole-grain breads and cereals instead of highly refined grains.
14. I eat whole fruit with the skin or peel.
15. I taste food before salting it.
16. I avoid eating too many salty snack foods.
17. I avoid alcoholic beverages.
18. I eat a nutritious breakfast.
19. I drink milk or juice at meals rather than soft drinks.
20. I snack mostly on foods from the five food groups, rather than on empty-calorie foods.
21. If I snack, I do so well before mealtime.
22. At potato and pasta bars, I avoid overloading on sauces, sour cream, and butter.
23. At salad bars I go heavy on fresh fruits and vegetables and light on creamed salads and desserts.
24. I use information on a nutrient label and the ingredient list of a food label when I shop for food.
25. I compare prices using the unit price label when I shop for groceries.

HOW DID YOU SCORE?

Give yourself 2 points for every *almost always* response; 1 point for every *sometimes* response; and 0 points for each *seldom* or *never* response. Find your total, and read ahead to see how you scored. Then proceed to the next section.

38 to 50
Excellent. Your food choices show that you are taking good care of your health.

13 to 37
Good. You may understand that good nutrition is important to your health, but you need to make wiser food decisions.

0 to 12
Needs Improvement. Your food choices may be putting your body at risk.

WHAT ARE YOUR GOALS?

If you scored between 38 and 50, complete the statements in Part A. If your score was under 38, complete Parts A and B.

Part A

1. I plan to learn more about making wise food decisions in these ways: ____.
2. My timetable for completing this is ____.
3. I plan to share food and nutritional information with others by ____.

Part B

4. The food behavior I would like to change or improve is ____.
5. The steps involved in making this change are ____.
6. My timetable for making this change is ____.
7. The people or groups I will ask for support or assistance are ____.
8. My rewards for making this change are ____.

Meeting Students' Needs

For students who score *Excellent*. Have students consider careers in the food industry, and continue taking courses, such as chemistry, to increase their knowledge of nutrition.

For students who score *Good*. Suggest that students keep diaries of all the foods they consume for one week. This diary will allow students to examine the nutritional level of the foods consumed.

For students who *Need Improvement*. Help students understand that teenagers literally are what they eat. Have students set short-term goals that will lead to a change in eating habits.

Building Decision-Making Skills

eon works at the newest restaurant in town, which is doing a thriving business. He really likes his job and the people that work there, and he definitely needs the money. However, he has discovered that other employees engage in unsanitary practices while they are at work. The manager, a family friend who hired him, is aware of what is happening but has not spoken to the other employees. In fact, the one time Leon tried to speak with the manager about the problem she told him she would take care of it. That was two weeks ago. Nothing has changed. What should Leon do?

WHAT DO YOU THINK?

1. **Situation.** Why does a decision need to be made?
2. **Choices.** What possible choices might Leon have?
3. **Consequences.** What are the advantages and disadvantages of each choice?
4. **Consequences.** How will the other employees and the manager probably feel about each choice?
5. **Consequences.** What risks are involved for Leon in this decision?
6. **Decision.** What do you think Leon should do? Explain your reasoning.
7. **Evaluation.** Have you ever been in a similar situation? If so, how did you handle it? What did you learn from the experience?

enise feels very strongly about eating wisely. She has made a commitment to avoid fat, refined sugar, salt, and red meat. However, she is in a social situation with friends who are going to a fast-food restaurant. What should she do?

WHAT DO YOU THINK?

8. **Choices.** What choices does Denise have?
9. **Consequences.** What are the advantages and disadvantages of each choice?
10. **Decision.** What do you think Denise should do?
11. **Evaluation.** Have you found yourself in a dilemma such as this? Describe the situation, how you handled it, and what you learned.

Kari's high school has a student body that includes many different cultures and ethnic groups. The cafeteria manager does a great job and has won considerable praise for the quality of the food. Although Kari likes the food, a group of friends have decided that the cafeteria does not serve enough ethnic foods. As part of a cultural awareness week, Kari's friends have made it a project to try to get the manager to add more ethnic foods to the menu. The manager was offended by their suggestion and refuses to consider it. Kari's friends are organizing a boycott of the cafeteria and have asked for her support. Students are not permitted off campus during lunch, and Kari hates to carry her lunch. Should Kari join the boycott?

WHAT DO YOU THINK?

12. **Consequences.** What are the advantages and disadvantages of joining the boycott?
13. **Consequences.** What are the advantages and disadvantages of not joining the boycott?
14. **Decision.** Which choice do you think is best for Kari?
15. **Evaluation.** Have you ever found yourself in a similar situation? Describe the situation, how you handled it, and what you learned.

Building Decision-Making Skills

Teaching Strategies

L1 **CLASS ACTIVITY.** Have students participate in a role-play situation in which Leon talks to his parents about the unsanitary practices he has witnessed at the restaurant where he works. Should Leon talk to his employer again? Should Leon remain working at this restaurant? Should Leon have his parents talk to his employer? What are possible benefits and drawbacks to each of these solutions?

L1 **CLASS ACTIVITY.** Have students role-play the part of Denise as she talks with her friends about eating lunch at a fast-food restaurant. What possible compromise might Denise be able to reach with her friends?

L1 **DISCUSSION.** Considering Kari's situation, have students discuss the purpose and appropriateness of the boycott itself.

L1 **CLASS ACTIVITY.** Another possible role-play situation pertaining to nutrition includes: Your mother always salts your food for you for dinner. You have asked her several times not to salt your food because you have been trying to cut down on your sodium consumption. Your mother continues to add table salt to your food.

L2 **DISCUSSION.** Have students debate the role that food plays in preventing illness. Are there any foods that really help to prevent cancer?

Discussing the Answers

Situation 1. Perhaps the best solution in Leon's situation would be for him to do his homework and find out exactly what sanitary practices the health department expects. If Leon presents these requirements to his employer and explains his concern that the restaurant may be cited, fined, or closed as a result of these violations, perhaps Leon's employer will listen.

Situation 2. Denise could pack a lunch and take it along or order something from the menu that is not terribly unhealthy.

Situation 3. Kari needs to consider the appropriateness of the boycott and stand by her principles. True friends will respect her decision to boycott or not. She should not allow peer pressure to influence her decision in this instance.

DID YOU KNOW?

■ Ethnic foods may be better nutritional choices than the typical American diet. Chinese food, for example, tends to be low in fat and high in vitamins and fiber. Most dishes have plenty of vegetables and steamed rice, but limited amounts of meat and dairy products.

Answers to Chapter 19 Review

Using Health Terms

1. Nutrients
2. Nutrition
3. Carbohydrates
4. Amino acids
5. Cholesterol
6. Adipose tissue
7. Fat-soluble vitamins
8. Daily Food Guide
9. Diet
10. Added sugars
11. Regular exercise
12. Sugars
13. Sodium
14. The Food and Drug Administration and U.S. Department of Agriculture
15. Fortification
16. Open-dating
17. Ingredient list

Building Academic Skills

18. Autobiographies will vary.
19. Summaries will vary.

Recalling the Facts

20. They are linked to one's physical needs, environment, and emotions.
21. One's cultural heritage, family and social relationships, media messages, and life-style influence one's food choices.
22. Answers may include but are not limited to: one may eat to relieve tension or boredom, one may lose one's appetite due to emotions.
23. The first year of life and adolescence.
24. Ounce for ounce, carbohydrates have the same number of calories as proteins and fewer calories than fat.
25. Sugars.
26. They are the nine amino acids that the body cannot make that must come from the food one eats.
27. Fiber.
28. Recommended Dietary Allowances—the amounts of 19 essential nutrients that most people need daily to stay healthy.
29. To provide nutritional advice on how to eat to stay healthy for Americans aged 2 years and over.

Using Health Terms

On a separate sheet of paper, write the term that best matches each definition given below.

LESSON 1

1. Substances in food that the body needs to function properly.
2. Study of how the body uses food.

LESSON 2

3. Starches, sugars, and fiber.
4. Building blocks of protein.
5. Fatlike substance found only in animal sources of food.
6. Body fat.
7. Vitamins A, D, E, and K.

LESSON 3

8. Guideline for helping people choose a varied, balanced, and moderate diet.
9. Everything you eat and drink.
10. Foods that provide calories but few essential nutrients.
11. Must accompany smart eating for weight control.
12. Food substances linked to tooth decay.
13. A nutrient found in salt, which is often linked with high blood pressure.

LESSON 4

14. A governmental agency that is responsible for food labels.
15. Substances added for a specific effect.
16. Consumer aid for judging foods' freshness.
17. Information on a food label that tells the specific contents of the product.

Building Academic Skills

LESSON 1

18. **Writing.** Write a food autobiography describing food habits unique to you.

LESSON 2

19. **Reading.** Read a magazine or newspaper article about a current nutritional issue. Summarize the article in writing.

Recalling the Facts

LESSON 1

20. Where do food preferences come from?
21. How does your environment affect your food choices?
22. Give two examples of how eating is tied to emotions.
23. What are the two fastest growth periods in your life?

LESSON 2

24. Refute the claim that carbohydrates are fattening.
25. What is the simplest form of carbohydrate?
26. Why are some amino acids known as essential amino acids?
27. What is the nondigestible part of some foods that helps move waste through the digestive tract?
28. What is the RDA?

LESSON 3

29. What is the purpose of the Dietary Guidelines for Americans?
30. Why should you eat a variety of foods from each of the five food groups?
31. What are the key nutrients supplied by each of the five food groups?
32. Why do fats and sweets not belong in any of the five food groups?
33. What are the benefits of controlling the fat and cholesterol in a person's diet?
34. List three ways you might reduce the fat in your diet. Which would be most effective for you? Why?
35. What are some benefits of controlling the amount of sugar in your diet?
36. Explain ways you could lower the amount of fat in food you order in a restaurant.

LESSON 4

37. What useful information can you find on food labels?
38. What is required on a nutritional information label?
39. What is the GRAS list?
40. How are ingredients listed on food labels?

30. To get all the nutrients one needs.
31. See page 386 for nutrients provided by each of the five food groups.
32. They provide few nutrients.
33. Reduction of one's risk of heart disease, obesity, and some cancers.
34. Accept three of the following: cut off the fat on meat; eat lean meat, fish, poultry; choose lower-fat milk, cheese, yogurt; eat less salad dressing; cut down on fried foods; eat steamed, boiled, or baked vegetables; eat plenty of vegetables, fruits, and whole-grain foods.
35. Reduces calories, reduces contribution to tooth decay, allows one to eat more nutritious foods.
36. See page 392.
37. See page 393.
38. Serving size; servings per container; calories per serving; grams of protein, carbohydrate, and fat per serving; percent of U.S. Recommended Daily Allowances for protein and several vitamins and minerals.

REVIEW

Thinking Critically

LESSON 1

41. **Synthesis.** Identify a holiday, and describe the food customs that usually surround the celebration.
42. **Evaluation.** Is it right or wrong for parents to reward or punish their child with food?
43. **Analysis.** How might a limited budget influence your food choices?
44. **Evaluation.** How do boredom, stress, frustration, and happiness affect eating habits? Give examples.

LESSON 2

45. **Evaluation.** What is the primary source of calories in your diet?
46. **Synthesis.** What would you expect of a product labeled *hydrogenated corn oil*?
47. **Synthesis.** Create an accurate and persuasive advertisement for a nutritious food.

LESSON 3

48. **Evaluation.** Compare your eating habits with those of a friend. Which of you makes more healthful choices?
49. **Synthesis.** Create a nutritious daily menu plan for someone who typically eats six minimeals during the day.
50. **Synthesis.** Suppose your friend skips breakfast because she does not like traditional breakfast foods. What advice might you offer?
51. **Evaluation.** What standards would you apply to decide if a snack is healthy?

Making the Connection

LESSON 1

52. **Home Economics.** Compare the fat content in 1/2 pound of various types of ground beef (regular, chuck, round) by breaking the ground beef apart and browning it with no additional fat. Remove the meat from the frying pan, pour the fat into a measuring cup, and measure. What conclusions can you draw from this experiment?

Applying Health Knowledge

LESSON 1

53. Discuss the pros and cons of food advertising on children's television.

LESSON 2

54. How might a vegetarian who eats no meat, poultry, or fish get all of the nutrients he or she needs?
55. Suppose your friend said, "Milk is only for children." How would you refute this?

LESSON 3

56. The typical fast-food meal (burger, fries, and shake) has over 800 calories. How could you lower this meal's caloric and fat content?
57. Suppose a family member has high blood pressure. How could you help control the sodium in his or her diet?
58. As a teenager, you probably enjoy snacks. What might you do to keep snacks from promoting tooth decay?

LESSON 4

59. You are buying a breakfast cereal. One has 100 percent of the Daily Value for all nutrients listed. The other has 25 percent of B vitamins, 15 percent of iron, and small amounts of other nutrients. Which would you buy? On what basis do you decide to buy a cereal? What factors do not enter into your decision?
60. If you had the opportunity, what information would you include on food labels?

Beyond the Classroom

LESSON 1

61. **Parental Involvement.** Ask your parents what criteria they use when shopping for food.

LESSON 4

62. **Further Study.** Research the recent food labeling debate, and report on its current status.

39. Generally recognized as safe—additives that can be used without permission of the FDA and USDA.
40. By weight, in descending order.

Thinking Critically

41. Answers will vary.
42. Answers will vary. Possible answer: Wrong—unwanted positive or negative associations may be made with food.
43. Answers will vary. Possible answer: One may choose less prepared items.
44. Answers will vary. Possible answer: These emotions may cause one to eat more or less than one normally would. Examples will vary.
45. Answers will vary.
46. Answers will vary. Possible answer: A more saturated fat with a firmer texture, such as margarine.
47. Answers will vary but might point out nutritional and caloric advantages.
48. Answers will vary.
49. Answers will vary but should reflect a fairly even distribution of servings for the five food groups.
50. Answers will vary. Possible answer: She should eat what she likes for breakfast as long as it stays within the guidelines for a balanced and moderate diet.
51. Answers will vary but might mention regulating fat, sodium, and caloric intake.

Making the Connection

52. Answers will vary.

Applying Health Knowledge

53. Answers will vary. Possible answers: Pro—children can choose from a wider variety of foods. Con—children see many prepared foods that are high in fat and empty calories; children are impressionable and cannot be expected to make wise dietary decisions when bombarded with foods with empty calories.
54. Answers will vary. Possible answer: He or she may eat alternates for meat, such as legumes.
55. Answers will vary. Possible answer: Tell him or her that

adolescence is the second fastest growth stage in one's life and milk is important for that growth.
56. Answers will vary. Possible answer: Have a salad plain or with low-calorie dressing instead of fries, and diet soft drink or milk instead of the shake.

57. Answers will vary. Possible answers: Take the salt shaker off the table; encourage fruit or vegetable snacks; use herbs and spices to season foods; encourage him or her to buy low-sodium foods.
58. Limit sugary snacks and brush your teeth after each snack.

59. Answers will vary.
60. Answers will vary.

Beyond the Classroom

61. Answers will vary.
62. Answers will vary.

Lesson Summaries

LESSON 1. Weight management is really an issue of energy intake and expenditure. A smart weight control plan doesn't require a diet, but rather eating wisely and exercising throughout life.

LESSON 2. An obsession with thinness, along with psychological pressures, can lead to eating disorders: anorexia nervosa and bulimia, requiring medical assistance and counseling. Sports may also cause individuals to modify their diets, when only good nutrition is necessary.

LESSON 3. Food safety may be the major health issue of the 1990s. Protecting oneself from foodborne illness comes with knowing the causes and ways to keep food safe.

Introducing the Chapter

Collect all the diet books you can from the school library, public library, and your own reference materials. Display these in your classroom. Read through the titles with the students so they can get an idea of the number of books available and the different topics related to weight control. Ask them why they think there are so many books written on this subject. Ask each student to select one book and read about the author's professional training and experience. Discuss the levels of training in nutrition for various professionals. Point out that nutritionists are the most highly trained in this field. Tell students they will learn more about weight control in this chapter.

Performance Assessment ✓

Refer to pages T 23 to T 25 for a Performance Assessment strategy for this chapter. See the *Performance Assessment Activities* booklet for additional suggestions.

CHAPTER
20 AVOIDING PROBLEMS WITH FOODS

LESSON 1
Weight Control

LESSON 2
Eating Disorders and Sports Nutrition

LESSON 3
Food and Your Safety

402   CHAPTER 20 AVOIDING PROBLEMS WITH FOODS

Key to Ability Levels

Teaching strategies have been coded for varying learning styles and abilities.

L1 Level 1 activities are basic activities and should be within the ability range of all students.

L2 Level 2 activities are average activities and should be within the ability range of average to above-average students.

L3 Level 3 activities are challenging activities designed for the ability range of above-average students.

LD LD activities should be within the ability range of learning-disabled students.

LEP LEP activities should be within the ability range of Limited English Proficiency students.

WEIGHT CONTROL

T o be truly fit, you need to maintain a healthy weight—now and throughout your lifetime. Your own healthy weight probably will not be the same as the weight of a high-fashion model or that of your best friend. You can use some general guidelines, however, to judge your weight and to keep it within a healthy range.

Calorie Basics

To understand weight management, you need to understand calories—what they are, where they come from, and how they affect body weight. When people hear the word *calories*, they often think of fattening foods. **Calories,** or more correctly, kilocalories, are simply a unit to measure energy. Calories are a measure of the energy in food and the energy your body burns. Calories are not nutrients.

Calories: Their Source

Some foods have more calories than others. The specific number depends on the amount of carbohydrate, fat, and protein in the food—as well as the portion size. The way a food is prepared or cooked also affects the calorie count.

In the previous chapter you learned about three nutrients that supply energy, or calories. Carbohydrate, the main source, and protein each supply four calories per gram. Fat supplies more than twice as much—nine calories per gram. For this reason, even small amounts of fat in a food significantly increase its calorie content.

The look and taste of many foods often provide clues to their calorie content. High-fat foods may be sweet and gooey, crisp and greasy, or oily. Low-fat foods may be watery, crisp (but not greasy), or bulky (high-fiber). Can you give examples of both types of foods?

Calories to Burn

Calories in foods provide your body's fuel. Your body uses calories 24 hours a day, even while you are asleep. You need a "full tank" to provide the fuel for basic metabolism, or all life-sustaining body processes, and all of your physical and mental activities.

How many calories do you need? Several factors play a role, such as rate of growth, body size, sex, age, and metabolic rate. For example, some people have a higher metabolic rate than others so they need more calories. Children and teens need more calories than adults because they are still growing. Taller and bigger people need more than shorter and smaller people. A person's activity level also plays a major role. Active people need more calories than sedentary people do in order to remain active.

LESSON 1 FOCUS

TERMS TO USE
- Calories
- Overweight
- Obesity (oh•BEE•suh•tee)
- Underweight
- Undernutrition
- Nutrient-dense
- Weight cycling

CONCEPTS TO LEARN
- Both obesity and being underweight are health risks.
- Exercise is an important part of weight management.
- Fad diets and gimmicks do not result in permanent weight loss.

ATTITUDES AND BEHAVIORS TO EVALUATE
- Self-Inventory, page 420.
- Building Decision-Making Skills, page 421.

Lesson Objectives
After studying this lesson, students should be able to:
- explain calories, their role as the body's fuel, and how they affect body weight
- contrast overweight and obesity
- identify the impact of obesity on overall health
- describe the health risks related to being underweight
- explain the relationship of weight control to eating behaviors
- discuss healthful weight-loss and weight-gain strategies
- identify advantages of exercise for losing, gaining, or maintaining weight
- evaluate popular diets and diet gimmicks

Bellringer
Write the following on the chalkboard for students to work on while attendance is being taken: *List all of the methods you can think of that people use in trying to lose weight. Then write the results you might expect from each.*

Introducing the Lesson
Refer to the Bellringer. Ask a few volunteers to share their lists of how people try to lose weight. Make a master list on the chalkboard. Discuss students' impressions of expected outcomes. Point out that exercise is just as important as food intake in maintaining a desired level of weight. Also, point out that extra weight took a period of time to put on, and it takes a period of time to take it off.

WEIGHT CONTROL **403**

Resources for Lesson 1

- **Transparency** 25
- **Guided Reading** Activity 53
- **Workbook** Vocabulary Activity 53
- **Reteaching** Activity 53
- **Lesson 1 Quiz**
- **BARN Software,** Body Management
- **Performance Assessment** Activity 20

Science and Technology Videodisc
Human Biology, Side 2
Ch 11 Obesity and Heredity

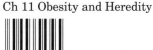

DID YOU KNOW?

- If both of a person's biological parents are overweight, his or her chances of also being overweight are 80 percent. However, people whose genes may be "weighted" against them can lower their risks of obesity by healthful eating and exercise.

Building Vocabulary

- Have students use the vocabulary terms in short stories about a teen having problems with food. Ask them to read their stories to the class.
- Have each student create a crossword puzzle or sentence-completion game, using all of the vocabulary terms. Afterwards, ask them to exchange their puzzles or games. Provide several minutes for them to complete one another's word challenge.
- Ask students to complete *Workbook Vocabulary Activity 53*.

Teach

Guided Practice

L1 EXPLANATION. Remind students that adding just 100 extra calories to their daily diets will add 12 pounds in a year if their activity levels remain the same.

LD CLASS ACTIVITY. Show LD students how to use calorie-counters. Have them plan a week's worth of healthful meals within a certain calorie limit.

L1 DISCUSSION. Talk about how modern life-styles encourage overeating.

L2 CLASS ACTIVITY. Have students survey the contents of any vending machine available in the school, and make a list of the foods and beverages offered. Have them analyze the nutrients in the foods and beverages as well as the number of calories in each. Ask them to report their findings to the class.

LEP CLASS ACTIVITY. Provide food-related magazines for students to collect pictures of high-calorie foods and drinks that total about 3,500 calories. Explain that this is the amount of calories (or food) that students would have to cut out each week to lose 1 pound (0.5 kg).

L1 USING LIFE MANAGEMENT SKILLS TRANSPARENCY 25. Refer to the Teaching Transparencies Binder.

Being active is a necessary factor in balancing the energy equation.

DID YOU KNOW?

- Regular exercise is one effective way to lose weight. These activities, performed by a 110-pound woman for just 10 minutes, can burn the following numbers of calories:

dancing	26
tennis	55
walking	41
sitting quietly	11
climbing hills	61
playing piano	20
running	97
swimming	78

Balancing the Energy Equation

Keeping a healthy weight is an issue of energy balance. Simply stated, calories consumed must equal calories burned. You gain or lose weight by tipping the balance. By taking in fewer calories than you expend, you lose body weight. When you take in more calories than you expend, you gain. Your body banks the extra calories as body fat.

Each pound (0.5 kg) of body fat equals about 3,500 calories. To lose 1 pound (0.5 kg) a week, which is a realistic, healthy goal, you need to consume 500 fewer calories than normal each day. Here is the calculation: 500 calories per day × 7 days = 3,500 calories = 1 pound (0.5 kg) of body fat. What will happen if you also burn 250 extra calories a day through exercise?

Weight Problems: Risky Business

Being too heavy or too thin increases the risk of developing health problems later on. In the meantime, weight problems can certainly affect the quality of life.

Body Fat versus Body Weight

Although we use the terms *overweight* and *obesity* interchangeably, these conditions are not the same. **Overweight** means weighing more than 10 percent over the standard weight for height; **obesity** means excess body fat, or adipose tissue. Usually obesity and overweight go together.

From a health standpoint, being overweight or being obese is risky. However, in certain situations, being overweight might not be a risk. A football player or bodybuilder may be overweight because of excess muscle but not have excess fat. Body composition, rather than weight, is a better measure of fitness.

Obesity: A Hazard to Health

Obesity is a common health risk in the United States. Excess body fat strains the body frame and increases the work load of the heart and the lungs. Obese people have a higher risk of health problems, including hypertension, diabetes, high blood cholesterol, atherosclerosis, and some cancers. Also, obese people are often inactive, which increases the health risks even more.

Adolescent obesity is increasing. Besides the health risks later in life, excess body fat during adolescence may affect self-esteem and social health. Unfortunately, many teens who are overweight or obese as adolescents continue to be so through adulthood.

Why do people gain too much weight? There are two main reasons:

- sedentary life-style
- poor food habits

Interestingly, studies show that many obese people actually eat less than normal-weight people who exercise more.

Obesity may be more complex, however. Heredity may play a role, but the exact relationship is unclear. Some scientists believe that obese

404 CHAPTER 20 AVOIDING PROBLEMS WITH FOODS

Across the Curriculum

Language Arts. Have students become consumer reporters and investigate the following approaches to weight control: diet candies, diet pills, liposuction, liquid meals, weight control clubs, intestinal bypass surgery, and a currently popular diet. Have them write a "Consumer Update" describing the approach, effectiveness, cost, and safety of each. Make copies of their reports to give to the entire class.

Math. Have students find the calories in a single serving of their favorite snacks. (Help students to understand what constitutes a serving size.) Ask volunteers to compile the calorie information into a one-page handout for the class.

people have more fat cells, which may get smaller but never go away. Other researchers are exploring the set point theory. This theory says that each person has a biological set point for weight and body fat. The body works to maintain that point by lowering metabolic rate when caloric intake goes down. Then it is hard to lose weight and keep it off.

Underweight: A Health Risk

Being thin does not mean being fit. With so much attention on obesity, we sometimes forget the health risks related to **underweight,** or being 10 percent or more below normal weight. Being too thin means a person has little body fat as an energy reserve, and perhaps less of the protective nutrients the body stores. This condition makes it harder for an overly thin person to fight off infection and increases the risk of health problems when surgery is needed.

Underweight people may be undernourished, too. **Undernutrition** is not consuming enough essential nutrients or calories for normal body functions. Among other health risks, underweight people have a greater chance for iron-deficiency anemia and osteoporosis.

Managing Body Weight

How many people do you know who have gone on a diet? How many lost weight only to regain it shortly afterward? Why? Perhaps they did not follow realistic weight-control strategies.

Determining a Healthy Weight

Height and weight charts are often used to determine a person's proper weight. However, the range of weights listed on these charts can vary a great deal when accounting for different size body frames. For example, two people who are the same height can have very different weights. A large-boned person will weigh more than a small-boned person of the same height.

Measuring a person's body composition is a more accurate way to determine a healthy weight. By measuring the thickness of skinfolds in three specific areas of the body with calipers, percent body fat can be determined when compared on a chart. For males 15 years and older, measurements can be taken at the chest, abdomen, and thigh. For females 15 years and older, measurements can be taken at the triceps,

There are expensive and inexpensive versions of calipers. All of them measure percentage of body fat.

K E E P I N G   F I T

Weight Placement

It may not be just how much a person weighs but where on the body his or her fat accumulates that may put a person at risk for particular diseases. Here are the steps to determine your "waist-to-hip ratio."

- First, measure around your waist at the thinnest part—over the navel.
- Measure at the widest part of your hips.
- Divide your waist measurement by your hip measurement to

determine your "waist-to-hip ratio." If the number is above .80 for a female or .95 for a male, you could be at increased risk for high blood pressure, cardiovascular disease, and diabetes.

WEIGHT CONTROL   **405**

Overcoming Misconceptions

Myth. The ideal female body shape is as thin as possible. **Fact.** Recent studies indicate that thin is out when describing the ideal female body shape. Instead, the new ideal female body is moderately well muscled, physically fit, and healthy. Most

women now would prefer an average body to a thin one. It is important that each individual find his or her own ideal body shape, accept it, and be comfortable with it.

L1 **DISCUSSION.** Ask students why males of a certain height and frame size weigh more than females of the same height and frame size. (Males' small frames are larger than females' small frames. Males tend to have more muscle tissue, which is dense. Females have more fat tissue, which is less dense.)

L1 **DISCUSSION.** Talk about the value of consulting a doctor, nurse, or dietician before starting a program to lose or gain weight.

L2 **CLASS ACTIVITY.** Select students to write and act out a conversation in which a doctor discusses the dangers of obesity and counsels an obese patient to start a weight-loss program. Remind students that tact can be very important in such a situation.

L1 **SPEAKER.** Invite a school nurse or dietician to class to talk about reaching and managing a healthy weight. Have students prepare a list of questions to ask the speaker.

L2 **DISCUSSION.** Have students debate this statement: *Prevention is the only true cure for obesity.*

L1 **CLASS ACTIVITY.** To help students lose weight and maintain their desirable weights, help them establish a weight-loss support club at school. Invite a school nurse to help direct the activities, which might include physical activity, snack selection, tips for behavior modification, etc.

DID YOU KNOW?

■ Losing weight too fast only makes you a fat person living in a temporarily thin body.

■ A healthful way to control your appetite is to drink a large glass of water before every meal.

Your Acceptable Weight

This chart provides a fairly simple way to determine whether you have too much body fat. Find your weight in the left-hand column (lb.) and your height in the right-hand column (in.). Then put a ruler between the two numbers. If the line the ruler forms falls within the acceptable range, in the middle of the chart, your weight is all right. If the line falls in the overweight or obese range, consult a physician.

This chart can only let you know whether you are overweight. It is not a scientific measure of healthful weight. Even if you come out in the acceptable range on the chart, talk with your physician if you think you may have a weight problem.

DID YOU KNOW?

■ Researchers from the United States and Sweden, looking over data from 247 sets of identical twins and 426 sets of fraternal twins, discovered that, whether or not the twins are raised apart, they are likely to end up with similar weights. They are also much more likely to have weights similar to natural parents rather than adoptive ones. This and other new research indicates that one's weight may have more to do with one's genes than previously thought.

thigh, and over the top of the hip. A desirable percent body fat is about 11 to 18 percent for males and 16 to 23 percent for females. A person with an excess of body fat is considered obese.

Knowing the amount of body fat you have is important for weight control. Equally important is the location of body fat. Excess abdominal fat increases the chance of heart disease and diabetes more than excess fat elsewhere, such as on the hips and thighs.

The chart shown above provides an indicator for acceptable weight. This chart uses a body mass index.

Starting a Weight Control Plan

The true meaning of the word *diet* is everything a person eats and drinks, not a restrictive eating plan. People who manage their weight well never need a restrictive eating plan. Instead, they eat and exercise to maintain a healthy weight throughout life.

These steps can get you started in a smart weight control plan:

■ Target your weight. Based on your body frame, choose a target weight that is within a healthy range, and not too thin. Ask your doctor what range is healthy for you.

■ Set smart goals. Losing or gaining 1/2 to 1 pound (0.2 to 0.5 kg) a week is realistic, attainable, and safe.

■ Make a personal plan, preferably one that includes both a nutritious diet and regular exercise. Consider your own food preferences and

Overcoming Misconceptions

Myth. A person can lose weight simply by dieting. **Fact.** Most people cannot permanently lose weight by dieting alone. The human body tries to maintain a fixed weight, or set point; and when one diets, the body thinks it is starving. It has a built-in safeguard to protect it from the famines human beings have had to face throughout history. As soon as an individual lowers the calories he or she consumes, the metabolic rate slows down, and the body begins to use fewer calories for all of its processes. However, a small amount of exercise added to daily activities can help speed up the metabolic rate and thereby lower the person's set point.

Regular exercise in some enjoyable form helps achieve the goals of any weight-control program.

life-style. Choose an exercise you will enjoy doing. It is easier to follow a plan that you create yourself.

- Put your goal and plan in writing.
- Stick to your plan. To help, keep a diary of what you eat and when, so that you become more aware of your food habits. Eat a variety of foods with at least the minimum number of servings from the Daily Food Guide. Avoid meal skipping; eat three or more meals a day.
- Think positively. If you slip up occasionally, that is okay. Focus on your progress, and get back on track.
- Evaluate your progress, but avoid weighing yourself every day. Instead, weigh yourself once a week at the same time of day.
- Recognize that plateaus are normal. Plateaus are a period of time when your weight does not change.

Smart Weight-Loss Strategies

The best weight-loss strategies are easily summed up as follows:

- Eat fewer calories (and make them nutrient dense). **Nutrient-dense** foods are those high in nutrients relative to their caloric content.
- Burn more calories through exercise.
- Better yet, do both.

This advice is the same no matter how much you need to lose—5, 15, even 50 pounds (2.3, 6.9, even 22.7 kg).

These strategies can help your weight-loss plan work for you:

- As a teen, eat at least 1,400 calories daily. Otherwise, you may miss out on essential nutrients.
- Eat mainly low-calorie foods from the five food groups, including fruits and vegetables.

DID YOU KNOW?

- Set point theory suggests that each body has a particular weight that it tends to maintain. As a person eats more or less, metabolism may adjust to expend more or fewer calories. The feeling of hunger also may adjust itself, so body weight doesn't alter much. That may be why it's hard to lose weight by dieting—and why lost pounds reappear. Research suggests that people may be able to alter their set point, however, by regular, moderate exercise.

L1 EXPLANATION. Tell students that TV viewing contributes to weight gain. On average, students up to 17 years of age watch at least 3 hours of television daily. Studies indicate that the prevalence of teenage obesity increases by about 2 percent for each additional hour of daily television viewing. Ask students why TV viewing would contribute to weight gain. (It is a sedentary activity. People snack while they watch programs. Many ads promote high-calorie snack foods, which, in turn, teens eat.)

L1 CLASS ACTIVITY. Have students brainstorm ways they can add extra physical activity to their day. (Taking the stairs rather than the elevator, walking around and visiting after lunch rather than standing or sitting, doing sit-ups while watching TV, etc.)

L2 CLASS ACTIVITY. Ask for volunteers to plan a daily exercise routine for themselves and keep a record of their efforts. Emphasize that a realistic plan that they will follow is better than an unrealistic plan that they will not keep up. Have students share their plans and report to the class on their results.

L1 CLASS ACTIVITY. Using the chart on page 406, have students judge their body weight. Reinforce that the chart is merely a guideline.

L1 EXPLANATION. Stress that slow, steady weight loss (or gain) is healthier and more likely to be permanent than rapid, variable weight loss (or gain).

L1 CLASS ACTIVITY. Have students design refrigerator magnets or signs to deter snacking and overeating. Choose some of the projects to display in the classroom.

L1 CLASS ACTIVITY. Ask students to brainstorm a list of non-food rewards they would find motivating during a weight control program.

Meeting Special Needs

Making Weight. Body weight is important in many sports. For example, extra weight is an advantage in football, but wrestling has weight restrictions.

Athletes should compete at a weight matching their desirable weight and work to keep their weight stable. Crash diets and sweat baths before weigh-in are unhealth-

ful. They result in fatigue, dehydration, muscle loss, and decreased performance.

Athletes who need extra weight for contact sports need a slow, steady program of weight gain. Building extra muscle takes time and exercise. Extra body fat, which can be gained more quickly, doesn't improve strength.

There is no safe way to take weight off quickly, no matter what claims and promises the ads make.

- Eat foods you like. If your favorites are high in calories, have just a tiny portion from time to time.
- Make meals last. Take small bites.
- If you are tempted to snack, do something else, even if you need to leave the house.
- Avoid shopping for food when you are hungry. This will help you avoid the temptation to buy empty-calorie desserts and snacks on impulse.
- Avoid rewarding yourself with food.

Smart Weight-Gain Strategies

Some people want to gain weight to look better; others want to gain for sports. Smart weight gain includes exercise and a diet higher in calories. Without exercise, extra food calories turn mainly to body fat. Consider these tips:

- Increase caloric intake, especially with foods high in complex carbohydrates, such as bread, pasta, rice, potatoes, beans, and vegetables.
- Eat more frequently. Take second helpings.
- Eat nutritious snacks, but space them two to three hours before meals to avoid spoiling your appetite.

Exercise and Weight Management

People can lose body fat just by dieting, but increased physical activity helps them reach their target weight faster, easier and, over the long run, more effectively. Whether you need to lose, gain, or maintain weight, you should exercise. Consider the following benefits of regular exercise:

- It burns calories, which promotes loss of body fat.
- It tones and builds muscles to give a firm, lean body shape. Without exercise, the weight lost may be lean tissue as well as body fat.
- It helps promote a normal appetite response, which helps anyone trying to gain, lose, or maintain weight.
- It helps relieve the stress that leads to overeating or undereating.
- It helps increase metabolic rate, so the body burns more calories even while resting. It takes more calories to maintain muscle tissue than body fat. Exercise may help lower your set point.
- It increases self-esteem, which helps keep your plan on track.

To build muscles and spend calories, you really need to work your muscles on a regular basis. Even adding exercise to your daily routine, such as using stairs instead of an elevator or walking instead of driving, helps. To set up a realistic, yet effective exercise program, refer to Chapter 18.

Popular Diets and Gimmicks

Perhaps no area of health receives more attention—or is more lucrative—than weight control. People want to take off the pounds quickly even though it took months, even years, to put them on. That is why

408 CHAPTER 20 AVOIDING PROBLEMS WITH FOODS

The Calorimeter

The calorimeter is a high-tech room that measures human energy. It monitors the number of calories a body takes in and gives off. On the outside, the calorimeter looks like a square space capsule. It has a control panel filled with mysterious dials. It also has an observation window and a special slot where food trays can be passed through to the interior. Inside, it is a small room equipped with a TV, bed, toilet, and sink plus enough room to do certain kinds of exercise. The purposes of the calorimeter, nick-named "The Box," are to try to determine why and how some people become over-weight and to understand how efficiently a particular body utilizes and produces energy.

How does "The Box" operate? A test subject enters the 9 × 12-foot metal box for a 24-hour period. The entire time the person is inside the enclosed environment, 80,000 energy sensors in the walls of "The Box" register how much heat the subject's body takes in and gives off. Also measured are the oxygen and carbon dioxide involved in the subject's breathing.

The calorimeter has already been used to dismiss the common myth that most people who get fat do so because of faulty or slow metabolisms. It will also be used to disprove other misconceptions about dieting, obesity, and the effectiveness of various diets.

fad weight-loss diets and gimmicks are so common. Fad diets are approaches to weight control that are very popular for a short time. Diet gimmicks are deceptive approaches that are costly, unsafe, and ineffective. You can find both in books, magazines, and newspapers. Health food stores, drugstores, and grocery stores provide products that promise weight loss in a few, short steps.

Dieting the Wrong Way

Many popular diets are extreme and hard to stick to. Many promise quick results without offering adequate nutrition. Some are dangerous; others are costly. Most do not result in long-term weight loss.

Quick weight-loss regimens may seem to work at first. However, the initial weight lost is usually water, not body fat.

Weight cycling, or the cycle of losing, regaining, losing, and regaining, is the result of following one weight-loss regimen after another. This is also called seesaw or yo-yo dieting.

Weight cycling may be more unhealthy than weighing a bit extra. The reason? Lean body tissue lost with body fat is replaced by more body fat. Because body fat burns fewer calories than muscle does, the person continues to require fewer and fewer calories to maintain weight. Weight loss gets harder and harder.

Culturally Speaking

Ice Cream Anyone?

Sometimes problems with food are genetically caused. Infants have an enzyme (lactase) that allows them to digest milk sugar (lactose). People from cultures with histories of dairy farming also are more likely to be able to digest milk sugar. For example, only 2 percent of Danish adults are lactose intolerant (cannot digest milk sugar).

Most adults worldwide, however, lose this ability. The Thai or Pima Indians, with no dairy farming heritage, have 98 percent lactose intolerance. If these adults eat milk products, they experience diarrhea and other problems.

Across the Curriculum

Home Economics. List three basic foods, such as eggs, green vegetables, and chicken. Have students give examples of how these foods can be high or low in calories and fat, depending on how the foods are prepared.

Science. Ask a science teacher to speak to the class about diet pills, powders, and liquids and their effects on the body.

Home Economics. Invite a registered dietician to talk to the class about weight control, reducing diets, and how patients are taught new eating habits.

L2 EXPLANATION. Stress how fad diets make it difficult to maintain an ideal weight once it is attained, since they do not teach new ways of eating.

Independent Practice

L2 PERSONAL INVOLVEMENT. Have students list all the activities they do in the course of a day. Next to each activity, ask them to estimate the amount of time spent in doing it. Have them use a calorie chart to determine how many calories are burned through their daily activities.

L1 SELF-ESTEEM. Point out the importance of setting and reaching short-term goals in order to achieve long-term goals. Have students set personal, private goals for the next week, month, and 3 months to gain, lose, or maintain weight. Discuss how one's level of self-esteem would affect a successful weight management program and how achieving short-term goals would reinforce self-esteem.

L2 COMMUNITY INVOLVEMENT. Ask students to identify sources of support in the community for people working to lose weight. Have them answer the following questions about each source: What type of support is provided? How does the program help dieters? What are the fees?

L2 COMMUNITY INVOLVEMENT. Have students investigate health clubs in the community. Have them find out the charges for joining, monthly fees, and any added fees for special programs. Also, request that students ask what programs or benefits are offered. Have students make a chart showing their findings.

L2 COMMUNITY INVOLVEMENT. Have students conduct research to learn about companies that have made health facilities available on their premises for employees. Ask students to find out the costs of the facilities, what the facilities offer, the percentage of employees who regularly use the facilities, and the benefits experienced by the companies and the employees who use the facilities.

L1 USING THE LESSON RESOURCES. For additional student activities, refer to the lesson resources on page 403.

Assess

Check for Understanding

■ Assign and discuss the lesson review. Encourage LD students to focus on questions 1, 3, and 5.

Evaluate

■ Administer, grade, and discuss the *Lesson 1 Quiz*.

Reteach

■ Ask students to identify weight-loss products that claim quick and easy weight loss. Have students explain why these claims are likely false.
■ Ask students to complete *Reteaching Activity 53*.

Enrich

■ Have students apply their understanding of sound nutrition to create menus for a restaurant for people who watch their weight. Their menus might include calorie information; tips for calorie trimming; and/or codes for low-sugar, low-sodium, and low-fat foods.

Close

Have students close their textbooks and write an outline of the lesson's major concepts. Ask them to write a summarizing sentence beside each concept. Afterwards, request that they open their textbooks to check the accuracy of their outlines. Conclude with a brief discussion of the most important concepts learned in the lesson.

HELP WANTED

Dietetic Technician

Here's a unique opportunity to combine your flair for cooking with your desire to help others. We need dietetic technicians to become members of the health-care team in our hospital and nursing home. These are management-level positions, requiring two-year associate's degrees in dietetics. Strong communication and organization skills are also essential. Working under the direction of a dietician, our dietetic technicians assist in planning menus and supervising food production operation. They are also responsible for providing dietary counseling and nutrition education to patients and their families. Want to learn more about this career opportunity? Please contact: American Dietetic Association 216 W. Jackson Blvd. Suite 800 Chicago, IL 60606

BEWARE

Many people look for quick, effortless weight reduction. Consumers need to be aware that many such diets or products may be not only ineffective but also unsafe. Beware of any diet or product that
■ consists of only one food;
■ promises quick results;
■ supplies too few calories (below 1,200 calories a day) for energy and health;
■ requires a weight-loss aid, such as a vitamin pill, a body wrap, a liquid shake, or an appetite suppressant;
■ promises spot reducing—an unrealistic claim because weight loss occurs all over;
■ does not teach a person how to make changes for permanent weight loss.

Other Risky Weight-Loss Strategies

Three other weight-loss approaches—fasting, liquid protein diets, and diet pills—are not worth the risks.

Fasting.   Avoiding food, or fasting, is dangerous even for a short time. For health, growth, and energy, you need a fresh supply of nutrients daily. For example, without protein, the body uses its own muscle tissue for energy.

Liquid Protein Diets.   High-protein, low-carbohydrate diets can have such serious side effects that the FDA requires a warning label on these products. Using them as the only source of nutrients can result in serious health problems, even death.

Diet Pills.   The side effects of diet pills can be very serious. Some cause drowsiness; others may produce anxiety. In addition, diet pills may be addictive. Most important, they do not result in permanent weight loss.

LESSON 1 REVIEW

Reviewing Facts and Vocabulary

1. Name three health risks related to being obese and being underweight.
2. What is a skinfold test? How is it used?
3. What is the set point theory?

Thinking Critically

4. **Analysis.** Compare being obese to being overweight.
5. **Synthesis.** How would you explain energy balance?

6. **Synthesis.** Suppose you want to lose 1 pound (0.5 kg) per week for the next five weeks. How would you change the calories you eat and the calories you burn in exercise to reach that goal?

Applying Health Knowledge

7. Find a magazine article about a current weight-loss or weight-gain plan. Evaluate it using principles of good nutrition and health. Discuss whether the program could allow permanent weight change.

Answers to Lesson 1 Review

1. See "Obesity: A Hazard to Health" on page 404. See "Underweight: A Health Risk" on page 405.
2. Calipers are placed on a fold of skin and measure the thickness of the fold. It determines percent of body fat.
3. Everyone has a biological set point for weight and body fat.
4. Answers will vary. Possible answer: Both have related health risks.
5. Calories consumed must equal calories burned to maintain weight.
6. Decrease caloric intake by 500 calories per day, increase activity to burn 500 calories per day, or a combination.
7. Answers will vary.

EATING DISORDERS AND SPORTS NUTRITION

F itness-minded people usually care about their diets. They choose what they eat to maximize their overall performance. Sometimes people take a wrong turn on the road to good nutrition, however. They may have misconceptions about the role of food in their lives. Others, obsessed by their body weight, may fall victim to eating disorders.

Eating Disorders—Serious Health Risks

Today's society is obsessed with being thin. The average high-fashion female model is about 5 feet 8 inches (1.7 m) tall and weighs less than 110 pounds (50 kg). Does this model represent an accurate picture of a healthy, typical female figure? In truth, no, but many people compare themselves to these models.

An obsession with thinness, along with psychological pressures and perhaps genetic factors, can lead to two eating disorders: anorexia nervosa and bulimia. Thousands of people in the United States, mainly females, suffer from these disorders.

Anorexia Nervosa

Anorexia nervosa involves the irrational fear of becoming obese and results in severe weight loss from self-induced starvation. Many adolescents who develop anorexia were not above a normal weight to begin with. This disorder often starts as ordinary dieting. *Anorexia* means "without appetite"; *nervosa* means "of nervous origin."

Anorexia nervosa is a psychological disorder with emotional and physical consequences. It relates directly to an individual's self-concept and coping abilities. Being thin becomes an obsession. Outside pressures, high expectations, the need to achieve, and the need to be popular help lead to this disorder.

What are the signs of anorexia? Each person with anorexia is different, but these behaviors and emotions are typical: a very low caloric intake, a great interest in food, an obsession with exercising, emotional problems, a distorted body image (feeling fat even though underweight), and a denial of an eating problem.

A person with anorexia has physical symptoms related to malnutrition and starvation: extreme weight loss, constipation, hormonal changes, heart damage, impaired immune function, decreased heart rates, and in females, no menstrual cycle. In severe cases, anorexia can result in death.

Most people with anorexia are females, in their teens or twenties. However, this eating disorder is not unknown among males. All cases of anorexia require professional medical help.

EATING DISORDERS AND SPORTS NUTRITION **411**

LESSON 2 FOCUS

TERMS TO USE

- Anorexia nervosa (AN•uh•REHK•see•uh nuhr•VOH•suh)
- Bulimia (byoo•LIHM•ee•uh)
- Glycogen (GLY•kuh•juhn)
- Carbohydrate loading

CONCEPTS TO LEARN

- Eating disorders are symptoms of other problems.
- Extra calories in a diet should come from nutrient-dense foods.

ATTITUDES AND BEHAVIORS TO EVALUATE

- Self-Inventory, page 420.
- Building Decision-Making Skills, page 421.

Resources for Lesson 2

- **Transparency 41**
- **Guided Reading** Act 54
- **Workbook** Voc Act 54
- **Reteaching** Act 54
- **Lesson 2 Quiz**

Science and Technology Videodisc
Human Biology, Side 2
Ch 13 Bulimia

Guided Practice

L1 DISCUSSION. Display photographs and advertisements from magazines and newspapers to represent the association between people's values and their food decisions. Examples might include pictures with food and people to emphasize physical fitness, family togetherness, friendship, community, and self-esteem. Ask volunteers to identify some of the values portrayed in the pictures. Emphasize that food decisions reflect people's values and the way they feel about themselves and others.

L1 DISCUSSION. Ask students to recall messages they were given about eating as they were growing up. Examples might include giving candy or other sweets as a reward, forcing vegetables on children as punishment, requiring that children clean their plates before leaving the table, or disciplining children by sending them to bed hungry. Discuss the impact of those early experiences on present food choices and behaviors.

L1 EXPLANATION. Mention that eating disorders are common among females, and many factors are involved, such as societal pressure, fashions, advertising, etc.

L1 EXPLANATION. Talk about how common it is for many people to respond to stress or anxiety by not eating or by overeating. Emphasize that these actions ultimately can result in long-term eating disorders. Explain to students that these activities do not eliminate stress. Explore with them ways of effectively dealing with stress.

DID YOU KNOW?

According to a federal study:
- 34 percent of high school females in the U.S. perceive themselves as overweight, though many of them are not;
- 15 percent of high school males in the U.S. see themselves as overweight;
- 20 to 25 percent of the U.S. high school population is actually overweight.

Taking care of your body's fluid requirements helps you perform at your best.

CONFLICT RESOLUTION

Her friends think Tracey has it all: she's a good student and very popular. However, Tracey is unhappy. She thinks she's overweight. Tracey's parents worry that she's getting too thin. Because they nag her to eat more, Tracey lies about how much food she eats away from home. As her weight drops, she feels more and more in control, but she still sees a chubby image in the mirror. Only the low numbers on the bathroom scale make her feel good.

How can Tracey be helped to resolve her unhappiness with herself?

Bulimia

Bulimia is another very serious eating disorder involving cycles of overeating and some form of purging, or clearing of the digestive tract. Often the person with bulimia follows a very restrictive diet, only to binge in response to hunger. To binge is to eat a large amount of food in a short time. This eating behavior is followed by self-induced vomiting or purging through laxative abuse. Often after a binge, a person may try to follow a severely restrictive diet in order to restore a sense of control and avoid the possibility of weight gain.

The desire to become thin, more attractive, and more physically perfect can be overwhelming until vomiting or purging becomes a daily routine. Associated with this behavior may be the misguided notion that once the perfect figure is attained, everything in life will be fine. Bulimics are often secretive, but they know they have a problem.

Bingeing, purging, or fasting should never be viewed as a smart way to control weight. Bulimia can lead to serious health problems, even death. Vomiting and diarrhea lead to dehydration, kidney damage, and irregular heartbeat. Chronic vomiting erodes tooth enamel, causes tooth decay, and damages tissue of the stomach, esophagus, and mouth. Because laxative abuse interferes with digestion and absorption, nutrient deficiencies may occur. Laxative abuse can also lead to serious damage of blood composition.

Anorexia and bulimia are not diseases; they are symptoms of other problems. Both are psychological in nature. People suffering from these disorders need medical help and qualified counseling immediately. Recovery is a long process, but early diagnosis and care improve the chance of recovery.

If you believe a friend has symptoms of anorexia or bulimia, advise your school nurse, or, in a caring way, encourage your friend to get help. Do not try to counsel your friend yourself.

Food for Sports

Are you a serious athlete? Do you engage in pick-up basketball or tennis? Do you swim for fun and relaxation? No matter what type of athlete you are, good nutrition can help you do your best. Smart food choices can help you reach your top physical performance as you train.

The Training Diet

No one food or nutrient builds muscle or increases speed. The best training diet is balanced, moderate, and varied. Athletic training does not significantly alter the body's requirements for protein, vitamins, or minerals. The main difference is the increased need for calories, or food energy. Nutrient-dense foods are the best sources.

Physical activity requires an increase in fluids, especially during hot weather, to prevent dehydration and heatstroke. Drink several cups of fluid two hours, and then 15 minutes, ahead of a heavy workout. During exercise drink a half cup of fluid every 15 minutes. Afterwards drink two cups of fluid for every pound of body weight lost through sweat. Water is an athlete's best source of fluid.

412 Chapter 20 Avoiding Problems with Foods

Overcoming Misconceptions

Myth. Fasting can be an easy, quick approach to maintaining weight. **Fact.** If uncontrolled, fasting can lead to anorexia nervosa. This eating disorder may result in severe damage to one's health or even death. Recovery from anorexia is a long process. Early diagnosis and care improve the chance for recovery. Although each victim is different, some signs of anorexia nervosa are low caloric intake; extreme interest in food; obsessive involvement in strenuous activity; intense fear of being obese; inaccurate image of one's body; attitude of extreme perfectionism; emotional problems; extreme weight loss; constipation; and, in females, absence of menstrual periods.

Making Weight

In some sports maintaining a certain body weight is important. For example, wrestlers compete in a specific weight class. In contact sports, a little extra body weight may offer some advantages. Athletes are wise to meet their weight requirements in a healthful way.

Trying to compete in a weight class that is below your healthy weight can be dangerous. Fasting, crash dieting, or trying to sweat off extra weight before weigh-in can cause dehydration and can compromise performance. Over time these practices may result in loss of muscle mass, too. If you do need to lose weight, follow the sensible plan—1/2 to 1 pound (0.2 to 0.5 kg) a week—described earlier in this chapter.

Athletes who train to gain weight need to follow a healthy diet and to exercise to build muscle mass. Extra calories should come mainly from nutrient-dense foods. Slow, steady weight gain, no more than 2 pounds (0.9 kg) a week, is best. Using hormones, such as steroids, to increase muscle mass is not healthy. They may stunt growth and damage the body's reproductive system.

Pre-Competition Meal

Many athletes ask, "What should I eat before competing, and how far ahead of the event?" Eating three to four hours before an event allows the stomach to empty, yet keeps the athlete free from hunger pangs while competing.

Before competing, choose a meal high in carbohydrates and low in fat and protein. Fats and proteins stay in the digestive tract too long. Good sources of carbohydrates are pasta, rice, breads, vegetables, and fruits. Drinking plenty of fluids before a workout is important, too.

Carbohydrates are stored in the body in the form of **glycogen.** Athletes who participate in endurance sports, such as cross-country running or long-distance bicycling, may benefit by **carbohydrate loading,** or storing extra glycogen in the muscle before strenuous exercise. Several days ahead, the athlete eats a high-carbohydrate diet to store plenty of muscle glycogen. Practice is light for two days before competition, too, so stored glycogen is not depleted.

Carbohydrate loading is not recommended for teenage athletes who are still growing. A balanced diet supplies enough glycogen for most sports as long as the diet includes a wide variety of foods and the recommended 55 to 65 percent from carbohydrates.

A balanced diet is an essential ingredient in achieving peak athletic performance.

K E E P I N G   F I T

Muscle Up and Trim Down

New research indicates that exercises that help you to build muscle mass, such as working out with weights or even just doing abdominal crunches, can help you lose weight. Why? Because such exercises get your "calorie-burning engines" working extra hard. The larger the muscle mass you are working, the greater the number of calories you will burn. So don't just rely on aerobic exercise to trim down or maintain your weight. Add strength training to your workout regimen.

EATING DISORDERS AND SPORTS NUTRITION   **413**

Across the Curriculum

Home Economics. Team up with a food and nutrition class for a demonstration of nutrient-dense versus empty-calorie foods. Also, have students gather recipes for pre-competition meals and nutritious fluids.

Science. Have students research the ingredients in sports drinks and report their findings to the class. Ask them to contrast the use of sports drinks and water in providing necessary fluids for athletes.

Language Arts. Have students write letters to their favorite athletes, asking about their training diets and pre-competition meals.

L1 DISCUSSION. Ask students what some of the health risks associated with bulimia are. Why is bulimia not considered a disease?

L1 USING CONFLICT RESOLUTION TRANSPARENCY 41. Refer to the Teaching Transparencies Binder.

L1 DISCUSSION. Have students describe the food choices they make when they are angry, sad, or frustrated. Ask them if the choices are different from the choices they make when they are happy, excited, or content. If so, have them describe how they are different and why they think this is so.

L1 EXPLANATION. Remind students that empty-calorie foods are the opposite of nutrient-dense foods. Have students give examples of empty-calorie foods (soft drinks, candy, salad dressings, etc.) and nutrient-dense foods (green beans, carrots, sweet potatoes, peanut butter, milk, dried fruit, eggs, dried peas and beans, etc.).

L2 CLASS ACTIVITY. Have students create a food package with a nutrient label for a nutrient-dense snack food. Ask them to be creative with brand names and designs yet accurate with information. Display and discuss the finished projects in the classroom.

L2 DISCUSSION. Have students prepare for and debate the statement: *Athletes should eat differently than nonathletes.*

L1 DISCUSSION. Ask students why there is so much misinformation regarding athletes and dieting. (People look for quick, easy answers to gain more speed, strength, etc.)

Independent Practice

L2 COMMUNITY INVOLVEMENT. Ask volunteers to research community sources of help for individuals suffering from anorexia nervosa and/or bulimia. Have them prepare a list of survey questions to find out about the kinds of treatment available, the length of most kinds of treatment, fees, training, and qualifications of personnel. Request that students share materials from the community programs and their findings with the class.

**Using
Overcoming the Odds**

■ **Discussion.** What are some of the costs of bulimia? (Deceitful behavior, shame, and guilt; large amounts of money spent on food—perhaps stolen from friends or relatives; erosion of tooth enamel by stomach acids due to repeated vomiting; dehydration and electrolyte imbalance, sometimes leading to heart problems and death.)

■ **Class Activity.** Ask students to write down whether they think they're too fat, too thin, or just right. Have them calculate their correct weight for their height and compare it with their actual weight. Is their fatness assessment in line with the figure on weight?

■ **Answers**

1. Janelle binged and vomited secretly; only food could fill the emptiness she felt. She got into recovery after passing out at a gymnastics meet.

2. Answers will vary. For female teens, especially, self-esteem may be almost completely dependent on feeling attractive, which usually means thin.

L3 PERSONAL INVOLVEMENT.
Select students to develop a plan for a campaign to encourage teens who suffer from eating disorders to get professional help. The plan might include posters, guest speakers, and newspaper articles. Encourage them to carry out the campaign.

L2 RESEARCH. Have students do library research to refute these common sports nutrition myths: (1) Honey provides immediate energy. (2) Tea and coffee are good pre-game beverages. (3) Sucking ice before a workout will prevent dehydration. (4) Taking a salt tablet will help prevent dehydration. (5) Drinking milk before competition causes cotton mouth.

**L1 USING THE LESSON
RESOURCES.** For additional student activities, refer to the lesson resources on page 411.

Overcoming The Odds

Janelle is 17. She is an A student and a fine gymnast. She is also a bulimic. She begins, "I have an eating disorder that will stay with me for the rest of my life. But now that I'm getting help, I know I can deal with it.

"All my life I've always had this older sister with this great figure. My mom was heavier when she was a kid, but she's really thin now and into exercise, so I had these women in my life who were living examples of what I wasn't: Thin. I felt like I could never measure up. But my real problem didn't take hold until I was about 13."

The "real problem" Janelle talks about is bulimia. Janelle continues. "It all started innocently. I went on a diet and lost some weight. So I figured I could reward myself and get away with it. I love ice cream. I crave it. So I started to buy pints on my own after school, scarf them down, then force myself to throw up. Then I started bingeing on other things like cakes and cookies and chips. I'd usually do it when I knew no one was at home, but when they were, I found ways

around it. It was all this massive shameful cover-up.

"By the time I was 15 I was doing this a lot. I was afraid of going out of control. I felt like there was this deep empty black hole inside me and

nothing could fill it up—except food. I got scared that my dentist would figure out what I was doing, so that's when I started using laxatives. In a while that got out of control, too. Finally, I started to look kind of bad. My energy level was down. Then, at a gymnastics meet, I just passed out. That was the beginning of the next stage."

The "next stage" to which Janelle refers was getting help. She was taken to her doctor for a full medical evaluation. "I was dehydrated. My electrolytes were way out of whack. So they got me physically straightened out, and then they started on my head," she laughs.

"I had individual therapy for a while. I've started to be able to look at myself for who I am, not for what I weigh or how well I compete. It isn't easy. It's a lifelong challenge, I know. But there are pluses. My family communicates better. I do, too. There's hope. That's not to say that the problem has gone away. It hasn't. But I realize that I don't have to be so perfect, that maybe I'm okay as I am."

1. What were some of the characteristic bulimic behaviors and feelings that Janelle exhibited? What caused her to get into recovery?

2. How do you feel about your body? Your weight? How is your self-esteem tied to your body image, your weight, and the comments others make about the way you look?

Additional Information

Weight-Loss Strategies. For students trying to lose body fat, here are some healthful hints: (1) Be patient. Don't try to lose weight in a hurry. Change your eating habits gradually. (2) If you have setbacks, don't panic or give up. Stay calm and analyze the situation. If you suddenly find yourself starting to eat a big chocolate bar, stop. Don't criticize yourself, but ask yourself why you want it. Sometimes old cravings win out, but they can be dealt with if you are willing to face them. Take charge of the situation. Be determined to eat healthful foods. Throw out the chocolate bar and go for a walk or call a friend—anything to take your mind off eating.

Do vitamin pills give extra energy? Because vitamins do not supply calories, extra amounts will not give extra energy. Although B vitamins help release energy from carbohydrates, fats, and proteins, athletes usually get enough in the extra foods they eat. No so-called energy-giving aids really work; these include bee pollen, wheat germ oil, and others.

Will extra protein or amino acid supplements build extra muscle? The only way to build muscle mass and strength is through exercise. The body does not store protein. Extra protein is expended as energy or stored as body fat.

Does eating a candy bar or honey before a workout provide quick energy? Energy for physical activity comes from foods you ate several days, not an hour or so, before a workout.

Will drinking tea, colas, or coffee before a workout improve performance? All three beverages contain the stimulant caffeine. A good warm-up gets you moving just as well. Caffeine can cause headaches, stomach upset, nervousness, irritability, and diarrhea. Caffeine has a diuretic, or urine-producing, effect, so it also increases the chance of dehydration.

Will sucking on ice before a workout prevent dehydration? Ice does not provide much fluid. To avoid dehydration and heatstroke, athletes need to drink enough fluid before, during, and after a workout.

Do athletes need salt tablets? A normal diet has enough sodium to replace losses through sweat. Salt tablets may worsen the problem of dehydration.

FINDING HELP

Overeaters Anonymous is a group of men and women who support one another in their attempts to deal with food addictions. The OA program is modeled on Alcoholics Anonymous. There are therefore no dues or fees. What is said at the meetings and who attends them remains anonymous, and members' last names are not used. People who join OA generally get special friends, called sponsors, who help to guide them through their recovery.

For more information about the OA program in your area, look in your phone book under Overeaters Anonymous.

For some athletes, eating special foods before competition offers a psychological lift. As long as those foods are part of a healthy diet, enjoy them!

Contrary to popular belief, having a steak dinner before competing has no physical benefits. In fact, a high-fat, high-protein meal will not digest as fast as one high in carbohydrates.

LESSON 2 REVIEW

Reviewing Facts and Vocabulary

1. What is anorexia nervosa? What is bulimia?
2. Write three health risks related to anorexia and to bulimia.
3. What is carbohydrate loading?
4. What characterizes the best training diet for athletes?

Thinking Critically

5. **Synthesis.** Why do you think that most people with anorexia are females in their teens or twenties?

6. **Synthesis.** If you had a friend who might have an eating disorder, how would you help?
7. **Synthesis.** What would you say to a friend who decided to double protein intake to build muscles?

Applying Health Knowledge

8. Using library resources, write a research report on eating disorders. Consider reading about a celebrity who struggled with the problem, such as performer Karen Carpenter, who died from the complications of anorexia. Share your findings with the class.

EATING DISORDERS AND SPORTS NUTRITION **415**

FOOD AND YOUR SAFETY

Focus

Lesson Objectives

After studying this lesson, students should be able to:
- identify symptoms of foodborne illness
- describe ways to select and handle food safely
- identify health conditions or stages of life when nutrient supplements may be beneficial
- point out misleading health and organic food claims
- explain food allergies, symptoms, and sources

Bellringer

Write the following on the chalkboard for students to work on while attendance is being taken: *Describe a time when you, a family member, or a friend experienced a foodborne illness. What were the cause, the symptoms, and the treatment?*

Introducing the Lesson

Have students share their responses to the Bellringer. Tell them that they will learn more about food safety, health foods, nutrient supplements, and food allergies in the lesson.

Building Vocabulary

- Ask students to find newspaper and magazine articles using as many of the vocabulary terms as possible. Select some of the articles to have students read to the class.
- Ask students to complete *Workbook Vocabulary Activity 55.*

DID YOU KNOW?

- When the U.S. sets up its first space station, potatoes will be one main focus of the space diet. Why are space spuds being suggested as the diet mainstay? They provide many nutrients, grow easily, and are highly digestible. In addition, they can be grown hydroponically—in water, without soil.

LESSON 3 FOCUS

TERMS TO USE
- Foodborne illness
- Cross-contamination
- Nutrient supplements
- Megadoses (MEHG•uh•doh•sehz)
- Food allergy
- Allergens (AL•uhr•juhns)

CONCEPTS TO LEARN
- Foodborne illness is caused by bacteria.
- Getting nutrients from a balanced, varied diet, rather than from supplements, is the safest, healthiest approach.
- Food allergies can come from food additives as well as various kinds of food.

ATTITUDES AND BEHAVIORS TO EVALUATE
- Self-Inventory, page 420.
- Building Decision-Making Skills, page 421.

How can you be sure the food you eat is safe? Are nutrient supplements necessary if you eat a balanced diet? How common are food allergies? Food is at the center of many issues related to health.

Food Safety

Food safety has been described as one of the major health issues of the 1990s. Foodborne illness is on the rise. The increased use of pesticides and additives has more and more people asking about their impact on health and on the environment.

Foodborne Illness

Reports suggest that millions of Americans experience foodborne illness every year. **Foodborne illness,** or food poisoning, comes from eating food contaminated by bacteria. Many times these bacteria cannot be seen, smelled, or tasted. Protecting yourself from foodborne illness comes from knowing the causes and ways to keep food safe.

Foodborne illnesses related to food spoilage are commonly caused by four types of bacteria: *Salmonella, Staphylococcus aureus, Clostridium perfringens,* and *Clostridium botulinum.* Parasites and intestinal viruses can cause other food-related diseases.

You may not realize when you have foodborne illness because many of the symptoms are similar to flu symptoms. Nausea, vomiting, diarrhea, fever, and body aches are common symptoms of foodborne illness. People often get over these symptoms in a few days. However, for those who are elderly, very young, ill, or malnourished, foodborne illness is very risky. One form of foodborne illness, botulism, is especially dangerous because it can be fatal. It comes from food contaminated in a canned or vacuum-packed container. If you come down with foodborne illness, rest, drink plenty of fluids, and, if the symptoms continue, call a doctor.

Health Foods

Is there really such a thing as health food? Not really; no food has special abilities to promote health. Whether you are active or sedentary, nothing beats a balanced, varied diet for good health.

The term *health food* has no legal definition. The Food and Drug Administration has called the health food business a racket and one of the most widespread forms of deception in the United States. Yet many people perceive that these higher-priced foods offer extra benefits. Foods or ingredients commonly sold as health foods include brewer's yeast, lecithin, honey, and alkaline salts. Some out-of-the- ordinary vegetables and grains may also be available in health food stores.

416 CHAPTER 20 AVOIDING PROBLEMS WITH FOODS

Resources for Lesson 3

- **Transparency** 26
- **Guided Reading** Activity 55
- **Decision-Making** Activity 20
- **Workbook** Vocabulary Activity 55
- **Workbook** Application Activity 20
- **Reteaching** Activity 55
- **Enrichment** Activity 20
- **Health Labs** Activity 20

- **Cooperative Learning** Activity 20
- **Lesson 3 Quiz**
- **Chapter 20 Test**
- **Science and Technology Videodisc**
- **Human Biology, Side 2**
- Ch 14 Measuring Calcium Deficiency

Many people are beginning to examine and question the impact that various pesticides may have on health.

Some health foods are referred to as organic foods. Actually, all foods are organic. However, some foods are organically grown, which means they are grown without pesticides or synthetic fertilizers. Production of organically grown foods is not monitored in most states, so you have no way of knowing whether the claims are true unless you actually see how the plants were grown.

KEEPING IT SAFE!

Bacteria need three conditions for growth: nutrients, moisture, and warmth. Bacteria in food multiplies rapidly between 40° and 140°F (4.4° and 60°C). At these temperatures, bacteria double in number in 30 minutes.

Keep food safe by selecting and handling it with care. Follow these guidelines:

- Do not buy or eat food from damaged packaging. Check all packaging for cracks, leaks, bulging lids, or popped safety buttons.
- Store and prepare foods according to package instructions.
- Keep hot foods hot. Bacteria is destroyed when food reaches an internal temperature of 160°F (71.2°C). Be especially careful with a microwave oven because cooking is uneven; that is why you need to rotate foods.
- Keep cold foods cold. Below 40°F (4.4°C), bacteria grow more slowly.
- Keep all foods and food preparation surfaces clean. Wash hands, work surfaces, and utensils with hot, soapy water to keep bacteria away.
- Avoid **cross-contamination,** or spreading bacteria from one food to another. Wash work surfaces, utensils, and hands after handling raw foods.
- Refrigerate leftovers so that they do not stay at room temperature longer than two hours. Do not thaw food on the counter!
- Throw away suspicious foods without tasting them.

FOOD AND YOUR SAFETY **417**

Across the Curriculum

Science. Working with the science department, provide slides or pictures of the bacteria that cause food poisoning. Ask students to describe these bacteria and compare their properties.

Social Studies. Food safety standards vary from country to country. Have students research foodborne illnesses occurring in various parts of the world. Have them create a bulletin-board exhibit, using a world map, pointing out places where these illnesses are most prevalent. Ask students to locate newspaper and magazine articles about food safety and foodborne illnesses to use as part of their exhibit.

Teach

Guided Practice

LD EXPLANATION. Due to high-level vocabulary, LD students may have difficulty reading this lesson independently. Point out specifics that you expect them to learn during class discussions.

L1 CLASS ACTIVITY. Arrange with the school cafeteria manager for the class to tour the cafeteria. Ask students to prepare a list of pertinent questions prior to the tour. Afterwards, discuss their observations, and ask for volunteers to send a note of appreciation to the manager.

L1 COOPERATIVE LEARNING. Divide the class into three groups. Ask each group to plan a meal for a barbecue, family holiday, or formal dinner. After the menu is selected, have students identify what measures they would take with each food to prevent foodborne illness. Discuss each group's menu and precautions.

LEP CLASS ACTIVITY. Ask a volunteer to demonstrate correct hand-washing techniques and how to avoid cross-contamination of food. Have other students critique the demonstration.

L1 DISCUSSION. Hands can be carriers of contamination. Lead students in brainstorming a list of other sources of kitchen contamination, such as pots and pans, towels, aprons, counters, hair, insects, etc.

L1 DISCUSSION. Ask students how organic and natural foods and other health foods would impact the family food budget. If you were trying to get the most nutritional value for your money, would you buy health foods? Why or why not?

L1 EXPLANATION. Point out some advantages of organic farming, such as organic farmers use no pesticides or chemical fertilizers, thus leaving no residues in food or sending chemicals to underground water supplies or spreading them through the air.

L1 USING LIFE MANAGEMENT SKILLS TRANSPARENCY 26. Refer to the Teaching Transparencies Binder.

If you use a wooden cutting board, be sure it has no cracks. Bacteria can get trapped in the cracks, multiply, and contaminate other foods.

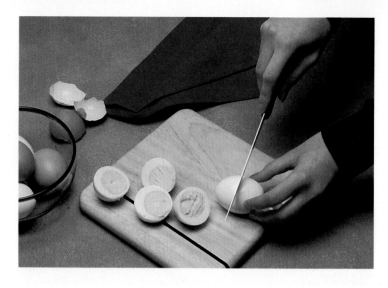

Nutrient Supplements

Nutrient supplements are pills, powders, and liquids—not foods—that contain nutrients. If you believe everything you hear or read, you might think that vitamin pills or protein supplements are the cure-all for just about any pain or disease. For some people nutrient supplements in safe amounts make health sense. Unfortunately, people also misuse them.

Under some health conditions or during certain stages of life, people can benefit from nutrient supplements. Following are some of these situations:

- Pregnant and nursing women have somewhat increased nutrient needs.
- Some illnesses affect appetite or nutrient absorption.
- Women may need extra iron to replace iron lost through menstruation.
- Menopausal women may need extra calcium to protect against osteoporosis.
- Elderly adults need a supplement if they do not eat adequately.
- Some medications may interfere with nutrient absorption.

KEEPING FIT

Nutrient Supplements

The annual sales of nutrient supplements has more than doubled during the last decade. But the use of supplements is often unnecessary, costly, and sometimes unsafe. It often keeps people from getting the medical attention they need.

- Supplements won't improve athletic performance. The extra food athletes eat provides the added vitamins they need.
- No evidence proves that vitamin B$_6$ supplements relieve menstru-

al cramps. In fact, large doses may cause nerve damage.
- Emotional stress doesn't require extra vitamins. So-called "stress" vitamins aren't needed, but rest and recreation are.

Additional Information

Cross-Contamination. Regardless of the season, germs can be spread from one area to another or from raw foods that need cooking to ready-to-eat foods such as produce and sandwiches. To help prevent cross-contamination, refrigerate raw chicken or other poultry in a pan or on a plate so it does not drip on food below. If possible, keep it on the bottom shelf. Also, throw out wooden cooking utensils that are splitting, because they harbor bacteria that can cause foodborne illness. Clean can openers regularly with hot, soapy water; and change dishcloths daily.

What dose of nutrient supplements is safe? Very large amounts, or **megadoses,** are an unnecessary cost and are potentially dangerous. Excess amounts of fat-soluble vitamins A, D, E, and K, for example, stay in the body and become toxic. Excess amounts of vitamin C, a water-soluble vitamin, are excreted, putting a heavy strain on the kidneys. A safe dosage of vitamins is near or less than the RDA levels. The supplement's label gives the dosage.

Fiber supplements are also on the market. However, the benefits of a higher-fiber diet come from high-fiber food, not fiber alone. The excess fiber from supplements may increase the risk of intestinal problems and decrease the absorption of some nutrients.

Getting vitamins, minerals, and other nutrients from a balanced diet, rather than from supplements, is the healthiest, safest approach.

Food Allergies

An *allergy* is the body's reaction to a toxin. With a true **food allergy,** the body's immune system overreacts to substances in some foods. These substances, called **allergens,** are usually proteins. The immune system responds to them as it would to pathogens, or foreign invaders. The body produces antibodies for defense.

Some people with food allergies show no symptoms. Others may experience one or more reactions: rash, hives, or itchiness on the skin; vomiting, diarrhea, or abdominal pain; or hay fever-like symptoms in the respiratory tract.

Most food allergies come from nuts, eggs, milk, wheat, and soy. Fish, shellfish, chicken, and tomatoes may cause problems, too. Sulfites, or food additives that help preserve food, cause allergic reactions in some people. To identify an allergy, doctors ask patients to cut out certain foods one at a time from their diet or to keep a food diary. They also test for antibodies.

A well kept food diary can provide invaluable information in tracking down an allergy.

Assess

Check for Understanding

- Assign and discuss the lesson review. Encourage LD students to focus on questions 1, 2, 3, and 4.
- Assign and discuss the chapter review.

Evaluate

- Administer, grade, and discuss the *Lesson 3 Quiz.*
- Administer, grade, and discuss the *Chapter 20 Test.*
- Refer to the Performance Assessment strategy for this chapter. See pages T 23 to T 25.

Reteach

- Choose students to make a video of someone pretending to be working in the food service industry. Have them display as many poor food safety habits as possible. Present the video to the class and ask, "What's wrong in this situation?"
- Ask students to complete *Reteaching Activity 55.*

Enrich

- Have each student make a checklist that an inspector might use to monitor restaurants for food safety violations.
- Ask students to complete *Enrichment Activity 20.*

Close

Divide the class into eight groups, and assign each group one of the tips for safe food selection and handling. Have each group rephrase their tip and provide several examples or situations that exemplify their tip.

LESSON 3 REVIEW

Reviewing Facts and Vocabulary

1. Define the term *foodborne illness.*
2. What are the common symptoms of food-borne illness?
3. List five ways to protect your food supply from bacterial growth.
4. Give three examples of situations in which nutrient supplements might be beneficial.

Thinking Critically

5. **Analysis.** Explain why some people may be more vulnerable to foodborne illness than others.

6. **Synthesis.** Describe how a doctor might find out if you are allergic to peanut butter.

Applying Health Knowledge

7. Plan a picnic meal, keeping in mind the principles of food safety. List what you could do to prevent foodborne illness. Report to the class.

Answers to Lesson 3 Review

1. Food poisoning.
2. Nausea, vomiting, diarrhea, fever, and body aches.
3. Accept five items from page 417.
4. Accept three of the following: pregnant and nursing women; illnesses that affect appetite or nutrient absorption; menstruating women; menopausal women; elderly adults; medications that inter-

fere with nutrient absorption.
5. Answers will vary. Possible answer: Certain individuals may be less able to fight the bacteria.
6. The doctor may ask you to stop eating peanut butter and keep a food diary and/or test for antibodies.
7. Answers will vary.

DID YOU KNOW?

- To avoid potential salmonella infection, after you prepare raw meat, especially chicken, wash your hands, counter tops, the cutting board, utensils—then go on to prepare the rest of the meal.

Helping Students Improve Their Health

Using the Self-Inventory

Teaching Strategies

L1 EXPLANATION. It is important to stress answering questions truthfully in order to get baseline data of knowledge and habits concerning food. Some students may have good knowledge of food and nutrition, but are unable to put this knowledge into practice. Encourage students to use scores on the inventory to set behavior goals.

L1 DISCUSSION. Ask students if they or someone they know has tried to lose weight. What were their results? Discuss why most diets are not successful in the long term. Discuss the key components of successful dieting.

L1 DISCUSSION. Have students write down the physical qualities of their "perfect" person. Discuss how many people actually fit those qualities. How much are we, as a society, influenced by advertising where all the models look "perfect"?

L2 DISCUSSION. Ask students if they can recall a time when they were influenced by advertising to buy a product. What were some of the things used in the ad to influence them? Can these types of ads affect dieting in an adverse way? If so, how?

L2 CLASS ACTIVITY. Have students figure what the weight gain would be if you consumed just 15 excess calories a day for 20 years.

Self-Inventory

How Do You Manage Your Weight?

HOW DO YOU RATE?

Number a sheet of paper from 1 through 20. Read each item below and respond by writing *yes* or *no* for each item. Then proceed to the next section.

1. Would you consider exercise to be as important as diet if you needed to lose weight?
2. Do you think that very slim models have the "perfect" body?
3. Would you eat all you could at all-you-can-eat places to get your money's worth?
4. If you had a weight problem, would you be satisfied to lose or gain one pound per week?
5. Do you think that your weight as a teenager will have any effect at all on your health 30 to 40 years from now?
6. Have you ever bought a book or magazine because it had a quick weight-loss or weight-gain scheme you might try?
7. Would you be willing to set 30 minutes aside 3 times a week to work out?
8. Do you think that being obese can effect the quality of your life?
9. Do you consciously try to eat a variety of nutritious foods, even when you are trying to lose or gain weight?
10. Would you ever eat just for something to do when you were bored or stressed?
11. Would you use stairs rather than an elevator if you had a choice?
12. If you had a choice, would you go grocery shopping on an empty stomach?
13. Do you reward yourself with food?
14. Do food advertisements on TV lure you to the refrigerator or kitchen cabinet?
15. Have you ever fasted or gone on a quick weight-loss or weight-gain diet?
16. Do you eat even when you are not hungry?
17. Do you keep snack foods around you?
18. Do you think you must give up high-calorie favorites to lose weight?
19. Would you be willing to put your fork down between bites to make meals last?
20. Are you willing to change your eating habits for your lifetime, if necessary, in order to control your weight?

HOW DID YOU SCORE?

Give yourself 1 point for each *yes* answer to these items: 1, 4, 5, 7, 8, 9, 11, 19, 20. Give yourself 1 point for each *no* answer to these items: 2, 3, 6, 10, 12, 13, 14, 15, 16, 17, 18. Add the total, and see how you scored. Then proceed to the next section.

15 to 20
Excellent. Your attitudes and behaviors toward weight management can help keep you at a healthy weight.

10 to 14
Good. Many of your attitudes and behaviors are positive, but you could benefit from a few changes.

5 to 9
Fair. You need to examine your attitudes and behaviors carefully to maintain your healthy weight.

0 to 4
Needs Improvement. You need to rethink your attitudes and behaviors toward food before your weight is out of control!

WHAT ARE YOUR GOALS?

If you scored *excellent* or *good*, complete Part A. If your score was *fair* or *needs improvement*, complete Parts A and B.

Part A

1. I plan to learn more about controlling my weight by ____.
2. My timetable for accomplishing this is ____.
3. I plan to share what I learn with others by ____.

Part B

4. The weight management attitude or behavior I would most like to change is ____.
5. The steps involved in making this change are ____.
6. To be successful, my support must come from ____.
7. I will be successful if ____.
8. If I slip along the way, I will ____.
9. My rewards for making this change are ____.

Meeting Students' Needs

For students who score *Excellent*. Have students do a report on how good weight management affects a person's health.

For students who score *Good*. Have students make a collage of people practicing healthful weight control habits.

For students who score *Fair*. Have students create a chart that will allow them to keep track of both positive and negative weight control behaviors and chart those behaviors for 1 week.

For students who *Need Improvement*. Have students go through the inventory and identify where they have faulty attitudes or behaviors. Then have the students make a list of ways to correct these attitudes or behaviors.

Building Decision-Making Skills

R amad's girlfriend, Felicia, has lost 20 pounds in the last couple of months. He really likes her new, 110-pound, trim look. However, he is concerned because she still thinks she is fat. She has become very irritable and seems obsessed with exercising. She has promised that she won't continue to lose weight. What should Ramad do?

WHAT DO YOU THINK?

1. **Situation.** Why does Ramad need to make a decision?
2. **Choices.** What possible choices might Ramad make?
3. **Consequences.** What are the benefits of each choice?
4. **Consequences.** What are the costs of each choice?
5. **Consequences.** What health risks are present here? Explain your answer.
6. **Consequences.** How will Ramad feel about each choice?
7. **Consequences.** How will Felicia feel about each choice?
8. **Consequences.** How will Ramad's health triangle be affected by each choice?
9. **Decision.** Which choice do you think is best for Ramad?
10. **Evaluation.** Have you ever found yourself in a situation in which you were faced with a decision that might jeopardize a relationship? Describe the situation, how you handled it, and what you learned from it.

L ing's boyfriend, Chris, is the star of the school's varsity wrestling team and a top prospect for a college scholarship. It is now wrestling season, and she has very mixed emotions. She loves the excitement of the sport and of being the star's girlfriend, but she hates the fact that he goes from the 185 pounds he weighed during football season to 157 for wrestling. To do this, he goes through all kinds of diets, exercises, and various other tricks to lose weight. In the meantime he becomes sullen and sometimes mean. He's counting on the scholarship to go to college. His parents and coach believe that he will be only an average wrestler if he competes at a higher weight class. Ling has spoken to Chris about her concerns. He says he has the situation under control, but he doesn't. What should Ling do?

WHAT DO YOU THINK?

11. **Situation.** How should Ling deal with her conflicting feelings (her pride and her concern for his health)?
12. **Situation.** How should Ling deal with people that reinforce the situation by complimenting Chris?
13. **Choices.** What possible choices might Ling make?
14. **Consequences.** What are the benefits of each choice Ling might make?
15. **Consequences.** What are the risks of each choice Ling might make?
16. **Consequences.** Does Chris's athletic success and college scholarship justify the risk to his health?
17. **Consequences.** How will Chris probably feel about each choice?
18. **Consequences.** How will Chris's parents probably feel about the choices Ling might make?
19. **Consequences.** How will Chris's coach probably feel about Ling's choices?
20. **Consequences.** How will Ling's health triangle be affected by each choice?
21. **Decision.** Which choice do you think Ling should make and how should she implement it?
22. **Evaluation.** Have you ever found yourself in a similar situation? Describe the situation, how you handled it, and what you learned.

Teaching Strategies

L1 CLASS ACTIVITY. Have students create a role-play with Ramad and Felicia discussing her recent and dramatic weight loss. Have Ramad really question her about her dieting and exercise regimen.

L1 CLASS ACTIVITY. Ask students to list some ways to safely lose weight. Then have them list the dangers of improper weight loss. Now divide the class into groups of 3 to 4 students and have them write a paper on proper dieting. Have them include why certain diet practices are all right, and why some could be a health hazard.

L1 CLASS ACTIVITY. Have students create a role-play with Ling discussing with her health teacher her concern about Chris's weight management. Have students include in their role-play conversations topics such as the use of diuretics, excessive sweating, and other ways to lose weight quickly and temporarily.

L2 DISCUSSION. Have students brainstorm to make a list of various weight-loss programs. From this list, discuss the pros and cons of each of the programs. Based on these pros and cons, try to make a decision as to which of the programs are healthful.

DID YOU KNOW?

- Anorexics often lose interest in almost everything but food—including sex, in part because their sex hormones diminish.
- Anorexia has been linked with depression and alcoholism in some individuals. The same underlying biochemical imbalance may lead to all three problems.

Discussing the Answers

Situation 1. There seems to be three key factors in the situation regarding Felicia—the amount of weight loss in such a short time, her obsession with exercise, and the fact that she thinks she is still fat. Together these factors may point to a eating disorder. It would seem important that Ramad bring this situation to the attention of people who could help.

Situation 2. In this situation, as well as others, there is no clear-cut solution. There are some key points to discuss with the class however. Is the weight loss dangerous to Chris? What is his percent of body fat? Is a scholarship worth risking health? Ling should express her concerns to other people, such as her parents or teachers.

Answers to Chapter 20 Review

Using Health Terms

1. Obesity
2. Skinfold caliper
3. Overweight
4. Nutrient-dense
5. Calorie
6. Pound of body fat
7. Underweight
8. Diet gimmicks
9. Bulimia
10. Bingeing
11. Carbohydrate loading
12. Water
13. Foodborne illness
14. Nutrient supplements
15. Food allergy

Building Academic Skills

16. 2,665 calories per day. 1 pound = 3,500 calories. 10 pounds ÷ 15 weeks = 2/3 pound per week. 3,000 calories × 7 days = 21,000 calories per week. 2/3 pound = 2,345 calories. 21,000 calories −2,345 calories = 18,655 calories per week. 18,665 ÷ 7 = 2,665 calories per day—a reduction of 335. Increasing the amount of exercise means not having to reduce the number of calories as much.
17. 281,474,976,710,656.

Recalling the Facts

18. Obesity strains the body frame, increases the work load for the heart and lungs, and increases risk of health problems.
19. They may be sweet and gooey, crisp and greasy, or oily.
20. It may affect self-esteem and social health.
21. One can have excess body fat without being more than 10 percent over the standard weight for height.
22. Your percent of body fat.
23. They take in more calories than they burn off.
24. Inability to fight off infections, iron-deficiency anemia, osteoporosis.
25. See bulleted items in "Exercise and Weight Management" on page 408.
26. Target your weight; set smart goals; make a personal plan of

Using Health Terms

On a separate sheet of paper, write the term that best matches each definition given below.

LESSON 1
1. Excess body fat.
2. Device used to measure body fat.
3. Weighing more than 10 percent over a standard weight for height.
4. Term used to describe foods high in nutrients compared with their caloric content.
5. Unit of energy.
6. Equals 3,500 calories.
7. Ten percent or more below normal weight.
8. Deceptive approaches to dieting that are costly, unsafe, and ineffective.

LESSON 2
9. Disorder characterized by an irrational fear of becoming obese.
10. Eating large amounts of foods in a short time, followed by self-induced vomiting.
11. Eating large amounts of starches on days leading up to athletic competition.
12. Best fluid replacement for sports.

LESSON 3
13. Comes with eating food contaminated by bacteria.
14. Pills, powders, and liquids that contain nutrients.
15. When the body's immune system overreacts to food substances.

Building Academic Skills

LESSON 1
16. **Math.** Suppose you need to lose 10 pounds (4.5 kg). Currently, you eat 3,000 calories daily. To lose this weight in 15 weeks, calculate how many calories you should eat and expend in extra daily exercise.

LESSON 3
17. **Math.** Bacteria double in number every 30 minutes. Determine how many bacteria are produced from one bacterium in 24 hours.

Recalling the Facts

LESSON 1
18. Why is obesity considered a health risk?
19. What are the characteristics of a high-caloric food?
20. What health problems do obese adolescents face?
21. Explain why a person might be obese but not overweight.
22. What do you learn from a skinfold test?
23. What is the main reason people gain weight?
24. What health risks are associated with being underweight?
25. How does exercise promote healthy weight?
26. List the steps in smart weight control.
27. Why does yo-yo dieting make permanent weight loss difficult?
28. What are five clues to an unsound weight-loss diet or product?

LESSON 2
29. What are four signs of anorexia nervosa?
30. What are the behavioral differences between bulimia and anorexia?
31. What is the best high-performance diet for sports?
32. Why is fasting an unhealthy way to make weight for sports competition?
33. Why is carbohydrate loading not recommended for teenage athletes?
34. How much fluid should a person drink to replace 2 pounds (0.9 kg) of weight lost through perspiration?
35. Can vitamin pills give a person extra energy? Why or why not?

LESSON 3
36. What conditions promote the growth of bacteria in food?
37. Who is especially vulnerable to foodborne illness?
38. What illness is associated with bulging canned foods? What is the risk?
39. Why can vitamin pills taken in large doses be unhealthy?

diet and exercise; put your goal and plan in writing; stick to your plan; think positively; evaluate your progress; recognize that plateaus are normal.
27. Yo-yo dieting eventually causes one to require fewer and fewer calories to maintain weight.
28. Accept five of the following clues to an unsound weight-

loss diet or product: consists of only one food, relies on special foods, supplies too few calories, requires a weight-loss aid, promises spot reducing, does not teach one how to make changes for permanent weight loss.
29. Accept four of the following: very low caloric intake, a great interest in food, an

obsession with exercising, emotional problems, a distorted body image, denial of an eating problem.
30. People who suffer from anorexia do not eat sufficient amounts of food. Those who suffer from bulimia eat and then purge themselves.
31. A light meal with variety from the five food groups

REVIEW

Thinking Critically

LESSON 1

40. Synthesis. Besides overeating, what personal habits could lead to the problem of obesity?

41. Evaluation. Why do you think many people fail in their attempts to lose weight?

42. Analysis. From what you know about the characteristics of high-caloric and low-caloric foods, make a list of snacks for each category.

43. Analysis. Why are teenagers urged to eat at least 1,400 calories a day in a weight-loss eating plan?

44. Analysis. Compare dieting the right way with dieting the wrong way.

LESSON 2

45. Synthesis. Discuss how the pressures faced by today's teenagers might lead to eating disorders.

46. Synthesis. How should you respond to someone who says, "Athletes need more protein than other people do"?

LESSON 3

47. Analysis. Why do food service establishments post signs for employees that say, "Wash hands before returning to work"?

48. Synthesis. Describe how you might decrease the risk of foodborne illness if you gave an afternoon barbecue party.

49. Evaluation. Explain how you would judge a food labeled "health food."

Making the Connection

LESSON 1

50. Social Studies. In many parts of the world starvation is the result of poverty, drought, political upheaval, poor transportation, insect infestation, and overpopulation. Choose an area of the world where people are starving, and research the causes, the public health consequences, and the aid provided to the victims.

Applying Health Knowledge

LESSON 1

51. Make an advertisement for a weight-loss program that follows the two basic principles of healthy weight loss.

52. Conduct a survey in your school to find out how teenagers lose, gain, or maintain their weight. Evaluate the responses based on good nutrition.

53. Study one weight-loss plan that is available to the public today. What questions would you ask yourself in determining whether this plan would or would not be a healthy approach to weight control?

LESSON 2

54. Suppose you have a friend who wants to put on a little weight for contact sports. What would you advise? Explain your response.

LESSON 3

55. Present a lesson for preschool or kindergarten children on the importance of washing hands before handling food.

Beyond the Classroom

LESSON 1

56. Community Involvement. Investigate three weight-loss programs available in your community. Judge them based on sound nutritional principles and their ability to sustain long-term weight loss. You might ask a local dietitian for advice.

LESSON 2

57. Community Involvement. Locate reliable services in your community for people with anorexia or bulimia. Learn about their programs, and report to the class.

LESSON 3

58. Further Study. Interview your school's food service director to learn the health department rules for maintaining food safety. Report to the class.

Applying Health Knowledge

51. Advertisements will vary but should mention reducing caloric intake and increasing exercise.

52. Answers will vary.

53. Answers will vary. Possible questions: Does it require any special foods, potions, or pills? Does it include a well-balanced diet with a variety of foods? Does it include an exercise program? How much weight loss is expected each week? Is weight maintenance education part of the program?

54. Answers will vary. Possible answer: Follow a healthy diet, exercise to build muscle mass, get extra calories for energy from nutrient-dense foods.

55. Answers will vary.

Beyond the Classroom

56. Answers will vary.

57. Answers will vary.

58. Answers will vary.

32. It can cause dehydration and compromise performance.

33. Teen athletes are still growing.

34. Four cups.

35. No, they do not supply calories.

36. Damaged packaging; improper storage, preparation, or temperature control; unclean foods or food surfaces; cross-contamination.

37. Elderly, very young, ill, or malnourished people.

38. Botulism. It can be fatal.

39. Fat-soluble vitamins A, D, E, and K stay in the body and become toxic; excess vitamin C is excreted, putting a heavy strain on the kidneys.

Thinking Critically

40. A sedentary life-style; heredity.

41. Answers will vary.

42. Answers will vary.

43. Teens are still growing and may miss out on essential nutrients if they eat fewer than 1,400 calories a day.

44. Answers will vary. Possible answer: Both are ways to lose weight. By dieting the right way, one forms lifelong healthful eating and exercise habits. By dieting the wrong way, one may lose weight quickly but fall into the habit of weight cycling which can actually make future weight loss more difficult.

45. Answers will vary.

46. Answers will vary but might include the information that the body does not store protein and protein does not digest as quickly as carbohydrates.

47. To avoid food contamination that would result in foodborne illnesses, such as hepatitis, parasites, and intestinal viruses.

48. Answers will vary but should mention keeping hot foods hot, cold foods cold, and storing foods correctly soon after people are done eating.

49. Answers will vary but should reflect the fact that no food has special abilities to promote health.

Making the Connection

50. Answers will vary.

Lesson Summaries

LESSON 1. Medicines are generally grouped according to their effect on the body. Commonly, they are used to prevent disease, fight pathogens, relieve pain, and regulate heart function and blood pressure. The effect of medicines on the body depends upon the type of medicine and each person's body chemistry. Individual differences in body chemistry sometimes cause side effects. Medicine interaction can result in synergistic, antagonistic, or additive effects. Drug tolerance and withdrawal are two major problems associated with medicine usage.

LESSON 2. The Food and Drug Administration has established a system to protect the consumer from medicines that are ineffective or harmful. All medicines in the U.S. must meet FDA standards before being approved and made available to the public. Over-the-counter and prescription medicines should be used as directed to reduce risks associated with medicine usage. Other precautions should be taken to prevent the misuse of medicines in the home.

Introducing the Chapter

Ask students to define the term *drugs* in their own words. You should get a variety of definitions, most of which will relate to drugs as illegal substances. Explain that the term's meaning changed as a result of the problems illegal drugs have caused in our society. Tell them that in this chapter they will study the benefits and risks of medicines that are available. The effects of illegal drugs will be discussed in Chapter 24.

Performance Assessment ✓

Refer to pages T 23 to T 25 for a Performance Assessment strategy for this chapter. See the *Performance Assessment Activities* booklet for additional suggestions.

CHAPTER
21 UNDERSTANDING MEDICINES

LESSON 1
How Medicines Help

LESSON 2
Medicines and the Consumer

Key to Ability Levels

Teaching strategies have been coded for varying learning styles and abilities.

L1 Level 1 activities are basic activities and should be within the ability range of all students.

L2 Level 2 activities are average activities and should be within the ability range of average to above-average students.

L3 Level 3 activities are challenging activities designed for the ability range of above-average students.

LD LD activities should be within the ability range of learning-disabled students.

LEP LEP activities should be within the ability range of Limited English Proficiency students.

HOW MEDICINES HELP

Years ago some people were crippled from polio. Others with tuberculosis spent time in sanitariums, isolated from family and friends. Thousands suffering from smallpox died. Since 1900 many medical discoveries and the development of more effective medicines have provided better treatment and prevention of medical problems. A **medicine** is a substance that, when taken into or applied to the body, helps prevent or cure some disease, injury, or medical problem.

At one time medicines also were called drugs. The term *drug* referred to any substance that, when taken into the body, caused a change in physiological or psychological activity. The term *drug* included medicines—both prescribed and over-the-counter (OTC), legal substances such as caffeine, and illegal substances such as marijuana, cocaine, and heroin. The term *drug* is now used primarily to refer to dangerous and illegal substances. Alcohol and tobacco, which are legal for adults but not for children and teenagers, are also considered to be drugs. Medicines sold on the street for purposes other than those intended by the manufacturer become dangerous drugs. Chapter 24 focuses on these drugs.

Classification of Medicines

Medicines are generally grouped according to their effect on the body. Some of the most widely used kinds of medicines

- prevent disease,
- fight pathogens,
- relieve pain,
- help the heart and regulate blood pressure.

Medicines That Prevent Disease

Your immunization schedule shows a record of what shots or vaccines you were given as an infant, child, and teen. You received these to help prevent you from contracting certain diseases. A **vaccine** contains weakened or dead pathogens of a particular disease. These weakened or dead pathogens stimulate your body to produce specific antibodies against these pathogens. Once these antibodies are produced, they give your body long-lasting protection against these specific pathogens should they enter your body in the future.

Antivenins are blood fluids that contain antibodies and act more quickly than vaccines. Antivenins are produced in animals, such as horses, sheep, or rabbits, in response to an infection or vaccination. The antivenin can then be used to help protect someone against certain diseases or poisonous bites or stings.

LESSON 1 FOCUS

TERMS TO USE
- Medicine
- Vaccine
- Synergistic effect
- Antagonistic interaction
- Additive interaction
- Tolerance
- Withdrawal

CONCEPTS TO LEARN
- A medicine helps prevent or cure some disease, injury, or medical problem.
- The term *drug* refers to dangerous and illegal substances.
- Medicines are grouped according to their effects on the body.
- Different reactions can occur when two or more different medicines are present in the body at the same time.

ATTITUDES AND BEHAVIORS TO EVALUATE
- Self-Inventory, page 436.
- Building Decision-Making Skills, page 437.

Lesson Objectives

After studying this lesson, students should be able to:
- define *medicine*
- define *drug*
- explain how medicines are grouped
- describe different reactions when two or more medicines are taken into the body at one time

Bellringer

Write the following on the chalkboard for students to work on while attendance is being taken: *Define* medicine *and name three medicines with which you are familiar. Write by each one what the medicine is used for.*

Introducing the Lesson

Make four columns on the chalkboard. Label each column with one of the following: Prevent Disease, Fight Pathogens, Relieve Pain, and Help the Heart and Regulate Blood Pressure. Have volunteers read one of their responses from the Bellringer. As they read what the medicine is used for, note the responses on the chalkboard in the appropriate column. Explain to students that in this lesson they will learn about the medicines that prevent disease, fight pathogens, relieve pain, and help the heart and regulate blood pressure. In addition, the students will learn how these medicines affect the body.

DID YOU KNOW?

- On any given day, 80 Americans die from bad reactions to legally prescribed medicines.
- The first drugstore was established in Baghdad in 754 A.D. It dispensed "medicines" such as camphor, cloves, and fruit syrups. These "drugs" seemed very attractive and modern compared to other prescribed "medicines" of the day, which included frog toes, antelope droppings, and lizard blood.

HOW MEDICINES HELP   **425**

Resources for Lesson 1

- **Guided Reading** Act 56
- **Workbook** Voc Act 56
- **Reteaching** Act 56
- **Lesson 1 Quiz**
- **Drugs in Society**
- **Performance Assessment** Activity 21

Science and Technology Videodisc
Human Biology, Side 1
Ch 16 Natural Time-Release Capsules

Human Biology, Side 2
Ch 8 Treating Motion Sickness

Building Vocabulary

- Copy each of the vocabulary terms on a 3-by-5 inch index card. Write each definition on an index card. Mix up the cards and give one to each of 14 students. At your signal, have students find a match for their term or definition. After they have finished, ask pairs of students to read their term and its matching definition. Have the rest of the class verify that a match has been made.
- Ask students to complete *Workbook Vocabulary Activity 56.*

Teach

Guided Practice

L1 DISCUSSION. Ask students if they have ever received medicines by injection. Ask them if they ever took prescription medicine by mouth. Discuss the reasons that some medicines are given by injection and some by mouth.

L1 DISCUSSION. Explain to students that some medicines may have to be administered for long periods—sometimes even for the rest of the patient's life. Ask students who take insulin, medicine for asthma, or allergy medicine to volunteer to share information with the class about their therapeutic routines.

L2 DISCUSSION. Ask students to describe the most positive aspect of medicines in our society, as compared with the most negative aspect.

L1 CLASS ACTIVITY. Ask students to get into groups and discuss entertainers or public officials who have mixed medicines and alcohol, resulting in health, family, and/or social problems. Ask students to include the ones who have died as a result of drug interactions. Have the students share their discussions.

L1 DISCUSSION. Ask students to discuss why medicines affect each person differently. Have students discuss which group of medicines in this lesson causes psychological and physical dependence. (Those that relieve pain.)

Aspirin and its substitute acetaminophen are medicines that relieve pain.

Culturally Speaking

Dietary Cures

Some diseases are controlled by avoiding certain foods. If someone with PKU, which is an inherited disorder, eats a food that contains phenylalanine, mental deficiency will result. If such foods are avoided, the person will develop normally. Some people in Mediterranean cultures must avoid the fava bean, or they become anemic.

The American Academy of Pediatrics (AAP) and the Advisory Committee on Immunization Practices (ACIP) issue recommendations for childhood vaccinations.

Medicines That Fight Pathogens

Sulfa medicines were the first disease-fighting medicines discovered. Today sulfa medicines are used to fight urinary tract infections and to treat malaria.

Antibiotics are medicines that kill or reduce harmful bacteria in the body. Antibiotics are made from bacteria, fungi, and some plants. The most commonly used antibiotics are penicillin and tetracycline.

Penicillin is an antibiotic that kills a wide variety of bacteria. It is the most effective and well-known antibiotic. When penicillin was first used, it was known as the wonder medicine because it was so effective in killing bacteria causing strep throat and pneumonia.

Tetracycline is a group of antibiotics used to treat infections and fight many microorganisms. Widespread use of tetracycline has resulted in some microorganisms becoming resistant to the effects of this antibiotic.

Medicines That Relieve Pain

Analgesics are medicines that relieve pain without loss of consciousness. Some can be bought without a prescription. Aspirin is by far the most widely used nonprescription analgesic medicine in the United States. Some 20 billion tablets are sold annually. Aspirin contains a chemical, acetylsalicylic acid, that helps relieve pain and reduce fever. Aspirin is used for headaches, toothaches, and muscular pain. Aspirin is one of the most effective anti-inflammatory medicines; that is why it is so effective with arthritis. Because of aspirin's wide and common use, many people do not realize that aspirin can be dangerous. Even small amounts can irritate the stomach, especially an empty one. Aspirin can interfere with blood clotting, and large doses can cause dizziness and ringing in the ears. Children who take aspirin are at risk of developing Reye's syndrome. Because this is a potentially life-threatening illness of the brain and liver, aspirin should not be given to children when illness with fever is present and undiagnosed.

Childhood Immunization Schedule

	2 months	4 months	6 months	12 months	15 months	15-18 months	4-6 years	11-12 years	14-16 years

Source: *American Health* June 1991

1 Earlier booster recommended in the event of local outbreaks.
2 Only for diphtheria and tetanus, not pertussis.
3 Shot may not be required, depending on the vaccine used.
4 May be given at 12 months, depending on the vaccine used.

■ = AAP   □ = ACIP

426 CHAPTER 21 UNDERSTANDING MEDICINES

Across the Curriculum

Social Studies. Have students ask a history teacher to help in researching information on the following medical pioneers to determine what major impact they made on disease prevention and/or treatment: Alexander Fleming, Frederick Banting and Charles Best, Louis Pasteur, Jonas Salk, and Albert Sabin. Have students write a report and share it with the class.

Math. Tell students to solve the following problem. If you were given a bottle of medicine containing 240 ml and the directions for dosage were one teaspoon every 6 hours, and one teaspoon of medicine equals approximately 6 ml, how many doses of medicine are in the bottle? (40) If a person takes three doses a day, how long will the medicine last? (13 1/3 days)

Some people who are sensitive to aspirin take acetaminophen, an aspirin substitute. It does not contain acetylsalicylic acid and does not cause most of the side effects of aspirin.

Codeine and morphine are much more powerful medicines than aspirin. They are narcotics—medicines that relieve pain and cause sleep by slowing down the brain and central nervous system. Narcotics are used for some types of cancer, pain resulting from severe injury, or for postoperative care. Codeine is often found in cough syrups and analgesics. Only a doctor can prescribe narcotics because they can cause both physiological and psychological dependence.

Medicines That Help the Heart and Regulate Blood Pressure

There are five main kinds of cardiovascular medicines:

- Beta blockers block the action of nerves that constrict blood vessels. This helps slow heartbeat and lower blood pressure.
- Diuretics increase urine production to reduce the amount of water and sodium in a person's body. Removing water from blood vessels helps reduce blood fluid volume. This is particularly important after heart failure.
- Vasodilators dilate the veins and arteries to increase the area for blood and oxygen flow. When there is a decreased blood supply in the arteries because of a spasm, blood clot, or a buildup of cholesterol, vasodilators are very useful.
- Antiarrhythmics are medicines given to help cases of arrythmia—any disturbance in the rhythm of the heart.
- Clot-dissolving medicines work to lower high blood pressure and to prevent blood clots.

Medicines in the Body

The effect of a medicine in the body depends on the type and amount of medicine a person takes and the method by which the person takes it. If the person swallows a medicine, it goes into the stomach, much like food. Sometimes the instructions on medicine labels will state that the medicine should be taken at mealtime. This allows absorption of the medicine with the least irritation to the gastrointestinal tract. Medicines usually dissolve in the stomach or small intestine. From there they are absorbed into the bloodstream and carried to the liver.

When a diabetic takes insulin intramuscularly, the insulin goes immediately to the bloodstream.

K E E P I N G   F I T

Read Medicine Labels Carefully

Many over-the-counter medicines contain some alcohol. This can be dangerous for alcoholics in recovery who do not want to relapse, or return to alcohol use. It can also be dangerous to others, including young children or people who are about to drive.

Before taking any medicine, read the ingredient label carefully. If a medicine contains alcohol, do not take it if you have to drive or operate machinery. Consult with your doctor to see if there are any alcohol-free alternatives. If there are not, beware. Let someone else drive you where you have to go while you are on the medication.

HOW MEDICINES HELP **427**

Overcoming Misconceptions

Characteristics of Medicine. Most medicines used today in the U.S. are allopathic, meaning "antagonistic to disease." Antibiotics work antagonistically by destroying disease-causing bacteria. Some medicines are homeopathic, meaning "similar to disease." Polio vaccine is a good example. Children are inoculated with a killed or milder version of the polio virus, which promotes the formation of antibodies without producing the disease. Other homeopathic medicines consist of less harmful strains of the bacteria that normally cause disease. The weaker strains stimulate an immune reaction to the more harmful bacterial invaders, thus enabling the body to heal itself.

Explain the potentially deadly effects of mixing alcohol with medicines. Give examples of the synergistic effect of alcohol on medicines that affect drowsiness and other medicines such as anticoagulants. (A great deal of alcohol consumed over a short period of time slows down the body's metabolism, causing the anticoagulant to produce a greater effect than it should. It can keep the blood from clotting in time to prevent serious blood loss from an injury.)

LEP **CLASS ACTIVITY.** Have students make a poster collage of OTC medicines advertised in magazines. Have the students categorize the medicines in groups relating to specific types of ailments or conditions they treat. Display the posters in the classroom.

Independent Practice

L2 **PARENTAL INVOLVEMENT.** Have students interview their parents and ask about any childhood diseases the parents survived or were vaccinated against that were deadly a century ago. Ask students to look at their own vaccination records to see the ages at which vaccinations were given and discuss their reactions, if any, to them. Have students write their findings in a one-page paper.

L2 **RESEARCH.** Ask students to poll three people about the first thought that comes into their minds when they hear the word *drug.* How many of the responses refer to medicines? How many refer to illegal drugs? Have students share the responses they gave and discuss what these responses suggest about our society today.

L1 **WRITING.** Ask students to clip newspaper articles relating to the use of medicines. Have students design their own newspaper on the use of medicines and explain how the use of these medicines relates to wellness.

L1 **USING THE LESSON RESOURCES.** For additional student activities, refer to the lesson resources on page 425.

When a medicine is taken intravenously, in the veins, or intramuscularly, in the muscles, by injection, the effects are much more immediate because the medicine goes directly into the bloodstream and then to the liver. A medicine that is inhaled must pass through the lungs before being absorbed into the bloodstream. A medicine that is sniffed must pass through the mucous membranes before being absorbed.

The Body's Reaction to Medicines

Each person's body chemistry is different. This means medicines will have different effects on different people. Some people experience side effects, or reactions, to certain medicines. They may even be allergic to a medicine. Several factors, including age, weight, and the use of other medicines, influence the effects of medicines. When you have questions about medicines, ask your doctor and pharmacist for accurate information.

HEALTH UPDATE

LOOKING AT THE ISSUES

Generic Versus Brand-Name Medicines

Though some people buy brand-name medicines at some times and generic drugs at others, there are people who feel strongly about choosing one or the other.

Analyzing Different Viewpoints

ONE VIEW. Some people are dedicated to using generic medicines. They cite the fact that they can cost from 30 to 80 percent less than the brand-name versions. In addition, brand-name and generic medicines not only contain the same chemical components, they are also often made by the same companies. Additionally, since generic medicines are so much less expensive than their often better-known alternatives, many people think they are essential in the treatment of the nation's elderly and poor, who otherwise might be even less likely to have necessary medications made available to them.

A SECOND VIEW. Recent reports that not all generic medicines are safe and that there are some abuses in the industry have kept some people from using them. Some critics of generic medicines call for the FDA to have stricter regulations for generic medicines. Other people buying brand names feel more secure dealing with established pharmaceutical companies. Still others claim that with certain medicines, such as thyroid medications, brand names offer greater control of dosages than generic versions.

Exploring Your Views

1. What are the advantages and disadvantages of using generic medicines?
2. The next time you might need a prescription, will you specify that you want a generic medicine or brand-name medicine or simply leave the decision up to your physician and/or pharmacist? Why?

Additional Information

Drug Interactions. There are two basic ways that food can affect the action of a medicine. Its presence in the digestive system can slow down or speed up the time it takes a medicine to go through the digestive tract to the site in the body where it is needed. A good example is the interaction between tetracycline compounds and dairy products. The calcium in milk and cheese, for example, impairs the body's ability to absorb tetracycline. The acidity in soft drinks and fruit juices causes some drugs to dissolve quickly in the stomach instead of the intestines, where they would be more readily absorbed. Antacids can also affect the absorption of medicines.

Medicine Interaction

Based on extensive scientific research, scientists can predict side effects that might be expected. These reactions, however, can be quite different when two or more medicines are present in the body at the same time. It is difficult to predict medicine interaction.

When medicines work together in a positive way, an **additive interaction** occurs. For example, both an anti-inflammatory and a muscle relaxant may be prescribed to treat someone with joint pain. A **synergistic effect** is the interaction of two or more medicines that results in a greater effect than when the medicines are taken independently. It occurs when one medicine increases the strength of the other. For example, the analgesic effect of a painkiller increases when cough medicine with codeine is taken at the same time. An **antagonistic interaction** occurs when the effect of a medicine is canceled or reduced when taken with other medicine. For example, someone who receives an organ transplant will take antirejection medicines. If this person is diabetic and takes insulin, the effectiveness of the insulin may be decreased.

Because of unknown effects, medicines should not be mixed without the advice of a doctor or pharmacist.

Problems Using Medicines

Sometimes people develop dependence on a particular medicine. In psychological dependence, a person believes he or she needs a medicine to feel good or to provide some form of an escape from reality. The medicine may be used to relax, sleep, or feel energetic. Soon the user is unable to relax, sleep, or feel energetic without the medicine.

Physiological dependence is a chemical need for a medicine. Physiological dependence is determined when a person experiences tolerance and withdrawal. **Tolerance** means the body becomes used to the effect of the medicine. The body then requires larger doses of the medicine to produce the same effect. **Withdrawal** occurs when the person stops taking a medicine to which he or she is physiologically dependent. Withdrawal symptoms include nervousness, insomnia, severe nausea, headaches, vomiting, chills, and cramps. These symptoms gradually ease or disappear after a period of time off the medicine. Withdrawal from certain medicines may require medical attention.

LESSON 1 REVIEW

Reviewing Facts and Vocabulary

1. Define the term *antibiotic* and list what antibiotics are made of.
2. Describe when withdrawal occurs and give examples of symptoms.

Thinking Critically

3. **Analysis.** Explain the difference between medicines and drugs.

4. **Analysis.** Compare psychological and physiological dependence. Give specific examples of each.

Applying Health Knowledge

5. Research the major health threats today and compare them to the leading killers 100 years ago. What are the differences? How can you account for the differences?

Answers to Lesson 1 Review

1. Medicines that kill or reduce harmful bacteria in the body. Antibiotics are made from bacteria, fungi, and some plants.
2. See "Problems Using Medicines" on this page.
3. Medicines help heal the body. Drugs are dangerous and illegal substances.

4. With psychological dependence, a person believes he or she needs a medicine to feel good or to provide an escape from reality. Example—being unable to relax or sleep without a medicine. Physiological dependence is a chemical need for a medicine. Example—a person experiences tolerance or withdrawal.
5. Answers will vary.

Assess

Check for Understanding

- Assign and discuss the lesson review.

Evaluate

- Administer, grade, and discuss the *Lesson 1 Quiz.*

Reteach

- Ask students to list the four major classifications of medicines presented in this lesson and to provide two examples of medicines in each. Have students explain the effects of medicines on the body, including the interaction of combining more than one medicine.
- Ask students to complete *Reteaching Activity 56.*

Enrich

- Ask students to investigate the beneficial use of hormone therapy on individuals who experience a hormone deficiency. Ask students to explain how steroid use is not beneficial and can be detrimental.

Close

Ask students to state the most important concepts studied in this lesson. Have students list alternatives to treating symptoms of common physical complaints without using medicines.

DID YOU KNOW?

- In 1825, Elias Durand installed the first soda fountain in a pharmacy. His Philadelphia innovation became an American institution for the next century and a half, and by 1929, almost two-thirds of drugstores in the U.S. included soda fountains. By the 1970s, however, this drug-and-fountain partnership had dwindled down to less than a third of all drugstores.

Focus

Lesson Objectives

After studying this lesson, students should be able to:
- describe the role of the Food and Drug Administration
- explain the purpose of guidelines for distributors of medicines

Bellringer

Write the following on the chalkboard for students to work on while attendance is being taken: *Why is consumer protection needed in the area of medicines? List examples of consumer protection that are medicine-related.*

Introducing the Lesson

Refer to the Bellringer. Ask volunteers to share their responses. Tell students they will learn more about consumer protection and medicines in this lesson.

Building Vocabulary

- Ask students to explain why a pharmacist is qualified to give us accurate information on medicine misuse. Have students list the most common ways medicine is misused.
- Ask students to complete *Workbook Vocabulary Activity 57.*

DID YOU KNOW?

- In 1240, Frederick II, Holy Roman Emperor, first placed regulations on pharmacists. By edict, he fixed the prices of drugs and forbade doctors and pharmacists from entering into secret contracts.

MEDICINES AND THE CONSUMER

LESSON 2 FOCUS

TERMS TO USE
- Medicine misuse
- Histamine
- Pharmacist

CONCEPTS TO LEARN
- The Food and Drug Administration helps regulate the use of medicines and drugs.
- Medicine misuse is using a medicine in a way that it should not be used.
- Guidelines for distributors of medicines help prevent improper use of them.

ATTITUDES AND BEHAVIORS TO EVALUATE
- Self-Inventory, page 436.
- Building Decision-Making Skills, page 437.

Throughout history in the United States, there have been medicines that did people little or no good. Because some of these medicines were actually harmful, the federal government set up a system for protection of the consumer.

Two forces regulate the use of medicines and drugs: the Food and Drug Administration (FDA) and increasing consumer awareness of what is available on the market.

Governmental Control

A consumer receives accurate information about the effectiveness and labeling of medicines from the FDA. In the United States all medicines must meet specific FDA standards before being approved and made available to the public.

The FDA requires a manufacturer of medicines to supply information about the chemical composition, the intended use, the effects, and the possible side effects of a medicine. Medicines are usually tested on animals first and then with different experimental groups of people. Since the FDA requires information about the long-term effects of a medicine, it takes about five years for a manufacturer of a medicine to meet all FDA requirements. The FDA decides which medicines require a doctor's prescription and which can be sold as OTC medicines. OTC medicines are safe to use without a doctor's supervision.

The FDA also controls all of the advertising of prescription medicines. These advertisements are generally found in medical journals and magazines because doctors make the decisions about particular prescription medicines to use. Laws also govern the advertising of OTC medicines. These advertisements cannot imply results that the medicines cannot provide.

When the FDA approves a medicine, it is saying that the medicine is safe when used as directed. FDA approval also means a medicine is effective in treating the illness or condition for which it was prescribed.

The FDA assists the consumer in using medicine properly by requiring companies to put certain information on all medicine labels. OTC medicine labels include more information than prescription medicines because they are self-prescribed and self-administered.

The FDA has many controls, but there are still risks and responsibilities when using medicines. **Medicine misuse** is using a medicine in a way that is not intended. Examples of medicine misuse include
- giving your prescription medicine to someone else,
- taking too much or too little of a medicine,
- taking someone else's medicine,
- discontinuing use of a medicine without informing one's doctor,
- taking medicine for a longer period of time than was prescribed,
- mixing medicines.

Resources for Lesson 2

- **Guided Reading** Activity 57
- **Decision-Making** Activity 21
- **Workbook** Vocabulary Activity 57
- **Workbook** Application Activity 21
- **Reteaching** Activity 57

- **Enrichment** Activity 21
- **Health Labs** Activity 21
- **Cooperative Learning** Activity 21
- **Lesson 2 Quiz**
- **Chapter 21 Test**

THE CONTROLLED SUBSTANCES ACT

The purpose of the Controlled Substances Act was to set guidelines for the distributors of medicines and to prevent improper use of medicines. As a result, medicines for use in the United States were categorized into five schedules based on their potential for improper use.

	Use of Medicine
Schedule I	Research only No current accepted medical use in United States Risk involved in use
Schedule II	Obtain with written prescription No refills Severe restrictions on medical use Improper use may lead to psychological or physiological dependence
Schedule III	Obtain with written or oral prescription Refill up to five times in six months Has accepted medical use Improper use may lead to high psychological or low physiological dependence
Schedule IV	Written or oral prescription Refill up to five times in six months Has accepted medical use Improper use may lead to limited psychological or physiological dependence
Schedule V	OTC or prescription limited to doctor's order Has accepted medical use in treatment Improper use may lead to limited psychological or physiological dependence

Over-the-Counter Medicines

OTC medicines include a wide variety of medicines you can buy without a doctor's prescription. These medicines can be purchased in pharmacies and other stores that sell medicines. They are not as strong as prescription medicines. However, any OTC medicine has the potential of being harmful if it is not used as directed.

The FDA governs the advertising and labeling of OTC medicines.

Teach

Guided Practice

L1 DISCUSSION. Discuss tips for using medicines safely. Ask students why it is important not to share a prescription. Why should medicines be destroyed after their expiration date? Why must medicines be kept away from small children?

L1 CLASS ACTIVITY. Have students list three common physical conditions that may result in a person taking a medicine. (Headache, heartburn, etc.) Next to each, have students suggest one way the condition might have been prevented and one way it may be relieved without the use of a medicine.

L2 DISCUSSION. Discuss ways an individual can assume responsibility when purchasing OTC medicines.

L2 EXPLANATION. Explain the marketing regulations of the FDA for prescription medicines.

L3 CLASS ACTIVITY. Discuss reasons for the length of time it takes for the FDA to approve a new medicine. Ask students if they think that function is an important safeguard. Discuss how students' feelings might be different if they were dying from a disease and a new medicine promised possible help. Ask for volunteers to participate on a debate team. Have students debate the issue of the length of time required by the FDA before a drug/medicine is approved. Write on the chalkboard any statements for or against the issue from each debate team.

L2 DISCUSSION. Ask students what antacids are used for. Why is their use so widespread? How do TV advertisers encourage use of antacids? What product qualities are emphasized? Do these product qualities relate to their use as an antacid or not? (Example: Some antacids are being promoted as good sources of calcium. Is this relevant to effectiveness as an antacid?)

Additional Information

Consumer Protection. Massive research and development efforts are required to create medications that treat specific diseases. Once identified, each one must go through exhaustive testing to determine effectiveness and safety. Most fail to measure up. Manufacturers estimate that only one medicine in 10,000 will be allowed to become available on the market. The average cost of finding that medicine, developing it, and testing it so that it can be sold in a pharmacy is $94 million. Discuss with students other costs the manufacturer would incur in marketing. (Service reps to sell to the doctors, advertising, obtaining patent, etc.)

FINDING HELP

There are many sources of up-to-date information about medicines. Some of these sources, such as the *Physicians' Desk Reference*, can be found at your local library, pharmacy, and family doctor's office.

Also, you can contact the U.S. Food and Drug Administration for information about medicines. First, look in your local telephone directory under U.S. Government, Health and Human Services Department, Food and Drug Administration. If it does not appear, write:

- Food and Drug Administration, Department of Health and Human Services 5600 Fishers Lane Rockville, MD 20857

OTC Medicines for Colds

Your nose is dripping, your eyes are watering, your head aches—you have a cold and want relief. You can find shelves of nonprescription cold remedies. There are hundreds of them, and people spend millions of dollars a year trying to cure their colds. The fact is, although cold remedies may relieve your symptoms, only time will cure a cold.

A virus in the respiratory system causes colds. When this pathogen invades your body, special cells release a substance called **histamine.** This natural body substance causes the blood vessels in the respiratory tract to dilate. It also causes tissues to swell, which accounts for a stuffed-up nose and a seepage of fluid into surrounding spaces. This causes a runny nose and watery eyes.

When taken orally, cold remedies containing antihistamines block the effects of the histamine. They can reduce swelling and a runny nose for up to 12 hours. They also can reduce sneezing and watery eyes. Antihistamines in decongestants relieve sinus congestion.

A person using an antihistamine should check the label closely. One side effect of most antihistamines is drowsiness. In addition, cold remedies containing antihistamines often contain a variety of other chemicals.

OTHER CHEMICALS IN COLD REMEDIES

Some or all of the following chemicals are often included in cold remedies:
- caffeine, a stimulant to counteract the drowsiness
- aspirin or acetaminophen, medicine to lower fever and relieve aching and inflammation
- codeine to suppress a cough
- antacids to counteract the burning quality of aspirin and nauseating effect of antihistamine

All of this information points to the fact that just because a product is sold over the counter does not mean that the consumer should not take precautions or consider side effects or possible dangers. If a person chooses to take a cold remedy, he or she should read the label and follow the directions for use.

K E E P I N G   F I T

Ask the Right Questions About Prescribed Medicines

Ask your doctor and pharmacist these questions before taking a prescription medicine:
- Why is the medicine being prescribed?
- Was the dosage tailored to your body's needs?

- Is this dosage the lowest possible level to be effective?
- What are the benefits and side effects of this medicine?
- Are there printed instructions?
- Is this medicine compatible with other medicine you take?

- When, how often, and how long should the medicine be taken?
- Is there a less expensive, yet still effective, generic medicine?
- Are there any storage requirements?
- Are there any food restrictions?

Overcoming Misconceptions

Generic Medicine. Many consumers don't buy generic medicines because they don't think they are getting the same medicine or that it is an inferior product when compared to a brand-name medicine. Consumers should consider these facts:

- Compared to brand-name medicines, generic medicines are safe when used as directed.

- A generic and brand-name medicine are tested and within a range set by the FDA. The medicines must be equivalent in the amount of active ingredients delivered to the body.
- Health-care professionals encourage the use of generic medicines and prescribe them.

Cold medicines containing anti-histamines can provide relief of cold symptoms.

Prescription Medicines

Prescription medicines require more controls because of their strength and potential harm. A prescription is a doctor's written order to a pharmacist to give a certain medicine to a patient. Only a physician can order them, and only a licensed pharmacist can sell prescription medicines.

Cautions about Medicines

Certain precautions should be taken with all medicines. Keep in mind the following guidelines for safe use of medicines.

- Keep medicines out of the reach of children. If anyone, particularly a child, takes a large dose, get medical help immediately.
- Do not use medicines for extended periods of time without medical supervision. If symptoms persist or unexpected symptoms develop, see your physician right away.
- Read the label on the container carefully. It will tell you how much medicine to take and when and how to take it.
- Do not take any medicine that contains aspirin if you are allergic to aspirin or have ulcers or a bleeding problem.
- Seek medical help immediately if you experience any bleeding or vomiting of blood after taking aspirin.

DID YOU KNOW?

- The average number of new approved medicines available to the consumer per year in the United States is about 25.
- Of every 5 medicines trying to be approved, only 1 makes it.
- In the U.S. there are over 1,000 pharmaceutical companies.
- The states that produce the most pharmaceuticals are New Jersey, New York, and Pennsylvania.

K E E P I N G   F I T

Avoiding Quacks

Medical quackery can result in a waste of money. Even more serious, it can result in injury, illness, or death. Be on the lookout for the following:
- "secret formula"
- "miracle cure"
- "overnight results"
- "limited offer"
- endorsements by stars
- availability only through mail order
- foreign medicine not usually available in the U.S.
- passionate testimonials of those supposedly "cured"
- hard-sell approaches

MEDICINES AND THE CONSUMER   **433**

■ **Discussion.** How is ALD inherited? What's the chance that another child of Michaela and Augusto Odone would be born with ALD? (ALD is a recessive disease like phenylketonuria. For a child with two normal parents to be affected by ALD, he or she must receive one ALD gene from each parent. With only one ALD gene each, the parents are unaffected. Each child has a 25 percent chance of being born with ALD.)

■ **Explanation.** Explain why little research and development of medicines is done for rare diseases like ALD, making the efforts of the Odone family that much more significant. (It takes millions of dollars and many years of research to develop a new medicine. Drug companies are profit-motivated, so unless a new medicine will be taken by relatively large numbers of patients, it is unlikely to be developed.)

■ **Answers**
1. The higher your self-esteem, the more likely you'll value your own opinions and not put doctors on a pedestal.
2. They're intimidated because they think doctors know everything in their areas of expertise, and they have little regard for their own opinions.

L3 RESEARCH. Ask students to research the education requirements for a pharmacist. Have them also determine the regulations regarding the filling and refilling of a prescription. Ask that they be prepared to share information with the class.

L3 RESEARCH. Ask student volunteers to contact the FDA to determine all of the procedures required by the FDA to manufacture and market a medicine until it reaches the pharmacy. Ask students to put the information on a chart to share with the class.

L1 USING THE LESSON RESOURCES. For additional student activities, refer to the lesson resources on page 430.

Overcoming The Odds

Lorenzo Odone is 13. As a small child, he spoke three languages and traveled to 16 different countries. These days, Lorenzo is an opera fan, loves to have the classics read to him, and still understands three languages. His mother, Michaela Odone, speaks with pride of her son's accomplishments. Unfortunately, Lorenzo can no longer speak. He is hearing impaired, and he cannot walk. His father, Augusto Odone, explains. "Our son was struck by a little-known, very rare disease. The medical establishment told us that he was going to die, and that he had about two years." Lorenzo's parents began a passionate search for a cure for the disease. They succeeded, inventing a treatment that saved his life.

The rare genetic disease that Lorenzo has is called ALD, which weakens, paralyzes, and kills young boys.

Refusing to accept the doctors' death sentence for their son, the Odones began doing extensive medical research. "We talked to everyone," Lorenzo's father says. "The world is large. There are other towns, other countries. We called everywhere." The next step was to get these experts from around the world together to brainstorm about the disease and its treatments. "We

organized the first international symposium on the disease," he continues. "This gave us ideas, and after gathering information, our next step was action."

Based on others' research and their own research and ideas, Augusto Odone eventually hypothesized that a combination of oleic acid and erucic acid might be the answer. He tested the oil on members of his wife's family, who are carriers of the disease. The experiment worked. "Then I immediately gave it to Lorenzo," he says. "In three weeks, his blood was normalized."

The treatment was not a cure, however. It did not reverse the symptoms already under way, but it stopped them in their tracks and kept Lorenzo from dying. The Odones have named the edible oil mixture "Lorenzo's Oil" in honor of their son, and it has now been patented. Still an experimental medicine in this country, the FDA has given permission for a U.S. doctor to prescribe the oil to patients with the disease. In addition, its use has been adopted in other nations, including the Imperial Institute of Neurology in Japan and a major children's hospital in London, England. So far, 30 boys with ALD have taken Lorenzo's Oil. All remain symptom-free.

Mrs. Odone advises young people to become responsible health consumers, to ask tough and thorough questions about their conditions and their treatment. "Don't run out and make your own medicine," she advises. "But do develop a very critical sense about what is being done to you."

1. How is the way you deal with doctors or experts in other areas of your life related to your level of self-esteem?
2. For what reasons do you think people sometimes accept the opinions of the experts as the final word without questioning them?

Across the Curriculum

Drama. Ask a drama teacher in your school to help students write a script for a skit on using medicines properly and the importance of responsible behavior in taking or using medicines. Students should make the script relevant for a fourth-grade student and present the skit to an actual fourth-grade class in your school district. Include in the skit information about over-the-counter medicines and prescription medicines. Inform the fourth graders of the importance of not taking medicine from anyone except their parents or certified personnel.

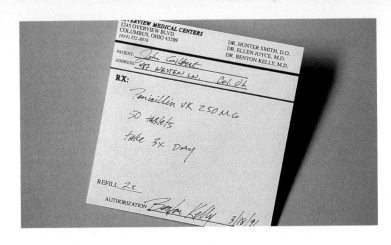

The law requires specific information to be included on a prescription medicine label.

The Pharmacist

A **pharmacist** is a person concerned with the preparation, distribution, and sale of medicines. A pharmacist is trained in medical therapy and therefore knows what a medicine is supposed to do and what adverse effects can occur. Pharmacists keep a profile of all medicines someone takes. The pharmacist can then monitor potential medicine interaction or medicine misuse. A pharmacist can fill your prescription, inform you of any side effects or precautions to take when using the medicine, and indicate the directions for taking the medicine.

Your pharmacist can provide the following information about prescriptions:

- the name and dosage of the medicine
- how and when it is to be taken
- possible side effects
- whether a prescription can be refilled
- whether an available generic medicine can be substituted
- what the shelf life of a medicine is—how long it can be kept before it becomes ineffective or dangerous
- how to store the medicine
- whether two or more medicines can be taken together safely.

HELP WANTED

Pharmaceutical Sales Representative

If science is your love, but sales is your game, maybe your career should be selling our products to doctors and hospitals. We need people who can sell in a highly competitive environment, but who have the scientific background to understand our products and the professional qualities to relate to our sophisticated clientele. High ethical standards, intelligence, an assertive attitude, and the ability to communicate are musts. You will likely have extensive college training in business as well as the sciences, especially chemistry. Experience in a medical field is a plus.

LESSON 2 REVIEW

Reviewing Facts and Vocabulary

1. What is the role of the FDA?
2. Define the term *histamine* and tell when it is released.

Thinking Critically

3. **Analysis.** Compare medicines with brand names with generic medicines.

4. **Synthesis.** Suggest possible reasons why a physician, not a pharmacist, is licensed to write prescriptions.

Applying Health Knowledge

5. Interview a pharmacist to determine what questions consumers most often ask about their medicines. Draw conclusions about how active consumers are in their own health care.

MEDICINES AND THE CONSUMER **435**

Answers to Lesson 2 Review

1. The FDA monitors the effectiveness and labeling of medicines and approves medicines before they are made available to the public.
2. A substance that causes blood vessels in the respiratory tract to dilate and tissues to swell. It is released when a virus enters the respiratory system.
3. Both have the same chemical substances and meet the same standards set by the FDA.
4. Answers will vary. Possible answer: Although both are trained in drug therapy, only a physician is trained to diagnose an illness.
5. Answers will vary.

Assess

Check for Understanding
- Assign and discuss the lesson review. Have LD students focus on questions 1 and 2.
- Assign and discuss the chapter review.

Evaluate
- Administer, grade, and discuss the *Lesson 2 Quiz*.
- Administer, grade, and discuss the *Chapter 21 Test*.
- Refer to the Performance Assessment strategy for this chapter. See pages T 23 to T 25.

Reteach
- Have students develop posters describing precautions teens should take before purchasing or taking medicine.
- Ask students to complete *Reteaching Activity 57*.

Enrich
- Have students go to the library to find out about a recent medicine approved by the FDA. What does the medicine do? How long was it tested before being approved? Is it a prescription or OTC medicine? How does the FDA decide how to classify the medicine? Find a medicine that used to be a prescription medicine that is now an OTC medicine. Why is it now an OTC medicine? Why was it changed? Have students summarize their findings in written reports.
- Ask students to complete *Enrichment Activity 21*.

Close

Ask students to state the most important concepts studied in this lesson. As consumers, what type of responsibilities do we have when using medicines?

DID YOU KNOW?

- Over-the-counter remedies provide relief, but not cures, for the 200 viruses that cause colds.

Helping Students Improve Their Health

Reinforcing Vocabulary

- **Tamper-proof seal.** A mechanism that protects a product from being altered once it has been packaged.
- **Side effects.** Any reactions to a medicine other than the one that is intended.

Teaching Strategies

L1 EXPLANATION. Students may not understand the history behind question 10. Students may benefit from understanding that certain medicines in the past have been tampered with and have caused loss of life.

L1 SELF-ESTEEM. Have students discuss methods for finding alternative medicines for the medicines advertised on TV. How might self-esteem influence a person's search for alternative medicines for stress or headaches, for example.

L1 CLASS ACTIVITY. Have students bring to class VCR clips from TV commercials. How many advertised products are OTC medicines? Do Americans appear to focus on a "quick fix" for many different ailments?

L2 CLASS ACTIVITY. Have students interview persons who regularly use medications for medical conditions, such as high blood pressure and diabetes. Have students find out how carefully amounts of medications are prescribed and used in such cases.

DID YOU KNOW?

- You shouldn't use a teaspoon from your kitchen to measure medicine—silverware spoons vary too much in size.

Self-Inventory

Using Medicines Carefully

HOW DO YOU RATE?

Number a sheet of paper from 1 through 15. Read each item below, and respond by writing *MT* if the statement describes you most of the time, *ST* if the statement describes you some of the time, and *N* if the statement never applies to you.

1. I try at least one healthful way to relieve physical discomfort before taking an OTC medicine.
2. I use OTC medicines only when necessary.
3. I use only one kind of medicine at a time, unless otherwise instructed by my physician.
4. If I am not sure about a medicine, I ask my parent, physician, or pharmacist.
5. I ask my physician for information about a medicine that is being prescribed for me.
6. I read all the enclosed information and follow the directions carefully when taking medicines.
7. I never take someone else's prescription medicines.
8. I take prescription medicine only according to my doctor's advice.
9. I check the expiration date on all medicines before taking them and properly dispose of those that are out of date.
10. I check all OTC medicines to see that the tamper-proof seal has not been broken.
11. I keep all medicines away from younger children.
12. I keep myself informed about types of medicines, the effects on the body, and their proper use.
13. I alert my parents or physician immediately if side effects occur when taking medicines.
14. I do not take OTC medicines for an extended period of time without my doctor's knowledge.
15. I compare the ingredients and prices on generic and brand-name medicines.

HOW DID YOU SCORE?

Give yourself 2 points for each statement that describes you *most of the time*, 1 point for each statement that describes you *some of the time*, and 0 points for each *never* response. Find your total, and read below to see how you scored. Then proceed to the next section.

23 to 30
Excellent. Keep it up. Your behavior and knowledge concerning medicines is healthful.

15 to 22
Good. You exercise some caution when taking medicines, but could improve your knowledge of medicines.

7 to 14
Fair. While you are acting carefully in some ways, you are omitting some important precautions that would protect you and others.

Below 7
Poor. You could be taking some unnecessary and dangerous risks with medicines.

WHAT ARE YOUR GOALS?

If you received an *excellent* or *good* score, complete the statements in Part A. If your score was rated *fair* or *poor*, complete Parts A and B.

Part A

1. I plan to learn more about medicines by ____.
2. My timetable for accomplishing this is ____.
3. I plan to share my information about medicine with others by ____.

Part B

4. The behavior I would most like to change is ____.
5. The steps involved in making this change are ____.
6. My timetable for accomplishing this is ____.
7. The people or groups I will ask for support and assistance are ____.
8. My rewards for making this change will be ____.

Meeting Students' Needs

For students who score *Excellent*. Suggest that students research careers in the field of medicine and determine their educational requirements.

For students who score *Good*. Suggest that students enroll in additional coursework to further their understanding of medicines, such as chemistry and physics.

For students who score *Fair*. Suggest that students become more familiar with the role that medicines play in society by researching the role of various medicines in changing the way Americans view diseases.

For students who score *Poor*. Have students help you organize a seminar to educate students on how to be an informed consumer/purchaser of medications.

Building Decision-Making Skills

H eather has suffered from severe allergies for which her allergist has prescribed regular injections and a nasal spray that has a steroid ingredient that violates the school's athletic policy. Heather was a good athlete long before taking the medication, and this particular medicine does not have a performance-enhancing element. What should Heather do? Some of her choices are:

A. Find a different therapy or medication that does not violate the policy.
B. Ask for an exception to the policy, pointing out the fact that it is prescribed by a doctor for a legitimate medical situation and not for performance-enhancing purposes.
C. Challenge the system in court.
D. Use the medication and try not to get caught.

WHAT DO YOU THINK?

1. **Choices.** What other options does Heather have?
2. **Consequences.** What are the probable consequences of each of the choices given?
3. **Decision.** Which strategy do you think Heather should choose? Explain your answer.

4. **Evaluation.** How will Heather know whether or not her decision was a good one?
5. **Evaluation.** Have you ever been affected—positively or negatively—by a bureaucratic policy that seemed very arbitrary and wrong to you? What did you do about it? Describe the situation, how it turned out, and what you would do differently the next time.

L ucia's twin, Alicia, has missed school again, complaining of a migraine headache. Lucia realizes Alicia has headaches but doesn't think they have ever been diagnosed as migraines. Alicia treats herself by taking over-the-counter medicine in excessive doses and going to bed. It seems to Lucia that these headaches occur at very convenient times, such as before school tests and unpleasant social situations. Lucia finds this especially irritating because her parents won't allow the girls to miss school for just any reason. Her sister is getting around the rule by being dishonest. How should Lucia handle this situation?

WHAT DO YOU THINK?

6. **Situation.** Is this a problem with which Lucia should concern herself?
7. **Choices.** If so, what are the possible solutions Lucia has for handling the situation with her sister?
8. **Consequences.** What are the advantages and disadvantages of each solution?

9. **Decision.** Which solution should Lucia choose?
10. **Evaluation.** How do you think Lucia will know whether or not her decision was a good one?

Teaching Strategies

L2 **CLASS ACTIVITY.** Conduct a court trial: "Heather vs. Athletic school policy." Allow a few undecided students to act as jurors who will hear Heather's case for being exempt from the athletic policy for prescribed medical purposes. Have a group of students act as Heather's defense and a group of students who will support the enforcement of the athletic policy. Allow the class to react to the jurors' decision.

L1 **CLASS ACTIVITY.** Present the situation between Lucia and Alicia. Ask students to remember if there was ever a time when they felt that someone was abusing a medical condition for selfish reasons. Ask students if they have ever been disbelieved when they truly felt ill. Have students brainstorm ways in which to handle this stressful situation. Have students role-play the part of Lucia and Alicia. Have Lucia respond in various ways to this situation.

L1 **CLASS ACTIVITY.** Other possible role-plays pertaining to understanding medicines include: (1) Your mother saves everything, including old medicines. One morning, after you wake up with a sore throat, your mother hands you an old bottle of an antibiotic that was prescribed for her. You have just learned in health class that taking someone else's medicine could be dangerous. Your mother is rather persistent. (2) Your parents sent you to the store to get some cough medicine. When you arrive at the pharmacy, there are several different brands to choose from. Each brand of cough medicine describes treatment of various symptoms. You are unsure which cough medicine is best for you to purchase.

Discussing the Answers

Situation 1. Perhaps the best way for Heather to handle this dilemma is to challenge the intent of the school's athletic policy. Heather has been prescribed medication for a legitimate purpose. She should present documentation of her condition to the school and give the school board an opportunity to allow Heather to be exempt from the school's athletic policy.

Situation 2. If Lucia is concerned about her sister's well-being, she should discuss this situation with her sister in a caring and nonjudgmental manner. If, however, Lucia's true motivation is jealousy, she owns this problem and it is up to her to resolve her feelings. This is probably a situation in which Lucia should not become involved.

Answers to Chapter 21 Review

Using Health Terms

1. Antivenins
2. Narcotics
3. Synergistic
4. Penicillin
5. Tolerance
6. Tetracycline
7. Aspirin
8. Histamine
9. Pharmacist
10. Medicine misuse

Building Academic Skills

11. Editorials will vary.
12. Answers will vary.

Recalling the Facts

13. Acetylsalicylic acid. Headaches, toothaches, muscular pain, pain of arthritis.
14. Type of medicine, method by which medicine is taken, body chemistry, allergies, age, weight, use of other medicines.
15. It used to refer to any substance that, when taken into the body, causes a change in physiological or psychological activity. Now the term is used mostly to refer to dangerous and illegal substances.
16. Prevent disease, fight pathogens, relieve pain, help the heart, and regulate blood pressure.
17. Synergistic—two or more medicines when mixed have a greater effect than either one independently; antagonistic—the effect of a medicine is canceled or reduced when taken with other medicines; additive—medicines work together in a positive way.
18. A condition in which a person believes medicine is needed to feel good or to provide an escape from reality.
19. A chemical need for a medicine characterized by tolerance and withdrawal.
20. In humans or animals, such as horses, sheep, or rabbits, in response to an infection or vaccination.
21. It occurs when a person stops taking a medicine to which he or she is physiologically dependent.

REVIEW

Using Health Terms

On a separate sheet of paper, write the term that best matches each definition given below.

LESSON 1

1. Blood fluids that contain antibodies and act more quickly than vaccines.
2. Medicines that relieve pain and cause sleep by slowing down the brain and central nervous system.
3. Interaction in which two or more medicines react with greater potency than each would when taken independently.
4. Antibiotic once known as the "wonder medicine."
5. Condition in which one's body becomes used to the effect of a medicine.
6. Antibiotic used in place of penicillin.
7. The most commonly used nonprescription analgesic medicine in the United States.

LESSON 2

8. Substance released in one's body when a cold virus invades the respiratory system.
9. A person trained in the preparation, distribution, and sale of medicines.
10. Using a medicine in a way that is not intended.

Building Academic Skills

LESSON 2

11. **Writing.** Using animals to test products is a controversial issue. However, some people believe that using animals to test medicines is necessary. Take a stand and write an editorial for your school or local newspaper.
12. **Reading.** Occasionally, an FDA approved substance becomes the subject of controversy. In recent years, red dye number 5 was one such substance. Research this substance or a current controversy involving the FDA. (News magazines are a good source.) Decide what position the news magazine has taken. Cite supporting facts and details.

Recalling the Facts

LESSON 1

13. What is the active ingredient in aspirin? What is aspirin used for?
14. What factors affect how one's body will interact with medicine?
15. How has the meaning of the term *drug* changed over the years?
16. What are the most widely used medicines used for?
17. Name and describe three types of medicine interactions.
18. Define psychological dependence.
19. Define physiological dependence.
20. Where and why are antivenins produced?
21. When does withdrawal take place?
22. What are the symptoms of withdrawal?
23. What is a vaccine?
24. How does a vaccine work?
25. Name four ways in which medicine can be taken into the body.

LESSON 2

26. How do OTC medicines differ from prescription medicines?
27. How long does it usually take for a medicine to be approved by the FDA?
28. What information must a manufacturer of medicines provide to the FDA?
29. What controls does the FDA place on the advertising of OTC medicines?
30. List four ways in which medicine might be misused.
31. Medicines are categorized into five schedules. How did this come about?
32. What are common chemicals found in OTC cold medicines?
33. Tell why generic medicines are just as good as those with brand names.
34. List five things a pharmacist can tell a person about a prescription.
35. What does FDA approval of a medicine mean?
36. What information is always given on OTC medicine labels?
37. What do cold medicines actually do?

22. Nervousness, insomnia, severe nausea, headaches, vomiting, chills, cramps.
23. A medicine to help prevent a person from contracting a disease.
24. Weakened or dead pathogens are introduced into the body, stimulating the body to produce specific antibodies against these pathogens.
25. Swallowed, injected either intravenously or intramuscularly, inhaled, sniffed.
26. OTC medicines can be bought without a doctor's prescription.
27. About five years.
28. Chemical composition of medicines, the intended use, the effects, possible side effects.
29. Ads cannot make or imply results that the medicine cannot provide.
30. By taking too much or too little, taking someone else's medicine, discontinuing use of medicine without a doctor's approval, taking medicine longer than prescribed.
31. Through the Controlled Substances Act of 1970.
32. Antihistamines, caffeine,

REVIEW

Thinking Critically

LESSON 1

38. Analysis. How would you answer a person who said that vaccines are dangerous substances because they contain pathogens?

LESSON 2

39. Evaluation. Do you think it is better to have a government agency or a privately owned company regulating approval of medicines? Support your answer.

40. Analysis. In later stages of development, experimental medicines are often tested on groups of people. Where do you think these groups of people come from? What would be the ramifications of being in this experimental group?

41. Evaluation. Sometimes insurance companies will not pay for a prescription if a generic equivalent was available but not dispensed. Do you feel this is justified? Support your answer.

42. Evaluation. What is the role of the Food and Drug Administration in monitoring medicines? Do you think this role should be altered in any way? Explain your answer.

Making the Connection

LESSON 1

43. Math. Study a newspaper or a magazine. Determine the percentage of ads for medicines. Display this information in a pie graph.

44. Home Economics. Conduct a home safety check by determining if all medicines at home are safely stored and outdated medicines are properly discarded. Summarize your findings and recommendations in writing.

45. Language Arts. In writing, describe one of the dilemmas teens may face in regard to OTC medicines. Then provide three different solutions to the dilemma.

Applying Health Knowledge

LESSON 1

46. If you had strep throat, the doctor might give you a choice between taking medicine orally or receiving an injection. Which would you choose and why?

47. Give an example of medicines that are taken into the body in each of the four ways described in this chapter.

48. You are watching your 3-year-old sister, and she develops a sudden fever. In the medicine cabinet, you find acetaminophen but the directions on the label only give dosage amounts for children six and older. Should this medicine be given to your sister? Why or why not?

LESSON 2

49. What are some appropriate questions to ask the doctor before he or she writes a prescription?

50. Select an advertisement of a medicine that is used to alleviate pain. Analyze the claims and benefits of the medication and determine the accuracy of the ad. Note ways the ad influences a person's decision to buy the medicine.

51. Look through a magazine and count the number of advertisements for OTC medications. What conclusions can you draw about the public's attitude toward taking medicines to relieve pain? Pick an ad and rewrite it, giving suggestions for relieving a health problem without medicine.

Beyond the Classroom

LESSON 1

52. Further Study. Some people still oppose mass vaccinations and reject these procedures as a requirement for admission to public schools. Is this the right of each family, or is it the responsibility of the school to protect the students? Defend your answer.

---

aspirin or acetaminophen, codeine, antacids.

33. They have the same chemical substances and meet the same standards set by the FDA.

34. Answers will vary. Accept five of the following: Name and dosage of the drug, how and when the drug is to be taken, possible side effects, number of refills allowed, if a generic substitute is available, shelf life of prescription, how to store the medicine, any drug interactions that might take place.

35. It means the medicine is safe when used as directed, and the medicine is effective in treating the illness or condition for which it is prescribed.

36. Directions for safe use, name and amount of all active ingredients, name and address of manufacturer, expiration date, cautions or warnings.

37. Relieve cold symptoms.

Thinking Critically

38. The pathogens are weakened or dead and are not usually harmful when administered to healthy individuals.

39. Answers will vary but should be supported logically.

40. These groups of people are probably sufferers of the ailment the medicine is meant to relieve. They have most likely volunteered to test the medicine. Answers will vary. Possible answers: These people may get relief from their ailment. They may get no relief. They may develop other problems associated with the medicine.

41. Answers will vary but should be supported logically.

42. The FDA reviews information about medicines supplied by manufacturers, controls advertising of prescription medicines, decides which medicines require prescriptions and which are OTC medicines, approves medicines for public use, requires manufacturers to put certain information on medicine labels. Answers will vary but should be supported logically.

Making the Connection

43. Pie graphs will vary.

44. Summaries will vary.

---

45. Answers will vary.

Applying Health Knowledge

46. Answers will vary. Possible answers: Orally, because of a fear of shots; injection, because it will provide relief faster.

47. Answers will vary. Possible answers: Swallowed— aspirin; injected—penicillin; inhaled—asthma medicine; sniffed—sinus medication.

48. No, one dosage would be too much medicine for a child of that age or weight.

49. Answers will vary. Possible answers: How often do I take it? If it says every six hours, does that mean I need to get up in the middle of the night to take it? What are the possible side effects? How long should I take it? Is there a generic form I can take?

50. Answers will vary.

51. Answers will vary.

Beyond the Classroom

52. Answers will vary but should be supported logically.

Lesson Summaries

LESSON 1. Emphasis on quitting smoking or never starting to smoke increases every day. Despite the dangers, some 50 million Americans still smoke. Peer pressure, a misconception that smoking affects health only after years of smoking, and the belief that smoking is a habit that they can drop any time they wish are major reasons teenagers begin to smoke. Smoking cigarettes, pipes, and cigars, as well as the use of smokeless tobacco, all carry significant health risks.

LESSON 2. Objections to smoking by nonsmokers is increasing. Not only is sidestream smoke offensive to many people, it is recognized to have unhealthy effects. With greater awareness of the effects of passive smoke, rights of the nonsmoker are increasingly being recognized and enforced. Many approaches exist to help individuals kick tobacco habits and deal with the problems and concerns associated with stopping.

Introducing the Chapter

Explain to students that some of the most conclusive research in the area of health behavior and wellness deals with the impact of smoking on one's health. Have students fold a sheet of notebook paper in half lengthwise and list on the left side some of the reasons they have heard smokers give for starting or not giving up cigarettes. Ask students to look for factual responses to the excuses they heard and note them in the second column as they read the chapter.

Performance Assessment ✓

Refer to pages T 23 to T 25 for a Performance Assessment strategy for this chapter. See the *Performance Assessment Activities* booklet for additional suggestions.

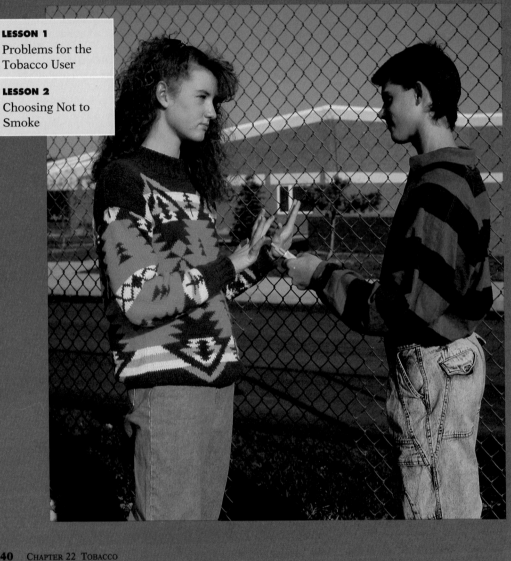

CHAPTER
22 TOBACCO

LESSON 1
Problems for the Tobacco User

LESSON 2
Choosing Not to Smoke

Key to Ability Levels

Teaching strategies have been coded for varying learning styles and abilities.

L1 Level 1 activities are basic activities and should be within the ability range of all students.

L2 Level 2 activities are average activities and should be within the ability range of average to above-average students.

L3 Level 3 activities are challenging activities designed for the ability range of above-average students.

LD LD activities should be within the ability range of learning-disabled students.

LEP LEP activities should be within the ability range of Limited English Proficiency students.

PROBLEMS FOR THE TOBACCO USER

When it comes to using tobacco, there is good news and bad news. The good news is that more and more people are becoming aware of the dangers of tobacco and are giving up the use of tobacco products. Consider these facts:

- At least 30 million Americans have quit smoking.
- An estimated 65 percent of doctors, 61 percent of dentists, and 55 percent of pharmacists who once smoked have now quit.
- In 1965, 40 percent of American adults smoked, while in 1990 that figure dropped to 29 percent.
- During the past 25 years almost half of the adults who once smoked have now given up the use of tobacco.

In short, emphasis on quitting smoking or never starting to smoke increases every day.

The bad news is that there are still some 50 million Americans who do smoke, despite the fact that most of them know of the dangers—from allergies, cancer, and heart and lung disease, to early death. According to the World Health Organization, in developed countries ". . . the control of cigarette smoking could do more to improve health and prolong life . . . than any single action in the whole field of preventive medicine." Yet too many people are still lighting up.

Why Young People Smoke

Every day in the United States 3,000 teens start smoking. Even though the media and schools keep sending out the message that tobacco use is hazardous to one's health, teens are smoking, chewing, and dipping tobacco in large numbers. Consider these facts:

- Teenage females are smoking more than ever before. The number of teenage females who smoke has doubled over the past 20 years.
- It is estimated that about 15 percent of 12- to 17-year-olds use cigarettes.
- In national samples of high school seniors, 13 percent of males and 12 percent of females describe themselves as daily smokers.
- One-quarter of high school seniors who smoke had their first cigarette by sixth grade, one-half by eighth grade.
- Over the last 20 years, the age at which teens start to smoke has continued to fall.
- According to the Centers for Disease Control and Prevention, an agency of the United States Public Health Service, each year an estimated 1 billion packs of cigarettes are sold to people younger than 18—even though it is against the law in many states.

According to U.S. Surgeon General Antonia Novello, "If current smoking rates were to continue in the United States . . . 5 million children now living in this country would die of smoking-related diseases."

PROBLEMS FOR THE TOBACCO USER **441**

Focus

Lesson Objectives

After studying this lesson, students should be able to:
- state reasons that some teens smoke
- explain how tobacco use is directly linked to respiratory and circulatory diseases, as well as a variety of other health-related problems

Bellringer

Write the following on the chalkboard for students to work on while attendance is being taken: *Respond in a brief paragraph to one of the two following statements: (1) I think it is okay to smoke or use tobacco orally. (2) I do not think it is okay to smoke or use tobacco orally.*

Introducing the Lesson

Refer to the Bellringer. Have students share their responses. Discuss smoker versus nonsmoker rights. Who has more influence today? Why has this happened? Should we have more restrictive laws against smoking? What types of laws would reduce the use of tobacco by young teenagers?

Building Vocabulary

- Ask students to find the definitions for all the vocabulary terms in this lesson. Ask them to locate any other words they feel need to be clarified. Define all the identified words. Ask students to explain how these words relate to the use of tobacco.
- Ask students to write sentences explaining each term or its relationship to tobacco. Have them leave the vocabulary term out of the sentence and replace it with a blank. Request that students exchange papers and, using the text as a resource if necessary, fill in the blanks. Ask original writers to check for correctness.
- Ask students to complete *Workbook Vocabulary Activity 58.*

Resources for Lesson 1

- **Transparency** 27
- **Guided Reading** Act 58
- **Reteaching** Activity 58
- **Lesson 1 Quiz**
- **BARN,** Smoking
- **The Reality of Drugs**

Science and Technology Videodisc
Human Biology, Side 2
Ch 15 Nicotine and the Lungs

ABC News InterActive Videodiscs
Tobacco, Side 1
Ch 5 Long-Term Consequences of Cigarette Smoking

Guided Practice

L1 DISCUSSION. Why do some people continue to smoke even though they are aware of the dangers of smoking? Why do you think the number of female smokers is increasing?

L1 DISCUSSION. Ask students how they can tell if someone smokes. List the clues on the chalkboard. Is the person who smokes aware of these clues? Why not?

L2 DISCUSSION. Ask students what products have been developed specifically for the smoking population. (Ashtrays, tooth whitener, breath freshener, smoker's toothpaste, extra filters, and smoke stopper strategies and gimmicks.) Why has this become a lucrative industry when the number of smokers is decreasing?

L3 CLASS ACTIVITY. Ask students to think of all the possible psychological appeals that someone marketing tobacco could use to convince someone to use the product. Have the class rank in order the ideas. Have students explain their reasoning for the ranking.

L2 CLASS ACTIVITY. Ask students to cut out as many advertisements for cigarettes or other tobacco products as they can find. Ask them to bring the ads to class and post them around the classroom. Have students rate which ads would have the most appeal to adolescents. Now ask what other groups would likely be influenced by the ads. Categorize the ads by the targeted audience. Ask students' opinions on the effectiveness of the ads to make a person purchase the product.

DID YOU KNOW?

- Nicotine accumulates quickly in the smoker's brain and, like other addictive drugs, affects certain nerve receptors.
- One study suggests that smokers experience twice as much pain as their non-smoking counterparts.

CONFLICT RESOLUTION

Several recent studies have found that passive smoke, the smoke inhaled by nonsmokers, is dangerous. As a result, efforts to discourage cigarette smoking are increasing.

Some people who continue to smoke complain of being treated as social outcasts. For this reason, some experts suggest a kinder attitude toward smokers. They argue that nicotine addiction is a medical problem, and smokers need treatment, not isolation.

What additional efforts can be used to discourage cigarette smoking and not have smokers feel like social outcasts?

So why do teens ever start to smoke? One major reason some teens smoke is that they feel insecure in social situations. Before they begin smoking, some teens believe that puffing on a cigarette will somehow remove their fears or insecurities, something a cigarette simply cannot do.

Teens may smoke because of peer pressure. Or they may smoke because advertising on billboards and in magazines has made them associate a particular brand with the attractive models pictured.

Teens may smoke because they think the bad effects of smoking on health occur only after many years of smoking. They may not realize that health risks begin from the moment the cigarette smoke from that first cigarette enters the body.

Perhaps the greatest reason young people smoke is that they believe that they can drop the habit at any time. They do not realize that for many smokers, smoking is no habit; it is an addiction that is difficult to shake. Still, some teens realize that people sometimes get addicted to cigarettes, yet feel certain that they are the exception and can stop at any time.

In a large survey of teens who smoke, half claimed they either definitely or probably would not be smoking after five years. They viewed it as a passing habit. The problem is that after five years of smoking, many of these same teens found that they had an addiction to cigarettes. Addiction includes physiological or psychological dependence. Many adult smokers who began smoking as teens are still at it because they are addicted.

Cigarettes

With each puff of a cigarette, a smoker comes in contact with more than 4,000 chemicals, and at least 43 of these are known to cause cancer. But the chemicals in tobacco can cause other ailments as well. Tobacco contains **nicotine,** the addictive drug in cigarettes. People smoke to reduce the craving for nicotine, which is a poisonous stimulant. A **stimulant** is a drug that increases the action of the central nervous system, the heart, and other organs. Nicotine raises blood pressure and increases heart rate.

The flavor of a cigarette is due mostly to the tar in tobacco. **Tar** is a thick, sticky, dark fluid produced when tobacco burns. Several substances in tar are known **carcinogens,** cancer-causing substances. Tar penetrates the smoker's airways and lungs. Combined with the drying

KEEPING FIT

The Benefits of Being a Nonsmoker

Nonsmoking means
- being able to take a deep breath,
- tasting food and having the full sense of smell,
- having good endurance during physical activity,
- using money for other things,

- preventing bad breath and having a clean mouth,
- unstained teeth and fingers,
- having hair and clothes that smell fresh,
- being free from addiction to nicotine,

- reducing the risks of heart disease, cancer, and leading respiratory diseases,
- taking pride that you are part of a growing, health-conscious no-smoking movement.

Additional Information

Smoking. A person who has one bad health habit is likely to have others. For example, in a 1988 survey of over 4,000 people conducted by the University of Michigan Fitness Research Center, results indicated that people who smoked were
- 2.5 times as likely as nonsmokers to have 8 or more drinks per week,
- 1.3 times as likely to take drugs,

- 1.2 times as likely not to exercise and to be absent from work more than 6 days a year,
- 1.4 times as likely to get less than 7 hours sleep a night and not to wear seat belts,
- 2.2 times as likely to be unhappy,
- 2 times as likely to report that they were not in good overall health.

effect of cigarette smoke, tar paralyzes or destroys cilia, the waving hair-like projections that work to keep the respiratory tract clear.

Carbon monoxide is a colorless, odorless, poisonous gas in cigarette smoke that passes through the lungs into the blood. This is the same gas in automobile fumes that, if inhaled, could prove fatal. It unites with the hemoglobin in red blood cells, preventing them from carrying the oxygen needed for energy to the body's cells.

Pipes and Cigars

Like smoking cigarettes, smoking pipes and cigars also presents major health risks. Pipe and cigar smokers usually inhale less smoke, yet they are more likely to develop cancers of the lip, mouth, and throat because more tar and other chemicals are generated by pipes and cigars. If the pipe or cigar smoker makes it a habit to inhale the smoke, his or her chances of lung cancer also increase.

Specialty Cigarettes

Specialty cigarettes are those prepared with tobacco and other ingredients. They are often made with strong tobacco and contain spices that make them taste and smell sweet. However, the effects they can have on the body of the user are anything but sweet. Experts say that specialty cigarettes actually contain more cancer-causing tars than standard cigarettes.

The most common specialty cigarette is the clove cigarette, which contains about 60 percent tobacco and 40 percent cloves. Most of these cigarettes are imported from Indonesia and have been used in the United States since the 1970s. Young people started smoking them in the early 1980s. Use of these cigarettes has dropped sharply in recent years for several reasons. There have been complaints of lung problems and possible deaths as a result of smoking clove cigarettes. The ingredient that produces the aroma of cloves anesthetizes the back of the throat and allows deeper inhalation.

Smokeless Tobacco

Use of smokeless tobacco has increased, especially among teenagers. Many people believe that using smokeless tobacco is safer than smoking it. These users claim it is safer because they are not taking in smoke or putting smoke into the air. In addition, advertisements using famous people to promote smokeless tobacco have contributed to an increase in its use, especially among teenagers. The picture of a cowboy or an athlete using smokeless tobacco gives the impression that chewing and dipping contribute to one's masculinity. They do not. Instead, they contribute to one's ill health. The fact that many teens who use smokeless tobacco started chewing tobacco or dipping snuff when they were between the ages of 13 and 15 means that they can develop serious health problems early in life. Some of those health problems include mouth sores that can turn into cancer of the lip, mouth, or throat; damage to teeth and gums; and damage to the digestive system.

Top: Normal lung.
Bottom: Cancerous lung.

PROBLEMS FOR THE TOBACCO USER **443**

Tell students what happens to the body when a person uses tobacco. Explain why, after about 30 minutes, the tobacco user wants more. (The constriction of the blood vessels causes a mild high. When the vessels return to normal, there is a sensation of restlessness and irritation. The smoker or oral tobacco user does not like the discomfort and will repeat the behavior that produced pleasure. This causes a cycle of use that becomes habitual. The frequent use builds up an addiction to nicotine.)

L1 **DISCUSSION.** What is the purpose of cilia? Explain what can occur when they stop functioning.

L1 **DISCUSSION.** Ask students to determine as many reasons as possible why an employer would rather hire a person who does not smoke over one that does. If they were an employer, how would they help their employees who smoke to stop?

L1 **CLASS ACTIVITY.** Have students debate this statement: *Smoking pipes and cigars is less dangerous than smoking cigarettes.*

L2 **CLASS ACTIVITY.** Select a group of students to develop and perform a skit about a female teen who objects to her boyfriend's use of smokeless tobacco; he chooses to dip because all the guys on the team do.

L1 **DISCUSSION.** What are some of the dangers of smokeless tobacco?

L1 **DISCUSSION.** Why do you think people continue to use smokeless tobacco even though they are aware of its dangers?

L1 **SPEAKER.** Invite a representative from the Dental Association, a school hygienist, or a local dentist to talk about leukoplakia. Ask the speaker to address the following questions: What is the frequency of occurrence? How does it look and feel? What can be done to eliminate this condition? Is it always cancerous? How fast does this condition turn into cancer? What other effects of oral tobacco use do dentists see in their practice?

Cigarettes and Health: A Body of Facts

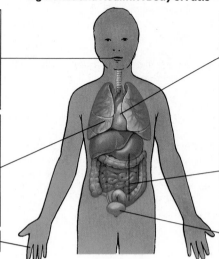

Mouth. Just one cigarette causes "cigarette breath" and dulls the taste buds. The hot smoke is harmful to the mouth and throat tissues. Cigarette smoking plays a major role in causing cancer of the oral cavity and larynx.

Teeth. Tar stains the teeth, causing brown spots.

Bronchioles. As smoke is drawn into the respiratory tract, harmful gases and particles settle into the surrounding membranes (bronchioles). One point of great concentration is where the bronchus divides into left and right bronchi. This is also where most lung cancer begins.

Lungs. Efficiency decreases.

Fingers. Cigarettes cause yellow stains on fingers.

Cardiovascular system. Nicotine causes blood vessels to constrict, forcing the heart to pump faster and increase blood pressure. Smokers have a higher death rate from strokes. Smoking is also a risk factor in the development of cardiovascular disease, affecting the circulation in the arms, hands, feet, and legs.

Gastrointestinal tract. Cigarette smoking appears to be connected to increased illness and a higher death rate from peptic ulcers. Cigarette smoking reduces the effectiveness of standard ulcer treatment and slows the rate of ulcer healing.

Bladder. Smokers have a greater risk of bladder cancer than nonsmokers.

Dangers of Smoking

Every day in the United States at least 1,000 people die from diseases caused from smoking. Cigarette smoking is responsible for well over 400,000 deaths in the United States each year.

Smoking and the Respiratory System

Cigarette smoking is a major factor associated with the two principal diseases that make up chronic obstructive pulmonary disease (COPD). These are chronic bronchitis and pulmonary emphysema, which are 10 times more likely to occur among smokers than among people who do not smoke.

Chronic bronchitis is a condition in which the bronchi are irritated. As cilia become useless, tar from cigarette smoke builds up, which results in chronic coughing and excessive mucous secretion of the bronchial tree.

Pulmonary emphysema involves the destruction of the tiny air sacs in the lungs through which oxygen is absorbed into the body. As the walls between the sacs are destroyed, they lose their elasticity, becoming larger and thus providing less total surface from which oxygen can be absorbed. More breaths are required, and instead of using 5 percent of one's energy in breathing, a person with advanced emphysema uses up to 80 percent of personal energy just to breathe.

Lung cancer, directly linked to cigarette smoking, is the leading cause of cancer deaths among males. With the increase in female smokers, lung cancer is becoming a more significant cause of cancer death among females, too.

Lung cancer begins as the bronchi are irritated by cigarette smoke. Cilia are destroyed and extra mucus cannot be expelled. The smoker develops a cough. Cancerous cells can grow in these conditions, block the bronchi, and move to the lungs. In advanced stages, cancerous cells can travel to other organs through the lymphatic system.

DID YOU KNOW?

According to *Prevention's Giant Book of Health Facts:*

- About 75 percent of deaths from lung cancer among women are caused by smoking.
- On average, a cigarette smoker is 10 to 15 times more likely to get lung cancer than a nonsmoker.
- Someone who smokes 2 or more packs of cigarettes a day is 20 to 25 times more likely to die from lung cancer.
- A male smoker who is between 30 and 40 years old can expect to lose about 8 years of his life because of smoking.

444 CHAPTER 22 TOBACCO

Additional Information

Nicotine and Smoking. It only takes 5 to 7 seconds for nicotine to reach the brain after a person inhales tobacco smoke. In those seconds, the nicotine is absorbed into the bloodstream through the lining of the mouth and through the lungs. The smoker's blood pressure goes up; heart rate increases by up to 20 beats per minute; oxygen supply to body tissues decreases; and blood circulation to the arms, hands, legs, and feet decreases. The first "rush" of stimulation of the brain is followed by depression and fatigue, leading the smoker to seek even more nicotine—another cigarette.

Overcoming The Odds

Todd and Ramon have been friends since junior high. They live in the same apartment building. They're on the same basketball team. They like to hang out together. Todd and Ramon have also been smoking together since eighth grade—at least until recently.

Not long ago Todd's dad was diagnosed with lung cancer. He was a two-pack-a-day smoker and thought nothing of it. Ramon's grandmother, a chain smoker, has emphysema. She can barely make it up the stairs. Both boys have seen firsthand what smoking can do to a person.

Then Todd's dad told him he was really sorry he'd ever set such a bad example for him by smoking all those years, and he begged Todd to stop smoking so he wouldn't end up like him—losing weight and gasping all the time—because of cigarettes. Todd decided to take action.

"I asked Ramon if he'd give up smoking, too," Todd says. "Ramon said he'd try but he didn't know for sure if he could do it. He said his grandmother had been trying to quit for 20 years, but he'd give it a shot.

"We worked out a system for helping each other," says Ramon. "We made a pact. We

decided we'd call each other or just drop in at least three times a day—unannounced—to make sure the other guy wasn't cheating. My sister said we should write up a contract

and sign it, but we told her we didn't need one—that we took each other's word for it."

Todd and Ramon started running in the park every day after school instead of hanging out with the other smokers. They cut down on the number of cigarettes gradually, and on the day of the last cigarettes, they chucked their ashtrays in the dumpster in a little ceremony. "We promised if we made it through the first week, we'd buy each other a new tape," says Todd, "and if we made it through the month,

we'd buy each other tickets to the playoffs. That took away some of the pain."

The first few days Todd says he felt like he would jump out of his skin. Ramon described it as feeling like his fingers were plugged into a socket.

Todd chewed packs and packs of gum. Ramon bit down on what seemed like hundreds of lollipop sticks but then, they actually started to feel better—calmer, less strung out than before.

It's been over four months now for Ramon. Todd, after one slip, is back on track, helping out his dad, and staying away from the cigarettes. He's running better than ever now, beating everybody's times, and his coach is talking about helping him apply for an athletic scholarship. "What I started out doing for my dad," he says, "I'm now doing for myself."

1. What factors motivated Todd and Ramon to try to stop smoking?
2. What strategies did they use for stopping? Do you think these methods will work over time? Why or why not?
3. How do you think this experience has affected their self-esteem? Their friendship?

Additional Information

Bronchitis. Acute bronchitis comes on suddenly and is usually caused by a virus entering the respiratory system and settling in the bronchial tubes. Treatment for acute bronchitis is medication to stop the infection. Chronic bronchitis is usually caused by smoking. The person with chronic bronchitis has a continuing heavy bark-like cough. The lungs secrete an excessive amount of sticky mucus as a means of dealing with the irritating smoke. The "smoker's cough" is a warning that the body may not be able to counteract this irritation of continual smoke and the passageways are narrowing. The narrowing causes pressure on the alveoli which sometimes collapse, leading to emphysema.

Using Overcoming the Odds

■ **Discussion.** What is the role of nicotine gum or patches in kicking the tobacco habit? Why not just go "cold turkey"? (Nicotine is highly addictive—more so than alcohol or cocaine for many people—so it's often easier to give it up gradually. Going "cold turkey" may cause such unpleasant withdrawal symptoms that the person trying to quit goes back to using tobacco. Nicotine patches and gum allow one to gradually cut down on the consumption of nicotine.)

■ **Speaker.** Invite someone to class who has recently given up smoking. Ask him or her to talk to students about the best and worst aspects of quitting.

■ **Answers**
1. Todd's father's lung cancer and Ramon's grandmother's emphysema.
2. They supported each other, substituted healthful activities for times they used to smoke, tapered off nicotine slowly, and rewarded themselves.
3. Increased their self-esteem and strengthened their friendship.

L1 **COOPERATIVE LEARNING.** Divide the class into groups of two or three. Assign each group an elementary grade level, K to 6. Ask them to develop a lesson on tobacco usage for their assigned level. The lessons could include visuals, a skit, discussion questions, student activities, charts, or displays. Meet with teachers from each grade level and explain your plans. Ask permission for students to teach their lessons to their classes.

Independent Practice

L3 **COMMUNITY INVOLVEMENT.** Have a group of students take training to become cofacilitators of classes to help their peers stop smoking. Training is offered through the American Lung Association or the American Cancer Society. Have an adult facilitator from the training agency work with the group.

Smokeless tobacco can present some serious health problems.

Smoking and the Circulatory System

You already know that nicotine makes the heart work harder and speeds up the pulse. Smoking constricts blood vessels, which cuts down on the circulation, or blood flow, to the limbs. This can result in a tingling feeling in a smoker's hands and feet. Nicotine contributes to plaque buildup in blood vessels. The formation of these fatty deposits in the arteries increases the chance of arteriosclerosis, or hardening of the arteries, and gradually clogs the blood vessels to the heart. This condition increases the risk of heart attack.

Cigarette smoking also damages the heart. The risk of sudden death from heart disease is three times greater for smokers than nonsmokers. This risk increases for those who smoke more than a pack a day.

Smoking raises blood pressure and leads to increased risk of stroke. If a smoker has high blood pressure and high cholesterol, the risks of coronary heart disease are even greater. Experts estimate that if all Americans stopped smoking, deaths from heart diseases could be cut by almost a third, saving more than 20,000 lives a year.

The Dangers of Smokeless Tobacco

Although smoke does not get into the lungs, smokeless tobacco presents other health problems, some of which can be serious, even life-threatening.

The nicotine in smokeless tobacco is as addictive as the nicotine in cigarettes. Once a person starts chewing and dipping, it can become very difficult to stop.

KEEPING FIT

Sixteen Good Reasons Not to Light Up

- lung cancer
- bad breath
- throat cancer
- yellow teeth
- stained fingers
- premature wrinkling of the skin
- birth defects
- irritated eyes
- increased heart rate
- increased blood pressure
- emphysema
- increased bronchitis
- sinus problems
- increased cholesterol, even as a teen
- lower life expectancy
- often being treated as a social outcast

Across the Curriculum

Science. Find a plant infested with aphids and cut off a twig or leaf cluster that has many insects on it. Remove the paper from several cigarettes. Boil the tobacco in a cup of water for 15 minutes. Strain the solution by pouring it through filter paper or a paper towel into a glass jar. Add a pinch of soap detergent to this tobacco solution to make it easier to spray. Pour the solution into an atomizer or other small spray bottle. Spray the leaves on top and bottom. Avoid breathing the spray. What happens to the aphids as a result of being sprayed with the nicotine in the tobacco? What does this tell you about nicotine?

SMOKING, APPEARANCE, AND SOCIAL HEALTH

Smoking not only can harm a person's insides, it can damage a smoker's outsides, too. In fact, cigarette smoking may be hazardous to a person's looks.

How? For one thing, it can yellow the smoker's teeth and stain the fingernails and fingers that hold cigarettes. In addition, according to a new study at the University of Utah, smoking can triple the average person's likelihood of getting wrinkled skin early. Heavy smokers studied were 5 times more likely to develop premature wrinkles than nonsmokers. According to the study, people who smoke and sunbathe have even greater wrinkling risks. They are 12 times more likely to develop wrinkles earlier in life than nonsmokers.

Smoking also causes bad breath, a smoke odor on clothes and in hair—as well as in a car, house, or workplace. All of this can have a negative impact on one's social health.

People who use smokeless tobacco have more saliva. Although the chewers usually spit out the saliva, they do swallow some without realizing it. This introduces tar and other chemicals into the digestive and urinary systems. Tobacco juices also contain chemicals that may delay healing of wounds.

Tobacco and its by-products are extremely irritating to the sensitive tissues in the mouth. Irritation from direct contact with tobacco juices is responsible for **leukoplakia,** thickened, white, leathery-appearing spots on the inside of a smokeless tobacco user's mouth. These areas can develop into cancer of the mouth.

Smokeless tobacco users also tend to show greater tooth wear than nonusers. The gums tend to be pushed away from the teeth where the tobacco is held. The roots of the teeth become exposed and more susceptible to decay. Dip and snuff products may cause people to lose their teeth while they are still young. Users of smokeless tobacco also develop bad breath and discolored teeth. Tobacco products decrease the user's ability to smell and taste, especially salty and sweet foods.

LESSON 1 REVIEW

Reviewing Facts and Vocabulary

1. Give three reasons some teens smoke.
2. Write a paragraph identifying some of the dangers of smoking, using the words *nicotine, carcinogens,* and *carbon monoxide.*

Thinking Critically

3. **Evaluation.** Do you think a doctor has the right to refuse to treat a person for a disease related to smoking if the individual refuses to quit smoking? Why or why not?

4. **Synthesis.** What would be the health risks to someone who smokes cigarettes *and* uses smokeless tobacco?

Applying Health Knowledge

5. Design a label that could be put on cigarette packs to alert the potential smoker to the many hazards of smoking.
6. Write a public service announcement for your school on the dangers of using any form of tobacco.

PROBLEMS FOR THE TOBACCO USER **447**

Answers to Lesson 1 Review

1. Answers may vary. Possible answers: Insecurity in social situations; peer pressure; attractive ads; a mistaken notion that health risks associated with smoking only occur after years of tobacco use; view it as a passing habit.
2. Paragraphs will vary. Definitions for terms can be found on pages 442 and 443 or in the Glossary.
3. Answers will vary but should be supported logically.
4. Answers will vary. Possible answers: Lung cancer, chronic obstructive pulmonary disease, heart disease, oral cancer, dental problems.
5. Designs will vary.
6. Announcements will vary.

Assess

Check for Understanding
- Assign and discuss the lesson review. Have LD students focus on questions 1, 3, and 4.

Evaluate
- Administer, grade, and discuss the *Lesson 1 Quiz.*

Reteach
- Ask students to use their text to identify some of the by-products of tobacco use. The list should include nicotine, tar, and carbon monoxide. Have students discuss the effects of these chemicals on the body.
- Ask students to complete *Reteaching Activity 58.*

Enrich
- Have students investigate court cases brought against tobacco companies. There have been many suits brought by "victims" of tobacco use. Have students determine what the issues of these cases are. Ask students to report their findings and share their opinions regarding these cases with the class.
- Have students research the trend of the tobacco industry to diversify its investments, companies, and products. Why is the industry taking this approach? What are the trends in the tobacco industry's economy? Why is the government still providing price support supplements for tobacco growers?

Close

Tell students that in this first lesson they studied the reasons some people use tobacco and the effects it has on the body. Explain that the next lesson will discuss the effects of smoking on people around the smoker. It will also present approaches to quitting smoking.

Focus

Lesson Objectives

After studying this lesson, students should be able to:

- describe the health hazards that nonsmokers face when in a smoke-filled environment
- discuss the rights of a nonsmoker
- discuss the challenge of quitting smoking and positive steps that smokers who want to quit smoking can take

Bellringer

Write the following on the chalkboard for students to work on while attendance is being taken: *List all the reasons you can think of for stopping smoking.*

Introducing the Lesson

Ask students to share their responses to the Bellringer. Write these on the chalkboard. If a reason is given by more than one student, place a check by the reason each time it is expressed. Rank in order the students' reasons by frequency. Ask the class to develop ways to present this reasoning to smokers to convince them to quit. For each reason to stop, formulate a strategy to help smokers modify their smoking behavior. For example—Reason: You will develop lung cancer. Strategy: Show the smoker pictures of smokers' lungs. Discuss the cancer rate among smokers. Have the smoker meet someone who has lung cancer.

DID YOU KNOW?

- Among the chemicals found in sidestream smoke are DDT and arsenic.
- A former smoker's risk of death continues to decline as the number of smoke-free years increases. It takes about 15 years of being smoke-free for an ex-smoker's risk of death to be the same as someone who never smoked.

CHOOSING NOT TO SMOKE

LESSON 2 FOCUS

TERMS TO USE
- Passive smoke
- Mainstream smoke
- Sidestream smoke

CONCEPTS TO LEARN
- There are many successful approaches to stopping smoking.
- Smokers must recognize their personal desire to quit and believe they are in control.

ATTITUDES AND BEHAVIORS TO EVALUATE
- Self-Inventory, page 454.
- Building Decision-Making Skills, page 455.

Increasingly, people who smoke cigarettes, pipes, and cigars are frowned upon by nonsmokers. They may be asked to move or to leave places where smoking is prohibited. More likely, individuals bothered by their smoke may simply cast them dirty looks or get up and move. In short, smoking can make a person feel like an outsider with strangers and friends—sometimes even in the smoker's own home.

In addition, many people object to the smell of smoke on hair or clothes. Even people who have already extinguished a cigarette, cigar, or pipe may experience disapproving looks from people who find the odor their tobacco has left behind offensive.

There is increasing concern and interest in the United States and around the world that the nonsmoker is being affected by the smoke of those using cigarettes, pipes, and cigars. In a recent report by the Environmental Protection Agency (EPA), it was estimated that being exposed to others' smoke kills 53,000 nonsmokers in the United States every year. In fact, passive cigarette smoke has recently been classified as a cause of cancer in its own right, and it is now considered the nation's third-leading preventable cause of death.

Environmental Tobacco Smoke

Each year the evidence grows that people who breathe someone else's cigarette smoke can receive the same unhealthy effects as the person who smokes. **Passive smoke** is cigarette, cigar, or pipe smoke inhaled by nonsmokers. It is also smoke that remains in a closed environment after the smoker is through smoking. Passive smoke includes **mainstream smoke,** what a smoker blows off, as well as **sidestream smoke,** what comes from burning tobacco.

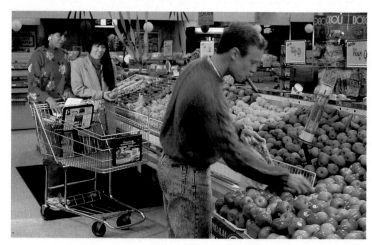

Passive smoke is cigarette, cigar, or pipe smoke inhaled by nonsmokers. Passive smoke is offensive to nonsmokers.

448 CHAPTER 22 TOBACCO

Resources for Lesson 2

- **Guided Reading** Act 59
- **Decision Making** Act 22
- **Enrichment** Act 22
- **Lesson 2 Quiz**
- **Health Labs** Act 22
- **Chapter 22 Test**

ABC News InterActive Videodiscs

Tobacco, Side 2
Ch 14 Ways to Say "No"

Tobacco, Side 2
Ch 9 Quitting Tobacco

Passive smoke contains large amounts of the same harmful ingredients as the smoke inhaled into a smoker's lungs. However, mainstream smoke may contain less nicotine and tar than sidestream smoke. This may be because sidestream smoke is hotter than mainstream smoke and has not been filtered through the cigarette.

A smoke-filled room may have levels of carbon monoxide and other pollutants as high as those that occur during an air pollution emergency. A nonsmoker could inhale enough nicotine and carbon monoxide in an hour to have the same effect as having smoked a whole cigarette.

Passive smoke causes eye irritation, headaches, and coughing. It causes more frequent ear infections, asthma attacks, and other respiratory problems, and aggravates existing heart and lung diseases, including lung cancer. Lengthy exposure to these conditions can result in the same kinds of health problems that the smoker may experience. Consider these facts:

- New studies indicate that passive smoke not only makes existing heart disease worse; it can actually cause it.
- Nonsmokers who live with smokers have a higher risk of dying from heart disease than do nonsmokers.
- An estimated 37,000 people die annually from heart disease directly caused by passive smoke.
- At least 3,700 people die annually from lung cancer and 12,000 from other forms of cancer because of exposure to others' smoke.

Smoking During and After Pregnancy

Cigarette smoking during pregnancy is associated with small fetal growth, an increased chance of spontaneous abortion and prenatal death, increased stillbirths, and a low birth weight, as well as growth and developmental problems during early childhood. Babies born to mothers who smoked during pregnancy may be adversely affected in intellectual development and behavioral characteristics.

Nicotine constricts the blood vessels of the fetus in the mother's uterus as carbon monoxide reduces the oxygen level in the mother's and fetus's blood. Smoking is especially harmful during the second half of pregnancy. After the baby is born, nicotine can be transferred during breast-feeding.

Most people would not give a child a cigarette, but people who smoke around children are doing the same damage to these youngsters that they would if they were helping them light up.

Most restaurants provide non-smoking sections.

K E E P I N G   F I T

Getting Smoke-Free: Some Things that Help

If you want to give up cigarettes, consider these steps:
- Decide once and for all that you want to quit.
- Make a list of what smoking is costing you, in terms of money, health, appearance, and social

acceptance.
- Set a target date for quitting and stick to it.
- Cut down on the number of cigarettes gradually.
- Begin an exercise program.
- Plan some fun to fill your time.

- Ask a friend to quit with you. Offer one another daily—or even hourly—support.
- Plan a healthy way to reward yourself when you have achieved a smoke-free status.

CHOOSING NOT TO SMOKE **449**

Additional Information

Smoking. Smoking kills more Americans each year than AIDS, cocaine, crack, heroin, alcohol, and fires combined. Smoking is related to thousands of deaths each year. The longer one smokes, the deadlier it becomes. Twenty-seven percent of American women smoke and 126,000 die each year from smoking-related disorders. Smoking is responsible for about 4,000 infant deaths in the U.S. each year. The tobacco industry spends billions of dollars on advertising to attract smokers. The Department of Health and Human Services has only a few million dollars to spend on anti-smoking campaigns. As the American Lung Association states, "Tobacco is the only substance that when used as intended causes disability and death."

Concentrating on an exercise program, such as running, is one way to overcome the urge to smoke.

Snacking on nutritious foods is a healthy substitute for smoking.

A federal study of 47,000 households shows that children of cigarette smokers are nearly twice as likely to be in poor or fair health as the children of nonsmokers. Among their ailments, they have more bronchitis and other respiratory problems. They have poorer lung function and a higher incidence of wheezing.

In addition, children of parents who smoke have twice the chance of developing lung cancer as children of nonsmokers.

Rights of the Nonsmoker

Despite the growing awareness of the dangers of passive smoke, nearly half of all smokers light up without asking those around them if they mind. According to a recent medical report, even though at least 80 percent of nonsmokers report that they are bothered by passive smoke, only about 4 percent actually ask smokers to stop. Because of the dangers of passive smoke, that fact has to change. You can help change it.

You have a right to express that you prefer that people not smoke around you. By doing so, you protect the air you breathe and the air of those around you. If you are allergic to smoke or the smell of it makes you sick, it is particularly important that you learn to speak up and let people know.

If you are out in a restaurant, ask for the nonsmoking section or at least ask to be seated away from smokers. If you are a member of some group or club, ask that no smoking be allowed during meetings or at least that the smokers sit near ventilated areas or windows.

It is considerate of smokers to ask others in an enclosed area if they mind their smoking. It is also important that smokers avoid smoking in very small or poorly ventilated areas, or in the presence of small children or people with allergy, lung, or heart problems. In fact, smokers should take responsibility to smoke elsewhere whenever nonsmokers are around. When they do not, nonsmokers also should take responsibility for their own health by asking smokers to extinguish their cigarettes or by moving to a smoke-free space.

Kicking the Habit

More and more people are taking responsibility for their health by giving up the use of tobacco. Giving up tobacco can be tough, but there are many ways to stop and many places that offer support and help with the process.

A person who wants to quit using tobacco should be reminded that he or she will probably go through a period of withdrawal. As you remember, withdrawal occurs when something on which a person is physiologically dependent is no longer used. During this period the person might feel nervous, moody, or have difficulty sleeping. These symptoms of withdrawal do not last long.

Some people may use a series of filters over a period of weeks to stop smoking. Each filter reduces the tar and nicotine levels so that withdrawal is gradual. Other people get a prescription from their doctors for gum that contains nicotine. The aim is to gradually cut down on the amount and frequency of gum use until they are eventually nicotine-free. A nicotine patch that is prescribed can also be used. This patch, placed on the body, gives off decreasing amounts of nicotine. The smoker can give up cigarettes while withdrawing gradually from the nicotine. Many people combine several of these approaches and techniques to get and stay tobacco-free. In addition, there is a variety of support groups for people to join when they want to stop smoking and need group support to do so.

Tips for Quitting

Those who want to quit smoking might take these steps:

- Identify the times when they usually reach for a cigarette out of habit.
- Change their daily routine so that they avoid situations that trigger smoking.
- Avoid people who smoke and situations that are conducive to smoking during the first few weeks.
- Make a list of the reasons they want to quit smoking, post it around the house, and read it when they feel like smoking.
- Chew sugarless gum, suck on sugarless candy, or munch on carrot sticks or other healthy snacks when they feel a desire for cigarettes.
- Drink plenty of water to flush out toxins.
- Avoid alcohol, coffee, tea, and colas for a while because these substances often stimulate the craving for tobacco.
- Exercise frequently.
- Think in terms of quitting for a few minutes, then an hour, and then a day, saying things to themselves like, "I choose not to smoke during this hour," or "I have to do this only one day at a time."
- Take deep breaths to aid relaxation when the craving to smoke gets strong.
- Brush their teeth often to remove tobacco residue.
- Stop buying cigarettes by the carton; buy them by the pack instead.
- Set a final target date for being tobacco-free and stick with it.
- Make a ceremony out of smoking the last cigarette, and declare their intentions to family and friends.
- Get rid of smoking reminders, such as ashtrays, matches, and lighters.
- Plan rewards for themselves each time they resist lighting up.
- Become aware of improvements in how they feel, in their senses of smell and taste, and in how they look.
- Get positive reinforcement and support from nonsmoking friends.
- If they relapse, or go back to smoking, know that they are not failures and that they can try to quit again.
- Think about all of the benefits of being smoke-free.

KEEPING FIT

More Ways to Give Up Smoking

- Surround yourself with people who support your decision and who, themselves, don't smoke.
- Decide how many cigarettes you will smoke that day. Stick to that plan.
- Find a substitute to put in your mouth such as sugar-free gum.
- Don't buy cartons of cigarettes.
- Ask nonsmoking friends what it's like for them to breathe your smoke.
- Try to stay smoke-free one day at a time.
- Have your teeth cleaned.
- If you do smoke again, don't give up. Many people have relapses. Start again on the smoke-free trail. It's worth it.

CHOOSING NOT TO SMOKE **451**

Overcoming Misconceptions

Myth. Low-tar, low-nicotine cigarettes are less hazardous to health than regular cigarettes. **Fact.** The tobacco is the same as in regular cigarettes, but their filters are designed to reduce the amount of tar and nicotine that enters the body. Studies have shown that smokers who switch to low-tar and low-nicotine cigarettes tend to smoke more and smoke cigarettes longer. As a result, the amount of tar and nicotine intake is probably not reduced.

Independent Practice

L2 RESEARCH. Ask students to research the different products sold to help people stop smoking. The pharmacist in a local drugstore may have knowledge of these products. Have students determine which are effective and why they work.

L1 PERSONAL INVOLVEMENT. Create a diet club for students who want to stop smoking, but are concerned about weight gain. Ask a school nurse or home economics teacher to help students develop a plan that provides increased oral satisfaction, but is low in calories.

L1 PERSONAL INVOLVEMENT. Organize students who want to stop smoking to form a support group to meet each morning before school. Train peers to be supporters. Have students post the number of days they have been smoke-free.

L2 COMMUNITY INVOLVEMENT. Have students find out when and where sessions of support groups for cancer patients are held. Have them explain what the class is learning and ask if student volunteers can visit and learn what it is like to live with cancer. The American Cancer Society should be helpful with this project.

L1 COMMUNITY INVOLVEMENT. Have students determine the locations of all the cigarette vending machines in their neighborhood. Are these easily accessible to underage buyers? What are the laws regulating the placement of cigarette vending machines for your area? How would you convince your town, area, or neighborhood to place cigarette vending machines in areas where underage buyers would not have access?

L2 COMMUNITY INVOLVEMENT. Have students ask officials in your town to support a local smokeout day during which residents and those who work in your area pledge not to smoke for one day. Assistance for the planning of such a day can be found through the American Lung Association and the American Cancer Society—who sponsor similar days. You may want to participate in their national day or create your own.

L2 **COMMUNITY INVOLVE-
MENT.** Have students create a
fund-raiser for the American Lung
Association or American Cancer
Society. The fund-raiser could be
a 5-K running event, dance-a-
thon, walk-a-thon, chances on a
donated prize such as a TV,
stereo, or gift certificate. Think
big! Get the entire community
involved and generate lots of publicity for your health class as the
sponsors of the event.

L1 **USING THE LESSON
RESOURCES.** For additional student activities, refer to the lesson
resources on page 448.

HEALTH UPDATE

LOOKING AT THE ISSUES

The Debate Over the Sale of Tobacco to Minors

Today in the United States,
45 states and the District of
Columbia have laws that out-
law the sale of tobacco to
people younger than 18. Now
there is a move by many
groups to get laws passed to
raise the age to 21.

Analyzing Different Viewpoints

ONE VIEW. Some people are
opposed to such laws. They
think that it is unfair to single
out teens when 18-year-olds
can perform other adult
responsibilities, such as enlist
in the military.

A SECOND VIEW. Other peo-
ple claim that these laws
could not be properly
enforced. They claim that
despite statewide bans on
tobacco sales for minors, it is
still very easy for most teen
smokers to buy cigarettes and
other tobacco products.

A THIRD VIEW. Still others
think that it is necessary to
protect the health of the
youth throughout the country
by passing and enforcing policies that prohibit the sale of
tobacco products to minors.

A FOURTH VIEW. Some anti-
tobacco activists think that

laws alone are not enough.
They believe that there should
be stiff penalties for stores
and store owners that allow
the sale of tobacco products
to minors. They also recommend that towns and cities
issue tobacco-selling licenses
that require store owners to
sign statements that indicate
they know that the sale of
tobacco to minors is against
the law. People who hold this
view advocate that tobacco-
selling licenses should then
be taken away from those
who do not comply with the
law.

Exploring Your Views

1. Which of these views
   seems most reasonable
   and fair to you? Which
   seems most likely to protect the health of young
   people?
2. Do you think tobacco sales
   should be banned for
   those younger than 18?
   Why or why not?
3. Should the buying age for
   tobacco products be raised
   to 21? Why or why not?
4. Should this age policy be
   decided by each state or
   should there be a uniform
   nationwide policy?
   Explain your reasoning.

Weight Gain: A Common Concern

A common concern of smokers is the risk of weight gain if they try to
quit. The following information has been reported about people who
have faced up to their habit or addiction and quit smoking:

■ One-third gain weight because they substitute eating for smoking.
■ One-third lose weight because they start a fitness program at the same
  time they stop smoking. They fill their need for smoking by eating carrot sticks or other low-calorie snacks.
■ One-third of those who quit find their weight remains the same.

Additional Information

**Smokeless Tobacco—Not a Safe
Alternative.** Between 1977 and 1988, the
number of young men using smokeless
tobacco, or chewing tobacco, doubled. It is
estimated that there are presently 4 million males age 21 and younger who use
smokeless tobacco, many of them believing it is safer than smoking cigarettes. But

they are wrong. Smokeless tobacco has
been associated with
■ lip cancer,
■ cancer of the mouth,
■ stained teeth,
■ bad breath,
■ gum disease,
■ cancer of the cheek and jawbones.

Many offices are now smoke-free.

A Smoke-Free Society

Increasingly, the American public is working toward becoming smoke-free. As people realize that the decision to smoke can affect not only their own health but also the health of loved ones, the drive to become a smoke-free society increases.

There are now whole towns that are banding together to restrict smoking. Tobacco licenses are being revoked by stores and store chains that sell cigarettes to minors. Vending machines are being moved out of unsupervised areas. Many cities are passing laws that restrict smoking in public places, such as in restaurants, civic buildings, business offices, even lobbies. Airplanes now prohibit smoking on commercial flights. Hotels have whole floors for nonsmokers. Laws are being proposed to ban smoking in all enclosed public spaces, and increasingly, the law is on the side of the nonsmoker.

These days smoking is less common in private social settings, too. Meetings of all kinds are now often designated as smoke-free. Even people giving parties no longer put out ashtrays; instead, they ask smoking guests to smoke outside. With continued commitment to health, the remaining bad news about tobacco use can be turned into good news about nonuse as Americans aim toward a smoke-free 2000.

FINDING HELP

STAT, which stands for Stop Teenage Addiction to Tobacco, is an organization dedicated to helping teens avoid the dangers of tobacco. This group works in a variety of ways to eliminate the sale of tobacco to minors. For more information, write to
STAT
121 Lyman Street
Suite 210
Springfield, MA 01103

LESSON 2 REVIEW

Reviewing Facts and Vocabulary

1. What is passive smoke?
2. What are some of the effects of passive smoke on the health of a nonsmoker?

Thinking Critically

3. **Evaluation.** Why do you think people sometimes do not stand up for their rights as nonsmokers?

4. **Synthesis.** In what ways do you predict American society will move toward becoming smoke-free?

Applying Health Knowledge

5. Make a booklet listing the programs and other resources available in your area to teens who want to get tobacco-free.

CHOOSING NOT TO SMOKE **453**

Helping Students Improve Their Health

Reinforcing Vocabulary

- **Smoke-free space.** An area where a person would not breathe cigarette smoke.

Teaching Strategies

L1 EXPLANATION. Frequently, nonsmoking students ask questions concerning a parent who smokes. Students can learn how to communicate effectively with parents in a caring and uncriticizing manner. Encourage class discussions that focus upon students helping other students deal with a parent, or loved one, who smokes.

L1 DISCUSSION. Tobacco products are harmful to one's health. Tobacco products are correlated strongly with the early death of tobacco users. Have students consider the premise that the tobacco industry must continually find new consumers of their product because the product kills their clientele. How ironic is this statement?

L1 CLASS ACTIVITY. Have students draw pictures of cigarette packages and replace the product name with terms such as *lung cancer, emphysema, heart attack,* and *stroke*. Do the same thing with actual magazine smoking advertisements.

L1 CLASS ACTIVITY. Help students understand the correlation between emphysema and smoking cigarettes. Have students actually experience how it feels to live with emphysema. Ask them to breathe through a cocktail straw for 1 minute, while plugging their nose. Explain to students that emphysema is a chronic, progressive disease and that people with emphysema experience this suffocating sensation when they breathe, every minute of their lives.

Self-Inventory

Are You Passive About Passive Smoke?

HOW DO YOU RATE?

Number a sheet of paper from 1 through 15. Read each item below and respond by writing *yes* or *no* for each item. Total the number of *yes* responses for items 1 through 5, 6 through 13, and 14 and 15. Then proceed to the next section.

1. Do you smoke?
2. Do you live with a smoker or smokers?
3. Do you have good friends who smoke?
4. Are you often exposed to other people's smoke?
5. Do you sometimes find yourself in enclosed spaces, where people are smoking?
6. When around people who smoke, do you let them know that you do not like to smell or breathe their smoke?
7. Have you ever given smokers disapproving looks to let them know indirectly that you are bothered by their smoke?
8. Have you ever made negative comments about someone's smoking to others but not directly to the smokers themselves?
9. Have you ever asked people who smoke to extinguish their cigarettes, cigars, or pipes?
10. Have you ever asked smokers to move so that you would not have to breathe their smoke?
11. If a smoker does not stop smoking or move, have you ever moved to a smoke-free space?
12. If you are in a car and someone is smoking, do you roll down the windows?
13. Instead of asking smokers to stop exposing you to their smoke, do you move away from them instead?
14. Are you ever passive about passive smoke, choosing to say and do nothing?
15. Are you afraid that if you speak up and ask a smoker to stop smoking or to move, that the person will laugh at you, get mad at you, or think you are not cool?

HOW DID YOU SCORE?

If you said *yes* to any of the first five questions, you may be at great risk from exposure to smoke.

Now look at your answers for questions 6 through 13. If you said *yes* to none of these, you are in the "passive zone" and need to stand up for your rights as a nonsmoker. If you said *yes* to one or two of these questions, you may be in the passive zone but are at least beginning to stand up for your right to breathe. If you said *yes* to three or four of these questions, you are heading for the "active zone," beginning to stand up for your health and your right to breathe. If you said *yes* to five or more questions, you are in the active zone, where people know they have a right to protect their health from others' smoke.

If you said *yes* to questions 14 and 15, it is very important that you learn to become assertive in standing up for your rights. Now proceed to the next section.

WHAT ARE YOUR GOALS?

If you are in or near the passive zone when it comes to standing up for your rights around smokers, complete Part A. If you are completely in the active zone, complete Part B.

Part A

1. I plan to take a first step in standing up for myself when I am exposed to someone else's smoke by ____.
2. The last time I was exposed to someone else's smoke and did not stand up for my rights, I was passive because ____.
3. I will take the following steps to become less passive and more active about avoiding passive smoke: ____.
4. The benefits will be ____.

Part B

5. I protect myself from exposure to passive smoke in the following ways: ____.
6. I will help others who are afraid or embarrassed to speak up for themselves on the issue of passive smoke by ____.
7. I will continue to give this person support for his or her rights as a nonsmoker by ____.
8. The benefits I will receive from sharing this information will be ____.

Meeting Students' Needs

Protecting Health and Personal Rights. Suggest the following activities for students to strengthen their resolve not to smoke and encourage a smoke-free environment. (1) Encourage students to do volunteer work for the American Lung Association or the American Heart Association. (2) Encourage students to organize and conduct workshops for elementary school students in order to help prevent young children from becoming future smokers. (3) Suggest that students organize peer-support groups to help students stop smoking. (4) Suggest that students brainstorm ways to create a smoke-free school environment. (5) Have students analyze how smoking affects their lives.

Building Decision-Making Skills

Karl is a popular student leader. A group of students in his school, including some of his friends, are lobbying the administration for a smoking area for students. Karl himself doesn't smoke, and he hates the smell of cigarette smoke, but his friends want his support for the idea that having such an area will reduce smoking in the bathrooms. This would eliminate a serious passive smoke problem for nonsmokers. Karl is concerned that, if he endorses the plan, he will be called a "grit," the label attached to the smoking group in the school.

WHAT DO YOU THINK?

1. **Situation.** What decision needs to be made?
2. **Situation.** What issues does Karl have to address in order to make this decision?
3. **Choices.** What possible choices does Karl have?
4. **Consequences.** What are the probable consequences of each choice?
5. **Consequences.** How will others be affected by this decision?
6. **Consequences.** How will Karl's health triangle be affected by this decision?
7. **Consequences.** How might the school board and the school administrators be affected?
8. **Decision.** What should Karl do?

Darlene's boyfriend smokes. She dislikes the fact that his clothes smell, his breath smells, and he spends so much money on cigarettes. She worries about the health risks to both of them, but she is afraid that he'll break up with her if she tries to get him to quit. What should Darlene do?

WHAT DO YOU THINK?

9. **Choices.** List three possible methods of dealing with this problem.
10. **Consequences.** What would be the probable outcome for each?
11. **Consequences.** How might Darlene address the problem and still be sensitive to her boyfriend's feelings?
12. **Situation.** Where might Darlene find help in addressing this problem?
13. **Decision.** What do you think Darlene should do? Why?
14. **Evaluation.** Have you ever faced a similar situation? If so, describe it and tell how you handled it. Would you handle a similar situation differently now? Explain your answer.
15. **Evaluation.** Every nonsmoker has experienced a situation where they have felt that their space was invaded by smoke. If you are a nonsmoker, are there certain situations that bother you? How do you handle these situations? Would you rather do it differently?
16. **Evaluation.** If you are a smoker, how do you feel about nonsmokers' rights? Have you ever been asked not to smoke? What have you done? How will you handle these situations in the future?

Helping Students Improve Their Health

Building Decision-Making Skills

Teaching Strategies

L1 CLASS ACTIVITY. Have students role-play Karl being approached by his lobbying, smoker friends. What message would Karl be sending people if he supported a smoking area, when he does not condone smoking? What message would it send students to provide an area in which students could smoke, when it is dangerous for their health? Is it fair to reward students with a smoking area in order to prevent these same students from breaking a school rule and smoking in the bathroom?

L2 CLASS ACTIVITY. Have students debate whether Darlene should talk to her boyfriend about his smoking. Should Darlene ask him to quit, not smoke around her, or say nothing?

L1 CLASS ACTIVITY. Other possible role-plays pertaining to tobacco products include: (1) Your best friend uses smokeless tobacco. Your friend has been complaining about a sore in his mouth for several weeks. The sore is not healing and your friend will not see a doctor. (2) Recently you found cigarettes in your younger brother's coat pocket. You confronted your brother and he denied they were his. You are aware that many of his friends smoke and fear that he is smoking, too.

Discussing the Answers

Situation 1. Karl needs to do something for which he can feel proud. Karl can begin organizing his own group of supportive friends who would confront smokers in the restrooms at school and would utilize positive peer pressure to stop smoking from happening. By using positive peer pressure, Karl can begin to make some changes for the better.

Situation 2. Darlene must decide if she cares more about her health or her boyfriend. Until she is ready to risk losing her boyfriend, she remains powerless. If Darlene decides that she cares more about her health, she can approach her boyfriend in a caring, nonjudgmental, and uncriticizing manner.

Answers to Chapter 22 Review

Using Health Terms

1. Addiction
2. Nicotine
3. Stimulant
4. Tar
5. Carcinogens
6. Carbon monoxide
7. Leukoplakia
8. Withdrawal

Building Academic Skills

9. A—tar; B—carbon monoxide; C—nicotine.
10. Letters will vary but should be appropriately worded for a 14-year-old and should present arguments that would be meaningful to a person of this age.

Recalling the Facts

11. A—false; B—true; C—true; D—true.
12. About one billion.
13. The United States Surgeon General.
14. Answers may include but are not limited to four of the following: Insecurity in social situations; peer pressure; attractive ads; a mistaken notion that health risks associated with smoking only occur after years of tobacco use; view it as a passing habit.
15. Cancers of the lip, mouth, and throat.
16. Those prepared with tobacco and other ingredients, such as spices that make them smell and taste sweet.
17. They are often more harmful because they contain more cancer-causing tars and some have been reported to cause hallucinations and seizures.
18. They may be bothered by the smoke, do not like the smell of smoke on hair and clothes, and are concerned about the risk of cancer from breathing passive smoke.
19. It is considered the nation's third-leading preventable cause of death.
20. Mainstream smoke is what a smoker blows off; sidestream smoke is what comes from burning tobacco.

21. Answers will vary. Accept five of the following: small fetal growth, increased chance of spontaneous abortion and prenatal death, increases stillbirths, low birth weight, growth and development problems in early childhood, increased chance of developing allergies.
22. Second half.
23. Answers will vary. Accept three bulleted items from page 451.
24. One-third gain weight, one-third lose weight, one-third maintain their weight.
25. Answers may include but are not limited to: Parts of restaurants, civic buildings, business offices, lobbies, airplanes.

Using Health Terms

On a separate sheet of paper, write the term that best matches each definition given below.

LESSON 1

1. A physiological or psychological dependence.
2. An addictive drug found in cigarettes.
3. The type of drug that increases the action of the central nervous system, the heart, and other organs.
4. A thick, sticky, dark fluid produced by burning tobacco.
5. Cancer-causing substances.
6. A colorless, odorless, poisonous gas found in cigarette smoke.
7. Thickened, white, leathery-appearing spots on the inside of the mouth of a smokeless tobacco user.

LESSON 2

8. A condition characterized by nervousness, moodiness, and difficulty in sleeping, caused by giving up a substance on which a person is physiologically dependent.

Building Academic Skills

LESSON 1

9. **Reading.** Below are three statements describing effects. Write *nicotine*, *tar*, or *carbon monoxide* as the cause of each effect.
   a. paralyzes or destroys the cilia that help keep the respiratory tract clear
   b. unites with the body's hemoglobins, preventing them from carrying oxygen to the body's cells
   c. increases the action of the central nervous system, raises blood pressure, and increases heart rate

LESSON 2

10. **Writing.** Write a letter to a 14-year-old who has just begun to smoke. Use your best persuasive arguments to convince this person to stop smoking.

Recalling the Facts

LESSON 1

11. Label each statement below *true* or *false*.
   a. Among high school seniors, more males than females smoke.
   b. Between 1965 and 1990, the number of adult Americans who smoked dropped by 11 percent.
   c. More than half of all doctors, dentists, and pharmacists who once smoked have quit smoking.
   d. During the last 20 years, teens who begin to smoke have been doing so at younger and younger ages.
12. According to the Centers for Disease Control and Prevention, about how many packs of cigarettes are sold each year to persons under the age of 18?
13. Who is Antonia Novello?
14. List four reasons some teens start to smoke.
15. What kinds of cancers are more likely to occur in pipe and cigar smokers than in cigarette smokers?
16. What are specialty cigarettes?
17. Are specialty cigarettes generally more or less harmful than standard cigarettes? Why?

LESSON 2

18. Why do many nonsmokers object to living, working, and socializing with smokers?
19. How serious is the threat of cancer from passive cigarette smoke?
20. What is the difference between mainstream smoke and sidestream smoke?
21. List five risks that have been associated with smoking during pregnancy.
22. Is smoking more harmful during the first or second half of pregnancy?
23. List three tips for quitting smoking.
24. What have studies shown about weight change in people who quit smoking?
25. List three places where smoking used to be allowed but is no longer permitted.
26. How does gum that contains nicotine help someone quit smoking?

REVIEW

Thinking Critically

LESSON 1

27. Evaluation. How effective are the warning labels on cigarettes in influencing people not to smoke?

28. Synthesis. Suggest ways that cigarette smoking is a problem for an entire society.

29. Analysis. Compare the amount of energy used for breathing by a person with advanced pulmonary emphysema and the amount used by a healthy person.

30. Analysis. Comment on this statement, "Smoking is the single, most preventable cause of death in the world."

31. Analysis. How addictive is the nicotine in smokeless tobacco compared to the nicotine in cigarettes?

LESSON 2

32. Analysis. How does the risk of developing lung cancer compare for children of smokers and children of nonsmokers?

33. Synthesis. Develop a list of protective measures that a nonsmoker can put into place to live in a smoke-free environment.

34. Evaluation. Three of your best friends have started to smoke. You have several choices. You can stop seeing these people. You can start smoking yourself, or you can try to convince your friends to quit. How will you decide what to do?

35. Evaluation. America is striving for a smoke-free society by the year 2000. What do you think about this goal?

Making the Connection

LESSON 2

36. Social Studies. Research the influence of tobacco production and sales on the United States economy. Something to consider: How would a ban on cigarette smoking affect tobacco growers and tobacco manufacturers? If cigarette smoking were banned, how would this affect the health of United States consumers?

Applying Health Knowledge

LESSON 1

37. You've noticed that some of the other members of the high school baseball team have begun chewing tobacco. They say professional players do it, and they are not hurting their lungs. What could you tell them about the effects of chewing tobacco?

LESSON 2

38. Which of the following would be good advice to give a person who wishes to quit smoking? Write *yes* for each one that should help. Write *no* for those that probably won't help. Give reasons for your answers.

a. Eliminate foods and beverages that stimulate the craving for tobacco, such as alcohol and beverages that contain caffeine.

b. Keep your intention to quit smoking a secret from friends and relatives.

c. Stay away from other people who have quit smoking.

d. Spend some time with people who still smoke to build up your resistance.

e. Eat healthy snacks when you feel a desire to put a cigarette in your mouth.

f. Drink lots of water to flush toxins from smoking out of your system.

g. Brush your teeth often so your mouth will feel clean.

h. Start an exercise program.

Beyond the Classroom

LESSON 1

39. Community Involvement. Interview 10 people who smoke or used to smoke. Choose people from different age groups. Prepare a list of questions to ask them about their smoking habit. Draw conclusions about your findings.

40. Parental Involvement. Ask your parents about changes in the smoking policies at work. Report your findings to the class.

CHOOSING NOT TO SMOKE **457**

26. By gradually reducing the amount and frequency of gum use until the person is eventually nicotine-free.

Thinking Critically

27. Answers will vary but should be supported logically.

28. Answers will vary. Possible answers: Since passive smoke is also a health risk, smokers put others at risk; it costs everyone in work time lost due to illness caused by cigarette smoke; cigarette butts are a litter eyesore.

29. A person with advanced pulmonary emphysema uses 80 percent of his or her energy to breathe compared to 5 percent for a healthy person.

30. Answers will vary. Possible answer: The risks from smoking are high for smokers and nonsmokers, but just as people choose to smoke they can also choose not to smoke, thus preventing the associated risks.

31. It is just as addictive.

32. It is twice as great for children of smokers.

33. Answers will vary. Possible answers: Ask smokers not to smoke in your presence; sit in no-smoking sections in restaurants; avoid clubs or groups that allow members to smoke.

34. Answers will vary but should be supported logically.

35. Answers will vary but should be supported logically.

Making the Connection

36. Answers will vary.

Applying Health Knowledge

37. That chewing tobacco can cause mouth sores that can turn into cancer of the lip, mouth, or throat; can damage teeth and gums; and damage the digestive system.

38. Reasons will vary. Possible reasons: A—yes, this would help one stop smoking out of habit when one might be tempted; B—no, they might be good motivators if they know; C—no, they could act as a support group; D—no, it would only be more temptation; E—yes, this could help one change one's habits; F—yes, this will help make one feel better; G—yes, if one's

mouth feels fresh, one may be less willing to smoke; H—yes, feeling good physically can be strong motivation to keep one's body healthy.

Beyond the Classroom

39. Answers will vary.
40. Answers will vary.

Lesson Summaries

LESSON 1. Some of the effects of alcohol are immediate. Other effects are not seen for some time, even years. Regular use of alcohol causes tolerance, dependence, liver problems, and brain damage. Drug interactions can occur when more than one drug is present in the body.

LESSON 2. There are more than 7.2 million problem drinkers today. Many young people will face pressures to drink. The reasons teenagers give for drinking are not very different from those reasons given by adults. Millions of young people have chosen not to drink, deciding they don't need it.

LESSON 3. For some people, alcohol becomes a serious problem that affects their lives and the lives of those around them. In some cases, it becomes life-threatening. Drinking during pregnancy can result in birth defects. Drinking and driving has become the most serious and widespread problem involving drinking.

Introducing the Chapter

Explain to students that the number one drug problem in the U.S. is alcohol. Despite the fact that there are more than 10.5 million alcoholics, many people do not even consider alcohol a drug. A great deal of misinformation and misunderstanding about alcohol exists. Getting the correct facts will help students to know the dangers when someone asks them to take a drink. Tell students they will learn more about alcohol and its risk to their well-being as they study this chapter.

Performance Assessment ✓

Refer to pages T 23 to T 25 for a Performance Assessment strategy for this chapter. See the *Performance Assessment Activities* booklet for additional suggestions.

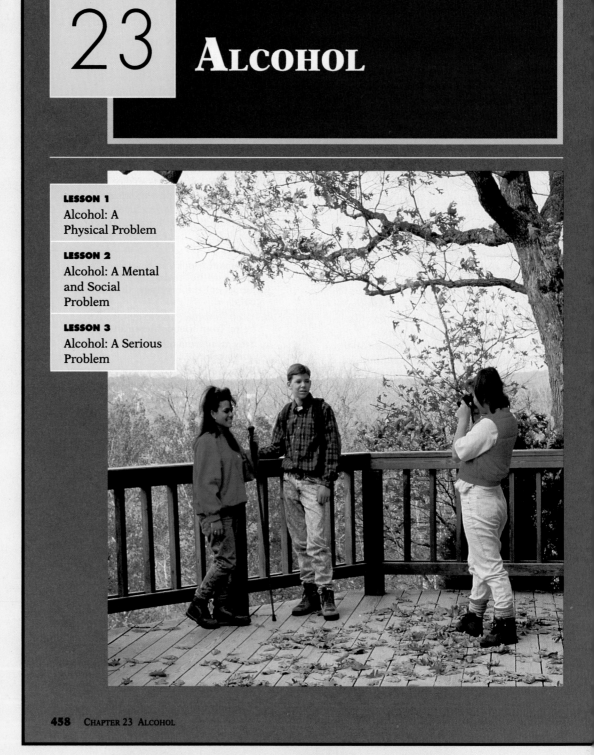

CHAPTER

23 ALCOHOL

LESSON 1
Alcohol: A Physical Problem

LESSON 2
Alcohol: A Mental and Social Problem

LESSON 3
Alcohol: A Serious Problem

Key to Ability Levels

Teaching strategies have been coded for varying learning styles and abilities.

L1 Level 1 activities are basic activities and should be within the ability range of all students.

L2 Level 2 activities are average activities and should be within the ability range of average to above-average students.

L3 Level 3 activities are challenging activities designed for the ability range of above-average students.

LD LD activities should be within the ability range of learning-disabled students.

LEP LEP activities should be within the ability range of Limited English Proficiency students.

ALCOHOL: A PHYSICAL PROBLEM

E thyl alcohol, also known as ethanol, is the type of alcohol found in alcoholic beverages, such as beer, wine, and liquor. It can be made synthetically, or it can be produced naturally by fermentation of fruits, vegetables, or grains. Fermentation is the chemical process that produces alcohol through the action of yeast on sugars.

The source of the sugar varies from drink to drink. In beer, malted barley is the sugar source; in wine, it is berries or grapes; in whiskey, it is malted grains, such as rye or corn. Potatoes are the source of sugar for vodka; molasses, the source for rum.

All alcoholic drinks are only partly alcohol. The rest is water, flavoring, and minerals. Beer is 4 to 6 percent alcohol; wine, 12 to 20 percent; and liquor, 40 to 50 percent. Yet there is the same amount of alcohol in 12 ounces (355 ml) of beer, 5 ounces (148 ml) of wine, and 1½ ounces (44 ml) of liquor.

Alcohol provides little of the taste but all of the intoxicating effect in alcoholic beverages. Because alcohol contains calories, it is a food substance. However, it is of little or no nutritional value. The term *empty calories* is often used with such food substances. Because of its effects on the body, alcohol is considered a drug.

How Does Alcohol Work in the Body?

When someone has a drink, the alcohol follows the same path that food does as it travels through the digestive system. About 20 percent of the alcohol passes directly into the blood from the stomach. So within minutes after a person takes a drink, some alcohol is circulated throughout the body. The majority of the alcohol passes into the small intestine, where it is absorbed into the blood.

Some of the effects of alcohol are short-term, or immediate. Others are not seen for some time, perhaps even years. These are called long-term effects.

Immediate Effects

Alcohol affects several parts of the body immediately. Several factors are involved, such as the amount of alcohol consumed, the size of the person, and whether or not there is food in the person's stomach.

Brain. Alcohol reaches the brain almost as soon as it is consumed. It depresses the activity of the brain, slowing the work of the nervous system. Thought processes are disorganized, and memory and concentration are dulled.

Liver. The liver, in a process called oxidation, changes alcohol to water, carbon dioxide, and energy. The liver can oxidize only about ½ ounce (15 ml) of alcohol an hour. There is no way to speed up this pro-

ALCOHOL: A PHYSICAL PROBLEM **459**

LESSON 1 FOCUS

TERMS TO USE
- Fatty liver
- Cirrhosis (suh•ROH•suhs)
- Multiplier effect

CONCEPTS TO LEARN
- Alcohol affects many parts of the body.
- Regular use of alcohol can result in tolerance and dependence.

ATTITUDES AND BEHAVIORS TO EVALUATE
- Self-Inventory, page 474.
- Building Decision-Making Skills, page 475.

Focus

Lesson Objectives

After studying this lesson, students should be able to:
- explain the effects of alcohol on the body
- describe special problems that occur when alcohol is mixed with other drugs

Bellringer

Write the following on the chalkboard for students to work on while attendance is being taken: *List as many parts of the body as you can think of that are affected by alcohol.*

Introducing the Lesson

Have students share their responses to the Bellringer. Explain to the students that alcohol affects a number of parts of the body. Some of the effects are immediate and others are long-term. This lesson details some of the effects of alcohol, as well as the effects of mixing alcohol with other drugs.

Building Vocabulary

- Ask students to use each of the vocabulary terms in a short public-service announcement about the effects of alcohol on the body. Select some of the announcements to be tape-recorded or videotaped for younger students.
- Ask students to complete *Workbook Vocabulary Activity 60.*

DID YOU KNOW?

- At low doses, alcohol functions as a stimulant; at high doses, as a depressant.
- Even small amounts of alcohol reduce one's sense of taste and smell.
- Alcohol can reduce one's field of vision.
- Alcohol causes the eyes to have difficulty discriminating between lights of different intensity.
- Alcohol decreases fear and increases one's likelihood of taking dangerous risks.

Resources for Lesson 1

- **Transparency** 27
- **Guided Reading** Activity 60
- **Workbook** Vocabulary Activity 60
- **Reteaching** Activity 60
- **Lesson 1 Quiz**
- **Poster** 8
- **The Reality of Drugs**
- **Performance Assessment** Activity 23

ABC News InterActive Videodiscs
Alcohol, Side 1
Ch 5 Alcohol and Your Body

Teach

Guided Practice

L2 CLASS ACTIVITY. Divide the class into seven groups. Have them give reports on alcohol's effects on one of the following parts of the body: brain, liver, bloodstream, kidneys, lungs, stomach, and small intestine. Have them condense and submit their reports to the student newspaper for a series on special problems associated with alcohol use.

L2 DISCUSSION. What signs indicate that alcohol has reached the brain of someone who is drinking?

L2 DEMONSTRATION. Set up an exhibit of colored water so students can see that there is the same amount of alcohol in 12 ounces (36 ml) of beer, 5 ounces (15 ml) of wine, and 1 1/2 ounces (4 ml) of liquor.

L3 COOPERATIVE LEARNING. Ask students to form small groups to write a skit about alcohol's travels through the brain, liver, and bloodstream. Have them present their skits to the entire class.

L2 CLASS ACTIVITY. Have students find newspaper and magazine advertisements of beer, wine, and liquor. Post the advertisements, and ask students to evaluate the ads' truthfulness about alcohol's effects on the body.

L2 DISCUSSION. Ask students what role food plays in slowing the absorption of alcohol in the body. What kinds of food might be more successful in slowing down the absorption process?

L3 CLASS ACTIVITY. Choose students to report on the process of the liver's oxidation of alcohol and the common use of coffee to "sober up" a person who is drunk. Discuss why this process does not work.

L1 CLASS ACTIVITY. Divide the class into small groups. Have them design mobiles showing the synergistic effect of alcohol with other drugs.

L1 USING LIFE MANAGEMENT SKILLS TRANSPARENCY 27. Refer to the Teaching Transparencies Binder.

1½ oz of 80-proof liquor is equal to 12 oz of beer or to 5 oz of wine. "Proof" is an indicator of the concentration of alcohol in a beverage. The higher the proof, the greater the intoxicating powers of the alcoholic beverage.

cess. Until the liver has time to oxidize all the alcohol, the alcohol keeps circulating through all body parts.

Blood Vessels. The blood carries the alcohol to all parts of the body, including the heart, liver, and brain. When alcohol enters the blood, it causes the blood vessels to dilate or widen. The result is an increased flow of blood, especially to the skin. This makes the skin feel flush and warm. However, it is an artificial warmth. The increase of blood flow near the surface of the skin causes the body to lose heat by radiation— body temperature actually decreases. Alcohol causes an increase in heart rate and an increase in blood pressure.

Kidneys. Alcohol affects the kidneys by causing them to produce more urine. (This is done indirectly. Alcohol affects the pituitary gland, which, in turn, acts on the kidneys.) This is one reason a person feels dehydrated the day after heavy drinking.

Stomach. Because the alcohol molecule is very small and water soluble, it does not have to be digested. It can be immediately absorbed into the blood from the stomach. Having food in the stomach slows the

KEEPING FIT

Alcohol and Tobacco: A Smoking Gun

The harmful physical effects of alcohol are well-known. So are those of tobacco. But combining alcohol and tobacco can cause added health risks. Overconsumption of alcohol and cigarettes has recently been linked to increased risks for various kinds of cancer, including cancer of the larynx, esophagus, and mouth.

Across the Curriculum

Science. Have students make a model of the ethyl alcohol molecule (C_2H_5OH). Next, discuss the different kinds of sugars used in the manufacture of beer, wine, and liquor. Demonstrate fermentation, using various sources of sugar and starches.

Home Economics. Discuss the term *empty calories*. Have students contrast the nutritional value (including number of calories) of various alcoholic and nonalcoholic beverages.

Language Arts. As a creative writing project, have students imagine they are an alcohol molecule entering a human body. Ask them to describe the molecule's journey through the brain, liver, bloodstream, kidneys, lung, stomach, and small intestine.

absorption process. Even so, food will not keep a person from getting drunk if he or she drinks too much. Alcohol increases the flow of gastric juices from the stomach lining. Larger amounts of alcohol cause a larger flow of these high-acid juices, irritating the stomach lining. Repeated irritation can cause an open sore called an ulcer.

Long-Term Effects

There are several long-term effects of alcohol use.

Tolerance. Regular use of alcohol may result in tolerance, making it necessary to drink more and more in order to produce the same effects. As tolerance develops, a person may drink an increasing amount without appearing to be intoxicated. The person may continue to function reasonably well until some severe physical damage results or until he or she is hospitalized for some other reason. Then the individual will experience withdrawal, symptoms that occur when the person stops drinking alcohol. These symptoms range from jumpiness, sleeplessness, sweating, and poor appetite to tremors, convulsions, and hallucinations.

Dependence. Some people become physiologically dependent on alcohol. The body develops a chemical need for alcohol. Physiological dependence is marked by tolerance and withdrawal. The symptoms of withdrawal are so unpleasant, a person tends to drink more alcohol in order to avoid the symptoms. As a result, the level of tolerance increases.

Liver Problems. Alcohol interferes with the liver's ability to break down fats. As fats build up in the liver, a condition known as a **fatty liver** develops. This increased amount of fat prevents the normal work of the

Alcohol in the Body

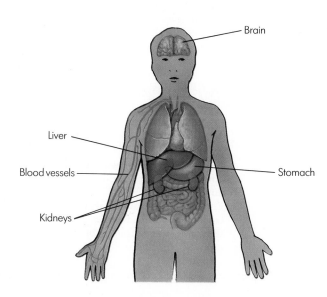

Alcohol affects various parts of the body.

L3 CLASS ACTIVITY. Ask for volunteers to work up a dramatic presentation or interpretive dance to signify the "feelings" of a human body that has been abused through the long-term use of alcohol.

LEP CLASS ACTIVITY. Provide basic art supplies for students to create a project representing one or more main concepts in the lesson. Set up a display of their projects in the classroom.

L3 COOPERATIVE LEARNING. Divide the class into small groups to create comic books for younger people, emphasizing the effects of alcohol on the body. Have students share their completed projects with the class.

Independent Practice

L2 WRITING. Ask students to write articles to submit to the school newspaper about the multiplier effect of alcohol and other drugs.

L2 COMMUNITY INVOLVEMENT. Have students collect brochures and flyers from local groups and agencies that work with individuals and families who have difficulty with alcohol. Ask them to make a display of the materials collected.

L2 RESEARCH. Have students use class and library resources to prepare written reports on some of the withdrawal symptoms experienced by heavy drinkers who quickly stop the intake of alcohol. Ask them to tell the class about what they learned.

L2 PERSONAL INVOLVEMENT. Have students divide a sheet of paper into two vertical columns. Ask them to label the left column "Goals" and the right column "Hindered." Students are to use the left column to list goals they hope to accomplish in their lifetime. Request that they list as many goals as they can. Next, in the right column, ask them to put an "x" beside each goal that could be affected by the short-term or long-term use of alcohol. Afterwards, ask for volunteers to share some of their goals and the effect that alcohol could have on these goals.

L1 USING THE LESSON RESOURCES. For additional student activities, refer to the lesson resources on page 459.

Across the Curriculum

Social Studies. The financial costs of alcohol's effects on the body are considerable. Ask a representative from a local medical facility to speak to the class about the costs of treating individuals with health problems related to alcohol. Discuss the impact of this expense on society.

Math. Using newspaper ads, ask students to compare the costs of alcoholic beverages with nonalcoholic beverages.

Science. Invite a doctor or psychologist to speak to the class about the effects of alcohol on the body (and brain).

- Assign and discuss the lesson review.

Evaluate

- Administer, grade, and discuss the *Lesson 1 Quiz.*

Reteach

- Help students present a mini-lesson about ways in which alcohol works in the body. Have them present their lessons to the rest of the class.
- Ask students to complete *Reteaching Activity 60.*

Enrich

- Ask for volunteers to design an educational game about the long-term risks of using alcohol. Have students demonstrate their completed projects to the class.

Close

Outline on the chalkboard the lesson's main ideas. Ask for volunteers to come to the board, select a main idea, and summarize it for the rest of the class.

DID YOU KNOW?

- Drinking even moderate amounts of alcohol can lead to hypertension, or high blood pressure.
- Heavy drinking has also been linked to an increased risk of stroke.
- Alcohol may contain dangerous levels of lead. The FDA currently allows lead concentrations in wine 20 times greater than what is allowed for water.

DID YOU KNOW?

- Alcohol is used by more Americans than any other drug. It is estimated that at least 1 in 20 Americans is addicted to alcohol.
- On average, alcohol shortens the life of an alcoholic by 10 to 12 years.
- One recent study of juveniles in jail indicated that 40 percent of them had been under the influence of illegal drugs and 33 percent had been under the influence of alcohol when they committed crimes.

liver cells. It also interferes with the growth of new liver cells. As a result, old liver cells are not replaced as quickly as they normally would be. The excess fat in the liver blocks the flow of blood in the liver cells, resulting in reduced oxygen, and eventually, cell death. This condition has been found in both moderate and heavy drinkers. It can be reversed when drinking stops.

Heavy alcohol use destroys liver tissue, which is then replaced with useless scar tissue. This condition is called **cirrhosis** of the liver. *Cirrhosis* means "scarring." There is no blood flow in the scarred area because there are no blood vessels, so the work of the liver is greatly reduced by cirrhosis. The symptoms of cirrhosis are high blood pressure, hemorrhages, abdominal swelling, tendencies toward infection, and a jaundiced appearance. Jaundice can be recognized by a yellowing of the skin or eyes.

Brain Damage. Long-term, excessive use of alcohol invariably leads to major brain damage. People have been hospitalized in mental institutions for severe brain damage caused by excessive alcohol use. Even moderate drinking can destroy brain cells. There can be a loss of intellectual abilities, such as remembering and problem solving. These losses can be enough to interfere with everyday functions.

Mixing Alcohol with Other Drugs

The interaction that occurs when a person takes alcohol with other drugs or medicines is called the **multiplier effect.** Alcohol is a depressant drug. When a person takes another depressant, such as a tranquilizer, with alcohol, the effects can be drastic. Impairment of both mental and physical abilities result. Many accidental deaths result from combining alcohol with other drugs or medicines. Some multiplier effects are not always predictable.

Both over-the-counter medicines like aspirin and prescription medicines can alter the way that alcohol affects the body. Medicines that might cause reactions with alcohol have warnings on their labels. The labels warn about drinking any alcoholic beverages while using the medicine.

LESSON 1 REVIEW

Reviewing Facts and Vocabulary

1. Name the major parts of the body that alcohol affects and tell how it affects them.
2. Explain what is meant by the *multiplier effect.*

Thinking Critically

3. **Analysis.** Compare the short- and long-term effects of drinking alcohol.

Applying Health Knowledge

4. Find two different magazine or newspaper advertisements for alcoholic beverages. How do they compare? What do they not tell you?
5. Consider the impact of labeling every alcohol container with the word *drug.* How do you think this would affect alcohol use or attitudes toward alcohol?

Answers to Lesson 1 Review

1. Brain, liver, blood vessels, kidneys, stomach. For effects, see pages 459 to 461.
2. Interaction that occurs when one takes alcohol with other drugs or medicines.
3. Answers will vary. Possible answer: Both are damaging to one's body. Short-term effects happen quickly and wear off fairly quickly, but long-term effects happen over time and can be permanent or difficult to overcome.
4. Answers will vary.
5. Answers will vary. Possible answer: To many people drug use is considered wrong, so if these people see alcohol labeled as a drug, they may not be so casual about its use and/or avoid it.

ALCOHOL: A MENTAL AND SOCIAL PROBLEM

In 1991 the average American drank 23 percent less hard liquor, 14 percent less wine, and 7 percent less beer than in 1980. What do these statistics have to do with you? At this stage of your life, you will undoubtedly be faced with increased pressure to use alcohol. You can learn about all the problems associated with drinking and the effect of alcohol on the body. However, what really matters are the decisions you make in regard to alcohol. Those decisions can mean the difference between life and death.

Why Young People Drink

The reasons that teenagers give for drinking often are not very different from the reasons that adults give:

- to escape pressures or problems
- to feel better; to get over being sad or lonely
- to relax
- to gain more self-confidence
- to get away with something that they are not supposed to do
- to fit in

Friends are often an important influence on a teenager's choice to drink. There is pressure to drink, and it can be very difficult to say no, especially when you want to be accepted as part of the group.

The family is another major influence on teenage drinking behavior. The example the family sets regarding drinking has much to do with the

There are many ways to have a good time without alcohol.

ALCOHOL: A MENTAL AND SOCIAL PROBLEM **463**

LESSON 2 FOCUS

TERM TO USE
- Alcohol-impaired driving

CONCEPTS TO LEARN
- Young people are influenced to drink or not to drink in a variety of ways.
- Drinking is a high-risk behavior at any age.

ATTITUDES AND BEHAVIORS TO EVALUATE
- Self-Inventory, page 474.
- Building Decision-Making Skills, page 475.

Focus

Lesson Objectives

After studying this lesson, students should be able to:
- list reasons young people choose to drink
- list reasons young people choose not to drink
- describe some of the negative social consequences of drinking

Bellringer

Write the following on the chalkboard for students to work on while attendance is being taken: *Make two vertical columns on a sheet of paper. In the left column, list at least three reasons teens give for drinking. In the right column, list at least three reasons teens give for choosing not to drink.*

Introducing the Lesson

Ask students to share their responses to the Bellringer. Reinforce the reasons given for teenagers' *not* drinking. Explain to students that alcohol not only is a physical problem but that it is also a mental and social problem, as they will learn from this lesson.

Building Vocabulary

- Have students design a bumper sticker (directed to teens) with a public-service announcement about alcohol-impaired driving. Have students choose the one they feel gets the message across in the most effective way.
- Ask students to complete *Workbook Vocabulary Activity 61*.

DID YOU KNOW?

- It's estimated that 9 out of 10 teens try alcohol, of whom 60 percent become social drinkers and 5 percent develop daily drinking habits.
- By the time the average child is old enough to drink legally, he or she has seen alcohol consumed on television thousands of times

---

Resources for Lesson 2

- **Guided Reading** Act 61   ▪ **Workbook** Voc Act 61   ▪ **Reteaching** Act 61
- **Lesson 2 Quiz**

ABC News InterActive Videodiscs
Drugs and Substance Abuse, Side 2
Ch 8 Media Images   Ch 14 Helping Yourself and Others

Guided Practice

L1 DISCUSSION. Talk about why alcohol intake is on the rise for teens and young adults even though the average American drinks less hard liquor, wine, and beer than in 1980.

L2 CLASS ACTIVITY. Set up a hypothetical social situation in which teens are pressuring others to drink. The ones not drinking have said "no" once, but their answer is not being accepted. Have students act out the situation, practicing ways to be assertive. Reinforce the reasons given for teenagers' not drinking.

L1 SELF-ESTEEM. Often someone who is drinking at a party will try to get others to drink. Ask students to share reasons why they think people do this. What can someone do to resist this pressure? How would self-esteem affect a person's ability to resist this pressure?

L1 DISCUSSION. Why is it difficult for some teens to say no to drinking?

L2 DISCUSSION. Ask students to look at each of the reasons for drinking as they relate to emotional needs. Drinking to meet these needs is not a very healthy choice. Why? What other reasons do students give for drinking?

L2 CLASS ACTIVITY. Have students debate the statement: *You have to drink to be popular.*

L1 DISCUSSION. What are some clues to indicate that drinking has become a problem for someone? Which of the reasons (pages 464 and 465) for not drinking have you heard (or given)?

L2 COOPERATIVE LEARNING. Divide the class into small groups; have students write commercials about not drinking. Present their commercials to the class.

L1 SPEAKER. Ask a representative from Mothers Against Drunk Driving to speak to the class about the problems of drinking and driving and the work the organization does to campaign against drunk drivers.

Culturally Speaking

A Nonalcoholic Drink, Please. . .

Evidence shows that early in human history, fermentation of sugar-containing mashes (crushed grains) was discovered, and alcoholic beverages became a part of many cultures. Drinking establishments are mentioned in the oldest known code of laws, the Hammurabi of Babylonia, from 1770 B.C. Choosing not to drink alcohol probably has almost as long a history. There are accounts of several attempts made by the Chinese to prohibit alcohol consumption, but all met with incomplete success. Religious prohibitions have been more successful. Buddhists in India have avoided alcohol since the 6th century B.C., as do the members of the Hindu Brahmin caste. The Qu'ran, written in the 7th century, prohibits drinking of alcohol for all faithful followers of Islam.

teenager's attitudes and behavior toward alcohol. If the teenager sees the parents use alcohol when they have problems, or when they want to socialize or celebrate, chances are the teenager will do the same.

Everyone has the need to belong, to feel loved, and to be important. You can go about meeting those needs in many ways. Drinking does not have to be one of them.

THE HIGH COST OF DRINKING

According to the Alcohol, Drug Abuse, and Mental Health Administration, alcoholism and problem drinking cost the economy over $136 billion in 1990 in lost work, accidents, health-care costs and treatments, research, education, and criminal justice costs. In addition, alcohol is

- a major factor in the four leading causes of accidental death in the United States (motor vehicle crashes, falls, drownings, fires and burns).
- a significant factor in 20 to 35 percent of all suicides.
- a factor in family violence, including spousal and child abuse.
- a major reason for marital separation and divorce.

Other facts about drinking are these:

- **Alcohol-impaired driving,** or driving under the influence of alcohol, is the leading cause of death among teenagers.
- The earlier one begins to use alcohol, the greater the chances of using other drugs later in life.
- Each day 11 teenagers are killed and over 350 are injured in alcohol-related car crashes.

Why Young People Choose Not to Drink

So much attention is focused on the reasons for teenage drinking that the nondrinking teenage group is often slighted. Why do millions of young people choose not to drink?

The most common reason given for not drinking is: "I do not need it." Perhaps the person is really saying, "I do not have to drink to be popular," or "I do not need to drink to be accepted, to have fun, or to act in some way that I usually would not." Other reasons given for not drinking include the following:

- It makes me sick.
- I hate the taste.
- It is fattening.

KEEPING FIT

What to Do If a Friend Who's Been Drinking Wants to Drive

- Don't let the person drive.
- Encourage him or her to ride home with a nondrinker.
- Walk the person home.
- Take away the person's car keys.

- Give the person bus, subway, or cab fare.
- Call a safe-rides service.
- Call the person's parents.
- Ask the host's family to let the person spend the night.

Do whatever you can to keep the person from getting behind the wheel. You could be saving your friend's or someone else's life.

Additional Information

Advertising. The alcoholic beverage industry's advertising efforts increase each year. In 1990, the industry spent more than $1.2 billion on advertising, more than that spent by the household equipment and electronic entertainment industries combined. The U.S. Surgeon General's Workshop on Drunk Driving recommends eliminating alcohol advertising and promotions on college campuses, where a high proportion of the audience is under the legal drinking age. According to a Gallup-Advertising Age poll, more than 74 percent of adults favor health warnings on ads for alcoholic beverages. Almost half felt alcohol advertising should be banned altogether.

- It costs too much.
- It leads to other problems.
- I do not want to lose control.
- I want to enjoy what is going on around me.
- It is harmful to my health.
- My parents are opposed to it.
- I would be breaking training rules.
- In most states, it is illegal for teenagers to buy or possess alcohol.

Negative Social Consequences of Drinking

Bad things can happen as a result of even one drinking episode. The negative consequences can affect not only the drinker but also the drinker's family and friends, as well as anybody else with whom the drinker comes in contact.

Whether drinking is a cause or a symptom, problem drinkers have difficulties with family, friends, school, and police. This situation becomes circular, meaning that if you had some problems at home in the first place, and then started drinking, the drinking would probably lead to more family problems.

Alcohol and Advertising

It is not very difficult to picture what is in a television beer commercial and why such commercials are so popular. Many, if not all, include the following:

- young people who are handsome, attractive, fit, and healthy-looking
- a partylike atmosphere with upbeat music
- an otherwise healthy environment, often in the beauty of the outdoors
- problem-free drinking
- a verbal message that really does not say anything about the product

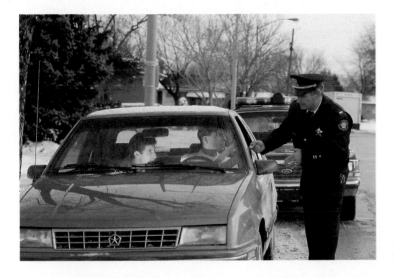

What penalties would these teens suffer for drinking and driving in your state?

ALCOHOL: A MENTAL AND SOCIAL PROBLEM **465**

L1 CLASS ACTIVITY. Discuss the attitude, "It can't happen to me." Ask students to design posters to reach drivers with this attitude. Also, have them create one or more slogans. When they are completed, ask students where the projects should be displayed, and try to arrange for such a display. (For example, at a supermarket, drugstore, laundromat, the lobby of a movie theater, etc.)

Independent Practice

L1 WRITING. Have students write a paragraph describing their views on drinking. Ask them to write a second paragraph describing their views on teen drinking. Request that they save these paragraphs until the end of the lesson. At that time, have students repeat the activity and compare their views, noting any changes.

L2 COMMUNITY INVOLVEMENT. Some schools have chapters of SADD—Students Against Driving Drunk. (Students sign contracts with their parents, saying they will call if they need a ride rather than drive while drunk. In return, parents will either pick them up or pay for a taxi.) Have students see about establishing a chapter in their school.

L2 RESEARCH. Ask students to find out what the state laws are regarding the purchase, possession, and consumption of alcohol by minors and the sale or delivery of alcohol to minors.

L1 PARENTAL INVOLVEMENT. Ask students to collect family recipes for tasty nonalcoholic drinks to be served at parties. Distribute copies of the recipes to the class.

L2 PARENTAL INVOLVEMENT. Ask for volunteers to interview their parents (or other adults) who do not drink. Have them find out reasons for the persons' choosing not to drink, whether they experienced peer pressure to drink, and what kinds of healthy alternatives to alcohol they enjoy.

L1 USING THE LESSON RESOURCES. For additional student activities, refer to the lesson resources on page 463.

Overcoming Misconceptions

Myth. "I can drink and still do well in school." **Fact.** Alcohol interferes with schoolwork when its use results in a changed attitude toward school, missing school, drinking during school hours, ignoring homework assignments, and/or hangovers on school mornings. **Myth.** "It's safe to drink if you're not an alcoholic." **Fact.** Off the highway, alcohol contributes to about 6 million non-fatal and 15,000 fatal injuries each year. In the workplace, up to 40 percent of industrial fatalities and 47 percent of industrial injuries can be linked to alcohol. Also, alcohol is closely connected to the four leading causes of accidental death in the U.S.: auto crashes, falls, drownings, and fires and burns.

- **Discussion.** What positive factors motivated Colleen in her decision to not drink? (She wanted to be in control of herself, live a long and healthy life, and not ruin hers or anybody else's life.)
- **Discussion.** In what way is Colleen influencing others not to drink alcoholic beverages? (Most effectively, she is influencing others by her actions—she realizes that individuals must choose for themselves not to drink.)
- **Answers**
1. Colleen has "overcome the odds" of not giving in to peer pressure and drinking alcohol.
2. She decided not to drink after seeing her brother and friends get drunk, seeing a wrecked car from a drunk-driving accident, and taking an alcohol and drug education program.
3. She was afraid of being different from her peers.
4. She would probably leave the party and reconsider her friendships.

Assess

Check for Understanding

- Assign and discuss the lesson review.

Evaluate

- Administer, grade, and discuss the *Lesson 2 Quiz.*

Reteach

- Divide the class into an inner and an outer circle. Choose five students to be in the inner circle and to list, and briefly discuss, five reasons that teens give for drinking. Next, select 12 students to sit in the inner circle and to list and discuss 12 reasons commonly given for not drinking. Afterwards, combine both circles, and close with a discussion of the negative social consequences of drinking.
- Ask students to complete *Reteaching Activity 61.*

Overcoming The Odds

My name is Colleen O'Conner. I want the people who read this book to know that there are teens out there who are popular, who do just fine in school and with friends, and who don't drink. I also want them to know that nothing grizzly out there got me to make the decision. It was more like a whole number of messages that added up over time that made me decide that I wasn't going to drink. And I don't. Sure, you hear in the news that ten or eleven million teens drink beer and other booze. But you don't hear enough about the other half— millions and millions like me who don't. So it's my turn, and I'm taking it.

"I saw what happened to my older brother when he became a teen. One time when he was about 15 he went to this 'All you can drink' party for three bucks. He came home crawling. And he swore he'd never do it again. Barry— that's my brother—had at least one friend who had a DUI, lost his license, had to go for special classes, the works. Then there are all those awful stories about drinking and driving and people losing legs and dying. When they brought a wrecked car to be displayed on the front lawn of our

school, I just stood there and stared. It really cut through me.

"In health class we had an alcohol and drug education program. It really hit home that you could mess up your

life and the lives of others in a big way if you let the drinking take over. And I guess I just decided one day that I wanted to be in more control than that, that I wanted to be healthy, live a long time, not ruin my life or anybody else's. I guess I 'got it' that nobody sets out to get addicted, but lots of people get that way anyway.

"After that, there was this growing level of disgust in me. Like, why are these people at

the parties I go to doing this to themselves? Seems like it's the only way they know how to fit in or have fun. And I've seen and heard enough about people throwing up or passing out or ending up with people they didn't want to be with or having to drink to get up the courage to do what they don't want to do anyway, and it's . . . well, really sad, I think. And I don't want any of it. Besides that, more and more of my friends are choosing not to drink, so that makes it easier.

"I used to be afraid of being singled out, but now I kind of like it. I let the negative comments roll. But it feels real good when someone knows they can always rely on me to drive because I'll always be able to see the road."

1. In what sense has Colleen "overcome the odds"?
2. What factors contributed to her decision not to drink?
3. What was her fear when she first decided to become a nondrinker?
4. What would Colleen probably do if she were at a party and her friends pressured her to drink and wouldn't take no for an answer?

Additional Information

Posting No-Alcohol House Rules. Tell students that one way to get the message across to guests that you don't allow alcohol at parties is to post a House No-Drinking Policy. Written out in bold letters and bright colors, the message can be posted all over the house on the night of a party. It might state policies such as these:

- Alcohol will not be served.
- There are plenty of great nonalcoholic drinks available.
- The host will not let anyone who uses alcohol or other drugs stay.
- The host will make sure that anyone who does come drunk will not be allowed to stay, but will also not be allowed to drive himself or herself home.
- This policy is because we care about you.

Is Advertising Effective?

Advertisers spend over $1 billion a year promoting alcoholic beverages. They want to paint an image of alcohol as an aid in successful and problem-free relationships, working situations, and recreational opportunities. Advertisers would not spend that kind of money if the ads did not accomplish their purpose.

It is rare to see a sporting event these days that is not sponsored in part by a liquor or beer company. Car races, boat races, and tennis events are just a few examples.

The brand names of alcohol are in abundance on college campuses where basketball and football scoreboards are sometimes donated to a school just to make the name of the company or product visible.

One of the most effective advertising gimmicks is having the consumer buy products with the name of the company on them. T-shirts and hats are examples of this type of promotion. By wearing the product, a person actually provides free advertising for the company.

You would probably have great difficulty remembering any advertising messages against drinking. While there are some, most are not nearly as appealing as the pro-drinking ads sponsored by the producers of alcoholic products. You need to learn to differentiate the facts from the implied messages in the ads.

You and Your Decisions about Drinking

Drinking alcohol in any form has no place in your life. It is unhealthy, unsafe, and in most places, illegal. As you apply your decision-making skills to the question of drinking or not drinking, you will see that the negative consequences far outweigh any positive benefits. You can live a fun-filled, active, and productive life without drinking alcohol.

CONFLICT RESOLUTION

While fewer teens are trying illegal drugs these days, nine out of ten say they've tried alcohol. The difference is due mostly to positive messages about alcohol in advertising. Many of these messages are aimed directly at young people. There's clearly a conflict between what's good for the alcohol industry and what's good for teens.

Make up a public service announcement for television that shows the risks of alcohol use by teens.

- Select students to interview college students about the role that drinking played during their high school years. Also, ask the interviewers to survey the students about the kinds of pressures to drink that they face at the college level. Have interviewers report their results to the class.
- Ask for volunteers to keep a journal about their experiences with alcohol (such as: dealing with peer pressure to drink, making decisions about drinking, observing friends and adults choosing to drink or not to drink, etc.) Assure them that their journals will stay in their possession and will not be turned in as an assignment.

Close

Ask students to state the most important concepts learned in the lesson.

DID YOU KNOW?

- A recent government report states that 10.6 million U.S. teens drink, 8 million drink weekly, and 500,000 have weekly binges.
- The same report says that 25 percent of teens drink because they feel bored, 25 percent use alcohol to get high, 41 percent because they are upset, and 31 percent because they feel lonely.
- All 50 states now prohibit the sale of alcohol to anyone younger than age 21.

LESSON 2 REVIEW

Reviewing Facts and Vocabulary

1. Identify four reasons young people choose not to drink.
2. What facts make drinking a special problem for teenagers?
3. What does *alcohol-impaired driving* mean?

Thinking Critically

4. **Analysis.** Describe three ways that alcohol is costly to our society.
5. **Analysis.** Select a current magazine and count the number of ads for alcohol products.

Select one ad and list the number of facts stated. What are the implied messages? Which message is the strongest? Why do you think purely factual ads are not used?

Applying Health Knowledge

6. How might you react in a healthy way at a party where most people are drinking beer and wine coolers?
7. What might you say to a younger brother or sister you caught drinking beer with friends after school one day?

Answers to Lesson 2 Review

1. See pages 464 to 465.
2. Problem drinkers experience difficulties with family, friends, school, and police. Drinking is unhealthy, unsafe, and, in most places, illegal.
3. Driving under the influence of alcohol.
4. Answers will vary. See page 464.
5. Answers will vary but implied messages may be that drinking is fun, glamorous, sexy, popular, friendly.
6. Answers will vary. Possible answers: Choose a nonalcoholic drink, keep busy with an activity, leave the party.
7. Answers will vary. Possible answer: Get him or her alone and discuss the problems and risks of drinking alcohol.

Focus

Lesson Objectives

After studying this lesson, students should be able to:

- explain what is meant by fetal alcohol syndrome
- describe the effects of drinking and driving
- explain what is meant by blood alcohol concentration
- list the costs of DWIs
- identify efforts to reduce DWIs
- describe the three stages of alcoholism

Bellringer

Write the following on the chalkboard for students to work on while attendance is being taken: *Discuss in writing why the boisterous drunk is no longer acceptable.*

Introducing the Lesson

Explain to students that attitudes about alcohol have changed dramatically over the past few years. Educational efforts have helped people better understand alcoholism as a disease. The grim statistics of deaths on the road due to DWI and the effects of fetal alcohol syndrome have awakened people to the risks and responsibilities of drinking. Refer to the Bellringer, and ask volunteers to share their written responses.

DID YOU KNOW?

- Each day in hospitals, 30 to 40 percent of patients have medical problems related to alcohol.
- About one-fifth of the total spent on hospital care is alcohol-related.
- It has been estimated that 65 percent of all domestic violence is related to the use and abuse of alcohol.
- Alcoholism is estimated to reduce one's life span by 12 years.
- Alcoholism has been linked to osteoporosis (bone loss) in men.

ALCOHOL: A SERIOUS PROBLEM

LESSON 3 FOCUS

TERMS TO USE
- Fetal alcohol syndrome (FAS)
- Blood alcohol concentration (BAC)
- Alcoholism

CONCEPTS TO LEARN
- The use of alcohol can lead to birth defects, driving accidents, and alcoholism.
- Blood alcohol concentration is affected by several factors.

ATTITUDES AND BEHAVIORS TO EVALUATE
- Self-Inventory, page 474.
- Building Decision-Making Skills, page 475.

For some people alcohol becomes a serious problem—one that changes their lives and the lives of those around them. In some cases the use of alcohol becomes life threatening.

Alcohol and Pregnancy

In recent years scientists have found a link between heavy drinking by pregnant females and birth defects in the babies born to them. This condition, which involves both mental and physical abnormalities, is called **fetal alcohol syndrome (FAS).** FAS is a leading cause of mental retardation in the United States.

FAS babies tend to be shorter and lighter in weight than normal, with impaired speech, cleft palate, general weakness, slow body growth, facial abnormalities, poor coordination, and heart defects.

Mental retardation, poor attention span, nervousness, and hyperactivity are also common in children born with FAS. All of these symptoms are present in some babies, while others may be affected by only some of the problems.

The alcohol the pregnant female drinks moves into her blood, then across the placenta through the umbilical cord into the blood of the unborn child. Any effects felt by the pregnant female as a result of drinking are also experienced by the unborn child.

Unfortunately, the unborn child cannot get rid of the alcohol as an adult can, so the alcohol remains in the baby's body much longer. If the pregnant female drinks three to four times a week, chances are the infant never rids itself of alcohol.

FAS is completely preventable. It does not occur in babies of nondrinking pregnant females. The public is becoming increasingly aware of the dangers of FAS. Each female, knowing the risks, must make the choice—to drink or not to drink.

In 1988 the United States Senate passed a bill that, in part, approved a label that warned of drinking during pregnancy. The warning reads: "According to the Surgeon General, women should not drink alcoholic beverages during pregnancy because of the risk of birth defects."

Drinking and Driving

The most serious and widespread problem involving drinking and the law is that of alcohol-impaired driving. This has become a serious problem for Americans of all ages. It is a problem for the nondrinker as well as the drinker—the nondrinker can easily become a victim in a crash caused by an alcohol-impaired driver.

For teenagers, alcohol-impaired driving is a particular problem. Alcohol-impaired driving is the leading cause of death among teenagers aged 15 to 19.

Resources for Lesson 3

- **Guided Reading** Act 62
- **Health Labs** Act 23
- **Decision-Making** Act 23
- **Lesson 2 Quiz**
- **Reteaching** Act 62
- **Chapter 23 Test**

ABC News InterActive Videodiscs

Drugs and Substance Abuse, Side 2
Ch 4 Drugs and the Family

Alcohol, Side 1
Ch 8 Alcohol and Pregnancy

This woman is protecting her unborn child by not drinking any alcohol.

What Effect Does Alcohol Have on Driving?

Driving experts and medical researchers have tested the effects of alcohol on driving and have found that drinking at any level

- reduces the ability to judge distances, speeds, and turns.
- reduces the ability to judge accurately one's own capabilities and limitations.
- increases the tendency to take risks.
- slows reflexes.
- adds to forgetfulness of taking precautions such as using signals when turning.
- reduces the ability to concentrate.

For these reasons, only one who has had no alcohol to drink should drive. Others should always refuse rides with anyone who has had any alcohol to drink.

DWI (driving while intoxicated) and *DUI (driving under the influence)* are two terms for the same situation. Driving while intoxicated means that the person's blood alcohol concentration level exceeds the limit allowed by law in that state.

KEEPING FIT

Drinking and Its Consequences

Increasingly, underage drinking and drinking and driving are being targeted as major social problems. Consider these facts:
- Every state now has a minimum drinking age of 21.
- In more and more states, drivers' licenses are revoked, or taken away, when drinking and driving violations occur.
- Sobriety checkpoints are becoming more numerous, as are the fines for drinking and driving violations.

- Fines are high and going up. According to a Gallup poll of almost 10,000 people, the average fine for a DUI or DWI is now more than $1,300.

ALCOHOL: A SERIOUS PROBLEM **469**

Overcoming Misconceptions

Myths. Using alcohol only on weekends is harmless. Drinking alcohol through a straw "filters out" the alcoholic content of a beverage. **Fact.** These myths are false, and the people who spread them are trying to delude themselves and others. **Myth.** People suffering from alcoholism don't need help to stop drinking. They can stop drinking on their own if they want to.

Fact. Alcoholics depend on alcohol to function physically and mentally; they are physically addicted. **Myth.** Only bums and street people are alcoholics. **Fact.** Alcoholism affects people of all social and economic backgrounds and of all ages. It can happen to anyone. In fact, many alcoholics are well-accepted members of their communities.

BAC	Approximate Alcohol Consumed in a Two-Hour Period	Effect on a 100-Pound Person
0.05%	1 to 2 ounces liquor 1 to 2 12-ounce beers	Mild impairment in reaction time and judgment, careless behavior, some loss of coordination and self-control.
0.1%	3 to 4 ounces liquor 3 to 4 12-ounce beers	Substantial impairment in muscle coordination, perception, and judgment. Emotions and inhibitions are relaxed.
0.2%	5 to 6 ounces liquor 5 to 6 12-ounce beers	Increased loss of self-control, difficulty in thinking clearly, impaired memory. Unpredictable emotional behavior. Entire motor area of brain is depressed. Slurred speech, staggered walk. Simple tasks, like buttoning a coat, become difficult to impossible.
0.3%	7 to 8 ounces liquor 7 to 8 12-ounce beers	Body thrown into state of confusion, sense organs seriously affected—double vision, hearing impaired, distances difficult or impossible to judge—may be in a stupor, walking is difficult and dangerous to person.
0.4%	9 to 10 ounces liquor 9 to 10 12-ounce beers	Brain can barely function, nervous system shuts down, may experience vomiting or uncontrolled urination, unable to move, may slip into unconscious state.
0.5%	More than 10 ounces liquor More than 10 12-ounce beers	Coma, brain unable to control body temperature—respiratory failure due to paralysis of breathing centers of brain. When this occurs, death will soon follow.

The Blood Alcohol Concentration

The amount of alcohol in a person's blood is expressed by a percentage called the **blood alcohol concentration (BAC).**

The chart on this page describes the effects of alcohol on the body at various BACs. This is based on a 100-pound (45-kg) person and the amount of alcohol consumed over a 2-hour period. Factors that affect the amount of alcohol in a person's blood include the following:

- gender
- the person's metabolism
- the amount of alcohol, not the number of drinks, a person consumes
- whether or not the person eats before or while drinking
- how much the person weighs
- how much time elapses after drinking stops or between drinks

Each state has determined the legal acceptable limit of alcohol in the blood. In most states, driving while intoxicated is defined as having a 0.1 percent BAC.

The Costs of DWIs

There are many problems that are created for the individual who is stopped for alcohol-impaired driving. Here are some:

Teacher Margin Notes

L1 DISCUSSION. Talk about the reasons someone might drive after drinking despite all the information and publicity about the dangers involved. Have students suggest ways to handle a situation in which someone they know insists on driving after drinking.

L1 CLASS ACTIVITY. Drinking while driving has become a national health and social problem. Thousands of innocent people die or are injured each year because of such irresponsible behavior. Ask students to complete the sentence: Even though I might not be a driver, I can work to reduce this tragic waste of lives by. . . .

L1 SPEAKER. Invite an attorney (or law student) to speak to the class about current laws regarding DWI. Ask them to discuss fees that might be involved in representing an individual who has been charged with driving while intoxicated.

L1 DISCUSSION. Ask students what the role of a "designated driver" is.

L2 DISCUSSION. Ask what the individual's responsibility is in not riding with someone who has had too much to drink. What can a person say or do to be assertive in this situation?

L1 CLASS ACTIVITY. Guide students in brainstorming ways for adults who drink to keep their blood alcohol concentration low during parties at which alcohol is served.

L1 DISCUSSION. Ask students what suggestions they would give someone whose date has had too much to drink.

L1 DISCUSSION. Ask why it is difficult for most people to admit they have a drinking problem.

L2 DISCUSSION. What are the differences between problem drinking being the cause and problem drinking being the symptom of other problems?

L1 DISCUSSION. Ask students what some of the behaviors of alcoholics are. In what way does each of the behaviors affect the others?

Overcoming Misconceptions

Myth. Alcoholics can safely drink socially if they limit their intake to no more than two drinks during a social event. **Fact.** The only way to recover from alcoholism is to stop drinking. Abstinence from alcohol is the only alternative. Recovering alcoholics should avoid drinking situations whenever possible. New activities and interests may be necessary. **Myth.** Recovering alcoholics who have a relapse probably will never stop drinking. **Fact.** Recovery takes time. Do not assume that once an alcoholic is committed to recovery, he or she will never have a relapse. A relapse does not mean treatment has failed. In fact, sometimes a relapse convinces the alcoholic that abstinence is the only alternative.

- immediate confiscation of driver's license
- arrest and a trip to jail
- court appearance
- fine
- possible suspension of driver's license
- possible mandatory jail sentence
- cost of bail to get out of jail
- higher insurance rates
- possible lawsuits

Efforts to Reduce DWIs

Because of the seriousness and extent of the alcohol-impaired driving problem, several efforts are being made to reduce it. Mandatory chemical tests for blood, breath, or urine exist in some states. Refusal to submit to a test can mean automatic suspension of one's driver's license.

Organizations such as MADD, Mothers Against Drunk Driving, and SADD, Students Against Driving Drunk, have been powerful forces in making the public and state legislators aware of the problem. Stricter enforcement of existing laws, tougher new laws, banning of open containers in cars, and abolishment of drive-through liquor stores are a few of the contributions that these organizations have made to the reduction of the problem of alcohol-impaired driving.

Alcoholism

Alcoholism, or addiction to alcohol, is a physical and psychological dependence on alcohol. It is a disease that may have a hereditary link. People with alcoholism are called alcoholics. They may have one or a combination of these behaviors:

- They cannot keep from drinking.
- They cannot manage tension without drinking.
- They cannot stop drinking once they have started.

Stages of Alcoholism

There are three clearly defined stages of alcoholism. They happen over a period of time. The time span can be long or short, depending on the individual and the age at which he or she started drinking.

Stage One. Alcoholism typically begins with social drinking, often to relax or to relieve stress. Gradually, this kind of drinking becomes necessary to manage stress. A physical and psychological dependency on alcohol develops. The person begins to drink and to become intoxicated regularly. The drinker cannot remember with whom he or she was drinking or what was said or done after each drinking episode. Often at this stage the drinker makes excuses and tries to rationalize his or her drinking behavior.

Stage Two. Gradually, the person reaches a point where he or she cannot stop drinking. Physical and mental problems become evident. At this stage of the disease, defensive behavior is evident. The drinker denies

Alcohol-impaired driving is the leading cause of death among teens.

HELP WANTED

Rehabilitation Counselor

If you think alcoholics should be locked up, you are NOT the person we are seeking. However, if you are committed to the disease model of substance abuse, you might be the one we are looking for. We need a person with a large measure of compassion and an equally large strength for providing direction during recovery. Your specific educational background is not as important as your experience and these personal qualities. You must be able to care, communicate, and confront. You will also need to be good at organizing programs and accomplishing many details at seemingly the same time.

For more information contact:
Council on Rehabilitation Education
185 N. Wabash Street
Room 1617
Chicago, IL 60601

ALCOHOL: A SERIOUS PROBLEM **471**

Across the Curriculum

Language Arts. Have students write a short story from the viewpoint of a fetus experiencing alcohol abuse. Have them include information about the physical, mental, and behavioral defects the fetus is likely to experience.

Science. Have students use library resources to research current surgical procedures to correct cleft palate. Ask them to share their

findings with the class.

Language Arts. Have groups of students write short scenarios in which group members discuss the behavior of a fictional person who they suspect is an alcoholic. Descriptions should reveal the symptoms of a person at one of the three stages of alcoholism. Have groups perform their scenes before the class.

collect newspaper and magazine
articles about accidents and
deaths caused by people with a
high blood alcohol concentration.
Have them circle the BAC, if identified in the article, and discuss
the effects listed in the chart on
page 470.

**L3 COMMUNITY INVOLVE-
MENT.** Have students find out
what your state considers acceptable and unacceptable blood alcohol concentrations. What kinds of
tests are administered to determine these levels? In your state,
what are the legal consequences
of being caught with higher
than acceptable alcohol levels?
The state police department
can provide students with this
information.

L2 COMMUNITY INVOLVE-
Ask for volunteers to
interview a local police officer to
determine what efforts have been
made to crack down on DWI
offenders. Have the efforts
worked? What age-group presents
the most serious problem? What
can the teenage driving population do to help fight this problem?
Request that students share the
findings of their interview with
the rest of the class.

L3 WRITING. Have students
write case studies showing the
progression of a person from
stage one to stage two and, finally,
to stage three of alcoholism.

L3 RESEARCH. Have students
research what is involved in the
detoxification of an alcoholic. Ask
them to share their research with
the class.

**L1 USING THE LESSON
RESOURCES.** For additional student activities, refer to the lesson
resources on page 468.

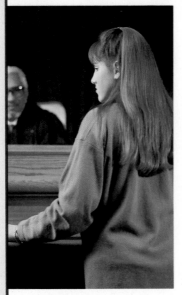

*Teens who drink and drive may
have their driver's licenses suspended, pay heavy fines, and
even go to jail.*

or tries to hide the problem. The body has developed a tolerance, and
more alcohol is necessary. Drinking becomes the central event in the
person's life. Performance on the job, at school, or at home decreases.
Frequent absences from school, work, or other commitments occur.

Alcohol, Advertising, and Adolescents

Recent polls show that up
to 73 percent of the American
public thinks that there is a
direct link between alcohol
advertising and teen drinking.
Companies that produce and
distribute alcoholic beverages
claim there is no connection.

**Analyzing Different
Viewpoints**

ONE VIEW. Some people
claim that the constitutional
rights to freedom of speech
and freedom of the press
should allow people to advertise their products how and
where they want as long as
they meet federal regulations
and are willing to pay for the
advertising.

A SECOND VIEW. Others
argue that people will drink if
they want to, regardless of
whether or not beer commercials are shown on television
or liquor ads fill billboards.
They point out that even
though cigarette and liquor
commercials have been
banned from TV, people continue to use these products,
which are now advertised on
billboards and in some magazines rather than on TV
screens.

A THIRD VIEW. Others,
alarmed by the vast number
of teens who drink, call for
strong measures, including
pulling all beer advertising
from television, particularly
during sporting events that
draw vast numbers of teen
viewers.

A FOURTH VIEW. United
States Surgeon General
Antonia Novello believes that
many alcohol advertisements
are geared specifically to
teens, that they try to sell a
life-style message that is inaccurate and unhealthy, and
that such messages need to be
regulated more fully. She
points out that many of the
industry guidelines, which are
voluntary, are not followed.
She also charges that the television networks have relaxed
their advertising standards.
She says it is very confusing
for teens when the law says
not to drink while advertisers
promote it.

Exploring Your Views

1. Do you believe alcohol
   products should be advertised on television? On
   billboards? Why or why
   not?
2. Does it seem to you that
   teens are targeted by alcohol producers and distributors? If so, how?
3. Do you ever feel caught in
   the middle of the
   drink/don't drink messages
   that the media send your
   way?
4. What do you think would
   be the most effective
   means of getting teens
   who drink to understand
   the dangers of drinking
   and to choose a healthy
   life-style that is alcohol-
   free?

472 CHAPTER 23 ALCOHOL

Overcoming Misconceptions

Myth. Treatment programs for alcoholics
cost more than they are worth. **Fact.** Successfully treating alcohol problems costs 10
times less than the current cost of alcohol
problems to society. **Myth.** Alcoholics seldom use other drugs. **Fact.** Alcohol users
frequently use other drugs. Close to half of
Alcoholics Anonymous members reported
addiction to other drugs as well as alcohol.

Also, over 90 percent of all alcoholics are
heavy cigarette smokers. **Myth.** The effects
of alcohol are identical among males and
females and among teens and adults. **Fact.**
Females become intoxicated faster and stay
that way longer than males of the same
size. Also, alcohol has a stronger effect on
teens and older people than on young
adults and middle-aged adults.

Stage Three. In the final and worst stage of the disease, the drinking is visible. It can no longer be denied, and it is also uncontrolled. Alcohol becomes a constant companion. The alcoholic becomes aggressive and is isolated from friends and family. Malnutrition becomes a problem because the drinker overlooks his or her need for nutritional foods. The body is addicted to the drug. If the alcoholic stopped drinking, he or she would experience the withdrawal symptoms associated with alcoholism, called delirium tremens (DTs). They consist of hot and cold flashes, tremors, nightmares, hallucinations, and fear of people and animals. DTs need prompt medical attention.

Although alcoholism cannot be cured, it definitely can be treated and arrested. As many as two-thirds of all alcoholics recover with proper treatment. The goal of the various programs to treat alcoholism is to stop or control the intake of alcohol. Several sources are available to help people who have a drinking problem. Help is also available for the families and friends of people who have a drinking problem. These are discussed in Chapter 25.

The heavy use of alcohol is often a cause of serious family problems. Alcohol is often a factor in spousal abuse, child abuse, and abuse of the elderly.

ALCOHOLISM AND THE FAMILY

One of the most tragic results of having an alcoholic in the family is what happens to the other family members. Here are some of the facts:
- There is prevalence of alcohol dependency in spousal and child abuse.
- Children of alcoholics are at greater risk of developing alcohol dependency than children of nonalcoholics.
- One in every eight Americans is the child of an alcoholic.
- Children of alcoholics exhibit symptoms of depression and anxiety more than children of nonalcoholics.
- Alcohol dependency and alcohol abuse are major factors in marital separation and divorce.

LESSON 3 REVIEW

Reviewing Facts and Vocabulary

1. What does *BAC* stand for, and what does it mean?
2. List three effects drinking alcohol at any level has on driving.
3. What are six factors that affect the amount of alcohol in a person's blood?

Thinking Critically

4. **Synthesis.** Explain why alcoholism is a problem for both drinkers and nondrinkers.
5. **Evaluation.** Do you think the Surgeon General and the United States Senate were justified in passing the bill to require a warning label on alcoholic beverages? Defend your answer.

Applying Health Knowledge

6. Interview five people. Ask each, "What is the cause of alcoholism?" Share your findings with the class. What do people believe about alcoholism?
7. Write a 30-second radio announcement warning of the dangers of fetal alcohol syndrome.

Answers to Lesson 3 Review

1. Blood alcohol concentration—the amount of alcohol in one's blood expressed by a percentage.
2. Answers will vary. Accept three effects from the bulleted list in "What Effect Does Alcohol Have on Driving?" on page 469.
3. See page 470.
4. Answers will vary. Possible answers: Family disharmony, damage done by drunk drivers, damage known as fetal alcohol syndrome.
5. Answers will vary but should be supported logically.
6. Answers will vary.
7. See page 468.

Check for Understanding
- Assign and discuss the lesson review. Have LD students focus on questions 1, 2, and 3.
- Assign and discuss the chapter review.

Evaluate
- Administer, grade, and discuss the *Lesson 3 Quiz.*
- Administer, grade, and discuss the *Chapter 23 Test.*
- Refer to the Performance Assessment strategy for this chapter. See pages T 23 to T 25.

Reteach
- Have students describe in their own words the symptoms of the three stages of alcoholism. Also, ask them to list five of the tragic results of having an alcoholic in the family.
- Ask students to complete *Reteaching Activity 62.*

Enrich
- Ask students to locate statistics about the incidence of fetal alcohol syndrome among live births in the U.S. Have them find out what recommendations the American Medical Association makes about the use of alcohol during pregnancy.
- Have students research the scientific explanation for a hangover. Ask them to discuss their findings, explaining the body's reaction to an excess of alcohol.
- Ask students to complete *Enrichment Activity 23.*

Close

Ask students to state the most important concepts learned in the lesson.

Helping Students Improve Their Health

Reinforcing Vocabulary

- **Designated driver.** An individual who does not drink alcohol so that he or she can safely drive home other individuals who have been consuming alcoholic beverages.

Teaching Strategies

L1 EXPLANATION. Students frequently argue that the legal drinking age is unfair. For example, students often argue that if an individual is old enough to vote or go to war, then that individual should be old enough to decide whether he or she drinks alcoholic beverages. It is important to help students understand that there is a very sound reason for picking the age of 21 as being the legal age to purchase and consume alcoholic beverages. Due to physiological development, persons younger than the age of 21 risk the progression of alcoholism much more so than if they were 21 years old or older. Teenagers simply cannot physically handle alcohol.

L1 DISCUSSION. Have students discuss the repercussions from drinking alcohol and driving an automobile. One factor is loss of potential. Cite examples, such as that of Bruce Kimble, the Olympic diver, who was imprisoned as a result of a drunk-driving manslaughter conviction.

L1 CLASS ACTIVITY. Arrange for students to visit an alcohol rehabilitation center for teenagers. Have students learn about the disease progression of alcoholism and how this progression is especially accelerated in teenagers.

L1 SPEAKER. Invite a police officer to come to your class to speak to students about the legal repercussions of consuming alcoholic beverages when one is under the age of 21.

Self-Inventory

Are You in Trouble with Alcohol?

HOW DO YOU RATE?

Number a sheet of paper from 1 through 20. Read each item below and respond by writing *yes* or *no* for each item. Total the number of *yes* responses; then proceed to the next section.

1. Have you ever had a drink containing alcohol?
2. Have you ever had more than one drink in a two-hour period?
3. Do you drink on a regular basis (every weekend, every day, at all parties, and so on)?
4. Do you drink to escape problems?
5. Do you drink to feel more comfortable with people?
6. When you get angry at other people, do you immediately think of taking a drink?
7. Have other people commented on your drinking?
8. Do you get angry when other people bring up your drinking or when one of your classes deals with alcohol or other drug use?
9. Do you gulp drinks or drink until the supply is gone?
10. Do you find it difficult to say no to your friends when they encourage you to drink?
11. Do you hide your use of alcohol from others?
12. Do you lose time from school or work because of your drinking?
13. Are your grades suffering because of your drinking?

14. Have you lost or changed friends since you started drinking?
15. Do you choose your friends because they drink?
16. Do you avoid situations and places where you know there will be no alcohol?
17. Is there alcoholism in your family?
18. Have you ever ridden in a car driven by someone who had been drinking?
19. Have you ever driven a car or operated other equipment after having had one or more drinks?
20. Have you ever turned down the opportunity to be the designated driver because you wanted to drink instead?

HOW DID YOU SCORE?

Give yourself 1 point for every *yes* response. Find your total and read below to see how you scored. Then proceed to the next section.

0 to 2
You do not have a problem with alcohol.

3 to 5
You could be on your way to a problem with alcohol.

6 to 8
Chances are you already have a problem with alcohol.

9 or more
You have a serious problem with alcohol and should get help now.

WHAT ARE YOUR GOALS?

If you do not drink at all, keep up the good work! Try using the following goal-setting process to help you stay alcohol-free:

1. The steps I can take to help me stay alcohol-free include ____.
2. To help another friend stay or get alcohol-free, I plan to ____.

If you ever drink and drive or ride with a driver who has been drinking, begin the following goal-setting process:

3. The steps I need to take to refuse rides with drinking drivers include ____.
4. The steps I need to take to stop driving after drinking include ____.
5. My timetable for making these changes is ____.

If you drink at all, use the following goal-setting process:

6. The way that I will stop drinking and avoid potential problems will be to ____.
7. My timetable for stopping drinking will be ____.
8. The people or program I will turn to for suggestions and support in stopping drinking include ____.
9. My rewards for stopping drinking will be ____.

Meeting Students' Needs

For students who score 0 to 2. Encourage students to join Students Against Driving Drunk, Youth to Youth, or other organizations that stress responsible, drug-free behavior.

For students who score 3 to 5. Encourage students to conduct a drug-free symposium in order to educate other students about the drug-free way of life.

For students who score 6 to 8. Encourage students to talk to a responsible adult about their drinking behavior.

For students who score 9 or more. Stress to these individuals that help is available. Consult specific treatment centers or talk to the school nurse, guidance counselor, or your school's drug education coordinator.

Building Decision-Making Skills

A llison's parents have gone away for the weekend, leaving her at home with specific instructions not to have anyone in the house. Allison invited her boyfriend and another couple over anyhow, but her boyfriend told some of his friends he was going to Allison's and the word "party at Allison's" got around quickly. She heard kids talking but didn't try to discourage it, because she thought she could control it and didn't want to be "uncool." Over 100 people, including some strangers, showed up, complete with beer and loud music. Things are getting rowdy, and some neighbors are at the door asking what's going on. What should Allison do? Some of her choices include:

A. Tell the neighbors she didn't invite anyone and ask them to help clear everyone out, knowing that some kids will probably resist forcefully.

B. Call the police.

C. Get her boyfriend and his friends to clear everyone out.

D. Let it go until someone else calls the police.

WHAT DO YOU THINK?

1. **Situation.** More than one decision needs to be made. What are they?

2. **Choices.** Think about what Allison should say to the neighbors. What are her choices?

3. **Consequences.** What are the advantages of each choice?

4. **Consequences.** What are the disadvantages of each choice?

5. **Consequences.** How are her parents probably going to react?

6. **Consequences.** What is the worst possible outcome of this situation?

7. **Decision.** What should Allison say to the neighbors?

8. **Decision.** What should Allison do after she talks to the neighbors?

9. **Evaluation.** Have you ever been in a similar situation? If so, what did you learn from it that you could apply to this situation? What advice would you give Allison?

H eidi and Kim, who are sophomores, agreed to go to the basketball game in the next town with two seniors. Kim had been trying to get her date to ask her out for weeks and was really excited about the evening. Since her parents weren't so excited, Heidi and Kim asked the guys to pick them up at the mall. After they got out of town, the guys opened beers for everyone from a fresh twelve-pack. The guys had smelled of beer when they first got into the car but said they hadn't been drinking. What should Heidi and Kim do?

A. Ask to be let out at a pay phone and call their parents to come for them.

B. Take the beer away and not let the guys drink any more.

C. Find a new way home when they get to the game.

D. Turn down the beer, knowing the guys will probably drink it if they don't.

E. Offer to drive, since Heidi just got her license. In fact, insist on it.

WHAT DO YOU THINK?

10. **Situation.** What risks are involved in this situation?

11. **Choices.** What other choices do Heidi and Kim have?

12. **Consequences.** What are the advantages of each choice?

13. **Consequences.** What are the disadvantages of each choice?

14. **Consequences.** What would Heidi's and Kim's parents probably want them to do?

15. **Decisions.** How do you think Heidi and Kim should handle this situation?

16. **Evaluation.** Have you ever been in a similar situation? How did you handle it? Would you handle it any differently today? Explain your answer.

ALCOHOL: A SERIOUS PROBLEM **475**

Helping Students Improve Their Health

Building Decision-Making Skills

Teaching Strategies

L1 CLASS ACTIVITY. Some teenagers may have found themselves in situations similar to Allison's. Have students discuss what consequences may exist for students who throw parties where alcohol is served to minors. How could Allison have avoided this situation?

L1 CLASS ACTIVITY. Have students role-play the part of Heidi and Kim as they discuss with their dates the concern that they have for their driving while under the influence of alcohol. What are the possible consequences for Kim and Heidi if they choose to stay in the car with their senior dates?

L2 DISCUSSION. Have students debate a situation in which a woman, eight months pregnant, orders an alcoholic beverage while in a restaurant. The waiter, shocked at the woman's drink order, clarifies for the woman that the drink that she has ordered contains alcohol. The woman is now getting upset and begins demanding her drink. Should the waiter be able to legally refuse to serve the woman alcohol? Should the woman have the right to decide for herself whether or not she can drink an alcoholic beverage while pregnant?

DID YOU KNOW?

■ Today's teens are almost as conventional as adults when it comes to using drugs: they're much more likely to drink alcohol or smoke cigarettes than take illegal drugs, and they view drugs in general with increasing disfavor.

Discussing the Answers

Situation 1. Allison has disobeyed her parents' directive and has chosen to invite a few people over while her parents are away. Given the situation, Allison has only one reasonable decision to make at this time. The best resolve in this situation would be for Allison to tell everyone to go home. If people refuse to leave, Allison should call the police.

Situation 2. The only responsible and safe choice for Kim and Heidi, at this time, would be to get out of the car and call their parents to pick them up. Kim and Heidi may be in trouble for lying to their parents, but getting into trouble is better than ending up dead.

Answers to Chapter 23 Review

Using Health Terms

1. Empty calories
2. Cirrhosis
3. Fermentation
4. Proof
5. Ethanol or ethyl alcohol
6. Oxidation
7. Multiplier effect
8. Alcohol-impaired driving
9. Driving while intoxicated or driving under the influence of alcohol
10. Fetal alcohol syndrome
11. Alcoholism
12. Alcoholics

Building Academic Skills

13. Answers will vary.
14. Answers will vary.

Recalling the Facts

15. Because of its effect on the body.
16. Withdrawal from alcohol when a dependence has developed.
17. Depresses the activity of the brain, the liver oxidizes the alcohol, blood vessels dilate, causes the kidneys to produce more urine, increases the flow of gastric juices from the stomach lining.
18. Tolerance, dependence, liver problems, brain damage.
19. Alcohol and other drugs or medicines will interact (multiplier effect), causing impairment of physical and mental abilities or possibly even death.
20. Lost work, accidents, health-care costs and treatments, research, education, and criminal justice.
21. By example—if a teenager sees his or her parent(s) using alcohol to help manage stress, the young person may, too.
22. Accidental death, suicide, family violence, marital separation and divorce.
23. Low birth weight and length, speech impairments, cleft palate, general weakness, slow body growth, facial abnormalities, poor coordination, heart defects.

Using Health Terms

On a separate sheet of paper, write the term that best matches each definition given below.

LESSON 1

1. Phrase that means food or beverage that has no nutritional value.
2. Condition in which liver tissue is replaced by scar tissue.
3. Chemical process in which yeast acting on sugar and starches produces alcohol.
4. An indicator of the concentration of alcohol in a beverage.
5. Type of alcohol in beer, wine, and liquor.
6. The process of changing alcohol to water, carbon dioxide, and energy.
7. The effect of mixing other drugs or medicines with alcohol.

LESSON 2

8. Driving under the influence of alcohol.

LESSON 3

9. A person who is driving and whose BAC exceeds the legal limit.
10. Birth defects caused by the consumption of alcohol by a pregnant female.
11. Addiction to alcohol.
12. People who have alcoholism.

Building Academic Skills

LESSON 2

13. **Math.** In 1990 alcoholism and problem drinking cost the economy over $136 billion. Do some research to find the most current population figure for the United States. Estimate and then calculate how much each U.S. citizen would have to pay to cover that expense. What percentage would each U.S. citizen be paying? How much would your entire family have to pay?

LESSON 3

14. **Reading.** Gather several ads for alcoholic beverages and brochures against drinking. Identify the stated and implied messages. Summarize your findings in writing.

Recalling the Facts

LESSON 1

15. Why is alcohol considered a drug?
16. What are the following symptoms an indication of: jumpiness, sleeplessness, sweating, poor appetite, tremors, convulsions, and hallucinations?
17. What are five immediate effects of alcohol?
18. What are four long-term effects of alcohol?
19. Why is it dangerous to drink after taking medicines?

LESSON 2

20. In what ways does alcoholism cost the economy every year?
21. How might family influence one's drinking behavior?
22. List four difficulties that problem drinkers may face.

LESSON 3

23. What are some of the problems children with fetal alcohol syndrome may encounter?
24. Describe the three stages of alcoholism a person may go through.
25. What are some symptoms of alcohol withdrawal?
26. Which of the following statements is true?
    a. Alcohol-impaired driving is the leading cause of death among 15- to 19-year-olds.
    b. Fetal alcohol syndrome is a leading cause of mental retardation in the United States.
    c. Driving under the influence of alcohol reduces one's ability to judge distances, speeds, and turns.
    d. Defensive behavior is common in the first stage of alcoholism.
    e. People in stage three of alcoholism suffer from DTs.
    f. Malnutrition becomes a problem in stage three of alcoholism.
27. Name at least five problems that someone stopped for alcohol-impaired driving may face.

24. See "Stages of Alcoholism" on pages 471 to 473.
25. Hot and cold flashes, tremors, nightmares, hallucinations, fear of people and animals.
26. A., B., C., E., F.
27. Answers will vary. Accept five of the following: Loss of driver's license, arrest and a trip to jail, court appearance, fine, possible suspension of driver's license, possible mandatory jail sentence, cost of bail to get out of jail, higher insurance rates, possible lawsuits.

Thinking Critically

28. Answers will vary. Possible answers: Decreased awareness could lead to frostbite; alcohol may make one sleepy or cause one to

REVIEW

Thinking Critically

LESSON 1

28. Synthesis. It is especially hazardous to use alcohol in cold climates. Give some reasons to support this statement.

29. Synthesis. List current slang terms that relate to alcohol or alcohol use. What can you infer about the role of alcohol in your environment from your list?

LESSON 2

30. Evaluation. Why do you suppose the average American drank less alcohol in 1991 than in 1980?

31. Evaluation. What responsibilities should people who sell alcohol to minors have?

LESSON 3

32. Synthesis. Penalties for drunk driving have become more severe. What reasons can you give for this trend?

33. Evaluation. Suppose you and a friend were on your way home from a football game and someone driving drunk hit you. Your friend was killed and you were badly hurt. How do you think you would feel toward the driver who hit you? What do you think should happen to that driver? How would you feel if you found out it was that driver's third DWI?

Making the Connection

LESSON 1

34. Music. Write a musical jingle encouraging students not to drink. Record the words and music.

LESSON 3

35. Language Arts. Interview a police officer in your community. What is being done to reduce the number of accidents caused by people who drive while intoxicated? Have the efforts worked? What age-group presents the most serious problem? How can teenage drivers help fight this problem? Summarize your interview in writing.

Applying Health Knowledge

LESSON 1

36. Look at the labels of medicines currently in your home. Which of these expressly state that alcohol should not be consumed while the medicine is in use?

LESSON 2

37. What are some ways a teenager can meet the needs to belong, to feel loved, and to be important without the use of alcohol?

38. Give examples to illustrate two situations that problem drinking has affected the economy.

LESSON 3

39. Find out what the legal acceptable limit of the blood alcohol concentration is in your state. How many 12-ounce beers is this for a 100-pound person? How many ounces of liquor is it?

40. Why do you think people who drink at parties try to get everyone else to drink also? What would you do in a situation in which your friends would not take no for an answer from you?

41. You are getting ready to leave a party. Your only way of getting home is with your friend who has had too much to drink. What would you do?

Beyond the Classroom

LESSON 2

42. Parental Involvement. Survey three popular magazines to determine which magazines have the most advertisements for alcohol. Determine the target market for each of the magazines. Discuss with your parents the conclusions that can be drawn from your survey.

LESSON 3

43. Further Study. Find out how MADD or SADD got started and what impact it has had.

become unconscious and freeze to death.
29. Answers will vary.
30. Answers will vary. Possible answers: Education; a more health-conscious society; less disposable income; a resurgence of traditional values.
31. Answers will vary.
32. Answers will vary. Possible answers: The influence of groups such as MADD and SADD; a reflection of societal awareness and demands for change.
33. Answers will vary.

Making the Connection

34. Musical jingles will vary.
35. Answers will vary.

Applying Health Knowledge

36. Answers will vary.
37. Answers will vary. Possible answers: Helping others, such as volunteering to read to or visit the elderly; joining clubs and sports teams; running for class officer; joining or organizing groups to fight drug and alcohol abuse.
38. Answers will vary. Possible answers: Lost work—hangovers, illness due to alcohol abuse; accidents—on-the-job accidents due to impaired judgment, auto accidents; health-care costs and treatments—free alcohol treatment centers, emergency room treatment because of alcohol-related injuries; research—for the causes of alcoholism, for better ways to treat the disease; education—campaigns to show the effects of alcohol abuse, public relations brochures for anti-alcohol programs; criminal justice costs—prosecution of drunk-driving charges, jail space occupied by those arrested on drunk-driving charges.
39. Answers will vary.
40. Answers will vary.
41. Answers will vary. Possible answers: Call your parents to come get you; call a cab; take a bus if it is available; take your friend's keys and drive your friend home and then yourself if you can.

Beyond the Classroom

42. Answers will vary.
43. Answers will vary.

Lesson Summaries

LESSON 1. The costs of using illegal drugs affect almost everyone, not just the people who use drugs, as cited by the increasing number of drug-related crimes and deaths and losses in productivity in the workplace. Drug use does nothing to help users deal with their problems, but instead introduces a host of other problems, including dependence, tolerance, withdrawal symptoms, and addiction.

LESSON 2. Psychoactive drugs affect the central nervous system and can result in mental and/or behavioral problems. Stimulants, depressants, and narcotics have medicinal value. Hallucinogens have no medicinal value. Each type of drug presents specific risks to the user's health.

LESSON 3. Common drugs, such as marijuana, inhalants, designer drugs, and steroids, have been determined to be dangerous. Each drug carries its own set of health risks ranging from lack of concentration and impaired judgment to severe damage to the body and even death.

Introducing the Chapter

Tell students that while alcohol abuse is the most prevalent drug abuse problem with young people, illegal drugs, or street drugs, also pose very serious problems. Tell them that after studying this chapter they will be able to explain the effects of various drugs and problems associated with their use. Have students write on file cards any questions they want answered. Collect the cards and, after discussing the chapter, read the questions and have students answer them.

Performance Assessment ✓

Refer to pages T 23 to T 25 for a Performance Assessment strategy for this chapter. See the *Performance Assessment Activities* booklet for additional suggestions.

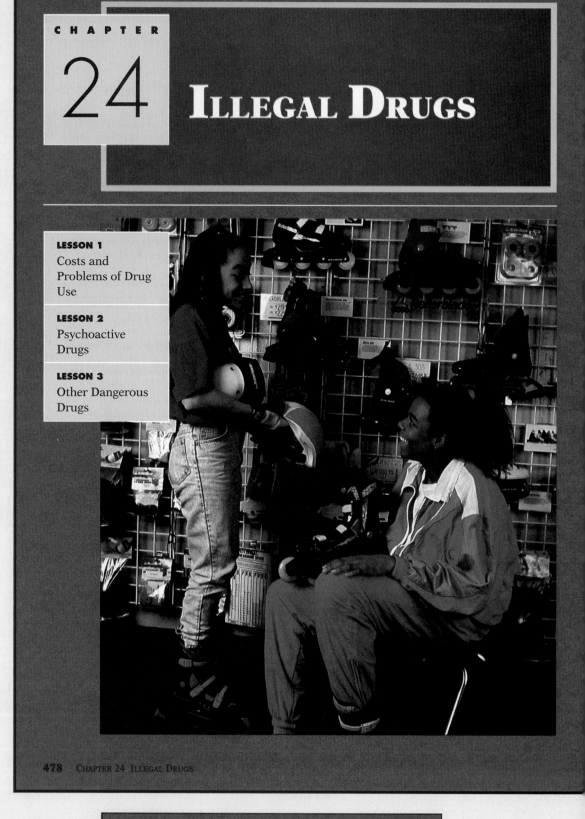

CHAPTER

24 ILLEGAL DRUGS

LESSON 1
Costs and Problems of Drug Use

LESSON 2
Psychoactive Drugs

LESSON 3
Other Dangerous Drugs

478 CHAPTER 24 ILLEGAL DRUGS

Key to Ability Levels

Teaching strategies have been coded for varying learning styles and abilities.

L1 Level 1 activities are basic activities and should be within the ability range of all students.

L2 Level 2 activities are average activities and should be within the ability range of average to above-average students.

L3 Level 3 activities are challenging activities designed for the ability range of above-average students.

LD LD activities should be within the ability range of learning-disabled students.

LEP LEP activities should be within the ability range of Limited English Proficiency students.

COSTS AND PROBLEMS OF DRUG USE

A s you know, the term *drug* is used to refer to dangerous and illegal substances, including alcohol and tobacco. Medicines sold on the street for purposes other than those intended by the manufacturer also become dangerous, illegal drugs.

The growing use of illegal drugs and medicines acquired illegally has captured the interest and attention of American families in the 1990s more than ever before. Almost daily in the newspaper, on television or the radio, there are stories about physical, mental, and social health problems resulting from illegal drug use.

Costs of Drug Use

The cost of using drugs affects almost everyone—not just the people who use drugs. Think about the number of drug-related crimes and deaths you read or hear about. Consider the effects of drugs in the work force in terms of lost productivity caused by absenteeism and accidents. Also consider the rising costs of consumer products and health care that result from drug use. Everyone pays a price for drug use.

Consider the cost to you and what happens if someone you know at school or at your job uses drugs. Drug use can

- hinder concentration,
- decrease memory function,
- affect attentiveness to tasks by causing either a drowsy, relaxed state or a highly anxious feeling,
- increase the possibility of making poor judgments and decisions,
- affect mood, and
- affect the senses and limit the ability to function.

Learning about the dangerous effects of drugs as well as ways to promote a healthy life-style is important in reducing or eliminating drug use and its costs.

Problems of Drug Use

People of all ages use drugs for many reasons. Some may use drugs because they feel pressure from others to do so. Others seek a good feeling, or high, in an attempt to ease boredom or forget problems. Still others use drugs because they have become addicted and have lost the power to choose. Unfortunately, drug use cannot make problems go away. In addition, using drugs can damage a person's health. Anyone who uses drugs will likely have one or more of the following problems:

COSTS AND PROBLEMS OF DRUG USE **479**

LESSON 1 FOCUS

TERMS TO USE

- Physiological dependence
- Tolerance
- Withdrawal
- Psychological dependence
- Addiction

CONCEPTS TO LEARN

- The cost of using drugs affects almost everyone.
- Using drugs damages a person's health.

ATTITUDES AND BEHAVIORS TO EVALUATE

- Self-Inventory, page 492.
- Building Decision-Making Skills, page 493.

Lesson Objectives

After studying this lesson, students should be able to:

- identify the costs of drug use to the user, the user's family and friends, and to society in general
- describe the effects of drugs on a person's health

Bellringer

Write the following on the chalkboard for students to work on while attendance is being taken: *List as many of the dangerous effects of drugs as you can think of that affect the user, the user's family and friends, and the rest of society.*

Introducing the Lesson

Collect students' responses to the Bellringer. On the chalkboard, write some of their responses. Explain that drug use affects almost everyone, not just the user. This lesson will focus on the dangerous effects of drugs and the physical and psychological problems that are likely to occur to anyone who uses drugs.

Building Vocabulary

- Divide the class into small groups. Have students brainstorm words that come to mind when the term *drug* is used. Afterwards, have students compare the definitions of *drug* in the dictionary with the definition in the textbook. Discuss the similarities and differences, if any. Ask students to look for the ways drugs can damage a person's health as they read the chapter.
- Ask students to complete *Workbook Vocabulary Activity 63.*

Resources for Lesson 1

- **Guided Reading** Act 63
- **Lesson 1 Quiz**
- **Workbook** Voc Act 63
- **BARN** Alcohol, Other Drugs
- **Reteaching** Activity 63
- **The Reality of Drugs**

ABC News InterActive Videodiscs
Drugs and Substance Abuse, Side 1
Ch 15 The Nature of Addiction

Drugs and Substance Abuse, Side 2
Ch 3 Cost to Society

DID YOU KNOW?

- In 1990, Americans paid 70 to 90 billion dollars—for illegal drugs.

Guided Practice

LD EXPLANATION. LD students should be able to comprehend the core subject matter of this chapter, but may have difficulty recalling the specifics of each drug presented.

L3 CLASS ACTIVITY. Have students write, plan, and practice skits to teach junior high school students some of the costs and problems of using drugs. With administrative approval, plan a field trip to a junior high class to present the skits. Make certain that the senior high presenters know they must be prepared to answer basic questions during any discussions that may follow the skits.

Using Overcoming the Odds

■ **Class Activity.** Ask students to compare steroid and alcohol abuse. (Consider addictiveness, legality, and purpose of use.)

■ **Discussion.** Why might rational pleas to give up the drug, as in Josh's case, tend to backfire for steroid abusers especially? (Rather than be convinced by rational pleas, steroid abusers are likely to feel paranoid and exhibit aggressive, irrational behavior, two of the most common characteristics of steroid users.)

■ **Answers**

1. You may be afraid of angering and losing your friend, who may be irrational some of the time.
2. The drug user's life may be saved and the friendship strengthened.

L3 SPEAKER. Invite a member of the emergency room staff at a local hospital to speak on treatment of overdose cases. Have students write short summaries of the presentation.

L1 CLASS ACTIVITY. Have students list ways to have fun at a party without the use of drugs or alcohol. Next, ask them to plan a party for an upcoming special occasion.

Overcoming The Odds

Ben is 16 and rather shy. "I've never been one to talk in public much, but I figured this was pretty important. The reason is because I know there are thousands more out there just like me who have friends in deep trouble with drugs, and nobody knows what to do about it." Ben continues, "Three of us—good friends from way back—watched what was happening to our friend, who I'll call Josh. He's this football fanatic, OK? He lives for it. So the coach told him if he could get some weight on and increase his strength, he'd be a starter on the team in the fall. So first he started to lift weights more. Then he started to use steroids. Pills. Sure we read all about steroids in health class and knew the dangers—on paper. But it's a different story when you see somebody you know real well starting to act differently, starting to go down the tube. We all just sat and watched it happening and didn't know what to do. I guess mostly what we did at first was either ignore it or razz him about it . . . till it got out of hand."

Ben goes on. "All of a sudden Josh just bulked up. Sure he was working out in the weight room a lot. That could account for some of the increase. But most of the rest

of us were working out, too, and we didn't look like him. Then Josh started to have headaches and act edgy a lot. He got this awful acne. He had to use the bathroom all

the time. He had this killer breath. All that was weird enough. But then, he started to behave weird, too. He got paranoid. He was either down or up. Sometimes he acted like he was going to take over the world. Other times, he just retreated. And then, there was the temper. He got really mean sometimes—even with us.

"Early this fall, some of us went away with the other peer helpers on a weekend training retreat. One of the things we talked about was what to do if you have a friend who is in

trouble with drugs. I realized I had to do something."

Ben talked to the peer helper advisor. She suggested some ways Ben and his friends might approach Josh. She urged them to tell Josh's parents that he needed help. She also gave them some telephone numbers for counseling and drug treatment centers that might be able to help. Ben continues, "So three of us ended up going to talk to Josh about the steroids. We told him how he'd changed, what we thought the drugs were doing to him, and that we were there because we were worried about him. We were prepared that he might get angry, and he did. But we expected that and didn't react to it. We told him where he could get help. We also told him that if he didn't, we'd probably have to involve some adults. That felt really weird. I don't know if what we did will help or not. It's been only a couple of weeks."

1. What are some of the reasons confronting a friend with a drug problem is so difficult?
2. What are the possible benefits of such a confrontation—both to the drug user and to the person who does the confronting?

Overcoming Misconceptions

Myth. Teens with high self-esteem and ambition are more likely to use drugs than their peers who are less ambitious and less sure of themselves. **Fact.** Those who have a high regard for themselves are more likely to resist group pressure to use drugs. Also, drugs can interfere with schoolwork

and career plans. Teenagers with a strong desire to achieve are less likely to let drugs get in their way. **Myth.** "If I choose to use drugs, it's nobody's business but my own." **Fact.** Others can get hurt, too. This is especially true for family and friends who care about the user's health and happiness.

Types of Drugs	Effects
Stimulants Amphetamines	Results include excitation, restlessness, rapid speech, irritability, convulsions, insomnia, hallucinations, severe mental disorders, anorexia, malnutrition, and/or death.
Ice	Lethargy, severe depression, paranoia, and possible cardiopulmonary effects are likely to occur.
Cocaine	Negative effects include irritability, depression, mental disorders, damage to lining of nose and blood vessels when sniffed, seizures, heart failure, stroke, and death. When taken during pregnancy, cocaine can lead to abruptio placenta, miscarriages, and fetal death. Infants exposed perinatally may have long-lasting effects that include tremors, seizures, learning problems, a delay in or difficulty bonding, and failure to thrive.
Crack (a crystallized derivative of cocaine)	Crack is an extremely addicting form of cocaine with the same effects and problems, including insomnia, agitation, and paranoia. Users experience a very short period of intoxication for 5 to 10 minutes.
Depressants Barbiturates	Effects include decreased alertness, confusion, drowsiness, irritability, poor coordination, lack of judgment, loss of appetite, sleep disorders, nausea, addiction, and possible death.
Tranquilizers Valium	Use may lead to dependence and withdrawal symptoms that include convulsions, tremors, cramps, and overdose.
Narcotics Methadone Opium Morphine Heroin Codeine	Use may result in decreased alertness, confusion, stupor, slurred speech, nausea, vomiting, unconsciousness, and possibly death.
Hallucinogens PCP (phencyclidine)	Use may cause perceptual distortions, confusion, agitation, impaired memory, anxiety, loss of coordination, delusions, panic, irrational thought patterns, violent behaviors, and/or long-term developmental consequences.
LSD	Delusions, illusions, hallucinations, increased panic, severe mental disorders, or death may result from use.
Cannabis Marijuana Hashish	Drug combines stimulant, hallucinogenic, and depressant effects. The effects of intoxication, or high, may last 48 hours, long after the individual considers him- or herself no longer under the influence. User may experience reduction of inhibitions, panic, impaired memory, paranoia, loss of concentration, loss of coordination, loss of interest, loss of ambition, goals, and motivation, changes in perception, sterility, impaired heart function, lowered resistance to infection, lung cancer, psychological dependence, delayed sexual development, and lung damage caused by exposure to the smoke. Fetal marijuana syndrome may result from use during pregnancy, causing low birth weight and developmental abnormalities of infants exposed to marijuana before birth.

Across the Curriculum

Language Arts. Have students write a fictional first-person story, assuming that they are the victim of a drug-related crime. Ask them to set the stage of the crime, the persons involved, the kind of crime committed, the effects of the crime on the victim and the victim's family and friends, and the cost of the crime to those involved.

Select the best stories to submit to the school newspaper.

Science. Ask for volunteers to research the types of chemical tests for blood, breath, and/or urine that currently are being used in different parts of the U.S.

L1 CLASS ACTIVITY. Have students find examples of drug-related crimes and deaths in newspaper and magazine articles. Discuss some of the examples, and list some of the victims (or probable victims) involved, such as family, friends, innocent bystanders, business owners, taxpayers, health-care workers, etc.

L1 CLASS ACTIVITY. Invite a panel of employers to talk about drug use in the workplace. Ask them to discuss the use of drug tests, health insurance costs, accidents, and other costs of drug use by workers.

L1 SPEAKER. Ask a police officer to speak to the class about the availability and use of drugs in the local community. Have them share their knowledge of what users pay for various drugs; the relationship between drugs, crime, and death; and the apprehension and conviction rates of users.

L2 CLASS ACTIVITY. Select students to design and complete a bulletin board or exhibit portraying some of the costs of drug use.

Independent Practice

L3 COMMUNITY INVOLVEMENT. Have students develop a handout of positive ways to deal with stress in their lives. Encourage them to contact professionals in the community who work with teens for ideas or resources. Make the handouts available to teens in your school or in your community.

L2 RESEARCH. Select groups of students to find out what the state law is regarding controlled substances, such as cocaine, heroin, morphine, etc. Have them share what they learned with the class.

L3 COMMUNITY INVOLVEMENT. Ask for volunteers to collect current statistics on the use of illegal drugs in your local community. Also, have them find out what the statistics were 5 years ago. Suggest that they make a bar graph to show the increase or decrease in use.

L1 USING THE LESSON RESOURCES. For additional student activities, refer to the lesson resources on page 479.

Check for Understanding

- Assign and discuss the lesson review.

Evaluate

- Administer, grade, and discuss the *Lesson 1 Quiz.*

Reteach

- Have students list ways in which drugs affect both the user and others.
- Select students to describe five negative effects of drug use on a person's health.
- Ask students to complete *Reteaching Activity 63.*

Enrich

- Assign each student to read a report, article, or book or to watch a movie about true experiences of Americans imprisoned in foreign countries for drug offenses. Ask students to find answers to the questions: What rights do the offenders have, if any? What kinds of punishments are handed out in various parts of the world? Afterwards, have students share what they learned with the class.

Close

Ask students to state the lesson's most important concepts.

DID YOU KNOW?

- Passive smoke does not just involve tobacco. It also involves cocaine. About 6 of every 100 children treated in emergency rooms have cocaine in their systems from breathing the smoke from adult crack-cocaine smokers.

DRUGS AND THEIR EFFECTS

continued

Anabolic steroids	Severe acne, nausea, vomiting, diarrhea, hair loss, deep depression, excitation, power delusion episodes, aggressive behavior, uncontrolled violence, heart disease, hypertension, stroke, kidney damage, and abnormal liver function are among the negative effects. May also cause sexual underdevelopment or delays. In males, problems may include atrophy of genitalia, sterility, and stunted growth. In females, a decrease in estrogen, deepening of voice, a masculine build, and an increased risk of cancer.
Inhalants Solvents Gasoline Model glue Felt-tip markers Aerosols Insecticides Freon	The easily available household compounds are most frequently abused. Use may cause poor coordination, stupor, impaired thought processes, unconsciousness, violent behavior, hallucinations, and damage to liver, kidneys, and bone marrow. Single use may cause permanent brain damage.

- **Physiological dependence.** The body develops a chemical need for a drug. Physiological dependence is determined when a person experiences tolerance and withdrawal. **Tolerance** occurs when the body adjusts to the effects of the drug. Larger doses of the drug are needed to achieve the same effect. **Withdrawal** is characterized by symptoms that occur when a person stops using a drug to which he or she is physiologically dependent. These symptoms can include nervousness, insomnia, severe nausea, headaches, vomiting, chills, and cramps and, in some instances, even death.
- **Psychological dependence.** A person believes a drug is needed in order to feel good or to function normally.
- **Addiction.** An addict has a physiological or psychological dependence on a drug. Negative effects of drug use will vary with each individual. Some people have very serious effects with first use while others may experience harmful effects only after chronic use. The earliest consequences are frequently behavioral or social, which may be the most critical health concern. Drug use is a learned behavior. It is important, then, not to begin using drugs. The chart on pages 481 and 482 gives an overview of the drugs you will study in this chapter.

LESSON 1 REVIEW

Reviewing Facts and Vocabulary

1. Tell how physiological dependence is related to addiction.
2. Explain the term *drug.*

Thinking Critically

3. **Analysis.** Explain the difference between tolerance and withdrawal.

4. **Synthesis.** List three costs of drug use and give examples of how each cost might affect you.

Applying Health Knowledge

5. Write a one-page report telling ways you would help reduce the costs of drug use in your school or community.

Answers to Lesson 1 Review

1. Addiction occurs when one has a physiological dependence on a drug.
2. *Drug* is used to refer to dangerous and illegal substances, including alcohol and tobacco. It also refers to medicines sold on the street for purposes other than those intended by the manufacturer.
3. With tolerance, the body becomes used to the effects of a drug and requires larger doses to achieve the same effects. Withdrawal is the body's reaction when one stops taking a drug on which one has become physiologically dependent.
4. Answers will vary. See "Costs of Drug Use" on page 479.
5. Reports will vary.

PSYCHOACTIVE DRUGS

L ike medicines, drugs are grouped according to their effects on the body. Many of the substances that will be discussed in this lesson promote health when used in a controlled medical situation. However, when not used for medical purposes, these substances can be very dangerous. They can cause irreversible harm and even result in death.

Psychoactive drugs affect the central nervous system and alter normal functioning of the brain, resulting in mental or behavioral changes. Stimulants, depressants, narcotics, and hallucinogens are psychoactive drugs. The first three have medicinal value. Hallucinogens have no medical use.

Stimulants

Stimulants speed up the central nervous system. They cause increased heart and respiratory rates, high blood pressure, dilated pupils, and decreased appetite. In addition, users may experience sweating, headaches, blurred vision, dizziness, and sleeplessness. Extremely high doses can cause irregular heartbeat, tremors, loss of coordination, and even physical collapse. Inhalation or injection of stimulants can cause a sudden increase in blood pressure that can result in stroke, high fever, or heart failure.

Psychological effects of stimulant use include moodiness, restlessness, and anxiety. Chronic users can experience hallucinations, delusions, and paranoia. These symptoms disappear when drug use ceases.

Amphetamines

Amphetamines are stimulants that have an effect similar to that of the sympathetic nervous system. They speed up the heart and breathing. They cause anxiety, sleeplessness, and loss of appetite. Medical use of amphetamines has declined greatly in recent years. They may be used in the treatment of narcolepsy, a disease that results in an uncontrollable need to sleep, as well as in some cases of brain damage resulting from senility. Some people use amphetamines illegally to stay awake and alert, to feel high and euphoric, to improve athletic performance, to lose weight, and to offset the effects of depressant drugs. Tolerance to amphetamines can develop. Psychological dependence also can result. The user can experience depression as the effect of the drug wears off.

Methamphetamine. Methamphetamine is an amphetamine that has been used medically in treating narcolepsy, Parkinson's disease, and obesity. When used illegally, this drug, which is also called crank, speed, or ice, may cause a person to be paranoid and violent. Because crank is made in labs, it is readily available. Crank can be smoked; snorted or sniffed up the nostrils; injected; or swallowed. The effects of this drug

PSYCHOACTIVE DRUGS **483**

- Have students write a sentence explaining the difference between stimulants and depressants. Next, ask them to write a sentence contrasting narcotics and hallucinogens.
- Ask students to complete *Workbook Vocabulary Activity 64.*

Teach

Guided Practice

L2 DISCUSSION. Talk about the different weight-loss systems advertised in the media. Have students research which systems are most likely to be healthy and permanent approaches to losing weight. Also, ask them to find out if any of the systems that use drugs for weight loss are regulated. Lead a discussion of their findings.

L1 EXPLANATION. Tell students amphetamines for losing weight are usually unsuccessful because, if eating habits do not change, the weight is regained as soon as one quits taking the pills or products.

L2 CLASS ACTIVITY. Have students design a bulletin board featuring some of cocaine's slang terms. *(Snow, C, coke, dynamite, flake, gold dust, happy dust,* and *paradise.)* Also, ask them to feature some of the symptoms of cocaine use. (Excitability, hyperactivity, irritability, restlessness, anxiety, euphoria, hallucinations, talkativeness, tremors, hyperactive reflexes, dilated pupils, loss of appetite, insomnia, etc.)

L2 CLASS ACTIVITY. Assign students to prepare case histories of cocaine abusers (such as Richard Pryor, Len Bias, etc.) based on several actual accounts. Using this information, have students list other healthy ways the abuser could have addressed his or her problems instead of taking cocaine. What other options were there for this person?

L1 DISCUSSION. Why did PCP get the nickname "bad drug"? (Its effects were extreme and varied, causing bizarre, unpredictable behaviors in users.)

DID YOU KNOW?

- Addiction to cocaine is increasing. Among those addicted in the United States, some 200,000 are in drug treatment, 55,000 are homeless, and 1,530,000 were arrested in one recent year.
- A new study shows that testing for cocaine by hair analysis is more effective than testing through urine analysis.
- Teens who smoke cigarettes are 14 times more likely to use cocaine and 10 times more likely to use marijuana as teens who do not smoke cigarettes.

Len Bias, a star college basketball player, had just signed a major contract with the NBA when he went out celebrating—used crack and didn't live to tell about it.

are long-lasting. Food and water become unimportant after taking crank. Seizures and death can result.

Cocaine

Cocaine is a white powder made from the coca bush, which grows in parts of South America. Cocaine was once widely available in the United States. In fact it was once an ingredient in a well-known soft drink. The drug was even used as a local anesthetic in the mid- and late nineteenth century. Other chemicals with stronger anesthetic effects and fewer side effects have almost eliminated cocaine's medical usefulness. Cocaine use and possession is now illegal under state and federal laws.

Cocaine is a rapid-acting, powerful stimulant. Its effects, which include increased heart rate, blood pressure, and respiration, can last from 20 minutes to several hours. The feelings of confidence that come from cocaine use are often followed by a letdown. Regular use can lead to depression, edginess, and weight loss. Physiological dependence occurs because the user wants to avoid the letdown feeling. As cocaine use increases, so does the danger of paranoia, hallucinations, and psychological dependence.

Cocaine is used in many ways. When snorted, the drug is absorbed into the bloodstream through the mucous membranes of the nasal cavity. It constricts, or contracts, the many little blood vessels in these membranes, reducing the blood supply to the nose and causing it to become dry. Repeated cocaine use can cause tissue damage in the nose and even holes in the nasal septum, the wall dividing the two halves of the nose.

Cocaine use can cause malnutrition and, especially among those with cardiac problems, an increase in the risk of heart attack. Even in healthy individuals who are not heavy users of cocaine, the drug may disturb the electrical impulses of the heart and cause death. An additional risk of cocaine use is the possibility of being infected with HIV when injecting cocaine with a shared needle.

Crack. Crack is a form of cocaine that can be smoked. Processing converts cocaine into lumps or rocks. This kind of cocaine is known as freebase. Preparing freebase may involve the use of dangerous solvents and can result in injury or death from an explosion or fire.

Crack is extremely addictive. Because it is smoked, its effects are felt within 10 seconds. The physical effects of crack include dilated pupils, increased pulse rate, elevated blood pressure, insomnia, loss of appetite, hallucinations, paranoia, and seizures. Crack users may develop a sore throat, hoarseness, and lung damage.

Using crack can cause death by cardiac or respiratory failure. Compared with other forms of cocaine, crack users are at increased risk because of the extreme dangers of this drug.

Depressants

Depressants, or sedatives, are drugs that tend to slow down the central nervous system. Depressants relax muscles, relieve feelings of tension and worry, and bring on sleep. They slow down the heart and breathing rates and reduce blood pressure. Depressants can easily cause physical and psychological dependence.

Across the Curriculum

Language Arts. After reviewing literature and personal accounts of people using crack and cocaine, have each student write a short essay on cocaine and crack. The essay should explore their personal feelings about this drug and its effects on individuals.

Language Arts. Have each student research the history of one psychoactive drug and prepare a one-page report to share with the class. Ask students to consider such questions as these: Does the drug have any positive, useful purposes? What effects does this drug produce? Is this drug addictive? How widespread is the abuse of this drug?

Babies born to mothers who use depressants illegally during pregnancy may be physically dependent on them and show withdrawal symptoms at birth. Birth defects and behavioral problems among these infants also are common.

Combining depressants and alcohol has a synergistic effect and increased health risks to the person who does this. Results include depression of the central nervous system and death.

Sedative-Hypnotics

Sedative-hypnotics are a type of depressant. They induce sleep and reduce anxiety. Motor coordination and judgment can be impaired. When these drugs are used in excess, the respiratory and cardiovascular systems are depressed. Sedative-hypnotics can produce physiological and psychological dependence.

Barbiturates. Barbiturate use can result in mood changes, more than normal sleep, or even a coma. Barbiturates are rarely used for medical purposes such as treating insomnia. They are used illegally to give a feeling similar to intoxication and to counteract the effects of stimulants.

Tranquilizers

Tranquilizers are depressants that reduce muscular activity, coordination, and attention span. Antianxiety tranquilizers, such as Valium, are used medically to relieve anxiety, muscular spasms, sleeplessness, and nervousness. Valium helps a person relax and have a feeling of well-being. However, when tranquilizers are used in excess, physiological and psychological dependence occurs. Withdrawal from Valium causes severe shaking. In severe cases, coma or death can result.

Antipsychotic tranquilizers are used to treat severe mental disorders, such as schizophrenia. These tranquilizers can help control violent behavior by decreasing brain activity. They reduce muscle tone and activity as well as blood pressure and pulse.

Narcotics

Formerly, the term *narcotic* referred only to drugs made from the opium poppy flower. These drugs were called opiates. Narcotics now also include medicines used to relieve pain.

Medicines combined with alcohol can be deadly.

K E E P I N G   F I T

Driving and Marijuana

You've probably heard of people arrested for driving drunk getting DUIs (Driving Under the Influence) or DWIs (Driving While Intoxicated). But driving under the influence of marijuana can also be very dangerous. Marijuana puts added "blindfolds" on a driver by
- interfering with the perception of distance,
- interfering with the perception of depth,
- impairing thinking and judgment skills,
- slowing reflexes, thus affecting one's ability to brake and negotiate curves,
- impairing the ability to stay in the proper lane.

Overcoming Misconceptions

Myth. Drugs affect all people the same way. **Fact.** Specific hazards of drug abuse differ from person to person. However, drug abuse can affect a person's physical and emotional health and social life. **Myth.** "Drug overdoses can't happen to me. I'm always in control of the situation." **Fact.** An overdose can happen due to uncertain purity, strength, or even type of drug you get illegally. It can also happen due to increased tolerance, because you need more and more of a drug to get the same effect. **Myth.** "Depressants are the safest of all drugs, because they just make you relax." **Fact.** Depressants can easily cause physical and psychological dependence.

L1 EXPLANATION. Stress that people who abuse drugs often become dependent on several different types of drugs. They may take amphetamines to get high and then take a depressant to settle down or to be able to sleep. Discuss the implications of this type of abuse on the body's ability to function on its own.

L1 DISCUSSION. Talk about how the symptoms of heroin use differ from those of cocaine use. Are there any positive uses for either heroin or cocaine? Compare the risks of abusing the two drugs.

L1 EXPLANATION. Tell students that the life expectancy of heroin addicts is quite short. The risks of overdose, hepatitis, AIDS (drug addicts have the second highest incidence of AIDS), and getting a bad mix are great. The monetary cost of maintaining the habit increases the abuser's risk of bodily harm through association with criminals. Many resort to crime to support their habit.

L1 DISCUSSION. Talk about why cough syrups with codeine are no longer available without a doctor's prescription. (Because people began abusing them.)

L3 COOPERATIVE LEARNING. Divide the class into groups. Ask each group to work up a brief skit depicting codeine's symptoms. (Drowsiness, anxiety, euphoria, slurred speech, impaired coordination, depressed reflexes, constricted pupils, loss of appetite, and constipation.)

L1 SPEAKER. Invite a hospice worker or intensive care nurse into class to talk about those narcotics and medicines most commonly and effectively used with dying patients to alleviate pain. Ask the speaker to discuss the average doses, how frequently and in what form they are administered, and what role the patients play in deciding on their dosage and use.

L1 DISCUSSION. Talk about reasons that malnutrition is often a side effect of drug abuse.

three or four cans of food or other household items with labels already removed. Let students examine the cans carefully and then guess what is in each can. Record all answers. Open the cans and find out what is inside. Compare this to the frequent deceptiveness involved in buying or selling drugs based on appearance.

L2 **CLASS ACTIVITY.** Have students prepare a table of signs and symptoms of drug overdose, with appropriate emergency actions. Ask for volunteers to computerize the information and to make printouts for the entire class.

L1 **CLASS ACTIVITY.** Have students develop a bulletin board describing information about psychoactive drugs. (Possible information to be included: street names, other descriptive information, how drug is taken, and its effects on a person.)

Independent Practice

L3 **COMMUNITY INVOLVEMENT.** Have students find out what types of drug rehabilitation programs are available both locally and nationwide. Stress the fact that almost all of these treatment programs involve the entire family, not just the person with the drug problem. Ask why this would be important to the success of a treatment program. Ask students to share their findings with the class.

L2 **COMMUNITY INVOLVEMENT.** Ask for volunteers to visit a local drugstore to examine labels on cough syrups. Have them find out what is used other than codeine to stop a cough. Request that they make an appointment to talk with the store's pharmacist to learn about the drugs used in cough medicines, which drugs actually suppress a cough, and the purpose of the other ingredients.

L1 **USING THE LESSON RESOURCES.** For additional student activities, refer to the lesson resources on page 483.

Culturally Speaking

Illegal Transport

International drug control has been a difficult issue for a long time. The Opium War, from 1839 to 1842, was the result of Chinese government restrictions on foreign merchants of opium. In 1909, President Theodore Roosevelt set up a meeting of 13 nations in Shanghai to look at the problem of opium importation into China. The first opium convention was held at The Hague in 1912 to regulate international transport of drugs. Later in 1946, the United Nations and World Health Organization took over as regulators and extended the rules to cover more types of drugs. In 1961 the International Narcotics Control Board was established.

Some medicines made from opium have valuable medical uses in relieving pain and suffering. For example, morphine is used to relieve pain, and codeine is used to stop severe coughing. Both cause drowsiness and can result in physiological dependence. Drugs made from opium can cause stupor or sleep and can result in coma or death.

Heroin

Heroin is made from morphine and has no medical use in the United States. It is an illegal drug. Using heroin depresses the central nervous system and slows breathing and pulse rate. Coma or death may occur with large doses. Tolerance develops very quickly with this drug. Pregnant females who use heroin risk having babies born who are addicted. Retardation and delayed growth of these babies' muscular and nervous systems can result. Withdrawal from this drug is very painful. As with any drug that is injected, there are risks of HIV infection from using contaminated needles.

Treatment for heroin use often involves methadone—a synthetic narcotic. *Synthetic* means made from laboratory chemicals. Methadone depresses the central nervous system, causing drowsiness, and blocks the craving for heroin. The use of methadone, however, is dangerous and must be monitored by qualified medical personnel. Methadone also is addictive. Using too much can result in a deep coma.

Hallucinogens

Hallucinogens, or psychedelics, first became popular during the 1960s. These drugs alter mood, thought, and the senses, including vision, hearing, smell, and touch.

PCP

Phencyclidine (PCP), or angel dust, is a powerful and dangerous hallucinogen. It is prepared synthetically. PCP is considered to be one of the most dangerous drugs.

Users report that PCP makes them feel distant and detached from their surroundings. Time seems to pass slowly; body movements slow down. Muscle coordination is impaired, and the sensations of touch and pain are dulled. PCP can make the user feel strong and powerful. This

KEEPING FIT

Dealing with the Dealers

What can you do when drugs are taking over your neighborhood and you feel unsafe?
- Call the police.
- Report license plate numbers of dealers.
- Get involved in a community

effort to rid your neighborhood of drugs.
- Let people know you are not interested in drugs.
- Protect yourself by staying away from trouble spots and from those dealing drugs.

- Keep reminding yourself that the fancy cars the dealers drive are temporary rewards. Many dealers wind up in prison, addicted, or dead by the time they reach their 20s.

486 CHAPTER 24 ILLEGAL DRUGS

Across the Curriculum

Math. The following data provided by the National Adolescent Student Health Survey indicate the percentage of tenth-grade males and females who have tried drugs at least once in their lifetime. Ask students to make bar graphs of this data and interpret the results. Ask them to compare male and female data and have them speculate about why certain drugs are tried more often than others.

Drug	Male	Female
Diet Pills	7	24
Stay-awake Pills	26	28
Inhalants	20	21
Marijuana	40	30
Cocaine	8	7
Crack	3	2
Amphetamines	11	13
Psychedelics	8	5

feeling has resulted in tragic deaths, serious accidents, and acts of violence.

While overdoses of PCP can cause death, most PCP-related deaths are caused by the strange, destructive behavior the drug produces in the user. PCP users have drowned in shallow water because they were so disoriented they could not tell where they were or which direction was up. Others have died in fires because they were disoriented and had no sensitivity to the pain of burning.

Using PCP repeatedly makes it difficult to remember specific facts; it impairs speech, sometimes causing the user to stutter. Judgment and concentration are impaired long after the user has stopped taking the drug. Long-term users may experience anxiety, depression, and violent behavior. Serious mental problems have also resulted from PCP, causing users to need psychiatric care and, sometimes, institutional care.

The effects of PCP are widely unpredictable and vary from person to person. Once taken, PCP remains in the body long after the initial effect has worn off. A flashback, or recurrence of the effect of the drug, may occur at a later time.

All illegal drugs are dangerous. Sharing needles adds other risks—HIV infection and AIDS.

LSD

Lysergic acid diethylamide (LSD) is probably the drug responsible for initiating an awareness of hallucinogens in American society. Use of LSD during the 1960s and the resulting tragedies—deaths from a false sense of security or hallucinations—received much publicity. Deaths resulted when people thought they could fly or could stop a train by standing on train tracks.

Current use of hallucinogens is illegal, although during the 1960s and 1970s, LSD was tried in different types of therapy. All medicinal use was stopped because the results were inconsistent and unpredictable.

LSD causes an increase in heart rate and a rise in blood pressure. The user may experience chills, fever, loss of appetite, or nausea. Bad experiences may lead to panic, anxiety, or accidental suicide. Flashbacks can occur even after use has stopped. Furthermore, much of the LSD currently being sold is mixed with potentially lethal substances like strychnine.

LESSON 2 REVIEW

Reviewing Facts and Vocabulary

1. Explain the effects of psychoactive drugs.
2. How do antipsychotics help in the treatment of severe mental disorders?
3. Describe what a flashback is and list with which type of drugs flashbacks occur.

Thinking Critically

4. **Analysis.** How do the effects of stimulants differ from those of narcotics?

5. **Synthesis.** What might happen if a person took alcohol with a tranquilizer?

Applying Health Knowledge

6. Make a poster that warns of the dangers of cocaine.

PSYCHOACTIVE DRUGS   **487**

Answers to Lesson 2 Review

1. See second paragraph on page 483.
2. They help control violent behavior by decreasing brain activity.
3. A flashback is a recurrence of the effect of a drug. Flashbacks occur with hallucinogens.
4. Stimulants speed up the central nervous system, causing increased heart and respiratory rates and high blood pressure.

Narcotics depress the central nervous system, slowing down breathing and pulse rates and causing drowsiness.
5. A synergistic effect would occur and the central nervous system would become depressed with the possibility that death could result.
6. Posters will vary.

Assess

Check for Understanding

■ Assign and discuss the lesson review.

Evaluate

■ Administer, grade, and discuss the *Lesson 2 Quiz.*

Reteach

■ Ask each student to make a cause-and-effect chart regarding psychoactive drugs. Have students title the left side of the chart "Cause," with a list underneath each drug discussed in the lesson. Ask them to title the right side of the chart "Effects," followed by physical and mental effect(s) of each drug.
■ Ask students to complete *Reteaching Activity 64.*

Enrich

■ Assign students to research endorphin (produced in the brain and believed to be the body's own morphine) to find out where and when it is produced and its effects on the body. Ask them to summarize their findings in a short paper.

Close

Divide the class into four groups. Assign one of the following types of drugs to each group: stimulants, depressants, narcotics, and hallucinogens. Ask each group to write a one-sentence summary of their assigned type of drug. Share the summaries with the class.

DID YOU KNOW?

■ Over 25 million Americans have used cocaine. Over 4 million of these are regular users. It is estimated that about 2.2 million cocaine users are addicted to it.

Focus

Lesson Objectives

After studying this lesson, students should be able to:

- explain the effects of marijuana on the body
- compare designer and look-alike drugs
- describe the dangers of anabolic steroids

Bellringer

Write the following on the chalkboard for students to work on while attendance is being taken: *List the following drugs in a vertical column: marijuana, inhalants, designer and look-alike drugs, and anabolic steroids. Beside each drug, write a sentence or two describing it.*

Introducing the Lesson

Ask students to share some of their responses to the Bellringer. Tell the class that this lesson will focus on the drugs listed on the chalkboard and how they affect a person's body and behavior.

Building Vocabulary

- Assign students to write a short commercial directed to teens, contrasting young people who are drug-free and those who use drugs such as marijuana, hashish, inhalants, designer drugs, look-alike drugs, and anabolic steroids. Ask for volunteers to present their commercials to the class.
- Ask students to complete *Workbook Vocabulary Activity 65.*

DID YOU KNOW?

- Underground chemists produce designer drugs today. They are synthetic copies of narcotics and hallucinogens changed chemically so they are not exactly the same as those known to be illegal.

OTHER DANGEROUS DRUGS

LESSON 3 FOCUS

TERMS TO USE
- Marijuana
- Hashish
- Inhalants
- Designer drugs
- Look-alike drugs
- Anabolic steroids

CONCEPTS TO LEARN
- Marijuana is a hallucinogen but also has the effects of a depressant and a stimulant.
- Inhalants are not meant for human consumption.
- Anabolic steroid use has serious side effects.

ATTITUDES AND BEHAVIORS TO EVALUATE
- Self-Inventory, page 492.
- Building Decision-Making Skills, page 493.

T he following types of drugs—marijuana, inhalants, designer drugs, and steroids—are additional dangerous drugs.

Marijuana

The scientific name for **marijuana,** a hemp plant, is *Cannabis*. The leaves and flowers of marijuana are smoked, eaten, or drunk for intoxicating effects. Scientists have been able to identify over 400 chemicals in marijuana.

The chemical that produces the psychoactive effect is delta-9-tetrahydrocannabinol (THC). Scientists measure the strength of marijuana by testing how much THC it contains. THC does not dissolve in water, and it is not easily flushed out of the body. It may take many weeks after heavy use for the body to excrete it. When THC enters the blood, some is stored in fatty tissue. The highest concentration of fat cells in the body is in the brain cells, liver, lungs, kidneys, and reproductive organs. In these cells, marijuana acts as a poison. It prevents the proper formation of DNA, proteins, and other essential building blocks for cell growth and cell division.

Hashish (hash) is the dark brown resin collected from the tops of the cannabis plant. Hash is stronger than marijuana because it contains more THC. Hash affects a user more strongly than marijuana. Both marijuana and hashish are illegal.

Marijuana is a hallucinogen but also has the effects of both a depressant and a stimulant. The effects of using marijuana include a calm state with a sensitivity to sight, touch, and sound. Time seems to pass slowly. Visual perception can change. Images may be seen. Marijuana lowers body temperature, but increases the heart rate and blood pressure. It stimulates the appetite. It reduces a person's control over behavior. Some people may become talkative and giddy, others quiet and withdrawn. The effects vary from person to person and can be influenced by a person's mood and surroundings.

Regular marijuana users tend to have personality problems that include loss of willpower and motivation, lack of energy, and paranoia. They tend to lose interest in activities that used to be important to them. Marijuana users may become apathetic and lethargic, withdrawing from academic and social activities. These problems, if not present before the beginning of regular marijuana use, develop and intensify as a result of regular use. Marijuana users often develop psychological dependence on the drug, wanting the feelings they experience to continue.

Studies have shown that marijuana affects memory, making it more difficult to recall and to pay attention. Concentration and coordination are impaired. Reaction time is slowed. Marijuana use definitely impairs driving ability. Drivers under the influence of marijuana react slower and make more accident-causing mistakes than drivers who are not

---

Resources for Lesson 3

- **Transparency** 27
- **Guided Reading** Activity 65
- **Decision-Making** Activity 24
- **Workbook** Voc Act 65, Appl Act 24
- **Reteaching** Activity 65
- **Enrichment** Activity 24
- **Health Labs** Activity 24
- **Cooperative Learning** Activity 24
- **Lesson 3 Quiz, Chapter 24 Test**

ABC News InterActive Videodiscs
Drugs and Substance Abuse, Side 1
Ch 6 Marijuana

Ch 8 Steroids

under the influence. Since some of the effects of marijuana—delayed reaction time and poor concentration—seem to last longer than the actual high, a person may not think he or she is driving under marijuana's influence. Research is still going on to determine whether marijuana destroys certain cells in the brain, causing permanent damage.

Research shows that marijuana smokers may be more susceptible than nonsmokers to infection by viruses, bacteria, and other pathogens. Marijuana smoke contains more cancer-causing chemicals than cigarette smoke. Studies have shown that marijuana interferes with the cells in the lungs that destroy disease-producing bacteria, making the user more susceptible to infections from bacteria. Because marijuana users often inhale unfiltered smoke deeply and hold it in the lungs, marijuana is damaging to the respiratory system. Deep, long breaths associated with smoking marijuana allow more time for harmful particles and gases to act on the lung cells. Smoking marijuana causes a narrowing of the respiratory passages, making breathing more difficult.

Regular use of marijuana lowers the level of testosterone in the blood. Testosterone is responsible for the development of male secondary sex characteristics. Sperm production can decrease with marijuana use. Females should avoid marijuana use especially during pregnancy. Some studies show that marijuana use during pregnancy results in decreased birth weight and a condition similar to fetal alcohol syndrome.

Inhalants

Inhalants are substances with fumes that are sniffed and inhaled to give a hallucinogenic high. Included among the inhalants are glue, spray paints, aerosols, and gasoline. Most inhalants depress the central nervous system and produce effects similar to those of alcohol. Immediate effects of inhalants include nausea, sneezing, coughing, nosebleeds, fatigue, lack of coordination, and loss of appetite. A person who regularly sniffs an inhalant has trouble keeping his or her balance, has a glassy stare, and finds it hard to talk. Judgment is impaired, and the behavior of the user may resemble the behavior of someone who is drunk.

Since inhalants were never meant to be taken into the body, any time they are not used according to the purpose for which they were made is considered illegal drug use. Heavy use of inhalants can result in fatigue, liver and kidney damage, changes in bone marrow, and permanent brain damage. High concentrations of inhalants can cause suffocation. "Clowning around" under the influence of an inhalant has been the cause of many accidental deaths.

Designer and Look-Alike Drugs

To avoid using illegal substances, street chemists make drugs with synthetic substances. These drugs are called **designer drugs.** One of the most well-known designer drugs is called ecstasy, or MDMA. Ecstasy's chemical composition is similar to that of methamphetamines and mescaline. It is a combination stimulant and hallucinogen. Use of this drug gives a feeling of euphoria and results in long-term damage to brain cells.

Federal and local governments are taking steps to destroy marijuana crops wherever they are found.

FINDING HELP

Many young people need treatment for drug and alcohol addiction, but the cost of that treatment is sometimes prohibitive. But now students in Little Rock, Arkansas, have complete insurance coverage for drug and alcohol treatment thanks to a new experimental approach. The district's 26,000 students in grades K through 12 now have 100 percent coverage. The program, which grew out of a community coalition, will include education, early intervention, treatment, and family therapy for young people with chemical dependency. The program is being financed by a grant and local fund-raising efforts.

OTHER DANGEROUS DRUGS **489**

CHAPTER 24 ILLEGAL DRUGS **489**

490 CHAPTER 24 ILLEGAL DRUGS

L1 **SPEAKER.** Invite emergency room workers to class to share experiences about the special problems in diagnosing look-alike drugs and drugs used in combination. Assign students to write a short paper summarizing what they learned.

L1 **EXPLANATION.** Tell students there are great risks in putting chemicals in the body. One never knows how the body will react. Compare this to mixing chemicals in a laboratory. Discuss the health risks of using the body as a chemical lab.

L1 **SPEAKER.** Ask a chemistry teacher to speak to the class about designer and look-alike drugs and the dangers they pose to the user.

L1 **SPEAKER.** Invite a doctor, athletic coach, or trainer to speak to the class about his or her observations of steroid use.

Independent Practice

L2 **COMMUNITY INVOLVEMENT.** Ask for volunteers to interview owners/managers of local gyms and fitness centers about the prevalence of steroid use among their clientele. Have students share what they learned with the class.

L1 **READING.** Ask students to locate and read newspaper and magazine articles about steroid use by well-known athletes. Lead a discussion of their findings. Ask who used the steroids. What side effects were noted? How was the steroid use discovered by authorities or medical personnel?

L1 **USING THE LESSON RESOURCES.** For additional student activities, refer to the lesson resources on page 488.

DID YOU KNOW?

■ A designer drug's changed molecular structure also changes the drug's potency, length of action, euphoric effects, and toxicity.
■ Overdoses are common. These drugs can be several hundred times stronger than the drugs they are designed to imitate.
■ Symptoms caused by designer drugs include uncontrollable tremors, drooling, impaired speech, paralysis, and irreversible brain damage.

Exercise is a healthy way to build muscle. Taking steroids is unhealthy and illegal.

CONFLICT RESOLUTION

Mike never saw anyone dealing drugs in his neighborhood—until yesterday. Then, he saw a neighbor pass a bag of white powder to a stranger in a car. Mike is pretty sure it was a cocaine deal. Mike wants his neighborhood to be safe, but he's afraid to report what he saw to the police. His neighbor might retaliate if Mike turns him in.

What should Mike do?

Look-alike drugs are made from legal substances to look like illegal drugs. With these drugs the user never knows exactly what he or she is getting. Using these kinds of drugs or mixing them with other drugs is very dangerous.

HEALTH UPDATE

LOOKING AT THE ISSUES

Drug Testing

According to the National Institute on Drug Abuse, on any given day in the United States, 25 percent of workers between the ages of 18 and 40 would test positive for drugs. Some experts estimate that drug use costs employers over $60 billion a year in decreased productivity, absenteeism, and accidents. Therefore, in the interest of health, safety, and economics, many companies are now testing employees for drug use, but the practice is stirring heated debate.

Presently, drug testing is used in hospital emergency rooms for suspected drug overdoses and when arrests for driving violations suggest drug use. Some schools are now suggesting random drug testing for students.

Analyzing Different Viewpoints

ONE VIEW. Some groups claim that randomly testing people for drug use without just cause is an invasion of their rights, including their right to privacy.

A SECOND VIEW. Others believe that drug testing should be restricted to those who are in jobs where public safety is involved—such as pilots or bus drivers— or to cases where there is just cause, such as after an accident where drug use is suspected.

A THIRD VIEW. Some people claim that widespread drug testing deters the use of drugs, and that, considering the size of the drug problem in the United States, such testing is needed.

A FOURTH VIEW. Others say that drug testing is one way to get those who use drugs to confront their problem and get help and treatment.

A FIFTH VIEW. Still other people argue the tests are not always accurate and can have severe consequences for the individual who incorrectly tests positive. These consequences include job loss or a damaged reputation.

A SIXTH VIEW. Some people believe that random drug testing is not enough—that to stop the drug problem in the United States, everyone in the workplace as well as in schools should be tested.

Exploring Your Views

1. Who, if anyone, do you think should be tested for drugs? Why? In what kinds of situations?
2. Do you think this testing should be random or "across-the-board"?
3. When people do test positive for drugs, what do you think should happen to them? Why?
4. What do you think about schools testing students for drugs? Why?
5. What other means of identifying and getting help for students in trouble with drugs can you suggest?

Overcoming Misconceptions

Myth. Look-alike drugs are made by some local guy trying to make a buck. **Fact.** These types of drugs are big business. Law enforcement authorities report that the sale of look-alike drugs has become a multimillion-dollar business in the U.S. **Myth.** The health effects of using marijuana are fewer now that a lot of marijuana is grown in the U.S. **Fact.** Today's marijuana is quite potent. It can contain 5 to 10 times more THC than marijuana available just 5 years ago. **Myth.** Drivers who smoke marijuana are just as safe as those who smoke tobacco. **Fact.** The use of marijuana definitely affects driving ability. The reactions of drivers under the influence of marijuana are slower.

Moderate doses of any one of these substances can produce nervousness, restlessness, insomnia, or increased blood pressure and heart rate. Regular use of look-alikes, and their use in combination with other drugs, can lead to the same behavior found with frequent use of amphetamines.

The use of look-alikes is hard to diagnose. This makes treatment very difficult. If look-alikes are taken with other drugs, such as alcohol, serious reactions can occur. If a user is admitted to an emergency room, the medical staff may not be able to treat the patient successfully because no one can know for sure what drugs the user took.

Anabolic Steroids

Anabolic steroids are synthetic derivatives of the male hormone testosterone. When used as medicine, these drugs help build muscles in patients with chronic diseases. They also have been used to treat bone diseases, burns, hormonal imbalances, and as protection for blood cells during treatment for cancer.

These drugs are used illegally by some athletes to enhance performance. Because steroids help the body synthesize protein for muscular growth, athletes who use them recover more quickly in practice or after a game. Use also increases aggressiveness and strength. Teens who want to look more muscular sometimes use steroids because steroids help make muscles stronger and bigger. This use of steroids is illegal and dangerous.

Steroid use has serious side effects, including high blood pressure, acne, and increased risk of liver damage, heart disease, and stroke, as a result of clogged arteries. Males can experience baldness, depression, aggressiveness, a decrease in sperm production and testicle size, and an increase in breast growth and body and facial hair. Females can experience breast shrinkage, growth of facial hair, and baldness. Teens who use steroids are at special risk because the reproductive and skeletal systems can be permanently affected. Steroid use causes mood swings and violent behavior. The super aggressive behaviors experienced are termed "'roid rages." The user exhibits behaviors that would never have occurred without using the drug. Because steroids can be taken by injection, risk of infection with HIV exists from shared needles.

HELP WANTED

Drug Enforcement Officer

The "army" needs you—the one fighting the war on drugs, that is. Your working conditions will be terrible and your hours long. You will face danger and will deal with the lowest of the low life. However, the opportunity for satisfaction is great, as you make a difference in one of the most important battles of our times. Integrity is a must as are physical fitness and some acting ability. You need solid policework skills, which you may have gained from a combination of classroom training and experience. We will be glad to consider your particular background.

For more information contact your local office of the U.S. Drug Enforcement Agency.

LESSON 3 REVIEW

Reviewing Facts and Vocabulary

1. Explain the dangers of using inhalants.
2. Relate how designer drugs came into being.

Thinking Critically

3. **Analysis.** Compare the immediate and long-term effects of marijuana use.

4. **Evaluation.** What do you think about steroid use for professional athletes? On what did you base your position?

Applying Health Knowledge

5. Develop a list of strategies that might be effective for reducing drug use in your community.

OTHER DANGEROUS DRUGS **491**

Answers to Lesson 3 Review

1. Inhalants depress the central nervous system and can result in liver and kidney damage, changes in bone marrow, and brain damage. High concentrations can cause suffocation.
2. They were originally made by street chemists with synthetic substances to avoid using illegal substances.
3. Immediate effects—increased heart rate and blood pressure; reduction in coordination, reaction time, and control over behavior. Long-term effects—greater susceptibility to viruses, bacteria, and other pathogens; reduced interest in previously important activities.
4. Answers will vary.
5. Answers will vary.

Assess

Check for Understanding

- Assign and discuss the lesson review.
- Assign and discuss the chapter review.

Evaluate

- Administer, grade, and discuss the *Lesson 3 Quiz.*
- Administer, grade, and discuss the *Chapter 24 Test.*
- Refer to the Performance Assessment strategy for this chapter. See pages T 23 to T 25.

Reteach

- Select students to design a bulletin board about marijuana smoking. Ask them to make the focus of the exhibit a diagram of the human body depicting how different body systems are affected by marijuana.
- Ask students to complete *Reteaching Activity 65.*

Enrich

- Have students prepare charts on the risks marijuana poses to various body systems, such as the lungs, brain, immune system, and the reproductive system. Let them use class and library resources to find out what is currently known and being researched about marijuana and the particular body system they choose to explore.
- Ask students to complete *Enrichment Activity 24.*

Close

Write the terms *marijuana, inhalants, designer drugs, look-alike drugs,* and *anabolic steroids* on separate slips of paper. Place the slips in a box. Divide the class into five groups, and let a student from each group draw a slip. Next, ask each group to write a short summary of their type of drug to present to the entire class.

Helping Students Improve Their Health

Reinforcing Vocabulary

- **High.** Altered mental state; usually referring to an altered state as a result of drug use.

Teaching Strategies

L1 EXPLANATION. Frequently, students who use illegal drugs will be in a state of denial and will have a tendency to underestimate how serious their drug problem actually is. This inventory may be a good opportunity for students to take a serious look at their drug use patterns. Be aware of students who may ask for help in subtle ways. It would be good to alert the guidance department of the possibility that students may want to discuss drug issues during this unit.

L2 DISCUSSION. Have students list characteristics of persons who use illegal drugs. Discuss how these characteristics may limit a person's potential to be the best that he or she can be.

L1 DISCUSSION. Discuss how adolescents who use addictive, illegal drugs remain emotionally at the same age as when they began using the drug, even though these same adolescents mature physically. What repercussions might this fact have in the successful drug recovery of youths?

L2 CLASS ACTIVITY. Possible debate topics that involve illegal drugs include: (1) The pros and cons of the legalization of marijuana and other illegal drugs. (2) The pros and cons of providing sterile needles to intravenous drug users in order to prevent the spread of the AIDS virus. (3) The pros and cons of mandatory drug testing of public employees, such as police officers, school bus drivers, and elected officials. (4) The pros and cons of random drug testing of high school and college athletes.

Self-Inventory

What Is Your Attitude About Drug Use?

HOW DO YOU RATE?

Number a sheet of paper from 1 through 20. Read each item below, and respond by writing *yes* or *no* for each item. Then proceed to the next section.

1. I avoid any type of drug use.
2. I have been encouraged to try drugs.
3. I choose friends who avoid drug use.
4. Some of my best friends use drugs.
5. I feel comfortable saying *no* to friends who want me to use drugs.
6. Most of my friends use drugs at parties.
7. When using an inhalant, such as spray paint, for its intended purpose, I am in a well-ventilated area.
8. I sometimes take medicines that are not prescribed for me.
9. I belong to an organization that promotes a drug-free life-style.
10. I get angry when someone tries to tell me not to use drugs.
11. I stay away from areas where I know drugs are used.
12. I have covered for someone who uses drugs.
13. Whenever possible I avoid peers who use drugs.

14. I sometimes attend parties when I know drugs will be available.
15. I know where to get help for drug problems and would feel comfortable passing the information along to someone who needed it.
16. I frequently am in areas where drugs are sold.
17. I want to remain in control of my actions at all times.
18. I think I would like the experience of getting high.
19. I understand the dangers involved in using drugs and want to avoid the high risks.
20. I think it would be fun to watch others get high.

HOW DID YOU SCORE?

Give yourself 1 point for every *yes* answer to an odd-numbered item. Give yourself 1 point for every *no* answer to an even-numbered item. Total the points, and find your score below. Then proceed to the next section.

19 to 20
Excellent. Your attitudes and behaviors related to drugs are commendable.

15 to 18
Good. Your attitudes and behaviors related to drugs are positive, but limited in scope.

11 to 14
Fair. You need to change your attitudes and behaviors.

Below 11
Needs Improvement. You need to get help to change your behavior and thoughts about drugs. Your health may be in danger.

WHAT ARE YOUR GOALS?

If you received an *excellent* or *good* score, complete the statements in Part A. If your score was rated *fair* or *needs improvement,* complete Parts A and B.

Part A

1. I plan to learn more about drug use and preventing drug use by ____.
2. I want to learn more about drug use because ____.
3. My timetable for accomplishing this is ____.
4. I plan to share my information with others by ____.

Part B

5. The attitude or behavior toward drugs I would most like to change is ____.
6. The steps involved in making this change are ____.
7. My timetable for accomplishing this is ____.
8. The people or groups I will ask for support and assistance are ____.
9. My rewards for making this change will be ____.

Meeting Students' Needs

For students who score *Excellent.* Suggest students become volunteers at a drug rehabilitation center or other community agencies that educate the public about the dangers of drug abuse.

For students who score *Good.* Have students research career opportunities in drug enforcement, pharmaceuticals, or controlled substance abuse counseling.

For students who score *Fair.* Have students organize a peer-support group for students who wish to remain drug-free.

For students who *Need Improvement.* Have students consider how drugs adversely affect society. Suggest that troubled students contact a counselor who is equipped to care for drug-dependent teenagers.

Building Decision-Making Skills

Nikita's friends smoke a joint almost every day during lunch in the restroom at school. While Nikita seldom participates, she helps her friends by being a "lookout" for school officials who occasionally happen by. The friends insist they could never put up with their afternoon teachers without mellowing out. Nikita thinks the smoking habit is getting worse. She also thinks it is affecting her friends; they are barely passing their courses. Nikita doesn't use drugs and wishes that her friends would stop. What should she do? Some of her choices are:

A. Tell the school counselor about the situation and ask for help in dealing with it.

B. Tell her friends she's not going to take the risks of being the "lookout."

C. Tell her friends she doesn't want to have anything more to do with them.

D. Think about what is important to her and which decision coincides with her value system.

WHAT DO YOU THINK?

1. **Choices.** What are some other choices Nikita has?

2. **Consequences.** What are the positives and negatives of each choice?

3. **Consequences.** What risks are involved in this decision?

4. **Consequences.** How will Nikita's health triangle be affected by this decision?

5. **Decision.** How do you think Nikita should handle this situation?

6. **Evaluation.** Have you ever been in a similar situation? If so, how did you handle it? What did you learn? Would you handle a similar situation differently now? Explain your answer.

Tom has been approached in the restroom by a student council officer selling pot and cocaine. He feels he should report it, but since Tom has been in trouble before, he doesn't think the principal will believe his word against a student leader. Even though Tom has had his share of trouble, he doesn't do drugs. Tom has a good relationship with his math teacher but doesn't know whether or not to get him involved. Tom has several choices. Some of them include:

A. Tell the principal or the assistant principal.

B. Tell the math teacher and ask him to pursue it but keep Tom's name out of it.

C. Forget the situation. Stay away from the pusher and let him get caught on his own.

D. Write an anonymous letter informing the school administration and the police of the situation.

WHAT DO YOU THINK?

7. **Choices.** What other choices might Tom have?

8. **Consequences.** What are the advantages and disadvantages of each choice?

9. **Consequences.** What risks does Tom face?

10. **Consequences.** Who will probably be affected by his decision? Explain your answer.

11. **Evaluation.** Have you ever been unfairly stereotyped by others because of your appearance or because of previous experiences? Explain the situation and how you dealt with it.

Discussing the Answers

Situation 1. The first thing Nikita may want to do is to stop standing guard at the door. Eventually, Nikita must decide how much she values her friendship with her joint-smoking friends. Nikita can be a true friend by actively confronting her friends about their use of marijuana. If her friends are psychologically addicted, however, her friends may not be able to quit on their own and may need outside help.

Situation 2. Perhaps the best way for Tom to handle this situation is to talk it over with a trusted adult, such as his math teacher. A trusted adult who knows the situation can objectively help Tom make an appropriate choice.

Building Decision-Making Skills

Teaching Strategies

L1 CLASS ACTIVITY. Have students discuss the manner in which Nikita should handle the situation with her friends smoking a joint in the restroom. Choose the top three possibilities and have students role-play all three.

L2 CLASS ACTIVITY. Tom has had a history of causing trouble at school, and yet he believes strongly that selling illegal drugs is wrong. Have students debate the best way in which Tom could handle the situation. Have students pick the top three responses and role-play all three.

L1 CLASS ACTIVITY. Another possible role-play pertaining to illegal drugs is: You are planning a small get-together with a few close friends while your parents are out of town. Your parents warned you not to have anyone over while they are gone. The word at school is that you are having a huge party and hundreds of people are planning to come and bring alcohol and illegal drugs. You know that you have to do something to stop this from occurring.

L1 DISCUSSION. Invite recovering drug abusing youths to lead a student-to-student discussion about the dangers of using illegal drugs.

DID YOU KNOW?

- Teen females who consider themselves unattractive are four times more likely to use illegal drugs than those with higher self-esteem.
- Now available on some college campuses are drug-free dormitories, where students pledge not to use any mood-altering substances.

REVIEW

Answers to Chapter 24 Review

Using Health Terms

1. Addiction
2. Physiological dependence
3. Tolerance
4. Psychological dependence
5. Psychoactive
6. Flashback
7. Crack
8. Depressants
9. Antipsychotic tranquilizers
10. Inhalants
11. Designer drugs
12. Anabolic steroids
13. Marijuana
14. Hashish

Building Academic Skills

15. Summaries will vary.

Recalling the Facts

16. Newspapers, television, radio.
17. Absenteeism and accidents cause lost productivity for companies.
18. The cost of lost productivity is passed on to consumers in terms of high prices.
19. Answers may include but are not limited to: their friends do, peer pressure, they like the "high" feeling, to ease boredom, to escape problems.
20. Physiological dependence, tolerance, withdrawal, psychological dependence, addiction.
21. With physiological dependence one's body has a chemical need for the drug. With psychological dependence one believes one has a need.
22. Those that affect the central nervous system and alter normal functioning of the brain.
23. Methamphetamine.
24. It constricts blood vessels in the mucous membranes, reducing blood flow to the area and causing it to become dry.
25. Crack.
26. A form of cocaine that can be smoked. It is extremely addictive; users can develop sore throat, hoarseness, and lung damage; it can cause death by cardiac or respiratory failure.
27. Definition for *stimulants* can be found on page 483 or in the Glossary. Examples:

amphetamines, ice, cocaine, crack.
28. Depression, edginess, weight loss, paranoia, hallucinations, physiological dependence, damage to tissues in the nose, holes in the nasal septum, liver damage, malnutrition, heart attack, risk of HIV infection if cocaine is injected.

29. Definition for *depressants* can be found on page 484 or in the Glossary. Examples: barbiturates, tranquilizers.
30. Babies can be born addicted, have birth defects or behavioral problems.
31. Depressants that reduce muscular activity, coordination, and attention span.

32. They help a person relax and have a feeling of well-being.
33. Definition for *narcotic* can be found on page 485 or in the Glossary. Examples: methadone, opium, morphine, heroin, codeine.
34. Definition for *hallucinogens* can be found on page 486 or in the Glossary. Examples: PCP, LSD.

Using Health Terms

On a separate sheet of paper, write the term that best matches each definition given below.

LESSON 1

1. A physiological or psychological dependence on a substance.
2. A chemical need for a drug.
3. The need for larger doses of a drug to achieve the same effect.
4. When a person believes a drug is needed in order to feel good.

LESSON 2

5. Drugs that affect the central nervous system and cause mental or behavioral changes.
6. Recurrence of the effect of a drug, often associated with PCP and LSD.
7. A smokable form of cocaine.
8. Drugs that slow down the central nervous system, relax muscles, relieve feelings of tension, and bring on sleep.
9. Tranquilizers used to treat severe mental disorders.

LESSON 3

10. Substances with fumes that are sniffed to give a hallucinogenic high.
11. Drugs that resemble the action but not the chemical makeup of a drug.
12. Synthetic derivatives of the male hormone testosterone.
13. A drug that is a hallucinogen but also has the effects of a depressant and a stimulant.
14. The dark brown resin collected from the tops of the cannabis plant.

Building Academic Skills

LESSON 1

15. **Reading.** Read a magazine article about an individual or family who has been affected by drugs. Summarize your conclusions about the impact of a life of drugs on the people around the individual.

Recalling the Facts

LESSON 1

16. How do average Americans learn about the growing drug problem in the United States?
17. What are some of the effects of drug use on the work force?
18. How does drug use contribute to rising consumer costs?
19. What are some reasons people give for using drugs?
20. List five problems an individual who uses drugs will likely experience.
21. Distinguish between physiological dependence and psychological dependence.

LESSON 2

22. What are psychoactive drugs?
23. What is the name of the drug commonly called crank, speed, or ice?
24. Explain the effects cocaine has on the nose.
25. What is freebase?
26. What is crack? Why is it so dangerous?
27. Define *stimulants* and give four examples.
28. What problems can result from regular cocaine use?
29. Define *depressants* and give two examples.
30. What may happen to babies born to mothers who use depressants during pregnancy?
31. What are tranquilizers?
32. Why are tranquilizers so popular?
33. Define *narcotic* and give five examples.
34. Define *hallucinogens*; give two examples.

LESSON 3

35. What health problems do look-alike drugs present?
36. What is THC? Where is it stored in the body? What parts of the body are most affected?
37. Why does hashish affect a user more strongly than marijuana?
38. Why is it dangerous to ride in a car with a driver who has been smoking marijuana?
39. Define inhalants and give five examples.
40. What are the risks of using steroids?
41. What are the dangers of inhalants?

REVIEW

Thinking Critically

LESSON 1

42. Analysis. Drug use takes an enormous toll on society, as well as on the individual. Explain this statement and provide several illustrations of the costs to both the individual and society.

LESSON 2

43. Synthesis. Drug use is not unique to the teenage culture. Many adults also use drugs. How might cocaine use affect the life of an adult user? How might it affect the children of the user?

44. Analysis. Talk with someone who was a young adult in the 1960s to learn more about the social climate of that time, especially the attitude toward drug use. What was his or her favorite music, dance, hairstyle, movie? What conclusions can you draw about life in the 1960s? How was the social climate of the 1960s similar to the social climate today? How was it different?

LESSON 3

45. Evaluation. The value of legalizing marijuana has long been debated. Take a stance and argue your position. You may need to find out more about this drug in order to make an intelligent argument. Support your opinion with facts.

Making the Connection

LESSON 1

46. Math. Find an article about drugs that has a chart or bar graph. Present the information in a different form, such as a pie chart.

LESSON 2

47. Language Arts. Work with classmates to write, edit, design, and print an informational leaflet, "Signs of Possible Drug Use." Distribute the leaflet with a school newsletter, at a parents' meeting, or at a shopping mall.

Applying Health Knowledge

LESSON 1

48. Write down three of your personal goals. Next to each goal write a statement about how involvement in drugs would interfere with your ability to reach your goal.

49. You have many learned behaviors. Make a list of five behaviors you practice and describe how you worked to learn each one. Then think of a behavior you have decided to change. Tell the process you followed to stop that behavior.

LESSON 2

50. Drug users often started experimenting occasionally with drugs and then became dependent on them. Explain how a change from experimentation to dependency can happen.

LESSON 3

51. Name some bacterial infections to which marijuana smokers may be more susceptible than nonsmokers.

52. What ramifications does the fact that marijuana lowers the level of testosterone have for a teenage male who uses marijuana heavily?

53. If you had a friend who told you he wanted to start taking steroids to develop his muscles, what advice would you give him?

Beyond the Classroom

LESSON 1

54. Parental Involvement. With your parents, read *Go Ask Alice* which is a true anonymous account of a 15-year-old's struggle with drugs. Discuss the thoughts and feelings you each had while reading this book.

55. Further Study. Read a newspaper from a major city in your area for a week. Clip each article that is somehow related to drugs or drug use. Draw conclusions based on these articles. Share your findings with your peers.

35. Emergency medical personnel may be unable to treat a patient because they don't know what chemicals are in the drugs.

36. The chemical that produces the psychoactive effect in marijuana. It is stored in fatty tissue. Brain cells, liver, lungs, kidneys, reproductive organs.

37. It contains more THC.

38. The driver has impaired visual perception, concentration, coordination, and slowed reaction time.

39. Definition for *inhalants* can be found on page 489 or in the Glossary. Examples (accept five of the following): solvents, gasoline, model glue, felt-tip markers, aerosols, insecticides, freon.

40. High blood pressure, acne, liver damage, heart disease, stroke; in males—baldness, depression, aggressiveness, decreased sperm production and testicle size, increase in breast growth, body and facial hair; in females—breast shrinkage, growth of facial hair, baldness; mood swings, violent behavior, risk of infection with HIV from shared needles.

41. Dangers with regular use—trouble maintaining balance, glassy stare, difficulty talking, impaired judgment. Heavy use—fatigue, liver and kidney damage, changes in bone marrow, permanent brain damage, suffocation.

Thinking Critically

42. Answers will vary.

43. Answers will vary. Possible answers: Money budgeted for food, clothing, house or rent payment, or entertainment may be used for buying cocaine. Purchasing and using cocaine may become the main goal. Children of cocaine users may feel unwanted or unloved, confused by parent's behavior, or be physically or mentally abused or neglected.

44. Answers will vary.

45. Opinions will vary but should be supported factually and logically.

Making the Connection

46. Pie charts will vary.

47. Leaflets will vary.

Applying Health Knowledge

48. Answers will vary.

49. Answers will vary. Accept any behavior that has been learned (as opposed to being innate).

50. Answers will vary. Possible answer: Many drugs cause a user to develop a physiological or psychological dependency without the user even realizing it.

51. Answers will vary. Possible answers: Pneumonia, bronchitis, pleurisy, tuberculosis, etc.

52. Answers will vary. Possible answer: It might interfere with the development of secondary sex characteristics.

53. Answers will vary. Possible answers: Steroid use has serious side effects; the drawbacks outweigh the benefits; it is illegal; work out to enhance muscle development.

Beyond the Classroom

54. Answers will vary.

55. Answers will vary.

Lesson Summaries

LESSON 1. Addiction is increasingly being recognized as a disease, though life-style decisions and messages society gives affect whether or not individuals acquire the disease. Addiction has physiological and psychological consequences.

LESSON 2. The process of recovering from addiction has emotional and social hurdles. Remaining drug-free is an ongoing concern for addicts. Treatment choices include counseling, support groups, and an assortment of treatment centers.

LESSON 3. Someone who is codependent is overly concerned with other people's behaviors and problems and feels driven to fix and control those problems. A common trait of codependency is trying to protect a person with substance addiction from facing the consequences of the addiction.

LESSON 4. Intervention may be required to recover from codependency. Support groups for substance addicts offer the codependent individual a support system for coping and structured programs for regaining emotional and social health.

Introducing the Chapter

Tell students that addiction for a long time was a misunderstood problem that was considered only to be a consequence of behavior. Research has led scientists to a better understanding of the causes of addiction and the problems an addict and his or her family face. This chapter will present some of these findings.

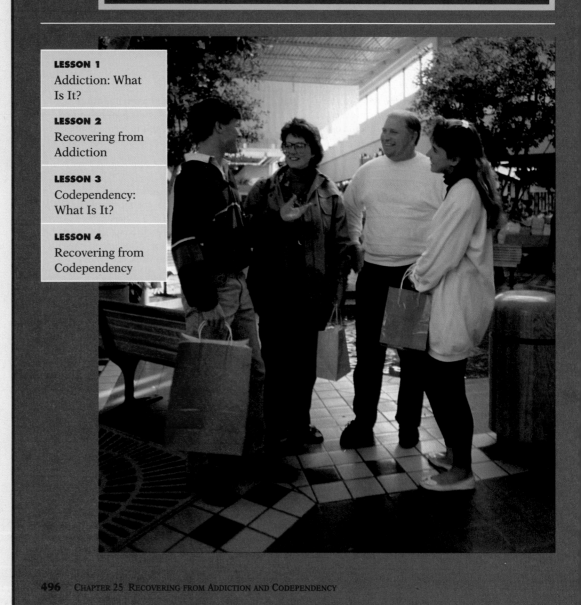

CHAPTER

25

RECOVERING FROM ADDICTION AND CODEPENDENCY

LESSON 1
Addiction: What Is It?

LESSON 2
Recovering from Addiction

LESSON 3
Codependency: What Is It?

LESSON 4
Recovering from Codependency

496   CHAPTER 25 RECOVERING FROM ADDICTION AND CODEPENDENCY

Performance Assessment ✓

Refer to pages T 23 to T 25 for a Performance Assessment strategy for this chapter. See the *Performance Assessment Activities* booklet for additional suggestions.

Key to Ability Levels

Teaching strategies have been coded for varying learning styles and abilities.

L1   Level 1 activities are basic activities and should be within the ability range of all students.

L2   Level 2 activities are average activities and should be within the ability range of average to above-average students.

L3   Level 3 activities are challenging activities designed for the ability range of above-average students.

LD   LD activities should be within the ability range of learning-disabled students.

LEP   LEP activities should be within the ability range of Limited English Proficiency students.

ADDICTION: WHAT IS IT?

A ddiction is a complex matter. Like a jigsaw puzzle, an addiction is made up of many interlocking parts. These puzzle pieces may fit together differently in different people.

These days some experts are comparing alcohol and drug addiction to illnesses such as diabetes and cardiovascular disease. They have found that the tendency to develop these diseases may be inherited. However, the life-style decisions people make and the messages society gives about the use of alcohol and drugs also affect whether or not people become addicted.

Addiction

An **addiction** is a physiological or psychological dependence on a substance or activity. One can be addicted to alcohol, drugs, gambling—even food. In this chapter we will discuss addiction to alcohol and other drugs. **Physiological dependence** means that the body has become accustomed to a drug or drugs and needs these chemicals just to function. The body of an addict craves these substances. Physiological dependence is determined when a person experiences tolerance and withdrawal. Tolerance means the body becomes used to the effect of the drug. The body then requires larger doses of the drug to produce the same effect. Withdrawal occurs when the person stops taking a drug to which he or she is physiologically dependent and experiences physical symptoms.

Psychological dependence means a person comes to depend on the feeling received from a drug. Psychological dependence often involves denial, which means that the addict does not admit or does not realize that he or she is in trouble with alcohol or other drugs. The person believes that he or she can control the use of the drug and is not causing any harm.

ALCOHOLISM

Alcoholism, or addiction to alcohol, is considered a disease by the American Medical Association (AMA). Since 1987 **drug dependence,** or drug addiction, has also been considered a disease by the AMA. Both of these diseases are described as chronic, progressive, and potentially fatal. *Chronic* means that the diseases are ongoing, and *progressive* means that they get worse over time. *Potentially fatal* means that people can die from the disease.

The Addiction Continuum

Addiction is a process—a series of gradual changes that happen over time. This process happens more quickly to some than to others. Some

---

LESSON 1 FOCUS

TERMS TO USE
- Addiction
- Physiological dependence
- Psychological dependence
- Alcoholism
- Drug dependence
- Intervention

CONCEPTS TO LEARN
- An addiction is a physiological or psychological dependence on alcohol or other drugs.
- Alcoholism and drug dependence are considered diseases by the American Medical Association.
- Addiction is a series of gradual changes that happen over time.

ATTITUDES AND BEHAVIORS TO EVALUATE
- Self-Inventory, page 512.
- Building Decision-Making Skills, page 513.

Focus

Lesson Objectives

After studying this lesson, students should be able to:
- explain addiction in terms of physiological and psychological dependence
- describe the process of intervention and how it helps get the alcoholic or other drug addict into recovery

Bellringer

Write the following on the chalkboard for students to work on while attendance is being taken: *How do you know if someone is addicted to a drug, such as alcohol or cocaine? How does the addicted person behave?*

Introducing the Lesson

Refer to the Bellringer. Ask volunteers to share their responses. Students may believe that someone is addicted only after he or she has reached a stage of total dependency on the drug. Emphasize that addiction is really a process and that someone may be on his or her way to becoming drug dependent even with just "social" use of the drug.

Building Vocabulary

- Discuss the terms *physiological dependence* and *psychological dependence* by asking the following questions: How do physiological and psychological dependency differ? How are they related to addiction?
- Ask students to demonstrate their understanding of intervention by describing what happens in a typical intervention.
- Ask students to complete *Workbook Vocabulary Activity 66.*

Resources for Lesson 1

- **Transparency** 28
- **Guided Reading** Activity 66
- **Workbook** Vocabulary Activity 66
- **Reteaching** Activity 66
- **Lesson 1 Quiz**
- **BARN Software,** Alcohol and Other Drugs
- **The Reality of Drugs**

- **Performance Assessment** Activity 25
ABC News InterActive Videodiscs
Drugs and Substance Abuse, Side 1
Ch 15 The Nature of Addiction

DID YOU KNOW?

- Drug use patterns may be determined by certain factors: (1) peer pressure, particularly when someone first tries using a drug (2) home, school, and work environments and (3) mental state.

Guided Practice

L1 DISCUSSION. What are the symptoms of physiological dependence on a drug like alcohol? How is physiological dependence related to the concepts of tolerance and addiction process?

L1 SPEAKER. Invite a drug counselor or addiction specialist to the class to describe the process of intervention.

LEP COOPERATIVE LEARNING. Select students to act out a typical intervention meeting with an alcoholic or other drug addict. They should decide who should be at the meeting and what should be said. Ask the rest of the class to decide whether or not they think the presentation will convince the addict to seek treatment.

L1 USING LIFE MANAGEMENT SKILLS TRANSPARENCY 28. Refer to the Teaching Transparencies Binder.

Independent Practice

L1 SELF-ESTEEM. How would you describe an individual who is psychologically dependent on a drug such as marijuana? How is psychological dependence related to the concept of denial? How would you describe the level of self-esteem of a person who is psychologically dependent? How might a person break the cycle?

L1 EXPLANATION. Explain what it means when alcoholism and drug dependence, in general, are described as chronic, progressive, and potentially fatal diseases. Ask for examples of other chronic, progressive, and potentially fatal diseases.

LEP CLASS ACTIVITY. Ask volunteers to explain the concept of addiction as a process or continuum by drawing a diagram on the chalkboard. What lies at the two ends of the continuum? What happens along the way? Ask them to explain how their diagram can be interpreted in two ways: to show what happens to a single individual over time; or to show variation among individuals who are at different stages in the continuum.

- Each year in the U.S., between 5,000 and 10,000 children are born with fetal alcohol syndrome.
- Up to 100,000 children may be born each year with fetal alcohol effects, the less severe but still serious results of drinking alcohol during pregnancy.
- Exposure of a fetus to alcohol is now a leading cause of mental retardation in the U.S.

people get hooked on a drug from the first time they take a drink, a pill, or an injection. For other people, an addiction develops more slowly, perhaps over a period of many years. Others do not become addicted at all. For this reason it is difficult to know or predict exactly when a person becomes addicted.

ADDICTION: THE DOWNWARD SLIDE

These steps show the way an addiction to alcohol or other drugs might develop.

Step 1: First use/occasional use
- Takes first drink or uses other drug for the first time
- Likes the way it feels and reduces stress
- Uses the drug in social settings

Step 2: Occasional trouble with drug
- Shows mood swings or personality changes (may happen on the first use)
- Has greater tolerance than others—for example, can outdrink others without seeming drunk
- May cry, get violent, or show high-risk behaviors while drinking and using drugs
- May have blackouts, not remembering what was said or done

Step 3: Regular use of drug
- Finds that tolerance increases—needs more of a drug and may crave it more frequently
- Tries to control drug use but cannot
- Feels guilty after binges, or episodes
- Hangs out with others who drink or use drugs
- Denies problem; gets angry when others suggest a drinking or drug use problem

Step 4: Multiple drug use
- May combine or switch drugs for new and stronger effects or to assure supply
- May become cross-addicted, or hooked on more than one kind of drug

Step 5: Increasing dependency
- Needs drug just to function
- Finds that drug no longer has same effect; needs drug just to stop shaking or feeling sick
- Loses interest in family, friends, school, job, sports—everything but drugs

Step 6: Total dependency
- Suffers major loss because of addiction, such as getting thrown out of school, losing a relationship, causing a car crash, being hospitalized, getting arrested
- Feels physically and emotionally defeated

K E E P I N G   F I T

The Gene Scene

Studies published in 1991 support the idea that there is a gene or family of genes at least in part responsible for alcoholism and other drug dependencies.

This idea is not accepted by everyone. Research does show that children of alcoholic parents are statistically at a greater risk than others of becoming alcoholics. However, the role of heredity versus environment remains unclear to many on this issue.

Knowing your family's medical history can provide important clues about your health and possible risks.

Additional Information

Addiction. It is estimated that there are over 2 million compulsive gamblers in the U.S. Many of these gamblers are teens. A 1989 study suggests that people with the compulsion to gamble may suffer from a biochemical craving much like that of alcoholics or other addicts. Though it has in the past been classified as a behavior disorder or an impulse control condition, new research indicates that for the truly compulsive gambler, the problem may lie in the person's central nervous system. Compulsive gamblers have been found to have higher than normal levels of norepinephrine, a brain chemical given off during periods of peak excitement—the kind that some people experience when gambling.

Overcoming The Odds

Sarah W. is 17. Her dad is an alcoholic, and last fall, her dad's drinking seemed to get worse. He started the day with whiskey and ended it with beer. He stayed home from work a lot. Whenever he drank, he seemed to change. "The slightest thing could set him off," she says. "Then he'd yell, slam doors, and threaten Mom, my brother, or me. A couple of times he slapped my brother Mark around, and once, he banged my head against the wall. It was really scary. I would lie awake nights listening to my mom yelling or crying or my father bad-mouthing my brother. It was always a bad scene, and it was ripping me up inside."

Finally, Sarah stopped having her friends over. She couldn't eat or sleep either.

Then, last winter, Sarah had a great health teacher named Mrs. Quintana. In her class, Sarah learned that alcoholism is a disease. She learned how it not only affected her dad but was affecting everyone in her family—that they all, not just her dad, needed help. She finally got up the courage to call a good friend whose mom was a recovering alcoholic, and she asked her what she should do.

The next week her friend took Sarah to her first Alateen

meeting. She was uncomfortable at first but says she soon felt like she belonged. "It was so great to learn that I'm not alone in this," she says. "What a relief to know I didn't need to keep it all a secret anymore and that I don't have to spend my whole life worrying about my dad's drinking."

Soon Sarah's mom started going to Al-Anon, and they both stopped covering up for her dad. Recently, they confronted her dad with just how bad the situation had gotten, and now her dad is in recovery, too. "True, my older brother is still drinking and using drugs," Sarah says, "but now I know there's help out there for him, too, when he's ready. I didn't use to know that. I didn't use to know that at all."

Sarah says she feels really good about herself and her own life these days and proud that her decision to help herself has begun to help her whole family. "I'm starting to learn that I'm not responsible for anybody's behavior except my own. I've also learned that with alcoholism in the family, I'm at risk of becoming an alcoholic myself, so I feel more committed to not drinking than a lot of my friends. The biggest change, though, is that I don't feel so numb. I feel more alive. I used to feel so ashamed, so afraid, so shut off from life. Yes, there are still scary times, but mostly I have hope now. And my dad, well, he's doing so much better. We jog together before dinner every night and talk. We joke around and call it our 'happy hour.' Life is really so much better around here since he quit drinking and agreed to get help."

1. In what ways does Sarah's story illustrate that alcoholism is a family disease?
2. Why should the first step in getting help for a family member's addiction be to get help for oneself?
3. Why do you think Sarah's brother's chances for recovery might be better than average?

Additional Information

Cultural Alcohol Use. Though alcoholic beverages have been manufactured and consumed for thousands of years, the acceptance and use of alcohol varies widely. In some countries, such as France and Nigeria, alcoholic beverages are consumed daily and play an important role in social interactions. To the contrary, in other cultures, such as Mormon and Muslim, drinking alcoholic beverages is forbidden.

The introduction of alcohol to people who did not use it before contact, notably Pacific Islanders and Native North Americans, has had long-range repercussions, leading to widespread addiction and contributing to social disruption.

Assess

Check for Understanding

- Assign and discuss the lesson review. Encourage LD students to focus on questions 1, 2, and 3.

Evaluate

- Administer, grade, and discuss the *Lesson 1 Quiz*.

Reteach

- Ask students to describe the behavior of six different individuals, one in each of the six steps of the downward slide to addiction.
- Ask students to complete *Reteaching Activity 66*.

Enrich

- Select students to research the history of alcohol use and how alcoholics have been regarded at different times in the past.

Close

Tell students that in this lesson they learned that addiction is a process or continuum that involves physiological and/or psychological dependence on a drug. They examined the behavior that characterizes individuals as they progress from their first drink or use of the drug—all the way to hitting rock bottom. They also learned how family members and friends can help get the alcoholic or drug addict into recovery through the process of intervention.

DID YOU KNOW?

Here's how some recovering addicts define addiction:

- an escape from reality that kills you while you think you're keeping yourself safe;
- excess without pleasure;
- when "want to" becomes "have to";
- when you have to rely on something else to make your life okay.

Intervention

Many families rely on a process called intervention. **Intervention** means interrupting the addiction continuum before the alcoholic or addict hits bottom. The process begins with meetings of family members and other significant people involved in the life of the chemically dependent person. These meetings take place without his or her knowledge. A certified drug and alcohol counselor and someone from a support group such as Alcoholics Anonymous usually oversee these meetings. Family members learn about addiction and the ways in which they have become affected by it. They do list work—listing all of the episodes they can remember when the person's drinking and drug use were involved and how it made them feel. They rehearse what might happen at the actual intervention—a surprise meeting with the alcoholic or addict when the list work is presented. Often this meeting forces the alcoholic or drug addict to face just how bad his or her addiction is and just how unmanageable his or her life has become because of it. The group presents the alcoholic or addict with a plan for immediate treatment. If the person refuses to get this needed help, the family, boss, or others taking part in the intervention process tell the person what steps they plan to take in response to the refusal to get help. For example, a wife might say, "If you will not get help, I will move out"; or a boss might say, "If you drink again at work, you're out of a job." Such ultimatums let the chemically dependent person know that all enabling has stopped and the person must now face the consequences of his or her addiction.

Imagine addiction to alcohol or other drugs as a downward slide. An addiction can begin with the first use of alcohol or other drug. Unfortunately, an addiction often ends at the bottom end of the continuum with irreversible damage to the body and mind—or with death. It is this side of addiction that has become a major health problem in the United States.

During an intervention, evidence of addiction is presented to the person with the drug problem.

LESSON 1 REVIEW

Reviewing Facts and Vocabulary

1. Define the term *addiction*.
2. How are alcoholism and drug dependence described by the American Medical Association?

Thinking Critically

3. **Analysis.** Compare physiological and psychological dependence.

4. **Synthesis.** What explanations can you give for why some people become addicts and some people do not.

Applying Health Knowledge

5. Draw an addiction continuum. Think about someone you know or know of who may have an addiction to alcohol or other drugs. Where would you place this person on the continuum? Which characteristics of the downward slide seem to apply to this person?

Answers to Lesson 1 Review

1. A physiological or psychological dependence on a substance or activity.
2. Both are considered diseases and are described as chronic, progressive, and potentially fatal.
3. With both one feels that one cannot do without a drug. Physiological dependence means one's body needs a drug. Psychological dependence means one thinks one needs the drug.
4. Answers will vary. Possible answer: Addiction is a process that occurs over a period of time. For some this process happens more quickly than for others.
5. Answers will vary. Refer to page 498.

RECOVERING FROM ADDICTION

Getting well again is known as **recovery.** Recovery from alcohol or drug addiction means learning to live an alcohol- or drug-free life. In addition to the physical aspects, there are also mental and social aspects to deal with for successful recovery from an addiction.

The Recovery Continuum

Like addiction, recovery is a process. It happens over time. It happens at different rates and in different ways for different people. Yet there are certain characteristics common to most recovery stories.

Imagine recovery on a continuum as you did for the addiction process. The first steps in recovery are to recognize that there is a problem with alcohol or other drugs and to make the decision to give them up. The next step is to actually remove these drugs from the body. This process is called **detoxification** and should take place under medical supervision. In addition to regaining physical health, recovery also involves restoring one's mental health by learning to build healthy relationships and by taking responsibility for one's own life.

People in recovery describe themselves as recovering rather than being recovered. This is because the recovery process is ongoing. The biochemical and perhaps genetic conditions that first set them up for addiction remain in their bodies and brains whether or not they use drugs. Alcoholism and drug dependence are therefore considered lifelong diseases. They cannot be cured. They can, however, be kept from progressing further.

Experts on the addiction and recovery process used to believe that people had to hit bottom, or suffer some major loss as a result of their

Experts recommend total abstinence for a recovering alcoholic.

LESSON 2 FOCUS

TERMS TO USE
- Recovery
- Detoxification
- Relapses
- Total abstinence
- Alcoholics Anonymous (AA)

CONCEPTS TO LEARN
- Recovery is a series of gradual changes that happen over time.
- There are many treatment options available for someone with an addiction who wants to obtain help.

ATTITUDES AND BEHAVIORS TO EVALUATE
- Self-Inventory, page 512.
- Building Decision-Making Skills, page 513.

Focus

Lesson Objectives

After studying this lesson, students should be able to:
- describe the process of recovery from addiction
- identify sources of help for the addict who wishes to enter recovery

Bellringer

Write the following on the chalkboard for students to work on while attendance is being taken: *If a friend or family member needed help with an alcohol or other drug addiction problem but didn't know where to turn, what advice would you give?*

Introducing the Lesson

Refer to the Bellringer. Ask volunteers to share their responses. Tell students that in this lesson they will learn about sources of help for people who want to recover from addictions. These range from support groups, like Alcoholics Anonymous, to special treatment centers, such as halfway houses. First, students will study how the recovery process progresses for the typical addict.

DID YOU KNOW?

- Rational Recovery is a new alternative to AA, a support group for people who believe that by finding logical solutions to their problems and finding group support they can overcome their alcohol problems. Instead of ongoing support, they suggest attendance at their meetings for from 6 months to 1 year. As of 1991 there were approximately 1,000 Rational Recovery groups in the U.S.
- Support groups like AA, NA, and CA suggest 90 meetings in the first 90 days of recovery, followed by ongoing meetings. Some people continue to attend daily, others every few days or weekly.

Resources for Lesson 2

- **Transparency** 28
- **Guided Reading** Activity 67
- **Workbook** Vocabulary Activity 67
- **Reteaching** Activity 67
- **Lesson 2 Quiz**

ABC News InterActive Videodiscs
Drugs and Substance Abuse, Side 1
Ch 15 The Nature of Addiction

Drugs and Substance Abuse, Side 2
Ch 3 Cost to Society

Building Vocabulary

- Ask students to write a concise paragraph that shows they understand how these three terms are related: *recovery, detoxification,* and *relapse.*
- Ask students to complete *Workbook Vocabulary Activity 67.*

Teach

Guided Practice

L1 DISCUSSION. Ask students what the steps involved in the process of recovery from addiction are.

L1 EXPLANATION. Explain why we say of alcoholics and other drug addicts that they are "in recovery" not that they have "recovered."

L1 DISCUSSION. Ask why alcoholism is considered to be a lifelong disease.

L1 EXPLANATION. Explain why detoxification is an important part of recovery from drug addiction.

L2 CLASS ACTIVITY. Ask volunteers to act out a scenario for the class in which an addicted individual is confronted by a family member or close friend about his or her abuse of alcohol or other drugs.

L1 DISCUSSION. Discuss how a relapse while in recovery from drug addiction does not mean that the person is hopelessly addicted to the drug.

L1 SPEAKER. Invite a drug counselor to class to share his or her experiences in dealing with recovering alcoholics and other drug addicts.

L3 DISCUSSION. Ask what the role of poor self-esteem is in the drug addiction and recovery process.

L1 SPEAKER. Invite a representative from the local Alcoholics Anonymous headquarters to speak to the class about the role of AA in recovery from alcoholism.

DID YOU KNOW?

- People in recovery sometimes develop transfer addictions. That means they go from being addicted to one substance to being addicted to another substance or behavior. For example, recovering alcoholics sometimes develop eating disorders or become compulsive gamblers.
- People in recovery do not concentrate on the fact that they will have to live a lifetime without drugs. Instead, they talk about staying sober or clean one day at a time.

---

drinking or drug use, before they would decide to get well. Now it is generally recognized that people can begin the recovery process at any point on the downward slide into addiction—even before they suffer major losses.

Most experts in the field of addiction recommend total abstinence for the recovering alcoholic and addict. **Total abstinence** means not using any mood-altering drugs including alcohol. Long-term studies show that attempts at controlled drinking and drug use usually fail. Even small amounts of alcohol or other drugs can send an addict back into addiction.

Many people in recovery manage to stay drug-free for the rest of their lives. Others may have **relapses,** or slips—periodic returns to drinking and drug use. Yet despite how far down the addiction continuum a person goes or how many times that person relapses, the choice of and chance for recovery are always there.

RECOVERY: THE UPWARD CLIMB

The following scale shows how a person's recovery from alcoholism or other drug dependency might progress:
- Decides to get help
- Actually asks for or goes for help
- Has medical evaluation, or checkup
- Detoxes (gets drug out of the system)
- Learns about the disease
- Finds that physical health improves
- Sees appearance improve
- Experiences improvement in mental health
- Gains emotional control
- Rebuilds or makes healthy relationships
- Sets and achieves new goals
- Rebuilds self-esteem
- Continues to stay drug-free
- Helps others with addictions to recover
- Takes responsibility for own life
- Continues lifelong adventure in recovery

Treatment Choices: Where to Go for Help

When someone wants help with an addiction, a first step in getting help may be to talk with someone whom that person trusts, preferably someone knowledgeable about addiction.

Counseling

A parent, teacher, school counselor, or peer counselor may be a place to start. A person in trouble with alcohol or other drugs might also call one of the toll-free drug and alcohol hot lines, the National Council on Alcoholism, or a drug and alcohol treatment center. Someone there would connect the caller with a counselor who specializes in drug and alcohol counseling.

Additional Information

Cocaine. Fifteen years ago nobody thought cocaine was addictive because it produced few withdrawal symptoms. Today, scientists consider it to be one of the most addictive drugs in existence because of the intense cravings it creates. Lab rats given the choice between cocaine, food, and water will starve themselves to get more and more of the drug.

More than 25 million people in the U.S. have tried cocaine. Ten million are regular users, 5 million suffer serious problems related to its use, and 1 million are addicted. Every day thousands of Americans try cocaine for the first time, and many of those who continue to use it will end up addicted.

just say no

A school guidance counselor can make referrals to a drug or alcohol counselor.

Support Groups

A support group is a group of people who share a common problem and work together to help one another and themselves cope with and recover from that problem. Regular attendance at such support groups is the most popular form of ongoing treatment for addictions. Support groups such as **Alcoholics Anonymous (AA)** have played a major role in helping people to get and stay alcohol- and drug-free. At meetings, which are held frequently all over the world, members provide support and help one another stay sober or otherwise drug-free. Such meetings are confidential; members can remain anonymous because no one has to give his or her last name. They are also free of charge. Each AA office can direct people to local AA meetings or to other support groups such as Narcotics Anonymous or Cocaine Anonymous.

Alcohol and Drug Treatment Centers

Alcohol and drug treatment centers offer a wide range of services to addicts who want to recover. Many centers specialize in treating teens with addictions or have special units solely for adolescents.

Some treatment centers are privately owned, but there are also state and community alcoholism and mental health clinics that offer professional care at a low cost or free of charge. Since drug and alcohol dependence are considered diseases, some health insurance plans may cover at least some of the costs.

Culturally Speaking

Busted

A group of young African Americans who are aspiring to be actors and actresses have produced an antidrug film, *Busted*, for the Partnership For a Drug-Free America. The Partnership wanted to "unsell" kids on drugs. So they tried something new. *Busted* is a 10-minute film that is shown before feature films aimed at teen audiences. During *Busted*, at a test run in a Harlem theater, the audience became so involved they were actually talking to the girl in the film encouraging her to choose her longtime, straight friends over those who use drugs. The Partnership hopes this scene will be repeated in real life as well.

K E E P I N G   F I T

Tips for Killing the Craving

After an addicted person goes through withdrawal he or she may still crave the drug for some time. A person newly into recovery may lessen such cravings by
- keeping in mind that a person only has to stay drug-free one

day at a time,
- eating fruit or drinking juice when cravings hit,
- avoiding places, people, or behaviors that he or she associates with drinking or drugging,
- getting lots of exercise,

- finding a sober friend whom the person can call to talk over problems and get reinforcement for staying drug-free,
- getting lots of sleep.

RECOVERING FROM ADDICTION **503**

L1 DISCUSSION. Ask students how residential treatment centers differ from outpatient treatment centers. What are some advantages and drawbacks of each?

L2 DISCUSSION. In addition to the withdrawal from physical addiction to alcohol or another drug, what are some of the mental and social aspects of recovery from addiction?

Independent Practice

L1 COMMUNITY INVOLVEMENT. Ask students to locate the names, addresses, and phone numbers of sources of help in their local community for people with alcohol and other drug addictions. Which, if any, are particularly oriented to teens? Have students make a poster or flyer that informs other students in their school of where to go for help—for themselves, for friends, or for family members.

L2 COMMUNITY INVOLVEMENT. Select students to find out if there are any alcohol and drug aftercare programs or halfway houses in their local community. If there are, ask students to investigate if there have been any problems with acceptance of the facilities within the neighborhoods where they're located.

DID YOU KNOW?

- Most alcoholism treatment programs follow some variation of what's known as the Minnesota model, which was developed more than 30 years ago. Such programs provide counseling aimed at behavior modification and education on the nature of addiction and the principles of recovery.

Additional Information

Marijuana. Marijuana—also known as pot, grass, dope, reefer, hashish, and more than 200 other names—is the most widely used drug in the world after caffeine, alcohol, and tobacco. In the U.S., about 66 million people have tried it. Although its use has declined steadily since 1979, about 12 million Americans were using marijuana in 1988.

Marijuana has been used since ancient times in China and India to treat a wide variety of ailments. In the U.S., it was used in some prescription medicines until 1937, when the Marijuana Tax Act outlawed its use for any purpose, recreational or medicinal.

L1 RESEARCH. Ask students to
research what the process of
detoxification from drug dependence involves. How long does it
take? What are the withdrawal
symptoms? Why should it often
be done under medical supervision? Have students present their
findings in an oral report to the
class.

L1 RESEARCH. Ask students to
research what the process of
detoxification from drug dependence involves. How long does it
take? What are the withdrawal
symptoms? Why should it often
be done under medical supervision? Have students present their
findings in an oral report to the
class.

L1 WRITING. Ask students to
write a brief account of how
someone typically recovers from
alcohol or other drug addiction.
Have them describe how counseling, a support group, or a treatment center plays a role in the
recovery process.

L1 RESEARCH. Ask students to
research the studies that have
been done on controlled drinking
and drug use versus total abstinence. What have they found?
Why does it seem to be more
difficult to control alcohol and
other drug use than to abstain
entirely?

**L1 USING THE LESSON
RESOURCES.** For additional student activities, refer to the lesson
resources on page 501.

Assess

Check for
Understanding

- Assign and discuss the lesson
  review. Encourage LD students
  to focus on question 1 independently. Allow several students to
  work together on question 3.

Evaluate

- Administer, grade, and discuss
  the *Lesson 2 Quiz.*

Reteach

- Ask students to research
  Alcoholics Anonymous. What
  are the basic principles it follows? What is the nature of its
  recovery program? What is a
  typical AA meeting like? What
  are the roles of anonymity and
  confidentiality? Have students
  find out where and when AA
  meetings take place in their
  local community.
- Ask students to complete
  Reteaching Activity 67.

HELP WANTED

Occupational
Therapist

An alcohol rehabilitation
center needs an occupa-
tional therapist to design
activity programs that
will allow recovering
addicts to return to independence and employ-
ment. Your contribution
to the rehabilitation process is a key part in helping recovering addicts
regain physical, mental,
and social health. Your
patience, perseverance,
and ability to plan a program suited to an individual's needs will make you
a success in this field,
which offers both per-
sonal and professional
satisfaction.
For more information
contact:
American Occupational
Therapy Association
P.O. Box 1725
1983 Picard Drive
Rockville, MD 20850-4375

HEALTH UPDATE

LOOKING AT THE ISSUES

Health Threats to Unborn Babies

When a pregnant female is
addicted to alcohol or other
drugs, her baby can be born
addicted. The health consequences of the baby's addiction and withdrawal can be
severe and long lasting. In
some states, mothers who
give birth to babies addicted
to cocaine and crack are now
being charged with endangering—even though those drugs
are given indirectly to the
babies before they are actually born.

In 1989, a young female
from Florida became the first
mother convicted of delivering drugs to her baby while
pregnant. She delivered those
drugs through the umbilical
cord by using them herself.
Found guilty, she was sentenced to 1 year in a drug
rehabilitation program and
15 years of probation. This
conviction was later over-
turned.

Analyzing Different
Viewpoints

ONE VIEW. Some people
think that pregnant females
who use drugs are unfit to be
parents at all and should have
their children removed from
them by the courts.

A SECOND VIEW. Others
believe such females should
be placed in prison just as
other parents who commit
life-threatening child abuse
sometimes are.

A THIRD VIEW. Still others
think that these females have
a disease and should be sentenced to treatment, followed
by close observation and drug
testing. People with this view
believe that by getting these
females into treatment, they
have a better chance at
becoming responsible, drug-
free parents.

Exploring Your Views

1. Which of these views
   seems most reasonable
   and fair to you? Why?
2. Do you think that children
   who are born addicted
   should be taken from their
   mothers? Temporarily?
   Permanently? Should they
   be put in foster care or put
   up for adoption? Should
   they be given back to the
   mothers when the babies
   are out of medical danger?
   When the mothers are in
   recovery for addiction?
   How far into recovery?
   Give reasons for each of
   your answers.
3. Should females also be
   prosecuted, or charged,
   with child abuse when
   they drink, smoke, or use
   other addictive drugs?
   Should they be charged
   only when their babies are
   born addicted to or showing harmful side effects
   from these drugs? Why or
   why not?

Detox Units. In some hospitals or treatment centers, there are medical
detox units for alcoholics and addicts undergoing the detoxification process. During this process, which usually lasts from three to seven days,
the person is under a doctor's care and may be given some medication
to ease the sometimes dramatic symptoms of withdrawal. Some people
go directly from detox to ongoing involvement in a support group.

Additional Information

Prescription Medicines. Many thousands
of Americans are addicted to prescription
medicines. Women and older Americans
are particularly at risk of becoming addicted, because they visit doctors more frequently and tend to be prescribed more
medicines.

Addiction to therapeutic medicines dates
back to the 1800s in the U.S., when lau-

danum and other opium tonics could be
ordered through the Sears, Roebuck catalog. Opium was marketed as a remedy for
various ailments, including alcoholism.
The federal government first regulated the
use of opium in the early 1900s.

Inpatient or Residential Treatment Centers. People generally stay in this kind of facility for a month or more. Such centers, often in peaceful and attractive surroundings, offer a time away from the person's usual environment so that full concentration on recovery can take place. The first few days are spent in detox. After that, people spend a month or more taking part in drug and alcohol education, individual and group counseling, and support group meetings.

Outpatient Treatment Centers. Outpatient treatment involves getting treatment for a few hours each day at a nearby treatment center but spending the rest of the time in one's regular surroundings and activities. This approach to treatment allows people to go to work or school and to live at home during the treatment process. It is less expensive than inpatient treatment, but it takes place over a longer period of time. For people with mild to moderate withdrawal symptoms, outpatient treatment is now being used even for the detoxification process.

Continuing Programs. Many inpatient and outpatient rehabilitation centers have long-term programs of counseling and support for people in recovery who have gone through their standard short-term treatment programs. These usually involve follow-up sessions, individual and group counseling, and family system therapy—counseling that gets the whole family involved in the recovery process.

Halfway Houses. Halfway houses, sometimes called continuing-care facilities, offer people housing, counseling, and support meetings as they are recovering from a severe addiction. People are generally admitted to halfway houses only after having completed at least a 28-day program of recovery at a treatment center. They stay for six months to a year as they learn coping and living skills they will need when they return to society. Residents are also sometimes channeled into vocational rehabilitation or job training programs.

At a residential treatment center, full concentration on recovery can take place.

Enrich

■ Have students research recovery rates for various types of treatment for alcohol and other drug addictions. Do success rates vary from one drug to another? Are there any figures on recovery rates for people who try to overcome addiction without help, other than that of friends and family members? In the studies reported on, how long were recovering addicts followed to see if they stayed drug-free? Ask students to prepare a concise report of their findings to share with the rest of the class.

Close

Tell students that in this lesson they learned that the process of recovery from alcohol and other drug addictions is difficult and lifelong, but that there are many sources of help available for the recovering addict. Some forms of treatment, such as detoxification in a hospital ward, are costly medical procedures, but others, including support groups like Alcoholics Anonymous, are free of charge and available to everyone.

DID YOU KNOW?

■ Although there is no one test to determine if someone is alcoholic, researchers at the National Institute on Alcohol Abuse and Alcoholism have shown that a series of blood profiles, or lab tests, looked at together can help identify alcoholics. These tests measure such things as liver function, blood fats, sodium levels, and size of red blood cells. Meanwhile, scientists continue to get closer to identifying a gene or genes that are at least partially responsible for the development of the disease of alcoholism.

LESSON 2 REVIEW

Reviewing Facts and Vocabulary

1. For what reasons do people in recovery describe themselves as recovering rather than being recovered?
2. Use the words *total abstinence* and *relapse* in a short paragraph that describes the dangers of trying controlled drinking.
3. Outline some of the treatment choices for an alcoholic who wants to recover.

Thinking Critically

4. **Analysis.** Compare inpatient and outpatient treatment centers.

5. **Evaluation.** Why do you think recovery includes more than just physical detoxification?

Applying Health Knowledge

6. Make a booklet that lists and describes alcohol and drug treatment services available in your community.

RECOVERING FROM ADDICTION **505**

Answers to Lesson 2 Review

1. The recovery process is ongoing.
2. Paragraphs will vary.
3. Outlines should reflect a basic understanding of counseling, support groups, and alcohol and drug treatment centers; detox units, inpatient or residential treatment centers, outpatient treatment centers, continuing programs, and halfway houses.

4. Both take place in treatment centers. Inpatient requires a long-term stay at the center. Outpatient requires only several hours a day at the center.
5. Answers will vary. Possible answer: Recovery includes all aspects of health.
6. Answers will vary.

Focus

Lesson Objective

After studying this lesson, students should be able to:
- describe codependent behavior and its relationship to alcoholism and other drug addictions

Bellringer

Write the following on the chalkboard for students to work on while attendance is being taken: *Write a definition of the word* codependency. *What does codependency have to do with alcoholism and other drug addictions? Can there be codependency without drug abuse?*

Introducing the Lesson

Refer to the Bellringer. Ask volunteers to share their responses with the class. Students may think codependency refers to dependence on multiple drugs, such as both alcohol and cocaine. There may be other misconceptions about this little understood problem. Explain that codependency refers to a certain type of behavior—being overly concerned with other people's problems and driven to fix them. Such behavior often characterizes people involved in relationships with alcoholics and other drug addicts.

DID YOU KNOW?

- There are over 28 million children of alcoholics in the U.S. There are over 7 million children under the age of 18 who live with at least one alcoholic. There are almost 21 million people over the age of 18 who grew up with at least one alcoholic in the household.
- Children of alcoholics are more often hyperactive than other children.

CODEPENDENCY: WHAT IS IT?

LESSON 3 FOCUS

TERMS TO USE
- Codependency
- Enabling

CONCEPTS TO LEARN
- Codependency means being overly concerned with other people's behavior and problems.
- Codependents learn rigid roles to play.

ATTITUDES AND BEHAVIORS TO EVALUATE
- Self-Inventory, page 512.
- Building Decision-Making Skills, page 513.

Being overly concerned with other people's behavior and problems and feeling driven to fix and control those problems is known as **codependency.** People who live with or are close to alcoholics and drug addicts and show this kind of behavior are called codependents. Their codependency is sometimes also referred to as co-addiction.

Common Traits of Codependents

Though each person who exhibits codependent behavior does so in a unique way, codependents share many traits in common:

- They feel like they have to fix other people's problems, particularly those related to another's drinking and drug use.
- They feel lost, bored, or bad about themselves when not rescuing someone in trouble.
- They feel responsible for other people's feelings, actions, and happiness.
- They have difficulty having fun, relaxing, or taking good care of themselves.
- They constantly seek others' approval.
- They do not meet their own needs and may not even know what their own needs are.

Enabling: Hurting by Helping

One of the most common traits of codependency is enabling. **Enabling** means trying to protect the person having trouble with alcohol or drugs from facing the consequences of his or her drug-related problems. Codependent people enable an addict by lying for him or her; lending money, which may be used to purchase more drugs or alcohol; or making excuses for him or her. Enabling is not healthful caring. Such actions do not help the addict. They just make it more comfortable and possible for the alcoholic or addict to keep on drinking or using drugs.

What Codependency Is Not

Codependent people are not physically addicted to a drug the way an addict is. Though codependency is often referred to as an addiction, it is neither an addiction nor a disease in the physical sense. It is, instead, a very damaging emotional and social preoccupation, or obsession, which often can have physical consequences. This type of obsession is different from drug addiction.

Codependents can suffer from a variety of stress-related mental or physical disorders, from depression and eating disorders to high blood pressure and digestive disorders.

506   CHAPTER 25 RECOVERING FROM ADDICTION AND CODEPENDENCY

Resources for Lesson 3

- **Transparency** 42
- **Guided Reading** Activity 68
- **Workbook** Vocabulary Activity 68
- **Reteaching** Activity 68
- **Lesson 3 Quiz**

ABC News InterActive Videodiscs
Drugs and Substance Abuse, Side 2
Ch 4 Drugs and the Family

Alcohol, Side 2
Ch 3 Alcohol and the Family: Disease

Addiction as a Family Disease

In a family where there is alcoholism or other drug dependence, both addicts and codependent family members are hurting and need help. That is why alcoholism and drug dependence are sometimes referred to as family diseases. They affect everyone in the family.

People in a family with drug or alcohol dependency experience terrible shame, fear, disappointment, guilt, and anger. They are embarrassed to admit these feelings, not realizing that millions of other families suffer from the effects of drug dependency.

Roles in Families with Addiction

In a healthful family system, rules are flexible and members play many roles based on changing situations and needs. In families with drug dependency, codependents instead learn to cope by acting out rigid, unchanging roles such as these:

- Main enabler. This role is usually played by the husband or wife. He or she may be a responsible caretaker who nags, blames, controls, rescues, and covers up for the alcoholic or addict in the family.
- The good child or hero. This role may be assumed by the oldest child in the family. He or she often gets straight As, wins awards, and tries to bring esteem to the family with his or her achievements.
- The troublemaker. This person may use drugs, fail in school, or show other self-destructive behaviors. The troublemaker's goal is to hold the family together by keeping it focused on his or her bad behavior.
- The sensitive child. This person may be the youngest in the family. He or she may be overly aware of everyone else's emotions, and despite hurting deeply inside, always puts on a smile. This child works to keep family peace. This child may also play the role of family clown.
- The invisible child. This person may withdraw from the family altogether, not wanting to add to the family's problems. He or she may try to live in a fantasy world or be very passive, adjusting to anything that happens without complaint.

Regardless of what role or roles family members play, they all make the alcoholic or drug addict the center of their lives. They adjust their needs, emotions, and behaviors to the unhealthy demands, behaviors, and emotions of the addicted person. In the process they, too, become unhealthy.

Lying to a parent's boss to cover up a drinking problem is an example of enabling behavior. It permits the individual to continue drinking.

KEEPING FIT

Excuses, Excuses

An enabler is someone who shields the addict from the consequences of his or her behaviors. In addition, the enabler may "buy the addict's line"—or believe the chemically dependent person's rationalizations—that he or she is drinking or drugging because of other great problems. For example, the addict might convince the enabler that he or she needs to drink or smoke because of stress at school or work, financial worries, other illnesses, broken relationships, and so on. What enablers and addicts do not realize is that continuing the addictive behavior creates problems and creates stress rather than relieving them.

CODEPENDENCY: WHAT IS IT?   **507**

Additional Information

Children of Alcoholics. One of the strongest feelings for children of alcoholics is a sense of powerlessness. This has three major causes. First, the child is powerless over the parent's drinking—the child can't stop the drinking or get sober for the parent. Second, the child is powerless over the relationship between the parents, which is often abusive. Unfortunately, the child usually doesn't believe that he or she is powerless in these first two cases, so the child may try almost anything to make things better—usually leading to a greater sense of powerlessness. Finally, children of alcoholics feel powerless because they can't leave the dysfunctional situation.

Building Vocabulary

- Have students define *codependency*. Ask why codependent individuals might sometimes be referred to as co-addicts.
- Ask students to complete *Workbook Vocabulary Activity 68.*

Teach

Guided Practice

L1 DISCUSSION. What are some of the characteristics and behaviors commonly found in people who are codependent?

L2 COOPERATIVE LEARNING. Ask a group of students to prepare and present a short skit to the rest of the class that demonstrates a codependent relationship. Ask the audience to identify particular dialogue or actions that reveal the codependency.

L1 DISCUSSION. How does the codependent person in a relationship or family often "hurt by helping" a person having trouble with alcohol or other drugs?

L2 CLASS ACTIVITY. Divide the class into two groups. Have one group make a list of ways in which a codependent person might act to enable a spouse or other family member to continue with an alcohol or other drug problem. Then have the other group revise the list so that it shows helpful, not hurtful, behaviors—behaviors that encourage the addicted person to accept and get treatment for the addiction.

L1 DISCUSSION. What are some ways in which children might deny the drug addiction problem of a parent?

L1 USING CONFLICT RESOLUTION TRANSPARENCY 42. Refer to the Teaching Transparencies Binder.

Independent Practice

L1 COMMUNITY INVOLVEMENT. Ask students to investigate local sources of information, support groups, and other assistance for children of alcoholics. Have students make a poster or bulletin board to inform other students of their findings.

L2 RESEARCH. Select students to research the effects on children growing up in an alcoholic family. What are their special problems and concerns? What are some common ways of coping? How are they likely to be affected into adulthood by the dysfunctional family they grew up in?

L1 USING THE LESSON RESOURCES. For additional student activities, refer to the lesson resources on page 506.

Assess

Check for Understanding

■ Assign and discuss the lesson review. Encourage LD students to focus on questions 1, 2, 3, and 5.

Evaluate

■ Administer, grade, and discuss the *Lesson 3 Quiz.*

Reteach

■ Ask students to list the common traits of codependents and explain how they may contribute to addicts' dependence on alcohol or other drugs.
■ Ask students to complete *Reteaching Activity 68.*

Enrich

■ What has led to the emergence of *codependency* as the "word of the decade," as one expert recently put it? Ask students to research the concept of codependency. When was the term coined, and what did it refer to? How has its place in the psychological literature and popular press grown? Have students write a summary of their findings.

Close

Tell students that in the next lesson they will study how codependents can recover from their destructive codependent behaviors and relationships.

Family members often put their life on hold hoping an addiction will go away. Some teens may delay going to college to help meet family expenses.

The Codependency Continuum

As a family member's alcoholism or addiction progresses, his or her family's codependency also gets worse. It, too, is a downhill process. The rage, sadness, excuses, and disappointment increase. People get sick. Violence may occur. Some family members may become overly involved in others' problems, taking the focus off themselves. Other family members may simply withdraw. In either case, family members put their lives on hold hoping the addiction will go away, but it does not. In turn, they may scream, cry, beg, threaten, nag, retreat, leave, come back, or even use alcohol or other drugs to avoid their pain. Like the alcoholic or addict, they may also be in denial, not realizing or being able to admit just how bad things at home have become.

LESSON 3 REVIEW

Reviewing Facts and Vocabulary

1. What is meant by the term *codependency?*
2. List some common traits of codependents.
3. Give three examples of enabling behavior.

Thinking Critically

4. **Synthesis.** Suggest ways that a family member could be supportive to an alcoholic family member and not be considered codependent.

5. **Analysis.** In what ways are chemical dependency and codependency similar? In what ways are they different?

Applying Health Knowledge

6. Write a skit or make a drawing in which you show the roles in families with drug or alcohol dependency. Include the dependent person actively drinking or using drugs. Show how everyone else in the family reacts to this behavior, each according to his or her role.

---

508 CHAPTER 25 RECOVERING FROM ADDICTION AND CODEPENDENCY

Answers to Lesson 3 Review

1. See definition on page 506 or in the Glossary.
2. See page 506.
3. Lying for the addict, lending money, making excuses for the addict.
4. Answers will vary. Possible answers: Acknowledge the family member's alcoholism and don't make excuses; realize that only the addict can help him- or herself.

5. Both cause people to suffer mentally and socially, can lead to physical illness, and cause people to live their lives around the addiction. Chemical dependency is largely a physical disease. Codependency is an emotional and social preoccupation.
6. Answers will vary.

RECOVERING FROM CODEPENDENCY

There are many ways for families with chemical dependency to get help. These days more families are seeking and getting that help.

The Recovery Continuum for Codependents

Just as addiction is not hopeless, neither is codependency. The downward slide into codependency, like that of addiction, can be turned around and changed into a process of recovery. Like recovery from chemical dependency, recovery from codependency takes time and effort. Different people may recover at different speeds and in different ways. Whatever anyone's timetable for recovery, the personal and family rewards can be great.

RECOVERY FROM CODEPENDENCY: THE UPWARD CLIMB

A codependent's recovery might progress like this:
- Hits an emotional bottom as a result of involvement with someone else's addiction
- Desires and goes for help
- Gets educated about the diseases of addiction
- Accepts the disease concept and his or her part in that disease
- Stops trying to control others, including the addict
- Focuses on self instead of the addict
- Begins to pay attention to personal appearance
- Experiences improvement in own physical, mental, and social health
- Rebuilds self-esteem
- Helps family become more flexible; aids in the process of redefining once-rigid roles
- Continues to attend support group meetings, helping other codependents and self
- Takes full responsibility for own life

Strategies for Getting Well

There are many ways that a person from a family with addiction as well as the addicted family member can get help. The first step is to admit that there is a problem. The next step is to reach outside the family system for help. This can seem like an impossibility to many people since families of active alcoholics and drug addicts have usually lived by the unspoken rules—"don't talk, don't trust, and don't feel."

Reaching outside the family for the first time can feel like a betrayal. However, it is a healthy step to take, and a sense of relief often results. Whatever the risks are in seeking outside help, not seeking it holds

---

LESSON 4 FOCUS
TERMS TO USE
■ Al-Anon
■ Alateen
CONCEPTS TO LEARN
■ The first step to recovery is admitting that there is a problem.
■ Seeking outside help is an important step in recovering from codependency.
ATTITUDES AND BEHAVIORS TO EVALUATE
■ Self-Inventory, page 512.
■ Building Decision-Making Skills, page 513.

Lesson Objectives

After studying this lesson, students should be able to:
- summarize the process of recovery from codependency
- identify sources of help for the codependent

Bellringer

Write the following on the chalkboard for students to work on while attendance is being taken: *"Unless the alcoholic or drug addicted family member seeks help, there is no way for other family members to recover from their codependency." Is this statement true or false? Why?*

Introducing the Lesson

Refer to the Bellringer. Ask volunteers to share their responses. Students may believe that codependents cannot get well as long as the addicted family member still drinks or uses drugs. Tell them that in this lesson, they will learn of several sources of assistance for codependents, which can help codependents get healthy even if the addicted family member continues with the addictive behavior.

Building Vocabulary

- Ask students to identify the specific group helped by each of the following: Alcoholics Anonymous, Al-Anon, and Alateen.
- Ask students to complete *Workbook Vocabulary Activity 69.*

RECOVERING FROM CODEPENDENCY **509**

Resources for Lesson 4

- **Guided Reading** Activity 69
- **Decision-Making** Activity 25
- **Workbook** Vocabulary Activity 69
- **Workbook** Application Activity 25
- **Reteaching** Activity 69
- **Enrichment** Activity 25
- **Health Labs** Activity 25

- **Cooperative Learning** Activity 25
- **Lesson 4 Quiz**
- **Chapter 25 Test**
- ABC News InterActive Videodiscs
Alcohol, Side 2 Ch 4 Alcohol and the Family: Recovery

DID YOU KNOW?

- In 1990, alcohol and drug dependence cost the U.S. an estimated $136.3 billion.
- It is estimated that from 25 to 63 percent of all homeless people in the U.S. are heavy drug and alcohol users.

Teach

Guided Practice

L1 DISCUSSION. What is the process of recovery like for the codependent?

L1 DISCUSSION. What are some sources of help for people with codependency who wish to start the recovery process? Why is it important to go outside the family for help?

L1 DISCUSSION. Why do children often adopt rigid roles in families with an alcoholic or other addict as a parent? What function does it serve in helping them to cope? What function does it serve in postponing their treatment and recovery?

L2 DISCUSSION. How do the following elements of all addictions apply both to the alcoholic or other drug abuser and to the codependent involved with the abuser: denial; loss of control or powerlessness; continued usage without regard for consequences; repression of feelings; obsessive-compulsive thoughts and behaviors; and withdrawal symptoms?

LD DISCUSSION. Describe the structures of each of the treatment programs and have students consider the pros and cons of each.

Independent Practice

L1 WRITING. Ask students to write a description of a scene between an addict and his or her codependent spouse that demonstrates students' understanding of codependent behavior.

L1 RESEARCH. Select students to research the topic of family therapy.

L2 COMMUNITY INVOLVEMENT. Ask students to research the sources of information, counseling, and support that are available in their local community for codependents. Ask them to prepare a pamphlet containing this information.

L1 USING THE LESSON RESOURCES. For additional student activities, refer to the lesson resources on page 509.

CONFLICT RESOLUTION

Fifteen-year-old David lives a secret life that no one at school knows about. He never invites friends home because his dad's an alcoholic. David's not only ashamed about this, but he's terrified his friends will witness one of the "scenes" his dad makes when he gets drunk. These "scenes" often result in physical abuse. When David and his mom get hurt and develop bruises, they lie about their cause. They also lie to his dad's boss about why he misses so much work.

How are David and his mom supporting his dad's alcoholism?

What could they do to resolve the conflict in their own lives as well as help his dad stop drinking?

---

greater risks. Continuing to adapt to an unhealthy family system can be far more damaging to everyone involved.

Sometimes only one person in a chemically dependent family seeks and gets outside help. Because of this, that person may feel very lonely. When everyone in the family seeks help and assumes responsibility for his or her own role in the family, recovery can occur more quickly.

Interventions can hasten the speed with which the alcoholic or addict gets into a treatment program. It also can speed up the rate of recovery for the co-alcoholics or co-addicts in the family. Sometimes intervention fails. In families where this happens the alcoholic or addict will continue to drink or take drugs. However, the rest of the family can work on being healthy again.

Abstinence, or staying away from all alcohol and other drugs, is particularly important for the child of an alcoholic or drug addict. Research indicates that having a chemically dependent parent does not necessarily mean a person will also become chemically dependent. However, research shows that a child of an alchoholic or drug addict has a better than average risk of developing an addiction.

Counseling

Many codependents need professional care. Individual and group counseling may be available with a psychiatrist, psychologist, social worker, or therapist trained in chemical dependency and codependency. Family therapy is often recommended and may help the family even if the alcoholic or addict refuses to participate.

Support Groups

There are many support groups for people involved in the lives of alcoholics and other drug addicts. The most widely known of these groups is **Al-Anon**. Like Alcoholics Anonymous, Al-Anon is a worldwide self-help organization. It welcomes family members and friends of alcoholics. It is open for the codependent whether or not the chemically dependent person decides to get well. Like AA meetings, Al-Anon meetings offer a support system for coping and a structured program for regaining emotional and social health. The program encourages detachment—the process of pulling back or separating from involvement with

---

KEEPING FIT

Smashing Stereotypes

There are many unfair stereotypes about people who suffer from addictions. What is your mental picture of a typical alcoholic? Is the person of a particular race, age, sex, or socioeconomic group? The fact is that alcoholism is an equal-opportunity disease that strikes people of all races, ages, sexes, and classes. Though some ethnic groups seem to be at greater risk for developing the disease, all groups are represented in statistics for active addiction and recovery from those addictions.

Meeting Special Needs

Children of Alcoholics. Some of your students may have alcoholic parents, so it's important to be aware of seven areas of concern for children of alcoholics. They feel: (1) worry about the health of the alcoholic parent, (2) anger over unpredictability and inconsistency, (3) worry about arguments and fights between the parents, (4) fear of violence or the threat of violence, (5) concern over a parent's deviant behavior, (6) disappointment over broken promises and feeling unloved, and (7) responsibility for the parent's drinking.

someone else's addiction and refusing to let that addiction rule one's life any longer. Al-Anon meetings are free, and what is said at the meetings remains confidential.

Other support groups such as Codependents Anonymous, the National Association for Adult Children of Alcoholics, The National Association for Children of Alcoholics, and Children of Alcoholics offer information and support at both national and local levels

Alateen, an offshoot of Al-Anon, is for teens and preteens between the ages of 12 and 20, whose parents or other family members or friends have drinking problems. Like Al-Anon, its members come together to share their experiences and discuss how the addiction of someone close to them has affected their lives and how they can cope and recover. Information about Al-Anon and Alateen can be found by calling the local Al-Anon office listed in the phone book. Other similar programs such as Nar-Anon and Coc-Anon are available to help families and close friends of narcotics and cocaine addicts.

Alateen is a support group for teens who have a family member with a drinking problem.

Family Programs

When an alcoholic or drug addict enters a rehabilitation or treatment center, the family is usually included in at least part of the program. During weekend visits or in a three- to seven-day program of their own, family members learn about the disease of addiction, how they have been affected by it, and how they can recover and support the recoveries of others in the family.

Assess

Check for Understanding

- Assign and discuss the lesson review.
- Assign and discuss the chapter review.

Evaluate

- Administer, grade, and discuss the *Lesson 4 Quiz.*
- Administer, grade, and discuss the *Chapter 25 Test.*
- Refer to the Performance Assessment strategy for this chapter. See pages T 23 to T 25.

Reteach

- Have students prepare a diagram that illustrates the "upward climb" that a codependent typically goes through in the process of recovery. Important steps along the way should be labeled.
- Ask students to complete *Reteaching Activity 69.*

Enrich

- Have students research the connection between alcohol or other drug abuse and physical abuse, particularly of wives and children of addicts. Ask them to summarize their findings in a written report.
- Ask students to complete *Enrichment Activity 25.*

LESSON 4 REVIEW

Reviewing Facts and Vocabulary

1. Where might the family of an addict or alcoholic turn to get treatment information?
2. Why is it important to seek help outside the family?
3. Give two examples of support groups often used by codependents.

Thinking Critically

4. **Analysis.** For what reasons do you think it is difficult for people to confront close friends with drinking and drug use problems?
5. **Analysis.** Why do you think it is possible for a codependent to recover even if the chemically dependent person in his or her life does not?

6. **Analysis.** Is there a danger that overinvolvement with support groups can keep someone from taking full responsibility for his or her life? Explain your reasoning.

Applying Health Knowledge

7. Write what you would say to a close friend or relative who was deeply depressed or otherwise upset by a parent's addiction. How would you guide that person for help?
8. Set up a Recovery Resource Table at your school. Provide information about local recovery resources for people suffering from chemical dependency and for those suffering from codependency.

RECOVERING FROM CODEPENDENCY **511**

Close

Tell students that in this lesson they learned how codependents, that is, people involved in unhealthy relationships with alcoholics and other drug addicts, can get help with recovery. They saw that the recovery process for codependents is typically an upward continuum, much like the recovery process for alcoholics and other drug addicts that was described earlier in this chapter.

Answers to Lesson 4 Review

1. See pages 509 to 510.
2. Getting help is a healthy step that will help family members assume responsibility for their roles in the family.
3. Al-Anon and Alateen.
4. Answers will vary. Possible answers: Embarrassment, fear of losing love or friendship, codependent need to keep rescuing, fear of anger.

5. Answers will vary. Possible answer: With group support, therapy, and practice in not enabling, codependents can learn to detach from the addict's behavior and emotions and get on with their own lives.
6. Answers will vary.
7. Answers will vary.
8. Answers will vary.

Helping Students Improve Their Health

Using the Self-Inventory

Reinforcing Vocabulary

- **Compulsive.** Having to do with an irresistible impulse to perform some irrational act.
- **Symptoms.** Any conditions resulting from a disease and serving as aids in diagnosis.

Teaching Strategies

L1 EXPLANATION. It is important to recognize that the codependent person will need to hide or outthink the inventory, using denial. In explaining the inventory, be sure to stress that it is confidential. This could be a breakthrough for individuals who are codependent, helping them admit the fact and seek help.

L1 EXPLANATION. Point out that the inventory is designed to give a general profile of codependency. It does not necessarily mean that individuals are codependent if they answer yes to some of the items.

L1 DISCUSSION. Ask students to recall a time when they were very angry at a friend or family member, but kept that anger inside. How did they feel? Why? How would a person who did this all the time feel? How could this possibly affect the person's health triangle?

L1 DISCUSSION. Ask students to list why people sometimes feel responsible for others' happiness. Discuss the reasons. Ask if all the reasons are viable. Should one ever feel responsible for another person's happiness?

Self-Inventory

How Codependent Are You?

HOW DO YOU RATE?

Number a sheet of paper from 1 through 15. Read each item below and respond by writing *yes* or *no* for each item. Total the number of *yes* and *no* responses. Then proceed to the next section.

1. Do you live with a person who is addicted to drugs or alcohol?
2. Do you have a close friend who is an addict?
3. Are your life and emotions totally wrapped up in the addiction of this person you care about?
4. Do you spend a great deal of time, energy, or money trying to fix this person's problems?
5. Has your involvement with his or her addiction affected your appetite, sleep habits, or mental or physical health?
6. Do you ever lie or cover up for the person when his or her drinking or drug use results in trouble?
7. Do you feel overly responsible for other people's feelings, behavior, and happiness?
8. Do you feel comfortable, happy, or useful only when you are trying to rescue someone in trouble?
9. Do you focus on others' needs before focusing on your own?
10. Do you try to control people, situations, and outcomes?

11. Are you compulsive? Do you overdo it in such areas as work or exercise, not knowing when to stop?
12. Do you feel you have to please everyone?
13. Do you avoid arguments at all costs?
14. Are you loyal to others even when they hurt you?
15. Are you uncomfortable when the tables are turned and someone asks you how *you* are feeling?

HOW DID YOU SCORE?

Give yourself 1 point for every *yes* answer and 0 points for every *no* answer. Find your total, and read below to see how you scored. Then proceed to the next section.

0 to 4
Good. You are concerned with what others think of you, but you probably are not codependent.

5 to 9
Fair. You are showing symptoms of codependence that may lead to further problems.

10 to 15
Watch out! There is a good chance that you are codependent.

WHAT ARE YOUR GOALS?

If you received a *good* score, complete the statements in Part A. If your score was rated *fair* or *watch out!* complete Parts A and B.

Part A

1. I plan to learn more about the subjects of codependency and recovery from codependency in the following ways: ____.
2. My timetable for completing this is ____.
3. I plan to share my information with others by ____.

Part B

4. The codependent behavior I would like to change or improve is ____.
5. The steps involved in making this change are ____.
6. My timetable for making this change is ____.
7. The people or groups I will ask for support or assistance are ____.
8. My rewards for making this change will be ____.

Meeting Students' Needs

For students who score *Good.* (1) Suggest students become involved with SADD. (2) Have students check to see if the school has an intervention program, and if so, to determine its effectiveness.

For students who score *Fair.* (1) Suggest students seek more information on code-

pendency. (2) Have them do an extra-credit book report on codependency.

For students who must *Watch Out.* (1) Discuss with these students how codependency affects one's health triangle. (2) Suggest further reading on codependency with extra credit for a book report on the topic.

Building Decision-Making Skills

C raig's younger brother has been admitted to a drug rehabilitation center. This program encourages counseling for the entire family. Craig loves his brother, but feels he and his brother now have very little in common. As a star athlete and president of his local Youth-to-Youth chapter, Craig is very antidrug and is embarrassed by his brother's problem. He'd like to avoid the counseling. What should Craig do? Some of his choices include:

A. Tell his parents why he doesn't want to go.

B. Find excuses, such as football or basketball practice, to keep away during the scheduled counseling sessions.

C. Realize that his brother's problem does not reflect on him and that as president of Youth-to-Youth, he should be involved in helping people overcome their problems.

D. Do it just to help his brother and his family.

E. Find out why he is embarrassed by his brother's problem with drugs.

WHAT DO YOU THINK?

1. **Situation.** Why do you think Craig feels embarrassed?

2. **Choices.** What other choices does Craig have?

3. **Consequences.** What are the costs and benefits of each choice?

4. **Consequences.** How will his brother, parents, the counselors, and Craig's friends feel about Craig if he participates in the counseling? How will he feel about himself if he participates?

5. **Consequences.** How will other people involved feel about Craig if he doesn't participate in counseling?

6. **Consequences.** What's the worst thing that could happen if Craig participates in the counseling? What's the best thing that could happen?

7. **Decision** What should Craig do? Explain your reasoning.

8. **Evaluation.** Have you ever been in a situation in which it was easier to respond positively to a stranger than to someone close to you with the same problem? How did you handle that situation?

J anet's older sister uses alcohol, pot, and cocaine. Janet loves her sister very much and wishes she could get her to give these drugs up as she has said so many times she would like to do. She is also into prostitution, theft, and selling drugs to support her habit. Janet is afraid of the people her sister associates with in these activities. She is not only afraid of what might happen to her sister but also what might happen to herself and their mother and younger sister. Their mother is a single parent who works long hours trying to support them. She may not be able to cope with this additional burden. What should Janet do?

WHAT DO YOU THINK?

9. **Choices.** What possible solutions can you come up with for Janet?

10. **Consequences.** What do you think the chances of success for each approach are? What are the costs of each approach?

11. **Consequences.** What risks exist for the older sister and for the rest of the family?

12. **Decision.** What do you think Janet should do? How should she go about implementing her plan?

13. **Evaluation.** What situations have you dealt with in which you felt too young and powerless to help? How did you handle the situation? What was the outcome? Who did you find to help? What advice would you give to others who find themselves in a similar situation?

Teaching Strategies

L1 CLASS ACTIVITY. Have students create a role-play with Craig discussing his embarrassment with his parents. Try to get students to cover all the bases, i.e., reasons for embarrassment, comparison of codependency to any other illness, etc.

L1 CLASS ACTIVITY. As a class, list what Janet's alternatives for a solution are.

L1 CLASS ACTIVITY. Have students participate in a role-play with Janet talking to her sister about her concerns. Those concerns should include such things as drug dependency and family health.

L2 DISCUSSION. Debate the value of drug intervention in high school. Would it be a step to curb dependency or an invasion of privacy?

L2 DISCUSSION. Make a list of the ways or reasons that people become drug-dependent. Compare the process of dependency between adults and adolescents.

L3 DISCUSSION. Discuss the effects, on any society, of widespread drug dependency within its population. Include finances and morals.

DID YOU KNOW?

If you need to seek treatment for addiction for a family member, first take the following steps:

■ learn all you can about addiction and recovery;

■ get help for yourself (and for your children if you're a parent);

■ consider a formal intervention.

Discussing the Answers

Situation 1. It is possible that in order to find a solution to Craig's embarrassment that the class consider why he is embarrassed. Is there a misunderstanding of drug dependency? Does he feel this is a sign of weakness on the part of his brother? Does Craig really need counseling?

Situation 2. In this situation, not only does Janet have to be concerned about the drug dependency, but also what the dependent person will do to maintain use. The dependency is important, but so is the possible harm, both mental and physical, to the family. Janet should seek help in coping with this situation.

Answers to Chapter 25 Review

Using Health Terms

1. Addiction
2. Physiological dependence
3. Psychological dependence
4. Detoxification
5. Abstinence
6. Relapses
7. Recovery
8. Main enabler
9. Codependents
10. Troublemaker
11. Enabling
12. Alateen

Building Academic Skills

13. Answers will vary.

Recalling the Facts

14. They are diseases that are chronic—ongoing, progressive—get worse over time, and potentially fatal—people can die from them.
15. As long as the addict denies the problem, it means he or she maintains the illusion of control over the drug and that it is not causing any harm.
16. First use of alcohol or drugs. Mind/body damage or death.
17. It varies—some become addicted the first time; for others it may take years.
18. It means that recovery happens over a period of time, at different rates, and in different ways for different people.
19. The biochemical and perhaps genetic conditions that contributed to addiction will always be part of the addict.
20. Because even a small amount of the drug or alcohol could cause the addict to suffer a relapse.
21. The drugs are removed from the addict's body. The addict is usually under a doctor's supervision and sometimes receives medicine. It usually takes 3 to 7 days.
22. Restoring one's mental health by teaching the addict to develop healthy relationships and to take responsibility for his or her own life.
23. It is a place where a recovering addict can receive housing, counseling, and support.

Using Health Terms

On a separate sheet of paper, write the term that best matches each definition given below.

LESSON 1

1. Physiological or psychological dependence on alcohol or drugs.
2. When a person's body has a need for a certain substance.
3. When a person comes to depend on the feeling received from a drug.

LESSON 2

4. The process of removing alcohol or other drugs from one's body.
5. The act of going without alcohol or other drugs.
6. Periodic returns to drinking alcohol and using drugs.
7. The ongoing process of getting well again.

LESSON 3

8. Role of a responsible caretaker who blames, controls, or covers up for the alcoholic or addict in the family.
9. People who are overly concerned with other people's behavior and problems.
10. Role played by a family member to get the family to focus on his or her bad behavior.
11. The act of trying to protect the alcoholic or drug addict from the consequences of his or her own actions thereby helping the addict to continue the self-destructive behavior.

LESSON 4

12. An organization for teens and preteens whose parents or other family members have drinking problems.

Building Academic Skills

LESSON 1

13. **Reading.** Many articles and books are available that deal with drug and alcohol dependency. Read one and summarize it in writing. Identify cause-and-effect relationships described in the article.

Recalling the Facts

LESSON 1

14. How does the American Medical Association describe the diseases of alcoholism and drug dependence? Explain what these terms mean.
15. Why is denial an important part of psychological dependence?
16. What is at the beginning of an addiction continuum? What is at the end?
17. How long does it take for one to become addicted?

LESSON 2

18. What is meant by the statement "Recovery is a process"?
19. What is it about an addict that causes his or her recovery process to be considered ongoing?
20. Why do experts on alcohol and drug addiction recommend total abstinence for the addict?
21. What happens at a detoxification unit? How long does detoxification usually take?
22. Besides regaining one's physical health, what factors are involved in an addict's recovery?
23. What is a halfway house? How does this facility help in the treatment of an addict?
24. What services do continuing programs provide for people in recovery?

LESSON 3

25. Name and describe three roles a codependent may play in a family with addiction.
26. List some emotions people in a family living with an addict might experience.
27. How might being a codependent adversely affect a person's physical and mental health?

LESSON 4

28. What part might a family play in an addict's recovery program?
29. Why is intervention important?
30. What is Al-Anon? What is a major purpose of this organization?

It helps ease the transition from severe addiction to returning to society.
24. Follow-up sessions, individual and group counseling, and family system therapy.
25. Answers will vary. Accept descriptions from "Roles in Families with Addiction" on page 507 for three of the following: main enabler;

the good child or hero; the troublemaker; the sensitive child; the invisible child.
26. Shame, fear, disappointment, guilt, anger, and embarrassment.
27. Codependents may suffer from stress-related mental or physical disorders such as depression, eating disorders, high blood pressure, and digestive problems.

They also may be victims of physical abuse.
28. Family members may go to the treatment center to learn about the disease of addiction, how it has affected them, how they can recover and support other family members with their recoveries.
29. Intervention gets an addict to a treatment program

REVIEW

Thinking Critically

LESSON 1

31. Synthesis. What might cause a person to experiment with drugs or alcohol? How could this be avoided?

32. Evaluation. Cigarette ads were banned from television in the 1970s. Do you think ads for alcohol should be banned? Support your answer.

LESSON 2

33. Synthesis. Most experts recommend that recovering addicts totally abstain from the substance(s) they have used. How long do you think the addict would have to abstain? What effects on the addict's future might this have?

LESSON 3

34. Evaluation. Years ago people often hid the problem of addiction within a family and suffered in silence. How are things beginning to change? What do you think is causing the change? How is this change for the better?

LESSON 4

35. Evaluation. Why do you suppose many codependents need professional help?

36. Analysis. How does Alcoholics Anonymous compare with Al-Anon?

Making the Connection

LESSON 2

37. Art. Design and paint a large two-panel mural. On one half, paint images that suggest addiction to alcohol or other drugs. On the other half, paint images that suggest recovery.

38. Art/Music. Make a sculpture or write a song about the *down* escalator of addiction and the *up* escalator of recovery.

39. Language Arts. Rehearse in writing what you would say if you were to confront someone close to you who was in trouble with drugs.

Applying Health Knowledge

LESSON 1

40. Watch television for one hour during a sporting event. Record the number of commercials aired that sell alcohol. How is the use of alcohol depicted? Discuss the influence these commercials could have on you and your peers.

41. Your friend wants to experiment with drugs and wants you to join him or her. What will you tell your friend? Explain your answer.

LESSON 2

42. Your friend lives in a single-parent household. His parent is an alcoholic who drinks in the evening and on weekends. What kind of treatment program do you think is best suited for your friend's parent?

43. Why do you suppose detoxification often takes place under medical supervision?

LESSON 4

44. Your friend and his younger sister live with alcoholic parents. You can see that their lives are very difficult because of their parents' actions. How can you help your friend?

Beyond the Classroom

LESSON 1

45. Parental Involvement. In recent years, programs have been developed encouraging young people not to get started with alcohol or drugs. With your parents, find out what similar programs are available in your community and what it takes to get involved in them.

46. Community Involvement. Research two support groups for addicts and codependents within your community. Interview a facilitator from each group to learn all you can about the program. If no group presently exists, research the need for such a group in your area.

and speeds the rate of recovery for family members.

30. A support group designed for family members and close friends of people with alcohol dependency problems. To offer a support system for coping and a structured program for regaining emotional and social health.

Thinking Critically

31. Answers will vary. Possible answers: Peer pressure, boredom, trying to escape reality, curiosity. Possibly by choosing friends who do not use drugs or alcohol, being active in school and community work, getting help.

32. Answers will vary but should be supported logically.

33. For the rest of their lives. Answers will vary. Possible answers: Avoiding events or places where drugs or alcohol are likely to be; may find him- or herself taking along a substitute drink, such as soda water, when it is known alcohol will be served.

34. Answers will vary. Possible answers: There seems to be more understanding within the public sector so that there is less of a negative impact. More public awareness and education may be causing the change. People dealing with this realize they are not alone.

35. Answers will vary. Possible answer: Because codependency is an emotional illness and a health-care professional can help a person develop awareness and understanding of the problem.

36. Answers will vary.

Making the Connection

37. Paintings will vary.
38. Sculptures/songs will vary.
39. Answers will vary.

Applying Health Knowledge

40. Answers will vary. Possible answer: Alcohol is depicted as being an essential and harmless element of any fun gathering, necessary for peer approval, and as an integral part of male/female relationships. Discussions will vary.

41. Answers will vary but should be supported logically.

42. An outpatient treatment program.

43. Once the body becomes dependent upon and adjusts to certain chemicals, the withdrawal process can be painful and/or dangerous.

44. Answers will vary but might include the idea of suggesting the friend and his sister look into Alateen.

Beyond the Classroom

45. Answers will vary.
46. Answers will vary.

Lesson Summaries

LESSON 1. Communicable diseases are spread by pathogens that invade the body and attack its cells and tissues. Bacteria and viruses are common pathogens. Others include rickettsias, fungi, protozoans, flatworms, and roundworms.

LESSON 2. For disease to develop, a pathogen needs an intermediary host, a means of transportation, and a host with lowered resistance to the pathogen. The body has mechanical, chemical, and biological barriers to prevent pathogens from entering, and the immune system assists in fighting pathogens once they have invaded.

LESSON 3. A person can prevent being infected by disease by avoiding contact with pathogens or by becoming immune either by having had the disease or by vaccination.

Introducing the Chapter

Ask students how many of them have had to miss school due to a cold or the flu. Have students estimate the number of days missed by the entire class last year as a result of cold or flu symptoms. Tell them that in a 1-year period, colds alone are typically responsible for absences of 30 million days from school and another 30 million days from work. Additionally, Americans spend an estimated $500 million a year on nonprescription medicines alone to fight cold symptoms. To avoid being plagued with these mild diseases, as well as more serious ones, it will help to understand our bodies' defenses against diseases and preventive measures that can be taken for communicable diseases.

Performance Assessment ✓

Refer to pages T 23 to T 25 for a Performance Assessment strategy for this chapter. See the *Performance Assessment Activities* booklet for additional suggestions.

LESSON 1
Causes of Communicable Diseases

LESSON 2
Body Defenses Against Communicable Diseases

LESSON 3
Preventing Communicable Diseases

516 CHAPTER 26 COMMUNICABLE DISEASES

Key to Ability Levels

Teaching strategies have been coded for varying learning styles and abilities.

L1 Level 1 activities are basic activities and should be within the ability range of all students.

L2 Level 2 activities are average activities and should be within the ability range of average to above-average students.

L3 Level 3 activities are challenging activities designed for the ability range of above-average students.

LD LD activities should be within the ability range of learning-disabled students.

LEP LEP activities should be within the ability range of Limited English Proficiency students.

CAUSES OF COMMUNICABLE DISEASES

Many of the most common diseases are caused by tiny microorganisms called pathogens. Pathogens infect, or invade, the body and attack its cells and tissues. Some bacteria, rickettsias, fungi, protozoans, certain types of worms, and all viruses are pathogens.

Diseases caused by the direct or indirect spread of pathogens from one person to another are called **communicable diseases.**

Bacteria

Bacteria are one-celled microscopic organisms that rank among the most widespread of living things. Some bacteria are so small that a single grain of soil may contain over 100 million of them. Of course, most bacteria do not cause disease.

In order to live, all bacteria must have a food supply, as well as suitable temperature, moisture, and darkness. Some bacteria digest nonliving food materials, such as milk and meat. These organisms are called **saprophytes.** If the food supply is a living plant or animal, the microorganism is called a **parasite.** The plant or animal that the parasite feeds on is called a **host.**

Resident Bacteria

Many kinds of bacteria, called **resident bacteria,** live in your mouth and intestines and on your skin. These help protect you from harmful bacteria.

Lactobacilli, found in the gastrointestinal tract, produce lactic acid from simple carbohydrates. Coliform bacilli, found in the intestines, help break down carbohydrates and combat disease-causing bacteria.

As you will read later in this chapter, the resident bacteria form one line of defense against disease. They cause disease only if they move to a place in the body where they do not belong. For example, if bacteria from your mouth move into your middle ear, you may develop an ear infection.

The Spread of Bacteria

Most diseases caused by bacteria begin when microorganisms not usually present in the body invade the body. When these bacteria enter the body, they multiply at a rapid rate through cell division. A fully grown cell divides, forming two new cells. If conditions are good, this division can repeat itself at intervals of 20 minutes. That may not sound like much, but calculate what this multiplication rate can mean.

CAUSES OF COMMUNICABLE DISEASES **517**

LESSON 1 FOCUS

TERMS TO USE
- Communicable diseases
- Saprophytes
- Parasite
- Host
- Resident bacteria
- Viruses

CONCEPTS TO LEARN
- Pathogens cause communicable diseases.
- Communicable diseases have various modes of transmission.
- The common cold is preventable, but not curable.

ATTITUDES AND BEHAVIORS TO EVALUATE
- Self-Inventory, page 532.
- Building Decision-Making Skills, page 533.

Focus

Lesson Objectives

After studying this lesson, students should be able to:
- describe six types of pathogens that cause disease
- explain the role of resident bacteria in protecting the body against disease
- describe the spread of bacterial infection through cell division
- explain effective ways to treat a cold
- identify symptoms of colds that may be dangerous
- explain how viruses differ from other pathogens

Bellringer

Write the following on the chalkboard for students to work on while attendance is being taken: *Describe the last cold you had. Tell how you believe you caught it and how you treated it.*

Introducing the Lesson

Have students share their responses to the Bellringer. Point out that colds are one type of disease that a person can catch or give to someone else. Such diseases are called communicable diseases. Tell students that this lesson explains how some of these diseases are spread.

DID YOU KNOW?

- The electron microscope was developed in the 1930s.
- Viruses are about one-half to one-hundredth the size of some bacteria.
- While only 3 types of viruses are responsible for influenza, or flu, over 200 viruses are responsible for colds.
- About 30 percent of the infections associated with the common cold are caused by a virus called rhinovirus.

Resources for Lesson 1

- **Guided Reading** Activity 70
- **Workbook** Vocabulary Activity 70
- **Reteaching** Activity 70
- **Lesson 1 Quiz**
- **Performance Assessment** Activity 26

Cold symptoms may include fever, sneezing, a runny nose, a cough or sore throat, and headache.

HELP WANTED

Medical Laboratory Technician

Can you do careful, painstaking work under time pressure? If you can, then a position as medical lab technician may interest you. We are looking for responsible graduates of accredited one-year technician training programs or two-year associate degree programs for our hospital labs. Individuals with on-the-job experience or certification in a specialized area are especially desired. The position involves doing routine lab tests necessary to diagnose and treat disease. Specific duties include preparing samples of patients' blood and other tissues and performing biochemical analyses of them. If you are interested in learning more about this position, please contact:
American Society for Medical Technology
2021 L St. NW, Suite 400
Washington, DC 20036

If a single bacterial cell divides, 30 minutes later the 2 cells become 4. After 30 more minutes (1 hour elapsed), the 4 cells become 8. In just 15½ hours, there would be more than 4 billion bacteria!

Obviously, if this multiplication continued for long, the bacteria would soon take over completely. Because the bacteria must compete with one another for food, competition kills many of them, which helps control their numbers.

Toxins

Some other bacteria cause disease by producing certain poisons called toxins. Botulism, a type of food poisoning, results from this type of bacteria. Bacteria that normally live in the soil can enter the body through a wound and produce a poison that affects muscles and nerves in the body. Tetanus, or lockjaw, is an example of the actions of such bacteria.

Bacterial diseases include certain types of pneumonia and food poisoning, diphtheria, tetanus, tuberculosis, strep throat, syphilis, and gonorrhea. We will discuss some of these diseases in greater detail in this unit.

THE COMMON COLD

Colds are caused by viruses that are spread through the air, through water, or by any direct or indirect contact with a contagious person. Once you have been exposed to a cold virus, it usually takes one to two days for the symptoms to appear.

The cold virus is most contagious the day before symptoms appear. Symptoms can include a mild fever, aching, sneezing, congestion, a runny nose, a cough, a mild sore throat, and a headache.

At present there is no cure for the common cold. Getting rest, drinking liquids, and maintaining good nutrition are the best methods of treating the cold virus. Americans spend millions of dollars each year on over-the-counter cold remedies. Some of these may help relieve the symptoms, but many are useless and some may even be harmful.

Although it may be difficult to prevent colds, you can keep your body healthy so that it can better resist infection. Good nutrition, regular exercise, adequate sleep, and good health care all contribute to prevention. Controlling stress levels and relaxing also help ward off infections.

Not smoking is another way you can help prevent infections. People who smoke get more colds, and their colds tend to last longer.

Colds can be dangerous. Call a doctor if any of these symptoms last two or more days:

- a fever of 101°F (38°C) or higher
- a sore throat with a 101°F (38°C) fever
- pain in the chest or shortness of breath
- continued coughing
- pain in the back of the throat or in the ears
- any of the above, even after taking over-the-counter medicines

Viruses

Viruses are small, simple lifelike forms—between one half to one hundredth the size of some bacteria. These organisms are also one of

Across the Curriculum

Home Economics. Invite a home economics teacher or a local health representative to talk to the class about salmonella, trichinosis, and other food-related bacterial problems. Ask the speaker to include information about methods of prevention.

Social Studies. Have students research and give reports on the great epidemics of communicable diseases throughout history, such as the Black Death in Europe in the fourteenth century and the Spanish influenza of 1919.

Math. Have students calculate how many bacteria there would be 4 hours after a single bacteria cell begins to divide if division occurs every 30 minutes.

the human body's worst enemies. Scientists had not actually seen viruses until the 1930s, when the high-powered electron microscope was developed. Using an electron beam instead of light and a photographic plate instead of the human eye, the electron microscope made the study of viruses possible.

An examination of viruses reveals that they are not cells. They have no nucleus, no cytoplasm, and no cell membrane. The virus particle consists of nucleic acid, a complex chemical that is an acid present in the cells of all organisms.

Viruses at Work

All viruses are parasites, requiring living cells for survival and reproduction. Viruses are highly specific in the kind of cells they invade. Only certain viruses invade animal cells, and these various viruses can attack only specific types of cells. For example, the rabies virus can enter only brain cells, polio viruses attack only the nervous system, and cold viruses enter only the cells lining the respiratory system.

Viral hepatitis is caused by a virus that affects the liver. Mumps and mononucleosis are caused by viruses that infect glandular tissues. Smallpox, chicken pox, shingles, and warts are infections caused by viruses that attack the skin tissues.

When a virus enters the body, it attaches itself to a cell and releases its nucleic acid into the host cell. The substance disrupts the cell's activities and causes it to begin producing more viruses identical to the one that attached itself to the cell wall. These viruses then spread to other body cells, where the process is repeated.

Rickettsias

Rickettsias are organisms that are considered intermediate, that is, somewhere between a virus and a bacterium. They are smaller than bacteria. Most of them grow in the intestinal tracts of insects, which then carry them to their human hosts. A rickettsia requires a living cell in order to grow and multiply.

Bloodsucking insects, such as lice, mites, and ticks, carry rickettsias to humans. Typhus fever and Rocky Mountain spotted fever are diseases caused by these organisms.

One disease caused by a virus is measles.

KEEPING FIT

Don't Let Strep Get You by the Throat

Streptococcal bacteria are the cause of strep throat. The classic strep infection can cause a severe sore throat, fever, and a general feeling of illness. However, a newly mutated strain of strep is becoming more common. The bacteria that cause this ferocious kind of strep have also been linked to rheumatic fever, which can lead to permanent heart damage. This new strain of strep, first reported in 1987, has also been linked to skin rashes and shock-like symptoms. About 10,000 cases of this severe strep are reported annually.

If you have a persistent sore throat or skin infections, see a physician. Most strains of strep can be treated.

CAUSES OF COMMUNICABLE DISEASES **519**

Across the Curriculum

Physical Education. Have students talk with coaches or physical education teachers about what processes the school follows in an attempt to decrease the incidence of athlete's foot transmission through locker rooms and showers.

Social Studies. Assign small groups of students to prepare reports to share with another class about protozoan-caused communicable diseases, such as malaria, African sleeping sickness, and amoebic dysentery. Have them find out how these diseases affected people in the past and if they are still affecting people today.

L1 EXPLANATION. Point out some of the complex problems presented by viruses. (There are so many different types causing different diseases. The diseases they cause cannot be prevented through vaccinations. The diseases can only be treated, they cannot be cured. With so many kinds of viruses, it can be difficult to pinpoint the type of disease to be treated. Viruses cannot be treated with antibiotics like bacteria can.)

L1 DISCUSSION. Ask students to explain how rickettsias are different from bacteria and viruses.

L1 EXPLANATION. Inform students that ticks attach themselves by embedding their heads under the skin. As they suck blood, their bodies grow. Encourage students who spend time outdoors to check their bodies for ticks at the end of the day. If they find a tick, they should smother it with rubbing alcohol or a thick substance, such as petroleum jelly. Once the tick dies, it can be taken out. Stress that the head of the tick should be removed.

L1 DISCUSSION. Ask students what fungi are. In what ways can they cause problems for humans?

L1 DISCUSSION. Have students explain why they should wear shower shoes when showering in public facilities, such as school locker rooms. (This is to prevent picking up fungi that can live on the base of shower stalls.)

L1 SPEAKER. Ask a home economics teacher or county extension agent to speak to the class about trichinosis and ways to prevent it by proper cooking of pork and other meat.

L1 SPEAKER. Ask a biology teacher to speak to the class about flatworms and roundworms, their prevalence, and the diseases they cause in the human body. Request that the speaker bring specimens to show the class. Have students prepare a list of questions to ask the speaker.

Independent Practice

L2 RESEARCH. Ask students to use classroom and library resources to research some of the resident bacteria and their functions in the body.

Overcoming The Odds

Dave Clowes is a saddle-maker. He loves to ride horses. As a teenager, he was a weight lifter and an award-winning gymnast. He is also one of the millions of people who contracted polio in the 1940s and 1950s before there was a vaccine to prevent it. Today, one of his legs is smaller than the other and he walks with a cane, but Dave is healthy and enjoying life. He says, "I was a year old when I got polio. I spent nine months in the hospital. A doctor told me years later that polio could be no worse than the flu, it could affect people as it did me, or worse. The point is that it affected different people in different ways. I remember having a brace when I was a little kid. The thing about me was that I never thought about it much. It wasn't as if I'd ever known differently, so it didn't feel like I had to overcome anything."

He continues, "I started lifting weights when I was thirteen. All of a sudden, I was stronger than everybody else, and I enjoyed that. I got involved in gymnastics in the eighth grade. I applied myself to that and got pretty good at it. I tied for metropolitan

champ in the AAU, the American Athletic Union. I tied for first place on the rings one year. I went to the AAU junior nationals that same year, and I got third on the rings. That was really fun.

"Back in the 50s, when everyone else had to line up for the polio shots (the Salk vaccine), I didn't get them because they thought I was immune. Then they found out there were three different strains of the disease, so I ended up having to take sugar cubes when I was in college." The sugar cubes contained the oral polio vaccine approved in 1961. This vaccine, called the

Sabin vaccine, is still given today. Decades after their initial polio infections, many people are suffering from recurring polio symptoms. "My doctor warned me about post-polio syndrome, but I don't worry about it," Dave says. "My friend with a bad back says I'm healthier than he is. We're all victims of some disease—or of ourselves. If you have a problem, it's your problem, not somebody else's, and it's your responsibility to do something about it. I did it. I overcame it. And I have a beautiful wife, two stepsons, a business, horses, five acres. I've done okay in life."

1. Dave realized what he could do and worked to excel at it, rather than dwelling on what he couldn't do. Do you take this approach, or do you dwell on your limitations?

2. One reason Dave was able to accept his disability was that he had never known any other way. How might a sudden change in health or ability later in life make it harder to adjust?

3. Why is it important to remember that diseases affect different people in different ways?

Additional Information

Communicable Diseases. Deer ticks can carry Lyme disease to humans. This is a condition that begins with a rash and is then followed by muscle and joint aches which can lead to the development of rheumatoid arthritis.

Rat fleas can carry tapeworms and even bubonic plague to humans.

Psittacosis, a lung infection, is spread by parakeets, parrots, and canaries. Human exposure occurs through inhalation of cage dust.

Salmonella is carried through turtles and hamsters, undercooked pork and fowl, and in eggs and egg products.

Mosquitoes, through their bites, spread malaria and encephalitis.

Fungi

Fungi are living organisms that cannot make their own food. Many feed off dead animals, insects, and leaves. Fungi are, therefore, saprophytes. They prefer dark, damp environments. Two of the most common fungi are yeast and mushrooms.

Disease-producing fungi invade mainly deep tissues of the hair, nails, and skin. Fungi cause infections of the scalp, such as ringworm, and of the feet, such as athlete's foot. Pathogenic fungi can also cause brain inflammation and serious lung infection.

Protozoans

Protozoans are single-celled organisms that are larger than bacteria and have a more complex cellular structure. Most protozoans are harmless. The disease-producing protozoans are most common in tropical areas that have poor sanitation. Protozoans cause malaria, African sleeping sickness, and amoebic dysentery, a severe intestinal infection.

Other Pathogens That Can Cause Infections

Certain flatworms and roundworms, while not microorganisms, are regarded as pathogens and cause diseases in the human body. Disease-producing flatworms include flukes, which can invade the blood, intestines, liver, or lungs, and tapeworms, which live in the intestines. Pathogenic roundworms can infect the intestines, muscles, and fluids under the skin. You may have heard of trichinosis, a disease caused by an intestinal roundworm. Trichinosis is usually transmitted when a person eats improperly cooked pork.

Trichinosis, a disease caused by an intestinal roundworm, can be transmitted when a person eats pork that has not been cooked properly.

LESSON 1 REVIEW

Reviewing Facts and Vocabulary

1. What is a communicable disease?
2. Name six types of pathogens that cause disease.
3. How are viruses different from other pathogens?

Thinking Critically

4. **Analysis.** Compare a parasite and a saprophyte. Give an example of each.
5. **Synthesis.** How might a communicable disease influence one's mental health?

Applying Health Knowledge

6. Contact a local veterinarian to find out about parasites (such as ticks and fleas) that affect pets. How do these microorganisms work? How can they be stopped from causing illness or discomfort to pets or people? How does warm weather affect the problems associated with fleas and ticks? Share your findings with your class.
7. On one side of a poster board, make a collage of ads for cold remedies. On the other side, create your own ad for preventing the common cold through good health habits.

CAUSES OF COMMUNICABLE DISEASES **521**

BODY DEFENSES AGAINST COMMUNICABLE DISEASES

LESSON 2 FOCUS

TERMS TO USE
- Phagocytosis (fag•uh•suh•TOH•suhs)
- Neutrophils (NOO•truh•fils)
- Lymphocytes (LIM•fuh•syts)
- Antibodies

CONCEPTS TO LEARN
- Pathogens can be spread in many ways.
- The body has many defenses against communicable diseases.

ATTITUDES AND BEHAVIORS TO EVALUATE
- Self-Inventory, page 532.
- Building Decision-Making Skills, page 533.

You may know someone who seems to get colds or flu a lot. Why do some people get these diseases often and others do not? How does anyone get a communicable disease? How does your body respond when a pathogen enters?

Ways Pathogens Are Spread

Pathogens are spread in many ways. As you learn the ways they can be spread, you can practice habits that help promote your health.

Indirect Contact

Many communicable diseases spread as a result of indirect contact with an infected person. The common cold, strep throat, and pneumonia are diseases that can be spread through the air. The pathogens that cause these diseases are in the tiny droplets of moisture expelled when a person coughs or sneezes. Anyone near the infected person can breathe in the pathogens in the airborne droplets.

Certain pathogens are spread when an uninfected person touches objects that an infected person has used. These objects can include eating utensils, combs, or toothbrushes. They also can include needles used to inject drugs that are shared with an infected person.

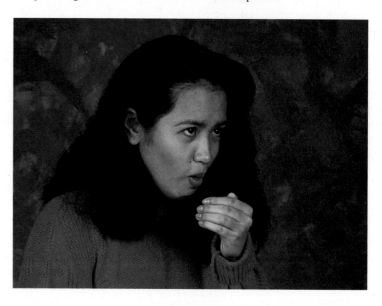

Pathogens are expelled into the air when a person coughs or sneezes.

Resources for Lesson 2

- **Guided Reading** Act 71
- **Workbook** Voc Act 71
- **Reteaching** Act 71
- **Lesson 2 Quiz**

Science and Technology Videodisc
Human Biology, Side 1
Ch 14 White Cells in Action

Ch 15 Combined Immune Deficiency

Human Biology, Side 2
Ch 23 Animal Models of Human Physiology

Direct Contact

Pathogens may be spread when an uninfected person comes into direct physical contact with an infected area on another person. Some skin rashes can be spread in this way. Sexually transmitted diseases are also spread when an infected person with sores comes in contact with an uninfected person.

Contact with Animals

Animals spread many serious diseases. When an insect, such as a mosquito, bites an infected person, the insect may take pathogens into its own body. The pathogens then continue their development within the insect.

When the insect later bites an uninfected person, it injects some of the pathogens into that person's body, thus spreading the disease. Some communicable diseases, such as rabies, are spread by contact with infected mammals and birds.

Your Immune System

Though you cannot see them, your body is exposed each day to millions of pathogens. Pathogens are in the air you breathe, and they cling to the surfaces you touch. Your body is constantly fighting pathogens that enter your body. When they enter your body, pathogens attack your body cells and use these cells to grow and multiply. The end result of such an attack is an infection.

Most of the time, your body manages to stay free of infection because of your immune system. Your immune system includes two main types of defenses. One type of defense is nonspecific resistance. Another type of defense is specific resistance. Both types work together to protect your body against pathogens that could harm you.

Nonspecific Resistance

Body defenses that are nonspecific respond in the same way each time your body is invaded by a foreign substance. Your body's nonspecific defenses include mechanical mechanisms, chemical barriers, cells, and inflammatory response.

Mechanical Mechanisms. Mechanical mechanisms form barriers to help keep pathogens out of the body. Your body's main mechanical mechanism is your skin. Unbroken skin helps prevent pathogens from entering body tissues. The tough dead cells that make up the outer layer of skin form a very effective barrier. Mucous membranes in your mouth, nose, and bronchial tubes produce a sticky substance called mucus that traps pathogens. Some mucous membranes have cilia, tiny hairs, that also trap pathogens, which are then expelled when you cough or sneeze. Tears and saliva are other mechanical barriers that help carry pathogens away.

Pathogens may be spread by sharing eating utensils—or even from your pet.

BODY DEFENSES AGAINST COMMUNICABLE DISEASES **523**

Building Vocabulary

- Ask students to find medical definitions of *communicable disease* and *immunity*. Then, have them rewrite the definitions in their own words.
- Ask volunteers to explain the following terms and phrases: *infectious disease, pathogen, immune system, phagocyte, inflammatory response, lymphocyte,* and *antibody.*
- Ask students to complete *Workbook Vocabulary Activity 71.*

Teach

Guided Practice

LEP **CLASS ACTIVITY.** Ask two students to act out in front of the class typical interactions between two family members in their kitchen. Instruct the two actors to pretend to touch the same utensils, foods, and each other's hands after miming coughs, sneezes, and nose blowing. They should avoid pretending to wash their hands. Have the rest of the class observe and make note of every occasion where the possibility of contagion occurs. Then, have the two students re-act the scene using behaviors, like frequent hand-washing, that would inhibit the spread of infection.

L1 **SPEAKER.** Invite a veterinarian or veterinarian's assistant to speak to the class about animal diseases that humans may contract. Ask the speaker to address questions like: who is most at risk; which animals are the greatest danger; and how can one avoid contracting diseases without isolating oneself from animals?

L1 **EXPLANATION.** Explain that most of us are constantly fighting pathogens in many ways. We do not get sick every time we come in contact with a pathogen because our immune system protects us on several fronts. People are most likely to get sick when their immune systems are compromised for some reason—lack of sleep, lack of food, use of some medications, stress, infection with HIV, etc.

Across the Curriculum

Language Arts. Have students review popular magazines and books for information about ways to strengthen the immune system. Have them determine why this is important and ways they can incorporate the information into practical steps in their own lives.

Science. Ask students to prepare a report on diphtheria and tetanus, explaining the two diseases, their symptoms, methods of treatment, and any long-term effects. Have them conclude their reports by discussing vaccines that are available to protect against these diseases.

L1 **SELF-ESTEEM.** Ask students what responsibility they feel an infected person has to tell other people that he or she may be contagious. Discuss what influence a person's level of self-esteem would have on his or her ability to act responsibly about the risks of spreading disease.

L1 **EXPLANATION.** Explain that a person can be contagious both before and after having symptoms of a communicable disease.

L2 **CLASS ACTIVITY.** Have students use class and library resources to research mucous membranes and where they are found in the body. Follow up with a discussion of the role of mucous membranes in the fight against invading pathogens.

L3 **COOPERATIVE LEARNING.** Choose students to work in groups to design and create board games based on the lymphatic system and its functions in defending against infection. Have each group demonstrate its completed game to the class.

L2 **CLASS ACTIVITY.** Ask one student to volunteer as scribe at the chalkboard. Have the rest of the class work together to name and give examples of the types of nonspecific resistance that help us fight off infections.

L1 **EXPLANATION.** Explain how the inflammatory response works to fight bacteria in a localized tissue.

L2 **COOPERATIVE LEARNING.** Divide the class into three or four groups of several students each. Have each group produce a diagram that illustrates the action of lymphocytes, including the roles of both T cells and B cells, in fighting off pathogens. Circulate the drawings. Have students give each other feedback on their diagrams to correct errors and misconceptions.

L3 **DISCUSSION.** Ask the class what "specific" means in the phrase "specific resistance to infection." Continue by asking why it is so valuable to have antibodies that can "remember" a pathogen and be available if it invades the body again. Suggest the analogy of a surprise attack in a game or warfare.

Chemical Barriers. Chemicals on the surface of cells can kill pathogens or prevent them from entering the body. Such chemicals can be found in tears, saliva, and sweat. The acidic digestive juices of the stomach also are chemical barriers. These juices destroy pathogens that are swallowed with food. Other chemicals cause body changes that help cells inside the body fight pathogens.

Cells. Certain types of white blood cells, called phagocytes, travel through blood and group together to destroy foreign substances. This action is called phagocytosis. **Phagocytosis** is the process by which phagocytes engulf and destroy pathogens. **Neutrophils** are one type of phagocyte that are most actively involved in the process of phagocytosis.

Inflammatory Response. After bacteria enter the body or cause damage to body tissue, chemical mediators are released. These cause the blood vessels to dilate and allow increased blood flow. Increased blood flow brings phagocytes to the area to leave the blood and enter the tissues. This process continues until the pathogens are destroyed. Once the pathogens are destroyed, tissues can be repaired. Symptoms of inflammation confined to a specific area include heat, redness, and swelling, which result from increased blood flow. Pain can result from swelling.

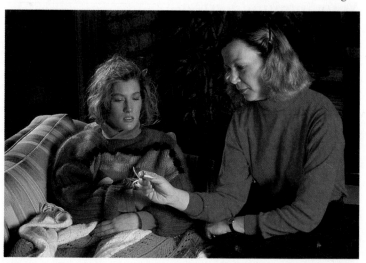

Fever is another way that the body fights infection by speeding up the activities of the immune system.

KEEPING FIT

The Spread of Disease

- Rumors are rampant about how disease-carrying organisms are spread—toilet seats, kissing, casual contact. All pathogens are different, so there is no single set of rules for all. Many pathogens need warm, moist,

dark environments to survive. Once these organisms leave the body, they die quickly.
- Many other organisms are resilient and can last a long time outside the body.

- Antiseptics, such as household disinfectants, inhibit the growth of bacteria and can be used to clean skin, wounds, and inanimate objects. Germicides, such as bleach, also kill bacteria.

Overcoming Misconceptions

Myth. The fight against communicable diseases has been won. **Fact.** Unfortunately, such diseases as measles, cholera, and typhoid fever, which are well on the way to extinction in the developed nations, remain major killers in areas where sanitary conditions and nutrition are primitive. Parents must continually be reminded of the need to have their children immunized against many communicable diseases.

LOOKING AT THE ISSUES

Should Animals Be Used for Medical Research?

Many people and organizations believe that the use of laboratory animals for medical research is critical. Animal-rights advocates, however, claim that such testing is not only unnecessary but also cruel and inhumane. This heated debate goes on.

Analyzing Different Viewpoints

ONE VIEW.   Those who support the use of laboratory animals for medical research maintain that various medical procedures or medicines must first be tested on animals to see if they will be safe and effective when used on humans. They state that animal research has led to a great many important medical advances for humans. Dogs were used in the perfecting of coronary artery bypass surgery. Mice have been used in the development of vaccines for various communicable diseases and are even now being used to test how some vaccines might trigger defenses in humans. Those in favor of using animals in biomedical research caution that if funding is cut for research, many humans suffering from diseases will not get the treatment, medi-

cations, or cures that might be available to them if testing were to continue.

A SECOND VIEW.   Many animal-rights advocates say that they are not against all animal research if the aim of such research is truly to aid human beings in the treatment or prevention of diseases rather than to make money for medical companies. Some animal-rights advocates add that more humane, less painful methods of testing than those presently used must be developed and implemented. They also claim that some animal testing, such as that for cosmetics, is completely unnecessary, since such products are not needed for improved health.

A THIRD VIEW.   Some people are opposed to any use of animals for research. They claim no human has the right to harm another living creature for any purpose.

Exploring Your Views

1. Do you favor the use of animals for medical research? Why or why not?
2. Are there any limitations or conditions that you would put on that research?

Spreading Diseases

Many human activities may unwittingly spread diseases. Some activities simply allow diseases to be carried to new populations. People and animals traveling by air may be infected with a disease, although they have no symptoms. Sometimes pathogens actually "catch a ride" to new areas in cargo shipments.

Other human activities spread disease by causing favorable environments for some disease carriers. Building highways and clearing land for farming have caused new mosquito breeding grounds in parts of South America, Asia, and Africa.

Independent Practice

L1 **RESEARCH.** Ask students to research the specific causes (i.e., species of pathogen) of several common communicable diseases. Have them present their results in a table. They also should write a summary paragraph that describes the types of organisms, in general, that cause most human communicable disease.

L1 **COMMUNITY INVOLVEMENT.** Ask students to survey friends, neighbors, and family members about how they think one can get a cold. (e.g., getting chilled, not getting enough sleep, etc.) Have them compile their answers in a list. Discuss the validity of each cause listed. Point out that, while the ultimate cause of a cold is a virus, many other factors can play a contributing role by weakening the body's ability to fight off infection.

L2 **RESEARCH.** Select students to learn about the role fevers play in fighting infection.

L2 **RESEARCH.** Ask students to research diseases spread by animals. Ask them to share what they learn with the class.

L3 **COMMUNITY INVOLVEMENT.** Select students to investigate the type of mosquito control, if any, used by any local or state health agency.

L3 **WRITING.** Ask for volunteers to design and demonstrate to the class computer games based on the communicable disease process. When the games are completed, assign students to groups to select names for the games and design brochures describing the purpose of the games and how to play them.

L2 **RESEARCH.** Select students to research different types of immunity, such as active immunity, passive immunity, temporary immunity, and permanent immunity. They should write a report that summarizes the differences among the various types of immunity and describes how each type comes about. They also should give examples of particular diseases that are characterized by each type of immunity

L1 **USING THE LESSON RESOURCES.** For additional activities, refer to the lesson resources on page 522.

Specific Resistance

The general response of your nonspecific defenses is not always enough to protect your body from disease. Another defense mechanism is specific resistance. This defense gives specific protection against specific types of pathogens. When this happens, another body defense goes to work. This defense is the cells that not only fight off pathogens but also keep a record of them in case they enter the body again.

BODY DEFENSES AGAINST COMMUNICABLE DISEASES   **525**

Overcoming Misconceptions

Leprosy and Tuberculosis. Two diseases that have caused a great deal of illness and death in human populations for millennia are leprosy and tuberculosis. They are caused by two different species of the bacterial genus *Mycobacterium*.

Historically, people infected with either of these two diseases have been shunned for

fear of contamination. However, their infectivity has been overestimated. Although both are communicable diseases (spread through sneezing and coughing or by direct contact), neither is very easy to pick up by people with normally functioning immune systems. Both require a long period of close contact with an infected person.

Assess

Check for Understanding

- Assign and discuss the lesson review.

Evaluate

- Administer, grade, and discuss the *Lesson 2 Quiz.*

Reteach

- Have students write a detailed outline of the material in the lesson, using two major headings: *Ways Pathogens Are Spread* and *Your Immune System.*
- Ask students to complete *Reteaching Activity 71.*

Enrich

- Have students research how malaria is transmitted. Based on their research, they should draw a diagram illustrating the transmission process and the organisms involved (malaria pathogen, mosquito vector, and human host). They also should provide a brief explanation of the role of each organism in the transmission cycle.
- Choose students to read about current research being done on interferon. Ask them to summarize what they read in a written report.

Close

Tell students that in this lesson they learned how we are exposed to communicable disease pathogens: indirectly through the air or through contaminated objects; directly through physical contact with an infected person; or through contact with infected animals. They also learned how our immune system fights off the pathogens we are exposed to: through nonspecific defenses such as mechanical and chemical barriers; and through the production of antibodies specific for a particular pathogen.

CONFLICT RESOLUTION

Tomorrow night is the senior prom, and Gloria's been looking forward to it for weeks. Everything was going to be perfect—until she woke up this morning with a sore throat. Now Gloria's mom thinks she should stay home from the prom so she won't "spread her germs." Gloria thinks that going to the last social event of her senior year is more important than protecting her date from a sore throat.

What do you think Gloria should do?

MONONUCLEOSIS

Mononucleosis is a communicable disease common among young people that is characterized by abnormal shapes of lymphocytes. It spreads primarily through direct contact, such as kissing. Symptoms include chills, fever, sore throat, fatigue, and swollen lymph nodes. Complete bed rest is needed. Treatment and recovery can take three to six weeks.

Lymphocytes. **Lymphocytes** are a type of white blood cell that fights pathogens. Lymphocytes travel through your body along two networks of vessels. One of these networks is your blood vessels. The other network is your lymph vessels, which are a part of your lymphatic system. Your lymphatic system also includes your spleen, tonsils, thymus gland, lymph, and lymph nodes. This system is part of your body's defense system. Lymphocytes multiply in the spleen, tonsils, thymus gland, and lymph nodes.

The immune system uses two major types of lymphocytes—T cells and B cells. T cells and B cells originate in bone marrow, the soft material at the core of your bones. T cells move through blood vessels and mature in your thymus gland. B cells mature in red bone marrow. Both T cells and B cells travel between your blood and your lymph tissues.

T cells and B cells both fight specific pathogens. Imagine that pathogens that cause a particular disease have entered your body. Your immune system searches your lymph nodes for the right T cell and B cell to fight those particular pathogens. When the right T cell and B cell are found, your body begins producing many copies of these cells to ensure that enough lymphocytes are on hand to attack the pathogens.

T cells and B cells work in different ways. There are many types of T cells, and these different types have different functions. Some T cells kill pathogens. Other T cells regulate other cell functions. B cells are stimulated by T helper cells, one type of T cell, to make antibodies. **Antibodies** are proteins that destroy or neutralize pathogens in your body. The antibodies for a particular pathogen remain in your blood to become active if you encounter the specific pathogen again.

LESSON 2 REVIEW

Reviewing Facts and Vocabulary

1. How are pathogens spread?
2. List the body's nonspecific defenses.
3. Explain the term *antibodies.*

Thinking Critically

4. **Analysis.** Explain why the presence of antibodies is often used to determine if an individual has a communicable disease.
5. **Analysis.** Compare B cells and T cells.

Applying Health Knowledge

6. In small groups make up a game or activity that explains ways your immune system works. Exchange completed projects with classmates as a review for this lesson.

Answers to Lesson 2 Review

1. Indirect contact through air or objects, direct contact through touch, contact with animals.
2. See pages 523 to 524.
3. Antibodies are proteins that destroy or neutralize pathogens in your body.
4. Antibodies are highly specialized so if certain antibodies are present, it is to attack one kind of pathogen.
5. Both are lymphocytes that serve as a defense against the spread of disease-causing pathogens. Some T cells kill pathogens; other T cells regulate other cell functions; B cells are stimulated by T helper cells to make antibodies.
6. Games and activities will vary.

PREVENTING COMMUNICABLE DISEASES

What can you do to protect yourself from being infected by disease? You have several choices. You can avoid contact with pathogens and you can avoid spreading pathogens to others. Follow these guidelines to reduce the spread of infection.

- Bathe or shower every day to keep your skin, hair, and nails clean.
- Avoid sharing eating or drinking utensils.
- Store and prepare food in a safe way to prevent food poisoning.
- Wash your hands after using the bathroom, after changing diapers, and before preparing or serving food.
- If you know you are sick, avoid giving your illness to someone else. Get medical treatment for your illness. Cover your mouth when you cough or sneeze to prevent spreading the germs. Use tissues only once and dispose of them immediately in a waste container.
- If you are well, avoid contact with people who are sick.

There are three other ways to protect yourself from communicable diseases. You can become immune by having the disease. You can be immunized by injection if a vaccine is available, and you can practice biofeedback.

Immunity

As you have read, immunity is the body's natural resistance to many pathogens. Certain pathogens cannot live in the body, while others are quickly destroyed if they enter the body.

One important feature of the body's immune system is that it remembers the pathogens it meets. This gives the body long-term protection—immunity—against many communicable diseases. For example, if you had chicken pox, your immune system remembers the chicken pox virus. If the virus enters your body again, cells designed specifically to combat the chicken pox virus will attack it immediately. In most cases, the virus does not get a chance to make you sick again.

This immunity your body develops to protect you from disease is called **active immunity.** Some types of immunity last a lifetime; others last only a short period of time. A single virus causes chicken pox, so once a person has had the disease, the body is usually protected against chicken pox for life. However, many different kinds of viruses cause the common cold. Because the body is continually exposed to different pathogens, immunity to colds is limited.

Vaccines Provide Active Immunity

Through the use of vaccines, the body can develop active immunity against a disease without actually having had the disease. **Vaccines** are

PREVENTING COMMUNICABLE DISEASES **527**

LESSON 3 FOCUS

TERMS TO USE
- Active immunity
- Vaccines
- Vaccination
- Passive immunity
- Biofeedback

CONCEPTS TO LEARN
- You can protect yourself from communicable diseases by avoiding contact with pathogens.
- There are many strategies to help prevent communicable diseases.

ATTITUDES AND BEHAVIORS TO EVALUATE
- Self-Inventory, page 532.
- Building Decision-Making Skills, page 533.

Focus

Lesson Objectives

After studying this lesson, students should be able to:
- cite specific ways to avoid contacting or spreading pathogens
- differentiate between active and passive immunity
- describe three major types of vaccines
- explain and give examples of biofeedback

Bellringer

Write the following on the chalkboard for students to work on while attendance is being taken: *Try to remember all the immunizations you have received, and list them on a sheet of paper.*

Introducing the Lesson

Check with a school nurse regarding immunizations required for school attendance. Refer to the Bellringer by asking students what immunizations or booster shots they can remember having before they could enter school. As each immunization for a disease is mentioned, ask what some of the basic symptoms of the disease are. (It may become necessary for you to add information.) Lead into a discussion of the material in this lesson by differentiating between active and passive immunities.

DID YOU KNOW?

- A new high-tech test that can diagnose measles in just 2 hours may help stop the disease from spreading as widely. How? By letting people know early that they have measles and may be contagious to others. Currently, it can take up to a week to get a firm diagnosis.
- According to the Centers for Disease Control, for every dollar spent on measles vaccinations, $11.90 in medical costs is saved.

Resources for Lesson 3

- **Guided Reading** Activity 72
- **Decision-Making** Activity 26
- **Workbook** Voc Act 72, Appl Act 26
- **Reteaching** Activity 72
- **Enrichment** Activity 26
- **Health Labs** Activity 26

- **Cooperative Learning** Activity 26
- **Lesson 3 Quiz, Chapter 26 Test**
Science and Technology Videodisc
Human Biology, Side 1
Ch 13 Diagnosing Disease With Glowing Cells

Storing food properly and keeping your hands clean are two ways to prevent becoming infected with a communicable disease.

DID YOU KNOW?

- People can infect themselves with cold viruses by rubbing their eyes or noses and giving the virus an easy entry into the body.
- Researchers claim that neither cold weather nor air conditioners cause people to catch seasonal cold viruses.

preparations that usually are composed of dead or weakened viruses. Vaccines provide immunity by causing the body to produce antibodies against the pathogen. The vaccine contains substances that are strong enough to cause the production of antibodies, but not strong enough to cause the disease. Through the process of **vaccination,** a vaccine is injected into the body.

The first vaccine was developed by Dr. Edward Jenner in 1798. In an effort to control the deadly smallpox disease, he injected people with pus from the sores of an animal with cowpox. (The cowpox and smallpox viruses are closely related.) People developed a mild case of cowpox but also developed an immunity to smallpox. Jenner's technique has been refined, and vaccinations are now used to protect people from a variety of crippling or fatal diseases.

At birth, babies carry in their blood small amounts of the antibodies that protected their mothers. Babies are thus protected from the same diseases as their mothers. This immunity lasts for a few months after birth until the baby can produce antibodies of its own. The temporary immunity that the infant acquires from the mother is called **passive immunity.**

Types of Vaccines

Some of the major types of vaccines include live-virus vaccines, killed-virus vaccines, and toxoids.

Live-Virus Vaccine. Some vaccines are made from weakened viruses. By using mechanical means or chemicals and growing the virus over and over until it is very weak, scientists develop a live-virus vaccine. In this weakened state, the virus cannot cause a disease, but the virus does stimulate the production of antibodies in the body. Measles, rubella, and oral polio vaccines all contain live viruses.

528 CHAPTER 26 COMMUNICABLE DISEASES

Overcoming Misconceptions

Myth. All U.S. children receive vaccinations for most childhood diseases. **Fact.** The successful use of vaccines for many childhood diseases has caused a complacency about getting regular immunizations. Some parents even withhold immunizations, thinking the risks associated with them are greater than those of getting the disease. This can prove dangerous. Some immu- nizations, such as those for measles and mumps, require only one inoculation for lifelong immunity. Others require boosters. For example, tetanus boosters are required every 10 years throughout life. A smallpox vaccination is no longer required in the U.S. because the disease has been eliminated in this country.

Killed-Virus Vaccine. Another type of vaccine is the killed-virus vaccine. Scientists use mechanical means or chemicals to kill the viruses. The killed-virus vaccine causes the body to produce antibodies, but it is not as powerful as the live-virus vaccine. Because it is less powerful, people need booster shots of killed-virus vaccines. Booster shots are injections given to add strength to the antibody in guarding against infection.

Toxoids. Diphtheria and tetanus are diseases caused by bacteria that release a toxin. Scientists have discovered that by chemically treating bacteria toxins, they can make very effective vaccines. The treated toxins, called toxoids, stimulate the production of antibodies and establish active immunity against diphtheria and tetanus.

Reactions to Vaccines

Vaccines are as safe as medical scientists can make them. However, vaccinations sometimes cause minor reactions, usually in the form of a mild fever or skin rash. On rare occasions more serious reactions may occur. Yet the risks from vaccines are far less than the risks from the diseases themselves.

Immunization for All

Immunization is more than just a good idea—the law often requires it. Each state has its own laws governing immunizations and school attendance. In most states, students cannot enter kindergarten without up-to-date immunizations. Several states now enforce laws that prevent teenagers from attending school without complete immunization. Why, do you think, are immunizations so important in the school setting?

Some communicable diseases are more common than others. Diseases that were once dreaded can now be controlled through immunizations. Some of these diseases have been completely eradicated. However, because some diseases are no longer the threat they used to

Vaccines may be administered with a "gun," or with a conventional needle.

L1 DISCUSSION. Ask students in what ways live-virus vaccines, killed-virus vaccines, and toxoids are different.

L1 SPEAKER. Invite a science teacher to talk about how live-virus vaccines are developed. Ask the speaker to name some vaccines that contain live viruses.

L1 DEMONSTRATION. Invite a school nurse to demonstrate the difference between a conventional needle and an injection gun used in giving group vaccinations.

L1 DISCUSSION. Ask students what biofeedback is. What is its purpose? What is its relationship to areas of the body that are involuntary?

LEP CLASS ACTIVITY. Provide a variety of magazines for students to locate pictures or articles about simple and basic examples of biofeedback, such as weighing oneself, taking one's pulse when exercising, and taking one's temperature when sick. Ask for a show of hands indicating what forms of biofeedback are commonly done by the class.

L2 DISCUSSION. Select students to research and debate the following statement: *Relaxation exercises are just as effective as, and less expensive than, biofeedback training in the treatment of tension headaches.*

L2 CLASS ACTIVITY. Have students make posters about preventing communicable diseases, using the title "Prevention Is Preferable."

L1 CLASS ACTIVITY. Help students develop a system to keep personal medical records.

Independent Practice

L1 PARENTAL INVOLVEMENT. Ask students to talk with their parents and/or grandparents about their experiences with and observations of communicable diseases. In preparation for this assignment, have the class work together in developing a list of questions to ask their parents or grandparents.

L2 READING. Have students use class and library resources to read about the chicken pox and smallpox viruses and their effects on the human body. Ask them to contrast the two viruses. Have them summarize their readings in a short report.

Across the Curriculum

Science. Assign students to read current findings on post-polio syndrome. Ask them to find out if there is a post-polio support group in the community; if so, have them interview members of the group about the syndrome.

Home Economics. Choose students to survey local pharmacies to investigate types of medical home-testing kits available. Ask students to suggest advantages and disadvantages of using these kits.

Science. Select students to present reports on diphtheria and tetanus. Ask them to explain the two diseases, their symptoms, methods of treatment, and any long-term effects. Have students conclude by discussing vaccines that are available to protect against these diseases.

L2 COMMUNITY INVOLVE-MENT. Arrange for students to volunteer their services to community immunization clinics or projects. Have them discuss their experiences with the class.

L3 COMMUNITY INVOLVE-MENT. Select students to visit the office of a private doctor to research the cost of vaccinations against some of the major childhood diseases. Also, have them ask about the recommended immunization schedule for children. Request that students make copies of the schedule to share with the class.

L1 PARENTAL INVOLVEMENT. If possible, have students obtain their immunization records. Discuss the importance of keeping them up-to-date. Stress that as they get older, keeping medical records becomes their responsibility.

L2 COMMUNITY INVOLVE-MENT. Have students investigate community sources of influenza vaccine during the flu season for young children and the elderly. Ask them to find out the cost, if any, to individuals.

L2 RESEARCH. Ask students to choose a foreign country they would like to visit. Have them find out what special health precautions are necessary to travel to that country and what immunizations or vaccines they would need.

L3 COMMUNITY INVOLVE-MENT. Ask for volunteers to visit the local blood donor center. Have them request information about current efforts taken to prevent the transmission of serum hepatitis through blood transfusions.

L1 USING THE LESSON RESOURCES. For additional student activities, refer to the lesson resources on page 527.

Weighing yourself regularly and taking your pulse before and after exercising are two examples of biofeedback.

be, people have become lax in obtaining immunization, and isolated cases of some diseases, such as polio, are being reported. An immunization program is essential, just as is the practice of simple biofeedback.

Biofeedback

One way to keep checking on yourself is through **biofeedback**—biological feedback about your body. Biofeedback is the process of becoming aware of physical events in your body that you normally are not aware of, with the intent of gaining voluntary control of such events.

Simple and basic examples of biofeedback include the following:

- weighing yourself
- taking your pulse when exercising
- taking your temperature when you are sick

Biofeedback provides a means for receiving feedback on functions of your body that are involuntary—that is, functions under the control of the autonomic nervous system. These functions include those of the brain, the heart, and the circulatory system.

Other Uses of Biofeedback

Besides the personal methods of biofeedback, other methods can be used to help restructure many body malfunctions. Using sophisticated instrumentation, muscle tension, brain waves, skin temperature, skin resistance, and other physical processes can be regulated.

The implications of biofeedback in preventive medicine are tremendous. Changes to the body's balanced healthy state can be prevented or overcome by consciously reestablishing normal body conditions. Biofeedback is used clinically to manage stress, to relieve migraine and tension headaches and anxiety disorders, to rehabilitate the neuromuscular system, and to ease gastrointestinal disorders.

Biofeedback Instruments

The principal instruments used in biofeedback training are as follows:

- Electromyogram (EMG). The feedback of bioelectric information from the muscles regarding muscle tension.
- Electroencephalogram (EEG). The feedback of bioelectric information from the brain regarding changes in the brain-wave status.

K E E P I N G   F I T

What to Do for Colds: Getting the Cold Facts

- Drink plenty of liquids.
- Get lots of sleep and rest.
- Wash your hands frequently to prevent spreading the virus.
- Use a humidifier or a vaporizer. When using a vaporizer, keep it clean to avoid infections.

- Don't take aspirin. You may have flu. Aspirin should never be taken when you have flulike symptoms. Instead, take an aspirin substitute.
- If you develop a severe earache, a sore throat, a fever of 101°F or

more, wheezing, difficult breathing, or a deep cough, consult a physician. You may have more than a cold. Also call your physician if you cough up greenish phlegm or blood.

DID YOU KNOW?

- Scholars estimate that 33 percent of the original population of the Americas died in smallpox epidemics introduced by Europeans.
- In 1980, smallpox became the first communicable disease ever declared to have been eradicated from the face of the earth—thanks to the smallpox vaccine.

Additional Information

Flu Vaccination. It is recommended that the following groups of people get flu shots yearly, generally in the late fall: people over age 65; children on long-term aspirin therapy; chronically ill people, such as those with heart disease, kidney disease, anemia, or diabetes; people with lung problems or asthma; and people who live or work with a high-risk flu group, such as workers in nursing homes.

However, the following groups of people should not get the flu vaccine: people allergic to eggs, since the vaccine is made with egg protein; people who have in the past had a bad reaction to a flu shot; and pregnant females in the first trimester of pregnancy.

- Thermal trainer. The feedback of changes in skin temperature, a result of blood flow.
- Electrodermal response (EDR). The feedback of changes in skin resistance, a result of perspiration.

Biofeedback may become increasingly popular in the future. However, the simple disease-prevention steps that we all take day after day are also invaluable.

HEPATITIS

Hepatitis is a disease involving an inflammation of the liver. There are two main types—viral hepatitis and toxic hepatitis. The two most comon forms of viral hepatitis are hepatitis type A and hepatitis type B.

Hepatitis A results from eating food or drinking water that has been contaminated with the virus. Symptoms include weakness, loss of appetite, vomiting, and jaundice—a yellowish discoloration of the skin. Symptoms usually appear three to four weeks after exposure to the virus and last from two to six weeks.

A person who has been exposed to the hepatitis virus receives a shot of gamma globulin, a protein fraction of blood rich in antibodies. If this vaccine is administered within a week of exposure to the hepatitis virus, the disease can be prevented.

Hepatitis B virus is found in all body fluids of an infected person, especially blood. Hepatitis B used to be transmitted through blood transfusions from an infected donor. However, tests that detect the virus in the blood have helped eliminate this means of transmission. Contaminated medical instruments, sexual contact with an infected person, and hypodermic needles shared by drug users are the main ways hepatitis B is spread. Symptoms usually appear six to twelve weeks after the infection. The treatment is the same for types A and B. Bed rest is prescribed for both.

Toxic hepatitis results from exposure to certain chemicals. The chemicals can enter the body by being swallowed, inhaled, injected, or absorbed through the skin. Symptoms will depend on the particular chemicals causing the hepatitis.

Assess

Check for Understanding

- Assign and discuss the lesson review. Have LD students work in groups to complete questions 6 and 7.
- Assign and discuss the chapter review.

Evaluate

- Administer, grade, and discuss the *Lesson 3 Quiz*.
- Administer, grade, and discuss the *Chapter 26 Test*.
- Refer to the Performance Assessment strategy for this chapter. See pages T 23 to T 25.

Reteach

- Have students design a comic book for grade school students. Have them feature ways to prevent communicable diseases. When completed, display and discuss some of the comic books. Then ask for volunteers to take the comics home, share them with their younger siblings, and report to the class their siblings' reactions.
- Ask students to complete *Reteaching Activity 72*.

Enrich

- Ask for volunteers to locate or design a computer program for keeping personal medical records and dates of immunizations. Have them demonstrate their results for the class.
- Ask students to complete *Enrichment Activity 26*.

LESSON 3 REVIEW

Reviewing Facts and Vocabulary

1. Define *active immunity* and *passive immunity*.
2. How can biofeedback benefit a person?
3. Name three major types of vaccines.

Thinking Critically

4. **Synthesis.** What are some major factors that would lessen the effectiveness of the body's immune system?
5. **Analysis.** When the polio vaccine first was introduced, some people actually contracted the disease from the vaccine. Explain how this could happen.

Applying Health Knowledge

6. Develop an information pamphlet on a common communicable disease. Include symptoms, mode of transmission, prevention, and treatment.
7. In recent years some groups have challenged the right of government to make laws requiring immunization of children before they enter school. If you were given the task of explaining the need for such laws, what would you say? Limit your response to two paragraphs.

PREVENTING COMMUNICABLE DISEASES   **531**

Answers to Lesson 3 Review

1. See pages 527 and 528 or the Glossary for definitions.
2. It can help one gain voluntary control over events in one's body that one is usually not aware of.
3. Live-virus, killed-virus, toxoids.
4. Answers will vary. Possible answers: Illness, a disease that attacks the system directly, lack of immunizations, lack of antibodies.
5. Answers will vary. Possible answer: Since the polio vaccine is a live-virus vaccine, perhaps the virus was not weakened enough before it was injected, thus causing the disease.
6. Answers will vary.
7. Answers will vary.

Close

Divide the class into small groups. Assign each group part of this lesson to rewrite in their own words, using their own case studies or examples. Afterwards, duplicate each group's work, and distribute them to the class. Close by having one person from each group summarize the major ideas within its part of the lesson.

Helping Students Improve Their Health

Reinforcing Vocabulary

- **Aerobic.** Occurring only in the presence of oxygen.
- **Poultry.** Domesticated birds, such as chicken and turkey.

Teaching Strategies

L1 EXPLANATION. Exception might be taken by parents to item 10. Most parents try to encourage regular attendance at school. Explain that this item is referring to definite signs of illness.

L1 EXPLANATION. It is important that students realize that not everyone does all of these things all of the time. The inventory is trying to give the individual an understanding of how they rate in the area of disease prevention. For this reason encourage students to answer according to their general daily behaviors.

L2 DISCUSSION. Divide the class into two groups. Have one group be for mandatory immunization before entering public school, the other be against it. Debate the value of this practice.

L2 CLASS ACTIVITY. Have students brainstorm a list of communicable diseases, both past and present. Which ones from the list are not very common? Why? Is it possible that common diseases of today may be gone in 50 years? Why?

Self-Inventory

Your Disease-Prevention Efforts

HOW DO YOU RATE?

Number a sheet of paper from 1 through 20. Read each item below and respond by writing *M* if the statement describes you *most of the time*, *S* if the statement describes you *some of the time*, and *N* if the statement *never* applies to you. Total the number of each type of response. Then proceed to the next section.

1. I keep my immunization records up-to-date.
2. I stay away from people who currently have a cold or the flu.
3. I eat a balanced diet daily.
4. I get at least eight hours of sleep each night.
5. I exercise aerobically at least three times a week.
6. I do not smoke.
7. I avoid using towels others have used.
8. I avoid using other people's combs and brushes.
9. I take a few minutes each day to relax.
10. I stay home at least the first day that symptoms of illness appear.
11. I listen and respond to my body's message that it is tired or that something may be wrong.
12. I wash my hands before every meal, before preparing food, and after using the bathroom.
13. I shower or bathe regularly.
14. I do not share eating utensils or glasses with other people.

15. I cover my mouth when I cough or sneeze.
16. I avoid walking barefoot in locker rooms and shower rooms.
17. I avoid eating dairy products and poultry that might not have been refrigerated.
18. I advise my parents to make sure that our pets have their shots.
19. I put food waste in closed containers.
20. I support efforts to enforce public health laws for immunization and for reporting communicable diseases.

HOW DID YOU SCORE?

Give yourself 4 points for each *most of the time* answer, 2 points for each *some of the time* answer, and 0 points for each *never* answer. Find your total, and read below to see how you scored. Then proceed to the next section.

60 to 80
Excellent. Your disease-prevention efforts are outstanding. Congratulations.

40 to 59
Good. You are doing very well in your efforts to prevent communicable diseases.

20 to 39
Fair. Disease prevention is not important enough to you. Some effort will be beneficial to you and others.

Below 20
Needs Improvement. Be careful. You may be spreading communicable diseases to yourself

and to others. Now is a good time to start taking better care of yourself.

WHAT ARE YOUR GOALS?

If you received an *excellent* or *good* score, complete the statements in Part A. If your score was *fair* or *needs improvement*, complete Parts A and B.

Part A

1. I plan to learn more about disease prevention by ____.
2. My timetable for accomplishing this is ____.
3. I plan to share my information with others by ____.

Part B

4. The behavior I would most like to change is ____.
5. The steps involved in making this change are ____.
6. The people or groups I will ask for support and assistance are ____.
7. My rewards for making this change will be ____.

Meeting Students' Needs

For students who score *Excellent*. Suggest students share their knowledge of communicable diseases in the form of public-service announcements in school.

For students who score *Good*. Suggest students work on a collage depicting ways to avoid illness.

For students who score *Fair*. Have students pick five items from the inventory

that they scored low on. Then, list and enact behavior modifications that could raise their score.

For students who *Need Improvement*. Have students list five diseases and list the pathogen, symptoms, and method of transmission for each. Then, list behaviors to avoid these diseases.

Building Decision-Making Skills

Lavonda is a major contributor to the school's select choir, which has a major performance tomorrow. This morning she noticed she had symptoms of chicken pox. What should Lavonda do?

A. Don't tell anyone and go ahead with the performance because it means so much to both her present happiness and future opportunities. She is a critical part of the group and doesn't want to let the other members of the group down.

B. Tell the teacher and let her decide, based on what is best for the group.

C. Tell her mother and let her decide. It may be that she doesn't really have chicken pox or that she isn't contagious or that no one else in the group is susceptible.

D. Go to the doctor and let him or her decide.

WHAT DO YOU THINK?

1. **Situation.** Why does a decision need to be made?
2. **Situation.** How much time does Lavonda have to make this decision?
3. **Choices.** What other possibilities exist for Lavonda?
4. **Consequences.** What risks are involved in this decision and to whom?
5. **Consequences.** What are the advantages of each approach to this problem?
6. **Consequences.** What are the disadvantages to each approach?
7. **Consequences.** What obligation does Lavonda have to the other members of the group both healthwise and musically?
8. **Consequences.** How will Lavonda's health triangle be affected by this decision?
9. **Decision.** What do you think Lavonda should do? Why?
10. **Decision.** How should Lavonda implement this decision?
11. **Evaluation.** Have you ever been in this type of situation? What process did you use to make your decision? Was it effective? What did you learn that could be applied to this situation?

Marco is captain of the school's wrestling team. In past years he has gotten strep infections from the mats, resulting in an athletic department policy that the mats be washed before every practice and match. The new coach is a "drill sergeant type" who believes wrestlers should be tough and worry only about getting in the maximum training time. On several occasions he has started practice without washing the mats. Marco's teammates have asked him to talk to the coach. What should Marco do?

A. Tell the guys to quit complaining and be tough.

B. Talk to the coach but say it's on behalf of his teammates.

C. Tell the coach he and his teammates are concerned about not only their health but the possible effects an absence would have on the team's success.

D. Go to the administration with the problem and ask for anonymity.

E. Wait and see if strep becomes a problem.

WHAT DO YOU THINK?

12. **Situation.** Why does a decision need to be made?
13. **Choices.** What other choices does Marco have?
14. **Consequences.** What are the advantages and disadvantages of each choice?
15. **Consequences.** Does Marco have different obligations as a result of being captain? If so, what are they?
16. **Consequences.** What are the risks involved in this situation?
17. **Decision.** How do you think Marco should handle this situation?

Building Decision-Making Skills

Teaching Strategies

L1 CLASS ACTIVITY. Have students role-play Lavonda discussing her problem with her parents. Lavonda really wants to perform, but her parents are against it. Really try to get students to anticipate what might be said by Lavonda to convince her parents.

L1 DISCUSSION. Ask students to remember when they were a major contributor to some event. Could they have been replaced if need be? Is any one person more important than the whole group?

L1 CLASS ACTIVITY. Role-play the situation of Marco approaching the coach about washing the mats. Have both suggest ways to compromise in order to get the mats cleaned.

L1 CLASS ACTIVITY. Have students participate in a role-play with the wrestlers talking among themselves trying to come up with a solution to the problem. Ideas tend to pop up better in a "brainstorm" type of role-play.

Discussing the Answers

Situation 1. In an important life event such as this, it is often easy to forget about the interests of others. It is important that Lavonda tell her parents what symptoms she has noticed so far. They may decide to allow her to perform, or take her to the doctor. If this is the case, the doctor may let her perform. It is important not to expose others to a suspected case of chicken pox.

Situation 2. Regardless of the athletic department's policy, it is important to take proper care of equipment to avoid spreading various infections. This is especially true with a sport like wrestling. Marco should go through proper channels to remedy the situation.

Answers to Chapter 26 Review

Using Health Terms

1. Pathogens
2. Saprophytes
3. Parasites
4. Toxins
5. Viruses
6. Rickettsias
7. Fungi
8. Phagocytes
9. Phagocytosis
10. Specific resistance
11. Lymphocytes
12. B cells
13. Immunity
14. Vaccines
15. Vaccination

Building Academic Skills

16. Articles will vary.

Recalling the Facts

17. A food supply, suitable temperature, moisture, darkness.
18. They are bacteria that live in the mouth or intestines or on the skin; they help protect against harmful bacteria.
19. They can cause disease if they move to a place in the body where they do not belong.
20. The competition for food kills many of the bacteria.
21. Tetanus.
22. Answers may include but are not limited to: Pneumonia, food poisoning, diphtheria, tetanus, tuberculosis, strep throat, syphilis, gonorrhea.
23. It enters the human body and attaches itself to a cell. Then it releases its nucleic acid into the host cell, disrupting the cell's activities and causing it to produce more of the virus. These viruses spread and continue this process.
24. Air from a cough or sneeze; touching objects an infected person has used; sharing needles.
25. Body defenses that respond in the same way each time your body is invaded by a foreign substance.
26. Chemicals on the surface of cells can kill pathogens or prevent them from entering the body. Such chemicals can be

Using Health Terms

On a separate sheet of paper, write the term that best matches each definition given below.

LESSON 1
1. Disease-producing organisms.
2. A type of bacteria that digest nonliving food materials.
3. Bacteria that live off plants or animals.
4. Poisons.
5. Small, simple lifelike forms—smaller than bacteria.
6. Organisms that are somewhere between viruses and bacteria and that grow in the intestinal tracts of insects.
7. Simple organisms that cannot make their own food, such as yeasts and mushrooms.

LESSON 2
8. White blood cells that travel through blood and destroy foreign substances; part of nonspecific resistance.
9. The process in which pathogens are engulfed and destroyed.
10. Body defense that gives specific protection against specific pathogens.
11. Cells that multiply in the spleen, tonsils, thymus gland, and lymph nodes.
12. Cells that are stimulated to make antibodies.

LESSON 3
13. The body's ability to resist disease.
14. Preparations that may be composed of dead or weakened viruses.
15. The injection of a vaccine into the body in order to provide immunity to a disease.

Building Academic Skills

LESSON 2
16. **Writing.** Look up information about a communicable disease that was not mentioned in this lesson. Write a newspaper article telling about this disease, i.e., how it is transmitted and how the body defends itself.

Recalling the Facts

LESSON 1
17. What do bacteria need to survive?
18. What are resident bacteria, and what purpose do they serve?
19. Although resident bacteria are generally helpful bacteria, they can be harmful. How can they become harmful?
20. Bacteria can multiply fast enough to take over one's body in a short time. What usually prevents this from happening?
21. Suppose you are planting some flowers and you cut yourself on one of the tools you are using. What disease could result if soil containing bacteria enters the open wound?
22. Name eight different bacterial diseases.
23. How does a virus work?

LESSON 2
24. List ways indirect contact spreads pathogens.
25. Explain nonspecific resistance.
26. Explain how chemical barriers work and where they can be found in the body.
27. Describe the role of chemical mediators during the inflammatory response.
28. List symptoms of inflammation confined to a specific area.
29. Explain specific resistance.
30. What tissues are part of your lymphatic system?
31. Describe how antibodies are made and their role in the blood.

LESSON 3
32. What are some behaviors that will help a person avoid communicable diseases?
33. In what two ways can a person become immune to a communicable disease?
34. If the body is able to remember a virus that has invaded it and fight against it in the future, why do people not develop an immunity to colds?
35. Name and briefly describe three types of vaccines.
36. In what ways might a person contract hepatitis?

found in tears, saliva, sweat, and the digestive juices.
27. These cause blood vessels to dilate and allow increased blood flow. This action brings phagocytes to the area.
28. Heat, redness, and swelling. Pain can result from swelling.

29. Specific protection against specific pathogens. Cells that keep a record of pathogens in case they enter the body again.
30. Spleen, tonsils, thymus gland, lymph, and lymph nodes.
31. B cells are stimulated by T helper cells to make antibodies. Antibodies destroy or neutralize pathogens in

your blood. Antibodies will remain in your blood to become active if you encounter the specific pathogen again.
32. See bulleted list on page 527.
33. By having the disease, by being immunized by injection of a vaccine.
34. Colds are caused by many different viruses.

REVIEW

Thinking Critically

LESSON 1

37. Analysis. Many people think they can catch a cold by becoming chilled, getting caught in the rain, or not dressing warmly enough in cold weather. Analyze why people might think this way.

38. Synthesis. Interview four people who are 35 or older about polio. What were some of the myths about this disease that existed during their youth? How do these myths compare to some early impressions about AIDS? Write some generalizations about why myths develop and how they affect people.

LESSON 2

39. Analysis. Compare and contrast the function of phagocytes during nonspecific resistance and lymphocytes during specific resistance.

LESSON 3

40. Evaluation. In the past, people usually visited a physician only when they were sick. Now many insurance policies reimburse people for wellness checkups. In your opinion, is this a good or bad practice? Support your answer.

Making the Connection

LESSON 1

41. Social Studies. Write a one-page report about a protozoan-caused communicable disease, such as malaria, sleeping sickness, or amoebic dysentery. How did the disease affect people in the past? Is it still affecting people today? If so, in what way? How is the disease treated?

LESSON 3

42. Physical Education. Talk with a coach or physical education teacher about what process the school follows to try to decrease the incidence of athlete's foot transmission in the locker rooms.

Applying Health Knowledge

LESSON 1

43. Discuss how a disease can affect a person's mental, social, and emotional health.

44. For many years Ellis Island in New York City harbor was a clearinghouse for millions of immigrants who came to the United States. Find out about the disease-prevention efforts that were carried out with the immigrants. Draw some conclusions about the effectiveness of these efforts.

LESSON 2

45. Your brother works at a day-care center. He says that the children there are always passing colds and flu to each other. What could you share with him about the spread of pathogens?

46. Make a chart with three columns. At the top of each column, write one of the following: indirect contact, direct contact, and contact with animals. List several examples of communicable diseases known to be spread in this way.

LESSON 3

47. Antibacterial soap is now available in many stores. What is the benefit of this kind of soap? What is a drawback?

48. Each year, as flu season approaches, a flu vaccine is made available. Who is usually advised to receive this vaccine? Why do you suppose this is?

49. Find out what the law is in your state regarding immunizations.

Beyond the Classroom

LESSON 1

50. Further Study. Find out how parasites such as ticks and fleas affect pets.

LESSON 3

51. Further Study. Find out more about Jonas Salk and A. B. Sabin. What was the difference in their discoveries? What impact did they have on public health?

35. See "Types of Vaccines" on pages 528 and 529.

36. Hepatitis A—eating contaminated food or drinking contaminated water; hepatitis B—unsterile medical instruments, sexual contact, sharing hypodermic needles; toxic hepatitis—exposure to certain chemicals by swallowing, inhalation, injection, or absorption.

Thinking Critically

37. Answers will vary. Possible answer: This is how people historically believed one caught a cold and many people still cling to these ideas, perhaps because it gives them a feeling of control over something they actually have minimal control over.

38. Answers will vary, depending on what information is gathered from the people who were interviewed.

39. Phagocytes are white blood cells that travel through blood and group together to destroy foreign substances. Lymphocytes also are white blood cells that travel in the body through lymph and blood vessels. Two major types of lymphocytes are T and B cells. Both of these fight specific pathogens. Some T cells kill pathogens. Other T cells regulate other cell functions. B cells are stimulated by T helper cells to make antibodies.

40. Answers will vary but should be supported logically.

Making the Connection

41. Answers will vary.
42. Answers will vary.

Applying Health Knowledge

43. Answers will vary. Possible answers: People may become preoccupied thinking about their disease and its ramifications; suffer mental impairment through the disease process and thus be less able to function to the best of their ability; may feel responsible for getting the disease because they did something wrong or did not try hard enough to prevent it; may begin a degree of the grieving process; may be embarrassed

or ashamed and become reclusive as a result.

44. Answers will vary.

45. Answers will vary. See pages 522-23.

46. Answers will vary. Direct contact—genital herpes, syphilis; indirect contact—cold, strep throat; contact with animals—rabies.

47. Unlike most soaps, this soap kills bacteria so one

may be preventing bacterial spread by washing with it. It will not kill other pathogens discussed in this chapter.

48. Answers will vary. Possible answers: Senior citizens, chronically ill people, people with heart problems. To these people, the flu could be very dangerous.

49. Answers will vary.

Beyond the Classroom

50. Answers will vary.
51. Answers will vary.

Lesson Summaries

LESSON 1. Gonorrhea is a disease caused by a bacterium. Its symptoms, which are not always obvious for the female, can be cured if treated early enough by antibiotics. Symptoms can go away on their own, but the disease may still be present. Many complications can result from untreated gonorrhea.

LESSON 2. Syphilis is a disease caused by a bacterium called spirochete. When left untreated, it can cause damage to vital organs. Syphilis can go through four stages, if penicillin is not used to treat it.

LESSON 3. The symptoms, diagnoses, and treatments for herpes simplex II, nongonococcal urethritis (NGU), chlamydia, and other STDs are presented in this lesson.

Introducing the Chapter

Introduce this chapter by contrasting people's reactions to various communicable diseases. For example, if an individual were diagnosed as having chicken pox, he or she might be upset because it would interfere with normal routines, but the individual would be comfortable telling family, friends, and acquaintances about the illness. However, if the same individual were diagnosed as having an STD, he or she would probably be hesitant to tell others of the illness. Because of the social stigma attached to STDs, many people ignore them and hope that the STD will just go away. In this chapter students will learn how dangerous this approach is. They will also gain specific, helpful information about many different kinds of STDs.

Performance Assessment ✓

Refer to pages T 23 to T 25 for a Performance Assessment strategy for this chapter. See the *Performance Assessment Activities* booklet for additional suggestions.

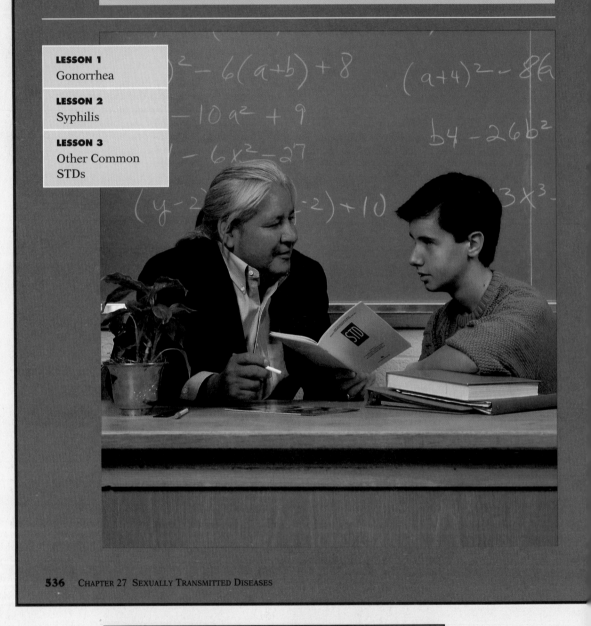

LESSON 1
Gonorrhea

LESSON 2
Syphilis

LESSON 3
Other Common STDs

536 CHAPTER 27 SEXUALLY TRANSMITTED DISEASES

Key to Ability Levels

Teaching strategies have been coded for varying learning styles and abilities.

L1 Level 1 activities are basic activities and should be within the ability range of all students.

L2 Level 2 activities are average activities and should be within the ability range of average to above-average students.

L3 Level 3 activities are challenging activities designed for the ability range of above-average students.

LD LD activities should be within the ability range of learning-disabled students.

LEP LEP activities should be within the ability range of Limited English Proficiency students.

GONORRHEA

A sexually transmitted disease (STD) is a communicable disease that is spread from person to person through sexual contact. While many of the common communicable diseases are being controlled, rates of STDs are rising steadily. STDs represent a serious threat to the health of all Americans, but particularly to young adults.

Nearly 3 million adolescents contract an STD each year. One in four of sexually active adolescents will become infected before graduating from high school. Although epidemics of STDs do occur in the United States, there are ways to control and even prevent these diseases completely. The first step is to remain sexually abstinent until marriage. Next, obtain accurate information about such diseases and recognize inaccurate information.

People often fail to seek medical attention for an STD. A social stigma exists about STDs, and some people are embarrassed. Others are not willing to take responsibility for their actions. Still others just will not believe that they could have an STD. Through denial and rationalization, they ignore the signs and symptoms. In many cases, symptoms are not obvious, and the person does not know that he or she has the disease.

Gonorrhea is a disease caused by bacteria that live in warm, moist areas of the body, primarily in the lining of the urethra of the male and in the cervix of the female. The bacteria are transmitted during sexual contact. A person cannot pick up the pathogens from towels or toilet seats because the bacteria cannot live outside the body.

Gonorrhea is one of the most frequently reported communicable diseases in the United States. Despite the fact that gonorrhea is a treatable disease and can be cured, about 2 million cases of it are reported in the United States each year. There is no way of knowing how many unreported cases there are.

Symptoms of Gonorrhea

Symptoms of gonorrhea are not always obvious. This is true particularly in the female, who may never know that she has gonorrhea. The symptoms may not be present or may be so slight that an infected person does not notice them.

In the female, symptoms may include a slight discharge from the vagina, a burning sensation during urination, abnormal menstruation, and abdominal pain or tenderness. In the male, symptoms may include a whitish discharge from the penis and a burning sensation during urination. The lymph nodes in the groin may also become enlarged and tender.

These symptoms usually appear between three days and three weeks after sexual contact with an infected person. These symptoms may go away on their own, but the disease is still present in the body.

GONORRHEA **537**

LESSON 1 FOCUS

TERMS TO USE

- Sexually transmitted disease (STD)
- Gonorrhea (gahn•uh•REE•uh)
- Pelvic inflammatory disease (PID)

CONCEPTS TO LEARN

- There are immediate and long-term consequences when one gets gonorrhea.
- The symptoms of gonorrhea are often difficult to detect, especially for females.
- The seriousness of gonorrhea warrants diligent protection and immediate treatment.

ATTITUDES AND BEHAVIORS TO EVALUATE

- Self-Inventory, page 550.
- Building Decision-Making Skills, page 551.

Focus

Lesson Objectives

After studying this lesson, students should be able to:

- define the term *sexually transmitted disease*
- identify and describe the symptoms and treatment for gonorrhea
- describe the problems that result from untreated gonorrhea

Bellringer

Write the following on the chalkboard for students to work on while attendance is being taken: *List three problems that can result from sexual contact.*

Introducing the Lesson

Have volunteers share their responses to the Bellringer. Students should understand that unwanted pregnancies, lowered self-esteem, feelings of guilt, and sexually transmitted diseases can be prevented by avoiding sexual contact. Explain that gonorrhea is a common sexually transmitted disease. Because of gonorrhea's prevalence, it is important to learn about its symptoms, treatment, prevention, and the problems associated with untreated gonorrhea. This lesson will address this sexually transmitted disease.

DID YOU KNOW?

- A sexually transmitted disease, or STD, may also be referred to as a venereal disease, or VD. The word *venereal* means "having to do with sexual intercourse." It is derived from the name for the Roman goddess of love, Venus.
- Several strains of gonorrhea have developed that are drug resistant.

Resources for Lesson 1

- **Transparency** 33
- **Guided Reading** Activity 73
- **Workbook** Vocabulary Activity 73
- **Reteaching** Activity 73
- **Lesson 1 Quiz**
- **BARN Software,** Human Sexuality
- **Education in Sexuality**
- **Performance Assessment** Activity 27

ABC News InterActive Videodiscs
Teenage Sexuality, Side 1
Ch 13 Sexually Transmitted Diseases

Building Vocabulary

- Ask students to attempt to write the correct spelling for each of the vocabulary terms as you pronounce them. After the test, have students exchange papers with a neighbor and correct the spellings as you read them aloud. Instruct students to look up the definitions for these terms in the lesson.
- Ask students to complete *Workbook Vocabulary Activity 73*.

Teach

Guided Practice

L1 DISCUSSION. Have students discuss how STDs are spread from one person to another through sexual contact. Then discuss how to prevent the spread of these diseases. Help students focus on the fact that some STDs are currently curable.

L2 CLASS ACTIVITY. Divide the class into two teams to debate whether STDs are just another group of communicable diseases or whether they are in a class by themselves. (Support for the position that STDs are special diseases include the following facts: no immunity to STDs can be built; there are no vaccines for them; the symptoms can be hidden.)

L1 EXPLANATION. There is no blood test for gonorrhea. Usually a male knows that he has the disease because of obvious symptoms. Since the female is asymptomatic, a simple test similar to a Pap smear is done in the doctor's office to detect the bacterium gonococcus.

L1 DISCUSSION. Have students discuss why drops are put in all babies' eyes when they are born.

L1 USING LIFE MANAGEMENT SKILLS TRANSPARENCY 33. Refer to the Teaching Transparencies Binder.

LD CLASS ACTIVITY. Have LD students compile a chart with the following headings: "Disease;" "Method of Transmission;" "Symptoms;" "Problems Caused;" "Cure."

DID YOU KNOW?

- Gonorrhea has several street names, such as "the drip," "the dose," "the clap," and "the strain." These names are associated with the symptoms of this disease.
- Males who contract gonorrhea have symptoms that cause such discomfort they usually seek medical help quickly. Symptoms in females, however, are more subtle and may be disguised by ovulation or menstrual cramps. Females are therefore more vulnerable to the complications of untreated gonorrhea.

The only way to be absolutely certain that you won't become infected with an STD is to practice abstinence.

Diagnosis and Treatment

Gonorrhea can only be confirmed by a medical diagnosis. This involves a laboratory culture at the sight of the infection. In a male, gonorrhea is diagnosed by examining discharge from the penis under a microscope. In a female, a culture test of the vagina is done to make the diagnosis. This involves taking a sample of cells from the vagina and examining them under a microscope. The Pap smear, which is a test for cervical cancer, does not test for gonorrhea.

Most cases of gonorrhea can be quickly and easily cured if diagnosis is made early. Antibiotics, such as penicillin or tetracycline, are usually used for treatment. However, there presently is a new strain of gonorrhea that is resistant to penicillin. With this particular strain, a different antibiotic is used to treat it. Follow-up visits to the health clinic or doctor's office also are suggested to be sure treatment is effective.

The body does not build an immunity to gonorrhea or any other sexually transmitted disease. So being cured of gonorrhea does not protect a person from getting the disease again. Furthermore, since a different pathogen causes each of the more than 50 different sexually transmitted diseases, a person can have more than one sexually transmitted disease at the same time. There is only one sure means of preventing gonorrhea or other sexually transmitted diseases—avoiding sexual contact.

Problems from Untreated Gonorrhea

If gonorrhea is not diagnosed and treated, the disease can spread in the body. In a small number of infected persons, the bacteria will enter the blood and spread throughout the body. This incidence causes high temperature, sores on the skin, and pain in the joints. Sometimes the joints, heart valves, and meninges will become infected.

Additional Information

PID. Pelvic inflammatory disease is a disease caused by untreated gonorrhea and chlamydia in females. This disease can lead to reproductive damage by causing obstruction and scarring of the Fallopian tubes, resulting in involuntary infertility. Thousands of females are affected each year by PID. In addition, females who have had PID are more likely to experience ectopic pregnancies. An ectopic pregnancy occurs when the Fallopian tubes are partially blocked and a fertilized egg becomes implanted in one of the tubes rather than in the uterus. As the cells multiply, there is danger of rupturing the Fallopian tube, causing a serious health risk to the female.

In both males and females, untreated gonorrhea can lead to infertility—the inability to reproduce. In the male, this can result from scarring from the infection, which obstructs the epididymis and the vas deferens.

This blocks the passage of sperm. The urethra can also be affected. In the female, the infection can move from the uterus to the Fallopian tubes. Scarring of both tubes can block the pathway of ova. Pelvic inflammatory disease can also result. **Pelvic inflammatory disease (PID)** is a painful infection of the Fallopian tubes, ovaries, and/or the uterus. If PID progresses, it also causes scar tissue to develop on the Fallopian tubes and results in infertility. Symptoms of PID include pain and tenderness of the lower abdomen and high temperature and chills. Because the incidence of PID is increasing, better diagnostic measures are needed for this situation.

In pregnant females, having gonorrhea increases the chance of premature labor and stillbirth—the birth of a dead fetus. If a female has gonorrhea when she gives birth, the bacteria that cause the disease can enter the baby's eyes. The baby can develop an eye infection that can lead to permanent blindness. For this reason, most physicians treat all newborn babies with special eye drops shortly after birth.

PROBLEMS WITH CHRONIC PID

Chronic PID can lead to temporary or permanent infertility. It also can lead to ectopic pregnancy. An ectopic pregnancy occurs when a fertilized ovum implants outside the uterus.

Even if the Fallopian tubes are partially blocked due to PID, fertilization can occur. However, a fertilized ovum may not be able to pass through the Fallopian tube to the uterus. In this situation, the fertilized ovum may implant at various places in the reproductive system of the female. The most common site is in the Fallopian tubes. As the embryo develops in this type of pregnancy, the wall of the Fallopian tube can rupture. Major internal bleeding results and surgery is needed to remove damaged tissue. Often the Fallopian tube cannot be repaired. If this type of pregnancy is not diagnosed and treated early, the mother may die.

LESSON 1 REVIEW

Reviewing Facts and Vocabulary

1. What are the symptoms of gonorrhea?
2. What is PID?
3. How is gonorrhea diagnosed and treated?

Thinking Critically

4. **Evaluation.** Do you think that giving someone an STD should be considered a criminal offense? Explain your answer.

5. **Analysis.** How might it be possible for a person to have more than one STD at a time?
6. **Analysis.** Why are sexually transmitted diseases a serious threat to one's total health?

Applying Health Knowledge

7. In small groups, role-play how you would give advice to a friend who complains of having symptoms of an STD and is embarrassed to go to the doctor.

GONORRHEA **539**

Answers to Lesson 1 Review

1. See "Symptoms of Gonorrhea" on page 537.
2. Pelvic inflammatory disease—an infection of the Fallopian tubes, ovaries, and/or the uterus.
3. It is diagnosed by a laboratory examination of secretions from the penis or vagina. It is treated with penicillin or tetracycline or other antibiotic.

4. Answers will vary but should be supported logically.
5. A different pathogen causes each of the different STDs.
6. Answers will vary. Possible answers: Sometimes one does not know one has an STD and much damage can be done before treatment is sought; the body doesn't build up immunities to STDs.
7. Answers will vary.

Independent Practice

L1 **RESEARCH.** Explain that the birth control pill has had an effect on the increase of gonorrhea in the U.S. Have students research the effects of the birth control pill on the incidence of gonorrhea. (Reduces the use of condoms and increases the alkalinity and moisture of the female genital tract, causing a rapid growth of the bacteria that cause gonorrhea.)

L1 **COMMUNITY INVOLVEMENT.** Have students send for materials from health departments to prepare posters and a bulletin board on STDs.

L1 **USING THE LESSON RESOURCES.** For additional student activities, refer to the lesson resources on page 537.

Assess

Check for Understanding

■ Assign and discuss the lesson review. For LD students, assign only questions 1, 2, and 3.

Evaluate

■ Administer, grade, and discuss the *Lesson 1 Quiz.*

Reteach

■ Ask students to write a one-page flyer called "Gonorrhea Alert" summarizing the lesson.
■ Ask students to complete *Reteaching Activity 73.*

Enrich

■ Ask students to do statistical research about the rise in the number of cases of gonorrhea during 5-year intervals from 1950 to the present. Ask them to present their findings in bar graphs.

Close

Ask students to summarize the most important concepts in this lesson.

Focus

Lesson Objectives

After studying this lesson, students should be able to:
- identify and describe the symptoms and treatment for syphilis
- describe the condition called congenital syphilis

Bellringer

Write the following on the chalkboard for students to work on while attendance is being taken: *Imagine that you have just received a letter from a friend saying that he or she may have syphilis. Write a brief response to the letter.*

Introducing the Lesson

Refer to the Bellringer. Ask volunteers to share their responses; then point out that syphilis is not as common as gonorrhea, but it is one of the oldest and most dangerous of the sexually transmitted diseases. Tell students they will learn more about syphilis in this lesson.

Building Vocabulary

- Ask students to differentiate between syphilis and congenital syphilis and write a definition of the term *chancre.*
- Ask students to complete *Workbook Vocabulary Activity 74.*

LESSON 2 FOCUS

TERMS TO USE
- Syphilis (SIH•fuh•luhs)
- Chancre
- Congenital (kahn•JEN•uh•tul) syphilis

CONCEPTS TO LEARN
- Syphilis is a dangerous disease that affects many parts of the body.
- Sexually active people must constantly be aware of the threat and symptoms of syphilis.
- The problems of syphilis worsen without effective treatment.

ATTITUDES AND BEHAVIORS TO EVALUATE
- Self-Inventory, page 550.
- Building Decision-Making Skills, page 551.

SYPHILIS

C aused by a small bacterium called a spirochete, **syphilis** is a disease that attacks many parts of the body. While syphilis is not as common as gonorrhea, it is one of the most dangerous of all the sexually transmitted diseases.

Historically, syphilis is supposed to have first been brought to the Old World 500 years ago by Christopher Columbus's crew. In 1494 syphilis appeared in Europe. It is likely that some of the crew or passengers on Columbus's ships had contracted the disease and brought it back to Spain on the return voyage after the discovery of the New World. It was present among Native Americans in the New World, but in a milder form. In Europe the disease took the most destructive form. With the introduction of penicillin in the late 1940s, syphilis cases in the United States declined by 99 percent. Beginning in 1985, however, the number of cases rose sharply and has now reached its highest level in 40 years.

Syphilis is dangerous because, when left untreated, it can damage vital organs, such as the heart, the liver, the kidneys, and the central nervous system, including the brain. It can cause heart disease, blindness, paralysis, and insanity.

Symptoms of Syphilis

Syphilis develops in stages. Symptoms appear and then go away on their own. However, if treated in the early stages, the disease can be cured.

Primary Stage

The first sign of syphilis is a **chancre,** a reddish sore at the place where the pathogen enters the body, usually on the genitals. It is a painless sore that appears within 10 to 90 days after contact with an infected person. The chancre lasts 1 to 5 weeks and will then go away, even if not treated. However, the disease continues to develop in the body.

Secondary Stage

The pathogen, if not treated early, will be circulated in the blood. Within one to six months after contact, the highly contagious second stage of syphilis appears. This is commonly characterized by a nonitching rash on the chest, back of the arms, and legs. In females, the rash is most often found on the outer edges of the vagina. Sores may develop from the rash. These sores will likely give off a clear liquid filled with the infectious spirochetes. Some swelling may occur in the lymph nodes under the arms and around the groin. Fever, sore throat, and a generally sick feeling are also common symptoms. Without treatment, these symptoms will disappear, but the disease continues to develop.

540 CHAPTER 27 SEXUALLY TRANSMITTED DISEASES

Resources for Lesson 2

- **Transparency** 33
- **Guided Reading** Activity 74
- **Workbook** Vocabulary Activity 74
- **Reteaching** Activity 74
- **Lesson 2 Quiz**

LOOKING AT THE ISSUES

Dangerous Liaisons: STDs and Lawsuits

There are an estimated 12 million new cases of STDs reported annually in the United States. The physical, emotional, and social costs of these diseases can be very high. The legal and financial costs can also be very high. Increasingly, people infected by partners who did not tell them of their known STD are taking these partners to court. Some people who have intentionally infected others have even ended up in jail.

Analyzing Different Viewpoints

ONE VIEW. Many people believe that anyone who knows he or she has an STD has an obligation to inform all sexual partners. Some people with this view also believe that if such a person does not inform his or her sexual partners, a lawsuit for medical bills and damages is justifiable if the partners become infected.

A SECOND VIEW. Some people state that anyone infected with an STD who knowingly has sex with someone without disclosing the presence of his or her STD should be charged with a crime—whether or not infection results. Such charges range from reckless endangering (for having sex under such conditions even if the partner does not become infected) to aggravated assault or attempted murder (when sex is used intentionally to harm another through infection).

A THIRD VIEW. There are also people who maintain that anyone who has sex outside of marriage is asking for trouble and has taken the risk of contracting an STD by being sexually active. They state that those infected made the decision to have sex and therefore should at least share the responsibility for getting an STD.

Exploring Your Views

1. What do you think is one's responsibility regarding sexual relations when a person knows he or she has an STD?
2. What do you think a person should do if he or she is infected by someone with an STD who knew he or she had it but did not disclose this information?
3. Do you think anyone planning to have sex should ask the prospective partner about his or her sexual history?
4. What is one sure way teens can make sure they do not contract or pass on STDs?

DID YOU KNOW?

- Syphilis is sometimes called "pox," "lues," "syph," or "bad blood."
- There are now more than 50,000 syphilis cases a year. That is the highest rate of syphilis since the 1940s.
- The number of cases of syphilis in the United States is increasing by 14 percent a year.
- The Earl of Condom, personal physician to King Charles II of England, was asked to make a protective prophylactic to prevent the king from getting syphilis. His protective sheath was made from sheep intestine.

Latent Stage

The third stage of syphilis usually begins about two or more years after the initial infection. All signs disappear, leading the individual to think that he or she is cured or never had the disease.

It is in this stage that syphilis begins to attack the heart and blood vessels and the central nervous system. The damage to these areas is slow and steady. Even though people have reached the latent stage, they can relapse into the second stage. Sores will reappear.

SYPHILIS   **541**

Additional Information

The Myth of Syphilis. The name *syphilis* comes from a popular poem written in the 1500s by Girolamo Fracastoro, an Italian doctor and poet. The poem was about a Greek shepherd named Syphilis, who was punished by Apollo with the disease that was then known as the "great pox" and the "serpentine disease," among many other names.

Fracastoro not only gave syphilis its name, he also devised one of the numerous treatments for it. Patients were placed in a chamber below which mercury ore was burned. It clearly was a treatment of last resort because the mercury fumes caused patients to lose most of their teeth and suffer bone destruction. Whether it cured the syphilis as well is unknown.

Teach

Guided Practice

L1 DISCUSSION. Explain that since the discovery of the birth control pill, cases of STDs have increased in number. Discuss how this discovery has affected the epidemic of STDs.

L1 DISCUSSION. Ask students when and how syphilis got to the United States.

L1 DISCUSSION. Ask what syphilis is. Why is it considered one of the most dangerous of all the sexually transmitted diseases?

L2 CLASS ACTIVITY. Ask students to get into debate groups. Prepare debates to determine if tests for STDs should be required in all physical examinations conducted by a doctor.

L1 DISCUSSION. Ask students to get into groups and discuss the following: If you were a parent, would you expect your teenager to tell you that he or she has contracted an STD? Why? Why not? How would you feel about your teenager receiving treatment without your permission? Share responses with the class.

L1 DEMONSTRATION. Borrow slides from the science department and show students the different organisms that cause STDs.

L1 SPEAKER. Ask a school nurse to speak to the class about local sources for help with STDs. Have the nurse discuss the laws related to STDs in your state regarding confidentiality.

L1 DISCUSSION. Have students discuss the methods or tests to determine if a person has an STD. Discuss the importance of seeking medical attention for any sign of an STD. Why is it not only important for the person with the STD, but also other people?

L1 USING LIFE MANAGEMENT SKILLS TRANSPARENCY 33. Refer to the Teaching Transparencies Binder.

L2 RESEARCH. Ask students to research how requiring a test for syphilis when applying for a marriage license and during pregnancy has affected the spread of syphilis in the United States. What are the advantages of STD testing? What are the disadvantages?

L1 COMMUNITY INVOLVEMENT. Ask students to survey your local area for a list of doctors and clinics that have facilities for STD testing.

L1 USING THE LESSON RESOURCES. For additional student activities, refer to the lesson resources on page 540.

Assess

Check for Understanding

- Assign and discuss the lesson review. For LD students, assign only questions 1, 2, and 3.

Evaluate

- Administer, grade, and discuss the *Lesson 2 Quiz.*

Reteach

- Ask each student to write a three-part article for the school newspaper. In the first part, have them describe the symptoms of syphilis and the stages; in the second, the treatment of the disease; and in the third, congenital syphilis.
- Ask students to complete *Reteaching Activity 74.*

A nonitching rash is a symptom of the second stage of syphilis.

Culturally Speaking

"Shadow" Disease

The origins of syphilis are not clear. Some suggest an American origin because there are no indisputable references to syphilis in European literature until after the American voyage of Columbus. Some skeletal remains of Native Americans dated before Columbus's voyage also show evidence of the disease. On the other hand, early accounts of leprosy in Europe describe symptoms that might be syphilis rather than leprosy. For example, there is reference to spread by sexual contact, and treatment with mercury. Mercury was the first recorded treatment for syphilis. Syphilis has been called the "shadow disease" and the "great imitator" because its symptoms can be mistaken for other diseases.

Neurosyphilis Stage

If untreated, syphilis moves into the neurosyphilis stage within 10 to 30 years. When the symptoms of this stage occur, the heart, skin, brain, and spinal cord are affected. A person loses the ability to coordinate muscular movements and may experience blindness or insanity. The central nervous system is affected resulting in a loss of mental abilities. A person in this stage of syphilis may experience paralysis and convulsions. Syphilis can be treated but not cured in this stage.

Diagnosis and Treatment

While gonorrhea is detected by means of a microscopic slide exam, the test for syphilis, called the Venereal Disease Research Laboratory, or VDRL, is a blood test. The presence of the spirochete in the blood or in sores indicates the presence of the disease. Some states require that couples who plan to marry be tested for syphilis.

Penicillin is the main drug used in the treatment of syphilis. Doctors strongly recommend follow-up to be sure the disease has been cured. However, no matter how effective the treatment is, it cannot undo any harm that has already been done. Early treatment of syphilis is crucial.

Syphilis has no immunity. One may become reinfected at any time. If a person goes through too many treatments, the body may become

K E E P I N G   F I T

STDs—A Major Problem

Most STDs could be completely eradicated if people practiced responsible health behaviors. Ignoring signs of a disease is not being responsible. Responding to symptoms, seeking treatment, and following medical care instructions will combat this serious epidemic.

But the best way teens can combat this serious health problem is by having no sexual contact. It is not only okay to say no—it is healthy.

Additional Information

Cures for Syphilis. Because the latent stage of syphilis is often associated with a long period during which the patient is symptom-free, many treatments for the disease were falsely lauded as cures. In fact, dozens of painful and frequently harmful treatments earned undeserved reputations for brief periods—until patients entered the neurosyphilis stage and symptoms recurred.

Mercury in one form or another, including ointments, pills, plasters, and fumigants, was used as a treatment for several hundred years. In fact, mercury was so much associated with syphilis that there was an aphorism that went: "One night with Venus—3 years with Mercury."

Many states used to require a blood test for syphilis before they issued marriage licenses. This practice was not effective in preventing the spread of syphilis.

immune to penicillin as a means of treatment. As in the case of all STDs, the only sure means of prevention is practicing abstinence.

Congenital Syphilis

A pregnant female who has syphilis is likely to transfer the infection to her unborn child. This condition is called **congenital syphilis.** *Congenital* means "existing at or dating from birth." The unborn child can develop syphilis any time after the fourth month of pregnancy. The mother's chances of having a miscarriage—the body's natural expulsion of a fetus prematurely—are greater if she has syphilis. In addition, her chances of having a stillborn baby are doubled.

If the baby is born, symptoms of congenital syphilis begin to appear within three to four weeks. If syphilis is diagnosed early enough in the mother, penicillin treatment will usually protect the fetus.

CONFLICT RESOLUTION

When leaving Health class, Kara heard some of her classmates continuing the class discussion about syphilis. A few were saying that getting syphilis doesn't seem to be a big deal, since it can be cured when treated in an early stage. They also think that once cured, a person need never worry about syphilis again. However, Kara knows that her cousin got syphilis twice, because he thought being cured gave him immunity to this disease.

What can Kara tell her classmates to convince them that getting syphilis is a big deal?

LESSON 2 REVIEW

Reviewing Facts and Vocabulary

1. What is a chancre?
2. How is syphilis diagnosed and treated?
3. What is congenital syphilis?
4. If syphilis can be treated and cured, why is early treatment critical?

Thinking Critically

5. **Analysis.** Compare complications resulting from syphilis to complications resulting from gonorrhea.

Applying Health Knowledge

6. Investigate the prevalence, spread, and treatments of syphilis in another period of history. Follow the case of one famous syphilis sufferer from the period, such as Christopher Columbus, King Henry VIII of England, or Al Capone. Write your findings in the form of a research paper, a medical report written from the point of view of a doctor from that period, or a journal entry from a patient's experience.

SYPHILIS **543**

Focus

Lesson Objectives

After studying this lesson, students should be able to:

- identify and describe the symptoms and treatment for herpes simplex II, NGU, and chlamydia
- discuss the importance of seeking medical attention for any sign of an STD
- discuss how to best prevent the spread of STDs

Bellringer

Write the following on the chalkboard for students to work on while attendance is being taken: *Why is it important for anyone being diagnosed as having an STD to tell his or her partner?*

Introducing the Lesson

Refer to the Bellringer. Ask volunteers to share their responses. Display several newspaper or magazine articles that relate to current research being done in the area of STDs. Tell students that these diseases are so prevalent that considerable research is being done to find cures. Tell students they will learn more about other STDs in this lesson.

DID YOU KNOW?

- Most sexually transmitted diseases occur in teens and young people up to about age 25.
- Except for the common cold and flu, sexually transmitted diseases are the second most common communicable diseases in the U.S.
- According to one study, even though most teens know condoms can offer some degree of protection against STDs, including HIV infection, less than half of sexually active adolescents use condoms during sexual intercourse.
- It is important to point out that condoms are not 100 percent effective in preventing the spread of STDs. The failure rate of condoms if not properly used is 12 percent.

OTHER COMMON STDs

LESSON 3 FOCUS

TERMS TO USE
- Herpes 2
- Dormant
- Nongonococcal urethritis (NGU) (nahn•gahn•uh•KAHCK•ul yur•i•THRYT•uhs)
- Chlamydia (kluh•MIHD•ee•uh)

CONCEPTS TO LEARN
- There are many myths and misconceptions centered around STDs.
- The number of STDs and the number of individuals affected are increasing.
- All sexually transmitted diseases require medical attention.

ATTITUDES AND BEHAVIORS TO EVALUATE
- Self-Inventory, page 550.
- Building Decision-Making Skills, page 551.

Other serious diseases transmitted through sexual contact are herpes 2, nongonococcal urethritis (NGU), and chlamydia. Acquired immune deficiency syndrome (AIDS), also a sexually transmitted disease, will be discussed in Chapter 28. Cures are available for NGU and chlamydia, but at present no cures or vaccines exist for herpes 2 or AIDS.

Herpes 2

Herpes simplex type 1 virus is a virus that causes herpes 1, cold sores on or around the mouth. Herpes simplex type 2 virus is a virus that causes genital herpes, blisterlike sores in the genital area. Genital herpes is sometimes called **herpes 2.** It is transmitted by sexual contact and is, at present, an incurable STD. An estimated 30 million Americans have genital herpes. The Centers for Disease Control and Prevention have declared the number of cases of this STD to be at an epidemic level.

Recently, medical professionals have decided not to distinguish between herpes 1 and herpes 2, because it is possible to find a type 2 infection on the mouth and a type 1 infection on the genitals. However, for the purpose of this text section, the infection that affects the genitals that is transmitted through sexual contact is described as herpes 2. It has certain characteristics.

Symptoms

Symptoms of herpes 2 include painful, itching sores in or around the genitals. Sores usually appear 2 to 20 days after contact with an infected person. They may last as long as three weeks. Other symptoms include fever and a burning sensation during urination. With the help of moisture and friction, the herpes 2 virus can spread to other areas of the body. This is why a person who has herpes 2 is told not to rub the skin and to keep it dry.

Diagnosis and Treatment

Herpes 2 is diagnosed by a medical examination of genital sores and verified by lab tests. Currently, no cure exists for herpes 2, but there are medications that treat the symptoms.

The blisterlike sores of herpes 2 go away, but the virus remains in the body. Blisters may reappear at any time. When the blisters are present, the disease can be transmitted to another person.

One of the problems with this virus is that the disease may be contagious for a period of time before the blisters appear and after they disappear. There is no sure way of knowing when the disease is in its contagious state. This makes controlling its spread very difficult.

544 CHAPTER 27 SEXUALLY TRANSMITTED DISEASES

Resources for Lesson 3

- **Transparency** 33
- **Guided Reading** Activity 75
- **Decision-Making** Activity 27
- **Workbook** Vocabulary Activity 75
- **Workbook** Application Activity 27
- **Reteaching** Activity 75
- **Enrichment** Activity 27
- **Health Labs** Activity 27

- **Cooperative Learning** Activity 27
- **Lesson 3 Quiz**
- **Chapter 27 Test**
- **ABC News InterActive Videodiscs**
- **Teenage Sexuality, Side 2**
- Ch 15 Fears, Risks and Consequences

Although the symptoms of herpes 2 disappear, the virus remains in the body in such a state that it may be reactivated and cause another rash. After the healing from the initial outbreak has taken place, the virus can enter nerve endings near the initial rash. The virus then moves away from the surface of the skin, thus escaping the body's defenses. It moves to nerve-cell bodies near the spinal cord, where it becomes **dormant,** or inactive. The dormant herpes 2 virus can remain in this state indefinitely without causing damage.

Some people never have another outbreak of the virus, while others experience periodic outbreaks. Different factors, which are very individual, influence recurring outbreaks. Stress is one factor thought to bring on recurrences.

Infected females should have regular Pap smears, because herpes 2 infections have been linked to the development of cervical cancer cells. A pregnant female infected with herpes 2 may infect her developing baby. Death or deformity may result to the baby if infected before birth. There also is a chance the baby may acquire the virus during delivery while passing through the birth canal. If herpes develops and is untreated, the baby may suffer permanent damage or die.

A pregnant female should inform her doctor if she knows or suspects she has herpes 2. A doctor may choose to perform a cesarean delivery—birth by surgical means—to avoid risk to the baby.

One of the problems in preventing the spread of herpes 2 is that an infected individual may be contagious even before the blisters appear.

Nongonococcal Urethritis (NGU)

Nongonococcal urethritis (NGU) is a disease caused by several different kinds of bacterialike organisms that infect the urethra in males and the cervix in females. This STD is called nonspecific, because the specific cause of it has not yet been discovered. Like all STDs, NGU is transmitted through sexual contact.

Symptoms and Treatment

Males notice symptoms of NGU more than females do. In males, there may be a discharge from the penis anywhere from one to three weeks

A pregnant female should inform her doctor if she suspects she has an STD.

OTHER COMMON STDs **545**

Building Vocabulary

- Scramble the letters for each of the vocabulary terms on each of four 3-by-5 inch index cards. (For example, *chlamydia* becomes *machiylad.*) Display one of the cards and read the definition of that term or phrase as it appears in the lesson to the class. Have students try to unscramble the letters and figure out what the term or phrase is.
- Ask students to complete *Workbook Vocabulary Activity 75.*

Teach

Guided Practice

L1 SPEAKER. Invite a health educator from the Public Health Department and an administrator from your school into class to discuss the efforts that are being made to control the spread of sexually transmitted diseases.

L1 DISCUSSION. Ask students why the rate of genital herpes is increasing, even with the widespread education about STDs.

L1 DISCUSSION. Ask why medical professionals have recently decided not to distinguish between herpes I and II.

L1 DISCUSSION. Ask why people with herpes II are told not to rub the skin and to keep it dry.

L1 DISCUSSION. Explain why people can't tell for sure when herpes II is in its contagious state.

L1 DISCUSSION. Ask students where the herpes II virus goes in the body after the healing from the initial outbreak has taken place.

L1 CLASS ACTIVITY. Contrast the symptoms of chlamydia in males and in females. Ask students to list reasons a female with chlamydia is more likely to exhibit no signs of the disease until it is in the advanced stage.

L1 USING LIFE MANAGEMENT SKILLS TRANSPARENCY 33. Refer to the Teaching Transparencies Binder.

Overcoming Misconceptions

Hepatitis. We tend to think of herpes, syphilis, gonorrhea and, more recently, AIDS as the major sexually transmitted diseases. But viral hepatitis, which causes a liver infection, also can be transmitted through sexual contact. For example, as many as 250,000 cases of hepatitis B occur annually in the U.S. as a result of sexual contact. Hepatitis A also can be transmit-

ted sexually, usually through oral-anal contact.

Hepatitis ranges in severity from symptomless to fatal, but even asymptomatic carriers have an increased risk of liver cancer. Vaccines are available for hepatitis B. Brief protection against hepatitis A is available with shots of serum globulin.

L1 **CLASS ACTIVITY.** Ask students to compare the symptoms in males of gonorrhea and nongonococcal urethritis (NGU). Write the reason why NGU is called a "nonspecific" disease.

L1 **DISCUSSION.** Ask students why STDs have been referred to as "love bugs."

L1 **DISCUSSION.** Ask what pubic lice are. What is the difference between pubic lice and crabs? Scabies and crabs?

L1 **COOPERATIVE LEARNING.** Arrange students in groups. Ask students to select individuals to participate in the role of a Public Health Administrator in developing laws related to the control of STDs. Each group should list laws that should be enacted, problems in implementing the laws, and the rationale for the laws.

L3 **CLASS ACTIVITY.** Tell students that although antibiotics can cure many STDs, some STD pathogens have become resistant to current medications. Have students define *resistant* in this context, and then have them write a paragraph about the problems this poses to individuals and society.

L1 **COOPERATIVE LEARNING.** Have students get a partner and prepare a role-play for the following situation: Your friend has been told that he or she has contracted an STD. What could you do to help the friend? What information could you share with the friend to prevent any future infections from occurring? Select several partners to role-play the situation for the class.

L1 **CLASS DISCUSSION.** Ask students why it might not be wise to share clothes and towels with others, even brothers and sisters. (Some STDs, such as lice and scabies, can be transmitted by sharing towels and clothes.)

L2 **CLASS ACTIVITY.** Have students write a solution to the following: Jane and John have been dating for a month and are very serious about their relationship. They know about the serious health and social problems associated with STDs and want to avoid getting one. What can they do to prevent getting or transmitting an STD? (Abstinence is the only 100 percent effective method of avoiding STDs.)

SEXUALLY TRANSMITTED DISEASES

Disease	Description	Cause	Symptoms	Treatment
Vaginitis	A common inflammation of the female genitals. Can be carried by males. Many types exist.	Microscopic organisms	Female—severe itching, discharge. Male—few or no symptoms.	Antibiotics
Moniliasis	Yeast infection	Fungus	Thick, white, cheesy discharge, general itching and irritation.	Antibiotics
Trichomoniasis	A vaginal infection that can lead to urethra and bladder infections. Males are rarely infected, but they can be carriers.	A protozoan parasite	Female—yellowish discharge, strong odor, irritation, itching. Male—slight or no symptoms.	Prescription medicine
Genital warts	Pink or reddish warts that have cauliflowerlike tops.	A virus	Warts appear on genitals 1 to 3 months after infection.	Application of a prescription skin medication
Infestation of pubic lice	Tiny insects called lice attach themselves to skin and hair in the pubic area. Lice feed on blood and cause intense itching.	Lice, insects that are parasites resemble tiny crabs	Intense itching, small nits (eggs) on pubic hair, small spots of blood on underwear.	Special medicated shampoo
Scabies	Infestation of skin by mites that cause red, swollen itchy bumps on the skin.	Tiny insects called mites that burrow into the skin	Itching in the genital area 4 to 6 weeks after infection. Mites can be spread to forearms or fingers.	Hot baths and medicated creams

K E E P I N G   F I T

Symptoms of STDs in Males

General symptoms of STDs in men include:
- difficult or painful urination
- penile discharge
- soreness inside the penis

- sores in the genital area
- itching genitals
- flulike symptoms
- painless rash on hands, feet, or body

The most important thing to do when such symptoms are present is to get medical attention as soon as possible.

546   CHAPTER 27 SEXUALLY TRANSMITTED DISEASES

Overcoming Misconceptions

Myth. You can get an STD from a toilet seat or doorknob. **Fact.** STDs are anaerobic organisms that cannot live in aerobic conditions. They are transmitted in bodily fluids. **Myth.** You cannot get two STDs at the same time. **Fact.** STDs are caused by several organisms and it is possible to get several at once. **Myth.** Once you have had an STD, you won't get it again. **Fact.** Once an STD is cured, the person can get the infection again if exposed to the organism. **Myth.** A person can keep from getting an STD by keeping himself or herself very clean. **Fact.** Cleanliness does not prevent STDs.

after infection. Males may also experience a mild burning during urination. Females may have a vaginal discharge and pain in the lower abdomen.

NGU can be treated and cured. Treatment consists of an antibiotic, usually tetracycline.

Chlamydia

Chlamydia is the most prevalent STD in the United States today. Annually, about 4 million cases are reported, which is 2 million cases more than gonorrhea. Chlamydia is an infection that affects the vagina in females and the urethra in males. If the infection is not treated, serious damage can be done to other reproductive organs. Chlamydia is a common cause of sterility. Chlamydia is caused by a special type of bacteria that has been only recently recognized.

Symptoms

In males, the symptoms include pain and burning during urination and an unusual discharge from the penis. These symptoms usually occur one to three weeks after exposure. If left untreated, chlamydia can result in chronic inflammation of the urethra.

In females, the symptoms are not always obvious. If symptoms do occur, they may include an unusual discharge from the vagina, pain in the pelvic region, and painful urination. If left untreated, chlamydia can cause pelvic inflammatory disease (PID). PID is a painful infection of the ovaries, Fallopian tubes, and/or uterus.

A pregnant female who has chlamydia can spread it to her baby during delivery. In infants, the disease can cause eye infection, blindness, and sometimes pneumonia.

Treatment

Chlamydia is diagnosed through a laboratory test. Certain antibiotics can cure chlamydia. However, if scar tissue has already formed, treatment cannot undo that damage. Chances of sterility in the male and in the female will remain.

K E E P I N G   F I T

Symptoms of STDs in Females

General symptoms of STDs in women include:
- abnormal discharge from the vagina
- difficult or painful urination
- warts, blisters, sores, bumps, or rashes in the pubic area

- itching in the pubic area
- unusual bleeding from the vagina
- stomach cramps not associated with menstruation
- flulike symptoms
- rash on hands, feet, or body

- painful intercourse

The most important thing to do when such symptoms are present is to get medical attention as soon as possible.

OTHER COMMON STDs **547**

Using Overcoming the Odds

■ **Discussion.** What steps should Andrea take to cope with her lifelong herpes infection? (Reduce the occurrence of lesions by staying healthy and stress-free; when outbreaks occur, avoid sexual contact to prevent infecting others.)

■ **Discussion.** How is syphilis worse than herpes? How is herpes worse? (Syphilis can be life-threatening if untreated; herpes is usually more annoying than dangerous. Syphilis is readily cured with antibiotics; there's no cure for herpes.)

■ **Answers**

1. Like most teens, she didn't think anything like that could happen to her.

2. So they can take precautions to end further spread of the disease.

3. Answers will vary. Telling previous sex partners you may have infected them with herpes is difficult, but it could spare scores of other people from being infected in the future.

L2 **RESEARCH.** Ask students to research the effects of STDs on an unborn child. Contact the March of Dimes for information relating to birth defects and other conditions related to STDs and newborns.

L1 **WRITING.** Have students work in small groups to create posters about preventing STDs. Students can display their posters throughout the school building. They might also create radio and television spots which can be aired using the school's audiovisual system.

L1 **USING THE LESSON RESOURCES.** For additional student activities, refer to the lesson resources on page 544.

Overcoming The Odds

Andrea is 18. "There's only one simple way to put it," she begins. "I have genital herpes—a very common sexually transmitted disease—something I thought I'd never get. I'm just your average high school senior, thinking a lot about the future, involved with my friends, active in school activities, all of it. I didn't do any more or worse than some of my friends, but here I am now paying for it."

Andrea continues, "I first noticed something wasn't right when I got this weird itching, then those painful sores. They were like blisters. It hurt when I went to the bathroom. After a while, they broke open and they became even more painful. I figured it was just some passing thing. But I did have swollen glands, a fever, and I felt like it was maybe the flu. Then the sores went away and I just brushed the whole thing off. Then, around exam time, when the pressure was on, the sores came back. I felt lousy. They hurt. Then I got the call."

The call was from her second boyfriend. He informed her that he had been tested, and genital herpes had been confirmed. "It was really the most awful and embarrassing phone call of my life," Andrea says. "But he said he knew he had to tell me. His sores were

recent, so he said he figured I'd given it to him, that I'd had it first, and that I'd better call my first boyfriend and tell him. He hung up, and I just wanted to throw up. Then I cried.

"After a while, I made that awful second call to the other guy. He just laughed it off. I was so angry. I can't even look at him in school. Then I used the anger to take action for myself. I finally got up the courage to go to the clinic. They told me there were no antibiotics I could take because it is not a bacterial infection. There is no cure. They also told me the disease would stay with me for the rest of my life. I had it, and whenever it was active, I could pass it on. They also said that if I have children someday I may have to have a cesarean section so my babies won't get the infection. They said stress could cause a flare-up, so now when I'm under stress, I'm really stressed because I don't want those lesions back."

1. Why was Andrea surprised that she got herpes?

2. Why was it important that all the sexual partners involved be informed that one of them had tested positive for the disease?

3. If you had been Andrea, how would you have felt about the first phone call? If you were she, would you have made the second phone call? Why or why not?

Additional Information

More About STDs. According to the Centers for Disease Control and Prevention, sexually transmitted diseases have increased each year in the United States. Human papillomavirus infection, which is the cause of genital warts, is considered the STD that is increasing at the greatest rate in the U.S. with an estimated 1,000,000 new cases every year. Chlamydia, which is the most common bacterial STD in the U.S., results in 4 million cases annually. Syphilis and gonorrhea, which have been controllable for years, are on the rise. The financial costs of treatment of STDs in the United States is several billion dollars a year. Every year 3 million adolescents contract an STD.

Other STDs

There are several other diseases that are spread through sexual contact. Some are more serious than others, but they all require medical attention. The chart on page 546 provides a description of some of the more common ones. You will notice that two of the conditions listed in the chart can be acquired in ways other than sexually.

Treatment

Treatment for sexually transmitted diseases is an important personal responsibility. Having an STD is not like having a cold. It will not simply go away if a person waits long enough. In fact, it is possible for a person to have more than one STD at the same time. The individual must do something about it. No one else can do it for that person.

It is understandable that a person may feel embarrassed about having an STD. However, a person who seeks treatment from a private doctor or a public health clinic is guaranteed by law that all information will remain confidential. It is important for the infected person to notify all people with whom he or she has had any sexual contact. A doctor or a public health clinic can help a person make these decisions.

If you think you have an STD, it is important that you get immediate medical help.

Prevention of STDs

Sexually transmitted diseases are different from other diseases. The body does not build up an immunity to any STD. No vaccination is available to prevent these diseases. Since STDs are spread by sexual contact with an infected person, the only sure way not to contract an STD is not to be sexually active. More and more young people are recognizing this choice as the only alternative to contracting STDs and experiencing their crippling effects. Abstinence is the only choice that is 100 percent effective in preventing the spread of STDs.

Why is it important that an individual infected with an STD notify all of his or her sexual partners?

Assess

Check for Understanding

- Assign and discuss the lesson review. For LD students, assign only questions 1 and 3.
- Assign and discuss the chapter review.

Evaluate

- Administer, grade, and discuss the *Lesson 3 Quiz.*
- Administer, grade, and discuss the *Chapter 27 Test.*

Reteach

- Have students use telephone books and library research to compile a list of hotline numbers that give out information and/or offer counseling about STDs.
- Ask students to complete *Reteaching Activity 75.*

Enrich

- Ask students to investigate one or more of the following subjects surrounding STDs: confidentiality of test results; treatment of minors without parental consent; legal suits against people who know they have an STD and intentionally infect someone else; the laws of the FDA on medicines available to treat STDs and the unavailability of certain experimental medicines; and prejudice against people with the diseases. Have students report their findings to the class. If possible, plan a panel discussion in which several or all of these issues are addressed in detail.
- Ask students to complete *Enrichment Activity 27.*

LESSON 3 REVIEW

Reviewing Facts and Vocabulary

1. What is chlamydia?
2. Why is NGU called nonspecific?
3. What is the best way to prevent STDs?

Thinking Critically

4. **Analysis.** Explain how good general health practices can be helpful in preventing STDs.
5. **Analysis.** What reasons can you give for chlamydia being so common?

6. **Evaluation.** Have the current practices for controlling STDs been effective? Explain your answer. What would you do differently?

Applying Health Knowledge

7. Many states now require screening for some STDs before granting a couple a marriage license. Do you agree with mandatory screening? Why or why not? State your position in a letter that could be sent to your local newspaper.

OTHER COMMON STDs **549**

Answers to Lesson 3 Review

1. An STD that affects the vagina in females and the urethra in males.
2. The specific cause of it has not yet been discovered.
3. Do not be sexually active.
4. Answers will vary. Possible answer: A couple of STDs can be transmitted other than through sexual contact.
5. Answers will vary. Possible answers:

Symptoms that are not obvious; embarrassment may keep people from seeking treatment, thus continuing to spread the disease.
6. Answers will vary. Possible answer: No, the evidence is in the high number of cases of STDs. Suggestions will vary.
7. Answers will vary but should be supported logically.

Close

Ask students to summarize the most important concepts in this lesson. Have students explain how taking responsibility for their behavior can prevent the possibility of contracting an STD.

Helping Students Improve Their Health

Using the Self-Inventory

Teaching Strategies

L1 EXPLANATION. There is much ignorance among adolescents about the contracting of sexually transmitted diseases. Teenagers typically feel they are invincible. Try to relate the inventory questions in a relevant manner to the students.

L2 DISCUSSION. Have students discuss the issue of whether a doctor should be required to contact a teenager's parent(s) before treating a sexually transmitted disease.

L1 CLASS ACTIVITY. Have students participate in an activity designed to show students how sexually transmitted diseases increase in numbers. Students will shake hands with six different people and write their names down. Have one student wear latex gloves to represent the wearing of a condom. Have one student refuse to shake hands, representing abstinence. Have two individuals shake hands only with each other, representing a monogamous relationship. After three rounds, name one person as being the original carrier of the sexually transmitted disease. For each round, tabulate all persons with which this individual came into contact. Now, include the partners of the persons with which the originally infected person came into contact.

L2 SELF-ESTEEM. How might the fear of getting an STD affect a person's self-esteem? How might a high level of self-esteem be an influence in a person's acting responsibly?

Self-Inventory

STDs: Where Do You Stand?

HOW DO YOU RATE?

Number a sheet of paper from 1 through 10. Read each item, and respond by writing *agree* or *disagree* for each statement. Total the number of each type of response. Then proceed to the next section.

1. Being in good health will keep a sexually active person from getting an STD.
2. A sexually active person can have only one STD at a time.
3. There is no known way to prevent the spread of STDs.
4. Untreated STDs usually go away in time.
5. Health problems associated with STDs are usually more serious in males.
6. STDs are basically a problem for adults.
7. Having only one sexual partner will prevent a sexually active person from getting an STD.
8. Once the symptoms of an STD have disappeared, the disease has been cured.
9. Having an STD is a private matter, so a sexually active person should not have to tell his or her partner if he or she has an STD.
10. All STDs can be treated and there are known cures for all of them.

HOW DID YOU SCORE?

Give yourself 1 point for each *disagree* answer and 0 points for each *agree* answer. Find your total, and read below to see how you scored. Then proceed to the next section.

9 to 10
Excellent. You are up-to-date in your knowledge of STDs, you have a healthy attitude about STDs, and how to protect yourself.

7 to 8
Good. You have a healthy attitude about STDs, but you could learn more about how the spread of STDs might be prevented.

Below 7
Needs Improvement. You need to learn more about STDs and how they are spread to protect yourself and others.

WHAT ARE YOUR GOALS?

If you received an *excellent* or *good* score, complete the statements in Part A. If your score was *needs improvement*, complete both Parts A and B.

Part A

1. I plan to rethink some of my attitudes and decisions about STDs after I ____.
2. My timetable for accomplishing this is ____.
3. I plan to share my knowledge with others by ____.

Part B

4. I plan to learn more about STDs by ____.
5. The steps necessary to do this are ____.
6. My rewards for making this change will be ____.

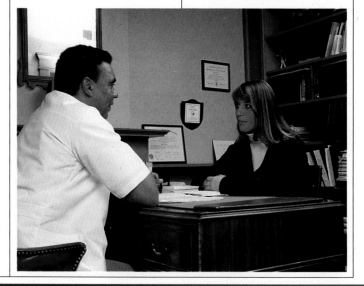

Meeting Students' Needs

For students who score *Excellent*. Suggest that students become involved in organizing a positive peer group to support those students who choose to be sexually responsible and abstain from engaging in sexual intercourse.

For students who score *Good*. Suggest that students organize a task force to help adolescents make informed decisions regarding sexual behaviors that risk contracting an STD.

For students who *Need Improvement*. Stress to students that sexually transmitted diseases adversely affect one's health and, if left untreated, may possibly prevent students from being able to have children some day. Reinforce the fact that not all STDs can be cured.

Building Decision-Making Skills

O ne of Angel's former boyfriends has just told her he has herpes. He suggests that because of their sexual contact she should see a doctor in order to be tested for the disease. In the meantime, Angel has had several other boyfriends but she has not had sex with any of them. Angel is embarrassed. She does not want her reputation to suffer by having people find out that she may have a sexually transmitted disease. What should Angel do?

A. Put the whole thing out of her mind and pretend it never happened.

B. Don't panic. Get medical attention immediately but don't tell anyone else until she gets the results of the test.

C. Share the news with someone she can trust so that she will have some emotional support.

D. Tell her current boyfriend if it turns out that she has the disease.

E. Protect her reputation by keeping the results of the test secret.

WHAT DO YOU THINK?

1. **Situation.** What should Angel do to get the facts about her situation?

2. **Situation.** Why does Angel need to make a decision?

3. **Situation.** Why is Angel in this situation?

4. **Situation.** Who is involved? Who will be affected?

5. **Situation.** How much time is there to decide?

6. **Choices.** What alternatives does Angel have?

7. **Choices.** What factors should Angel consider in making her decision?

8. **Consequences.** How will Angel's decision affect her former boyfriends, her current boyfriend, her parents, her friends, and the people who have respected her in the past?

9. **Consequences.** How will Angel's decision affect the various sides of her health triangle?

10. **Consequences.** Are there any legal obligations involved in Angel's situation? What are they?

11. **Consequences.** How will Angel's decision affect her self-esteem and her plans and goals for the future?

12. **Consequences.** How might Angel's decision affect her ability to bear healthy children?

13. **Decision.** What decision do you think would be best for Angel?

14. **Evaluation.** In an age when sexual activity is obviously increasing, do you think the stigma attached to sexual diseases has changed? Do you think it should?

15. **Evaluation.** Should past sexual experiences and exposure to STDs be discussed by teens who are currently going out together?

16. **Evaluation.** Have you ever known anyone who had been involved in a situation involving moral and legal obligations? What did the individual do? Do you think it was a good decision? Why or why not? How would you handle such a situation in the future?

B etsy's older sister, Sue, is about to get married. Her fiancé just told Sue he has an STD. What should Sue do?

WHAT DO YOU THINK?

17. **Choices.** What are several choices Sue has?

18. **Consequences.** What are the advantages of each choice?

19. **Consequences.** What are the negative consequences of each choice?

20. **Consequences.** What are the health risks to Sue and to her fiancé?

21. **Decision.** What do you think Sue should do? Explain your answer.

22. **Decision.** How should Sue go about implementing her decision?

OTHER COMMON STDs **551**

Discussing the Answers

Situation 1. Angel needs to be prepared to handle the consequences from her sexual behavior. These consequences may include contracting an STD, becoming pregnant, and having her reputation soiled. Perhaps the best alternative is for Angel to see her gynecologist and discuss the situation. Her doctor may be able to advise her more appropriately, based on medical information.

Situation 2. There is a possibility that Sue also is infected if they have been sexually active together. First, Sue needs to be examined by her gynecologist and treated if she is infected. Later, Sue and her fiancé need to discuss the situation.

Answers to Chapter 27 Review

Using Health Terms

1. Sexually transmitted disease
2. Sterility
3. Stillbirth
4. Syphilis
5. Congenital
6. Miscarriage
7. Herpes simplex type 1 virus
8. Herpes simplex type 2 virus
9. Cesarean delivery
10. Nonspecific

Building Academic Skills

11. Answers will vary.
12. Inactive.

Recalling the Facts

13. Primarily in the lining of the urethra in males; the cervix in females.
14. Three days to three weeks.
15. No, the disease can only be cured through the use of penicillin or tetracycline.
16. Avoiding sexual contact.
17. The body does not develop an immunity to any STD.
18. Each STD is caused by a different pathogen.
19. If untreated in males, it can damage the tubes from the testes to the urethra through which sperm move. In females, scar tissue may form in the Fallopian tubes, blocking the pathway of the ovum.
20. Eye infections that may lead to permanent blindness.
21. If left untreated, it can damage vital organs, such as the heart, the liver, the kidneys, and the central nervous system. It can cause heart disease, blindness, paralysis, and insanity.
22. Syphilis cases declined by 99 percent.
23. On the genitals.
24. Ten days to 3 months.
25. Two or more years.
26. Two to 20 days.
27. To detect any cervical cancers in an early stage.
28. They have a higher risk of being miscarried, born prematurely, or stillborn; or suffering brain damage if they pass through the birth canal at a time when the infection is active.

Using Health Terms

On a separate sheet of paper, write the term that best matches each definition given below.

LESSON 1

1. A communicable disease that is spread from one person to another through sexual contact.
2. The inability to conceive children.
3. The birth of a dead fetus.

LESSON 2

4. A sexually transmitted disease that is caused by a bacterium called a spirochete.
5. Existing at or dating from birth.
6. The body's natural expulsion of a fetus prematurely.

LESSON 3

7. A virus that causes cold sores on or around the mouth.
8. A virus that causes blisterlike sores in the genital area.
9. Birth by surgical means.
10. A term used to describe a disease for which the exact cause has not yet been discovered.

Building Academic Skills

LESSON 1

11. **Writing.** Abstinence is the only 100 percent effective method of avoiding STDs. Write an editorial or letter to the editor of your school newspaper explaining the health issues of STDs and encouraging your fellow students to remain abstinent or to return to abstinence.

LESSON 3

12. **Reading.** Use the context clues in the following sentences to define the word *dormant*.
    The quiet volcano had been dormant for years, but no one knew how long it would remain inactive. Some believed it would erupt at any moment.

Recalling the Facts

LESSON 1

13. In what part of the body do the bacteria that cause gonorrhea usually live?
14. How long might it take symptoms of gonorrhea to occur after sexual contact with an infected person?
15. If the symptoms of gonorrhea occur and later disappear, does it mean that the person is free of the disease? Explain.
16. What is the only sure means of preventing gonorrhea?
17. Why can a person get the same STD more than once?
18. How is it possible for a person to have more than one sexually transmitted disease at the same time?
19. How can gonorrhea lead to sterility in males? In females?
20. What is the major danger to a baby born to a woman who has gonorrhea?

LESSON 2

21. Why is syphilis a dangerous disease?
22. What effect did the introduction of penicillin have on the number of syphilis cases in the United States?
23. Where on the body is the first sign of syphilis, a chancre, likely to be found?
24. How long after sexual contact with an infected person will a syphilitic chancre appear?
25. How long after initial infection does the third stage of syphilis begin?

LESSON 3

26. How long after sexual contact with an infected person will the symptoms of herpes 2 usually appear?
27. Why is it important for women to have regular Pap smears?
28. What special risks do babies of females with herpes 2 experience?
29. What part of the body does nongonococcal urethritis (NGU) affect?

29. The urethra in males and the cervix in females.

Thinking Critically

30. The chart should include the following information: Disease: gonorrhea. Description: an infection that occurs primarily in the urethra in males and the cervix in females. Cause: bacteria. Symptoms: female—slight vaginal discharge, burning sensation during urination, abnormal menstruation, abdominal pain or tenderness; male—discharge from the penis, burning sensation during urination, enlarged or

REVIEW

Thinking Critically

LESSON 1

30. **Synthesis.** Make a chart similar to the one in Lesson 3 and complete information for gonorrhea. Do some additional research to fill in any information not provided in the text.

LESSON 2

31. **Synthesis.** Add syphilis to the chart you began in item 30 above.
32. **Synthesis.** Some states have a law requiring couples who apply for marriage licenses to be tested for syphilis. What is the purpose of such a law? Why is such a law not as effective in controlling the spread of syphilis as it might have been fifty years ago?
33. **Synthesis.** Develop a law of your own that you think would be effective in the control of syphilis. Explain your thinking.

LESSON 3

34. **Synthesis.** The only known way to prevent any kind of sexually transmitted disease is to abstain from sexual contact. What strategies can you suggest that would be effective in "selling" this concept to teens who are already sexually active?
35. **Analysis.** Why is a person who has many different sexual partners more likely to contract a sexually transmitted disease than a person who has only one sexual partner? Explain your answer.

Making the Connection

LESSON 1

36. **Math.** Do some research on the number of cases of gonorrhea during 5-year intervals from 1950 to the present. Present your findings in a bar graph. Develop a comparable bar graph for population increases during the same period. Compare the two graphs.

Applying Health Knowledge

LESSON 1

37. Contact your local health department to find out about the relationship between gonorrhea and arthritis and gonorrhea and heart trouble. Share your findings with the class.
38. Design a booklet entitled "Gonorrhea Alert" that summarizes the major points presented in the lesson.

LESSON 2

39. What steps could public health agencies take to further control the spread of syphilis? What steps could individuals take?
40. Why is it inadvisable for females with syphilis to become pregnant? When can an unborn baby develop syphilis during pregnancy?

LESSON 3

41. If an individual is diagnosed as having a sexually transmitted disease, who should he or she tell in order to prevent further spread of the disease?

Beyond the Classroom

LESSON 1

42. **Parental Involvement.** Ask your parents or other adults at home how they learned about STDs. Ask about the quality of that information. Talk with them about the best ways for young people to learn about STDs.

LESSON 3

43. **Further Study.** Use a dictionary to find the etymology, or origin, of the words *gonorrhea, syphilis,* and *herpes.* Which of these words has an alternate spelling and what is it?
44. **Community Involvement.** Find out what kinds of assistance are available to help people who have STDs in your community. Prepare a report to share your findings with your classmates.

Beyond the Classroom

42. Answers will vary.
43. Etymologies will vary.

Gonorrhea may also be spelled gonorrhoea.
44. Answers will vary.

31. Disease: syphilis. Description: an infection that attacks many parts of the body. Cause: a bacterium called a spirochete. Symptoms: chancres; rash on chest, arms, and legs or vaginal area in females; sores that secrete a clear liquid; swelling of lymph nodes under the arms and in the groin area; fever; sore throat; loss of muscular coordination; blindness; insanity; senility. Treatment: penicillin.
32. To prevent the spread of syphilis; to identify people who have the disease and recommend they seek treatment. Answers will vary. Possible answer: Many cases of syphilis are spread by and to people whom partners do not intend to marry.
33. Answers will vary but should be supported logically.
34. Strategies will vary.
35. Each partner one has may have had sexual contact with several other partners, each of whom may have had sexual contact with several partners, and so on. When two noninfected persons have only each other as a sexual partner, there is virtually no chance of contracting a sexually transmitted disease.

Making the Connection

36. Answers will vary.

Applying Health Knowledge

37. Answers will vary.
38. Booklets will vary but should include symptoms, diagnosis, treatment, and problems of untreated gonorrhea.
39. Answers will vary. Possible answers: Providing education to grade schools and high schools, abstaining from sex.
40. The risks of miscarriage, having a stillbirth, or transferring the infection to the fetus are too great. Anytime after the fifth month of pregnancy.
41. Anyone with whom he or she has had sexual contact.

tender lymph glands in the groin. Treatment: antibiotics.

Lesson Summaries

LESSON 1. AIDS is a fatal communicable disease with no effective treatment and no known cure. The virus that causes AIDS—HIV—attacks the body's immune system. HIV must enter a person's bloodstream to infect the person. Transmission can occur during sexual intercourse with an infected person or sharing a contaminated needle. Infected blood used in transfusions has caused AIDS, but blood is routinely tested now to detect HIV antibodies, greatly reducing blood transfusion risks. Teenagers are a primary risk group for contracting AIDS due to their high-risk behaviors. Prevention can be achieved by staying informed and avoiding high-risk behaviors.

LESSON 2. Testing for HIV is recommended for foreign service employees, persons in the medical profession, and individuals who have practiced risk behaviors. Infection can be detected by the presence of HIV antibodies. Its symptoms may not appear for 6 months to 10 to 12 years, though the person will eventually develop AIDS. Diagnosis of AIDS is based on the presence of HIV antibodies and the presence of an opportunistic disease. Researchers continue to search for effective treatment and possible vaccines.

Introducing the Chapter

Tell students that this chapter will investigate AIDS, a disease that attacks the body's immune system. Ask them to brainstorm what they already know about AIDS. List their facts on the chalkboard. Copy the list and provide copies for all students. Have students verify the facts and identify any misinformation or misconceptions as they study the chapter.

Performance Assessment ✓

Refer to pages T 23 to T 25 for a Performance Assessment strategy for this chapter. See the *Performance Assessment Activities* booklet for additional suggestions.

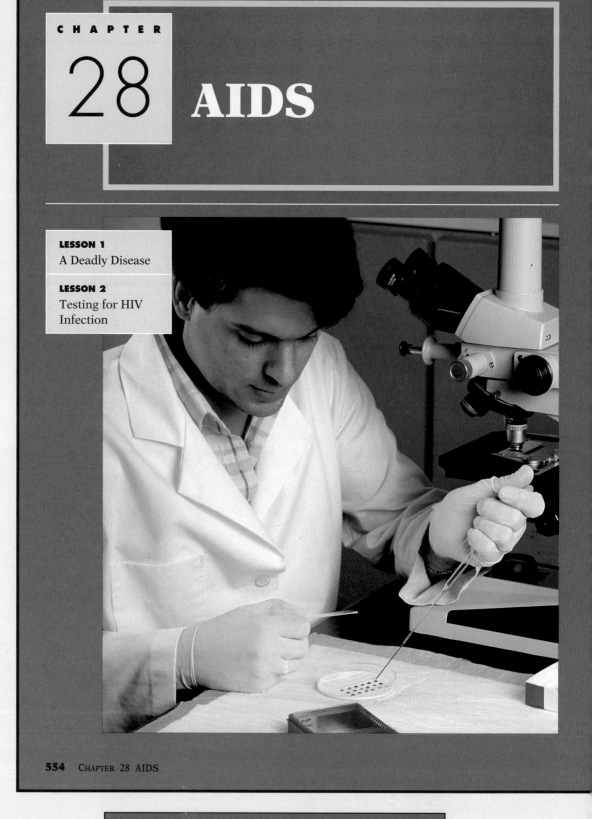

CHAPTER

28 AIDS

LESSON 1
A Deadly Disease

LESSON 2
Testing for HIV Infection

554 CHAPTER 28 AIDS

Key to Ability Levels

Teaching strategies have been coded for varying learning styles and abilities.

L1 Level 1 activities are basic activities and should be within the ability range of all students.

L2 Level 2 activities are average activities and should be within the ability range of average to above-average students.

L3 Level 3 activities are challenging activities designed for the ability range of above-average students.

LD LD activities should be within the ability range of learning-disabled students.

LEP LEP activities should be within the ability range of Limited English Proficiency students.

A DEADLY DISEASE

Today more Americans are infected with STDs than at any other time in history. The most serious of these diseases is AIDS. Since the first cases were identified in the United States in 1981, AIDS has touched the lives of millions of families. This deadly disease is unlike any other in modern history.

What Is AIDS?

Acquired immune deficiency syndrome (AIDS) is a fatal communicable disease with no effective treatment or known cure. AIDS is the final stage of infection caused by the **human immunodeficiency virus (HIV).** When HIV enters the body, it attacks the body's immune system.

How Does HIV Affect the Body?

In order to understand how HIV attacks the body's immune system, it is necessary to review the function of lymphocytes. HIV causes specific changes in the functions of the lymphocytes, which differ from changes caused by other kinds of viruses.

Lymphocytes and Antibodies

As you know, **lymphocytes** are white blood cells made in bone marrow. Lymphocytes move throughout your lymphatic system between blood and lymph tissue, and help your body fight pathogens, disease-causing organisms. There are two major types of lymphocytes—B cells, which mature in bone marrow and T cells, which mature in the thymus gland. T helper cells, a type of T cell, stimulate B cells to produce antibodies. **Antibodies** are proteins that help destroy pathogens that enter the body.

When HIV enters the body, it enters certain cells, including T helper cells. Here HIV reproduces its genetic material, which causes more T helper cells to become infected and to be destroyed. This decrease in the number of T helper cells affects the ability of the immune system to fight pathogens. As a result, many illnesses can occur in the body. Indicator illnesses are those illnesses associated with a person who has AIDS. These include opportunistic infections, which are infections a healthy immune system would usually be able to fight. A person is said to have the disease AIDS when he or she is infected with HIV, has a low T helper cell count, and has one or more indicator illnesses.

Origin of HIV

There are many theories as to where HIV originated and how it spread to the United States. It is thought that the virus spread as people

A DEADLY DISEASE **555**

LESSON 1 FOCUS

TERMS TO USE
- Acquired immune deficiency syndrome (AIDS)
- Human immunodeficiency (IM•yuh•noh•di•FISH•uhn•see) virus (HIV)
- Lymphocytes (LIM•fuh•syts)
- Antibodies

CONCEPTS TO LEARN
- AIDS is the final stage of infection caused by the human immuno-deficiency virus (HIV).
- To date HIV is known to be transmitted only through blood, vaginal secretions, semen, and breast milk.
- Specific behaviors are known to transmit HIV from an infected to an uninfected person.
- HIV is not transmitted through casual contact.

ATTITUDES AND BEHAVIORS TO EVALUATE
- Self-Inventory, page 564.
- Building Decision-Making Skills, page 565.

Focus

Lesson Objectives
After studying this lesson, students should be able to:
- define AIDS
- list body fluids through which HIV is known to be transmitted
- list behaviors known to transmit HIV
- discuss ways in which HIV is not transmitted

Bellringer
Write the following on the chalkboard for students to work on while attendance is being taken: *Write an example of how your immune system helps prevent you from getting diseases.*

Introducing the Lesson
Have volunteers share their responses to the Bellringer. Tell students that the virus that causes AIDS attacks the body's immune system. This lesson discusses how the immune system is affected by the virus, ways the virus is transmitted, and how to avoid becoming infected.

Building Vocabulary
- Write the vocabulary terms on the chalkboard. Ask volunteers to use a dictionary to find the meanings of these words and parts of words: *acquired, immuno-, deficiency, syndrome, lymphocytes, anti-, bodies.* Have another volunteer write the meanings on the board. Have each student write a sentence about each term that demonstrates the meaning.
- Ask students to complete *Workbook Vocabulary Activity 76.*

DID YOU KNOW?

- In 1991 the Centers for Disease Control and Prevention proposed a broadened definition for AIDS that would include anyone whose blood had a count of less than 200 CD4 lymphocyte cells per cubic millimeter—a sign that one's immune system is being attacked, even if the person still feels okay.

Resources for Lesson 1

- **Transparencies** 33, 34
- **Lesson 1 Quiz**
- **Guided Reading** Act 76
- **BARN**, AIDS
- **Reteaching** Act 76
- **AIDS and Society**

ABC News InterActive Videodiscs
AIDS, Side 1
Ch 3 What Is AIDS?

Ch 4 Your Immune System & AIDS

Ch 5 How You Can Become Infected

Guided Practice

L2 DISCUSSION. Have students discuss why AIDS is the most serious communicable disease known today that can be passed through sexual intercourse.

L2 EXPLANATION. Explain to students that so far, in the United States, more than 90 percent of people with AIDS have been: homosexual or bisexual men, IV drug users, or people who received donated blood or blood products prior to March 1985. These are referred to as "high risk groups." But anyone can get AIDS if they engage in high-risk behaviors. Engaging in sexual intercourse with anyone can put you at risk for HIV. There is an increase in the number of females that are contracting the virus. The Centers for Disease Control and Prevention indicates that as of March 31, 1993, 289,320 people in the United States have been diagnosed with AIDS. AIDS has been responsible for 182,275 deaths in the United States.

L2 DISCUSSION. Ask students what AIDS is. Discuss how HIV affects and changes the normal function of the T4 lymphocyte cell. How does this affect our immune system?

L2 CLASS ACTIVITY. Explain the school policy on students attending your school who have been diagnosed with AIDS. Ask students why an AIDS patient would need certain rights. Have students write a paragraph telling how the rights of someone with AIDS can be protected.

L1 USING LIFE MANAGEMENT SKILLS TRANSPARENCIES 33 AND 34. Refer to the Teaching Transparencies Binder.

Blood that is donated in the United States is tested for the presence of HIV antibodies.

traveled. It is also known that the virus assumes many different forms within the body.

The first group of people in the United States diagnosed with AIDS were male homosexuals. Many people then believed AIDS was a disease only homosexuals could contract. This is not true. Anyone who participates in behaviors known to spread HIV is at risk of becoming infected, regardless of age, race, or sexual orientation.

How HIV Is Transmitted

There are many myths about how HIV is or is not spread. The fact is, HIV must enter a person's bloodstream to infect the person. HIV has been found in body fluids such as blood, semen, and vaginal secretions of infected persons. Small concentrations have also been found in saliva, sweat, tears, feces, urine, and breast milk. To date, HIV is known to be transmitted only through blood, vaginal secretions, semen, and breast milk. Certain behaviors and situations are known to transmit HIV from an infected to an uninfected person because the exchange of body fluids is involved.

Behaviors Known to Transmit HIV

About 93 percent of adults and teenagers testing positive for HIV have acquired the virus through sexual intercourse or IV drug use. These two actions are high-risk behaviors for HIV infection.

Sexual Intercourse. HIV can be transmitted during any form of sexual intercourse. During intercourse, secretions containing HIV can enter a partner's blood through tiny cuts in the body. The risks of HIV infection increase with the number of sexual partners a person has or by having sexual contact with someone who has had many sexual partners. Having an STD that results in sores and bleeding or discharge also increases the risks of HIV entering the blood.

Contaminated Needles. If a person who is infected with HIV injects drugs into his or her veins with a syringe, drops of that person's blood are left on the needle. If another person uses the same needle, it is very likely that the infected blood will be passed to this person's blood. Sharing any needle, including one used to inject steroids, make tattoos, or pierce ears, puts a person at risk of becoming infected with HIV.

Situations Known to Transmit HIV

HIV is carried in the blood. Any transfer of blood from one person to another is a potential risk for HIV infection.

Blood Transfusion. Prior to March 1985, before donated blood was tested for HIV, people who received blood transfusions were at risk of being exposed to HIV. All blood donated in the United States is now tested for the presence of HIV antibodies. This testing has almost eliminated the risk of receiving contaminated blood or blood products from a transfusion. There is no risk when donating blood because disposable needles are used. These needles are used only one time.

CONFLICT RESOLUTION

Assume you have a friend who is infected with HIV.

Would you advise your friend to tell other classmates and teachers about the infection or keep the infection a secret?

How would you convince your classmates and teachers that they are a greater health risk to your friend than your friend is to them?

Across the Curriculum

Social Studies. Have students contact the Centers for Disease Control and Prevention for more information on the epidemiology (the study of how a disease comes about) of AIDS. Ask a social studies teacher to help you to compare the worldwide spread of AIDS to the spread of bubonic plague. Investigate the similarities in that disease and AIDS. Were individuals with plague ostracized and not cared for properly? Are people with AIDS treated warmly and accepted by our society? How does fear and prejudice for the people then compare to current treatment of AIDS patients? Compare the effective treatment and medicine available for both diseases. Investigate how the plague was finally eradicated.

Overcoming The Odds

Henry Nicols is 18. He loves to swim, do karate, backpack, and hike. He is an Eagle Scout. He is also a hemophiliac, and he has AIDS.

Henry begins, "I was diagnosed with hemophilia when I was just 18 months old. Hemophilia is an inherited bleeding disorder that prevents blood from clotting. So when I get a cut or a bruise, I need a blood transfusion. I've had more than 300 transfusions over the years." It was one of those transfusions that infected Henry with HIV. Because of his condition, sports were out. But illness did not stop Henry from being active. "I swim quite a bit, and I started taking karate classes about three years ago. I've also been involved with the Boy Scouts for a long time."

He continues, "In 1985, when they developed a test for HIV infection, I was taking part in an experimental test of a new medicine for hemophilia. As part of the program, they tested my blood for HIV. It was positive. They called my father and asked if he wanted to know the results. At first my father said "no," but later, he changed his mind. He waited a week before telling my mother. He waited two more weeks before telling me and my sisters."

Neither HIV nor AIDS has stopped Henry, however. In fact, he has turned his illness into a passionate mission to educate other young people about the disease. He explains. "The highest rank in scouting is the Eagle Scout Award," he says. "To get it, you have to

complete a number of requirements, and one of them is an Eagle Scout Project. The project has to be a service to the community and has to demonstrate leadership. I chose speaking about AIDS and educating other young people about the disease as my project. I earned the badge in July. But I didn't feel I should end it there. I talk in high schools and colleges across the country now. The support is usually overwhelming. There's very little negative reaction."

There has been some prejudice, though, Henry says, "but mostly in the form of ignorance. For example, in our scout troop, one of the mothers didn't want her son eating out of the same potato chip bag as I.

"My family has been behind me 100 percent. This has brought us closer together.

Some people figure they have a long time to tell their parents they love them or to make up for mistakes. We know better.

"I have very good self-esteem," he continues. "I think family support helped me to feel good about myself and what I'm doing."

In closing, Henry says with great seriousness and directness, "You have to change the way you think about HIV, AIDS, and those infected. You need to recognize that not everyone with AIDS contracted the virus through high-risk behavior. And you must take action to avoid high-risk behaviors. That may mean changing your behavior. It should mean choosing abstinence."

1. How can ignorance about AIDS or any other disease be a form of prejudice?
2. If you knew you had a terminal disease, how might you live your life differently?

■ **Discussion.** How does Henry deviate from the stereotypical AIDS patient? In what way is he like most other AIDS patients? (Henry was infected with HIV as a child as a result of a blood transfusion. However, like other AIDS patients, he must come to terms with the fact that he's likely to die of AIDS at a young age.)

■ **Explanation.** Explain what Henry had going for him to maintain his high self-esteem in light of the double whammy he was dealt—a life-threatening genetic disorder and a fatal infectious disease. (Henry had a loving, supportive family; he set and attained long-term goals; he kept physically active; he mastered a new skill; and he became actively involved in helping others.)

■ **Answers**
1. You may be misinformed about the dangers of infection and treat infected individuals unfairly.
2. Answers will vary. The exercise will serve to give students some notion of what it's like to have AIDS.

L2 CLASS ACTIVITY. Have students write a mock advice column for teens asking about AIDS. What questions do teens usually ask?

L2 DISCUSSION. What do current research studies cite as the number of years that may be the incubation period of HIV? Discuss how a teenager could be a carrier of HIV and not get AIDS until he or she is an adult.

Overcoming Misconceptions

Myth. People who have daily contact with someone at school who has AIDS are likely to get it, too. **Fact.** HIV is transmitted by sexual intercourse, needle sharing, or infected blood. The virus cannot be passed through ordinary activities at school. **Myth.** A person can become infected with HIV from "French" kissing. **Fact.** Not likely. HIV has been found in saliva, but in very low concentrations—so low that scientists believe it is virtually impossible to pass through deep kissing. **Myth.** A person who has never used IV drugs and has had sexual intercourse only with a person of the opposite sex cannot become infected with HIV. **Fact.** HIV does not discriminate. Both males and females can become infected and transmit the infection to another person.

HIV is not transmitted through casual contact.

Before, During, and After Birth. A pregnant female who is infected with HIV can pass the virus to the baby in blood exchanged through the umbilical cord. A baby also could be infected with HIV during birth if the virus enters a cut on the baby's body. A nursing baby could receive HIV while breast-feeding.

Teenagers at Risk

Teenagers are at primary risk for contracting HIV. The Centers for Disease Control and Prevention (CDC) is part of the United States Department of Health and Human Services. The CDC gathers statistics regarding disease throughout the world. According to the CDC:

- Over one-fifth of the people with AIDS are in their 20s. Most of these people probably became infected with HIV as teenagers.
- As of March 30, 1993, 1,167 cases of AIDS had been reported among teenagers.
- AIDS is the seventh leading cause of death among 15- to 24-year-olds in the United States.

A teen who chooses to abstain from sexual intercourse and who does not use intravenous (IV) drugs virtually eliminates the risk of HIV infection. In addition, abstaining from the use of alcohol and other drugs, which can impair a person's judgment in regard to sexual activity and drug use, can also reduce the risk of HIV infection. Making responsible decisions means protection from HIV infection.

How HIV Is Not Transmitted

Fear of AIDS has caused people to react negatively and sometimes violently toward people known to be infected with HIV. Ignorance feeds this fear. Remember, HIV is transmitted in body fluids. It is not an airborne pathogen.

HIV cannot be transmitted through casual contact. Casual contact includes sharing towels, combs, eating utensils, bathroom facilities, or having close physical contact, such as touching or hugging. In studies of families who have a member infected with HIV, no incidence of the virus spreading to other family members through casual contact has been found. In addition, according to the Centers for Disease Control and Prevention, HIV is not spread through an insect bite.

K E E P I N G   F I T

Facts You Should Know

- A person cannot get HIV from casual contact with someone who is infected.
- A person cannot get HIV from swimming in a pool with someone who is infected.
- A person cannot get HIV from

being sneezed on by someone who is infected.
- A person cannot get HIV from donating blood. Blood banks and other blood collection centers are very careful to use sterile equipment. Do not let the

fear of AIDS stop you from donating much-needed blood. All donated blood is now vigorously tested for HIV so that the risk to those receiving blood transfusions is extremely low.

Additional Information

AIDS Statistics. As of March 31, 1993, the Centers for Disease Control and Prevention reports that, in the U.S., 40 percent of women and 3 percent of men with AIDS contracted the disease through heterosexual sex. AIDS will soon become the fifth leading cause of death among American women ages 15 to 44.

Among American women with AIDS, IV drug use is the number one means of transmission, followed by having sex with an IV drug user.

It is estimated that at least 1.5 million Americans are now infected with HIV, and many of them do not know it.

How Infection with HIV Can Be Prevented

Although AIDS is not curable, being infected with HIV is preventable. Knowledge is the first step in prevention. Because HIV and AIDS research is ongoing, scientists are learning more and more about HIV and AIDS. New information is continually being updated and changing what is known about HIV infection.

Facts about HIV infection and AIDS can be obtained from a variety of sources. Newspapers, professional journals, and health news reports on television and radio often report the latest scientific findings. The Centers for Disease Control and Prevention, as well as state and local health organizations, are excellent resources for accurate information about HIV infection and AIDS. Parents, teachers, school counselors, church leaders, and doctors also can be sources or provide guidance about where to find information.

The second step in preventing HIV infection is applying information learned. This includes avoiding those behaviors known to transmit HIV—sexual intercourse and using illegal IV drugs. Teens who practice abstinence, or voluntarily refrain from sex, help prevent the spread of HIV to themselves and to others. Teens who avoid using drugs and the people who use them, do the same.

Saying no to behaviors known to transmit HIV may not be easy, especially when the person you are saying it to is someone whose friendship you value. Using refusal skills may help you save both your friendship and your health.

Unfortunately, despite the life-threatening risks involved, some persons will continue to participate in behaviors known to increase their risk of HIV infection. You may feel a responsibility to share the information you know about HIV infection and AIDS, or have someone you know talk with them. Each person must accept responsibility for decisions he or she makes about behaviors, including the ones that involve risks of HIV infection.

LESSON 1 REVIEW

Reviewing Facts and Vocabulary

1. What is AIDS?
2. What is the function of T helper cells?
3. Explain the ways HIV is known to be transmitted.

Thinking Critically

4. **Evaluation.** Do you think an individual infected with HIV is responsible for informing others of the infection? Why or why not?

5. **Synthesis.** Why is AIDS a serious threat to public health?

Applying Health Knowledge

6. Design a poster that tells teens how to avoid HIV infection.

Answers to Lesson 1 Review

1. Acquired immune deficiency syndrome—a fatal communicable disease with no effective treatment or known cure.
2. They stimulate B cells to produce antibodies.
3. It is transmitted in bodily fluids through sexual intercourse; by sharing contaminated needles; in transfusions with infected blood or blood products; by an infected pregnant female in blood exchanged through the umbilical cord or, after birth, through breast milk.
4. Answers will vary but should be supported logically.
5. Answers will vary. Possible answers: Costs of health care, increasing number of those infected, effects on victims and families.

Focus

Lesson Objectives

After studying this lesson, students should be able to:

- describe the two tests that detect the presence of HIV antibodies
- explain the factors that determine a diagnosis of AIDS

Bellringer

Write the following on the chalkboard for students to work on while attendance is being taken: *Should certain groups of people be required to be tested for AIDS? If yes, who are they and why did you select them?*

Introducing the Lesson

Have students share their responses to the Bellringer with the class. Explain that there are special groups of people that are required to be tested for AIDS to prevent the spread of the disease. For instance, pregnant women, people who donate blood, body organs, or tissues, and those who join the armed forces are required to be tested. Tell students that this lesson discusses testing for HIV infection and treatment for infected persons.

Building Vocabulary

- Ask students to attempt to write the correct spelling for each of the vocabulary terms as you pronounce them. Have students exchange papers with a neighbor and correct the spellings using the Glossary. Have them read the term out loud and define each term for the neighbor.
- Ask students to complete *Workbook Vocabulary Activity 77.*

DID YOU KNOW?

- In 1988, Illinois became the first state to require an AIDS test for marriage licenses. As a result, the number of Illinois marriages decreased, and marriages of Illinois couples in neighboring states doubled or even tripled. The law was later repealed.
- Most states require that a positive test be reported to the state health department.

TESTING FOR HIV INFECTION

LESSON 2 FOCUS

TERMS TO USE
- ELISA
- Western blot
- Pneumocystis carinii (NYOO•mo•sis•tis CAR•in•nee) pneumonia (PCP)
- Mycobacterium avium intracellulare (MAI)
- AIDS dementia (dee•MEN•shuh) complex

CONCEPTS TO LEARN
- Two tests detect the presence of HIV antibodies.
- A diagnosis of AIDS is based on several factors.

ATTITUDES AND BEHAVIOR TO EVALUATE
- Self-Inventory, page 564.
- Building Decision-Making Skills, page 565.

Presently, testing for HIV is required for people who donate blood, body organs and tissue, and for those who join the armed forces. Testing is recommended for State Department Foreign Service employees and people in the medical profession. It also is recommended for people who have practiced behaviors known to transmit HIV. Because of the stigma associated with HIV infection and AIDS, results of tests for HIV are kept confidential.

Detecting HIV Antibodies

As you know, when a pathogen enters the body, the immune system produces antibodies to fight and destroy the pathogen. The immune system does produce antibodies to fight HIV, but these antibodies are not effective in preventing HIV infection. However, finding these antibodies in the blood indicates a person is infected with HIV.

ELISA and Western Blot

In 1985 the ELISA test was developed to detect the presence of antibodies for HIV. **ELISA** means enzyme-linked immunosorbent assay. ELISA is a test for HIV infection, not a test to determine the disease AIDS. ELISA is used for screening donated blood. ELISA also is used on persons who suspect they are infected with HIV because of behaviors they have chosen. One ELISA is given. If a person tests positive, two more tests are done. If after the three tests, two or three are positive, then the Western blot is done to confirm the test results. The **Western blot** is a more expensive test to use but is very specific in identifying HIV antibodies.

Test Results. A positive test means that the person has HIV antibodies in his or her blood. This person is infected with HIV although he or she may show no signs of the disease. In fact a person infected with HIV can feel and look fine. However, this individual can still infect others when practicing behaviors known to transmit HIV. A person can be infected with HIV for 10 to 12 years or longer before showing signs of infection. Many people who have the disease AIDS actually became infected with HIV years earlier.

A negative test means that there were no HIV antibodies in the sample of blood. It does not mean, however, that the person is uninfected. After being infected, it may take the body anywhere from two weeks to six months or longer to develop HIV antibodies. If a person concerned about possible exposure to HIV does test negative, he or she should be retested in six months. During that six-month period, behaviors known to transmit HIV must be avoided. If the second test is negative, the person is probably not infected with HIV.

Resources for Lesson 2

- **Guided Reading** Activity 77
- **Decision-Making** Activity 28
- **Workbook** Voc Act 77, Appl Act 28
- **Reteaching** Activity 77
- **Enrichment** Activity 28
- **Health Labs** Activity 28
- **Cooperative Learning** Activity 28
- **Lesson 2 Quiz, Chapter 28 Test**

ABC News InterActive Videodiscs
AIDS, Side 1
Ch 16 The First Decade of AIDS

Ch 17 United States Statistics

Basketball star Magic Johnson stunned the world when he announced he was HIV-positive.

Symptoms of HIV Infection

Although symptoms of HIV infection may not appear for 6 months to 10 to 12 years, a person infected with HIV will eventually develop the disease AIDS. A person infected with HIV will experience many signs and symptoms before a diagnosis of AIDS is made. Symptoms include fever, rash, headache, body aches, swollen glands, and the decreasing ability to fight pathogens. T helper cell count decreases. In a later stage, thrush appears. This fungal infection results in white spots and sores in the mouth and infections on the skin and in mucous membranes.

Diagnosis of AIDS

Diagnosis of AIDS is based on several factors, including a positive test for HIV antibodies and the presence of an opportunistic infection. As mentioned earlier, these illnesses result from a breakdown of the immune system. A person who has been diagnosed with AIDS may live only a few months or for several years. AIDS patients die from the effects of opportunistic infections. Several opportunistic infections are associated with AIDS. **Pneumocystis carinii pneumonia (PCP)** is a

---

K E E P I N G   F I T

Volunteering Helps

What can you do to help in the AIDS crisis?
- Work to educate fellow teens about AIDS and how to prevent it. Organize an AIDS awareness week at your school.
- Work to organize a fund-raiser

for a local AIDS hospice or AIDS education program.
- Consider becoming an AIDS buddy, doing food shopping and other chores for people who are too sick to do these things for themselves.

- Check yourself for any judgments or prejudices you may have about people with AIDS. Do you really know and believe that you cannot get AIDS from casual social contact?

TESTING FOR HIV INFECTION **561**

Additional Information

AIDS Victims. Persons with HIV infection and AIDS have distinct needs that are unlike others having any other disease in history. These people live in fear knowing that there is no cure and death is imminent. They also know the stigma associated with the disease. Some are ostracized from friends and family. Some are denied medical care. Many are denied insurance. In addition, the types of infection that will lead to death are so horrible that some of these people will commit suicide.

Independent Practice

L3 **WRITING.** Have students use past issues of news magazines such as *TIME, NEWSWEEK, INSIGHT,* and *U.S. NEWS & WORLD REPORT* to research and report on the latest developments in the research for a vaccine, treatments, and a cure for AIDS. Have students summarize their findings.

L1 **USING THE LESSON RESOURCES.** For additional student activities, refer to the lesson resources on page 560.

DID YOU KNOW?

■ All 50 states in the United States, the District of Columbia, U.S. dependencies and possessions, and independent nations in free association with the United States report AIDS cases to the Centers for Disease Control and Prevention (CDC).

■ The CDC releases a report quarterly that includes the information received through the last day of the previous quarter.

DID YOU KNOW?

■ At age 13, Ryan White became infected with HIV from a blood transfusion he received because he was a hemophiliac. In the years in which he was sick, he became a national spokesperson for people with AIDS, speaking in schools, appearing before a presidential AIDS panel, and being the subject of a movie about his life and his battle against the disease. He died at age 18 but not in vain. In 1990, The Ryan White Comprehensive AIDS Resources Act was passed, approving funds for AIDS testing, counseling, and treatment to cities and states hardest hit by the disease.

---

form of pneumonia with symptoms that include difficulty in breathing, shortness of breath, fever, and persistent cough. **Mycobacterium avium intracellulare (MAI)** is the leading cause of wasting syndrome, a gradual deterioration of all body functions. It is characterized by fatigue, sudden high fever, severe night sweats, cramps, and weight loss.

HEALTH UPDATE

LOOKING AT THE ISSUES

Testing for HIV

Questions surrounding this issue include whether these tests should be voluntary or mandatory, who should be tested, and if those with positive test results should be identified.

Analyzing Different Viewpoints

ONE VIEW. Many health-care professionals call for mandatory testing for HIV in patients undergoing surgery, pregnant women, and IV drug users. Why? Because such persons could put others at risk. For example, surgeons operating on infected patients could become infected.

A SECOND VIEW. Other people believe that HIV testing should be voluntary. The Centers for Disease Control has recently proposed widespread voluntary tests for hospital patients. Under these proposals, patient test results would be kept confidential.

A THIRD VIEW. Some people claim that health-care workers should be tested. New federal guidelines urge testing for health-care workers such as surgeons or dentists who may have blood-to-blood contact with patients. The American Medical Association (AMA) is opposed to mandatory testing for health-care workers, but it is calling for routine, voluntary screening for doctors at risk either because of their work or their

life-styles. The AMA would also ask HIV-positive doctors to stop performing invasive surgical procedures.

A FOURTH VIEW. Some people are calling for mandatory testing for everyone. They state that no safety precautions are foolproof. They fear that some health-care workers infected with HIV may continue to practice, putting patients at risk because they are afraid of losing their jobs and medical benefits if they disclose that they are infected.

A FIFTH VIEW. Others maintain that mandatory testing infringes on the right to privacy. They state that testing health-care workers is discriminatory, because the risk of infection from health-care workers is small.

A SIXTH VIEW. Others think that taking precautions such as disposing of needles, wearing gloves and masks, and avoiding contact with body fluids are safeguards enough, so that in most cases not even voluntary testing is necessary.

Exploring Your Views

1. Who do you think should be tested for HIV?
2. Should that testing be voluntary or mandatory? Explain your answer.
3. If you had to be admitted to the hospital, would you agree to voluntary testing for HIV? Why or why not?

AIDS dementia complex is a progressive disorder that destroys brain tissue of a person with AIDS. Symptoms range from mild confusion to inability to control one's muscular movement.

Research and Treatment

There is no cure for HIV infection or AIDS. However, since 1981 the world's scientific community has made great progress in AIDS research. Scientists have gained enough information to develop experimental treatments and possible vaccines. Through concentrated efforts in researching HIV, scientists' understanding of the immune system has increased. It is hoped this knowledge will help advance the fight against this disease.

Medical Research

In March 1987 the medicine zidovudine (AZT) was approved for use in treating persons infected with HIV. AZT slows the multiplication of HIV and seems to help delay the onset of opportunistic infections. It also can help reduce the severity of some AIDS symptoms and prolong life. AZT does not cure AIDS. With estimated annual costs of treatment ranging from $2,000 to $4,000 per patient, AZT is an expensive medicine. Almost half of all AIDS patients must stop taking AZT because it damages their bone marrow. Other medicines, ddI and ddC, have also been approved for use. These medicines also delay the onset of serious illnesses. However, both can cause side effects.

A variety of approaches is being used in an attempt to discover a vaccine against the AIDS virus. A main focus has been finding a protein that will cause the body's immune system to produce effective HIV antibodies. Experimental vaccines have been developed through gene splicing. Only time will tell whether the antibodies produced by the vaccines can protect the body against HIV.

HELP WANTED

Epidemiologist

Are you part doctor, part researcher, part scientist, and part detective? Do you welcome the challenge of dealing with the most serious medical problems worldwide, utilizing the most scientific equipment and knowledge, and solving the most complicated and elusive problems? If so, Uncle Sam wants you to work at the Centers for Disease Control as an epidemiologist, identifying mysterious diseases and hopefully recommending successful treatments. We would like to review your medical school and experiential background.

For more information contact:
American Medical Association
535 N. Dearborn Street
Chicago, IL 60610

LESSON 2 REVIEW

Reviewing Facts and Vocabulary

1. What determines a diagnosis of the disease AIDS?
2. List two medicines currently being used to treat AIDS.
3. What precautions should a person take whose first test for HIV antibodies is negative?

Thinking Critically

4. **Analysis.** Compare and contrast the ELISA and Western blot tests.

5. **Synthesis.** Why do you think the number of AIDS cases continues to increase?

Applying Health Knowledge

6. Develop a one-minute public service announcement (PSA) to inform others about the spread of HIV. Submit the PSA to your school office to be read over the intercom during announcements.

TESTING FOR HIV INFECTION **563**

Answers to Lesson 2 Review

1. A positive test for HIV antibodies and the presence of an opportunistic infection.
2. Zidovudine (AZT), ddI, and ddC.
3. Avoid behaviors known to transmit HIV and be retested in six months.
4. Both are blood tests to check for the presence of antibodies for HIV. The

Western blot is more expensive and more specific and is done after three ELISA tests.
5. Answers will vary. Possible answers: People are not taking proper precautions, people believe it will not happen to them.
6. Answers will vary.

Assess

Check for Understanding

- Assign and discuss the lesson review. Encourage LD students to focus on questions 1 and 5.
- Assign and discuss the chapter review.

Evaluate

- Administer, grade, and discuss the *Lesson 2 Quiz.*
- Administer, grade, and discuss the *Chapter 28 Test.*
- Refer to the Performance Assessment strategy for this chapter. See pages T 23 to T 25.

Reteach

- Invite a health educator from the Public Health Department and an administrator from your school into class to discuss efforts that are being made to control the spread of AIDS in your community. Ask students to report on treatment available and testing procedures used to determine HIV infection.
- Ask students to complete *Reteaching Activity 77.*

Enrich

- Ask each student to investigate one or more of the following subjects surrounding the AIDS issue: confidentiality of test results; mandatory AIDS testing; legal suits against people who have transmitted the disease; the FDA and the unavailability of certain experimental drugs; group homes for AIDS children; hospices for AIDS patients; and prejudice against people with the virus. Have students report their findings to the class. If possible, plan a panel discussion in which several or all of these issues are addressed in detail.
- Ask students to complete *Enrichment Activity 28.*

Close

Ask students to state the most important concepts learned in this lesson. Ask students to determine what role they can play in preventing the spread of AIDS.

CHAPTER 28 AIDS **563**

Helping Students Improve Their Health

Reinforcing Vocabulary

- **Abstain.** To voluntarily do without.
- **Intimacy.** An intimate act, especially sexual intercourse.

Teaching Strategies

L1 EXPLANATION. Occasionally parents may attempt to point out that discussion of certain behavior, i.e., sexual intimacy, or the use of illegal drugs, only leads to experimentation on the part of young people. Stress to your students that the inventory is not meant to be suggestive in any way. It is only a tool to measure past or present behavior.

L1 EXPLANATION. The inventory questions past behavior in an attempt to stress that a disease like AIDS can occur from past behaviors. In other words, your past can catch up with you. Encourage students to answer the questions truthfully for their own sake.

L1 EXPLANATION. Tell students that inventory questions regarding the use of illegal drugs or alcohol are included due to the fact that drugs may decrease inhibitions and result in a person doing something he or she wouldn't normally do.

L1 SELF-ESTEEM. Discuss the value of sexual abstinence as being 100 percent effective in preventing the transmission of STDs (including HIV) and also pregnancy. Consider questions 1 to 15 on this page and how they relate to a person's self-esteem. Is a person with a high level of self-esteem more likely to make responsible choices?

DID YOU KNOW?

- Unprotected sex with HIV-infected partners is riskier for females than it is for males.

Self-Inventory

Are You at Risk?

HOW DO YOU RATE?

Number a sheet of paper from 1 through 15. Read each item below and respond by writing *true* or *false* for each item. Then proceed to the next section.

1. I have not used illegal drugs, including alcohol, in the past.
2. I do not use illegal drugs, including alcohol, now.
3. I have abstained from sexual intimacy in the past.
4. I abstain from sexual intimacy now.
5. I keep informed about HIV infection and AIDS.
6. I can say no to something I do not want to do or do not feel ready for.
7. I am not easily influenced by peer pressure.
8. I like myself and feel good about the decisions I make.
9. I do not use needles, including tattoo needles, razors, or other items that have been used by someone else.
10. I have not received a blood transfusion prior to 1985.
11. I have not been treated for an STD in the past.
12. I avoid those behaviors that can transmit HIV.
13. I know who to talk to and where to get information when I have questions about HIV infection and AIDS.
14. I know how HIV is not transmitted.
15. If I suspect I have an STD, I will see my physician for treatment.

HOW DID YOU SCORE?

Give yourself 2 points for each *true* response and 0 points for each *false* response. Find your total, and read below to see how you scored. Then proceed to the next section.

25 to 30
Excellent. You do not take unnecessary risks, and you use decision-making skills in addressing problems. You like yourself and feel comfortable with your decisions. You are not easily influenced by others.

19 to 24
Good. You use decision-making skills in solving some of your problems. However, you would be wise to look at your behavior to see whether some risks you are taking could prevent you from achieving your goals.

0 to 18
Watch out! You take too many risks and do not use decision-making skills in solving problems. You are taking risks that could cause you to contract STDs or HIV infection and to be involved in situations that could harm you for the rest of your life.

WHAT ARE YOUR GOALS?

Select one area in which your behavior needs improvement. Then complete each statement below.

1. I plan to learn more about HIV infection and AIDS by ____.
2. My timetable for accomplishing this is ____.
3. I plan to share my information with others by ____.
4. The attitude or behavior about HIV infection I would most like to change is ____.
5. The steps involved in making this change are ____.
6. My timetable for accomplishing this is ____.
7. The people or groups I will ask for support and assistance are ____.
8. The benefits I will receive for making this change are ____.

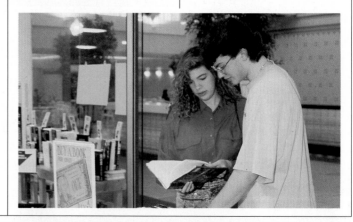

564 CHAPTER 28 AIDS

Meeting Students' Needs

For students who score *Excellent*. (1) Suggest that these students develop an AIDS policy, addressing how a person infected with HIV should be treated by peers. (2) Have students, with administration approval, write AIDS awareness messages to be read to the student body for a week.

For students who score *Good*. (1) Have these students write down ways they can reduce risk behaviors. (2) Suggest supplemental reading on high-risk behaviors associated with AIDS.

For students who must *Watch Out*. (1) Suggest these students reread the section on high-risk behaviors. (2) Suggest supplemental reading on specific high-risk behaviors and have them write an extra-credit report on a related topic.

Building Decision-Making Skills

Meredith's neighbor Jansen goes to school at the state university. The last time Jansen was home, he told Meredith that he was being treated for an ear infection at the university's health center. He also told her that there were rumors that there was a doctor on staff at the health center who was infected with HIV. He said that the doctor who treated him was the one rumored to be HIV-infected. Jansen said he is scheduled to go back to this doctor to see if the infection has been cleared up and if he would need another prescription for antibiotics. Jansen is concerned about being treated by this doctor. What should Jansen do?

A. Not worry about the office procedure unless either the doctor's or Jansen's body fluids are involved.

B. Make sure the doctor wears gloves and a face mask while treating Jansen.

C. Make an appointment to see another doctor on the health center's staff.

D. Cancel the appointment and treat the ear infection with any remaining antibiotics and OTC medicines.

WHAT DO YOU THINK?

1. **Situation.** What possible risks are involved in this situation?

2. **Choices.** What other choices can you think of for Jansen?

3. **Consequences.** What are the costs and benefits of each choice?

4. **Consequences.** Who will be affected by Jansen's decision?

5. **Choices.** Where might Jansen go for more information? Whom should he talk with about this situation?

6. **Decision.** What do you think Jansen should do? Explain your answer.

7. **Evaluation.** Have you ever been involved in something that posed a risk of harming your health? How did you handle the situation?

Trisha's little brother Vince, who is a freshman, just found out that he is infected with HIV. Because Vince has hemophilia, his blood does not clot properly. As a result he may bleed excessively from a minor injury. Vince can receive a clotting factor through injections or transfusions. Unfortunately, Vince obtained HIV through a transfusion years ago. The word about Vince has now spread throughout their small town. There has been a negative reaction to his returning to school. Fear and misunderstanding are widespread. Trisha has overheard some very harmful statements from her friends. She doesn't know how to handle this. She has considered five options.

A. Take the offensive, challenging her friends and school officials to show some understanding of the disease and compassion toward her brother.

B. Stay out of it and let the professionals, and the lawyers if necessary, handle the matter.

C. Try to convince her brother that he would be better off being tutored at home.

D. Suggest to her parents that they move to another state where they can start over and lead normal lives.

E. Finish her senior year as quietly as possible and go off to college where she can be away from the problem.

WHAT DO YOU THINK?

8. **Choices.** What other choices does Trisha have?

9. **Consequences.** What are the probable consequences of each choice?

10. **Consequences.** How honest should Trisha be with her brother and family about her feelings in each case? Explain your answer.

11. **Decision.** What do you think Trisha should do?

12. **Evaluation.** Would your opinion in these two cases change depending on which side of the situation you were on?

TESTING FOR HIV INFECTION **565**

Helping Students Improve Their Health

Building Decision-Making Skills

Teaching Strategies

L1 CLASS ACTIVITY. Have students make up a skit with Meredith discussing with Jansen his different options. Classmates may suggest other possible situations.

L2 DISCUSSION. Debate the pros and cons of regulations that would require medical workers to inform patients if they are HIV positive.

L2 DISCUSSION. Discuss with students precautions health-care workers are using to protect themselves from HIV infection. These precautions include wearing gloves, face masks, and gowns.

L1 CLASS ACTIVITY. Role-play each option that Trisha has considered. Discuss the consequences of each.

L1 CLASS ACTIVITY. Have each student get with a friend and talk about AIDS prevention. Have them address such questions as: What are high-risk behaviors to HIV transmission? Is there such a thing as safe sex?

DID YOU KNOW?

■ Recent guidelines of the National Association of State Boards of Education state that HIV-infected children should be allowed to attend school without restriction.

Discussing the Answers

Situation 1. Stress that it is important for Jansen to have as much accurate information as possible. Jansen must then weigh the consequences of every choice and make a decision.

Situation 2. If Trisha has good self-esteem, it might be best to meet the situation head on, not to hide from the problem. She could not only stand up for her brother, but also use this opportunity to inform people about some of the not-so-obvious ways to contract HIV.

Answers to Chapter 28 Review

Using Health Terms

1. AIDS
2. Lymphocytes
3. T cells
4. Antibodies
5. Western blot
6. Opportunistic infection
7. Mycobacterium avium intracellular
8. AIDS dementia complex
9. AZT

Building Academic Skills

10. Compositions will vary.
11. Compositions will vary.
12. IV drug use—about 13 percent; hemophilia—31 percent; receipt of blood transfusion or tissues—6.5 percent.

Recalling the Facts

13. AIDS is the final stage of infection caused by HIV.
14. HIV reproduces its genetic material in T helper cells, destroying the T helper cells. This affects the body's ability of the immune system to fight pathogens.
15. Throughout one's lymphatic system; help one's body fight pathogens.
16. B cells mature in bone marrow; T cells mature in the thymus gland.
17. They stimulate B cells to produce antibodies.
18. In T helper cells.
19. The body can no longer fight pathogens; the ability of the immune system is affected, allowing many infections to occur in the body.
20. Blood, vaginal secretions, semen, breast milk.
21. Stay well-informed, avoid high-risk behaviors, make responsible decisions about sex and drug use.
22. Avoid sexual intercourse and drug use.
23. They impair judgment in regard to sexual activity and the use of shared needles in drug-taking situations.
24. During sexual intercourse, body fluids are exchanged, and this is one of the most

REVIEW

Using Health Terms

On a separate sheet of paper, write the term that best matches each definition given below.

LESSON 1

1. The final stage of infection caused by HIV.
2. White blood cells that are made in bone marrow.
3. Lymphocytes that mature in the thymus gland.
4. Proteins that help destroy pathogens in the body.

LESSON 2

5. A test that is very specific in identifying HIV antibodies.
6. A term that describes an infection that results from a breakdown of the immune system.
7. The leading cause of wasting syndrome, characterized by fatigue, sudden high fever, night sweats, cramps, and weight loss.
8. A progressive disorder that destroys brain tissue of a person with AIDS.
9. Medicine that slows the multiplication of HIV and seems to help delay the onset of opportunistic infections.

Building Academic Skills

LESSON 1

10. **Writing.** Write a narrative composition describing the life of a person who becomes infected with HIV.

LESSON 2

11. **Writing.** Write a composition titled, "People Who Should Be Tested for HIV." Include reasons for your choices.
12. **Math.** According to the CDC, 872 cases of adolescents with AIDS had been reported through June 1992. The following are some of the causes with the number of cases: IV drug use—112; hemophilia—267; receipt of blood transfusion or tissues—55. Determine what percentage of the total each of these cases represents.

Recalling the Facts

LESSON 1

13. What is the connection between HIV infection and AIDS?
14. How does HIV attack the body's immune system?
15. Where do lymphocytes move and what function do they serve?
16. Name the two major types of lymphocytes and tell where they mature in the body.
17. What is the function of T helper cells?
18. In what kinds of cells does HIV reproduce its genetic material?
19. What happens when T helper cells become infected and are destroyed?
20. Through which body fluids is HIV known to be transmitted?
21. AIDS is not curable, but it is preventable. What are the best methods of prevention?
22. Name two ways teens can reduce their risk of HIV infection.
23. How can using alcohol and illegal drugs increase a person's risk of HIV infection?
24. What role does sexual intercourse play in the spread of HIV?

LESSON 2

25. For what groups of people is HIV testing now required?
26. What are the two main tests for detecting HIV? Which is more specific?
27. Which HIV test is used for screening donated blood?
28. How long may it take the body to develop antibodies to HIV after being infected?
29. How long can HIV stay in the body before a person shows signs of infection?
30. What are the advantages and disadvantages of the medicine AZT in treating AIDS patients?
31. What does a positive test for HIV mean? A negative test?
32. Which of the following are AIDS researchers hoping to find in order to cure people who are suffering from AIDS: a vaccine, a surgical operation, a new vitamin?

common ways of transmitting HIV.
25. Blood, body organ, or tissue donors; those who join the armed forces.
26. ELISA and Western blot. Western blot.
27. ELISA.
28. Two weeks to 6 months or longer.
29. Six months to 12 years.
30. Advantages—slows the multiplication of HIV, helps delay the onset of indicator illnesses, helps reduce the severity of some AIDS symptoms, prolongs life. Disadvantages—does not cure AIDS, is very expensive.
31. A person has HIV antibodies in his or her blood, therefore he or she is infected with HIV. A nega-

REVIEW

Thinking Critically

LESSON 1

33. Analysis. Indicate which of the following behaviors are known to transmit HIV from an infected to an uninfected person.
   a. sexual intercourse
   b. shaking hands
   c. kissing with the mouth closed
   d. sharing contaminated needles
   e. sharing bathroom facilities
   f. eating at the same table
   g. receiving a blood transfusion
   h. being stung by a wasp
   i. donating blood
   j. breast-feeding a baby

34. Evaluation. Do you think all health-care providers should be tested for HIV? Do you think the results should be made known to a provider's patients? Why or why not?

35. Evaluation. Why do you think many people are uninformed about HIV infection and AIDS?

LESSON 2

36. Synthesis. Design a care facility for people with AIDS. Describe the physical, mental, and social services that would be provided.

37. Evaluation. Do you feel that people who are known to have AIDS should be legally banned from entering the United States? Why or why not?

38. Evaluation. Do you believe that people should be required to undergo a test for AIDS before being considered for employment? Why or why not?

39. Evaluation. Do you think required HIV testing for groups such as organ donors is an invasion of privacy? Explain.

Making the Connection

LESSON 1

40. Language Arts. Write a letter to someone who is afraid of becoming infected with HIV. Explain behaviors and situations known to transmit HIV and how the virus is prevented.

Applying Health Knowledge

LESSON 1

41. Your friend Sam will be undergoing surgery in a few months that will require several blood transfusions. How much risk does Sam run because of this? How can Sam minimize the risk of receiving blood contaminated with HIV?

42. How can having sex only in a marital relationship minimize the risk of contracting AIDS?

LESSON 2

43. Why is confidentiality an important aspect of HIV testing?

44. Your friend has been engaging in behaviors that could lead to HIV infection. He has had his blood tested for HIV antibodies, and the result has been negative. What should he do next?

Beyond the Classroom

LESSON 1

45. Community Involvement. Where can a person get information about HIV infection and AIDS?

46. Community Involvement. Interview five people in your neighborhood. Ask them what they think are the five primary causes of infection with HIV. Are their ideas based on fact or fiction?

47. Community Involvement. Find out what organizations in your community are helping people with AIDS. Make a list of these organizations and tell what specific steps each is taking to help AIDS patients.

LESSON 2

48. Further Study. At the present time, AIDS is an incurable disease. Many diseases of the past were also incurable until medical researchers found a way to combat them. Choose one of the following diseases and write a report on its history: polio; tuberculosis; pneumonia; bubonic plague; malaria.

tive test means there were no HIV antibodies in the blood at the time of the test.
32. A vaccine.

Thinking Critically

33. A—yes; B—no; C—no; D—yes; E—no; F—no; G—yes; H—no; I—no; J—yes.
34. Answers will vary but should be supported logically.
35. Answers will vary. Possible answers: Fear, apathy.
36. Answers will vary.
37. Answers will vary but should be supported logically.
38. Answers will vary but should be supported logically.
39. Answers will vary but may include the argument that it is necessary for the protection of the organ recipient.

Making the Connection

40. Answers will vary.

Applying Health Knowledge

41. Sam's risk is small because all blood donated in the U.S. is tested for HIV antibodies. Answers will vary. Possible answers: Sam can minimize his risk by having people he knows are not infected donate blood for him ahead of time or by stockpiling his own blood prior to surgery if possible.
42. Answers will vary. Possible answers: The fewer sexual partners one has, the lower one's risk is.
43. Answers will vary. Possible answer: For some people that is the only way they will be tested because of the stigma attached to HIV infection.
44. Avoid behaviors known to transmit HIV and be retested in 6 months.

Beyond the Classroom

45. Answers will vary. Possible answers: Parents, teachers, doctors, the Centers for Disease Control, public health organizations, AIDS hotline.
46. Answers will vary.
47. Answers will vary.
48. Reports will vary.

Lesson Summaries

LESSON 1. Cardiovascular disease is closely related to one's lifestyle. The symptoms and causes of various cardiovascular diseases and stroke are presented in this lesson.

LESSON 2. Instruments and techniques have improved for clearing or bypassing blocked arteries, performing heart transplants, implanting pacemakers, replacing heart valves, and even providing artificial blood vessels. Prevention is best achieved through life-style intervention.

LESSON 3. Generally, all cancers constitute abnormal, uncontrolled cell growth. There are about 250 different types of cancer. Diagnosis is best achieved by a medical exam, though early warning signs can alert one to its presence. Various carcinogens and treatments for cancer exist.

LESSON 4. This lesson describes how diabetes functions and the types of diabetes. Diabetes cannot be cured, though it can be controlled.

LESSON 5. The types and treatment of arthritis are presented in this lesson.

Introducing the Chapter

Ask students to make a list of any 10 diseases. Remind them that a disease that can be passed from one person to another is called a communicable disease. Have students identify the diseases on their lists that a person cannot "catch" from another person. Identify those diseases as noncommunicable diseases. Tell students they will learn about these conditions in this chapter.

Performance Assessment ✓

Refer to pages T 23 to T 25 for a Performance Assessment strategy for this chapter. See the *Performance Assessment Activities* booklet for additional suggestions.

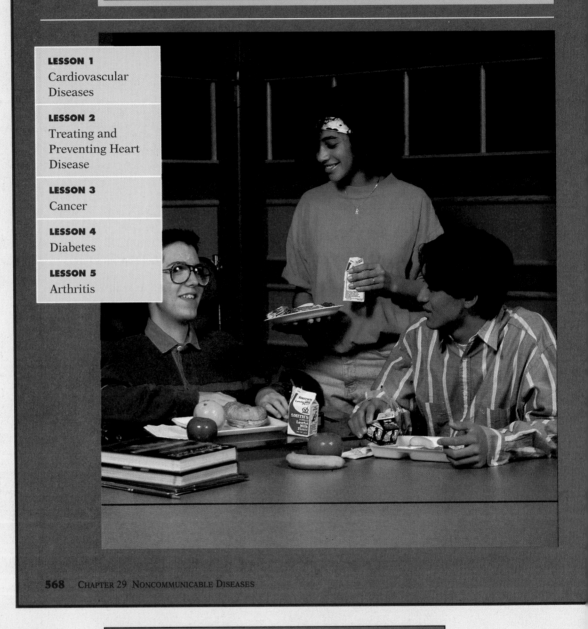

CHAPTER

29 **NONCOMMUNICABLE DISEASES**

LESSON 1
Cardiovascular Diseases

LESSON 2
Treating and Preventing Heart Disease

LESSON 3
Cancer

LESSON 4
Diabetes

LESSON 5
Arthritis

568 CHAPTER 29 NONCOMMUNICABLE DISEASES

Key to Ability Levels

Teaching strategies have been coded for varying learning styles and abilities.

L1 Level 1 activities are basic activities and should be within the ability range of all students.

L2 Level 2 activities are average activities and should be within the ability range of average to above-average students.

L3 Level 3 activities are challenging activities designed for the ability range of above-average students.

LD LD activities should be within the ability range of learning-disabled students.

LEP LEP activities should be within the ability range of Limited English Proficiency students.

CARDIOVASCULAR DISEASES

There are many diseases that are not caused by pathogens. These are **noncommunicable diseases,** meaning diseases that are not transmitted through contact with others. The diseases that are perhaps most closely related to one's life-style are **cardiovascular diseases**—those of the heart and blood vessels. Cardiovascular disease is the number one killer in the United States.

Over half of all Americans die of some form of cardiovascular disease. The importance of this statistic to young people is great because many cardiovascular diseases are the result of life-style choices and health habits that people adopt early in life.

Learning about cardiovascular diseases is also important because knowing how to recognize these diseases, what to do in an emergency, and where to get help may mean the difference between life and death.

Hypertension

Blood pressure is the force of blood against the walls of blood vessels as blood flows through the cardiovascular system. The force is created by the contraction of the heart muscle and the resistance of the vessel walls. Normal blood pressure varies with age, height, weight, and other factors. If a person's blood pressure stays above his or her normal pressure, the person has high blood pressure, or **hypertension.**

Approximately 60 million people have some elevation of blood pressure, and many of them do not know it. Hypertension has been detected in children as young as 6 years old.

Hypertension can be a silent mysterious killer. It is silent, because in early stages there may be no symptoms that alert a person that medical attention is needed. It is mysterious, because in more than 90 percent of all cases the cause is unknown, and because no cure exists. Since there is no cure, prolonged hypertension can result in major complications, such as stroke, heart attack, heart failure, or kidney failure.

Causes

In many cases the exact cause of hypertension is not known. However, many factors have been identified as being related to it. For example, people in highly stressful environments seem to be more susceptible to hypertension. Another factor is heredity. Children of parents who have hypertension will most likely also have high blood pressure.

Another factor that has definitely been identified as a contributor to hypertension is excessive sodium intake. What is excessive? The recommended daily allowance is 3 grams of sodium. One teaspoon of salt provides about 2 grams of sodium. The average American consumes two to three times this amount. Some people have a natural sensitivity to sodium, which elevates blood pressure.

CARDIOVASCULAR DISEASES **569**

LESSON 1 FOCUS

TERMS TO USE
- Noncommunicable diseases
- Cardiovascular diseases
- Hypertension
- Arteriosclerosis (ahr•TIR•ee•oh•skluh• ROH•suhs)
- Atherosclerosis (ath•uh•ROH•skluh• ROH•suhs)
- Angina pectoris (an•JY•nuh PEK•tuh•ruhs)
- Fibrillation (FIB•ruh•LAY•shuhn)
- Stroke

CONCEPTS TO LEARN
- Cardiovascular diseases have serious consequences to a person's life.
- Many cardiovascular diseases are related to a person's habits and life-style.

ATTITUDES AND BEHAVIORS TO EVALUATE
- Self-Inventory, page 592.
- Building Decision-Making Skills, page 593.

Focus

Lesson Objectives
After studying this lesson, students should be able to:
- describe how one's life-style relates to chronic and degenerative diseases
- describe hypertension and identify factors related to it
- define and describe arteriosclerosis
- explain what happens when a person has a heart attack
- explain what happens when a person has a stroke

Bellringer
Write the following on the chalkboard for students to work on while attendance is being taken: *Write a definition for the term* noncommunicable disease *and list three examples of this type of disease.*

Introducing the Lesson
Refer to the Bellringer. Ask volunteers to share their responses. Write the correct definition and the correct examples given by the students on the chalkboard. Explain that this lesson will focus on two noncommunicable diseases—cardiovascular disease and stroke. Tell students this lesson will help them learn the types and causes of these noncommunicable diseases that are the leading causes of death.

DID YOU KNOW?

- Heart-attack victims have a higher rate of survival if they own a pet than if they do not.
- The average time an American has to wait for a heart and lung transplant is 657 days; for a heart, 141 days; for a lung, 327 days.
- When you have an allergic reaction, your heart rate can double.

Resources for Lesson 1

- **Guided Reading** Act 78
- **Workbook** Voc Act 78
- **Reteaching** Activity 78
- **Lesson 1 Quiz**
- **Performance Assessment** Activity 29

Science and Technology Videodisc
Human Biology, Side 1
Ch 5 Blood Clot Treatment

Ch 9 Patient Simulator

Ch 11 Through-the-Skin Heart Drug

Building Vocabulary

- Write each of the vocabulary terms on a 3-by-5 index card. Copy the definitions of these terms as given in the lesson on each of eight more cards. Mix up the cards and give one card to each student. You may need more than one set of cards. When you signal, students should find a match for their term or definition. When they have finished, ask each student pair to read the term and its definition. Have the class verify each match.

- Ask students to complete *Workbook Vocabulary Activity 78.*

Teach

Guided Practice

LD **CLASS ACTIVITY.** LD students may have difficulty reading this lesson independently. Provide a skeletal outline for them to follow and fill in during class discussion.

L2 **DEMONSTRATION.** Bring an anatomical model of a heart to class and demonstrate the chambers of the heart and how cardiovascular problems can occur. Display a chart of the circulatory system and explain how the blood is pumped throughout the body, carrying oxygen and nutrients to each cell.

L2 **CLASS ACTIVITY.** Have students draw a heart and label the parts. Color the oxygenated blood red and the blood without oxygen blue. Use arrows to indicate the direction of the flow through the heart. Students can also use clay to construct a heart.

L1 **DISCUSSION.** How do the life-style choices students are making today (the health habits they have developed and practiced) relate directly to their potential for developing a cardiovascular disease? Is it easier to change unhealthy habits now or when recovering from a heart attack?

High blood pressure, hypertension, is called a silent killer.

As you know, sodium is essential for cellular function, but the body needs it only in small amounts. Most foods contain some sodium without adding table salt. Table salt provides more than enough sodium for almost everyone. You can reduce your sodium intake by checking food labels and limiting foods high in sodium. Taste your food before salting it, and try to substitute other seasonings.

Treatment

Hypertension cannot be cured, but 90 percent of cases can be controlled with medicine and by diet. Diet controls, besides limiting sodium intake, include maintaining desirable weight, reducing sugar consumption, and reducing intake of foods high in cholesterol and saturated fats. Regular exercise also helps reduce blood pressure.

Diseases of the Arteries

At birth the lining of the blood vessels is very smooth. Over the years fatty deposits, called plaque, build up along the inner lining of the arteries. This buildup is due mainly to dietary choices.

Arteriosclerosis

Arteriosclerosis is a condition in which the walls of arteries become thick and lose their elasticity. The condition is commonly called hardening of the arteries. It is by far the most common cause of death in the United States.

Atherosclerosis is a form of arteriosclerosis. Fatty deposits gradually collect in blood vessels. These deposits clog the vessel so that blood flow is affected. As blood flow is slowed, blood tends to thicken. This can result in the formation of a thrombus, or blood clot. In some cases, an embolus may develop. An embolus is a blood clot that moves from the point where it was formed. Fatty deposits, a thrombus, or an embolus can block a blood vessel. If a coronary vessel becomes blocked, the heart

Culturally Speaking

Salt and Hypertension

Some African cultures have a high frequency of salt-sensitive hypertension—blood pressure problems that increase with salt intake. These groups live in areas where salt is scarce, so usually salt is not a problem. However, if salt intake is increased, they may have blood pressure problems. African Americans show even higher frequencies of salt-sensitive hypertension than Africans.

570 CHAPTER 29 NONCOMMUNICABLE DISEASES

Overcoming Misconceptions

Myth. Only people over 40 have heart attacks. **Fact.** Congenital heart defects, diseases, and use of drugs can cause heart attacks at an early age. **Myth.** Most people with heart disease die suddenly. **Fact.** Heart disease is a silent killer and the progression of the disease can take years before actually causing a heart attack. **Myth.** Cigarette smokers do not have a

higher death rate from heart attack than nonsmokers. **Fact.** Smoking does increase the risk of heart attack. It causes the blood vessels to constrict, decreasing blood flow to the cells; increases blood pressure and strains the heart; carbon monoxide released into the blood decreases the oxygen supply in the blood.

Atherosclerosis

Normal artery

Blood flow
Smooth lining

Blood flow
Fatty deposits

Advanced
atherosclerosis

Blood flow
Buildup of
fatty deposits

As fatty deposits collect along artery walls, the flow of blood is seriously affected.

muscle is deprived of the normal supply of oxygen. The result is a heart attack.

Diseases of the Heart

Heart disease, or heart attack, is a common way to refer to a number of disorders that involve the heart and blood vessels.

Heart Attack

A heart attack occurs because the heart muscle cells are not getting the oxygen and nutrients they need. Any part of the heart that does not get nourishment dies. The severity of the heart attack is determined by how much heart tissue dies.

The heart can keep functioning if the damaged area is not too great. Scar tissue will gradually form over the damaged area, and other arteries will assume the work of the blocked ones. However, because scar tissue is not elastic, it does not contract when the heart does, so the heart is never again able to function at its highest capacity.

A heart attack can occur at any time; it usually is sudden and happens without warning. However, immediate response to the early signs of such an attack can mean the difference between life and death. These early signs include discomfort in the center of the chest. The sensation may be one of pressure, fullness, squeezing, or aching. The distress may extend into one or both arms, the neck, jaw, upper abdomen, and even

---

KEEPING FIT

Reducing the Risks of Cardiovascular Disease

- People who smoke a pack of cigarettes a day are twice as likely to have heart attacks as nonsmokers. The risk increases with the amount smoked. Cigarette smoking also

increases a person's risk of having a stroke.
- After quitting smoking, the risk of heart attack becomes the same as that of a nonsmoker.
- Consuming a diet high in fat is

a risk factor in atherosclerosis. Reduce your intake of cholesterol and fat simply by cutting down on butter, mayonnaise, beef, pork, and lamb.

CARDIOVASCULAR DISEASES **571**

Additional Information

Heart Disease. The gender gap in cardiovascular disease is narrowing. Once thought to be primarily a man's disease, heart disease now leads all other causes of death in women. Just fewer than one-half of those who die of heart disease are women. The same risk factors that for years have put men at risk for heart attacks now affect women equally: smoking, high-fat diet, stress, sedentary lifestyle. Additionally, women who smoke and take oral contraceptives are 39 times more likely to experience a heart attack than women who do neither. The good news is that, by controlling risk factors, women as well as men can reduce their chances of developing heart disease.

L1 **CLASS ACTIVITY.** Have students fold a sheet of paper into three columns. In the first column have students list the noncommunicable diseases that might be caused by how people live. In the second column have them list the diseases that could be caused by a problem a person is born with. In the third, have them list the diseases that might be caused by hazards in the environment. Ask students which diseases people have the most control over. Have them explain their answers.

L1 **COOPERATIVE LEARNING.** Have students form groups. Provide each with a poster board. Have one group feature the warning signs of stroke. Have another list factors including stress that are responsible in the occurrence of stroke. Have another list the effects of stroke on the body and life of an individual. Have another make a list of healthful behaviors that can reduce the possibility for having a stroke.

Independent Practice

L2 **RESEARCH.** Have students make a chart of foods preferred by teens and society as a whole. Have students include the number of calories and amount of cholesterol in each.

L1 **PARENTAL INVOLVEMENT.** Ask students to take home a copy of the RISCO health appraisal from the American Heart Association. Have them explain the factors on the health appraisal to their parents. Have students take the RISCO health appraisal with their parents to determine their risk of cardiovascular disease. Encourage the parents to also determine their level of risk. Have students and parents discuss ways to reduce their risk of heart disease.

L1 **PARENTAL INVOLVEMENT.** Ask students to discuss with their family what changes would occur in a family when any member suffers from a cardiovascular disease. (Diet change, reduction of salt and fat intake, increase in exercise, stress management, and smoking cessation.) Why do individuals wait for cardiovascular disease to occur before making the changes that would have prevented the disease? Have the family develop a plan to make healthful choices to avoid cardiovascular disease.

Electrical shock may be given to someone with ventricular fibrillation.

the back. Nausea, vomiting, sweating, and shortness of breath may also accompany the attack.

A person can easily mistake some of these signs for other problems, such as heartburn or indigestion. Self-diagnosis in this case could be fatal. A person with these symptoms should seek medical attention immediately.

Angina Pectoris

Many people who have atherosclerosis experience a condition known as angina pectoris. In the case of **angina pectoris,** pain and tightness or pressure in the chest occur as a result of the heart's not getting enough oxygen. People who have never had a heart attack may experience angina pains, which are intense attacks of chest pain. Medication can relieve the pain. In addition, these people may have to limit their physical activity to avoid the pain.

Fibrillation

Fibrillation is a rhythmic disturbance that occurs when the muscle fibers of the heart contract in an uncoordinated manner. The rhythm is irregular and is usually at a very fast rate.

K E E P I N G   F I T

Reducing the Risks of Cardiovascular Disease

Don't watch ball games, play them. Even though watching games can be exciting, the games you watch do nothing for your heart, lungs, or weight. But the ball games you play—softball, football, tennis, handball, racquetball, basketball or volleyball—do help. Stop being a fan and start being a player. You'll find that the game is far more exciting from the inside!

Additional Information

Stroke. Due to improving diagnosis and treatment of strokes, the survival rate has increased by more than 50 percent in the last 20 years. As with heart attacks, early recognition and medical intervention are keys to surviving a stroke. With increasing survival rates, stroke victims are requiring more rehabilitative assistance. When speech is lost, a stroke victim requires speech therapy to learn to understand and use spoken language. When muscle strength and coordination are lost, a stroke victim requires physical therapy. When job skills are lost, occupational therapy is needed to learn new job skills. For fun and motivation, recreational therapy provides sports, games, and mental activities.

When this condition occurs in the ventricles, it is called ventricular fibrillation. If not corrected it is usually fatal because the ventricles stop pumping blood efficiently out of the heart. Doctors can sometimes correct ventricular fibrillation by sending a powerful jolt of electricity into the heart muscle. The treatment is successful if the heart muscle responds by resuming normal rhythm.

Fibrillation can occur in the atria, the upper chambers of the heart. Although this is a serious condition, blood can continue to flow into the ventricles and be pumped out if the ventricles are still functioning.

Cardiac Arrest

Cardiac arrest occurs when the heart stops completely. In the case of cardiac arrest, circulation stops, and the brain can live for only about five minutes.

If cardiac arrest occurs in the hospital, the doctors and hospital staff will attempt external heart massage first. If that procedure does not revive the heart, electrical shock may be administered.

If cardiac arrest occurs, medical help is needed immediately. The victim's life may be saved if someone administers cardiopulmonary resuscitation (CPR) until medical help is available. This lifesaving skill, explained in Chapter 36, forces blood out of the heart and into the arteries. It includes mouth-to-mouth resuscitation, so that the victim gets oxygen. Only someone properly trained in the technique should administer CPR.

Stroke

A **stroke** occurs when the blood supply to a part of the brain is cut off and, as a result, the nerve cells in that part of the brain cannot function. In order to function, brain cells must have a continuous and ample supply of oxygen and nutrients. If brain cells are deprived for five minutes, they will die. The nerve cells of the brain control most of our body movements and the way we receive and interpret sensations.

Any part of the body can be affected by a stroke—it all depends on what area of the brain was deprived of oxygen and nutrients. Because the brain controls the body's movement, a stroke may affect any part of the body. Suppose an artery is blocked in the area of the brain that controls speaking. Then speech will be affected. If the blocked area controls leg muscles, then those muscles will be affected. Even memory can be affected.

Sometimes a stroke will have little effect on the person. At other times the effect will be severe. Some people recover quickly, while others may not recover at all.

Interference with blood supply to the brain may be due to a number of causes. It is not always possible to determine the particular cause of a stroke.

Cerebral Thrombosis

One of the most common causes of stroke is the blocking of a cerebral artery by a thrombus that forms inside the artery. This condition is

L3 **READING.** Select students to read about and report on the roles sodium and cholesterol play on cardiovascular disease. Have them explain the importance of reading food labels.

L2 **RESEARCH.** Ask students to research athletes who have suffered heart attacks at a young age while performing in their sports. Were any related to drug use, including steroids?

L2 **RESEARCH.** Ask students to determine the steps of first aid for a person complaining of chest pain, shortness of breath, and weakness. Have students make a chart of the ABCs of CPR. Students can contact the American Red Cross or the American Heart Association for materials, including posters for the class. Share and display the materials.

L2 **RESEARCH.** Ask students to research the changes in the leading causes of death since 1900 in the U.S. Ask them to explain what this tells us about how life-styles have changed over the decades.

L2 **RESEARCH.** Have students research and report on local medical assistance available to stroke victims.

L3 **RESEARCH.** Select students to research the relationship of strokes to the following risk factors: obesity, high-fat diets, and smoking.

L3 **RESEARCH.** Ask students to research the most recent statistical data on the number of deaths related to heart disease and stroke. Have students make a bar graph indicating the increase in the number of deaths from these two diseases over the past 50 years.

L3 **READING.** Assign students to read articles about transient ischemic attacks, or TIAs—warning signs of an impending stroke. Have them research the treatments used for TIAs. Select other students to report on stroke-preventing procedures.

L1 **USING THE LESSON RESOURCES.** For additional student activities, refer to the lesson resources on page 569.

Additional Information

Blood Pressure. Blood pressure is expressed as two numbers, X over Y. X is the blood's pressure against the arteries when the heart is contracting and is called the systolic pressure. Y is the pressure against the arteries in between contractions, when the heart is resting; it is called the diastolic pressure. A healthy teen or adult has a blood pressure in the range of 120/80, read "120 over 80." During heavy exercise, both the systolic and diastolic pressures rise. The instrument for measuring blood pressure is called a sphygmomanometer. Low blood pressure can be as unhealthy as high blood pressure. It causes transient lightheadedness, dizziness, and even fainting.

- Assign and discuss the lesson review. Encourage LD students to focus on questions 1, 2, 3, 5, and 6.

Evaluate

- Administer, grade, and discuss the *Lesson 1 Quiz*.

Reteach

- Ask students to define *cardiovascular disease* and list the types and causes of the disease studied in this lesson. Relate high blood pressure to heart disease and stroke.
- Ask students to complete *Reteaching Activity 78*.

Enrich

- Have each student choose a particular congenital heart disease and write a brief report about it, including what causes it and what types of treatment are available.

Close

Have students recall the major concepts of this lesson. Clarify any misconceptions.

DID YOU KNOW?

- Almost 62 million Americans have high blood pressure.
- Children over the age of 2 should have their blood cholesterol monitored if either parent's cholesterol level is over 240 or if a parent or grandparent had cardiovascular disease before age 55.

---

known as cerebral thrombosis. Sometimes the thrombus occurs in one of the four neck arteries that supply the brain with blood.

A clot is not likely to occur in a healthy artery. One may occur in an artery that has been damaged by atherosclerosis.

Cerebral Embolism

A cerebral embolism occurs if an embolus becomes wedged in one of the cerebral arteries. The result is an interference with the flow of blood to the brain.

Cerebral Hemorrhage

A diseased artery in the brain can burst and flood the surrounding brain tissue with blood. This condition is called a cerebral hemorrhage. The brain cells that the artery nourished do not get the food and oxygen they need. A cerebral hemorrhage is more likely to occur when a person suffers from a combination of atherosclerosis and high blood pressure.

Warning Signs of a Stroke

Following are the major signs of a stroke:

- sudden, temporary weakness or numbness of the face, arm, and leg on one side of the body
- temporary loss of speech, or trouble in speaking or understanding people
- temporary dimness or loss of vision, particularly in one eye
- unexplained dizziness, unsteadiness, or sudden falls.

If you notice one or more of these signs, be sure to tell your doctor.

LESSON 1 REVIEW

Reviewing Facts and Vocabulary

1. What factors are associated with hypertension?
2. How does atherosclerosis develop?
3. Define *thrombus* and *embolus*.

Thinking Critically

4. **Evaluation.** Why do you think that the noncommunicable diseases have replaced the communicable diseases as the leading causes of death?
5. **Analysis.** How is a heart attack different from a stroke?

Applying Health Knowledge

6. If you or someone you know is in a high-risk group for heart disease, what life-style changes could you suggest to reduce the risks of heart attack? Design a poster that lists those factors that could be changed to reduce the risks of developing cardiovascular disease or suffering a heart attack.
7. Research a recent discovery or development in heart surgery. Write a one-page descriptive report on your findings.

574 CHAPTER 29 NONCOMMUNICABLE DISEASES

Answers to Lesson 1 Review

1. Stress, heredity, diet (especially excessive sodium intake).
2. Fatty deposits called plaque build up along the inner lining of the arteries.
3. Thrombus—a blood clot; embolus—a moving blood clot.
4. Answers will vary. Possible answer: Immunizations and modern medicines have helped control communicable dis-

eases, but noncommunicable diseases are related to one's life-style and health habits.
5. Answers will vary. Possible answer: A stroke damages brain cells, but a heart attack damages heart tissue.
6. Posters will vary.
7. Reports will vary.

TREATING AND PREVENTING HEART DISEASE

I n recent years amazing advances have been made in treating heart disease. However, medical professionals still believe that preventive measures are the best solution.

Instruments and Techniques

An **electrocardiogram** (EKG or ECG) produces a graph of the electrical activity of the heart. The resulting pattern indicates the heart activity and rhythm. An EKG can help detect the nature of a heart attack and how the heart is behaving. It can indicate if the heart is beating regularly or irregularly, fast or slow, and if the heartbeat is weak or strong.

Phonocardiography involves placing a microphone on a person's chest to record heart sounds and signals, transferring them through photography to graph paper. A professional can then examine the tracings for heartbeat irregularities.

Coronary angiography is a procedure that is used to help evaluate the extent of coronary artery disease. This procedure uses a catheter, which is a thin, flexible tube that can be guided through blood vessels to certain body organs. When checking the vessels and chambers of the heart, the catheter is first inserted into an artery or a vein in either an arm or a leg. Then it is threaded to the aorta and through a coronary artery. When dye is injected into the catheter, X rays can be taken with a fluoroscope. A **fluoroscope** is similar to an X-ray machine except that it gives a moving image instead of a still photograph. This moving image allows narrow or obstructed areas of the heart to be detected.

An EKG is a recording of the electrical changes during a cardiac cycle, which is a complete heartbeat.

TREATING AND PREVENTING HEART DISEASE **575**

LESSON 2 FOCUS

TERMS TO USE

- Electrocardiogram (EKG or ECG) (i•LEK•troh•KAHRD•ee•uh•GRAM)
- Phonocardiography (FOH•nuh•KAHRD•ee•AHG•ruh•fee)
- Coronary angiography
- Fluoroscope (FLUR•uh•SKOHP)
- Balloon angioplasty
- Coronary bypass surgery

CONCEPTS TO LEARN

- Many preventive measures can be taken to reduce the risks of cardiovascular diseases.
- Your daily decisions about diet and exercise can do much to prevent cardiovascular diseases later in life.

ATTITUDES AND BEHAVIORS TO EVALUATE

- Self-Inventory, page 592.
- Building Decision-Making Skills, page 593.

Focus

Lesson Objectives

After studying this lesson, students should be able to:
- describe instruments and techniques for treating heart disease
- identify preventive measures for heart disease

Bellringer

Write the following on the chalkboard for students to work on while attendance is being taken: *Write two sentences about the prevention and treatment of heart disease.*

Introducing the Lesson

Have students share their responses to the Bellringer. Students should understand that heart disease can be prevented and treated effectively. This lesson will provide information on the importance of prevention and describe the types of treatment available for heart disease.

Building Vocabulary

- Write the vocabulary terms on the chalkboard. Ask students to rewrite the terms on a sheet of paper in alphabetical order. Then ask them to circle individual words that begin with the same letter and count the number of letters they need to scan to determine correct order for these words. (a: angiography and angioplasty (6 letters); b: balloon and bypass (2 letters)
- Ask students to complete *Workbook Vocabulary Activity 79.*

DID YOU KNOW?

- People who drink alcohol are more likely to have high blood pressure than people who do not.
- Smoking and alcohol both increase the rate of strokes. So does the use of cocaine.
- Men develop heart disease earlier than women, but women after menopause are just as likely to die as men from cardiovascular disease.

Resources for Lesson 2

- **Guided Reading** Act 79
- **Workbook** Voc Act 79
- **Reteaching** Activity 79
- **Lesson 2 Quiz**

Science and Technology Videodisc
Human Biology, Side 1
Ch 6 Heart Valve Balloon

Ch 7 Heart By-Pass Surgery

Ch 10 Electric Heart

Guided Practice

LD EXPLANATION. Due to the complexity of this lesson, hold LD students responsible only for the section on the prevention of heart disease.

L1 EXPLANATION. Explain the process of ventricular fibrillation.

L1 EXPLANATION. Contrast the artificial pacemaker and the implantable defibrillator.

L1 EXPLANATION. Bypasses and transplants are both types of open-heart surgery, which requires that a doctor operate directly on the heart. The first surgery of this kind was done in 1952. The first heart transplant was done in 1967. The first time an artificial heart was given to someone was in 1982.

L2 DISCUSSION. Ask students what a fluoroscope is. How does it differ from a chest X-ray machine? What are some symptoms of disease that it can detect?

L1 EXPLANATION. Explain that in 1980, more than 135,000 coronary artery bypass operations were performed. According to the Harvard Medical School, about 200,000 people undergo bypass surgery each year in the U.S. In 1988 an estimated 353,000 were performed in the U.S. Death rates from this type of surgery range from 1 to 2 percent in major medical centers.

L1 EXPLANATION. Explain the procedure of coronary bypass surgery. What is its purpose?

L2 DISCUSSION. Ask students what the definition of a risk factor is. What are some risk factors over which you have no control? What are some factors that can be controlled to avoid heart disease and stroke?

L1 DISCUSSION. Ask what a catheter is. How is it used in cardiac catheterization?

L2 DISCUSSION. Ask what an angiocardiography is. Why is it often considered the most valuable tool in a coronary-care unit?

L2 DISCUSSION. Ask students what risk factor is considered the single most important factor in atherosclerosis. Have students name some simple ways to reduce their intake of cholesterol and fat.

Recently ultrasound, or high-frequency sound waves, has been used with catheters to collect images of the heart.

If the doctor detects a blocked artery, then balloon angioplasty can be performed at the same time. **Balloon angioplasty** involves threading a balloon-tipped catheter through the body to the site of the blockage. As the balloon is inflated, it pushes the plaque against the artery wall, opening a path for the blood to flow through.

Open-Heart Surgery

In 1952 the first successful open-heart surgery was performed by an American surgeon, Dr. F. John Lewis. He used ice to lower body temperature and to slow circulation to lessen the heart's need for oxygen. A heart-lung machine performs the job of the heart and lungs for several hours during such an operation. The development of this machine has resulted in many advances in open-heart surgery.

Coronary Bypass Surgery

In 1967 a surgical technique for treating heart disease—coronary bypass surgery—was introduced to the medical profession. **Coronary bypass surgery** creates detours around obstructed or narrowed coronary arteries so that more blood can reach the heart.

In this operation a portion of a vein is removed from the patient's leg. One end of the vein is connected to the coronary vessel below the blocked area. This allows blood to flow to the area that was not getting enough blood.

Heart Transplants

Imagine having your heart completely removed and another one put in its place. In South Africa in 1967 Dr. Christiaan Barnard first used

Coronary Bypass

Left atrium

Damaged coronary artery

Left ventricle

Point of connection of transplanted vein

Bypassed area

Point of connection of transplanted vein

Across the Curriculum

Science. Have students research the history of transplantation. People have always been interested in replacing parts of the human body. A thirteenth-century medieval story tells of a leg being transplanted from a deceased Moor to a Christian who lost a leg. Begin the research here and write the progression of organ transplantation to the current status in the United States. Include information on procurement of organs relating to the Uniform Anatomical Gift Act of 1960 and the current procedures for organ procurement.

the heart transplant procedure. Most patients died within the first year, however, mainly because their bodies rejected the organ.

The Artificial Pacemaker

The heart has a natural pacemaker responsible for initiating electrical impulses that cause the heart to beat. When something interferes with this natural pacemaker, regular, strong heartbeats are not initiated.

An artificial pacemaker is a small unit that is implanted in the chest muscle and wired to the heart. It transmits an electrical impulse to the heart, causing the heart to beat. Many pacemakers are battery-operated, and the batteries must be replaced every four to five years. In the 1970s surgeons began using nuclear-powered and rechargeable battery-powered pacemakers.

Heart Valve Surgery

Valves control the proper flow of blood through the heart. Defective valves may be present at birth or develop later in life. A valve may be too tight, in which case the flow of blood is restricted. Or, a valve may not close tightly enough, which can cause blood to flow backwards.

A common surgical procedure involves replacing a defective valve. Three types of valves can be used to surgically replace a nonfunctioning valve. One type is a valve from a pig's heart and functions like a human valve. Another is a transplanted human valve. The third is a cage-ball valve, which involves a heat-treated carbon ball enclosed in a tiny stainless steel cage. This valve is sewn into the heart and allows blood to pass in only one direction. The pressure from the blood as it tries to flow backward forces the ball into the mouth of the cage, closing the valve.

Artificial Hearts and Blood Vessels

In the United States in 1982 a man whose heart was expected to collapse within hours was given the first artificial heart as a stopgap measure until a human transplant was arranged. Experiments involving the development of an artificial heart are still ongoing.

Some scientists are now working on a device that would duplicate the work of the left ventricle. This part of the heart often wears out before

A cage-ball valve allows a normal flow of blood through the heart.

Check for Understanding

- Assign and discuss the lesson review. Exempt LD students, and instead have them list and discuss the five risk factors they can control.

Evaluate

- Administer, grade, and discuss the *Lesson 2 Quiz.*

Reteach

- Have students list the factors that cause heart disease and specify which ones they can/cannot change. Have students develop a plan with their parents on the behaviors they will change to reduce the possibility of heart disease.
- Ask students to complete *Reteaching Activity* 79.

Enrich

- Have students investigate the use of an aspirin a day as a means of preventing strokes and heart attacks. What studies have been done? What are the potential risks of such a regimen? Have students write summaries of their findings along with their recommendations regarding the use of aspirin.

Close

Have students recall what techniques are used for treating heart disease and preventive measures they can take.

the other parts. The device would pump blood into the aorta for distribution throughout the body. Presently, experiments are being done on artificial blood vessels. If the research is successful, 300,000 to 500,000 people may benefit from these artificial vessels each year.

Prevention of Heart Disease

So far, the focus has been on identifying heart disease—its causes and signs, its care and treatment. These are all important areas and many lives have been saved through scientific and medical advances.

However, prevention offers the most promise. To help prevent cardiovascular diseases, it is necessary to look at the risk factors associated with contracting these diseases. A risk factor is a characteristic that has been shown to increase the chances of contracting a disease.

Obviously, you have no control over the factors of age, sex, race, and family medical history. However, you can significantly lower your risk by paying attention to the factors over which you do have control.

- People who smoke a pack of cigarettes a day are twice as likely to have heart attacks as nonsmokers. The risk increases with the amount smoked. Smoking also increases a person's risk of having a stroke.
- Within two years of giving up smoking, the risk of heart attack drops significantly. Within 10 to 15 years, the ex-smoker's risk of heart attack is no greater than that of a nonsmoker.
- Diet is an important factor in atherosclerosis. Reduce your intake of cholesterol and fat by cutting down on butter, mayonnaise, and fried foods. Choose a diet with plenty of vegetables, fruits, and grain products.
- Being overweight or obese is a contributive factor to heart disease. A middle-aged overweight person is two to three times more likely to have heart disease than a person of normal weight.
- Sodium intake is directly related to hypertension. You can control it by not adding salt to food and limiting your intake of salty foods.
- People who exercise regularly reduce their risk of heart disease.
- Managing stress in your daily life can be an important factor in reducing your risk of heart disease.

LESSON 2 REVIEW

Reviewing Facts and Vocabulary

1. How does an artificial pacemaker work?
2. Define and describe *balloon angioplasty*.
3. List at least seven ways of treating heart disease.

Thinking Critically

4. **Analysis.** Compare two types of artificial valves used during surgery.

Applying Health Knowledge

5. Investigate the kinds of chemicals that are injected during cardiac catheterization. What purpose does each serve? Are there any health risks associated with using these chemicals?
6. Heart transplants and artificial hearts are in the news almost daily. Look for articles in newspapers and magazines about this subject. Display the articles on a classroom bulletin board.

578 CHAPTER 29 NONCOMMUNICABLE DISEASES

Answers to Lesson 2 Review

1. It transmits an electrical impulse to the heart, causing it to beat.
2. It is a procedure in which a balloon-tipped catheter is used to push plaque against the artery wall to open a path for blood to flow through.
3. See pages 576 to 578.
4. Both types of valves used in surgery control the flow of blood through the heart.
5. Answers will vary.
6. Articles will vary.

CANCER

C ancer is the second leading cause of death among adults in the United States. Cancer is not one disease, but many diseases, and it is difficult to define cancer by using only one definition. Generally, all **cancers** constitute abnormal, uncontrolled cell growth. Cancer cells are more powerful than normal cells because they can travel beyond their environment and invade other cells. In the process of growth, the cancer cells take over and destroy normal cells and tissues.

Cell division produces new cells; however, some cell divisions result in abnormal cells. Abnormal cells reproduce by dividing, but not at a controlled rate as do normal cells. The uncontrollable division of abnormal cells produces more abnormal cells.

As these cells reproduce and multiply, a mass of tissue, called a **tumor,** develops. Some of these tumors are **benign,** that is, noncancerous. They do not spread to healthy tissue or other parts of the body. Other tumors are **malignant,** or cancerous. Malignant tumors invade and eventually destroy surrounding healthy tissue.

Cancer cells can break away from a malignant tumor and move through lymph or blood vessels to other parts of the body. New tumors, called secondary tumors, can then develop. This process of cancer cells spreading is called **metastasis.** Once a tumor has metastasized, it is very difficult to control. This is the reason early detection of cancer is so important. The sooner cancer is detected, the better the odds are of curing it. Today, half of all cancer cases are curable.

Types of Cancer

About 100 different kinds of cancer affect humans. Cancers are classified in two ways: by the part of the body where the cancer cells first develop, and by the type of body tissue within which the cancer begins.

Cancers that develop in epithelial tissue, tissue that forms the skin and linings of body organs, are called carcinomas. Sarcomas are cancers that develop in connective and supportive tissues such as bones, muscles, and tendons. Lymphomas are cancers that develop in the lymphatic system. Hodgkin's disease is a type of lymphoma.

Diagnosing Cancer

During a physical examination, a doctor can detect many types of cancer. This is one reason regular physical exams are important. If a tumor is found, a physician may do a biopsy. A **biopsy** is the removal of a small amount of tissue that is examined for the presence of abnormal cells. A doctor can check for cervical cancer in women by ordering a Pap smear. The Pap smear detects unusual cells or potentially cancerous tissue long before any symptoms might appear.

LESSON 3 FOCUS

TERMS TO USE

- Cancers
- Tumor
- Benign
- Malignant (muh•LIG•nuhnt)
- Metastasis(muh•TAS• tuh•suhs)
- Biopsy
- Melanoma
- Chemotherapy

CONCEPTS TO LEARN

- There are several warning signs of cancer.
- Early diagnosis of cancer is important so that appropriate treatment can begin.
- An increasing number of kinds of cancer are curable.
- Life-style, environment, and genetic factors can increase an individual's risk of developing cancer.

ATTITUDES AND BEHAVIORS TO EVALUATE

- Self-Inventory, page 592.
- Building Decision-Making Skills, page 593.

CANCER **579**

Focus

Lesson Objectives

After studying this lesson, students should be able to:
- explain how cancer develops
- describe cancer symptoms and treatment
- identify known carcinogens
- discuss what is being done to combat cancer in the U.S.

Bellringer

Write the following on the chalkboard for students to work on while attendance is being taken: *List three types of cancer.* (Examples: skin, colon, rectum, lung, breast, prostate, cervix, leukemia.)

Introducing the Lesson

Ask students to share their responses to the Bellringer. Introduce this lesson by stating that cancer is the second leading cause of death among adults in the U.S. Cancer is unique because it is not a single disease but many diseases. Tell students this lesson will examine the basics of what is currently known about various kinds of cancers, the known causes of cancer, treatment for the disease, and the little that is known regarding prevention.

DID YOU KNOW?

- A promising new vaccine in the works may help stop the growth of malignant melanoma, the deadliest of skin cancers. It works by boosting the immune system's ability to destroy tumor cells.
- Malignant melanoma has increased 1,500 percent since 1935.
- For every 1 percent decrease in ozone—the layer of the atmosphere that blocks the sun's ultraviolet rays—there is between a 3 to 6 percent increase in skin cancer.

Resources for Lesson 3

- **Transparency** 22
- **Guided Reading** Act 80
Science and Technology Videodisc
Human Biology, Side 2
Ch 18 Laser Treatment of Bladder Cancer

- **Workbook** Voc Act 80
- **Reteaching** Act 80
- **Lesson 3 Quiz**
ABC News InterActive Videodiscs
Tobacco, Side 1
Ch 6 Lung Cancer Victim: Roger Sharp

- Instruct students to attempt to write the correct spelling for each of the vocabulary terms as you pronounce them. Next, have students exchange papers with their neighbors and correct them as you read aloud the proper spelling of the terms. Have students locate the vocabulary terms in the Glossary and define each term.
- Ask students to complete *Workbook Vocabulary Activity 80.*

Teach

Guided Practice

L2 DISCUSSION. Ask students how cancer cells differ from normal cells. What do cancer cells do during their growth process?

L1 DISCUSSION. Ask why it's difficult to present a single definition of cancer.

L1 DISCUSSION. Ask students to explain the process of metastasis.

L1 EXPLANATION. Cancer is classified in two ways: (1) from the part of the body where the cancer cells first developed; (2) from the type of body tissue where the cancer begins.

L1 DISCUSSION. Have students explain the difference between a benign tumor and a malignant one. (A benign tumor is not cancerous; a malignant tumor is.) Stress that any tumor should be examined by a doctor.

L1 COOPERATIVE LEARNING. Divide the class into four groups. Give one of the following topics to each group: cancer treatment with radiation, treatment with surgery, treatment with chemotherapy, treatment being studied or experimented with. Have groups research their treatment, finding out the latest information available. Each group should present a 5- to 10-minute presentation of its findings.

L1 EXPLANATION. On the chalkboard, list several known carcinogens, such as radiation, tobacco, toxic waste, and certain food additives.

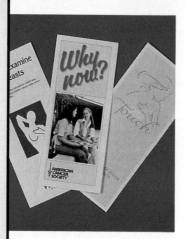

Regular self-examinations help prevent cancer. Your doctor will have pamphlets that show you how.

Identification of colon and rectal cancer has improved as a result of two developments: the fecal occult blood test and the flexible fiberoptic endoscope. The development of the computerized axial tomography (CAT) scan and magnetic resonance imaging (MRI), two techniques that provide clearer, more detailed images than ordinary X rays, are also used to detect cancer.

Cancer's Warning Signs

Early detection of cancer is the most critical factor in treating or curing the disease. The individual should be alert to the seven warning signs of cancer.

- **C**hange in bowel habit. Either loose stools, or constipation.
- **A** sore that does not heal.
- **U**nusual bleeding or discharge (as from the uterus, bladder, bowels, or with coughing).
- **T**hickening or a lump in the breast, or elsewhere (let your doctor decide what the lump means).
- **I**ndigestion or difficulty in swallowing.
- **O**bvious change in a wart or mole.
- **N**agging cough or hoarseness.
  Other symptoms include fatigue and unexplained weight loss.

Carcinogens

Carcinogens are substances that cause cancer. Carcinogens include many chemicals, such as those in tobacco smoke. Asbestos is also a known carcinogen. Radiation from X rays, exposure to the ultraviolet rays in sunlight, and certain viruses are also cancer-causing substances. Some dietary factors such as contaminated water may also be substances. Not everyone is equally susceptible to the same carcinogen. You can control your exposure to, and ingestion of, many carcinogens.

Despite the documented dangers of exposure to the sun, millions of Americans continue to bask in it and increase their risk of developing **melanoma,** or skin cancer. People who work out-of-doors and people who have fair skin are particularly susceptible to skin cancer. This is the reason those people need to use sunscreen lotions that protect the skin from the ultraviolet rays of the sun.

Although radiation is often used in the treatment of cancer, it is in itself a cancer-producing agent in humans. The overuse of X rays in past years exposed people unnecessarily to potential harm from radiation.

K E E P I N G   F I T

Avoiding Unnecessary Cancer Risks

Many cancer specialists recommend that people follow these guidelines to avoid unnecessary cancer risks:
- Maintain an ideal weight.

- Limit your consumption of preserved foods.
- Limit your consumption of prepared meats.
- Avoid artificial sweeteners.

- Limit foods with artificial flavors and colors.
- Increase dietary fiber and bulk.
- Limit your time in the sun.
- Avoid using all forms of tobacco.

580 CHAPTER 29 NONCOMMUNICABLE DISEASES

Additional Information

Cancer. The American Cancer Society estimates the following statistics for cancer deaths in 1993.

Cancer Deaths by Site for Males.
Lung, 93,000; Prostate, 35,000; Colon and Rectum, 28,800; Pancreas, 12,000; Lymphoma, 11,500; Leukemia, 10,100; Stomach, 8,200; Esophagus, 7,600; Bladder,

6,500; Kidney, 6,500; Liver, 6,800; Brain, 6,600; All Sites, 277,000.
Cancer Deaths by Site for Females.
Lung, 56,000; Breast, 46,000; Colon and Rectum, 28,200; Pancreas, 13,000; Ovary, 13,300; Uterus, 10,100; Lymphoma, 10,500; Leukemia, 8,500; Liver, 5,800; Brain, 5,500; Stomach, 5,400; Multiple Myeloma, 4,600; All Sites, 249,000.

We are constantly being exposed to the cosmic rays in the universe, so any unnecessary exposure through X rays is unwise. When considered absolutely necessary in medicine, X rays are used in diagnosis.

Our quality of health is directly related to the air we breathe. Lung cancer has shown the greatest increase of any form of cancer in the past 35 years. The increase in lung cancer is due essentially to smoking tobacco. In addition, air pollution caused by industrial wastes and automobile exhausts is a source of lung cancer concern.

The decision about cigarette smoking is an individual one. Air pollution from industrial sources is really a matter of community responsibility.

DIFFERENT TYPES OF CANCER

Body-Site Type	Organ(s) Most Often Affected	Occurrence
Skin cancer	Skin	Most common type in United States
Digestive system	Colon and rectum	Second most common type in United States
Respiratory system	Larynx and lungs	Occurs mainly in males; increase in incidence of lung cancer in females
Breast	Breast	Occurs mostly in females
Reproductive system	Males—prostate gland, testicles Females—cervix, ovaries, uterus	
Blood and lymph system	Bone marrow, lymph	Occurs in males and females

Treatment of Cancer

Treatment of cancers is directed at confining and killing the cancerous cells. At present, this is accomplished by three basic approaches: surgery, radiation, and chemotherapy.

Surgery

Surgery has been a standard method used for removing tumors and affected areas. Today with improved surgical techniques cancer patients have a longer life expectancy and an improved quality of life. For example, amputation used to be standard practice for treating cancer of arm and leg bones. One way doctors can successfully treat many patients is by removing the diseased bone tissue and transplanting healthy bone tissue from another part of the patient's body.

CANCER **581**

CONFLICT RESOLUTION

Tina is being treated for cancer and has lost most of her hair. "Sometimes when I go out," she says, "I won't cover up my head just to see what people will say about my baldness. Little kids don't know any better, so I don't mind when they stare and point at me. It's their parents' attitudes that I can't stand—they tell the kids not to stare and then turn around to stare themselves. I've heard people say I'm a drug addict, a skinhead, or I shaved my head on purpose just to get attention. It really makes me mad to overhear total strangers talking about me like that. I like it a lot better when people come right up to me and ask me why I'm bald."

In what ways do you think Tina and other cancer patients would like to be treated?

Additional Information

Cancer Diagnosis. Over a million Americans face a diagnosis of cancer every year. It strikes fear unlike almost any other diagnosis. Not too many years ago, a diagnosis of cancer was the equivalent of a death sentence. In the early 1900s, only 1 in 10 cancer victims had any hope of long-term survival. But today survival statistics promise a more optimistic outlook. Now almost half of all cancer victims will be alive 5 years after diagnosis. The odds of recovery from cancer are closely tied to how early the cancer is detected. Self-detection has led to early diagnosis of some tumors. During the teen years girls should begin breast self-exams and boys should begin testicular self-exams.

Someone undergoing bone marrow transplantation is carefully protected from possible infection.

Radiation

Radiation energy from cobalt or radium can penetrate a tumor. The energy destroys the tumor cells by damaging DNA in the nuclei. DNA is responsible for cell division.

With radiation therapy there is always the risk of causing damage to normal cells near the cancerous area. However, with today's more sophisticated equipment, doctors are able to aim radiation more directly at tumors while sparing surrounding healthy cells.

Radiation therapy is very successful in arresting certain kinds of cancer, such as cervical cancer. It is also very helpful in areas of the body where surgery is difficult, such as the head and neck.

Chemotherapy

Chemotherapy is the use of anticancer medications in the treatment of cancer. The goal of chemotherapy is to destroy malignant cells without excessive destruction of normal cells.

Anticancer medicines interfere with cell division of the cancer cells. The idea is that if the medicine can break up the process of growth, the cancer will not spread.

Unfortunately, some unpleasant side effects, such as nausea and vomiting, occur with the use of these strong medicines. However, new

---

HEALTH UPDATE

LOOKING AT THE ISSUES

Do Electromagnetic Fields Cause Cancer?

Sometimes research results are contradictory or inconclusive, and they may take years, even decades, to sort out. An example of one such debate is whether or not there is a link between electromagnetic fields (EMFs) and cancer. EMFs are emitted from power lines, computer monitors, microwave ovens, other home appliances, or any time an electric current passes through a wire.

Analyzing Different Viewpoints

ONE VIEW. Many people believe that claims of the dangers of EMFs are unfounded, even hysterical. They say the exposure from standard power lines and appliances is minimal.

A SECOND VIEW. Some people believe that exposure to EMFs can be linked to birth defects, high incidences of miscarriage, and even increased cancer rates.

A THIRD VIEW. Some people and organizations remain unsure and cautious. Many experts feel the evidence is unclear and more studies are needed to make definitive claims about the EMF/cancer link.

Exploring Your Views

1. When you hear about controversial health issues that are not yet resolved, how do you usually handle the situation?

Meeting Special Needs

Cancer Patients. Teens with cancer say one of the most difficult things about living with cancer is the loneliness. They often feel isolated and set apart. They look different—surgical scar, lost weight, lost hair. Their lives are different—missed school, some restrictions on recreation. If their friends do treat them differently or ostracize them, it's usually out of ignorance or fear. Friends often want to know if cancer is contagious, which of course it's not. They want to know if it hurts. Sometimes it does, and sometimes the treatments are uncomfortable and frustrating. They may be afraid of getting close to someone who's ill, in pain, and possibly going to die.

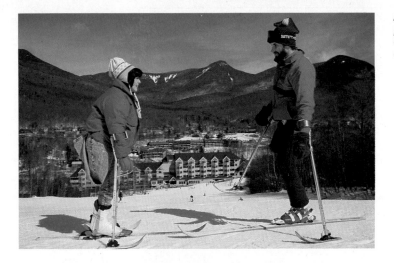

Many former bone cancer patients resume physical activities despite their disabilities.

techniques are allowing physicians to administer chemotherapy more safely and with fewer complications.

Efforts to Combat and Prevent Cancer

The United States began its war against cancer in 1971 when President Richard Nixon signed into law the National Cancer Act. The National Cancer Act established 15 comprehensive cancer centers around the country and greatly increased funding for research and treatment. Since 1971 federal spending for cancer research and treatment has totaled more than $21 billion.

Cancer is being attacked on many fronts. In some cases, we are winning the war. More cancer patients are living longer, better lives; more types of cancer are now curable; diagnosis has greatly improved and so have the three forms of treatment. Most importantly, scientists are learning more about why normal cells become cancerous and how to fight them.

Four main resources have contributed to the control of cancer.

- Education—for medical professionals and the public
- Research programs
- Public interest and support
- Organizations—such as the American Cancer Society and the National Cancer Institute

Prevention is possible in the case of some cancers, but not all. By avoiding exposure to harmful chemicals and excessive radiation, an individual can greatly reduce the risk of some forms of cancer.

There is evidence that there is a relationship between diet and cancer. However, no single vitamin or food has been proven to prevent cancer. Foods rich in vitamins A and C may help lower the risk for certain cancers. Choose to eat a variety of foods including dark green and yellow vegetables as well as cauliflower, broccoli, cabbage, carrots, and other foods high in fiber.

DID YOU KNOW?

- About half a million Americans die from cancer each year—about one every 63 seconds.
- It is predicted that by the year 2000, cancer, not heart disease, will be the number-one killer in the United States.
- According to the American Cancer Society, 49 percent of people with cancer are still alive 5 years after the diagnosis.
- About 90 percent of lung cancer cases in men and 79 percent of cases in women are attributable to cigarette smoking.

CANCER **583**

Additional Information

Skin Cancer. The most common malignancy in the U.S. today is skin cancer. More than 600,000 cases are reported each year, with an estimated 8,500 deaths. The two most common skin cancers (basal cell and squamous cell) have a 95 percent cure rate if detected and treated early. A rarer form, malignant melanoma, has a 90 to 95 percent survival rate.

Eighty percent of a person's skin exposure is acquired in the first 20 years of life. Wearing a sunscreen with an SPF of 15 during those years lowers skin cancer risks by 78 percent. One serious childhood or adolescent sunburn doubles the chances of developing skin cancer.

L2 READING. Have students read articles about chemotherapy—its risks, myths about it, drugs that are used, coping with the side effects, and new advances in chemotherapy. Ask students to summarize the articles in writing.

L1 READING. Ask students to read and make short reports on articles and books about people who have recovered from cancer.

L1 PARENTAL INVOLVEMENT. Ask students to share the seven warning signs of cancer with their parents. Have students ask their parents if they know someone who has had cancer and recovered. Has a member of the family had cancer? What kind, and what type of treatment was used? How were the families affected? Ask students to write a report on their findings.

L3 RESEARCH. Ask for volunteers to study benign breast disease (sometimes called fibrocystic disease, chronic cystic mastitis, or cystic breast disease). Have them describe the condition, its symptoms, current treatments, foods to avoid, and its relationship to women's risk of breast cancer.

L3 RESEARCH. Have students use classroom and library resources to find answers to the following questions: What factors influence the total amount of UV radiation that reaches the earth at any given time? During what hours of the day are you most likely to get a sunburn? Which state in the U.S. has the highest incidence of melanoma?

L2 RESEARCH. Have groups of students survey various packaged foods. Have each group compile a list of 20 products that use chemicals and a list of 20 products that do not. Allow time for the groups to compare and discuss their findings.

L2 RESEARCH. Select students to report on mammography: what it is, who should have a mammogram, how often one should have a mammogram, and what its possible risks are.

L2 WRITING. Ask students to consider that the place where they live might determine whether or not they get cancer. Have them suggest what they can do about human-made carcinogens in the environment. Have interested students write to the Environmental Protection Agency (EPA) in Washington, D.C., for further information.

Using Overcoming the Odds

■ **Discussion.** In what ways was Lea Ann lucky in how her leukemia case progressed? (A bone marrow donor was available right away, she had someone go through it ahead of her, and the donor marrow "took.")

■ **Explanation.** Explain why Lea Ann had to go through the worst 3 days of her life having massive doses of chemotherapy and radiation before her transplant operation. (To destroy the cancerous marrow so the donor marrow could take hold and eventually replace all of her own marrow.)

■ **Answers**

1. She had high self-esteem and a positive attitude.
2. The first step is most crucial—identify areas where you don't have control and decide if they can be changed. Taking control improves self-esteem.
3. Answers will vary. To most people it means learning to accept what they can't change and changing what they can if it leads to ill health.

L2 WRITING. Ask students to locate articles evaluating alternative therapies in the treatment of cancer, such as visualization, imagery, meditation, and humor. Have students summarize the articles in writing.

L1 RESEARCH. Ask students to volunteer to go to a pharmacy or store and look at labels for sun screens. Compare the labels according to the number level on the container. Why do babies and children need to use an SPF of 25 when out in the sun? Report results to the class.

L2 SELF-ESTEEM. How does one's level of self-esteem help in struggling with a debilitating disease?

L1 USING THE LESSON RESOURCES. For additional student activities, refer to the lesson resources on page 579.

Lea Ann Baldwin is 17. She used to play basketball and loved to bike and run—until she got sick. "I never understood why everyone else could run and run and why I couldn't." She soon discovered the reason. Lea Ann had leukemia. At Minneapolis Children's Hospital she was diagnosed with chronic myelogenous leukemia on her fifteenth birthday. "They said I'd have between five and six years to live unless I had a bone marrow transplant, the only possible cure.

"My whole family was tested to see if their HLA type (tissue type) matched mine, and none of them matched. My name was put on a computer list at the Red Cross and they searched for a match. I was lucky because they found my donor in a couple of months. A boy named Jason was ten days ahead of me in the transplant process. He would prepare me for what to expect. . . . That really helped."

Lea Ann wanted to make her hospital stay as happy and home-like as possible. "My mom brought sheets that made my room so colorful. I also covered the walls with posters. I painted my windows. I went wild."

Lea Ann goes on to describe the transplant process. "First

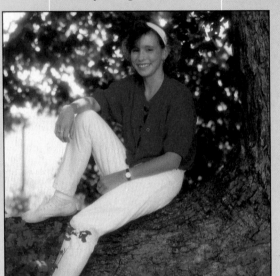

you have five days to get used to everything. Then for three days you have massive doses of chemotherapy and radiation. It's the worst three days of your life. You can't eat. You throw up. You get mouth sores. After the three days, the donor donates the bone marrow. The donated marrow for me was flown in a cooler and brought to the hospital by cab. They checked it, and put it into an IV. The whole process took only about an hour, and I was awake. They told me that afterward I'd feel like I'd been kicked in the lower back by a horse. After twenty-eight days, they gave me a biopsy to see if the other person's marrow was growing in my bones, and at that point I had 50 percent bone marrow, which was a good sign. My last checkup, my 2-year checkup, showed 100 percent donor bone marrow, which is great. They now say I'm cured.

"The donor who donated marrow to me is 31. She's a doctor of immunology, and that's special to me. Her name is Judy Scheppler, and I have not met her, but I really want to. We were a great match, even better than identical twins. I don't know if I'm quite ready to call her yet. I will eventually. She saved my life. It's just that I'm not sure what to say. Thank you just doesn't seem to cover it."

Lea Ann encourages everyone who can to become a donor. "Then everyone who needs a transplant will be able to get one."

1. What factors helped Lea Ann to face her health struggles?
2. Lea Ann made her environment colorful and homey. Doing so gave her a sense of control. What steps can you take to shape your environment so that you feel more in control of it and more positive about it? How might taking these steps affect your self-esteem?
3. What does it mean to you to have control over the things that affect your health and your life?

584 CHAPTER 29 NONCOMMUNICABLE DISEASES

Additional Information

Cancer Therapies. Several new cancer treatments are being studied.
■ Transplant: Cancerous organs or parts of organs can be removed and replaced with healthy tissue.
■ Chemoprevention: Using controlled megadoses of vitamins and minerals may prevent cancer recurrences and reduce chances for high-risk persons.

■ Transfusion: Giving blood cells and platelets controls the symptoms of cancer and the side effects of some treatments.
■ Hyperthermia: Applying localized or total body heat destroys some tumors without damaging surrounding healthy tissue.

Today early diagnosis and treatment remain the most effective ways of treating all types of cancer. Although many cancer researchers hope for a vaccine that could prevent some types of cancer from occurring, the discovery of a vaccine is probably 20 years or more away. Meanwhile, scientists are learning more about the role of heredity in families that experience multiple cases of the same type of cancer. New ways to treat the disease by enhancing the body's immune system are also being studied.

CANCER QUACKERY

In the United States, laetrile is an illegal drug that contains cyanide, a potentially lethal poison, as well as many impurities. Laetrile is available in Mexico and some people from the United States go there in the hope of finding a cure. Drugs like laetrile will always be available as long as cancer exists, because people want to be free of pain, either from the cancer itself or from the effects of chemotherapy.

When a person reaches a terminal stage, he or she is more likely to try anything. People involved in cancer quackery can influence a desperate person and make money.

As long as we have no known cure for cancer, there will be many drugs, treatments, and devices that people will sell to unknowing and desperate people. Sometimes the cancer patients convince themselves that such unproven practices work, often because they want to believe it. Also, cancer patients tend to have periods when they seem to improve. The patient often interprets this as a sign that the unproven practice or drug is actually working. Sadly, these people invest money in worthless attempts to cure their cancer. Valuable time is wasted. They may delay getting medical assistance that could provide them with the only real chance they might have for cure and survival.

DID YOU KNOW?

- Donated bone marrow can mean the difference between life and death for many leukemia patients and patients with other fatal blood and genetic diseases. Often, family members donate marrow. However, sometimes family members cannot or will not donate their marrow or their marrow is not a match.
- The chances of finding a marrow match outside the family, however, are low. Matches are most likely to be found within a person's ethnic group.

LESSON 3 REVIEW

Reviewing Facts and Vocabulary

1. What is the difference between normal cells and cancerous cells?
2. Why is early diagnosis and treatment of cancer so important?
3. Define *benign* and *malignant*.

Thinking Critically

4. **Evaluation.** Use the library to locate a magazine article about the controversies surrounding animal testing in medical research, particularly in cancer research. Explain the different viewpoints. What do you think about the use of animals for medical research?

Applying Health Knowledge

5. Interview someone in your school or neighborhood who has successfully undergone cancer treatment. Get details about the treatment, any side effects, and time required. Summarize your findings in a one-page report.

CANCER **585**

Answers to Lesson 3 Review

1. Normal cells reproduce at a controlled rate, but cancerous cells have abnormal, uncontrollable growth. Cancerous cells can move to other parts of the body and invade healthy tissue.
2. Early diagnosis means treatment can begin earlier to prevent cancer cells from spreading and to inhibit their growth.
3. Benign—noncancerous; malignant—cancerous.
4. Explanations will vary. Opinions will vary but should be supported.
5. Answers will vary.

Assess

Check for Understanding

- Assign and discuss the lesson review.

Evaluate

- Administer, grade, and discuss the *Lesson 3 Quiz.*

Reteach

- Have students make lists of the following information: three health steps that help prevent cancer; the seven warning signs of cancer; and three treatments for cancer.
- Ask students to complete *Reteaching Activity 80.*

Enrich

- Ask students to read about the controversies surrounding animal testing in medical research, particularly in cancer research. What are both sides of the controversy? What do they think of each? What is the Ames test, a test sometimes viewed as an alternative to animal testing? What are its benefits? Its drawbacks?

Close

Have students recall the major concepts of the lesson. Clarify any misconceptions.

DID YOU KNOW?

- Cancer is the leading cause of natural deaths in children.
- Depression is not linked to cancer, contrary to some previously published studies. A new 10-year study found no association between being depressed and developing cancer.

586

Focus

Lesson Objectives

After studying this lesson, students should be able to:
- describe diabetes and its progression
- describe the types of diabetes

Bellringer

Write the following on the chalkboard for students to work on while attendance is being taken: *What is diabetes? How can knowledge of diabetes be helpful?*

Introducing the Lesson

Have students share their responses to the Bellringer. If a student in the class is a controlled diabetic, ask ahead of time if he or she would like to explain the condition to the class. Ask the diabetic to include information regarding his or her diet, eating schedule, medications, activity levels, and emergency treatments. Because they concern a peer, these details will be relevant. If this is not possible, quickly survey the class to see how many have a diabetic in the family. More than likely there will be several. Tell students that diabetes is one of the leading health concerns in the U.S. and that they will learn more about this disease in this lesson.

DID YOU KNOW?

- Though severe complications from diabetes are often associated with type I, insulin-dependent diabetes, not all long-term sufferers of this disease experience such dramatic effects. According to one study at the Joslin Diabetes Center in Boston, among a group of people who had juvenile diabetes for over 40 years, 75 percent had only minor or mild complications, 87 percent were married, and only about 4 percent were unable to work because of their disease.

DIABETES

LESSON 4 FOCUS

TERMS TO USE
- Diabetes
- Glucose
- Insulin
- Type I diabetes
- Type II diabetes

CONCEPTS TO LEARN
- Metabolism of carbohydrates is the main source of energy for body cells.
- The release of energy from carbohydrates is a function of insulin, a hormone produced by the pancreas.
- There are two classifications of diabetes— type I and type II.

ATTITUDES AND BEHAVIORS TO EVALUATE
- Self-Inventory, page 592.
- Building Decision-Making Skills, page 593.

Diabetes is one of the leading health problems in the United States and a leading killer of adults. It affects an estimated 12 million Americans, and the number seems to be increasing. Many people have diabetes and do not know it.

About 700,000 new cases of diabetes occur each year. Persons with diabetes are more prone to suffer from heart disease and stroke; more prone to blindness; and more prone to kidney disease than persons who do not have diabetes.

Diabetes lessens the chance of a female's maintaining a full-term pregnancy and increases the frequency of birth defects in babies. The economic toll of diabetes in hours of work lost and in medical costs is over $20 billion annually.

How Diabetes Affects the Body

Diabetes is a chronic disease that affects the way body cells convert food into energy. Diabetes can be controlled but as yet cannot be cured. In the normal digestive process carbohydrates are changed to a sugar called **glucose,** absorbed into the blood, and delivered to body cells. Normally, with the help of **insulin,** a hormone produced in the pancreas, glucose is converted into energy for use by the cells. In the case of diabetes, this process is interrupted.

Diabetes develops either because no insulin or insufficient insulin is produced or because the insulin produced is not used efficiently. When glucose is unable to enter the cells, it accumulates in the blood until the kidneys filter out some of the surplus and it is passed off in urine. High sugar content in urine and in blood is one of the surest signs that a person has diabetes.

Types of Diabetes

The National Diabetes Data Group has established two classifications of diabetes: type I, insulin-dependent diabetes, and type II, noninsulin-dependent diabetes.

Type I, Insulin-Dependent Diabetes

Type I diabetes (formerly called juvenile-onset diabetes) occurs most often before the age of 15 and accounts for about 10 percent of all cases of diabetes. Type I usually appears abruptly and progresses rapidly. Symptoms of type I diabetes include frequent urination, abnormal thirst, unusual hunger, weight loss, irritability, weakness, fatigue, nausea, and vomiting.

Because the pancreas produces little or no insulin, these patients must take daily injections of insulin to stay alive. Before the discovery of

Resources for Lesson 4

- **Guided Reading** Act 81
- **Workbook** Voc Act 81
- **Reteaching** Activity 81
- **Lesson 4 Quiz**

Science and Technology Videodisc
Human Biology, Side 2
Ch 9 Insulin Pills

Ch 10 Insulin Pump

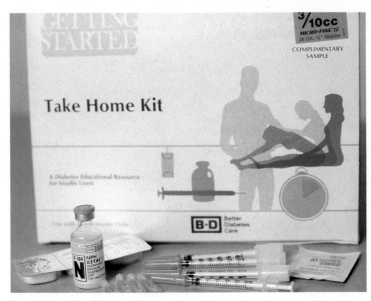

This diabetes kit is for use at home.

insulin, persons with type I diabetes usually lived no more than two years after diagnosis. Today, because of advanced methods of treatment, many persons with diabetes live near-normal life spans.

Type II, Noninsulin-Dependent Diabetes

Type II diabetes (formerly called adult-onset diabetes) occurs usually in adults over 40 years of age. This is the more common form of diabetes and accounts for about 90 percent of all cases of diabetes. In type II diabetes, the pancreas produces some insulin, but because of a cell receptor defect, the cells cannot use the insulin effectively.

Type II diabetes can usually be controlled by diet and exercise. In some cases, oral medications or injections of insulin are also required. Problems related to circulation are common in this type of diabetes. Because the onset of type II diabetes is gradual, the disease often goes undetected for years. Symptoms of type II diabetes include excess

---

K E E P I N G   F I T

Diabetes and Exercise

Research continues to support the fact that regular exercise helps to prevent or control a variety of diseases. Now studies suggest that regular exercise not only helps to control blood sugar levels in cases of diabetes, but it can also help prevent the disease. As little as 20 minutes of moderate aerobic exercise 3 times a week can help prevent diabetes. So can controlling one's weight.

DIABETES   **587**

Building Vocabulary

■ Write each of the vocabulary terms on a 3-by-5 inch index card. Write the definition of each on another card. Two or more sets of cards may be needed. Mix up the cards and give one to each student. At your signal, have students find a match for their word or definition. After they have finished, have each pair of students read the term and its matching definition. The rest of the class should verify that a match has been made.

■ Ask students to complete *Workbook Vocabulary Activity 81.*

Teach

Guided Practice

L1 **COOPERATIVE LEARNING.** Divide the class into groups. Give each group a poster board. Assign each group one of the following: (1) List all of the types of diabetes and the symptoms/characteristics of these diseases. (2) Describe healthful habits such as diet and exercise needed to control diabetes. (3) Provide pictures of unhealthful habits that contribute to diabetes. (4) Describe the types of treatment available for diabetics besides diet and exercise.

L1 **DISCUSSION.** Have students explain how diabetes functions. What happens when glucose is unable to enter the body cells?

Independent Practice

L2 **RESEARCH.** Have students read about hypoglycemia, sometimes referred to as low blood sugar. Then, have them compare and contrast hypoglycemia with diabetes. How are their symptoms, treatments, diagnoses, and long-term effects on the body similar and different? What roles does insulin play in each? How can hypoglycemia lead to diabetes? What does it mean to be "prediabetic"? Ask them to present their findings in writing.

Additional Information

Diabetes. Diabetes is the seventh leading cause of death in the U.S. As many as 12 million may have the disease. It is the leading cause of blindness in persons 25 to 74. It is estimated that 150,000 will die this year as a result of complications from diabetes. Persons with diabetes are twice as likely to suffer from heart disease and 2 to 6 times as likely to suffer from stroke. It is the most frequent cause of non-traumatic lower limb amputation. Congenital abnormalities of newborns are more frequent in women with diabetes. Hispanics have the highest rate of diabetes. It is the third leading cause of death in African Americans.

L1

L1 **PARENTAL INVOLVEMENT.**
Ask students to share the warning signs of diabetes with their parents. Have them explain that diabetes can be hereditary and ask if anyone in their family has had diabetes and, if so, what type was diagnosed. Have them ask if the family doctor has ever tested a family member for diabetes and what type of test was used. Ask students to write a report on the results of their interview.

L1 **USING THE LESSON RESOURCES.** For additional student activities, refer to the lesson resources on page 586.

Assess

Check for Understanding

- Assign and discuss the lesson review.

Evaluate

- Administer, grade, and discuss the *Lesson 4 Quiz.*

Reteach

- Have students label a sheet of paper "Type I Diabetes" and another "Type II Diabetes," then fill in the causes, signs, and treatments for each type. Have students refer to the lesson as they complete each outline.
- Ask students to complete *Reteaching Activity 81.*

Enrich

- Have students research the various ways insulin can be administered. (Hypodermic needle, orally, insulin pump.) Have them read about the future possibilities for pancreatic transplants.

Close

Have students recall major concepts of the lesson. Clarify any misconceptions.

Type of Emergency

Low blood sugar

Signs
- Staggering, poor coordination
- Irritability, belligerence, hostility
- Pale color
- Sweating
- Stupor or unconsciousness

Possible Causes
- Delayed or missed meals
- Too much insulin, by overdose or error
- Extreme exercise

Treatment
- Look for diabetic identification bracelet or necklace.
- The diabetic may carry candy or special quick-sugar commercial preparations in plastic soft-tipped containers. Squeeze the contents into the person's mouth.
- If the person can swallow without choking, offer any food or drink containing sugar, such as soft drinks, fruit juice, or candy. Do not use diet drinks!
- If the person does not respond in 10 to 15 minutes, take him or her to a hospital.

Type of Emergency

High blood sugar

Signs
- Thirst
- Very frequent urination
- Flushed skin
- Vomiting
- Fruity or winelike odor of breath
- Stupor or unconsciousness

Possible Causes
- Insulin forgotten or omitted
- Stress, such as illness or injury
- Overindulgence in certain foods or beverages

Treatment
- Look for diabetic identification bracelet or necklace.
- If unsure, contact a physician.
- Take the person to a hospital.

weight, drowsiness, blurred vision, tingling or numbness in hands and feet, skin infections, and itching and slow-healing cuts.

Type II diabetes has been linked to heredity, obesity, and inactivity. About 80 percent of all patients are overweight at the time they are diagnosed. People can prevent many cases of type II diabetes if they maintain a desired weight and keep physically active.

LESSON 4 REVIEW

Reviewing Facts and Vocabulary

1. In one sentence, describe diabetes.
2. How can a person help prevent type II diabetes?
3. What is a sure sign that a person has diabetes?

Thinking Critically

4. **Evaluation.** Is the presence of sugar in urine an effective test for diabetes? Explain.

Applying Health Knowledge

5. Find out why people with diabetes should wear emergency medical symbols.
6. Ask people who have diabetes to speak to your class about the effect of diabetes on lifestyle.

Answers to Lesson 4 Review

1. It is a chronic disease that affects the way body cells convert food into energy.
2. Maintain a desired weight and keep physically active.
3. High sugar content in blood and urine.
4. Partially right—a finding of too much sugar content in the urine should be followed up by a blood test.
5. Answers will vary but should mention that if people with diabetes are in a situation in which they cannot speak, the emergency medical symbol can aid medical personnel in diagnosing and treating them.
6. Answers will vary.

ARTHRITIS

T he term *arthritis* means "inflammation of a joint." **Arthritis** covers at least 100 different conditions that cause aching, pain, and swelling in joints and connective tissue throughout the body. It can and does occur at all ages, from infancy on. The National Center for Health Statistics estimates that about 37 million people have arthritis severe enough to require medical care. Arthritis costs the national economy over $18 billion yearly in lost wages and medical bills. It is likely that someone you know has arthritis, since it affects one in seven people and one in three families. The two most common kinds of arthritis are rheumatoid arthritis and osteoarthritis.

Rheumatoid Arthritis

Rheumatoid arthritis is the most serious type of arthritis and is mainly a destructive and disabling inflammation of the joints. It affects primarily the joints of the hands and arms, the hips, and the feet and legs. Rheumatoid inflammation also attacks connective tissue throughout the body, and this causes symptoms such as fever, fatigue, and swollen lymph glands.

Rheumatoid arthritis causes the joints to stiffen, then swell and become tender. The inflammation can do progressive damage inside the joint if it is not diagnosed and properly treated.

What Rheumatoid Arthritis Does

The area where two bones meet is enclosed in a capsule, containing fluid. The capsule has an inner lining called the synovial membrane.

Rheumatoid arthritis causes joints to stiffen and swell.

ARTHRITIS **589**

LESSON 5 FOCUS
TERMS TO USE ■ Arthritis ■ Rheumatoid arthritis ■ Osteoarthritis (AHS•tee•oh•ahr•THRYT•uhs) **CONCEPTS TO LEARN** ■ Arthritis can affect people of any age. ■ Treatment programs are available to ease the discomfort of arthritis. **ATTITUDES AND BEHAVIORS TO EVALUATE** ■ Self-Inventory, page 592. ■ Building Decison-Making Skills, page 593.

Focus

Lesson Objective

After studying this lesson, students should be able to:
■ describe the two most common types of arthritis

Bellringer

Write the following on the chalkboard for students to work on while attendance is being taken: *List as many words or terms as you can that relate to arthritis.*

Introducing the Lesson

Refer to the Bellringer. Ask volunteers to share their responses. Point out that most people tend to associate arthritis with old age. However, it can and does occur at all ages.

Building Vocabulary

■ Write the vocabulary terms, along with their pronunciations, on the chalkboard. Ask students to volunteer to pronounce the terms. After all the terms have been pronounced correctly, have the entire class repeat each term.
■ Ask students to complete *Workbook Vocabulary Activity 82.*

DID YOU KNOW?

■ Acupuncture, a 3,000-year-old technique, helps some people control arthritis pain. How it works is not known, but some scientists believe that acupuncture causes the brain to release endorphins, a natural painkiller.

Resources for Lesson 5

- ■ **Guided Reading** Activity 82
- ■ **Decision-Making** Activity 29
- ■ **Workbook** Vocabulary Activity 82
- ■ **Workbook** Application Activity 29
- ■ **Reteaching** Activity 82
- ■ **Enrichment** Activity 29
- ■ **Health Labs** Activity 29
- ■ **Cooperative Learning** Activity 29

- ■ **Lesson 5 Quiz**
- ■ **Chapter 29 Test**
- **Science and Technology Videodisc**
- **Human Biology, Side 2**
- Ch 19 Arthritis Research

A hip joint damaged by arthritis can be replaced with an artificial joint.

DID YOU KNOW?

■ Self-help aids allow people crippled by arthritis to lead independent lives. Raised seats on chairs or toilets make sitting down and standing up easier. Handrails along walls and by the bathtub are also helpful. A shower chair eliminates the need for sitting in a low tub or standing in a shower. For people with a weak or limited grasp, brushes, writing utensils, and eating utensils can be strapped to the hand or wrist. Velcro fasteners on clothing are also helpful. Self-help aids can be purchased at drugstores, at medical supply stores, and from the Arthritis Foundation.

Inflammation starts here, causing the membrane to swell and spread to other parts of the joint. Outgrowths of inflamed tissue invade the cartilage surrounding the bone ends, eventually eroding the bone tissue. Finally, scar tissue can form between the bone ends and sometimes change to bone, so that the joint becomes fused, and immovable.

Inflammation can also lead to distortion of the joint. This is most apparent when the disease attacks the hands. The fingers become drawn back and angled sideways, so that the hands are deformed and difficult to use properly in performing common daily tasks. These conditions can develop at any age. With proper treatment started early, some of the symptoms can be relieved.

Treatment of Rheumatoid Arthritis

Scientists do not know the cause of rheumatoid arthritis, and at the present time there is no cure for it. Treatment programs are designed to relieve pain, reduce inflammation, prevent damage to joints, prevent deformities, and keep joints movable and functioning properly.

A full treatment program for rheumatoid arthritis may include the following: medication (aspirin is the most frequently used anti-inflammatory medicine), rest, exercise, good posture, splints, walking aids, heat, surgery, and rehabilitation.

KEEPING FIT

Understanding People with Chronic Diseases

If you are close to someone who is chronically ill, remember these guidelines.
■ Offer help when it is needed or asked for. Allow the chronically ill person to be as independent as possible.

■ Be patient. Imagine what it would be like to be in the other person's place.
■ Don't always focus on the other person's condition. Talk about yourself, your own life, the outside world.

■ Don't underestimate the power of touch. Just holding a hand or giving a hug can do a lot for someone who is ill.
■ Don't forget humor.

Additional Information

Arthritis and Aerobics. In the early 1900s, people who had arthritis had very limited options about treatment. In fact, it was believed that participation in any kind of exercise was the wrong thing to do. It was thought that exercise would aggravate the problems with joints. As a result, arthritic patients were told that rest was the only option they had. Today the thinking is much different. Researchers have studied the effects of vigorous exercise on people with arthritis. The results indicate that aerobic exercise is safe and beneficial. Brisk walking is encouraged as an excellent form of exercise for people with arthritis.

Compare the normal knee joint on the left with the one affected by osteoarthritis on the right.

Osteoarthritis

Osteoarthritis is the most common type of arthritis, affecting about 16 million people. It results from wear and tear in the mechanical parts of a joint. Unlike rheumatoid arthritis, inflammation is rarely a problem. Osteoarthritis affects primarily the weight-bearing joints of the knees and hips.

In osteoarthritis, the cartilage becomes pitted and frayed and, in time, may wear away completely. Bone ends then become thicker and bony spurs may develop. As a result, surrounding ligaments and membranes become thickened, changing the whole structure and shape of the joint.

Aching and soreness around the joints, especially when a person moves, are the major symptoms of osteoarthritis. Although there is no cure, treatment can slow down and even control the disease process.

Aches and pains in or around joints can mean different things. Early detection and diagnosis of arthritis is essential and can prevent unnecessary damage and pain. Yet, arthritis specialists report that people suffering from arthritis wait an average of four years after their first symptoms appear before seeking assistance.

DID YOU KNOW?

- Joints that are damaged by severe arthritis, other disease, or injury can be replaced by artificial ones. Joints that can now be replaced include ankles, elbows, fingers, hips, knees, and toes. Most recipients of joint replacement have this surgery to reduce pain and improve joint function because of arthritis.

LESSON 5 REVIEW

Reviewing Facts and Vocabulary

1. What are the early signs of arthritis?
2. How is arthritis treated?

Thinking Critically

3. **Analysis.** Compare rheumatoid arthritis and osteoarthritis.
4. **Synthesis.** What effect could arthritis have on physical, social, and mental health?

5. **Synthesis.** Develop a short oral presentation that could be used to get people with arthritis to seek medical treatment.
6. **Analysis.** Explain why people with arthritis would be very susceptible to quackery.

Applying Health Knowledge

7. Invite a physical therapist to your class to discuss rehabilitative therapy for people with arthritis. Summarize the main points in writing.

ARTHRITIS **591**

Answers to Lesson 5 Review

1. Aching, pain, swelling in joints; stiffness, tenderness in joints, fever, fatigue, swollen lymph glands.
2. Medication, rest, exercise, good posture, splints, walking aids, heat, surgery, rehabilitation therapy.
3. Answers will vary. Possible answers: There is no cure for either, but both can be treated. Both affect joints.
4. Answers will vary. Possible answers: Loss of mobility, inability to maintain relationships with others, depression, stress.
5. Oral presentations will vary.
6. Answers will vary. Possible answers: Because there is no cure, inability to deal with pain.
7. Summaries will vary.

Assess

Check for Understanding

- Assign and discuss the lesson review.
- Assign and discuss the chapter review.

Evaluate

- Administer, grade, and discuss the *Lesson 5 Quiz*.
- Administer, grade, and discuss the *Chapter 29 Test*.
- Refer to the Performance Assessment strategy for this chapter. See pages T 23 to T 25.

Reteach

- Have students make a chart that compares and contrasts rheumatoid arthritis with osteoarthritis.
- Ask students to complete *Reteaching Activity 82*.

Enrich

- Have students read about lupus (systemic lupus erythematosus). What is the disease? How many lives does it claim each year in the United States? How did the disease get its name? What populations does the disease most commonly affect? What are the treatments, research, and advancements? Why is the disease so difficult to diagnose? Why is it sometimes associated with arthritis? Why do people with lupus get sent to rheumatologists, as arthritics do? Ask students to summarize their findings in writing.
- Ask students to complete *Enrichment Activity 29*.

Close

Have students recall the major concepts of this lesson. Clarify any misconceptions.

Helping Students Improve Their Health

Using the Self-Inventory

Reinforcing Vocabulary

- **Sunscreen lotion.** Lotion that protects the skin from ultraviolet rays.
- **Smokeless tobacco products.** Tobacco products that are placed within the mouth, but are not smoked.
- **Cholesterol.** A substance naturally produced by the body and found in animal fats.

Teaching Strategies

L1 EXPLANATION. Students frequently do not believe that there are long-term health consequences for many behaviors, such as smoking, tanning, and eating foods that are not healthful. It is important to focus upon healthful behavior issues in which students may see immediate effects.

L1 CLASS ACTIVITY. Have students experience the symptoms of arthritis today. Adolescents frequently become impatient with individuals who drive or walk too slowly. Many times this inability to maneuver one's body is a result of an arthritic condition. Have students place restrictive tape on various joints of the body, such as the fingers, knees, and elbows. Allow students to attempt to maneuver through various activities that will become difficult to perform. Stress to students that many individuals are permanently experiencing the lack of ability to move that the students have experienced. Encourage students to be patient when dealing with individuals with arthritis.

Self-Inventory

Risky Business!

HOW DO YOU RATE?

Number a sheet of paper from 1 through 18. Read each item below and respond by writing *yes* or *no* for each. Total the number of each type of response. Then proceed to the next section.

1. I avoid sitting or standing near people who are smoking.
2. I put salt on my food.
3. I smoke cigarettes.
4. I avoid eating fried foods.
5. I limit the amount of fat in my diet.
6. When I am in sunlight during midday, I use a sunscreen lotion.
7. I use smokeless tobacco products.
8. I exercise aerobically at least three times a week.
9. I eat foods high in fiber.
10. Fresh fruits and vegetables are a major part of my diet.
11. I avoid long exposure to dust, fumes, and industrial chemicals.
12. I limit my intake of foods high in cholesterol.
13. When I get upset, I take some action to relax.
14. I keep my weight under control.
15. I wear protective clothing when I am in the sun for long periods of time.
16. I use some effective ways to relax.
17. I avoid smoke-filled rooms.
18. I eat a lot of greasy foods.

HOW DID YOU SCORE?

Give yourself 1 point for each of these items you answered *yes:* 1, 4, 5, 6, 8, 9, 10, 11, 12, 13, 14, 15, 16, 17. Give yourself 1 point for each of these items you answered *no:* 2, 3, 7, 18. Find your total and read below to see how you scored. Then proceed to the next section.

17 to 18
Excellent. You are doing a great job of reducing your risk of getting heart disease and cancer.

15 to 16
Good. You are certainly on the right track, doing many positive things to protect yourself. Keep moving forward.

9 to 14
Fair. Obviously you are doing some things to protect yourself, but not as much as you could possibly do.

Below 9
Look out! It is time you realized that there is much that you should be doing to reduce your risk of heart disease and cancer.

WHAT ARE YOUR GOALS?

If you received an *excellent* or *good* score, complete the statements in Part A. If your score was rated *fair* or *look out!*, complete Parts A and B.

Part A

1. I plan to learn more about reducing my risks by ____.
2. My timetable for accomplishing this is ____.
3. I plan to share my information with others by ____.

Part B

4. The behavior toward heart disease and cancer I would most like to change is ____.
5. The steps involved in making this change are ____.
6. My rewards for making this change will be ____.

Meeting Students' Needs

For students who score *Excellent*. Encourage students to be a volunteer for the American Cancer Society or the American Heart Association.

For students who score *Good*. Suggest that students research their family history of illness and disease to determine possible genetic predispositions.

For students who score *Fair*. Suggest that students interview a member of the medical profession who is knowledgeable about noncommunicable diseases.

For students who need to *Look Out*. Take a field trip to a local cancer ward or heart surgery ward. Have students ask patients what behaviors may have contributed to their present health condition.

Building Decision-Making Skills

Even though Paige's grandfather had a heart attack over a year ago, she is still concerned about his health. He is trying hard to follow his doctor's orders of regular exercise, and he is taking his medicine faithfully. However, Paige is concerned about his diet. She knows that certain foods do not promote a healthy heart, and her grandparents have not changed their eating habits. Paige's grandmother says she is too old to change her habits and if you cannot enjoy a good meal, then why live? She thinks she'll die in a few years anyway. Paige has tried hard to convince her grandmother that choices a person makes can affect the quality of life, but she will not listen. Paige lives close to her grandparents, so she sees them often. What should Paige do next?

WHAT DO YOU THINK?

1. **Choices.** What choices does Paige have?
2. **Consequences.** What are the advantages and disadvantages of each choice?
3. **Consequences.** What risks are involved in this decision?
4. **Consequences.** How might Paige feel about each choice now and several years from now?
5. **Decision.** What should Paige do?
6. **Evaluation.** What do you do when you cannot convince someone you love and respect about the benefits of an idea that is new to them?

Diabetes runs in Rachel's family. Both her father and his brother have this disease. Now Rachel's aunt was just diagnosed as having type II diabetes. She is very worried. She has seen how this disease has affected older family members. One relative lost a leg, and another lost his eyesight. As a result Rachel's aunt is afraid to eat much of anything. She has lost a lot of weight and looks too thin. Rachel is concerned about her aunt. What should Rachel do?

WHAT DO YOU THINK?

7. **Situation.** Why does a decision need to be made?
8. **Choices.** What could Rachel do to help her aunt?
9. **Consequences.** What are the advantages of each choice?
10. **Consequences.** What are the disadvantages of each choice?
11. **Decision.** What do you think Rachel should do?

Bill and Linda have been going together for over a year. Both of them like to have fun and have many friends. They are anticipating the school dance that is coming up in two weeks. Bill and Linda will be meeting a group of friends there. Today in the cafeteria, many were talking about the upcoming dance. Sally told Linda that her brother, Marcus, was coming home from college the weekend of the dance. Sally asked Linda if she would like to go with Marcus to the dance. Sally knows that Linda goes with Bill, but said, "I just thought that since Bill is in a wheelchair because of his arthritis, you might want to go with someone who might be more fun at a dance." What should Linda do?

WHAT DO YOU THINK?

12. **Choices.** What are Linda's choices?
13. **Consequences.** What are the advantages and disadvantages of each choice?
14. **Decision.** What do you think Linda should do?
15. **Evaluation.** What do you usually do when you find yourself in a position where you must deal with negative stereotypes?

ARTHRITIS **593**

Building Decision-Making Skills

Teaching Strategies

L1 CLASS ACTIVITY. Have students participate in a role-play situation in which Paige is discussing her concern for her grandparents' eating habits with (a) Paige's parents, (b) a friend, (c) a guidance counselor, (d) her doctor. How might these different support structures differ in their suggestions? How might these individuals be similar in their advice? Which individual might possibly have the best advice to offer?

L1 CLASS ACTIVITY. Have students brainstorm the many different ways that Rachel might handle the situation with her aunt not eating. After brainstorming, have students vote on the top three suggestions. Have students form three different groups. Assign one strategy to each group. Have students role-play each situation for the class.

L1 DISCUSSION. Have students discuss possible adjustments Bill and Linda may have established to allow each other to enjoy and participate in any situation, while remaining together.

Discussing the Answers

Situation 1. Paige can continue to talk to her grandparents and she could also encourage her parents to do the same. Paige could even consult her grandfather's doctor in order to help convince her grandparents that a change in their eating habits is necessary.

Situation 2. It is time for a caring conversation between Rachel's aunt and their family doctor. Rachel can help arrange the visit to the doctor.

Situation 3. Students should consider responsibility and sensitivity that is necessary in a relationship. Bill and Linda have apparently learned to cope with Bill's disability and enjoy their relationship. Linda clearly should not forsake a good relationship for one evening.

Answers to Chapter 29 Review

Using Health Terms

1. Hypertension
2. Stroke
3. Heart disease or heart attack
4. Noncommunicable
5. Pacemaker
6. Transplant
7. Tumor
8. Carcinogens
9. Malignant
10. Cancer
11. Benign
12. Glucose
13. Synovial membrane
14. Osteoarthritis

Building Academic Skills

15. Answers will vary.

Recalling the Facts

16. See pages 571 to 572.
17. About 5 minutes.
18. It leads to atherosclerosis, which can result in a heart attack.
19. Stroke, heart attack, heart failure, kidney failure.
20. See page 574.
21. A device that would substitute for the work the left ventricle does; artificial blood vessels.
22. Do not smoke, watch cholesterol and fat intake, control one's weight, watch sodium intake, exercise regularly, manage stress.
23. Excessive sodium intake.
24. In air, water, food, the workplace, X rays, sunlight, and certain viruses. Examples may include but are not limited to three of the following: Tobacco smoke, asbestos, radiation, ultraviolet rays, industrial wastes, automobile exhausts.
25. Smoking tobacco.
26. Early diagnosis and treatment—surgery, radiation, chemotherapy.
27. The medicine can reach to all parts of the body wherever cancer might be but surgery and radiation are localized.
28. It was responsible for establishing 15 comprehensive cancer centers in the United States and increased funding for research and treatment of cancer. In 1971 during

---

REVIEW

Using Health Terms

On a separate sheet of paper, write the term that best matches each definition given below.

LESSON 1
1. High blood pressure.
2. A condition that occurs when a blood vessel in the brain is blocked.
3. Diseases of the heart and blood vessels.
4. Diseases that are not transmitted by contact with others.

LESSON 2
5. Responsible for initiating electrical impulses that cause the heart to beat.
6. A procedure in which a damaged or nonfunctioning organ is removed and replaced with one from a donor.

LESSON 3
7. A mass of tissue formed by cells multiplying faster than normal.
8. Cancer-causing substances.
9. Cancerous.
10. Abnormal, uncontrolled cell growth.
11. Noncancerous.

LESSON 4
12. A form of sugar produced by the digestion of carbohydrates.

LESSON 5
13. Inner lining of capsule where two bones meet.
14. A condition in which cartilage becomes pitted and may eventually wear away completely.

Building Academic Skills

LESSON 1
15. **Writing.** Keep a log of your sodium and fat intake and your activity level for one week. Analyze your diet and activity level and write a one-page paper, evaluating your potential risk for heart disease based on your log and making specific suggestions for improvement.

Recalling the Facts

LESSON 1
16. What are the early signs of a heart attack?
17. How long can the brain live once the heart has stopped?
18. What happens as a result of plaque buildup in the arteries?
19. What might hypertension lead to?
20. What are the signals that indicate a stroke may be occurring?

LESSON 2
21. What are two developments in the treatment of heart disease currently being studied?
22. What can a person do to lower his or her risk factor for heart disease?
23. What causes high blood pressure?

LESSON 3
24. Where can carcinogens be found? Give three examples of carcinogens.
25. What factor is the leading cause of lung cancer?
26. What are strategies for treating cancer?
27. What is an advantage of chemotherapy over surgery or radiation in the treatment of cancer?
28. What benefits were realized from the National Cancer Act? When was it signed into law, and under whose administration?
29. What kind of cancer can be detected by a Pap smear?
30. What are seven warning signs of cancer?

LESSON 4
31. Who is most likely to suffer from type I diabetes and what are its symptoms?
32. Who is most likely to suffer from type II diabetes and what are its symptoms? Why might a case of type II diabetes go undetected for several years?

LESSON 5
33. Why is early diagnosis of arthritis vital?
34. What are the goals of treatment of rheumatoid arthritis? What might treatment of rheumatoid arthritis involve?

Richard Nixon's administration.
29. Cervical cancer.
30. See page 580.
31. Children and young adults—frequent urination, abnormal thirst, unusual hunger, weight loss, irritability, weakness and fatigue, nausea, vomiting.
32. Adults over 40 who are overweight, inactive, and genetically disposed to it—excess weight, drowsiness, blurred vision, tingling or numbness in hand and feet, skin infections, itching and slow-healing cuts. The onset is gradual.
33. So it can be properly treated and avoid progressive damage and pain.
34. Relieve pain, reduce inflammation, prevent damage to joints, prevent deformities, keep joints movable and functioning properly. Treatment involves medicine (often aspirin), rest, exercise, good posture, splints, walking aids, heat, surgery, rehabilitation.

REVIEW

Thinking Critically

LESSON 1

35. Synthesis. What kind of life-style is associated with the development of hypertension? Why do hypertension and atherosclerosis increase the risk of stroke?

36. Synthesis. Explain how a stroke, which causes the death of brain cells, can cause paralysis of a leg or similar loss of motor function elsewhere in the body.

LESSON 3

37. Synthesis. How is early detection of cancer related to the likelihood of cure and to the increase in reported cancer cases?

38. Evaluation. Why do you think people knowingly expose themselves to carcinogens and so increase their risk of developing cancer later in life? Consider carcinogens such as ultraviolet rays on the skin from sunbathing and nicotine in the lungs from smoking cigarettes. What role does age play in such risky behaviors?

LESSON 4

39. Synthesis. Although persons with diabetes can die because of too much or too little sugar in their blood, they are more likely to die from heart or kidney disease that has progressed over many years. Why? What is the connection between diabetes and these other life-threatening illnesses?

LESSON 5

40. Evaluation. What can you do to help prevent osteoarthritis?

Making the Connection

LESSON 2

41. Language Arts. Research the history of one of the treatments for heart disease. How did the treatment develop? How long was research done before the treatment was tried on humans? How effective has this particular treatment been?

Applying Health Knowledge

LESSON 1

42. One of the factors related to hypertension is a highly stressful environment. Stress occurs as a result of good and bad events. List events or activities you consider stressors. Include both kinds of stressors on your list.

43. Why do you think noncommunicable diseases have replaced communicable diseases as the leading causes of death?

LESSON 2

44. Talk to someone who has survived a heart attack. Find out how his or her life has changed.

45. Many foods are now labeled with words such as *low-fat, low-cholesterol, low-sodium,* and *lite.* Are these labels encouraging people to buy certain products? Are they misleading? Do they provide people with a false sense of security? Explain.

LESSON 3

46. If someone you loved was diagnosed with cancer and wanted to go to Mexico for laetrile treatment, how would you react?

LESSON 4

47. What would you do if you knew your insulin-dependent brother had intentionally not taken his insulin?

LESSON 5

48. Arthritis affects one in seven people and one in three families. Do the people you know typify this statistic? Explain.

Beyond the Classroom

LESSON 1

49. Further Study. Find out what is a recommended daily sodium intake. Then read the labels of the food you consume most often to estimate about how much sodium you consume in an average day. Include estimates of table salt you use.

ARTHRITIS **595**

Thinking Critically

35. A highly stressful, sedentary life-style with a diet high in sodium, sugar, cholesterol, and saturated fats. Prolonged hypertension can lead to strokes; with atherosclerosis, blood flow is slowed and the blood thickens, forming clots. If one of these clots goes to the brain, it would cause a stroke.

36. The brain controls all bodily motor functions so when brain cells die, the messages from that part of the brain to certain parts of the body cease.

37. Answers will vary. Possible answers: With early detection, it may be possible to stop the cancer cells before they move to other parts of one's body; awareness encourages people to seek treatment earlier.

38. Answers will vary. Possible answers: Some habits are hard to break, people don't think it will happen to them, some people live for the present and don't worry about the future. Some habits or beliefs are begun when one is too young to be fully aware of the impact of the decisions he or she is making.

39. Answers will vary. Possible answers: Glucose that would normally enter the body cell cannot and so stays in the blood, putting added strain on the heart and kidneys to filter the blood. People who suffer from diabetes are 2 times more likely to suffer from heart disease and 17 times more prone to kidney disease than people who do not have diabetes.

40. Answers will vary. Possible answers: Maintain an ideal weight, choose exercises that are low impact.

Making the Connection

41. Answers will vary.

Applying Health Knowledge

42. Answers will vary. Possible answers: Births, deaths, moving to a new house or city, tests, getting or changing jobs, personal relationships.

43. Answers will vary. Possible answer: Medical technology has advanced so that many communicable diseases are controlled or cured by medications or vaccines. Prevention is the best approach to controlling many of the noncommunicable diseases and this often depends on one's life-style, which many people are unwilling or unable to change or regulate.

44. Answers will vary.

45. Answers will vary. Possible answers: Yes. Yes, they infer that these products fulfill requirements as healthful foods.

46. Answers will vary.

47. Answers will vary. Possible answers: Talk to your brother, your parents, or your brother's doctor.

48. Answers will vary.

Beyond the Classroom

49. The recommended daily allowance of salt intake is three to eight grams. Estimates will vary.

Lesson Summaries

LESSON 1. In every country, increasing numbers of individuals and groups of people are becoming aware of environmental problems. The causes and harmful effects of photochemical smog, acid rain, depletion of the ozone layer, untreated sewage, solid garbage, toxic industrial wastes, and oil spills are discussed in this lesson.

LESSON 2. A population explosion, along with increasing technology and a growing desire for more material goods, is challenging the future of our global environment. The growing population is affecting the land, while technology is introducing complex environmental changes. Natural catastrophes contribute major changes as well.

Introducing the Chapter

Introduce this chapter by asking for student input in listing environmental threats in your geographic area. Discuss local problems that may have received media coverage, such as landfills, city dumps, and air pollution. Then help students expand their thinking to environmental problems associated with other localities. Help students recognize that environmental problems that face other communities now may someday affect their local area, too.

Performance Assessment ✓

Refer to pages T 23 to T 25 for a Performance Assessment strategy for this chapter. See the *Performance Assessment Activities* booklet for additional suggestions.

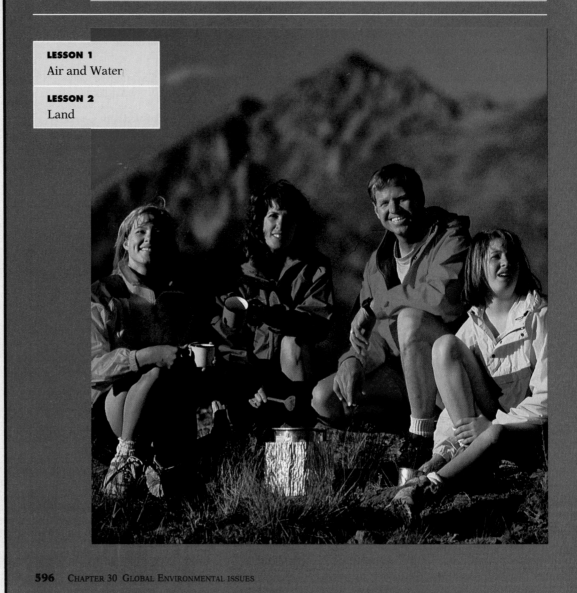

CHAPTER

30 GLOBAL ENVIRONMENTAL ISSUES

LESSON 1
Air and Water

LESSON 2
Land

Key to Ability Levels

Teaching strategies have been coded for varying learning styles and abilities.

L1 Level 1 activities are basic activities and should be within the ability range of all students.

L2 Level 2 activities are average activities and should be within the ability range of average to above-average students.

L3 Level 3 activities are challenging activities designed for the ability range of above-average students.

LD LD activities should be within the ability range of learning-disabled students.

LEP LEP activities should be within the ability range of Limited English Proficiency students.

AIR AND WATER

Y ou do not have to leave your home to see that the planet is in trouble. Almost any newspaper or newsmagazine carries headlines and articles about the health—or illness—of our world. Reports about acid rain, oil spills, global warming, droughts, famine, destruction of rain forests, and other disasters often fill the pages. Television reports show forests that are being destroyed and deserts that are expanding. There are scenes of the world's lakes, rivers, oceans, and air that are being degraded and polluted.

In every country increasing numbers of individuals and groups of people are becoming aware of environmental problems and are working to change things for the better. Let us review some of the environmental issues throughout the world, including what is being done to help protect and restore the planet.

Global Air Pollution

In just five days in 1952, one of London's smogs killed more than 4,000 people—a tragedy that still holds the record as the worst air pollution disaster in the world. London smogs were caused by a combination of fog and pollution. The pollution was mainly sulfur dioxide released when sulfur-containing coal and oil were burned in homes and power plants. After the tragedy the whole city, like many others in the United Kingdom, was declared a smoke-free zone. No one was allowed to burn a coal fire unless a preprocessed sulfur-free fuel or a more efficient smoke-eating stove was used. Industrial chimneys were required to be higher and to have built-in dust precipitators to remove some of the worst of the pollution. London smog is now mostly a thing of the past, and there have been no serious outbreaks of air pollution in London since the early 1960s.

Unfortunately, the story in developing nations of the world is another matter. There, many people continue to depend on coal or, more often, wood or charcoal for their cooking and heating needs. Controls either have not been introduced or have been difficult to carry out.

Photochemical Smog

Smog in the United States is an entirely different problem. It was first noticed in the early 1940s when residents of Los Angeles began to detect a tint in the air coupled with a stinging sensation in their eyes. Comparing their problems with what they knew of London, local authorities blamed sulfur dioxide and took steps to reduce it. However, the smog got worse.

Researchers named this new pollution **photochemical smog.** It occurs when vehicle exhausts, activated by sunlight, combine with other hydrocarbons in the atmosphere. One of the other hydrocarbons is the fumes from the fuel itself.

LESSON 1 FOCUS

TERMS TO USE
- Photochemical smog
- Estuaries (ES•chuh•wer•ees)
- Phytoplankton
- Chlorofluorocarbons (CFCs) (KLOHR•oh•FLOHR•oh•kahr•buhns)
- Carcinogenic (KAHR•SIN•uh•JEN•ik)

CONCEPTS TO LEARN
- Air pollution can be caused by smog, lead in the atmosphere, and acid rain.
- Damage to the ozone layer and the greenhouse effect may someday change the earth's atmosphere.
- Global water pollution has several causes and effects.

ATTITUDES AND BEHAVIORS TO EVALUATE
- Self-Inventory, page 610.
- Building Decision-Making Skills, page 611.

AIR AND WATER **597**

Resources for Lesson 1

- **Guided Reading** Activity 83
- **Workbook** Vocabulary Activity 83
- **Reteaching** Activity 83
- **Lesson 1 Quiz**
- **Performance Assessment** Activity 30

Science and Technology Videodisc
Human Biology, Side 2
Ch 16 Children and Smog

Focus

Lesson Objectives

After studying this lesson, students should be able to:
- give examples of global air pollution in the environment
- point out the effects of chlorofluorocarbons on the ozone layer
- explain the greenhouse effect
- point out some of the effects of global water pollution on the environment

Bellringer

Write the following on the chalkboard for students to work on while attendance is being taken: *Use your own words to define* pollution, *then list as many types of pollution as you can.*

Introducing the Lesson

Have students share their responses to the Bellringer. Introduce the lesson by stating that there are many types of pollution and that pollutants in one part of the world can affect the entire global environment. Tell students that this lesson will focus on pollution of the world's air and water.

DID YOU KNOW?

According to Tom Parker's book *In One Day*, each day in the U.S.
- Americans use 450 billion gallons of water on their farms, in their factories, and in their homes.
- Americans use 150 billion gallons of water to irrigate their land.
- Americans use 6.8 billion gallons of water in flushing their toilets.
- Americans pump 82 billion gallons of water out of the ground.
- Americans drink 115 million gallons of water.

Building Vocabulary

- Have students work in pairs to write a short paper, using each of the vocabulary terms. Afterwards, ask them to test each other's understanding of the terms' definitions.
- Have each student create a simple crossword puzzle or sentence-completion game, using all of the vocabulary terms. Afterwards, ask students to exchange their puzzles or games. Provide several minutes for them to complete each other's word challenges.
- Ask students to complete *Workbook Vocabulary Activity 83.*

Teach

Guided Practice

L1 CLASS ACTIVITY. Ask students to collect newspaper and magazine articles about global environmental issues. Discuss reasons the information in the articles is important to students and their families.

L1 DISCUSSION. Ask students what smog is. What are some of its effects on the environment?

L2 DISCUSSION. Ask from what sources does carbon dioxide enter the atmosphere. How do plants take carbon dioxide from the air?

L1 DISCUSSION. Have students describe acid rain. Talk about why it is a relatively new phenomenon.

L2 CLASS ACTIVITY. Select a small group of students to create a bulletin board about the effects of acid rain in the global environment. Have them title the board "Acid Rain Around the World."

CONFLICT RESOLUTION

Theresa Bennett lives with her mother and three-year-old sister in an old apartment building. In health class, Theresa learned that lead paint in old buildings is a possible cause of brain damage in young children. She and her mother are concerned that her sister may be at risk, but they can't convince their landlord to repaint their apartment. They feel trapped because they can't afford to move to a newer apartment. Theresa has considered organizing the other tenants and reporting the situation to city inspectors.

What other options can you think of to resolve Theresa's conflict?

Photochemical smog is a big problem in large cities.

Photochemical smog is found in many parts of the world, especially where there is dense traffic and a warm, sunny climate. In all of these places visibility is seriously reduced, and sometimes as little as one-tenth of the available sunlight actually penetrates the smog and reaches the ground.

Lead

Another toxic chemical pollutant in the atmosphere is lead—which spews from the exhausts of cars and other vehicles. Lead is still used as an anti-knock agent in gasoline in many parts of the world. In some urban areas toxic levels have been found in the bloodstream of traffic police officers and other outdoor workers. Scientists also have found that pigeons living in urban areas have as much as 10 times more lead in their blood than birds who live in rural areas.

Current research is being done on the long-term effects of lead poisoning. It is known that toxic effects of lead include loss of appetite, anemia, damage to the nervous system and, possibly, brain damage leading to a lowering of intelligence levels in young children.

Acid Rain

Air pollutants rarely go away; some return to the earth in rain, as in the case of sulfur and nitrogen from vehicles, industry, and home heating. Since the 1950s the acidity of rainfall in some parts of the world has increased dramatically. Acid rain can be 4 to 40 times more acidic than normal rainwater, sometimes as acidic as lemon juice or vinegar.

In industrial regions of England and Germany, acidic pollutants are damaging lakes, streams, and large tracts of forests. These pollutants are also becoming a serious problem in heavily industrialized parts of Asia, Latin America, and Africa.

Acid rain is spread over the earth by air currents. It is associated with depletion or total elimination of fish in lakes and **estuaries,** or ecosystems where seawater mixes with fresh water from rivers, streams, and runoff from the land. Besides damaging crops and forests, acid rain also damages steel and stone structures, outdoor artworks, and even nylon stockings.

Some responses to local air pollution standards have added to acid rain problems in other parts of the world. For instance, very tall smokestacks are sometimes added to power plants and smelting plants for dumping acid-laden smoke high in the atmosphere so that winds can distribute it elsewhere. For example, the world's tallest smokestack, which is in Ontario, Canada, accounted for 1 percent of the annual worldwide emissions of sulfur dioxide.

It is important to realize that Canada is not alone in this situation. In fact, Canada presently receives more acid deposits from industrialized regions of the northeastern United States than it sends across its southern border. Most of the acidic pollutants in Finland, Norway, Sweden, the Netherlands, Austria, and Switzerland are blown there from industrialized regions of western and eastern Europe. As you can see, prevailing winds do not stop at national boundaries; the problem of air pollution is of global concern.

598 CHAPTER 30 GLOBAL ENVIRONMENTAL ISSUES

Across the Curriculum

Science. Have students research and describe what happens to the human body when carbon monoxide is inhaled.

Home Economics. Have students see if there are aerosol cans at school and at home. Discuss alternate products that could be used.

Science. Ask students to investigate the use of lead in gasoline, paints, ceramics, glassware, city water supply pipes, and other products. Why is/was lead used in these products? In what ways is lead still used today? In which countries is the use of lead widespread?

Damage to the Ozone Layer

The ozone layer in the lower atmosphere absorbs most of the ultraviolet wavelengths from the sun. Unfortunately, this layer is being changed by the effects of man-made chemicals. In addition, each spring an ozone hole appears over the Antarctic. It extends over an area about the size of the continental United States.

Presently there is a large increase in skin cancers, which is believed to be related to increases in ultraviolet radiation from the sun. Cataracts may become more common because of the radiation; and the immune system may be weakened, making people more vulnerable to some viral and parasitic infections. In addition, reduction in the ozone layer may adversely affect the world's populations of **phytoplankton,** microscopic organisms, such as green algae, found in open, sunlit waters. These organisms are the basis of food webs in freshwater and marine life and are a factor in maintaining the composition of the atmosphere.

Chlorofluorocarbons. The causes of ozone reduction are being debated in the scientific community. To be sure, large volcanic eruptions, such as the recent eruptions of Mount Pinatubo in the Philippines, and cyclic changes in solar activity have serious effects. However, the major factor in ozone reduction is **chlorofluorocarbons (CFCs),** which are compounds of chlorine, fluorine, and carbon. They are odorless and invisible and are widely used as propellants in aerosol spray cans and as coolants in refrigerators and air conditioners. They are also used in making industrial solvents and plastic foams. CFCs enter the atmosphere slowly and resist breakdown.

The United States, Canada, and many other countries have reduced or banned the use of CFCs. Nonaerosol use of CFCs throughout the world has increased.

The Greenhouse Effect

Before the Industrial Revolution fossil fuels such as coal, oil, and gas were locked up within the earth's crust. Virtually all of the carbon dioxide that was released by people came from wood fires. Today carbon dioxide is being sent into the atmosphere from a whole range of sources, including human and animal respiration and decay, forest clearance, open fires, stoves, central heating, power station burners, and cars and other vehicles.

K E E P I N G   F I T

Protection Against Air Pollution

Protect yourself during pollution emergencies or when pollution levels are high:
- Avoid strenuous outdoor activities.

- Do not smoke.
- If you exercise outdoors, work out early in the morning when the concentration of pollutants in the air is lowest.

- Eat well-balanced meals; good nutrition enables your body to better handle toxic substances.

AIR AND WATER **599**

Additional Information

Lead Poisoning. Lead poisoning is the effect of a gradual accumulation of lead in body tissues. It occurs from repeated exposure to lead-containing substances. The most common route of exposure is inhalation of leaded fuel vapors. Lead also can be ingested from drinking water supplied through lead pipes. Unknowing children can eat lead-based paint from walls, toys, or furniture. Also, workers in agriculture, manufacturing, and mining are at risk for lead exposure.

Lead can affect the gastrointestinal and nervous systems. Anemia may result from lead's effect on bone marrow. Unless there is severe brain damage involved, lead poisoning can be reversed by chemically binding the lead to carry it out of the body.

L2 DISCUSSION. Ask students why many of the world's scientists are concerned about the greenhouse effect. How might it alter the global environment?

L1 SPEAKER. Ask a science teacher to speak to the class about the process of temperature inversion and its role in air pollution.

L1 CLASS ACTIVITY. Have students create bumper sticker designs and slogans to inform the public about global air pollution—its dangers and what can be done to combat it. Ask students to share their finished projects with the class. Create a display using some of the designs.

L1 DISCUSSION. Talk about some of the damaging effects of ozone depletion.

L1 CLASS ACTIVITY. Ask students to collect magazine and newspaper articles about the greenhouse effect. Afterwards, ask them to design and administer a simple survey of their friends' knowledge and concerns about the situation. Discuss the results of their surveys.

L2 COOPERATIVE LEARNING. Ask small groups of volunteers to create a board game or a computer game based on the greenhouse effect. Have students demonstrate their completed projects.

L2 CLASS ACTIVITY. Ask the class to assume that the earth's atmosphere can tolerate only a certain amount of a pollutant without serious damage to life on the planet. Tell them to call that certain amount the "allowable burden." Next, ask them to debate the following: No country has the right to contribute more pollutant to the allowable burden than the country's population size warrants. (For example, a country with 1 percent of the world's population would have the right to emit 1 percent of the world's total release of that pollutant, but no more than that.)

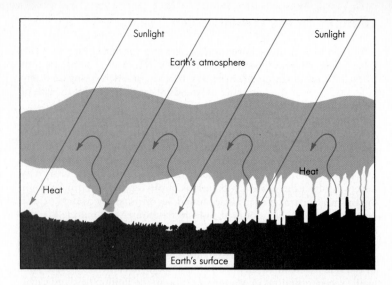

In the greenhouse effect, large quantities of carbon dioxide, caused by the burning of fossil fuels, form a cloud around the earth. Heat is kept near the surface, thus causing higher temperatures and humidity.

L2 COOPERATIVE LEARNING.

Divide the class into four groups to develop presentations or demonstrations. Assign one group to research the chronological history of the greenhouse effect. Have a second group investigate the impact of the greenhouse effect on people and the environment around the world. Ask a third group to report on current efforts that are being done to counteract it. Assign a fourth group to set up an actual demonstration of the greenhouse effect. Have the groups present their projects to the class.

L1 CLASS ACTIVITY.
Read the following statement to the class: *A developing country that chooses to burn its forests in order to create farms and grazing land has the right to do so, even though the resulting carbon dioxide contributes to global warming.* Next, have students indicate on a slip of paper their opinion of the statement by writing "agree," "disagree," or "not sure." Tally the slips, and ask students to discuss reasons for their opinions.

L1 SPEAKER.
Ask a representative from your local public school system to speak to the class about asbestos in schools. Ask the speaker if there is asbestos in your community's schools. If so, what steps are being taken to correct the problem? What precautions are required of the workers? What safeguards are provided to students and school personnel? What is the cost to the community?

L1 EXPLANATION.
Talk about the fact that although about 70 percent of the earth's surface is water, water is a limited resource. Have students identify some causes of water pollution around the globe.

L2 CLASS ACTIVITY.
Have students use library resources to find out which parts of the world are facing a water shortage problem and what steps, if any, are being taken to deal with the situation. Ask them to share what they learn with the class.

Although it makes up only a tiny fraction of the earth's atmosphere, carbon dioxide is vitally important because it regulates the amount of heat that the earth absorbs from the sun. The more carbon dioxide there is, the better an insulator the atmosphere becomes. It reflects heat that normally would escape from the earth into space. As current carbon dioxide levels rise, a growing proportion of the solar radiation is becoming trapped inside the earth's atmosphere and is being reflected back to the earth's surface. This condition, known as the greenhouse effect, results in higher temperatures, more water vapor, and steam.

There are about as many opinions on the results of the greenhouse effect as there are scientists studying it. One view is that the earth will get increasingly warmer. Other scientists predict that the results will be more complex and that some parts of the world might even get colder.

Global Water Pollution

Many people do not have enough water, or if they do, it is contaminated or too salty. There are about 336 million cubic miles (1,400 million cubic km) of water on the earth, but 97 percent of it is seawater—nearly all of it permanently held in the oceans. The rest is fresh water; and at any one time about 77 percent of it is stored in ice caps and in glaciers. A little over 22 percent is groundwater stored beneath the surface of the earth, and about 0.035 percent is held in the atmosphere. Surprisingly, surface water, such as the water in rivers and lakes, accounts for only 0.33 percent of all the fresh water on the earth.

In arid areas of the world, there may be no rain at all in some years. The tropics, by contrast, are deluged with water every day during the rainy season. The distribution of rainfall is so uneven over the earth's surface that one-third of all surface water is carried into the sea by only 15 rivers. The Amazon River carries 15 percent of this amount.

Each year the growing world population makes increasing demands on the world's water supply. Industry, mining, power generation, agriculture, and irrigation call for vast amounts of water. For example,

---

Additional Information

Air Pollution. Tell students to try the following to keep the air clean:

- Make sure that your home has proper ventilation.
- Have your furnace cleaned and tested for combustion efficiency.
- Avoid using commercially produced cleaning products which give off fumes. Substitute vinegar, baking soda, salt, and borax.
- Don't burn leaves. Instead, rake them and put them in a compost pile.
- Write to elected officials asking them to support clean air legislation.
- Avoid synthetic carpets, which give off chemical vapors.

about half the food being produced today grows on irrigated land. Water is piped into agricultural fields from groundwater or from lakes and other sources of surface waters. Many of these groundwater sources, which took thousands of years to create, are being used up or polluted.

Unfortunately, many people have taken water for granted over the years. Just as it was assumed that our vast atmosphere could absorb, dilute, and detoxify whatever was dumped into the air, it was believed that our water supplies had an unlimited capacity to wash away anything that was thrown into them. Tons of untreated sewage, solid garbage, and barrels full of toxic industrial wastes have ended up in streams, lakes, rivers, and oceans all over the world. For many years, this practice seemed to work. The "dilution solution to pollution" appeared to be a good one. Now, however, we know this solution is not effective.

The dumping of raw sewage into the world's rivers and oceans occurs almost everywhere you find human populations. Around the Mediterranean 70 percent of the coastal cities dump untreated sewage directly into the sea. In India the sacred Ganges River is among the most revered of rivers, yet it is the most polluted. The Hindu religion views the Ganges as bringing spiritual cleanliness through daily immersion rituals. In the meantime billions of gallons of raw sewage are dumped into the river each year. Although many Americans may not be aware of it, or prefer not to admit it, many of the cities in the United States dump raw or inadequately treated sewage, solid garbage, and industrial and hospital wastes into our oceans and waterways.

Despite efforts to provide more people with water and sanitation, the number of people without clean water increased during the past decade by 100 million. One of the greatest threats posed by contaminated water is the spread of water-borne diseases, such as cholera, typhoid, and amoebic dysentery.

In some cases specific illnesses have been traced to chemical water pollutants. In Japan in the late 1950s, for example, large quantities of mercury-containing wastes were dumped into a bay by a fertilizer manufacturer. The mercury settled, was picked up by bottom-dwelling organisms, and traveled up the food chain to fish, livestock, pets, and people. Thousands of people were stricken with muscular paralysis, impaired vision, and mental retardation. Many died—all from eating mercury-contaminated seafood. Other chemicals, often leaking into water supplies from industrial plants, have been linked to bone disintegration and cancer.

K E E P I N G   F I T

Chlorofluorocarbon Gases

Chlorofluorocarbon gases are gases used in spray cans to force out their contents. These chlorofluorocarbons float up into the air when they are released from the aerosol can. In the atmosphere, the chlorofluorocarbons release chlorine, which destroys ozone.

The first alert about the danger to the ozone layer was in 1974. However, not until 1978 did the United States ban the use of chlorofluorocarbons in aerosols.

Check for any aerosol cans in your home. Is their use absolutely necessary? Could you use a non-aerosol alternative?

Overcoming Misconceptions

Myth. Staying at home, you can avoid harmful air pollution. **Fact.** The air in a tightly sealed house may be polluted and make you sick. Common indoor contaminants in the home may include air filled with carbon monoxide (from kerosene heaters, poorly ventilated wood heating systems, tobacco smoke, etc.), radon, nitrogen oxides (from natural gas stoves), fumes (from plastics, evaporating cleaning fluids, refrigerant gases, and insecticides). Since 1900, over 30 million tons of asbestos have been used in the United States. When asbestos particles are inhaled, respiratory illnesses, and even lung cancer, may result.

L3 **RESEARCH.** Have students use classroom and library resources to find out about asbestosis, or white lung disease. Have them locate information about government regulations for workers who handle asbestos. Request that they share what they learn with the class.

L3 **RESEARCH.** Ask students to investigate some of the uses of asbestos around the world. Have them identify possible sources of asbestos in their current home, school, work, and recreational environments.

L3 **RESEARCH.** Have students use classroom and library resources to research which illnesses related to water pollution are most common around the world. Have them write a short report describing the causes, symptoms, and treatments of the illnesses. Ask them to share their findings with the class.

L1 **COMMUNITY INVOLVEMENT.** If applicable to your area, have students find out when and where beach cleanups are scheduled. Ask for volunteers to participate in a cleanup and to report back to the class about the experience and the kinds of trash picked up on the beach.

L1 **USING THE LESSON RESOURCES.** For additional student activities, refer to the lesson resources on page 597.

DID YOU KNOW?

- Early in 1992, scientists were alarmed to find that a huge hole in the ozone layer would soon appear over populated areas of Canada and the northern U.S.

DID YOU KNOW?

- It is estimated that costs from air pollution in southern California amount to more than 7 billion dollars annually. These include health, agricultural, and environmental costs.
- Air pollution results in 100 million dollars lost in crops and livestock in the United States annually.
- Breathing polluted air results in ailments such as burning eyes, lung and other cancers, pneumonia, aggravated asthma, bronchitis, sinus infections, and emphysema.

It has become apparent that dilution of toxins and other pollutants will not solve pollution in the world's lakes, streams, and oceans. While it may still be possible to find patches of clean air, there are very few large bodies of clean water left in most parts of the earth.

Oil Spills

In 1989 the oil tanker *Exxon Valdez* emptied 10 million gallons (38 million l) of crude oil into the waters around Prince William Sound in Alaska. Over 800 miles (1,287 km) of what had been one of the earth's most unspoiled and picturesque coastlines had been fouled, perhaps permanently. The accident, the largest oil spill in U.S. history, followed closely on the heels of two other major oil disasters. In December 1988, Grays Harbor in the state of Washington was the site of a 300,000-gallon (1,136,400-l) accidental spill. In January 1989, a calamity began at the opposite pole when an Argentine ship struck a reef and began leaking 3,000 gallons (11,364 l) of fuel and crude oil each day into the previously fresh and clean waters surrounding the Antarctic Peninsula. Many other less publicized spills have occurred in recent years. In fact, hardly a day goes by without a spill of some sort.

Studies by the National Academy of Sciences and other groups have found that the largest single source of oil pollution in ocean regions is the discharging of tank flushings and gravel used to help stabilize a ship, such as a crude oil tanker. In the North Sea alone, it is estimated that 400,000 tons of oil are released into the water each year from offshore oil rigs and ships emptying their tanks at sea. Additionally, oil from blowouts of offshore wells contaminates the seas.

Evidence shows that crude oil not only fouls our water and beaches but also contains **carcinogenic,** or cancer-causing, substances or substances that are poisonous. Though our energy-hungry world demands petroleum, we need to acquire our fuel in environmentally responsible ways. In addition, by developing and using alternative forms of energy, the world can reduce its fuel consumption and slow down oil drilling, thus helping preserve our oceans and beaches.

Oil spills harm our water, beaches, fish and wildlife.

Across the Curriculum

Language Arts. Have students locate recent magazine and newspaper articles about oil spills and other instances of global water pollution. Ask them to write letters to oil companies, government agencies, and groups such as the National Academy of Sciences that have experienced or studied oil spills. Ask students to request information about the spills, methods of cleanup used, costs of cleanup, and current research being undertaken on prevention and cleanup. Ask students to share their findings with the class.

Science. Ask students to present an illustrated report on the condition called pulmonary edema and the role of ozone, a poisonous form of oxygen, in that illness.

LOOKING AT THE ISSUES

The Ozone Layer

Ozone is the protective layer around the earth that is needed to shield humans from the sun's ultraviolet light. The ozone layer is being destroyed by gases found in freon (used in refrigerators and air conditioners), Styrofoam (polystyrene foam), and propellants in some aerosol cans. How quickly is ozone being destroyed and what should be done about it?

Analyzing Different Viewpoints

ONE VIEW. According to the United Nations Environmental Program, the ozone situation is getting worse fast. U.N. scientists are predicting that at least 3 percent of the ozone layer could be destroyed within the next 10 years.

A SECOND VIEW. According to the Environmental Defense

Fund, the depletion rate for ozone is much greater—in the 10 to 12 percent range over the next decade. The Environmental Protection Agency projects that for every 1 percent decrease in the ozone, 20,000 more people will develop skin cancer.

A THIRD VIEW. Others believe that such predictions of health catastrophe are overstated and hysterical and that technology can be created to deal with the problem effectively.

Exploring Your Views

1. What global steps do you think could be taken to ensure that the ozone layer will not be further destroyed?
2. What steps can you take to become active in environmental issues? How will doing so affect your self-esteem?

DID YOU KNOW?

- According to the Environmental Protection Agency, the use of pesticides has more than doubled in the past two decades.
- About 820 million pounds of pesticides are used by farmers every year.
- Despite spraying, about one-third of all United States crops are destroyed each year by a variety of pests.

Assess

Check for Understanding

- Assign and discuss the lesson review. Encourage LD students to focus on questions 1 and 2. Allow them to complete question 1 as a small group.

Evaluate

- Administer, grade, and discuss the *Lesson 1 Quiz.*

Reteach

- Lead students in a discussion of some of the causes of global air pollution. Ask them to explain how "acid rain" and the "greenhouse effect" got their names.
- Ask students to complete *Reteaching Activity 83.*

Enrich

- Select students to prepare a short illustrated report describing how weather conditions affect air pollution.

Close

Have students close their textbooks, and write an outline of the lesson's major concepts. Ask them to write a summarizing sentence beside each concept. Afterwards, request that they open their textbooks to check the accuracy of their outlines. Conclude with a brief discussion of the most important concepts learned in the lesson.

LESSON 1 REVIEW

Reviewing Facts and Vocabulary

1. Write a public service announcement about air pollution, using the terms *photochemical smog, chlorofluorocarbons,* and *carcinogenic.*
2. What are CFCs, and what are they suspected of causing?

Thinking Critically

3. **Analysis.** Find out the major sources of air pollution in your area. Decide whether or not sufficient efforts are being made to reduce the problem.

4. **Synthesis.** Investigate which water pollution dangers appear to be the most prevalent in today's world. Prepare an oral report to describe the causes and effects of these dangers.

Applying Health Knowledge

5. Develop and administer a student survey to determine the student body's awareness of global air and water pollution.
6. Use the results of the above survey to write an article for the school newspaper about global environmental issues.

Answers to Lesson 1 Review

1. Public service announcements will vary. Definitions for terms can be found on pages 597, 599, and 602 respectively, or in the Glossary.
2. Chlorofluorocarbons—compounds of chlorine, fluorine, and carbon used as propellants in aerosol spray cans, coolants in refrigerators and air condi-

tioners, and in making industrial solvents and plastic foams; it is the major factor in ozone reduction.
3. Answers will vary.
4. Reports will vary.
5. Surveys will vary.
6. Articles will vary.

604 CHAPTER 30 GLOBAL ENVIRONMENTAL ISSUES

Focus

Lesson Objectives

After studying this lesson, students should be able to:

- describe the effects of a growing human population on the environment
- explain the difference between deforestation and desertification
- describe the environmental problems associated with waste disposal
- list environmental problems resulting from war and civil conflict
- identify the effects of natural catastrophes on the environment

Bellringer

Write the following on the chalkboard for students to work on while attendance is being taken: *Imagine that you own all of the world's land. Write a short paper describing how you feel, as the owner, about people's treatment of your land.*

Introducing the Lesson

Have students share their responses to the Bellringer. Talk about how the future of the world's land is up to each of us. Explain that this lesson will be about some of the major crises facing the planet and some of the steps being taken to deal with them.

Building Vocabulary

- Have students use the terms *deforestation, desertification,* and *biosphere* in a written paragraph. Ask them to read their paragraphs to the class.
- Assign students to work in pairs to write a short public service announcement, using each of the vocabulary terms. Afterwards, ask them to test each other's understanding of the terms' definitions.
- Ask students to complete *Workbook Vocabulary Activity 84.*

LAND

LESSON 2 FOCUS

TERMS TO USE
- Deforestation
- Biosphere
- Desertification

CONCEPTS TO LEARN
- Population growth, technological developments, and wars cause changes in the earth's environment.
- Natural catastrophes can affect air quality and weather.
- Many environmental problems are also social, economic, and political problems.

ATTITUDES AND BEHAVIORS TO EVALUATE
- Self-Inventory, page 610.
- Building Decision-Making Skills, page 611.

The health and future of the earth are in the hands of its people. A population explosion, along with increasing technology and a growing desire for more material goods, is challenging the future of our global environment.

The World's Growing Population

More than 1½ million people are born each week—about 240,000 each day, which is about 10,000 each hour. The total world's population is more than 5.4 billion people. During most of our existence as a species, human population growth has been slow. For example, it took half a million years for humankind to achieve a population size of 1 billion. The next 1 billion people were born between 1850 and 1930, a total of 80 years. The third billion arrived between 1930 and 1960, in only 30 years. The fourth billion came along even more quickly, between 1960 and 1975 in just 15 years. About 1.4 billion more have been born since 1975.

This incredible growth of the human population is occurring when at least one person in six is hungry or malnourished and without adequate housing. One in four lacks clean drinking water, and one in three lacks access to adequate sewage facilities or effective health care. In a given year between 5 and 20 million people now die of starvation and malnutrition-related diseases.

Human Population and Changes in the Land

A growing human population is changing the land. Human beings are covering the surface of the earth with new highways, buildings, factories, and landfills, clearing billions of acres of what were once wilderness areas or rain forests, and cultivating crops needed to feed additional people.

Disappearing Forests. The number of people in developing countries in Central America, Africa, and Southeast Asia is increasing rapidly. By some estimates, 90 percent of the total population growth is occurring there. These countries have been clearing their tropical forests on a massive scale, mostly for fuel, farm, and ranchland. **Deforestation,** or destruction of forests, means extinction for thousands of plant and animal species.

The world's great forests play major roles in the **biosphere,** the thin layer of soil, water, and air near the earth's surface. Forested watersheds are like giant sponges that absorb, hold, and release water gradually. By influencing the downstream flow of water, forests help control soil erosion, flooding, and sediment buildup in rivers, lakes, and reservoirs. Deforestation, especially on steep slopes, leads to loss of the fragile soil

604 CHAPTER 30 GLOBAL ENVIRONMENTAL ISSUES

Resources for Lesson 2

- **Guided Reading** Activity 84
- **Decision-Making** Activity 30
- **Workbook** Vocabulary Activity 84
- **Workbook** Application Activity 30
- **Reteaching** Activity 84

- **Enrichment** Activity 30
- **Health Labs** Activity 30
- **Cooperative Learning** Activity 30
- **Lesson 2 Quiz**
- **Chapter 30 Test**

layer and disrupts the watershed. In the tropics, soil loss means long-term fertility loss as nutrients are quickly washed out of the system, leaving nutrient-poor soil behind.

Deforestation can also change regional patterns of rainfall as a result of altered rates of evaporation, transpiration (the exhaling of vapor from the surface of green tissues in plants), and runoff. Between 50 and 80 percent of the water vapor above tropical forests is released from the trees themselves. Without trees, annual precipitation declines and a region gets hotter and drier. The rain that does fall rapidly runs off the bare soil. As the local climate gets hotter and drier, soil fertility and moisture levels decline even more. Eventually, sparse grassland or even desertlike conditions may prevail where there had once been a rich tropical forest.

Clearing large tracts of tropical forests may also have global repercussions. These forests absorb much of the solar radiation reaching the equatorial regions of the earth's surface. When the forests are cleared, the land becomes shinier, so to speak, and reflects more incoming energy back into space. In addition, the trees of these forests help maintain the global cycling of carbon and oxygen through their photosynthetic action. When they are harvested or burned, the carbon stored in their biomass is released to the atmosphere in the form of carbon dioxide—and this may play a role in the greenhouse effect.

Almost half of the world's expanses of tropical forests has already been cleared for cropland, grazing land, timber, and fuelwood. Deforestation is greatest in Brazil, Burma, India, and Indonesia. At present rates of clearing and damage, only Brazil and Zaire will have large tracts of tropical forest in the year 2010; by 2035 those forests may also be gone.

Expanding Deserts. The world has always had deserts. Never before, however, have new ones been created as fast as now. Eighty percent of the productive land in the arid and semi-arid areas of the globe—or about one-third of Earth's surface—is believed to be affected by **desertification,** the conversion of grasslands, rain-fed cropland, or irrigated cropland to desertlike conditions, with a drop in agricultural productivity of 10 percent or more. The problem concerns both developed and developing countries. In the United States 10 percent of the land has already been affected, and a further 20 percent is threatened. About 2 billion acres worldwide have turned into deserts over the past 50 years. At least 44 million acres are still being transformed each year.

Today large-scale desertification is occurring mainly as a result of overgrazing on marginal lands. With a growing world population and an increasing requirement for food, scientists believe that food production must be increased by one-third by the end of the century simply to maintain present levels of nutrition. The desertification of once productive land poses a great threat to the health of the world's people.

Solid Waste. Resources are scarce in developing countries, and very few materials are discarded. However, in more affluent countries, a "throwaway" mentality often prevails. People use something once, discard it, and buy another.

Billions of tons of solid waste are dumped, burned, and buried annually in the United States alone. Instead of recycling most of these materials, as is done in natural ecosystems, people bulldoze them down the

Is there a better way to dispose of solid waste? Could some of these waste products be recycled?

Overcoming Misconceptions

Population and Resource Use. Many believe that the population explosion in economically deprived countries is a major contributor to resource depletion. In fact, while these countries have over 75 percent of world population, they use less than 20 percent of world energy.

The U.S., by contrast, has only about 5 percent of world population, and uses about 25 percent of its resources. This is much higher than in the economically deprived countries.

L1 SPEAKER. Ask a physics teacher to speak to the class about nuclear power and its cost, efficiency, environmental impact, safety, and the problem of radioactive waste disposal. Have students prepare a list of questions to ask the speaker.

L2 DISCUSSION. Ask students what the consequences are of depending so heavily on petroleum as a primary source of energy. Have students list alternative forms of energy.

L2 CLASS ACTIVITY. Ask students to take a stand for or against the further development of nuclear energy. Each must find two facts to document his or her stand. Divide the class into two groups—those for and those against. Give them time to research and arrange their facts to develop their argument. Then hold a debate on the topic.

L2 CLASS ACTIVITY. Have students use classroom and library resources to prepare for a discussion of the following questions: What are some of the environmentally safe and effective ways of disposing of or treating hazardous waste? Why is only 10 percent of the hazardous waste in the United States disposed of in a safe manner? What chemicals used in pesticides are commonly used in the community? What are some of the dangers of these products?

L3 COOPERATIVE LEARNING. Divide the class into small groups to report on information about DDT, such as its history, where it is manufactured, its dangers, current restrictions on its use, and parts of the world where it is still freely used. Have them share what they learned with the class.

L1 CLASS ACTIVITY. Invite a panel of individuals and representatives of businesses that encourage the use of organic methods of pest control. Afterwards, have students make a display or bulletin board to summarize what they learned from the speakers.

LEP CLASS ACTIVITY. Have students find magazine and newspaper articles about natural catastrophes and their effects on the environment. Lead a discussion based on some of the articles.

sides of canyons or dump them in wetlands, oceans, or landfills. There are only so many canyons; people must now deal with the pressing issues of solid waste disposal; air, water, and ground contamination; diminishing resources; and the growing unavailability of landfill space.

Technology and the Environment

There was a time when humankind took tens of thousands of years to accomplish much change. Then the intervals became just a few thousand years, then just a few hundred. Now these intervals are occurring in tens of years—or less—in terms of our capacity to alter our planetary living space. We have probably accomplished as much change in the years since 1950 as we did during the previous 2,000 years. One of the reasons for this decrease in time is the rapid increase in population.

Fossil fuels, such as petroleum and natural gas, have enabled people to develop agricultural technology that has brought about many changes, some good and some bad. For instance, modern farming has brought an abundance of food to people in many parts of the world. However, it has also resulted in the use of ever-increasing amounts of chemicals, such as pesticides and fertilizers. Some of these chemicals have contaminated parts of the world's food and water supplies. In addition, fertilizers, pesticides, tractor fuel, farm electricity, food processing, and food transportation all require fossil fuels—gasoline, oil, and natural gas.

Nuclear Energy. Today nuclear power plants dot the world's landscape. Industrialized nations that are poor in energy resources depend heavily on nuclear power. However, in many countries, plans to extend reliance on nuclear energy have been delayed or canceled. The cost, efficiency, environmental impact, and safety of nuclear energy are being seriously questioned. The overall net energy produced by nuclear reactors is relatively low, and the cost of constructing nuclear power plants is high—much higher than initially expected.

What about safety? Radioactivity escaping from a nuclear plant during normal operation is actually less than the amount released from a coal-burning plant of the same capacity. Nuclear plants do not add carbon dioxide to the atmosphere, as coal-burning plants do.

However, there is the potential danger of a meltdown. As nuclear fuel breaks down, it releases considerable heat, which is usually absorbed by

K E E P I N G   F I T

Conserving Energy

■ Save energy by washing clothes in warm water and rinsing in cold instead of using the hot water cycle.
■ Clean the lint trap in the dryer, and the dryer will run more efficiently.

■ Try drying your clothes outside on a line.
■ Put insulated wrap on the water heater but follow manufacturer's advice first.
■ Insulate and weatherstrip your home.

■ Draw curtains and shades at night to keep in heat when it is cold outside.
■ In winter, set the thermostat lower; in summer, set the air conditioner higher or consider not using it at all.

Across the Curriculum

Language Arts. Have students read about Love Canal, New York, where chemical wastes, buried for years, began to cause serious health problems. Ask when the situation erupted. What medical conditions arose? What chemicals were buried there? How did the federal government get involved? What happened to Love Canal and the people who lived there? Have students write reports of their findings.

water circulating over the fuel. The heated water produces steam, which drives electricity-generating turbines. If a leak should develop in the circulating water system, water levels around the fuel might drop. The nuclear fuel would heat rapidly, rising above its melting point. The melting fuel would pour onto the floor of the generator. There it would come into contact with the remaining water and instantly convert it to steam.

Formation of enough steam, along with other chemical reactions, could blow the system apart, releasing radioactive material into the surroundings. In addition, the overheated reactor core could melt through its thick concrete containment slab and into the earth, causing groundwater contamination.

All reactors have secondary cooling systems designed to flood the reactor if the initial cooling water is lost. In 1979 the Three Mile Island nuclear plant located in Pennsylvania underwent a partial meltdown. This was a result of the combination of equipment failure and human error. Some critics believe a meltdown was avoided only by luck. Others believe the incident proved the effectiveness of multiple backup safety systems in nuclear power plants.

In 1986 a meltdown occurred at the Chernobyl power station in the former Soviet Union. Radiation was released into the atmosphere, spreading to eastern Europe or beyond. A number of people died immediately; others died of radiation sickness weeks after the accident. Throughout Europe today people are still concerned about the long-term consequences. How long will the environment, including the land, water, produce, fish, and livestock, be contaminated? What are the risks of cancer from such exposure?

Nuclear Wastes. The Chernobyl incident underscores the consequences of nuclear accidents. What about routine nuclear wastes? Nuclear fuel cannot be burned to harmless ashes, as coal can. Nuclear wastes are a radioactive, extremely dangerous collection of materials. The decay rates of some nuclear wastes mean they must be isolated for 10,000 years or more.

The costs of simply cleaning up after currently operating nuclear facilities can range in the billions or trillions of dollars. The costs are so staggering that there remains the possibility that many sources of contamination will be abandoned because the money needed to adequately clean up the nuclear waste is not available.

War and the Planet

Battles among humans have probably always resulted in some damage to the environment. At no time in history has this been more true than today. Deliberate oil spills and the burning of hundreds of oil wells during the 1991 war in the Persian Gulf caused untold damage to the earth and its inhabitants.

The prospect of nuclear war is horrifying. Consequences would be measured in terms of billions of people who would be killed immediately and another billion who would die in the aftermath from radiation, starvation, and other effects. Many scientists predict that a nuclear war could bring about an effect called nuclear winter, which could lead to global extinction. They foresee that nuclear detonation would inject a

What are the advantages and disadvantages of nuclear power?

■ **Discussion.** In what ways is community service, as in Shawn's case, a better punishment than detention or similar curtailment of freedom? (It's a more positive response to negative behavior, and it may result in the individual learning something new; the individual may gain satisfaction and self-esteem in doing something useful for others or for the environment.)

■ **Discussion.** What did Shawn learn from his punishment of picking up trash? (That he loved nature; that the environment mattered to him; that he really could make a difference.)

■ **Answers**

1. As a punishment for getting into a fight; he gained self-esteem by helping save the river and wildlife.

2. Answers will vary. If nothing else, bad experiences can usually be learning experiences—the good comes from learning how to avoid the situation in the future.

Independent Practice

L3 **RESEARCH.** Have students study current information about how the increasing human population is changing planet Earth. Have them prepare an illustrated report to present to the class.

L1 **PARENTAL INVOLVEMENT.** Explain that if every American family planted just one tree, over a billion pounds of "greenhouse gases" would be removed from the atmosphere every year. Ask volunteers to purchase and plant a tree at home. Others might want to hold a fund-raising event to purchase trees to donate to parks and neighborhoods in your community.

L2 **COMMUNITY INVOLVEMENT.** Ask for volunteers to interview people in the community who are originally from other countries. Have students find out some of the environmental concerns of those countries. Ask students to report their findings to the class.

L1 **USING THE LESSON RESOURCES.** For additional student activities, refer to the lesson resources on page 604.

Overcoming The Odds

Shawn Gibbs is 18. He loves basketball and singing. He also has a special interest in the environment, but he did not develop this interest in the usual way.

Shawn begins, "When I was growing up, I lived with my mom, just me and my brother and my mom. Most of the time we lived with my grandmother. We didn't have very much. While my mom was at work working real hard, I took care of my brother a lot and did things around the house and we all did the best we could."

He goes on, "I wasn't doing real well in school—it was when I was in eighth grade. We came over some real hard times then. My mom was really struggling. So that eighth grade year I did really bad. We moved from the city, and I did better after that. I tried a lot harder. And when I came to my present high school, the associate principal, Mr. Arnell, helped me a lot and opened my eyes. In school I'd gotten into a fight with some guy. I had to do work as a punishment, and that is how I got involved with Mrs. Dean, a social studies teacher, and her environmental project. As my punishment, I had to go once or twice to the St. Jones River and pick up trash." Shawn had such a positive experience there by the river, however, that he continued to go there to work long after his punishment time had been served. "I liked it so much, to be out there by

ourselves," he says. "It's beautiful out there. So I asked if I could go back. I made new friends out there and was with some old friends, too. We picked up two or three tons of trash. It was a big accomplishment. We were trying to save the river from the highway being built over it. We found a rare tree called a Bald Cypress. We found out that this kind of tree doesn't grow around here usually. We mostly picked up trash but we also took pictures of a blue heron and other animals in the area to show that there was wildlife to save and that we'd be killing them off or forcing them to move if we didn't save the area."

Shawn plans to continue caring for the environment. "I'll try to help the environment in the future as much as I can." He concludes, talking about how he first got involved with the river, "The thing that works for me is that out of something bad can come something good if you just hang in there."

1. How did Shawn first become involved in cleaning up the river? What personal and environmental benefits grew out of Shawn's initial punishment?

2. Shawn points out that "out of something bad can come something good." Can you apply this statement to your own life? If you can't apply it to your past, how might you apply it to some area of your life right now that seems bad but might eventually prove to be good?

Overcoming Misconceptions

Myth. Most hazardous waste in the U.S. is disposed of in a safe manner. **Fact.** The Environmental Protection Agency (EPA) estimates that only 10 to 15 percent of all hazardous waste in the U.S. is disposed of properly. Because of the high cost of proper disposal, many companies take the risk of midnight dumping—illegally dumping hazardous waste into public waterways or secretly burying it underground. This pollutes water sources, and it contaminates soil. Not all hazardous waste is generated by industry. Household trash may contain materials such as drain cleaners, paint thinner, and automotive fluid—ultimately polluting landfills.

huge dark cloud of soot and smoke over most of the earth, which would block out the sun. Much of the planet would be thrown into darkness, and temperatures would fall below freezing for months.

Natural Catastrophes

Although many of the recent assaults upon the earth have been caused by its human population, natural events cause major changes as well. Earthquakes, hurricanes, tornadoes, and volcanic eruptions affect the environment and its inhabitants. Some of these, such as volcanic eruptions, not only change the nearby environment but also can affect air quality and weather conditions over large parts of the world.

Addressing the Issues

Many environmental problems are basically social problems. They begin with people as the cause and end with people as the victims. People and nature need each other; by hurting one, we wound the other. Fortunately, there is action being taken to stop the destruction of our global environment. In some countries, governments or conservation groups have turned abandoned land into wildlife parks. A number of countries and international groups have been working together on a comprehensive plan to preserve tropical forests, and the plan is already being implemented. A few developing countries have been reevaluating their agricultural policies. Brazil has designated some of its tropical rain forest as unsuitable for agriculture. This region has been set aside for ecological research and for recreation.

The world's efforts must go into renewing the environment by reducing pollution and waste and bringing back at least part of the earth's natural clothing of vegetation. All nations—and individuals—must work to put an end to deforestation, desertification, acidification, contamination and erosion of the soil, and the destruction of living species.

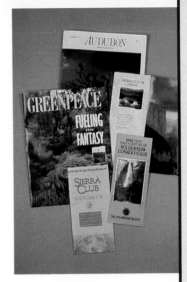

Many organizations are working to make people aware of environmental concerns.

Assess

Check for Understanding

- Assign and discuss the lesson review. Encourage LD students to focus on questions 1 and 3.
- Assign and discuss the chapter review.

Evaluate

- Administer, grade, and discuss the *Lesson 2 Quiz*.
- Administer, grade, and discuss the *Chapter 30 Test*.
- Refer to the Performance Assessment strategy for this chapter. See pages T 23 to T 25.

Reteach

- Have students write a short article for the school newspaper, focusing on a major idea in the lesson.
- Ask students to complete *Reteaching Activity 84*.

Enrich

- Have students study patterns of rainfall in different areas of the world throughout this century. Ask them to use library resources to find some of the reasons for the changing patterns. Request that they make an illustrated report of their findings.
- Ask students to complete *Enrichment Activity 30*.

Close

Make a one-page copy of a world map, and cut the map into jigsaw puzzle pieces. On the back of each piece write one of the lesson's major concepts. Give pieces of the map to students, and ask them to prepare a written summary of the concept printed on the back. Place a poster board at the front of the classroom, and have students pin their puzzle piece to the appropriate location to form a world map. Ask students to share their summaries with the class.

LESSON 2 REVIEW

Reviewing Facts and Vocabulary

1. Explain the difference between deforestation and desertification.
2. Write a paragraph using the term *biosphere* in which you point out its relation to global environmental issues.

Thinking Critically

3. **Synthesis.** Find examples in newspapers and magazines of land pollution and its effects on the global environment. Write a summary of your findings.

4. **Analysis.** Use a current and an older world map to compare the growing effects of deforestation and desertification.

Applying Health Knowledge

5. Develop an exhibit depicting some aspect of excessive population and its effect on the earth.
6. Write a letter that could be sent to a national or international organization, such as the Red Cross, asking what students and families can do to assist victims of a natural catastrophe. Share the information with the class.

LAND **609**

Answers to Lesson 2 Review

1. Deforestation is the destruction of forests; desertification is the conversion of grasslands or croplands to desertlike conditions.
2. Paragraphs will vary but should reflect an understanding of the impact that changes in the biosphere will have on global environmental issues and on the

population. Biosphere—the thin layer of soil, water, and air near the earth's surface.
3. Summaries will vary.
4. Answers will vary.
5. Exhibits will vary.
6. Letters will vary.

Helping Students Improve Their Health

Reinforcing Vocabulary

- **Recycle.** To treat or change waste so that it can be reused.
- **Toxic.** Poisonous.
- **Disposable.** Can be thrown away after use.

Teaching Strategies

L1 EXPLANATION. For the sake of convenience, many parents may buy products that are not environmentally healthful. Encourage students to talk with their parents about what they studied in this chapter and about their own concerns.

L2 CLASS ACTIVITY. Have students write letters to elected officials about the concerns that they have for the environment. Encourage students to become aware of environmental issues.

L3 CLASS ACTIVITY. Encourage students to investigate the current purchasing practices of your school. Does this school recognize environmentally safe practices? If not, encourage students to campaign for change through their student government.

L2 SELF-ESTEEM. Have students choose 8 items from the Self-Inventory. For each item, have students write a statement showing how the item relates to a person's self-esteem.

DID YOU KNOW?

- During a 1988 beach cleanup along the Texas shoreline 15,600 plastic 6-pack rings were found—in just 3 hours!
- Most of the 25 percent of world oil that Americans use each year provides fuel for our millions of motor vehicles.

Self-Inventory

Environmental Alert Checklist

HOW DO YOU RATE?

Number a sheet of paper from 1 through 14. Read each item below, and respond by writing *often, sometimes,* or *never* for each item. Total the number of each type of response. Then proceed to the next section.

1. I avoid buying things just for the sake of having them.
2. I recycle whatever is possible when disposing of a product or package.
3. I reuse things instead of disposing of them and buying new things.
4. I consider what pollution and wastes were created in the manufacture of the things I buy.
5. I read labels and buy the least toxic products available.
6. I shop at secondhand stores, garage sales, consignment shops, and flea markets.
7. I avoid buying disposable items when longer-lasting alternatives are available.
8. I avoid short car trips by walking, riding a bicycle, or using public transportation.
9. I refuse packaging for products that are already packaged.
10. I read consumer information articles to learn about the quality, durability, and toxicity of the products I buy.
11. I ask that less wrapping be used for my order at fast-food restaurants.

12. I reuse paper and plastic bags that are brought home from the store.
13. I recycle aluminum cans, newspapers, glass jars, and plastic bottles.
14. I share old magazines, books, and items of clothing I no longer need or want.

HOW DID YOU SCORE?

Give yourself 2 points for every *often* answer, 1 point for every *sometimes* answer, and 0 points for every *never* answer. Find your total, and read below to see how you scored. Then proceed to the next section.

25 to 28
Excellent. You are serious about caring for the environment.

17 to 24
Good. You are doing some reusing, reducing, and recycling, but you could do more to protect the earth.

9 to 16
Fair. Get serious about doing your share of planetary housekeeping, and try to do more to make the environment a better place for all of us.

Below 9
Poor. Not only are you not helping to clean up the environment, you are contributing to its destruction.

WHAT ARE YOUR GOALS?

If you received an *excellent* or *good* score, complete the statements in Part A. If your score was *fair* or *poor*, complete Parts A and B.

Part A
1. I plan to learn more about saving the global environment by ____.
2. My timetable for accomplishing this is ____.

Part B
3. The behavior or attitude that I would most like to change is ____.
4. The steps involved in making this change are ____.
5. My rewards for making this change will be ____.
6. My timetable for making this change is ____.
7. The people or groups I will ask for help are ____.

Meeting Students' Needs

For students who score *Excellent*.
Encourage students to lobby politically for environmental issues by writing letters and making phone calls.

For students who score *Good*.
Encourage students to develop an organization to address your school's or your community's environmental concerns.

For students who score *Fair*. Suggest that students spend 1 week investigating environmental issues. Encourage students to make one small change that will positively affect the environment.

For students who score *Poor*. Suggest that students recycle aluminum cans at home. They could save or donate the money earned from their efforts.

Building Decision-Making Skills

E lizabeth Tremain is a member of the high school environmental club. The club has decided that local and national environmental issues are so significant that it is going to take an active part in the next congressional election, based on how the candidates stand on these issues. The incumbent in the district is a friend of Elizabeth's parents, and Mr. and Mrs. Tremain have been active in supporting him and his party. However, his voting record has been unacceptable by the environmental club's standards. The club prefers to vote for his challenger, whose platform lines up with the club's views. This will be Elizabeth's first chance to vote in an election and be active in a campaign. How should Elizabeth vote?

WHAT DO YOU THINK?

1. **Situation.** Why does Elizabeth need to make a decision?

2. **Choices.** What choices does Elizabeth have?

3. **Consequences.** What are the advantages and disadvantages of each choice?

4. **Consequences.** How will Elizabeth's family feel about her decision? How will the rest of the community react? How will the con-

gressman and his opponent react?

5. **Decision.** What should Elizabeth do?

6. **Decision.** How should Elizabeth explain her decision? What advice would you give her?

R ico's school and other community buildings have been common targets for graffiti. They have become environmental eyesores. Rico and his friends have been as guilty as anyone of contributing to this problem. The new principal, whom Rico likes, has called on students to help clean up the school and to come up with a solution to the graffiti problem. As Rico has matured, he has regretted his contribution to this problem and become interested in helping to "save the city."

WHAT DO YOU THINK?

7. **Situation.** Why does Rico face a dilemma?

8. **Choices.** In what ways can Rico affect the situation?

9. **Consequences.** How will Rico's old friends respond to his actions?

10. **Consequences.** How will the community respond to Rico's actions?

11. **Consequences.** How will students, especially those who are still a part of the

problem, feel about students who are part of the solution?

12. **Decision.** What should Rico do? Why? How should he carry out his decision to get the most people on his side?

13. **Evaluation.** Have you ever been in a situation similar to Rico's? What did you do? Was your decision a good one, and how did you decide that?

Building Decision-Making Skills

Teaching Strategies

L1 CLASS ACTIVITY. Have students participate in a role-play situation in which Elizabeth is discussing her political concerns with her parents. Have students practice how to maturely discuss a heated topic with one's parents. Allow students to practice disagreeing with parents without becoming argumentative.

L1 CLASS ACTIVITY. Have students brainstorm in order to determine different ways in which Rico may begin to make up for his past mistakes that have involved vandalizing the school and other community buildings. Have students choose the best two responses. Have students form two groups and work toward creating a plan that students may use in your school building.

L1 CLASS ACTIVITY. Another possible role-play pertaining to global environmental issues is: At your local grocery store, you are given a choice to have your groceries bagged using plastic or paper bags. Your mother likes using the paper bags for the convenience, but she does not recycle or reuse these bags. Every time you say something to your mother about this issue, she gets angry. You want to do something to encourage her to recycle.

Discussing the Answers

Situation 1. It is up to Elizabeth to follow her conscience and vote in a manner that she can respect. Perhaps the best resolve is for Elizabeth to not discuss politics with her parents, unless her parents wish to discuss this topic. If Elizabeth presents her political views in a mature and unemotional manner, her parents are bound to respect her for her interest and perseverance.

Situation 2. Rico now has a chance to make up for past mistakes. Perhaps the best resolve in this situation would be for Rico to go to the principal and to ask how he can help. Perhaps Rico can exert some positive peer pressure on his friends to do the same.

Answers to Chapter 30 Review

Using Health Terms

1. Photochemical smog
2. Estuaries
3. Phytoplankton
4. Chlorofluorocarbons
5. Carcinogenic
6. Biosphere
7. Meltdown

Building Academic Skills

8. Cause—lead poisoning; effects—loss of appetite, anemia, damage to the nervous system, brain damage, lower intelligence in children.
9. Compositions will vary.
10. Less than two tablespoons.

Recalling the Facts

11. People were prohibited from burning coal fire unless they used a preprocessed, sulfur-free fuel or a more efficient smoke-eating stove. Industrial chimneys were required to be higher and to have built-in dust precipitators to remove pollution.
12. A tint in the air and a stinging sensation in people's eyes.
13. Air pollutants, such as sulfur and nitrogen, that return to the earth in rain.
14. Pollutes lakes, streams, and forests; depletes or eliminates fish in lakes and estuaries; damages crops, steel and stone structures, outdoor artworks, and even nylon stockings.
15. Tall smokestacks may be added to industrial plants to emit acid-laden smoke high into the atmosphere, but that smoke is spread over the earth by air currents and falls to the earth as acid rain.
16. It absorbs most of the ultraviolet wavelengths from the sun.
17. Chlorofluorocarbons.
18. Aerosol spray cans, refrigerators, and air conditioners.
19. Advantage—it regulates the amount of heat the earth absorbs from the sun, keeping the earth from becoming too cold. Disadvantage—too much carbon dioxide could trap too much heat, causing the earth

Using Health Terms

On a separate sheet of paper, write the term that best matches each definition given below.

LESSON 1

1. Air pollution that occurs when vehicle exhaust, activated by sunlight, combines with other hydrocarbons in the atmosphere.
2. Ecosystems where seawater mixes with fresh water.
3. Microscopic organisms, such as green algae, found in open, sunlit waters.
4. Contain chlorine, fluorine, and carbon.
5. Cancer-causing.

LESSON 2

6. The thin layer of soil, water, and air near the earth's surface.
7. A condition that occurs when an overheated nuclear reactor core melts through its concrete containment slab into the earth.

Building Academic Skills

LESSON 1

8. **Reading.** Identify cause and effect in the following sentence.
   Lead poisoning can lead to loss of appetite, anemia, damage to the nervous system, and possibly, brain damage leading to a lowering of intelligence levels in young children.
9. **Writing.** Air conditioning is one of the major sources of damage to the ozone layer. Write a composition of at least five paragraphs defending the use of air conditioning or persuading people to consider living without it.
10. **Math.** Imagine that all the earth's water is represented by one gallon of water. How much of that gallon would be the amount of water contained in rivers and lakes: about a cup, about half a cup, or less than two tablespoons?

Recalling the Facts

LESSON 1

11. What steps were taken to eliminate smog in the city of London?
12. What were the first signs of smog in Los Angeles in the 1940s?
13. What is acid rain?
14. List three effects of acid rain.
15. How can efforts to reduce air pollution in one place add to acid rain problems in other parts of the world?
16. How does the ozone layer protect people living on Earth?
17. What is the major cause of damage to the ozone layer?
18. What are the three main sources of chlorofluorocarbons?
19. What are the advantages of carbon dioxide in the atmosphere? The disadvantages?
20. Explain the meaning of the phrase "the dilution solution to pollution."
21. Name three water-borne diseases.
22. Name three effects of mercury poisoning.
23. List three ways water can become polluted, and explain the effects.

LESSON 2

24. How does an increasing population affect land use?
25. Why do people cut down forests?
26. What advantages for the environment do forests have over cleared land?
27. How does deforestation affect rainfall?
28. Explain the relationship between deforestation and the greenhouse effect.
29. What are the advantages and disadvantages of pesticides and fertilizers used by farmers?
30. What are the benefits and dangers of nuclear power plants?
31. How can an accident at a nuclear power plant affect the environment?
32. What is the cause of most environmental problems?
33. Who are the victims of most environmental problems?

to become too warm.
20. It refers to the practice of dumping waste into bodies of water and assuming that water will absorb, dilute, and detoxify whatever is dumped into it.
21. Cholera, typhoid, amoebic dysentery.
22. Answers will vary. Accept three of the following: Muscular paralysis,

impaired vision, mental retardation, death.
23. Oil spills, raw sewage, chemical wastes from factories, farms, homes, and nuclear plants; each type can contaminate drinking water, kill fish and animals, and cause illness.
24. It leads to more land being used for highways, buildings, factories, landfills,

and agriculture, at the expense of wilderness areas and rain forests.
25. For fuelwood, cropland, grazing land, and timber.
26. Forests control soil erosion, flooding, and sediment buildup in rivers, lakes, and reservoirs. Cleared land leads to loss of the soil layer and disrupts the watershed.

REVIEW

Thinking Critically

LESSON 1

34. Analysis. How is London smog different from Los Angeles smog?

35. Evaluation. Describe two conflicting views on the greenhouse effect. Do some research on this topic and decide which view you agree with.

LESSON 2

36. Analysis. Label each of the following causes of environmental change *air, water,* or *land,* to indicate which part of the environment it has the most serious effect on.
  a. deforestation   **e.** oil spills
  b. desertification   **f.** smog
  c. volcanic eruptions
  d. vehicle exhaust emissions

37. Synthesis. How can a volcanic eruption affect air quality over a large part of the world?

38. Synthesis. Invent one or more new ways for society to dispose of trash or garbage. Be creative. Present your plan to the class. Draw pictures or diagrams to illustrate your presentation. You may work on this project with two or three classmates.

39. Evaluation. If you could pass one law to protect our environment and address the pollution problem, what would it be? How would you enforce it? Explain why you chose the law you did.

Making the Connection

LESSON 1

40. Science. Fill a shallow pan half full of water. Pour in one cup of salad or cooking oil. Devise several ways to remove the oil from the water. (You might try a lettuce leaf, cotton balls, a piece of absorbent fabric, a suction tube, or anything else you can think of.) Which of your cleanup devices worked best? What does this experiment tell you about the difficulty of cleaning up oil spills in the environment?

Applying Health Knowledge

LESSON 1

41. Describe the environmental advantages and disadvantages of living where you do. Consider how your area is affected by each problem described in this lesson.

42. Your aunt Hildegarde used to be a lifeguard on a Florida beach. She has been treated for cataracts and several cancerous moles. What may have caused these health problems? What advice would you give her?

LESSON 2

43. What could happen to the drinking water in an area served by a nuclear power plant if a meltdown occurred?

Beyond the Classroom

LESSON 1

44. Community Involvement. Find out how your community treats water before it is consumed. Report your findings to the class.

45. Further Study. Choose one of the pollution problems described in this lesson. Read at least five articles related to the problem. Write a report describing the problem, its causes, and possible cures.

LESSON 2

46. Further Study. Do some research on the deforestation problem in Brazil. Find out why Brazilian forests are being cleared and how deforestation in Brazil will affect Brazil and the rest of the world.

47. Parental Involvement. Observe and keep track of your trash for a week. Then talk to your parents about a family recycling plan. Identify the items you throw away that could be recycled, such as aluminum cans, plastic and glass bottles and jars, and newspapers. Decide which family members will be responsible for each kind of item and what will be done with the items to be recycled.

27. As a result of altered rates of evaporation, transpiration, and runoff. Without trees, annual precipitation declines.

28. Forests help maintain the cycling of carbon and oxygen through photosynthetic action. When they are cleared, the carbon stored in their biomass is released to the atmosphere in the form of carbon dioxide; this may play a role in the greenhouse effect.

29. Advantage—make it possible for farmers to grow more food and thus feed more people; disadvantages—contaminate food and water supplies, require the use of fossil fuels.

30. Benefit—can provide energy to countries that are poor in natural energy resources; dangers—cost of construction is high, unresolved questions about safety.

31. It can cause death to people living in the immediate area. Others may die of radiation sickness weeks after the accident. Long-term consequences, caused by winds bearing contaminants, may occur over large areas. Land, water, produce, fish, and livestock may be affected.

32. People.

33. People.

Thinking Critically

34. London smog contained sulfur dioxide from burning coal and oil. Los Angeles smog is caused by vehicle exhaust emissions, activated by sunlight, combined with other hydrocarbons in the air.

35. Answers will vary. Possible answer: Some scientists believe the greenhouse effect will cause the earth to become warmer; others believe some parts of the earth will get colder. Opinions will vary but should be supported.

36. A—land; B—land; C—air; D—air; E—water; F—air.

37. Answers will vary but should include the idea that air currents may spread volcanic ash far beyond the area of the eruption.

38. Plans will vary.

39. Answers will vary but should be supported logically.

Making the Connection

40. Answers will vary.

Applying Health Knowledge

41. Answers will vary but should address smog, acid rain, damage to the ozone layer, water pollution, oil spills, global warming.

42. Overexposure to the ultraviolet rays of the sun. Answers will vary. Possible advice: Wear sunglasses and sunscreen when working, get a job indoors.

43. Answers will vary. Possible answer: Groundwater could become contaminated and eventually flow into lakes and rivers that may be the source of drinking water.

Beyond the Classroom

44. Answers will vary.
45. Reports will vary.
46. Answers will vary.
47. Answers will vary.

Lesson Summaries

LESSON 1. Everyone has a responsibility to protect the earth. Individuals can reduce waste and conserve natural resources by following certain guidelines at home. As consumers, they can precycle, by avoiding buying unnecessary things that need to be disposed of, and recycle those wastes that can be reused.

LESSON 2. It is important that business people, legislators, and individuals look ahead to consider the effects of their decisions regarding the environment. Short, quick answers in the past have often introduced new and greater problems. A step an individual can take now is to choose products that are safe for the environment. By being aware of environmental issues and becoming involved in their resolve, individuals promote health for themselves and others.

Introducing the Chapter

Ask students to think of energy conservation measures they are aware of and/or practice. (Possible responses might include ride-share programs, turning off lights, turning down thermostats in winter, etc.) Explain that on an individual basis it may seem that our efforts to conserve fuel are futile; however, the whole conservation movement started with one person's efforts and has continued to grow. It is important that each of us becomes a part of the solution, not part of the problem. Tell students that in this chapter they will study about conservation and steps they can take to protect the environment.

Performance Assessment ✓

Refer to pages T 23 to T 25 for a Performance Assessment strategy for this chapter. See the *Performance Assessment Activities* booklet for additional suggestions.

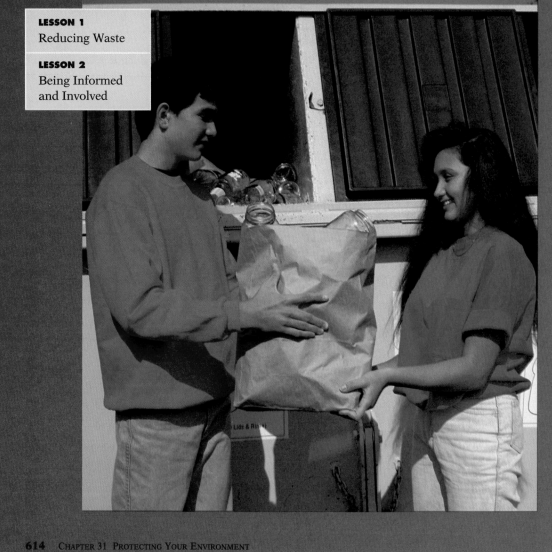

CHAPTER

31 PROTECTING YOUR ENVIRONMENT

LESSON 1
Reducing Waste

LESSON 2
Being Informed and Involved

614 CHAPTER 31 PROTECTING YOUR ENVIRONMENT

Key to Ability Levels

Teaching strategies have been coded for varying learning styles and abilities.

L1 Level 1 activities are basic activities and should be within the ability range of all students.

L2 Level 2 activities are average activities and should be within the ability range of average to above-average students.

L3 Level 3 activities are challenging activities designed for the ability range of above-average students.

LD LD activities should be within the ability range of learning-disabled students.

LEP LEP activities should be within the ability range of Limited English Proficiency students.

REDUCING WASTE

W ith so many people in the world, it may be hard for you to realize that you can make a difference in regard to environmental issues. Behaviors you choose can not only promote your personal health but also can help protect the environment. If you decide you have no responsibility to care for the environment, who will? Everyone has a responsibility to protect the Earth.

Conservation

Concern about preserving the environment, or **conservation,** is not new. After the Civil War there was great destruction of forests due to industrialization. Such events sparked the founding of our nation's two oldest environmental organizations, the Sierra Club and the Audubon Society. Both of these groups attempted to organize public opposition to the exploitation of the environment.

Theodore Roosevelt, the president of the United States between 1901 and 1909, is the president best known to support the cause of environmental conservation. He is known as the father of the national park system because of his great interest and love of nature. He is honored on the face of Mount Rushmore for his contributions to the preservation of our natural environment. Conservation is more than preserving national parks such as Yosemite or Yellowstone or our delicate wilderness.

Civilization and industrial development have resulted in life-styles that separate most people from direct contact with the resources that keep us alive. We buy food from stores, get water from faucets, and throw our waste in plastic bags. We sometimes take for granted our essentials in life.

Much responsibility and power in regard to conservation lies with you. You can help reduce waste and conserve precious natural resources by being aware of environmental issues. You also can protect the environment and conserve our resources by making good decisions as a consumer.

Guidelines for Saving Energy at Home

Energy conservation involves helping protect the environment and avoiding the use of irreplaceable resources. Of great significance to health is the fact that energy conservation reduces pollution of the environment.

About 70 percent of the energy we use at home is for heating or cooling. We use an additional 20 percent for heating water. The remaining 10 percent goes for lighting, cooking, and running small appliances.

Refer to the chart on page 616 to determine what you can do to conserve energy at home. Some of the actions may involve decisions that are not yours to make. You might discuss them with your family as ways to save money and conserve energy.

REDUCING WASTE **615**

LESSON 1 FOCUS

TERMS TO USE
- Conservation
- Precycling
- Recycling

CONCEPTS TO LEARN
- You can practice conservation by not using irreplaceable resources.
- Precycling is making environmentally sound decisions at the store, thereby reducing waste before it occurs.
- Recycling is treating or changing waste so that it can be reused.

ATTITUDES AND BEHAVIORS TO EVALUATE
- Self-Inventory, page 628.
- Building Decision-Making Skills, page 629.

Focus

Lesson Objectives

After studying this lesson, students should be able to:
- describe ways to avoid using irreplaceable resources
- list ways to precycle
- list products that can be recycled

Bellringer

Write the following on the chalkboard for students to work on while attendance is being taken: *In your own words, write a definition for the term* conservation.

Introducing the Lesson

Refer to the Bellringer. Ask volunteers to share their responses. Combine these responses to develop the definition used in the text. Explain to students that this lesson will explain the importance of conservation in protecting the environment and discuss ways to conserve.

Building Vocabulary

- Ask students to explain how conservation, precycling, and recycling can protect our environment.
- Ask students to complete *Workbook Vocabulary Activity 85.*

DID YOU KNOW?

- According to the American Aluminum Association, about 42.5 billion aluminum cans were recycled in the United States in one recent year.
- According to Recycle America, if only 250 people recycled a can a day, the energy equivalent of up to 3,500 gallons of gas a year would be saved.
- Almost three-quarters of the garbage Americans generate could be composted.

Resources for Lesson 1

- **Transparencies** 10 and 36
- **Guided Reading** Activity 85
- **Workbook** Vocabulary Activity 85
- **Reteaching** Activity 85
- **Lesson 1 Quiz**
- **Poster** 10
- **Performance Assessment** Activity 31

Teach

Guided Practice

L1 CLASS ACTIVITY. Ask students to complete some or all of the following open-ended statements: I could improve my conservation of resources by. . .; I could be a wiser user of resources if I. . .; Some of the ways in which I waste resources are. . .; Since studying about conserving resources, I have. . . .

LD DISCUSSION. Have students relate how they and their families reduce wastes. Discuss ways to improve community action and awareness in recycling.

L1 EXPLANATION. Buying recycled products reduces air and water pollution and mining wastes by 70 percent. Using recycled aluminum reduces pollution by as much as 95 percent. Every ton of recycled paper bought in America saves 17 trees, 7,000 gallons of water, and enough energy to heat or air condition a house for 6 months.

L1 COOPERATIVE LEARNING. Arrange students in groups. Ask one group to write ways to conserve energy, another group to conserve water use, another to reduce waste disposal, and another to explain how the world will be in an ecocrisis if Americans do not begin to protect their environment. Have each group report their findings to the class.

L1 DISCUSSION. The first Christmas tree recycling program was begun in 1971, in San Diego, California. In Austin, Texas, the program has saved more than $20,000 in hauling and disposal costs alone. The trees are collected and turned into mulch for gardening. Currently over 100 communities in the U.S. recycle Christmas trees. Discuss how this could be implemented in your community, if it is not already.

L1 USING HEALTH AWARENESS TRANSPARENCY 10. Refer to the Teaching Transparencies Binder.

L1 USING LIFE MANAGEMENT SKILLS TRANSPARENCY 36. Refer to the Teaching Transparencies Binder.

SAVING ENERGY AT HOME

Action	Effect
Heating and Cooling	
In hot weather use exhaust fans when cooking, bathing, or doing laundry.	Reduces heat gain that would increase the need for artificial cooling.
Close window drapes at night.	Reduces heat loss.
Have at least 6 inches (15 cm) of insulation over the top floor ceiling and 3 inches (7.6 cm) on an exterior wall.	Helps keep hot air in and cold air out during the cold season and does the reverse during the hot months.
Keep doors and windows shut during the air-conditioning season. Close fireplace vents.	Reduces the strain on the air-conditioning unit.
Keep air conditioning at a constant temperature and on automatic control.	Reduces the load on the system.
During the heating season turn down the thermostat 5 or 10 degrees at night.	Provides savings of 9 to 15 percent on heating bills.
Keep windows near the thermostat tightly closed.	Saves energy by preventing variations in temperature near the thermostat, which would cause the unit to run hotter or colder.
Water	
Insulate the water heater.	Saves energy.
Wash clothes only when you have a full load.	Saves water.
Use less detergent than suggested by the manufacturer.	Reduces the amount of phosphates in the detergent from going into the environment.
Wash clothing in warm or cold, not hot, water; use cold-water detergents.	Reduces energy costs.
Wash the car with water in a bucket instead of using a hose.	Saves gallons of water.
Place a filled plastic bottle in the toilet tank to displace water.	Saves 1 to 2 gallons (4 to 8 l) of water per flush.
Place a faucet aerator on water faucets.	Reduces water flow up to 50 percent by mixing air with water as it leaves the tap.
Fix leaky hot-water faucets.	Saves energy costs of heating water.
Never leave hot water running unnecessarily.	Saves electrical or gas energy and water.
If you have a food disposal, run it using cold water rather than hot water.	Saves electrical or gas energy and water.
Lighting	
Use fluorescent bulbs when possible. They now come in compact sizes.	Saves energy because fluorescent bulbs last longer and use less energy.
Use one higher-watt bulb rather than two lower-watt bulbs in a two-bulb fixture.	Saves electrical energy.
Cooking	
If you have a gas stove at home, be sure that it has a blue flame in the pilot light.	Saves fuel; a blue flame is a sign of a more complete burn.
When you have a choice, cook on top of the stove rather than in the oven.	Saves energy and uses less heat.

Across the Curriculum

Language Arts. Have a language arts teacher help students write a research paper on the use of nuclear power in conserving energy. Explain that one uranium pellet is equivalent to 1,780 pounds of coal, or 149 gallons of oil, or 157 gallons of regular gas, or 19,200 cubic feet of natural gas. Have students explain the following: Why is nuclear energy cheaper to use? What are other advantages to using nuclear power? How is uranium used as fuel? What are the hazards involved in using nuclear energy? Ask students to make a diagram explaining how a power plant operates. Students can get information by contacting Westinghouse Nuclear Energy Systems in Pittsburgh, Pennsylvania.

Precycling

Precycling, a new concept in protecting the environment, is a strategy to help avoid many problems of waste and recycling. **Precycling** means making environmentally sound decisions at the store, thereby reducing waste before it occurs. This strategy means that you, as a consumer, would avoid buying unnecessary things that need to be disposed of or recycled.

It will not be possible for you to precycle everything that you buy because there may not be choices for every purchase you need to make. However, the more you precycle, the less trash you will generate.

Guidelines for Precycling

Some basic guidelines for precycling are as follows:

- Be selective about packaging. When you are about to buy something, look at the way it is packaged. Determine whether or not the package can be reused, refilled, or recycled.
- Choose products packaged in recyclable materials. This includes packages made of paper, glass, aluminum, or cardboard.
- Do not pay for overpackaging, or layers of unnecessary packaging. If the packaging is not necessary to protect the product, buy products with more simple packaging. You might also save money by choosing these products.
- Avoid buying plastic. Even plastic that can be recycled cannot be reused as many times as glass, aluminum, or cardboard.
- Avoid forms of polystyrene, such as Styrofoam. Styrofoam contains chlorofluorocarbons, gases that harm the ozone layer and that are released when Styrofoam crumbles. Styrofoam is not biodegradable.
- Avoid buying disposable items, such as razors, diapers, cups, and plates. These items often end up as waste in already overflowing landfills.
- Buy in large or bulk quantities. This not only saves money but also helps eliminate unnecessary packaging. Single-serving items, such as individual juice drinks, small packages of raisins, and individual candies, are very overpriced and overpackaged.
- Look for products in refillable containers. Many manufacturers package products so that the consumer can buy one container and just buy refills after that. This eliminates the need to buy unnecessary, additional containers.
- Say, "No bag, please," when making few or small purchases. Instead, use a cloth bag for shopping.

Recycling

Recycling involves treating or changing waste so that it can be reused. Recycling has become very popular in many communities as individuals are taking responsibility to help protect the environment. Recycling more products means less need for incineration and landfills. Recycling pays off in many ways. Here are some examples:

- Recycling can produce six times as many jobs as when landfills and incineration are used.

Using a cloth bag for shopping eliminates the need for paper and plastic bags.

L2 DISCUSSION. Explain that several states have returnable aluminum can and bottle laws. These states have 30 to 40 percent less litter by volume than other states without the law. Discuss how this law could be enacted in your state.

L1 SPEAKER. Invite people who carpool to talk to the class. Ask them to describe advantages and disadvantages of carpooling, identify costs, give scheduling tips, and make suggestions for setting up carpools.

L1 DISCUSSION. Ask students to discuss how their families' lives would be affected if Americans were given gas stamps similar to the ones used in World War II when gas was rationed to each family. Discuss situations in the past that required gas rationing in the U.S. What would be alternatives if this were to occur?

L1 DISCUSSION. Have students name and explain some of the advantages of carpooling. Why is carpooling not used in every community?

L1 DISCUSSION. What are some ways that water can be conserved? How does water pollution threaten our water supplies of the future?

L1 CLASS ACTIVITY. Have students work in groups to list ways to conserve water at home and at school. Ask the students to share their lists.

L1 CLASS ACTIVITY. Have students make a class list of everything in a house that requires energy. Have them identify ways energy is commonly wasted and ways it could be conserved in the home. Discuss the fact that we sometimes take the availability of energy for granted.

L1 DISCUSSION. Have students discuss the possibility of electric companies controlling thermostats in homes or businesses by computers in order to conserve energy.

L1 DEMONSTRATION. Demonstrate the use of incandescent, fluorescent, and halogen lamps. Compare purchase prices, light output, and energy usage.

Across the Curriculum

Math. Help students realize how carpooling, using a bicycle, public transportation, and walking could conserve energy and save precious energy sources. Ask students to compute the amount of gasoline used by their own family each month. Have them get the approximate number of gallons of gas the family uses each month through bill statements or records kept by their parents, and then compute fuel consumption based on 15 miles per gallon and 30 miles per gallon. Have students determine the approximate number of miles traveled by family members in a week. Ask them to develop a plan with family members to decrease the number of gallons of gas the family uses in a month.

students in groups. Provide them
with posters and pamphlets or
brochures from companies on
how to conserve energy and
water. Have students design
posters for the class on conservation. Display the posters in the
class.

Independent Practice

L3 **COMMUNITY INVOLVE-
MENT.** Assign volunteers to
investigate whether or not their
community has an energy conservation program.

L2 **COMMUNITY INVOLVE-
MENT.** Ask volunteers to make a
map of the city, county, or just the
neighborhood marking all of the
sites where local recycling centers
are located. Include places where
secondhand merchandise can be
sold, such as flea markets, salvage
yards, and used book stores. Have
them include the name, address,
and phone number for each location. Share the map with the class
and put the map in the school
newspaper with an article about
conservation.

L1 **READING.** Have students
collect magazine and newspaper
articles about conservation issues
on the local, national, and world
levels. Have students report ways
in which the information in the
articles is important to them.

L1 **COMMUNITY INVOLVE-
MENT.** Recycling oil can be a
way to conserve and protect the
environment. Car owners in the
U.S. throw away more than 120
million gallons of motor oil that
could be recovered every year.
Have volunteers contact the EPA
to find what oil recycling facilities
are available in your area. Find
out who to contact in your state,
or ask at gas stations and auto
repair shops. Share the information with the class.

L3 **COMMUNITY INVOLVE-
MENT.** Assign students to investigate volunteer opportunities for
cleaning the environment in your
local community. What success
has your community had in recycling glass, aluminum, and paper
products?

DID YOU KNOW?

- Every hour,
  Americans collectively
  throw out 2.5 million
  plastic bottles.
- The American Paper
  Institute concludes
  that each American
  uses, on average, 120
  pounds of newsprint
  each year.
- Between 50 percent
  and 60 percent of
  American garbage is
  paper, much of that
  packaging.
- Every year, each per-
  son in the U.S. uses
  paper, paper products,
  wood, and wood prod-
  ucts that equal one
  100-foot-tall tree.
- Recycling paper uses
  55 percent less energy
  than producing paper
  the first time around
  and causes 95 percent
  less pollution in the
  process.
- For every 2,000
  pounds of paper that
  is recycled, 7,000 gal-
  lons of water and
  3,700 pounds of lum-
  ber are spared.

- Whatever does not have to be burned or buried is money saved.
- Recycling saves energy by requiring far less energy than using raw
  materials. For example, making a can out of recycled aluminum takes
  only 10 percent of the energy needed to make an aluminum can from
  its original source, bauxite ore.
- Recycling saves resources by reducing the need for foresting, mining,
  and drilling activities.
- Recycling preserves air and water quality because using recycled
  materials causes less pollution than when using raw materials.

According to the Institute of Scrap Recycling, producing a ton of
paper from waste paper requires 64 percent less energy, needs 58 percent less water, results in 74 percent less air pollution and 35 percent
less water pollution, and can result in 5 times more jobs than producing
a ton of paper from virgin wood pulp. In addition, it saves 17 pulp trees
and reduces solid wastes going into landfills.

Guidelines for Recycling

Not everything can be recycled. However, more than four out of five
items of household waste can be recycled in some form.

Different recycling centers accept different products. To shorten handling time and conserve space that is used for recycling, most centers
require that all items be clean, dry, sorted, and condensed. The following sections identify common recyclable products with guidelines for
each. It is important to recycle, but it is more important to consider limiting your use of each of the following materials.

Aluminum. Aluminum is one of the most expensive and polluting metals to produce. Fortunately, aluminum is totally recyclable. Recycling it
saves money and prevents pollution. About 55 percent of all aluminum
cans are recycled. Recycling aluminum is easy. Rinse cans and crush
them to save space. You can include pie pans, frozen food trays, and foil
in this group. In some states and national park areas, cans may be
returned for a refund.

Batteries. Dry-cell batteries range from the large flashlight type to the
small batteries used in cameras, calculators, and watches. These items
often are so small that they appear harmless, but they do contain toxic
materials.

K E E P I N G   F I T

Organize a Cleanup

One way that you can help the
environment is to do a beach
cleanup. Each year in September,
the Center for Marine Conservation sponsors the nationwide
effort. The debris picked up not
only makes beaches look cleaner,
it also helps to save the lives of
seabirds, fish, and mammals that
might choke or be poisoned by litter. To organize a group for a
local beach cleanup, write the
Oceanic Society at 218 D Street
SE, Washington, DC, 20003. If
you do not live near a beach, organize a group cleanup at a local
park, lakefront, zoo, or other public place.

618 CHAPTER 31 PROTECTING YOUR ENVIRONMENT

Additional Information

Water Conservation. Tell students they
could take a shower every day with the
waste water used when the tap runs while
brushing their teeth and shaving. Leaving
the water running can waste up to 20,000
gallons a year for one household. A running faucet uses as much as 3 to 5 gallons
of water a minute. Leaving the tap running
while brushing their teeth can use up to 5
gallons of water. By only wetting and rinsing their toothbrush they would use 1/2
gallon of water. Shaving with a tap running can use 5 to 10 gallons of water.
Filling the basin with water would use
only 1 gallon. Washing a car at home with
a hose can use up to 150 gallons of water.
If they use a hose with a shut-off apparatus, they would use only 15 gallons.

When burned in incinerators, metals from batteries, such as cadmium, lead, mercury, zinc, and nickel, pollute the air. When thrown into landfills, they leak into groundwater supplies.

Battery recycling is not yet very popular in the United States, although it is common in Japan and Europe. Ask your local recycling center or waste management (trash pickup) company for more information. Try to buy rechargeable batteries. Auto batteries, containing lead, are dangerous. They can best be disposed of by taking them to a service station or an auto parts dealer for recycling or safe disposal.

Cardboard. This product, used primarily in boxes, is fully recyclable. Cardboard is in short supply, so it is highly valued. About half is recycled in the United States. To recycle cardboard, flatten boxes, tie them together, and take them to a recycling center.

Clothing and Household Items. You might throw away clothing after buying something new. What do you do with a broken radio you cannot get fixed? What happens to an old refrigerator? Recycle all clothing and household items you no longer want by donating them to a community organization that can use them.

Glass. Like aluminum, glass is 100 percent recyclable. Glass accounts for 10 percent of household waste. It is among the easiest materials to recycle. Old glass is melted down and added to new glass to be used again hundreds of times.

There are three types of glass: clear, green, and brown. Check with your recycling center to see which types it accepts. Glass should be separated according to color. It does not matter if it is broken or cracked. Usually, paper labels need not be removed.

Most recycling centers will not accept auto glass, window glass, plates, ceramics, or light bulbs. Bottles and jars are usually the most common glass products recycled. Glass should be well rinsed. Caps, stoppers, wires, or lids should be removed.

Oil. More and more people change their own car oil. Some do not dispose of it properly. Just one quart of oil from a car can contaminate 250,000 gallons (946,350 l) of drinking water. A single gallon (3.8 l) of motor oil can form an oil slick for nearly 8 acres (32,376 square m).

Used oil is very valuable. About 2½ quarts (2.4 l) can be extracted from 1 gallon (3.8 l) of used oil. This oil is valuable as lubricating oil, road oil, wood preservatives, and oil for starting fires. Take used oil to a service station, auto garage, or oil change shop for proper disposal.

Paper. More paper is consumed in the United States than in any other country. Of the 72 million tons (65.5 million t) produced each year, about one-fourth is recycled. That amount saves 200 million trees per year. Paper accounts for more than one-half of all household waste.

Even though there is a demand to recycle paper, not all paper is desired. Some recycling centers will not take yellow paper, brown bags, or junk mail. Newspaper is excellent to recycle and should be bundled with cotton string or placed in paper bags. Do not mix magazines, catalogs, books, phone directories, and junk mail with newspapers.

Reuse the backs of envelopes and paper from junk mail. Reuse paper bags from stores, and use rags instead of paper towels.

REDUCING WASTE **619**

FINDING HELP

The Sierra Club works on hundreds of conservation issues at the local, regional, national, and international levels. To find out more about the organization—and the chapter or group nearest you—write to: Sierra Club Public Affairs 730 Polk Street San Francisco, CA 94109

L1 PARENTAL INVOLVEMENT. Explain to students that Americans use an average of 1.5 billion aluminum cans a week. Ask students to help parents and family members establish a system for recycling aluminum in their homes. Have them share their plans with the class.

L2 RESEARCH. The Environmental Defense Fund, the Audubon Society, the Sierra Club, and about 75 other environmental groups have made arrangements with banks to sponsor credit cards called "affinity cards." Research how these cards are used to benefit our environment.

L2 RESEARCH. Ask volunteers to go to a hardware store and check to see how many energy-saving and water-saving products it carries. Products should include plumbing items, such as low-flow shower heads, ultra-low-flush toilets, toilet dams, and water-saving faucet aerators. Examples of lighting items are compact fluorescent lightbulbs, energy-saving floodlights, and energy-efficient outdoor fixtures. Compare the prices on different brands of a product.

L2 COMMUNITY INVOLVEMENT. Ask students to contact local energy or water utility companies to see if rebate coupons are available for conservation products. Also, ask these companies to provide information on conservation. Share pamphlets, brochures, and other advertising information with the class.

L2 RESEARCH. Ask students to research economical sources of energy that are not fossil fuels. Have students design energy-efficient models that would provide energy for their homes, such as solar panels.

L2 PARENTAL INVOLVEMENT. Ask students to do an energy inventory with their parents to see what energy-efficient measures are used in their homes to conserve energy. What could family members do to make their home more energy efficient?

L2 SELF-ESTEEM. "I used to recycle, but what difference can one person make?" How does one's level of self-esteem affect decisions about environmental protection? How would doing your part in recycling contribute to your self-esteem?

Additional Information

Recycling. Recycling paper not only reduces the amount of waste in the environment, but also saves beautiful trees that are needed to remove over a billion pounds of greenhouse gases in the atmosphere every year. Americans use 50 million tons of paper each year. In order to provide this paper, 850 million trees are consumed. It takes over 500,000 trees to provide Americans with a Sunday newspaper every week. The average use of paper each year by Americans is 580 pounds. Recycling old paper uses 30 to 55 percent less energy than making paper from trees. However, recycled paper prices are higher than virgin paper because the demand for it has been low and manufacturers don't use it.

L2 **RESEARCH.** Americans use approximately 18 billion disposable diapers every year. Ask volunteers to study the different theories on the effects of disposable diapers on our environment. Compare the differences in the disposable and cloth diapers as to waste disposal and energy conservation.

L1 **WRITING.** Assign students to write compositions describing what their community might be like in the year 2025 if all environmental conservation efforts were suddenly stopped. Ask them to share their essays with the class.

L1 **RESEARCH.** If students have a leaky faucet at home, they can find out how much water is being wasted. Have them put a measuring cup or other container below the faucet and catch the water. Have them measure the amount of water the container collects in half an hour. Multiply that figure by 48 and they will know how much water is wasted each day.

L2 **COMMUNITY INVOLVEMENT.** Ask students to interview a city official about the status of carpooling and mass transit in their local community. Ask if any incentives are provided for people who carpool. What incentives are offered by other cities or communities? Report results to the class.

L1 **USING THE LESSON RESOURCES.** For additional student activities, refer to the lesson resources on page 615.

DID YOU KNOW?

- Actor Dennis Weaver lives in a luxury home built from thousands of old tires and aluminum cans.

Look for the recyclable and the recycled symbols when making purchases.

Plastics. Only a small percentage of plastics can be recycled. Unlike paper, glass, and aluminum, plastics can be recycled only a limited number of times, so try to buy beverages in glass or aluminum containers. Remove lids; then wash and squash plastic bottles you recycle.

Tin Cans. Tin cans are steel cans with a thin coating of tin inside of them. In the United States 30 billion tin cans are thrown away each year. Tin cans should be separated from aluminum cans when being recycled.

Tires. Almost one tire for each American is thrown away each year. Old and worn tires are a major source of litter, and they present a major fire hazard. Old tires can be recycled and used as padding for play equipment, as gardening containers, and as bumpers. Parts of the rubber also can be used in roads, playground surfaces, and running tracks. You should give your business to tire stores and service stations that recycle old or worn tires. Keep your tires properly inflated to extend their use. Doing so also saves gas.

Yard Waste. Leaves, grass clippings, and other yard wastes represent about 20 percent of all waste that ends up in landfills. Yet these materials can be of use, and recycling them can save money.

One option is to keep lawn mower blades sharp and high. Doing so enables grass to develop strong, healthy roots. Clippings can be left on the lawn to act as a natural fertilizer.

Composting is another option for yard waste. Composting refers to the biological decomposition of organic waste material under controlled conditions. Compost can be used as a soil conditioner, mulch, or plant cover. Food and yard waste can all be used in compost. A florist or gardener can give you details on how to start a compost pile.

Identifying Recycled and Recyclable Products

Using recycled products and products that can be recycled not only reduces waste but also reduces pollution and energy costs. To identify recycled packaging, look for one of these three indicators:

- the recycled symbol on the package
- a statement such as: "This package made from recycled materials."
- a gray interior such as that found in cereal and cake mix boxes

Recyclable products also carry an identifying symbol.

K E E P I N G   F I T

Becoming a Concerned Shopper

When going grocery shopping, show your environmental consciousness by
- bringing your own cloth or mesh shopping bag
- asking the grocery checker to pack your food in biodegradable

paper bags
- buying products with limited packaging
- buying milk in cartons rather than plastic containers
- buying rechargeable batteries
- buying bulk and unpackaged

goods instead of packaged goods
- buying locally grown and seasonal produce
- avoiding single-serving containers

Additional Information

Toxins in the Home. According to a new report, the amount of chemicals inside homes may be many times higher than outside. If you use air freshener, for example, you're not only masking odors but also creating a fine mist containing chemicals.

The three cancer-causing chemicals most commonly found in homes are benzene from smoking, paint supplies, and stored

fuels; perchloroethylene from dry cleaned clothes; and paradiochlorobenze in mothballs, air fresheners, and toilet deodorizers. These and many other home products containing hazardous chemicals contribute to indoor air pollution, hazardous waste, environmental illness, household poisonings, and smog.

LOOKING AT TECHNOLOGY

Jason, the Sludge-Detecting Robot

Industries and individuals have been dumping chemicals and other pollutants into waterways for years. Medical waste washing up on beaches has become a widespread problem in the United States. Drinking water is threatened with pesticides, hazardous wastes, solid wastes, and toxic chemicals. Many United States waterways now have thick black sludge on their bottoms sometimes referred to as "black mayonnaise." Originally, it was assumed that such sludge buildup would only occur in shallow or landlocked waterways. But now the evidence is mounting that sludge is even accumulating on the ocean floor.

Scientists know that ocean dumping may have serious consequences for the environment, and they are studying what the potential long-term health and environmental

hazards of this dumping may be. One way that they are doing this is with Jason, a sludge-detecting robot working on the ocean floor off the coasts of New Jersey and New York. The robot, attached by fiber optic cables, is operated by a scientist on a research ship who watches the robot on a video screen and moves a joystick to make the robot perform various operations. Using a variety of monitors and video screens, scientists aboard the ship study the remote-controlled robot's movements 9,000 feet below the water's surface as it moves across the ocean floor scooping up sediment and water samples. The samples will be studied to determine the long-term damage of the millions of tons of sewage and other pollutants that have been dumped into the ocean.

DID YOU KNOW?

- At least 35 states in the United States now have comprehensive recycling programs.
- Recently, a controversy has started about the use of juice boxes and whether or not they are recyclable. Some states have already banned them. Others are beginning to try to recycle them, turning them into, among other things, plastic timber used in building park benches and decks.

LESSON 1 REVIEW

Reviewing Facts and Vocabulary

1. How does recycling contribute to protecting the environment?
2. Define *precycling* and tell how consumers benefit from doing this.

Thinking Critically

3. **Analysis.** Compare precycling and recycling. Include examples of both.
4. **Analysis.** Why do you think only 10 percent of recyclable household products are actually recycled?

5. **Evaluation.** Why do you think recycling is more popular today than it was 25 years ago?

Applying Health Knowledge

6. Find out how to make a compost pile. How can doing this save money?
7. How would driving a car a few extra years be a good example of precycling?
8. Write a report on recycling efforts in your community. Evaluate the success of these efforts.

Assess

Check for Understanding

- Assign and discuss the lesson review. Encourage LD students to focus on questions 1, 2, 3, and 4.

Evaluate

- Administer, grade, and discuss the *Lesson 1 Quiz*.

Reteach

- Have students make a list of the ways to conserve and reduce wastes mentioned in this lesson and make a chart using this list for the class.
- Ask students to complete *Reteaching Activity 85*.

Enrich

- Have students write a description of a utopia. Ask them to pay particular attention to the ways in which water, wastes, and energy are managed in the utopia. What does the environment look like? How is it kept pollution-free? What effects do these perfect surroundings have on the humans who live there?

Close

Have students summarize the most important concepts in this lesson.

Answers to Lesson 1 Review

1. It involves treating and changing waste so it can be reused, and it means less need for incineration and landfills.
2. See "Precycling" on page 617.
3. Both are measures designed to protect the environment by reducing waste. Examples will vary.
4. Answers will vary.
5. Answers will vary.

6. Composting eliminates costs involved in trash pickup, incineration, and landfill fees and eliminates the need to buy soil conditioners and mulch.
7. Answers will vary. Possible answer: It would save on energy and materials needed to make a new car.
8. Reports will vary.

622 CHAPTER 31 PROTECTING YOUR ENVIRONMENT

Focus

Lesson Objectives

After studying this lesson, students should be able to:

- discuss the meaning of the terms *nontoxic, biodegradable,* and *organic*
- describe current environmental issues
- list ways they can become involved in protecting the environment

Bellringer

Write the following on the chalkboard for students to work on while attendance is being taken: *In your own words, explain the following statement: You are your environment.*

Introducing the Lesson

Refer to the Bellringer. Ask volunteers to share their responses. Explain to students that each person is responsible for the protection of the environment. This lesson will explain how people can be involved and make a difference in solving environmental problems. Students will learn how their actions can determine the type of environment that surrounds them.

DID YOU KNOW?

- Cities and states are working to achieve new recycling goals. For example, Florida requires its cities and counties to recycle 30 percent of their trash by 1994. Austin, Texas, plans to increase residential recycling from 4 to 15 percent by 1995.

BEING INFORMED AND INVOLVED

LESSON 2 FOCUS

TERMS TO USE
- Biodegradable (by•oh•di•GRAYD•uh•buhl)
- Organic

CONCEPTS TO USE
- Your personal health is related to environmental health; you can become an informed environmental consumer.
- There are many current environmental issues.
- You can become involved in protecting the environment.

ATTITUDES AND BEHAVIORS TO EVALUATE
- Self-Inventory, page 628.
- Building Decision-Making Skills, page 629.

Business people, government leaders, and individuals like yourself make decisions that affect the environment. It is important to look ahead to consider the effects those decisions have on future generations.

Sometimes in the past, short, quick answers were given to problems. Some of these answers caused new problems that, in time, proved to be greater than the original ones later on. The development of pesticides, the gasoline combustion engine, and nuclear power are all examples of inventions that were immediately beneficial to human life but later resulted in other problems to the environment.

Be Aware as a Consumer

Your personal health is related to environmental health. It is important to choose products that are safe for you and the environment.

There are a growing number of terms used on product labels to attract consumers who are interested in shopping for environmentally safe products. As a consumer, become aware of and familiar with the following terms:

- *Nontoxic* is a term that is meant to imply a product is not harmful or poisonous to humans. However, it could be harmful to plant and animal life, or the product's packaging could be harmful. What could happen to such a product when it becomes waste?

- When an item can eventually be broken down by microorganisms, it is **biodegradable.** The time for this process to occur can vary greatly. Some products may take up to several hundred years or more to decompose.

- You see the term *natural* on the packaging of many products. There are many natural ingredients that can also be dangerous and even poisonous. For example, lead and mercury are both natural and poisonous.

- The word **organic** means a product is derived from living organisms without the use of chemicals. For example, organic food is grown with fertilizer of plant or animal origin. Chemical fertilizers are not used. While some states have defined this term, there is no legal requirement to meet this claim. All living matter and even hazardous chemicals can properly be called organic.

- Consider the phrase *environmentally safe*. Does it refer to the contents of the package, the package itself, or both? Remember, almost everything has some impact on the environment.

Many common household products or chemicals for the yard are toxic. Disposing of them down a drain or in the ground could result in toxic chemicals reaching nearby water sources.

The Environmental Protection Agency (EPA) can give you advice about which products to avoid and can suggest safe alternatives. This

622 CHAPTER 31 PROTECTING YOUR ENVIRONMENT

Resources for Lesson 2

- **Transparency** 36
- **Guided Reading** Activity 86
- **Decision-Making** Activity 31
- **Workbook** Vocabulary Activity 86
- **Workbook** Application Activity 31
- **Reteaching** Activity 86

- **Enrichment** Activity 31
- **Health Labs** Activity 31
- **Cooperative Learning** Activity 31
- **Lesson 2 Quiz**
- **Chapter 31 Test**

Overcoming The Odds

Meg Chandler is 15. She keeps a journal and is thinking about a career in journalism in the future. She is on the newspaper staff at her school, and she has a part-time job working in a shoe store. But her real interest for the past several years has been working with Kids Against Pollution, an organization devoted to getting young people involved in helping to protect the environment.

She begins, "I became involved in environmental issues when I was in the sixth grade. That's when Kids Against Pollution was first started by the fifth grade class of Mr. Byrne. He asked me to help him with a presentation to the board of education about banning the use of Styrofoam in the town's three schools. After that, I became involved in making presentations in front of state legislators on issues like Earth Day 2000 and making environmental education mandatory."

Meg's environmental efforts are not just public ones. They are also private and personal. "I try to implement environmental awareness in my day-to-day routines," she says, "by buying only cleaners that are packaged in environmentally conscious ways and products that do not contain ingredi-

ents that are particularly harmful to the environment. A lot of it is also common sense, like turning off lights when you leave the room or turning off the water when you're not using it. The Earth is running out of resources," Meg says, "and facing the environmental problems in our world are odds that all of us have to overcome."

She goes on, "One particular set of odds stacked against people like me and others in Kids Against Pollution is simply the fact that we are just kids. But we also have the odds stacked in our favor because we are kids. We're open to new ideas. We aren't jaded about the situation we live in. We have a wonderful advantage because from the beginning we are being taught to be environmentally conscious, and these lessons are more likely to stick with us for the rest of our lives.

"Working with Kids Against Pollution has dramatically increased my self-confidence," Meg says. "It's shown me I can accomplish things. There are now over 1000 chapters of Kids Against Pollution, and several in foreign countries, too."

Meg concludes, "If you are like most teenagers, you are probably underestimating what you can do. One thing that I wish I could say to every kid in America is not to underestimate yourself—that if you see something that you would like to change, then by all means give it your best shot."

1. How did one individual's concern for the environment grow? How did many individuals pooling their commitment, energy, and talent make an even greater difference?
2. How has Meg's involvement in Kids Against Pollution affected her self-esteem?
3. What are your primary concerns about the environment? What commitment, talents, and energy can you give to an environmental effort?

Additional Information

Overpopulation. One reason for our environmental crisis is overpopulation. Not only are people living longer, but 16,000 babies are born each hour on the earth.

Water Conservation. Over 40 percent of the water used in the average house is flushed down the toilet. Many toilets use 5 to 7 gallons (19 to 27 l) of water per flush. An inexpensive way to cut down the amount of water used is by installing a water displacement device in the toilet tank. A small dishwashing soap bottle with the label removed will work. Stones in the bottle will help weigh it down after it is filled with water. The size of the bottle should not hinder the flushing mechanism. About 1 to 2 gallons (4 to 8 l) of water can be saved per flush.

624 CHAPTER 31 PROTECTING YOUR ENVIRONMENT

L1 DISCUSSION. Ask students to list current environmental conservation issues that are relevant to your community. Examples might include cleaning up an area, dealing with a landfill area, organic farming, recycling projects, erosion control, protection of water resources, disposal of city wastes, etc. Share the lists and discuss what the community is doing to address the issues and how students can help.

L1 DISCUSSION. Why are many people more concerned now than in the past about environmental issues in their communities?

L1 EXPLANATION. Composting yard waste is cleaner and healthier than dumping it in landfills and burning it. Each year, Americans throw away 28 million tons of mowed grass, dead leaves, and branches. Burning a ton of the waste emits 117 pounds of carbon monoxide, 41 pounds of particulate, and 7 or more carcinogens. Yard waste is responsible for 20 percent of all garbage Americans throw away. Have students determine how composting could be done in their yard.

L1 LAB. This activity will help students understand the effects of phosphates in our water supplies. Phosphates are used to increase suds in soap products to make them last longer. Phosphates are not necessary and pollute our waterways. One-half of the phosphates in lakes and streams comes from detergents. Bring to class a tablespoon, different brands of laundry or dish detergent, four identical jars with lids, masking tape, scissors, a ruler, a pen, water, and a clock or watch. Cut a piece of masking tape the height of each jar. Mark one-inch increments on the tape. Write the name of the detergent on the tape and affix it on each jar. Place one tablespoon of each detergent or soap in separate jars. Fill each half full with water. Mark the water line on the tape. Screw the lids on the jars and shake each one vigorously for 1 minute. Mark the suds lines on the tape. Leave the jars for 10 minutes and mark the suds lines again. Compare the difference in the brands of detergents. Are the ones with the most suds better for the water?

The term *natural* appears on many products. It is important to know that this term does not mean a product is safe or better than others.

CONFLICT RESOLUTION

Catching a fish in a local river last June has impacted Tosh's life. The fish he caught was a carp with a huge tumor on its head. Tosh caught the carp downstream from an oil refinery and the city's sewage treatment plant. Tosh wants to convince the public that the river must be cleaned up. So he's gone fishing in the river just about every day. So far, more than half the fish Tosh has caught have had deformities, such as eroded fins, misshapen skeletons, tumors, and lesions. Tosh's kept a careful record of every catch and put the most gruesome examples in his parents' freezer.

How should Tosh use his evidence to convince local residents to act against the polluters?

United States agency sets up and enforces standards to help protect the environment from pollution. The EPA also does research on the effects of pollution.

Current Environmental Issues

Every person who lives on Earth has some responsibility for what happens to it. We vary greatly in our knowledge, skill, interests, and needs concerning the environment. So it is not likely that every person can learn all there is to know about each environmental issue that faces humankind. Perhaps there is an issue that is of great interest to you, or that is a particular problem in your area. Here are some major environmental issues that might be of interest to you:

- Futuristic thinking. Nations of the world need to consider the long-range effects of short-range decisions, such as unrestricted use of nuclear power. Many environmentalists are investigating alternate sources of energy for the future.

- Population growth. Throughout the world and in certain areas of the United States where there is rapid population growth, there is low quality of life and much human suffering. Rapid population growth also leads to rapid deterioration of the land and to a severe drain on resources, such as water and minerals.

- Development and environment. Most people realize that development brings jobs and helps the income of the local population. However, development also brings problems that can negatively affect land, resources, air, and water.

- Food and agriculture. Problems of hunger, poor food distribution, destruction of usable cropland, poor irrigation methods, and extensive use of chemicals are part of this area of concern.

- Biological diversity. There is concern throughout the world that the habitats of many species of plants and animals will be destroyed as population, mineral extraction, and development increases.

- Tropical forests. About half of all tropical forests are gone, and along with them, many species of plants and animals. Forest loss causes many problems for people, including soil erosion, flooding, shortages of fuelwood and timber, loss of food from tropical plants, and displacement of whole groups of people.

- Ocean and coastal resources. Overfishing is a major problem in the oceans of the world. Some species of whales are near extinction. Pollution from large municipal areas, oil spills, and waste dumping have all created major problems for aquatic life.

- Fresh water. Many people do not have access to clean water. Unsafe water causes millions of deaths. Surface and groundwater are being polluted by municipal, industrial, and chemical wastes. Increasing population creates more demand for water.

- Nonfuel minerals. More people and increased consumption from development results in a greater need for minerals such as copper, zinc, lead, and mercury. At the current rate, some of these minerals will be gone within 50 years. Mining of these minerals can also cause great environmental damage.

Additional Information

Plants as Resources. The following are just a few of the many scientific and medicinal potentials of plants that could be affected by environmental problems. (1) Milkweed plants can convert sunlight into hydrocarbons—just as those found in petroleum. (2) The guayle plant found in the desert of Mexico is 10 to 20 percent rubber and is being tested by manufacturers for tires. (3) Evening primrose seeds contain an oil rich in an acid that scientists believe may help control heart disease. (4) Extracts from cucumber skins and bay leaves are being synthesized to possibly produce cockroach repellents. (5) The drug Cyclosporin A, that is used to prevent the body from rejecting transplanted organs, is derived from two strains of fungi.

Many tropical forests are being deforested. Saving these forests is an environmental concern. Forest loss causes many problems.

- Energy. Industrial development and transportation are highly dependent upon fossil fuels. Use and need are increasing rapidly. War and pollution are just two of the problems associated with this issue.

- Air, atmosphere, and climate. Increased use of fossil fuels, chlorofluorocarbons, and other chemicals is severely damaging the ozone layer, and there is danger of seriously warming the earth's climate and changing the way of life for many people.

- Hazardous substances. Products such as plastics, pesticides, and radioactive wastes, while contributing to development, have created significant health problems for large groups of people.

- Solid waste management. The problems of insufficient space to dispose of all our waste and how that waste affects the air and water are major problems in the United States today. These problems will get worse as population increases.

Culturally Speaking

Reforestation Efforts

Every day, 12 million trees are lost in the tropics. The trees are cut down for fuel or cleared to provide farmland.

In Brazil, some companies that cut down trees are also replanting. In Haiti, farmers are planting fast-growing trees that help the soil and later may be harvested for fuel. Easter Island, known for the giant stone heads erected by a thriving civilization 400 years ago, was nearly destroyed by deforestation and the resulting soil erosion. Today the islanders are planting fast-growing eucalyptus trees along mountain slopes. The soil now can support mahogany and coconut groves as well.

KEEPING FIT

Cleaning Up After Large Events

Litter picked up after large events such as concerts and fairs is rarely recycled even though up to 60 percent of the debris is recyclable. According to the James River Corporation, after the International Special Olympics in Minneapolis, 2 million Styrofoam cups were picked up for recycling, as were 50,000 bottles and cans, 800,000 napkins, and 10,000 pounds of food.

The next time your school is planning a large event, make arrangements to make it an environmentally sound event. Precycle when planning for what will be sold. Recycle after the event, providing labeled bins for different kinds of trash, and cleaning up litter left behind.

BEING INFORMED AND INVOLVED **625**

Additional Information

The Need for Trees. Our primary source of air pollution is the burning of fossil fuels for energy. In developing countries, air pollution results when large areas of forest and grassland are burned to clear land for farming. In both cases, burning releases large quantities of carbon dioxide and other gases into the atomsphere. Because of this, and with so many trees destroyed, less carbon dioxide is removed from the atmosphere. The greenhouse effect results. Planting trees will help relieve this effect. In addition to consuming carbon dioxide, a group of trees near a building can provide shade and cooler temperatures. Energy saved by not using air conditioning saves fuel and also helps alleviate the effects of global warming.

L1 DISCUSSION. Ask students how modern technology has influenced environmental problems. Discuss examples such as the invention of the microwave, instant foods, frozen foods, disposable containers, plastic trash containers, etc.

L1 EXPLANATION. Explain to students that if a family of 4 takes a 5-minute shower each day, the family will use more than 700 gallons of water every week. This amount of water is equivalent to a 3-year drinking supply of water for 1 person. Showers account for 32 percent of water use in the home. Explain that a low-flow shower head can save water and reduce water use by 50 percent. In addition, it will decrease the energy used for heating the water for the shower as much as 50 percent.

L1 CLASS ACTIVITY. Polystyrene foam, Styrofoam, is not biodegradable. It is estimated that Americans produce enough Styrofoam cups each year to circle the earth 436 times. These products will remain on our planet for 500 years after use. This product is deadly to marine life. At the current rate of use by Americans, what will be the ultimate effect on our landfills and waterways from the use of Styrofoam? How can we eliminate this problem? Ask students to write solutions and discuss them with the class.

L1 CLASS ACTIVITY. Divide the class into groups. Give each group a large sack. For 1 week, spend the first 15 minutes of class having each group circle certain sections of the school to pick up trash. At the end of the week, have students make environmental posters using the trash and displaying them throughout the school for awareness.

Independent Practice

L2 WRITING. Explain to students that the government has been hesitant in protecting consumers' interests relating to environmental claims manufacturers make about their products. A few states have passed laws prohibiting false environmental claims, but the majority of states and the federal government have not done anything. Ask students to write a letter to a politician asking why we don't have laws to protect consumers against false environmental claims made by manufacturers.

MENT. Arrange students into groups to organize a recycling campaign for your school. Have one group decide how to get containers for aluminum cans for the school. Have another group be responsible for finding a way to get the cans picked up from the school and taken to a recycling center. Have other groups do the same with paper products. Have students work with the student council so that any money collected from the project will be spent on trees to be planted around the school or in your city.

L1 PARENTAL INVOLVEMENT.
Ask students to help their family clean out the attic, garage, or storeroom. They could take items to be recycled to the proper facilities, donate items to be reused by the needy, or have a garage sale. Items could be taken to a flea market to be sold.

L1 PARENTAL INVOLVEMENT.
To determine how dependent we are on water, have students give each member of their family a sheet of paper to carry with them. Ask family members to record each time they use water. At the end of the day the list should be very long. Have family members compare lists. Ask students to discuss how the family could save water.

L1 USING THE LESSON
RESOURCES. For additional student activities, refer to the lesson resources on page 622.

DID YOU KNOW?

- Air pollution is one of the greatest environmental risks to human health, causing asthma, bronchitis, emphysema, and lung cancer.
- Lead poisoning is the most prevalent environmental threat to the health of children in the U.S.

Solid waste management is a major problem in the United States as communities try to determine what they should do with it.

Becoming Involved

Here are some practical suggestions for becoming involved in protecting the environment:

- Become an informed consumer by evaluating advertising, labels, contents, and packaging as it relates to the environment. Give feedback to companies on positive ways they can affect the environment.

- Get more information about environmental issues that are of concern to you.

- Contact organizations that conserve resources, and educate people on environmental issues that are of interest to you. Ask for information and ideas for conservation.

- Review how your own habits and life-style affect the environment.

- Write letters to elected officials letting them know your environmental concerns.

- Write letters to newspapers, and seek opportunities to have your opinions and concerns about the environment voiced on radio or public television.

HELP WANTED

Environmentalist

Do you believe that we can prevent many health problems by eliminating the many ways we poison ourselves in our environment? Your commitment to that ideal and willingness to tackle problems that seem too large to be solved will help make you a success in this field. You can't be impressed by wealth or power or discouraged by apathy or the enormity of the task. You must have a thorough, professional, scientific, and realistic approach to problem solving. A bachelor's degree in an appropriate field is a must.
For more information contact your local office of the state or federal Environmental Protection Agency.

K E E P I N G   F I T

Toxins in Art Supplies

According to the U.S. Public Interest Research Group, many art products do not contain warning labels mandated by the 1988 Labeling of Hazardous Art Materials Act. Yet the products have been known to cause serious health problems.

Before using any of the following products, you should look for safer, nontoxic alternatives, or provide proper ventilation while using them. These include

- rubber cement
- permanent markers
- water-based spray paints
- products with turpentine or toluene
- products with spray adhesive
- aerosol cleaners
- antiquing solutions

Additional Information

Right-to-Know Initiative. Concerned citizens in Ohio are trying to get a law passed, similar to one passed in California in 1986, which reduces exposure to toxic chemicals. The law would:

- establish individuals' right to know when they are exposed to chemicals that cause cancer or birth defects;
- mandate warnings in the form of labels on consumer products or mailings to neighbors of polluting factories;
- list 458 chemicals known to cause cancer and birth defects that are subject to the law;
- be enforced by the Attorney General, local prosecutors, and citizens;
- establish civil penalties (fines and jail terms) for violators.

Be aware of companies in your community that may be polluting the environment.

- Join an environmental organization. Most of these organizations can provide you with resources for understanding current issues. Being part of such a group can often provide you with suggestions on ways you can promote environmental health. Planned activities will help you put your concerns into practice. There are many examples of action and change coming from the work of small local groups made up of individual citizens working on issues.

- Take action against local polluters. The environmental problems in your community directly affect your health and your way of life. Targeting local polluters is a very effective way of protecting your health and that of your family and neighbors. Unfortunately, this is not an easy task. Local and national laws may not be adequately enforced. Some companies continue to pollute for years before the government can make them stop. Even then, the fines are often small compared with the cost of modernizing the facilities or cleaning up toxic wastes. Joining with others to let elected officials become aware of the problem is a start.

LESSON 2 REVIEW

Reviewing Facts and Vocabulary

1. Why can the term *biodegradable* be misleading to consumers?
2. Describe two current environmental concerns.

Thinking Critically

3. **Evaluation.** Explain whether or not you think individuals can make a difference in environmental problems. Support your opinion with examples.

4. **Analysis.** Compare the terms *natural* and *organic*.

Applying Health Knowledge

5. Begin a recycling project at your school. Make posters and pamphlets describing what can be recycled and where you can take recyclable materials.
6. Write a letter to your local newspaper stating your concerns and suggestions about an environmental problem in your community.

Answers to Lesson 2 Review

1. It means capable of being broken down by microorganisms, but the time required to do this can vary greatly.
2. Answers will vary.
3. Opinions will vary but should be supported logically and with examples.
4. Both are used on product labels to attract consumers who are interested in shopping for environmentally safe products. Both can refer to healthful items and hazardous materials.
5. Answers will vary.
6. Letters will vary.

Check for Understanding

- Assign and discuss the lesson review. Encourage LD students to focus on questions 1 and 2.

Evaluate

- Administer, grade, and discuss the *Lesson 2 Quiz.*
- Administer, grade, and discuss the *Chapter 31 Test.*
- Refer to the Performance Assessment strategy for this chapter. See pages T 23 to T 25.

Reteach

- Ask students to research labels on products that claim the products are environmentally safe. Ask students to describe the labels on the products and determine if indeed the products are safe to use.
- Ask students to complete *Reteaching Activity 86.*

Enrich

- Have students research biodegradable products. What are they? How do their ingredients differ from products that are not biodegradable? What difference might their use make in the overall health of the environment? What governmental actions could be taken to ensure labeling on products is accurate in relation to environmental standards?
- Ask students to complete *Enrichment Activity 31.*

Close

Ask students to summarize the most important concepts in this lesson. Ask students to list the ways they are going to be involved in improving the environment.

Helping Students Improve Their Health

Using the Self-Inventory

Reinforcing Vocabulary

- **Charitable.** Kind and generous to those in need.
- **Conserve.** To keep from being wasted.

Teaching Strategies

L1 EXPLANATION. Some parents may have stressed for years that their children not pick up others' trash for hygienic reasons, or take offense to wearing others' clothing. Try to stress that there are many ways to save our environment and that these are just two examples and are not meant to be offensive. You might want to mention the adopt-a-highway program as an example of picking up after others.

L1 EXPLANATION. In order to score higher on the inventory, a student may try to outguess the items. Stress that students should be honest with their answers and use the inventory knowledge gained to begin conservation measures in their own home.

L2 DISCUSSION. Ask students what precycling and recycling measures could be implemented at school. How can the students help instigate such measures?

L1 CLASS ACTIVITY. Have students brainstorm a list of things their school could do to better conserve energy. From this list, write a letter to school officials about student concerns and possible solutions.

DID YOU KNOW?

- Chili powder makes a safe, nontoxic ant repellant. Simply sprinkle it where you see ants crawling.

Self-Inventory

Are You Involved in Protecting the Environment?

HOW DO YOU RATE?

Number a sheet of paper from 1 through 20. Read each item below, and respond by writing *yes* if the statement is true most or all of the time or *no* if the statement is not true most or all of the time. Then proceed to the next section.

1. Do you consider waste when you buy things?
2. Do you store newspapers for recycling?
3. Do you litter?
4. Do you shut off lights in a room when you or someone else has left and does not plan to return?
5. Do you participate in any type of recycling program?
6. Do you accept unnecessary packaging in fast-food restaurants?
7. Do you use the toilet as a waste basket for paper, gum, and other waste?
8. Do you take a clean glass each time you get a drink at home?
9. Do you put on more clothing rather than turn up the heat when it is cold in the house?
10. Do you recycle aluminum cans?
11. Do you make others aware when they are littering?
12. Do you do anything specifically to conserve water in your home?
13. Do you shower longer than 5 minutes at a time?
14. Do you reuse paper that has been used only on one side?

15. Do you pick up litter even though you did not drop it?
16. Will you wear hand-me-down clothing?
17. Do you give used clothing and other items to friends or charitable organizations?
18. Do you let water run while shaving or brushing your teeth?
19. Do you clean the lint filter in your dryer after using it?
20. Do you buy recycled paper when you have a choice?

HOW DID YOU SCORE?

Give yourself 1 point for every *yes* answer to items 1, 2, 4, 5, 9, 10, 11, 12, 14, 15, 16, 17, 19, and 20.

Give yourself 1 point for every *no* answer to items 3, 6, 7, 8, 13, and 18. Then proceed to the next section.

18 to 20
Outstanding. Your concern for the environment is an example for others.

14 to 17
Very Good. You are doing much to protect the environment.

10 to 13
Good. You are on the right track. With some awareness and effort, you can improve.

5 to 9
Fair. While you are doing some things to help protect our environment, there is much more you can do.

0 to 4
Poor. Try to remember that we all have a shared responsibility for protecting Earth.

WHAT ARE YOUR GOALS?

If you received an *outstanding, very good,* or *good* score, complete the statements in Part A. If your score was rated *fair* or *poor,* complete Parts A and B.

Part A

1. I plan to learn more about protecting the environment by ____.
2. My timetable for accomplishing this is ____.
3. I plan to share my information with others by ____.

Part B

4. The attitude or behavior toward protecting the environment I would most like to change is ____.
5. The steps involved in making this change are ____.
6. My timetable for accomplishing this is ____.
7. The people or groups I will ask for support and assistance are ____.
8. My rewards for making this change will be ____.

Meeting Students' Needs

For students who score *Outstanding* or *Very Good*. Suggest these students survey surrounding communities to see what, if anything, they are doing with recycling.

For students who score *Good*. (1) Suggest these students do a collage depicting recycling efforts. (2) Suggest they do extra reading on energy conservation or recycling.

For students who score *Fair* or *Poor*. (1) Suggest these students do an extra-credit report on your community's recycling efforts. (2) For extra credit suggest they create a board game dealing with energy conservation/recycling.

Building Decision-Making Skills

A s part of a science fair program, Doug has discovered that his old school building has serious asbestos levels. He has proposed some solutions to the administration but has received little support. Doug isn't sure what he should do, but he has considered the following:

A. Organize a student protest.

B. Release his results to the news media.

C. Report his results to the health department.

D. Go to someone higher in the school administration.

E. Forget it, to avoid bad publicity for his school.

WHAT DO YOU THINK?

1. **Situation.** Why does a decision need to be made?

2. **Choices.** What other choices does Doug have?

3. **Consequences.** What are the advantages and disadvantages of each strategy?

4. **Consequences.** How might Doug's status in the school be affected by each strategy?

5. **Consequences.** How might Doug's relationship with his teacher or school principal be affected?

6. **Consequences.** How might Doug's parents be affected?

7. **Consequences.** How might Doug's health triangle be affected by this decision?

8. **Decision.** What do you think Doug should do? Explain your answer.

9. **Evaluation.** What do you do when you find yourself disagreeing with those in authority? What has been the outcome? What makes such a decision very difficult? What advice would you give Doug?

A s part of a community service project by the school's service club, Brooke and some friends cleaned up a weedy area near the elementary school playground. While doing this they discovered a number of used hypodermic needles. Brooke's friends are looking to her for guidance in how to handle this situation. Brooke isn't sure, but she's considering the following:

A. Contact the health department immediately.

B. Contact the news media so attention can be drawn to this serious incident.

C. Let the administration handle it, though they want to keep everything quiet.

D. Keep quiet to avoid bad publicity for the school and town.

WHAT DO YOU THINK?

10. **Choices.** What other choices does Brooke have?

11. **Consequences.** What are the advantages and disadvantages of contacting the health department right away? What are the advantages and disadvantages of contacting the health department later?

12. **Consequences.** What are the advantages and disadvantages of contacting the news media?

13. **Consequences.** What are the advantages and disadvantages of letting the school administration handle the situation?

14. **Consequences.** What are the advantages and disadvantages of keeping quiet about this?

15. **Consequences.** What other people could be affected by this situation? Explain your answer.

16. **Decision.** What do you think Brooke should do?

17. **Evaluation.** How would you handle a situation in which keeping quiet about a problem could result in harm to others?

BEING INFORMED AND INVOLVED **629**

Discussing the Answers

Situation 1. Try to bring out the health hazards associated with asbestos in your discussion. Along with the importance of this disclosure, have students consider the consequences of Doug intentionally going over school administrators' heads without first giving the proper chain of command a chance to respond.

Situation 2. It is probably important in this situation to allow the proper chain of command to respond to the situation. If school administrators do not respond in a favorable way, then it may be appropriate to move to the next higher level. Stress the importance of the continuation of projects like this regardless of the outcome.

Answers to Chapter 31 Review

Using Health Terms

1. Precycling
2. Chlorofluorocarbons
3. Aluminum
4. Conservation
5. Recycling
6. Nontoxic
7. Organic
8. Biodegradable
9. Environmental Protection Agency

Building Academic Skills

10. Proposals will vary.
11. At 20 miles per gallon, a family that travels: 5 miles a day will use .25 gallon; 15 miles—.75 gallon; 30 miles—1.5 gallons; 60 miles—3 gallons. At 36 miles per gallon, a family that travels: 5 miles a day will use .14 gallon; 15 miles—.42 gallon; 30 miles—.8 gallon; 60 miles—1.7 gallons. Answers will vary. Possible answers: Car pool, keep vehicle in good running order, walk when possible, avoid quick starts, keep tires properly inflated; number of drivers in a family, number of activities family participates in.

Recalling the Facts

12. Treating or changing waste so it can be reused.
13. Answers will vary. Accept two of the following: Glass, aluminum, cardboard, clothing.
14. Padding for play equipment, gardening containers, bumpers, in roads, playground surfaces, running tracks.
15. Seventy percent is used to heat or cool the environment, 20 percent is used to heat water, 10 percent is used for lighting, cooking, and running small appliances.
16. **A.** precycling—using less packaging.
    B. precycling—using less packaging; or recycling—using something like a cleaned out plastic milk jug.
    C. recycling—reusing an item.
    D. recycling—saves using

Using Health Terms

On a separate sheet of paper, write the term that best matches each definition given below.

LESSON 1

1. The process of reducing waste before it occurs by making environmentally sound decisions at the store.
2. Gases that harm the ozone layer.
3. An abundant metal that is expensive and polluting to produce.
4. Concern about saving or protecting the environment and its natural resources.
5. Treating or changing waste so it can be reused.

LESSON 2

6. Product not harmful or poisonous to humans.
7. Product that is derived from living organisms without the use of chemicals.
8. An item that can eventually be broken down by microorganisms.
9. Agency that enforces standards to help protect the environment from pollution.

Building Academic Skills

LESSON 1

10. **Writing.** Write a proposal to your principal on some aspect of conservation that can be utilized in your school, such as recycling paper or cans or turning lights off in rooms not in use.

LESSON 2

11. **Math.** Determine the number of gallons of gasoline burned by hypothetical families traveling 5, 15, 30, and 60 miles per day to work, school, and stores. Compute fuel consumption based upon 20 miles per gallon and compare with computations based upon 36 miles per gallon. How might these families reduce the amount of gasoline they consume? What factors will determine how much gasoline is needed by a particular family?

Recalling the Facts

LESSON 1

12. What does recycling involve?
13. Name two materials that are 100 percent recyclable.
14. What might old and worn tires be used for?
15. What is the distribution of energy use in an average household?
16. Which of the following situations demonstrates precycling and which shows recycling? Explain.
    a. Buying food products in bulk.
    b. Taking your own container to buy apple cider.
    c. Using the same piece of aluminum foil more than once.
    d. Using old envelopes for notes.
    e. Using cloth diapers.
    f. Collecting beverage cans and selling them.
    g. Using a cloth bag to carry home groceries and other items from the store.
17. What about modern life has enabled people to take the environment for granted?
18. What are significant benefits of conserving energy?
19. List three energy-saving actions an individual could practice at home, and tell how each helps protect the environment.

LESSON 2

20. Name three technological advances that were quick answers to problems and were immediately beneficial to humans but later caused environmental problems.
21. What are some issues that have become major problems for aquatic life?
22. What problems does forest loss cause people?
23. What is the Environmental Protection Agency and what does it do?
24. Identify three ways that conservation contributes to your life.
25. How can the term *biodegradable* be misleading?

new paper.
E. precycling—eliminating the need for disposable diapers.
F. recycling—enabling companies to buy them back and recycle them.
G. precycling—eliminating need for paper and plastic bags.
17. Civilization and industrial development have separated people from direct contact with resources. For example: buying food in stores, getting water from faucets, throwing away waste in plastic bags.
18. Protects the environment; avoids using irreplaceable resources; reduces pollution.

REVIEW

Thinking Critically

LESSON 1

26. **Evaluation.** Some places of business offer incentives for recycling, such as selling a product for less money if you bring your own container. Why do you think incentives are necessary to get people to recycle? What incentives do you need to motivate you to recycle?

27. **Analysis.** Each person in the United States uses about 80 gallons of water a day with about 50 gallons wasted. How can you conserve water that you use?

LESSON 2

28. **Synthesis.** Summarize reasons that environmental laws are necessary.

29. **Analysis.** What could be misleading about labels that read "made from natural materials"?

30. **Evaluation.** Investigative reporting often brings public attention to environmental problems or companies that might be contributing to these problems. What value, if any, do you feel these stories have for the general public?

31. **Evaluation.** Of the current environmental concerns defined in this chapter, which do you feel you could make a commitment to? Support your answer.

Making the Connection

LESSON 2

32. **Language Arts.** Write to one of your community officials or state legislators to find out his or her position regarding local environmental issues. Discover what his or her proposals are for environmental health for the future. Share the response you receive with your class.

33. **Social Studies.** Research an environmental catastrophe of your choice. Report what happened and what we learned from the situation.

Applying Health Knowledge

LESSON 1

34. Identify the item in each pair that would be better for the environment. Explain.
    a. paper towels or cloth towels
    b. paper plates or Styrofoam plates
    c. popcorn or Styrofoam for packing material
    d. aluminum can or plastic bottle

35. Tell how the following items can be reused:
    a. plastic grocery bags
    b. plastic milk jugs
    c. paper grocery bags
    d. used envelopes

LESSON 2

36. What hazardous chemicals are used in your home? What disposal options for these substances are available in your community?

Beyond the Classroom

LESSON 1

37. **Parental Involvement.** Along with your parents, evaluate your home and life-style and determine several changes or behaviors you are willing to practice to help the environment. Use the suggestions in this chapter or some found in any other good sources about the environment.

LESSON 2

38. **Further Study.** Research any of the following or other environmental organizations of which you have interest: Greenpeace, World Wildlife Fund, Water Pollution Control Federation, Sierra Club, or the Cousteau Society. Find out what contributions the group is making toward saving the environment.

39. **Further Study.** Find and share examples of advertisements that reflect current societal concerns regarding the environment.

19. Answers will vary. See page 616.
20. Pesticides, gasoline combustion engine, nuclear power.
21. Overfishing, pollution from large municipal areas, oil spills, waste dumping.
22. Soil erosion, flooding, shortages of wood and timber, displacement of groups of people, the loss of some species of plants and animals.
23. It is a governmental agency that enforces standards to help protect the environment from pollution, researches the effects of pollution, and gives advice about whether or not a product is good for the environment and can offer suggestions for safe alternatives.
24. It reduces waste, conserves natural resources, protects the environment.
25. Nearly everything can be broken down, but it may take as long as several thousand years.

Thinking Critically

26. Answers will vary. Possible answer: Some people need a monetary, concrete, or personal reason to recycle. Answers will vary.
27. Answers will vary. Possible answers: Shower instead of bathe; shorten showers; don't let water run while washing dishes or brushing teeth; use a bucket instead of a hose when washing the car.
28. Answers will vary but should be supported logically.
29. Answers will vary. Possible answers: The term *natural* has many definitions; some materials are natural and yet still may be dangerous.
30. Answers will vary but may reflect the idea of informing and educating the public.
31. Answers will vary but should be supported.

Making the Connection

32. Letters will vary.
33. Reports will vary.

Applying Health Knowledge

34. **A.** cloth towels—reusable.
    B. paper plates—Styrofoam releases chlorofluocarbons and is not biodegradable.

C. popcorn—completely natural and biodegradable.
D. aluminum can—totally recyclable

35. Answers will vary. Possible answers: A—to line waste baskets; B—to water plants, to hold motor oil; C—to bundle newspapers to be recycled, to line waste baskets, to store off-season clothing; D—to write notes or lists on.

36. Answers will vary.

Beyond the Classroom

37. Answers will vary.
38. Answers will vary.
39. Answers will vary.

Lesson Summaries

LESSON 1. Consumer health is concerned with helping consumers select products and services more wisely, and letting them know what to do if they need help. Individuals should know the rights that are guaranteed to them by law and they should understand the factors that influence their purchases.

LESSON 2. It is illegal to make false claims, promising that a drug, a food, or a cosmetic will do something that it really cannot. Consumers should become aware of the types of treatments and products that are most susceptible to such claims.

LESSON 3. Consumers depend upon others to provide them with products and services to protect their health. They should, however, become aware of the many agencies that can assist them in any claims against a product or company.

Introducing the Chapter

Compile a short videotape of TV commercials for health-related products. Introduce this chapter by showing the videotape to the class. Ask for students' reactions to any or all of the segments. What caught their eye? Which was most effective? Was there any information presented that did not sound accurate or possible? Tell students that in studying this chapter they will become wiser health consumers by looking at their rights as consumers, examining the factors that influence their choices, learning to recognize quackery, and examining consumer protection agencies.

Performance Assessment ✓

Refer to pages T 23 to T 25 for a Performance Assessment strategy for this chapter. See the *Performance Assessment Activities* booklet for additional suggestions.

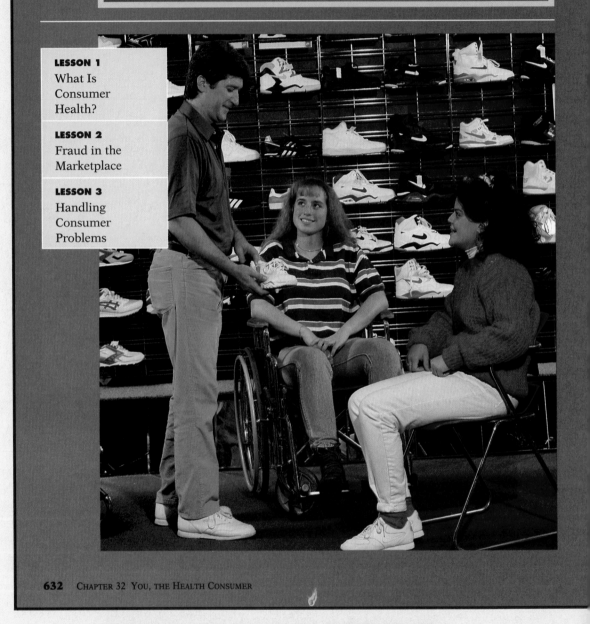

CHAPTER

32 YOU, THE HEALTH CONSUMER

LESSON 1
What Is Consumer Health?

LESSON 2
Fraud in the Marketplace

LESSON 3
Handling Consumer Problems

632 CHAPTER 32 YOU, THE HEALTH CONSUMER

Key to Ability Levels

Teaching strategies have been coded for varying learning styles and abilities.

L1 Level 1 activities are basic activities and should be within the ability range of all students.

L2 Level 2 activities are average activities and should be within the ability range of average to above-average students.

L3 Level 3 activities are challenging activities designed for the ability range of above-average students.

LD LD activities should be within the ability range of learning-disabled students.

LEP LEP activities should be within the ability range of Limited English Proficiency students.

WHAT IS CONSUMER HEALTH?

A s you work to promote or take care of your health, you probably purchase many products and services. A **consumer** is anyone who uses a product or a service. Obviously, you have all been consumers for many years. When you consider the products that you buy that in some way affect your health, you also realize you are a *health* consumer.

Consumer health is concerned with helping you select products and services wisely, and with letting you know where to go or what to do if you have been treated unfairly or need help.

Benefits of Being a Wise Health Consumer

There are three major benefits to being a wise health consumer:

- Being a wise health consumer saves money and time, and increases your satisfaction. You are able to make the best purchases for the least amount of money and time. It may take preparation time to collect information and to compare products or services, but it usually pays off in the long run.
- Being a wise health consumer protects your health. A wise consumer is not swayed into buying health products that are worthless or that may be harmful. A wise consumer knows when to seek medical help and does so without delay. Recognition and treatment of early symptoms is an important consumer skill.
- Being a wise health consumer builds your self-confidence as you speak up for your rights. If you have been sold a defective product or service, you protect yourself, as well as others, from future deception when you take action. Much of the progress that has been made in protecting consumers has resulted from people's willingness to speak up when they were treated unfairly. Such basic assertiveness skills can be helpful to you in all facets of your daily life.

Your Rights as a Consumer

As a consumer you have rights. In 1962 President John Kennedy introduced the Consumer Bill of Rights. It includes the following:

- The right to safety. Consumers are protected from dangerous products.
- The right to be informed. Consumers are protected from misleading advertising. They can ask for all of the facts they need to make good choices.
- The right to choose. Consumers have the right to make their own choices.
- The right to be heard. Consumers can speak out when they are not satisfied. They have a voice in making consumer laws.

WHAT IS CONSUMER HEALTH? **633**

LESSON 1 FOCUS

TERMS TO USE
- Consumer
- Consumer health
- Unit price
- Advertising
- Testimonial

CONCEPTS TO LEARN
- There are a variety of benefits in being a wise consumer.
- Consumers have several basic rights.
- Many factors influence a consumer's choice of products and services.

ATTITUDES AND BEHAVIORS TO EVALUATE
- Self-Inventory, page 648.
- Building Decision-Making Skills, page 649.

Focus

Lesson Objectives

After studying this lesson, students should be able to:

- identify the benefits of being a wise consumer
- list their rights as a consumer
- describe five factors that influence their choices of products and services

Bellringer

Write the following on the chalkboard for students to work on while attendance is being taken: *Define* consumer. *Then make a list of 10 products you buy or use at least once a week.*

Introducing the Lesson

Have students share their responses to the Bellringer. Point out that everyone is a consumer of products and services. Ask what they would do if they bought a product and it was defective. Point out that being a smart consumer is a skill that people acquire. Explain that this lesson establishes rules for becoming a wise health consumer.

Building Vocabulary

- Have students write public service announcements about consumer health, using each of the vocabulary terms in the lesson. Select some of the announcements for students to videotape and share with the class.
- Ask students to complete *Workbook Vocabulary Activity 87.*

DID YOU KNOW?

- At-home medical testing continues to gain in popularity. Tests already on the market include pregnancy tests, ovulation-prediction tests, and tests to detect sugar in urine, for example. Tests being developed include those for strep throat, Pap smears, and screenings for some STDs. Medical experts warn that these tests should not be used in place of proper medical care.

Resources for Lesson 1

- **Transparency** 29
- **Guided Reading** Activity 87
- **Workbook** Vocabulary Activity 87
- **Reteaching** Activity 87
- **Lesson 1 Quiz**
- **Performance Assessment** Activity 32

ABC News InterActive Videodiscs
Tobacco, Side 2
Ch 6 Advertising and the Media

L1 DISCUSSION. Remind students that when they buy grooming products they are making health decisions. Ask them if they can think of other consumer decisions that affect their health.

L1 SPEAKER. Ask a local merchant to visit your class to share consumer tips with students. Have students prepare questions for the speaker.

L1 CLASS ACTIVITY. Have students rate the stores where they regularly shop on the basis of price, quality of merchandise, convenience, and return policy. Lead them in a discussion of their ratings.

L2 CLASS ACTIVITY. Select students to write and present a skit about the effect of peer pressure on teens' purchases.

L1 CLASS ACTIVITY. Have students make lists of items they have purchased on impulse and place a check mark beside those items that turned out to be good buys. Discuss what factors influenced them to make the purchases.

L1 DISCUSSION. What types of advertising are geared toward adolescents? How successful do you think they are?

L2 CLASS ACTIVITY. Have students compare types of advertising found in various magazines and sections of the newspaper. Ask them to observe what products are advertised in the sports section of the paper, the life-style section, etc. Have students debate whether the ads suggest some stereotypes.

L1 SPEAKER. Invite a person from a local advertising agency or the advertising department of a company to speak to the class about his or her job in developing ads. Have the class prepare a list of consumer-oriented questions to ask the speaker.

L1 USING LIFE MANAGEMENT SKILLS TRANSPARENCY 29. Refer to the Teaching Transparencies Binder.

Generally, the more preparation that has been done for you, the higher the cost. Are there times when it pays to buy convenience foods?

During the 1970s President Richard Nixon added another right: the right to redress. This right means that consumers who have had a wrong done to them have the right to get that wrong corrected. There are many city, state, and federal agencies that help the consumer in these matters. President Gerald Ford also added a right—the right to consumer education.

What Factors Influence Your Purchasing Decisions?

Think of a health product you bought recently. What factors influenced your decision to buy that particular product? Did your friend have it? Was it on sale? Did you see it advertised?

Five main factors influence your choices as a consumer: price, convenience, family and friends, quality, and advertising. Be aware of these factors. You will be better able to make wise consumer health choices.

Price

Several factors influence price. Brand-name products cost more. They are usually well-advertised, and the cost of that advertising is passed on to the consumer. The size of the product also affects the price. Unit pricing tells how much different sizes of the same product cost per unit. The **unit price** is determined by dividing the price of the item by its weight, volume, or count—depending on how it is packaged. Many stores have unit pricing information on the shelves to help the consumer.

Another factor that affects price is where the product is sold. Products in convenience stores and specialty shops usually cost more than those in grocery stores or general department stores.

Convenience

Convenience, the labor-saving feature of a product, has a big impact on what we buy. In general, we pay more for convenience. Buying frozen macaroni and cheese may be more convenient than buying the ingredients and making it. When we are often in a hurry or want to save time, convenience becomes a significant factor in our purchases. Sometimes it is worthwhile to pay more, but making a habit of buying convenience products becomes expensive and can put a sizable dent in your budget.

KEEPING FIT

Fast Food—What's the Cost?

Your school has open lunch hour, and everyone likes to eat out at a fast-food restaurant. However, when eating fast food, there are hidden "costs"—additional calories, fat, and sodium. These "costs" also have a "cost"—

obesity, heart disease, and high blood pressure.

To lower these "costs," choose roast beef over a burger, a plain burger over one with cheese or sauce, a baked potato instead of fries, and milk over a milkshake.

Or, select a salad with low-fat dressing. Bring fruit to eat.

Be sure to read and compare the restaurant's nutritional information, and offer any suggestions you have for healthy food alternatives.

634 CHAPTER 32 YOU, THE HEALTH CONSUMER

Across the Curriculum

Home Economics. Remind students that they are consumers and that their parents are consumers on their family's behalf. Ask students to keep a record of how much money they spend in a week, and, if possible, how much more is spent on them by their parents. In class, have them calculate and discuss how many hours of employment, at minimum wage, an individual

would have to work to earn this amount of money.

Math. Have students go to a local supermarket to check the unit prices of five different brands of a product. Ask them to rate the products from most to least expensive (per unit) and to make and present an illustrated report of their calculations.

Family and Friends

Your family influences your purchasing decisions. You may or may not buy an item because of comments family members may make. You also may choose to buy a certain brand of product if your family has used it a long time. Friends also influence your purchases. You probably have bought an item because your friend had one. You may have bought a certain type of shirt or jeans because everyone else had them, or you wanted to identify with a certain group.

Quality

Have you ever bought a product only to have it not work or fall apart? Decisions about the quality of a product can be difficult. Just because something costs more does not mean it is of better quality. Examining the ingredients or the parts of a product and the guarantees that accompany the product will help you assess its quality.

Advertising

Advertising is the way by which a manufacturer gains your attention for its product. You may not be aware of how much advertising you are exposed to in a day. Think of the signs, the T-shirts, or the bumper stickers you have seen today that advertise something.

Advertising works in subtle ways, often on the subconscious level. It takes a very sharp consumer not to be influenced by advertising. Catchy jingles, tunes, and rhymes have a way of staying with us. That recognition factor is just what the advertiser wants.

Culturally Speaking

Foreign Language
The Nova car did not sell well in Latin America where "no va" means "it doesn't go." Pepsi's "Come Alive with Pepsi" slogan became "Come out of the grave with Pepsi" in one German translation. In China, shopkeepers made signs and used characters that sounded like "Coca-Cola," but were translated as "bite the waxed tadpole." Different characters with a similar sound had a more positive message: "Let the mouth rejoice."

What other forms of advertising can you name? Which form do you think is most effective?

WHAT IS CONSUMER HEALTH? **635**

Overcoming Misconceptions

Myth. Because of government regulations, all advertising must be accurate. **Fact.** Many forms of advertising praise an item with inflated opinions and exaggerations. This practice is called "puffery," and it uses words to make products seem far better than they really are. Puffery statements are not illegal because they cannot be proven false by the Federal Trade Commission. They cannot be proven true either, and can be very misleading to consumers. Here are some examples of puffery: "Three out of four doctors recommend _____." (How many were surveyed?) "_____ gives fast relief for _____." (How fast is it?)

Overcoming The Odds

Margaret Lofner knows firsthand what it's like to be a health-care professional and not be able to get health insurance. Born and raised in England but living in Texas since 1972, she has worked as a nurse in both the British and American health-care systems. Mrs. Lofner left her job of 14 years when her medical insurance was canceled and no one would insure her. "My former job was in a family practice clinic. "I have a pre-existing condition called a Protein S. Deficiency, a deficiency in an anti-coagulant factor. This causes my blood to clot much faster than other people's blood, which can cause clots in the deep veins. It can be fatal. My condition was discovered when I was 18, but it hasn't stopped me. I lead a very full, active life. I've never missed a day of work. But insurance companies don't look at your health history or attendance record. They just look at your diagnosis.

"Then, in February, I had to have surgery for endometrial carcinoma, cancer of the endometrium, the lining of the uterus. The outcome was very favorable. The cancer hadn't spread. I didn't need radiation or chemotherapy. The surgery was very risky because of the blood clotting, but I sailed through it.

"Soon after that, our

MARGARET LOFNER, R.N.

employers, who are physicians, called a meeting. They told us that the cost of the practice's health insurance premiums had skyrocketed, they were canceling the policies. I was told I couldn't get any coverage for three to five years—not just for cancer problems, either, but for anything at all. So I wrote to a consumer publication and called the American Cancer

Society and was told there were a lot of other people just like me. Very soon I realized that if I was going to have health insurance, I'd need to be part of a large group where my high-risk premiums would be offset by lots of medium-risk or low-risk ones. It was a tough decision to make, but I knew I'd have to change jobs to get insurance. Leaving my job was an emotional decision just like the one I'd made in 1972 to come here from England and leave my family behind."

Mrs. Lofner concludes, "Good health insurance coverage should be foremost among the factors you consider in making a decision about which job to take."

1. Mrs. Lofner investigated options, then made the necessary changes to ensure that she could get health insurance. When you face obstacles, do you gather information, investigate options, and make necessary changes in the interest of your health? If so, how? If not, for what reasons?

2. What steps can you take to become an advocate for your own health care? What might the benefits to your self-esteem be? To your health?

Across the Curriculum

Social Studies. Ask students to examine their belongings for the country of origin. Afterwards, write the products on the chalkboard. Beside each, have students name some of the countries of origin.

Math. Have students write a list of four brand-name products. Instruct them to leave one line on the paper after each product. Ask them to go to a store, and next to the brand-name products on their lists, record the prices. Then have them locate a generic equivalent of the items they listed and record those prices. Have students calculate the differences in prices between the brand-name and generic products. Discuss the pros and cons of buying generic goods.

Manufacturers spend billions of dollars to advertise their products. They use many different techniques to sell health products. Advertisements usually play on our emotions and our needs. They may promise popularity, sex appeal, or pain relief. Are you influenced by certain messages more than others? Do some ads turn you off? Look at some common techniques that are used in advertising.

Testimonials. Testimonials often use famous people to tell you how they use and like the product. A **testimonial** is a person's enthusiastic recommendation of a product. Because you like or identify with that person, you may be influenced to buy the product. The law says that the person who gives the testimonial must have actually used the product. This does not mean, however, that he or she really believes in the product or has purchased the product to use it. Companies pay famous people large sums of money for promoting their products.

Buy One, Get One Free. This is a common approach used in advertising. It makes consumers feel like they are getting something for nothing. Look closely at the advertisements. Often the price of one item has been raised, so you might pay more than you normally would. Remember, rarely, if ever, will you get something for nothing.

Emotional Pleas. Many ads play on people's emotional needs. Here are some examples:
- "Be the first on your block to have a . . . ."
- "Be happy, be smart, buy . . . ."
- "When you want only the best for you and your family . . . ."

All of these pleas encourage you to buy something for an emotional reason. Do not be tricked into spending more or buying something you normally would not buy.

FINDING HELP

In many communities, a library of tape-recorded health information is as close as your telephone. The Tel-Med Tape Library includes more than 500 tape-recorded messages on various health topics. The service is free. You simply call the Tel-Med number, located in your telephone directory, and ask for the topic on which you want information.

For a list of topics and phone numbers, write to Tel-Med Corporation, P.O. Box 22700, Cooley Drive, Colton, CA 92324.

LESSON 1 REVIEW

Reviewing Facts and Vocabulary

1. List two benefits of being a wise consumer.
2. What five factors influence one's choice of products or services?
3. What is a testimonial?

Thinking Critically

4. **Synthesis.** Could there be an honest purchasing system in our country if consumers had no rights? Explain your answer.
5. **Evaluation.** What criteria would you use to critique an ad for a particular product?

Applying Health Knowledge

6. Make a list of five common advertising slogans or jingles. Next to each one, write a consumer awareness warning. Your warning might point out something for the consumer to look for beyond what is being promoted in the ad.
7. Form a survey team to observe television commercials on different channels between 6:00 P.M. and 10:00 P.M. Answer the following questions, and then report your findings:
   a. How many commercials were for health products?
   b. How many were for beauty products?
   c. How many products used youth and beauty as part of the sales pitch?
   d. How many had pretty nature scenes?
   e. How many used music?
   f. Was the volume on the television louder during the commercials?

WHAT IS CONSUMER HEALTH? **637**

Answers to Lesson 1 Review

1. Answers will vary. Accept two of the following: Saves money and time; protects one's health; helps to build one's self-confidence.
2. Price, convenience, family and friends, quality, advertising.
3. An advertising technique in which a person endorses a product.
4. Answers will vary. Possible answers: Maybe not. There may be an increase in inferior products, consumer confusion or mistrust, and little or no recourse against poor products.
5. Answers will vary. Possible answers: Hidden messages, honesty of ad, amount and quality of information.
6. Answers will vary.
7. Answers will vary.

Assess

Check for Understanding
- Assign and discuss the lesson review. Encourage LD students to focus on questions 1, 2, 3, and 4.

Evaluate
- Administer, grade, and discuss the *Lesson 1 Quiz*.

Reteach
- Assist students in finding examples of advertisements that are informative or that appeal to emotions. Have them label each as "informative" or "emotional."
- Ask students to think of a limerick, jingle, or mnemonic device that will help them remember the five factors that influence purchasing decisions.
- Ask students to complete *Reteaching Activity 87*.

Enrich
- Ask students to keep a diary for one day in which they record the following information: each time they encounter any type of advertising (billboard, magazine ad, television commercial, etc.); what the advertisement is for; and whether their reaction to it is negative, positive, or neutral. Then ask students to evaluate how susceptible they are to this daily barrage of advertising, how they might protect themselves from its influence, and what kinds of advertising approaches resulted in positive responses.

Close

Remind students that it is important to realize their rights as consumers as well as to be aware of factors that influence their purchases.

Focus

Lesson Objectives

After studying this lesson, students should be able to:

- define *quackery*
- identify popular types of product fraud
- explain how to recognize medical quackery
- describe the dangers of quack remedies

Bellringer

Write the following on the chalkboard for students to work on while attendance is being taken: *Write the names of two health-related products or services that you have seen advertised that you do not think would really do what the advertising promises.*

Introducing the Lesson

Have students share their responses to the Bellringer. (Possibilities might include wrinkle creams, weight-loss clinics, diet supplements, etc.) Tell students that this lesson describes different forms of quackery and some of their dangers.

Building Vocabulary

- Ask students to write paragraphs, using each of the vocabulary terms.
- Ask students to complete *Workbook Vocabulary Activity 88.*

FRAUD IN THE MARKETPLACE

LESSON 2 FOCUS

TERMS TO USE
- Quack
- Quackery
- Placebo

CONCEPTS TO LEARN
- Many health-care products are susceptible to quackery.
- Quackery and fraud in the marketplace can be recognized.

ATTITUDES AND BEHAVIORS TO EVALUATE
- Self-Inventory, page 648.
- Building Decision-Making Skills, page 649.

It is illegal to make false claims, promising that a medicine, a food, or a cosmetic will do something that it really cannot do. You have probably heard the terms **quack** and **quackery** used to describe a dishonest promoter of medicinal products and the useless products or treatments. Quackery plays on human emotions, weakness, and fear to get money from people who want fast cures or relief from pain. The most prevalent areas of quackery are those in which there is no cure or instant relief.

How Quackery Works

The promoter deals with magic, miracles, and fast painless cures. Amazingly, even intelligent people can become victims of these false claims. Many times it is because the people want to believe what they hear or because they are hoping for something that does not exist.

Take, for example, the person who is 20 pounds overweight and does not like to exercise. Exercise is hard work, especially for overweight people. Now "Slim-Ex," a new candy, claims that this person will lose weight without exercise and while continuing to eat whatever he or she likes. An overweight person may purchase the product, wanting to believe that there is an easy way to lose weight without exercising.

Popular Types of Product Fraud

Here are types of products that are most susceptible to quackery:

- Beauty aids. These play on people's fear of growing old or fat and promise youth, beauty, and sex appeal forever. Included are cures for baldness; products that promise quick, painless weight loss; and products for the prevention of wrinkles.
- Diet aids. Their appeal is to our need to be trim and energetic. They include vitamin and diet supplements.
- Food. Food fads represent one of the most lucrative areas of quackery. Relying on special foods, diets, or diet supplements is not only a waste of money—it also is not healthy.
- Fraudulent devices. This group of products includes devices that are promoted as being capable of curing ailments. For example, excess body weight is said to be melted away by wearing special clothing. Sometimes the devices are legitimate but are promoted improperly. Such cases involve, for example, getting eyeglasses, contacts, or dentures through the mail without seeing a doctor or dentist.

Medical Quackery

Quackery offers hope. Therefore, the most susceptible people are those suffering from diseases or conditions without known cures.

Resources for Lesson 2

- **Guided Reading** Activity 88
- **Workbook** Vocabulary Activity 88
- **Reteaching** Activity 88
- **Lesson 2 Quiz**

Even if a product claiming a fast cure will not do any harm; the danger is that the individual may postpone seeking medical attention.

The problem with quack products is not so much the harm that may be done. Medical authorities point to quackery as being dangerous because the patient delays seeking sound medical advice and treatment until it may be too late.

Quack cures are offered most often for diseases or conditions for which treatment is apt to be lengthy and unpleasant, with uncertain results. Three areas susceptible to quackery are cancer, arthritis, and weight problems.

Cancer

In contrast to the standard treatment for cancer, which may involve surgery, radiation, and chemotherapy—all of which may be painful and disfiguring—the quack remedy is usually simple and painless. It may be a pill, an injection, a trip to the mountains, or a special diet. The quack remedy offers hope. Often, because hope is vital to a patient's survival, there may be apparent remission of the disease. This effect makes people more likely to believe in the product and continue to use it.

Have you ever heard of a **placebo?** It is a substance that has no medical value, but which is given for its psychological effect. The placebo effect comes about when people think that they are taking medicine and

> ### DID YOU KNOW?
>
> ■ It is estimated that each year one in four Americans will use some kind of medical treatment that is considered quackery, or not medically sound.
> ■ The American Medical Association estimates that 25 billion dollars a year is spent in the United States on quack medicines.

KEEPING FIT

Be Alert to Health and Medical Frauds

Here are some ways that you can be alert to any signs of fraudulent practices or products. If you can answer yes to any of these questions, you should be wary.
■ Is the product advertised as a scientific breakthrough without

any particular reference to a medical school, study, or journal? If one is mentioned, have you ever heard of it?
■ Does the product claim to be effective for a large variety of ailments?

■ Do the promised benefits seem too good to be true?
■ Does a "health consultant" sell the product door-to-door?

FRAUD IN THE MARKETPLACE **639**

Across the Curriculum

Science. Have students read about laetrile and the controversy surrounding the drug. Ask them to find answers to the following questions: What is laetrile? From what is it made? What disease is it used to treat? Has it been approved by the FDA? Why or why not? What are the medical claims made by those who prescribe its use? What are the arguments against the drug

by those who oppose its use? What generalizations can be made about such substances and the regulation of their use? Discuss students' findings.

Language Arts. Ask students to select and read a book or article that promotes a useless product or treatment. Have them list claims that are not based on fact.

Teach

Guided Practice

L1 DISCUSSION. Ask students to relate personal experiences during which they bought worthless products or services. Have students discuss what convinced them to make the purchases in the first place. Follow up by brainstorming ways to avoid quackery.

L1 CLASS ACTIVITY. Provide copies of supermarket tabloids, and have students find and discuss examples of quackery and unsupported claims.

L3 COOPERATIVE LEARNING. Divide the class into small groups to create simple comic books to inform children about quackery and product fraud. Display and discuss the completed projects.

L1 SPEAKER. Invite a dietician to class to contrast weight-loss plans that are credible with those that are fraudulent and/or misleading.

Independent Practice

L2 COMMUNITY INVOLVEMENT. Have groups of students make lists of questions they would like answered about cold remedies. Then have the groups choose representatives to pose those questions to a pharmacist, a sales clerk, and a supermarket employee. Have groups compare the types of information they were able to get from the various sources. Ask them to share their results with the class.

L1 PARENTAL INVOLVEMENT. Have students ask their parents, grandparents, or other adult relatives about types of product fraud that they have observed over the years. Have students ask questions such as: Did you, or your friends or family members, use any of the products? What were some of the claims made about the products? What were the results, if the products were used? Request that students share some of their interviews with the class.

L1 USING THE LESSON RESOURCES. For additional student activities, refer to the lesson resources on page 638.

Check for Understanding

- Assign and discuss the lesson review. Encourage LD students to focus on questions 1, 2, 3, and 4.

Evaluate

- Administer, grade, and discuss the *Lesson 2 Quiz*.

Reteach

- Collect a variety of newspaper and magazine advertisements of products that are susceptible to quackery, such as beauty and diet aids, diet supplements, or devices that supposedly cure ailments. Have students analyze the ads and make a list of reasons why they think the product is legitimate and another list of reasons why they think the product is fraudulent. Discuss their analyses as a class.
- Ask students to complete *Reteaching Activity 88*.

Enrich

- Have students read about Ralph Nader and the work he and his organization have done in the areas of consumer health and fraud. Ask them to summarize their findings in oral reports to the class.

Ask students to state the most important concepts studied in the lesson.

Weight control gimmicks attract a lot of attention.

therefore the symptoms are relieved. This effect illustrates the power of the mind over the body and the positive effect our beliefs can have on health. However, it also makes us quite susceptible to quackery.

Arthritis

The pain and suffering of arthritis, a condition that afflicts about 40 million Americans, makes sufferers of this disease a likely target for the quack's false promises. Medical science has no cure for arthritis, and even its control is complicated and not always effective. Some of the quack remedies are harmless enough, but they are still a waste of money. Wearing a copper bracelet, for example, is said to ease the discomfort of arthritis. It does no harm, but it cannot do what is claimed. However, other remedies that quacks offer are highly dangerous. The Arthritis Foundation estimates that arthritis victims spend millions of dollars a year on quack remedies.

Weight Problems

Unlike most quack remedies, many of the weight-loss plans that quacks offer may, if one faithfully follows them, actually work, resulting in a real loss of weight. The secret is not in the trick diet or the magic medicine the advertising features, but in the fact that most reduction plans involve a cutback in the amount of food consumed.

Weight control is perhaps the most lucrative area for unnecessary products and devices. There is only one way to lose weight—you must use up more calories than you consume. Buying products that claim to make weight loss effortless wastes your money and leads to more disappointment, making it even harder to deal successfully with the problem. Yet people spend billions of dollars annually on over-the-counter products that claim to aid in weight reduction.

LESSON 2 REVIEW

Reviewing Facts and Vocabulary

1. Name three types of product fraud, and describe what makes people susceptible to them.
2. What is the greatest danger to ill people who seek quack cures?
3. Why are cancer, arthritis, and weight loss the most susceptible areas of quackery?
4. What is a placebo?

Thinking Critically

5. **Evaluation.** What criteria would you use to select a shampoo or body lotion?

6. **Synthesis.** Imagine that advertising did not exist. Suggest some ways that our lives would be changed.

Applying Health Knowledge

7. Five classmates have been given $20 each to purchase health products. You are asked to give them some suggestions about the use of their money. What wise consumer practices would you share with them?
8. In a store you observe two people shopping for an item. What are some ways that you can tell if either one is a wise consumer?

Answers to Lesson 2 Review

1. Answers will vary. Accept three of the following: Beauty aids, diet aids, food, or fraudulent devices. Emotions, weakness, fear.
2. They delay seeking medical treatment, sometimes until it is too late.
3. All are conditions in which treatment may be lengthy and unpleasant, with uncertain results.
4. See pages 639 and 640.
5. Answers will vary. Possible answers: Quantity, unit price, ingredients, advertisements.
6. Answers will vary. Possible answer: It may be harder to find goods and services.
7. Answers will vary.
8. Answers will vary.

HANDLING CONSUMER PROBLEMS

E ach of us is a consumer. We depend upon others to provide us with products and services to protect our health. Many fine companies and businesses do their jobs well in providing us with what we want and need. Most businesses depend on satisfied customers to stay in business. Honest firms will make an effort to resolve problems, but you, as a consumer, must bring these problems to the attention of the company or store.

BEING AN ASSERTIVE CONSUMER

Being a wise consumer can protect your health and save you money, and it also can be fun and challenging. Think of a time when a salesperson was being pushy or pressuring you. How did you feel—uncomfortable, nervous, imposed upon? Next time, assert yourself. Challenge the person with consumer-oriented questions. If you are not interested or want to be left alone, simply state that. Compare what you stand to lose with your potential gains for being an assertive consumer.

Steps to Follow

Even the most careful shoppers find themselves buying products or securing services that do not work right or serve them well. Sometimes merchants and manufacturers are less than enthusiastic about resolving difficulties. This is why it is necessary for you, as a consumer, to know what to do and where to go for help. Here are some tips to follow:

1. Identify the problem and what you feel would be a fair way to solve it.
2. Have some documentation available to back up your complaint, for example, a sales receipt, a canceled check, or a warranty.
3. Go back to the person who sold you the item or performed the service. State the problem and how you would like to have it solved.
4. If this person is not helpful, ask to see the store manager or supervisor. Repeat your story. Most problems are resolved at this level.
5. If you are not satisfied with the response at this level, do not give up. If the company operates nationally or the product is a national brand, write a letter to the president or the director of consumer affairs of the company. Your letter should include these points:
   a. name and title of the person you're writing
   b. name of product and serial number or model number, or type of service
   c. date and location of purchase or service
   d. statement of the problem
   e. request for action within a reasonable time
   f. your address and phone number

LESSON 3 FOCUS

TERMS TO USE

- Better Business Bureau (BBB)
- Small-claims court
- Advocate
- Recall
- Food and Drug Administration (FDA)
- Federal Trade Commission (FTC)

CONCEPTS TO LEARN

- There are a variety of agencies that help protect the consumer.
- Consumer complaints need to be handled in an appropriate manner.

ATTITUDES AND BEHAVIORS TO EVALUATE

- Self-Inventory, page 648.
- Building Decision-Making Skills, page 649.

HANDLING CONSUMER PROBLEMS **641**

Focus

Lesson Objectives

After studying this lesson, students should be able to:

- list steps to follow in resolving consumer difficulties
- describe the various agencies and other sources that help to protect the consumer

Bellringer

Write the following on the chalkboard for students to work on while attendance is being taken: *List the steps you would take if you had a problem with a product or service you purchased.*

Introducing the Lesson

Have students share their responses to the Bellringer. Then demonstrate a product that does not work or is defective in some way. List the steps to follow in resolving the problem.

Building Vocabulary

- Have students use the terms *advocates* and *recall* in a written paragraph. Ask them to read their paragraphs to the class.
- Ask students to find examples of people who have served as consumer advocates. Ask them to discuss their findings with the class.
- Ask students to complete *Workbook Vocabulary Activity 89.*

DID YOU KNOW?

- The modern flush toilet was developed in England in 1778.

Resources for Lesson 3

- **Guided Reading** Activity 89
- **Decision-Making** Activity 32
- **Workbook** Vocabulary Activity 89
- **Workbook** Application Activity 32
- **Reteaching** Activity 89
- **Enrichment** Activity 32
- **Health Labs** Activity 32

- **Cooperative Learning** Activity 32
- **Lesson 3 Quiz**
- **Chapter 32 Test**

Guided Practice

L1 DISCUSSION. Ask students to state and discuss reasons why many people are not wise health consumers. Have students evaluate which of these reasons seem most widespread. (They may include lack of knowledge, convenience, laziness, fear, faulty advertising, or even self-destructive tendencies.)

L2 CLASS ACTIVITY. Have students work in pairs to act out a dispute between a consumer and a store owner or manager about a consumer problem, such as a defective appliance or skin-care product that did not work. Each partner should keep his or her own interests in mind, but work at reaching a fair solution. (The consumer wants satisfaction on the purchase and the store owner wants to incur as little loss as possible, yet still keep the customer.) Select pairs to act out their dispute for the class. Ask the class to critique each dispute, and offer suggestions for fair resolution of the problem.

L1 DISCUSSION. Ask students why some people do not file formal complaints or return merchandise even when they have received poor service or defective merchandise. In what kinds of situations would you be willing to compromise to get a complaint settled and in what kinds of disputes would you be unwilling to compromise?

L1 CLASS ACTIVITY. Have several students write and present a skit about a customer dealing with a pushy or high-pressured salesperson. Then divide the class into small groups, and have each group write and present similar skits, portraying various ways to be an assertive consumer.

L1 SELF-ESTEEM. Ask why it is best to remain calm when making a consumer complaint. (Staying calm might help the other person remain calm, thus increasing your chance of getting satisfactory results.) Discuss how a person with a high level of self-esteem might be assertive while remaining calm. How might being assertive affect a person's self-esteem?

A well-written letter will usually bring positive results.

Your address

Name and title of person you're writing

Today's date

Name and address of store where you made the purchase

The problem

Request for action

Copies of receipt and warranty

Your phone number

```
                                    926 Eastwind Drive
                                    Westerville, OH 43081
                                    October 27, 1993

Ms. Mary Reece
President
Universal Appliances
322 West 12th Street
Anderson, IN 46798

Dear Ms. Reece:

Last week I purchased a hair dryer, model
ST-1062, at Dave's Discount Appliances, 200
Pioneer Parkway, Columbus, Ohio, 43093.

Unfortunately the hair dryer has not
performed satisfactorily.  It doesn't heat.
The hair dryer has not been mistreated or
dropped.  To solve this problem, I would
like you to repair the hair dryer or
replace it.  Enclosed are copies of my
receipt and warranty.

I look forward to your reply and resolution
to this problem, and will wait three weeks
before seeking third-party assistance.  I
can be reached at the above address or by
phone at 817-555-1234.

                                    Sincerely,

                                    Ava Stinnett
```

One of the first steps in solving a consumer complaint is to take the product back to the store and tell the clerk what the problem is and how you want it resolved.

Getting Help

If you are not satisfied with the company's response, even after writing to the president, you may wish to contact one of several agencies outside the company for help. These sources vary greatly in services offered, approach taken, and type of complaint that will be handled. By becoming familiar with the existence and work of these agencies, you can improve your skill as a consumer.

The Better Business Bureau

The **Better Business Bureau (BBB)** is a nonprofit organization sponsored by private businesses. It offers a variety of services. These services include providing general information on products and services, reliability reports, background information on local businesses and organizations, and records of companies' complaint-handling performances.

The BBB attempts to settle consumer complaints against local business firms. It accepts written complaints and will contact a local firm on your behalf. The BBB considers a complaint settled when one of the following courses of action has taken place:

- The customer receives satisfaction.
- The customer receives a reasonable adjustment.
- The company provides proof that the customer's complaint is unreasonable or not backed by facts.

642 CHAPTER 32 YOU, THE HEALTH CONSUMER

Additional Information

Quackery. Quacks often have their own publications. They also advertise in magazines and newspapers and on radio and television. Usually, they have introductory offers with a guarantee that customers can get their money back if not satisfied. However, few people ever take the time and effort to get a refund.

Anyone can legally write a book or pamphlet on a subject whether the person is knowledgeable or not. Before you believe what you read, consider the background and qualifications of the author. Look for specific information about the author and the sources of the author's information.

BBBs also handle false advertising cases. To find a BBB, check your local phone book, local consumer office, or local library. Most of them are located in major cities.

Media Programs

If you live in or near a large city, you may be aware of one of the more than 100 newspapers and 50 radio and TV stations that offer action or hot line services for consumers who need help. These programs often get successful results because of the powerful influence of the media. Unfavorable publicity may be one of the best encouragers to get a merchant or business to take action to resolve a consumer complaint.

"Call for Action" is one of the larger media help lines. Staffed by 800 volunteers, it helps about 250,000 people each year. The volunteers relay complaints to the proper individuals, business people, or public agencies, and then check back with you—usually in about two weeks. If you have been satisfied, the incident is closed. If not, then "Call for Action" will intervene in your behalf. It generally turns public attention on a case to get results.

Small-Claims Court

You might imagine that seeking satisfaction in small-claims court is an expensive and drawn-out procedure. It is not. If you have a complaint that you are not able to resolve, then consider going to the small-claims court. This is a very important alternative for consumers. Court procedures are simple, inexpensive, quick, and informal. There are court fees involved, but you often get most or all of them back if you win your case. Generally, you do not need a lawyer. In fact, in some states, lawyers are not permitted in small-claims courts.

Small-claims courts deal with claims that range from $100 to $3,000, with an average of around $500. Locate the small-claims court in your area in your local phone book. When you reach the court on the phone, ask the clerk how to use the court. Sit in on a court session before taking a case to small-claims court, so that you become familiar with the operation.

Occupational and Professional Licensing Boards

If you have a problem with professional or occupational services, such as with a physician, a dentist, or a physical therapist, you may be able to get some help from a state licensing or regulatory board. There are an estimated 1,500 state boards that license or register more than 550 health-related occupations. The practice of licensing was first started to protect the public in matters of health and safety and to guard the public from incompetency and fraud.

To be licensed, a professional must have a certain level of education and experience and must pass a qualifications test. State boards set licensing examinations; issue, deny, or revoke licenses; take disciplinary action; and handle consumer complaints.

If you contact a state board for help, it will usually bring your complaint to the attention of the person whom you filed against, known as

A small-claims court can be used for a quick, effective means of settling a minor claim.

HELP WANTED

Ombudsman

If you have a compassionate and assertive personality and love to solve problems for other people, we'd like to talk to you. The person in this position will listen to people's problems within our business system and then help them find solutions. You will be an advocate for people and will tactfully yet forcefully get the cooperation of various departments. We are looking for a person with a degree in public relations or organizational communications, a proven record of dealing positively with people, and either the knowledge of our business or the ability to learn it quickly and well.
For more information contact:
Public Relations Society of America, Inc.
33 Irwing Place
New York, N.Y. 10003

HANDLING CONSUMER PROBLEMS **643**

Across the Curriculum

Language Arts. Divide the class into small groups. Assign each group one of the services or agencies discussed in the lesson. Have each group develop a one-page report, describing the availability of the service/agency in their community. Ask them to answer questions such as: If the source is not available in the area, where is it located? What exactly does the agency/service do? What must the consumer do to get help? What are the most common problems seen by the agency? Have the groups give an example of their agency's actions, if possible. Follow up by allowing time for the groups to present their findings to the class.

COOPERATIVE LEARNING.
Ask students to research the process used to recall or correct hazardous products. Have them find out what laws require manufacturers to notify people about product defects and to control product quality. After students have discussed this information, divide the class into groups. Assign each group one major product that has been recalled, such as rototillers, toys with small parts, cribs, bunk beds, hair dryers, coffeemakers, etc. Have each group study the complete course of that recall and report the findings to the class.

COOPERATIVE LEARNING.
Divide the class into five groups. Assign each group one of the following government agencies: the Consumer Product Safety Commission, the Food and Drug Administration, the Food Safety and Quality Service of the Department of Agriculture, the Federal Trade Commission, and the Bureau of Consumer Protection of the Civil Aeronautics Board. Have each group compose and send a letter to their assigned government agency, requesting information about its services to consumers. Display and discuss the responses when received.

Independent Practice

READING. Assign students to read about three pieces of consumer protection legislation, such as the Consumer Product Safety Act, the Child Protection and Toy Safety Act, the Fair Packaging and Labeling Act, the Truth-in-Advertising Act, the Truth-in-Lending Act, the Textile Fiber Products Identification Act, or the Fur Products Labeling Act.

WRITING. Ask students to read about arbitration as a means for settling consumer and business disputes. Have each student summarize his or her readings in a short report.

FINDING HELP

If you have been unsuccessful in resolving a consumer problem where you originally did business, the next step is to contact the company's headquarters or the manufacturer of the product.

Often you can find the name and address of the manufacturer on the product's label. If not, check your local library for the *Thomas Register*, which lists the manufacturers of thousands of products or *Standard and Poor's Register of Corporations, Directors, and Executives*, which lists the addresses of over 50,000 American business firms.

The postal service handles fraud or misleading promotions involving the use of the mail. If you have a complaint, contact your local postmaster.

the licensee. The board will seek a satisfactory solution to your problem. If necessary, the board can conduct an investigation. Some state boards even have consumer education materials to help you in selecting a health professional.

You can find out about a state licensing board by contacting your local consumer office. Check your phone book under state government offices or under professional listings. You can also ask professionals about the board that is responsible for their licensing. In fact, you should ask to see the person's license or registration before you use his or her services.

State, County, and City Consumer Affairs Offices

If you are not satisfied with a company's or person's response to your complaint about a product or service, a good place for an inquiry or a complaint is the local consumer affairs office. Local consumer offices can be particularly helpful because a person can contact them easily by phone or in person, and they are usually familiar with local businesses and regulations. Keep all receipts and other papers to show or to use when talking to the local agency.

If there is no consumer office where you live, contact a state consumer office. These consumer offices are set up differently from state to state. Many state and local consumer offices have a large selection of educational materials and information available. Your phone book should give you a listing under city, county, or state government.

Private Consumer Groups

In addition to the many governmental and business organizations that can be of assistance to the consumer, private consumer groups exist in all 50 states. In almost all cases, these are made up of individual consumer members who join together to support consumer interests. They are called advocates. An **advocate** is someone who speaks out for a position.

The private consumer groups are usually started and staffed by volunteers, although some have paid staff members. Some of the private consumer groups help individual consumers with complaints. Others are dedicated to serving the broad needs of special populations, such as the elderly, women, minorities, and low-income people. They represent consumers by using their collective energy to focus on critical consumer issues in the marketplace.

For more information about consumer groups in your area, you can contact your local or state government consumer affairs office. If you cannot locate a group in your area, you can try one of these organizations:

- The National Office of the Consumer Federation of America, 1424 16th Street, N.W., Washington, DC 20036
- National Consumers League, 815 15th St., N.W., Washington, DC 20005
- Ralph Nader's Public Citizen, P.O. Box 19404, Washington, DC 20036

Additional Information

Consumer Protection. The Better Business Bureau was started in the early 1900s in response to unrestrained commerce and freewheeling advertising. Unscrupulous people of the day advertised things such as "Complete Sewing Machines for 25 Cents," mailing out 12 needles in packages. Around 1910, a publisher and a lawyer drew up a model law concerning fraud and deception in advertising, which is now law in most states. Meanwhile, a committee was formed to fight dishonesty in advertising. Within a year, most large cities had formed similar groups. Local groups tested various names, and the name Better Business Bureau was born.

Help through Government Services

The federal government has established a number of specialized agencies that deal with health-related products and services. Taxes support these agencies. You have a right as a citizen to make use of their services, and these agencies have a responsibility to help you.

The important skills of being an effective consumer are knowing where to get help and what services are provided. Such information will save you money, protect your safety and health, and often keep merchants honest in their dealings with consumers.

Product Safety. The Consumer Product Safety Commission (CPSC) protects consumers against the manufacture and sale of hazardous appliances, toys, games, and so forth. It has the power to ban hazardous products and also to order a recall when a product is thought to be dangerous to the public. A **recall** occurs when a product that is already on the market has been considered unsafe for use and the CPSC has instructed the manufacturer to take the product off the shelves.

It is the CPSC that requires oral prescription medicines and aspirin to be packaged in child-resistant containers. These containers are designed so that children will have difficulty opening them.

For more information about this agency, contact the Director, Office of Communications, Consumer Product Safety Commission, Bethesda, Maryland 20207.

Consumer Information. The Consumer Information Center (CIC) distributes consumer information that the federal government publishes. It also works with other related agencies to develop and distribute new consumer information materials. The CIC publishes a listing of over 200 federal consumer publications, many of which are directly related to health. For a free copy of the Catalog of Consumer Information, send a postcard to Consumer Information Center, Pueblo, Colorado 81009.

Food, Cosmetics, and Medicines. The **Food and Drug Administration (FDA)** ensures that all food and food additives, other than meat and poultry or those containing meat and poultry, are safe, pure, wholesome, and honestly and correctly labeled. If you find unsanitary, contaminated, or mislabeled foods, contact the FDA and it will review the complaint, which may lead to an investigation.

The FDA also ensures that cosmetics are safe and pure. The FDA requires that cosmetics be truthfully labeled and that the ingredients be listed on each package. If you have an unusual physical reaction to a cosmetic, report it to the FDA.

In addition, the FDA ensures that medicines are properly labeled and safe and effective for their intended uses. The FDA determines whether a medicine should be a prescription medicine, one that is obtainable only with a doctor's order, or whether a medicine may be sold over-the-counter, so that it is available by individual choice. The FDA regulates the advertising of prescription medicines, while the Federal Trade Commission (FTC) regulates the advertising of over-the-counter medicines in all their forms.

For more information, contact the Director, Consumer Communications, Food and Drug Administration, 5600 Fishers Lane, Rockville, Maryland 20857.

When a consumer receives a recall notice, it means a product that was bought has a defect. Ignoring a recall can put you at risk.

HANDLING CONSUMER PROBLEMS **645**

Across the Curriculum

Home Economics. Ask students to find newspaper and magazine ads that claim "quick, easy, painless weight loss without dieting." Have students evaluate the ads, reading the fine print carefully. Do the ads appear to be legitimate? Why or why not? What is the cost of the product or service? Where could you go in the community for help in evaluating the product or service?

Language Arts. Have students write a consumer information column for the school newspaper. They can ask for letters from classmates and the faculty and try to answer them. (This will give students practice in identifying places from which to seek help for various consumer problems.)

L3 COMMUNITY INVOLVE-MENT. Ask students to find one product in a store that is advertised as "new and improved." Have students compare and contrast the new form of the product with the old, trying to determine what changes in its form, packaging, safety, ingredients, or price have been made. Ask them to write the manufacturer, requesting specific information about the "new and improved" feature. Follow up by having students report on responses, if any, from the manufacturers.

L1 USING THE LESSON RESOURCES. For additional student activities, refer to the lesson resources on page 641.

Assess

Check for Understanding

- Assign and discuss the lesson review. Encourage LD students to focus on questions 1, 2, and 3.

Evaluate

- Administer, grade, and discuss the *Lesson 3 Quiz*.
- Administer, grade, and discuss the *Chapter 32 Test*.
- Refer to the Performance Assessment strategy for this chapter. See pages T 23 to T 25.

Reteach

- Divide the class into small groups, and give each group a case study of a consumer problem. Have them determine appropriate sources of help and write a specific plan of action. Then bring the class together, letting each group describe their assigned consumer problem and plan of action.
- Have each student prepare a draft of a letter to a consumer advocate about a problem with a product or service. Then have students exchange papers with a partner and imagine they are the consumer advocate. Ask pairs to discuss the solutions they propose to each other's problems, and then compile a master list on the chalkboard.
- Ask students to complete *Reteaching Activity 89*.

DID YOU KNOW?

- When you are in the hospital, hospital staff will keep records about your condition, diagnosis, and treatment.
- Your chart may contain your medical history, lab test results, dietary restrictions, medications and other treatments, scheduled tests or therapies, and more.
- Though the chart technically belongs to the hospital, you have a right to know what is on it.

CONFLICT RESOLUTION

Travis is a bike-racing enthusiast. To help keep in shape over the winter, he saved his money for months to buy an exercise bike. Now, Travis has received the bike from the mail order company, and he's very disappointed. The bike doesn't seem worth the money he paid for it. Travis called the company to ask about sending it back and getting a refund. The sales rep he spoke with told him the bike was a nonreturnable sale item. Travis thinks he's being ripped off.

What can Travis do to get his money back?

HEALTH UPDATE

LOOKING AT THE ISSUES

Health Insurance

There are about 35 million people in the United States who have no health insurance—including 9 million children. As insurance companies become stricter about who they are willing to insure, more and more Americans are finding themselves unable to get insurance. Wanting to protect themselves from huge costs, insurance companies now often refuse to insure people with catastrophic illnesses like AIDS or cancer or even some people with chronic health problems such as diabetes or hypertension.

The issues of whether or not everyone should be insured and, if so, how this insurance should be financed remain in the forefront of health-care debates.

Analyzing Different Viewpoints

ONE VIEW. Some legislators propose making a requirement that employers have to provide health insurance for workers. In Hawaii, where a law was adopted requiring employers to insure all employees, the state's uninsured rate fell to 2 percent. Under the law, employees pay at least half the cost of health insurance for full-time workers. Hawaiians now have the greatest longevity in the United States and among the lowest health-care costs.

A SECOND VIEW. Other people in government propose a health-care plan covering every American that would be financed by a 5 percent payroll tax—80 percent on employers and 20 percent on employees.

A THIRD VIEW. Others call for a national health insurance program. They want a universal health-care plan for everyone who cannot afford their own insurance. They suggest moving Medicaid benefits into the universal health-care program. They call for coverage of basic benefits, including hospital and physician services. One such plan would call for everyone to pay based on income. They point to the Canadian system, which since 1971, has mandated that the government pay for all medically necessary doctor and hospital costs. It also allows the provinces and territories to run their own programs and set fees and hospital budgets.

A FOURTH VIEW. Others opposed to plans like the Canadian plan say that health-care insurance should remain in the private sector. They point out that in Canada, because of government restrictions, there are long waiting lists for elective surgery and equipment is often outdated.

Exploring Your Views

1. Do you think every United States citizen should have health insurance? Why or why not?
2. Who should pay for this insurance?
3. Are there certain kinds of procedures or tests you think health insurance companies should not pay for? If so, what are they? Why do you feel this way? Who should decide who should and should not get necessary care?

Additional Information

Product Recalls. When a product is unfit for use, the government can recall it. For example, a manufacturer can be asked to remove a food from the marketplace. Sometimes the company removes the food on its own without any action from a federal agency. Most industries want to be sure their products meet the highest standards possible. When a product is recalled by the FDA, agents keep close watch to be sure it is removed completely from the marketplace. Products are generally recalled by brand name and specific manufacturing lot number. Most products have the lot number stamped on the container. Some products may have been distributed only in certain areas, while others are spread nationwide.

Meat and Poultry. The Food Safety and Inspection Service (FSIS) of the Department of Agriculture ensures that meat, poultry, and the products made from them are safe, wholesome, and labeled properly. This branch ensures that meat-packing plants are clean and that any potential hazards are kept at safe levels. If you have suffered from suspected food poisoning from meat or poultry, contact a doctor of the local public health office who will contact the Meatborne Hazard Control Center, Agriculture Research Center, Beltsville, Maryland 20705.

This same agency also provides information on its activities and publishes a variety of educational materials on such subjects as food safety and purchasing. For copies of any of these materials, contact the Information Division, Food Safety and Inspection Service, Department of Agriculture, Washington, DC 20250.

Advertising. As you have studied, advertising is designed to influence you and your decision about a product or service. Sometimes this advertising is honest, and sometimes it is not. The **Federal Trade Commission (FTC)** prevents the unfair, false, or deceptive advertising of consumer products and services. This includes television, radio, and print ads.

For more information about false advertising of consumer products and services, contact the Office of the Secretary, Federal Trade Commission, Washington, DC 20580.

Transportation. The Bureau of Consumer Protection of the Federal Aviation Administration (FAA) handles complaints against airlines. If you have been misled about discount fares or types of service, this is the agency with which to register a complaint. Usually you can get your problem taken care of by contacting the customer service representative of the airline. If this does not work, write to the airline's consumer affairs department. If this fails, then the Bureau of Consumer Protection is a good choice. Its address is Bureau of Consumer Protection, Federal Aviation Administraton, Washington, DC 20428.

Enrich

■ Have students design and demonstrate a board game, featuring places for consumers to get help with problems and complaints. Set up a mock contest to choose the best name for the game.

■ Work with students in setting up a consumer fair that includes booths to convey information about steps to follow in resolving problems and complaints and places to get help with consumer problems. Request administrative approval to invite other students and parents to the fair. Choose students to write an article about the fair to submit to the school and/or community newspaper. Ask other students to create educational flyers to distribute during the fair.

■ Ask students to complete *Enrichment Activity 32.*

Close

Stress that consumers have both rights and responsibilities. A complaint must be genuine; and when consumers handle a problem in a professional and organized way, they are more likely to achieve a satisfactory resolution of the difficulty. Summarize the lesson by listing the sources of help and information available to consumers.

LESSON 3 REVIEW

Reviewing Facts and Vocabulary

1. Define the terms *advocate* and *recall.* Use each in a sentence.
2. What are the monetary limits of a case that could be taken to small-claims court?
3. How might an advocate group help the consumer?

Thinking Critically

4. **Analysis.** Compare five government agencies that protect consumers.

Applying Health Knowledge

5. Make up a situation in a store or restaurant in which a person is not treated well. Compose a letter of complaint to the appropriate place.
6. Identify three organizations that would be helpful to you as a consumer if you bought a package of pills that guaranteed weight loss, and the pills did not work.

HANDLING CONSUMER PROBLEMS **647**

Answers to Lesson 3 Review

1. Advocate—one who speaks out for a cause. Recall—the removal of unsafe products.
2. Range—$100 to $3,000.
3. Help with complaints and/or represent special populations.

4. Answers will vary. See pages 645 and 647.
5. Answers will vary.
6. Answers will vary. Possible answers: BBB, Federal Trade Commission, Ralph Nader's Public Citizen.

Helping Students Improve Their Health

Using the Self-Inventory

Reinforcing Vocabulary
- **Warranties.** Guarantees.
- **Impulsive.** Acting momentarily.

Teaching Strategies

L1 EXPLANATION. Several of the items deal with the question of avoiding waste and recycling from a consumer standpoint. Some parents may feel recycling is being forced on them. Stress that for their health and for future generations recycling is of utmost importance, and that it is a lifestyle just as eating right and exercising are.

L1 EXPLANATION. Because students may not have been exposed to much consumer health education, students may score poorly on this inventory. Stress that the inventory is an attempt to find where they stand at the present time. Hopefully the knowledge gained will allow them to improve.

L1 DISCUSSION. Ask students if they can remember a time when a pushy salesperson kept badgering them. How did they deal with the situation? What are some different ways to deal with this type of situation?

L1 DISCUSSION. Have students make a list of things that they have purchased on an impulse or under the influence of a friend. Discuss different ways they can avoid making purchases under these conditions.

Self-Inventory

Are You a Wise Consumer?

HOW DO YOU RATE?

Number a sheet of paper from 1 through 21. Answer *yes* or *no* to each of the items below. Total the number of *yes* responses. Then proceed to the next section.

1. I buy products I want only when I can afford them.
2. Before I buy food products, I compare ingredients.
3. Before I choose grooming products to buy, I compare ingredients.
4. Before I buy a product, I compare packaging.
5. I make an effort to avoid products sold with excess packaging.
6. I make an effort to purchase products packaged in recyclable containers.
7. I compare prices of different brands in the same store before I buy.
8. I compare prices of the same item in different stores.
9. I shop at stores that offer the best prices.
10. I read the local papers to find out where the best buys can be found.
11. I compare warranties before purchasing.
12. I read labels before I buy.
13. I am aware of factors such as advertising and peer pressure that might influence my purchase.
14. I return products if I am not satisfied with them or if they are defective.

15. I buy what I want or need without the influence of gimmicks.
16. I understand the purpose of advertising and how it is designed to make me want a product or feel that I need a product.
17. I check the material, product, or device before I buy it to be sure that the item is in good working order or is in its original packaging.
18. I read advertisements closely so that I am clear about what they are saying and not saying.
19. I avoid emotional or impulsive buying.
20. I am not intimidated by a high-powered, pushy salesperson.
21. I do not let myself be talked into things because they are on sale.

HOW DID YOU SCORE?

Give yourself 1 point for each *yes* response and 0 points for each *no* response. Total your points, and read the next column to see how you scored. Then proceed to the next section.

17 to 21
Excellent. You are an alert consumer and are probably getting the most for your money.

12 to 16
Good. You are on the right track.

Below 12
Needs Improvement. By changing a few of your behaviors you could get more for your money.

WHAT ARE YOUR GOALS?

Identify an area in which your score is low. Then complete the statements below.

1. The behavior I would most like to change or improve is ____.
2. The steps involved in making this change are ____.
3. My timetable for accomplishing this is ____.
4. People I will ask for support and assistance are ____.
5. The benefits I will receive are ____.
6. My reward at the end of each week will be ____.

Meeting Students' Needs

For students who score *Excellent.* Have students make lists of things they could do to reinforce wise consumer habits.

For students who score *Good.* Have students analyze situations when they made unwise purchases. Based on these situations, how could they improve their purchasing habits?

For students who *Need Improvement.* Have students go shopping with their parents to see what they buy and ask how they made their selections. Have them list helpful techniques used by their parents. How could their parents' consumer habits be improved?

Building Decision-Making Skills

I n March Janet placed an order with ABC, Inc. Two months later, she still had neither heard nor received anything. She tried to contact the sales rep who helped her, but he was at lunch and never returned her phone call. Two weeks later she phoned customer relations to complain about the poor services and request a refund. Finally her order arrived, but it was incomplete. A refund check was enclosed to cover the missing items—but it was $50 more than it should have been. What should Janet do?

WHAT DO YOU THINK?

1. **Choices.** What choices does Janet have?

2. **Consequences.** What are the advantages of each choice?

3. **Consequences.** What are the disadvantages of each choice?

4. **Consequences.** How might Janet's self-esteem be affected by this decision?

5. **Decision.** What do you think Janet should do?

6. **Decision.** Do you think Janet's decision would be different if no one knew about this problem?

7. **Evaluation.** Have you ever had bad service or bought something that was broken or didn't work properly? What did you do? Was your action effective? What could you have done that would have been more effective?

T odd and his friend Joe are in a store looking at stereos. The salesperson asks if they need any help. They both say that they are just looking. The salesperson asks if they know the difference between the two models they're looking at. They shake their heads to indicate that they do not. The salesperson swings into a full-blown presentation complete with a "special deal" where they can charge a stereo and the charge won't appear for 60 days. Todd's mother has a charge account at this store. What should he do?

WHAT DO YOU THINK?

8. **Choices.** What are Todd's choices?

9. **Consequences.** Which of those choices is totally inappropriate? Why?

10. **Consequences.** What are the advantages and disadvantages of each choice

that is not identified as inappropriate?

11. **Consequences.** Who is likely to be affected by this decision?

12. **Decision.** What do you think Todd should do? Why?

13. **Decision.** What would you do if you were Todd?

14. **Evaluation.** Have you ever been in a situation where you were really tempted to buy something you didn't have money for? How did you handle the situation? Would you handle it differently now? Explain your answer.

J oyce and Meg were having lunch at a restaurant. They were seated in the nonsmoking section. Halfway through their meal a customer at the next table started smoking. The smoke was coming right across the girls' table. What should they do?

WHAT DO YOU THINK?

15. **Choices.** What are their choices?

16. **Consequences.** What are the advantages and disadvantages of each choice?

17. **Decision.** What do you think they should do? Why?

Helping Students Improve Their Health

Building Decision-Making Skills

Teaching Strategies

L1 CLASS ACTIVITY. Have students create a role-play with Janet talking with someone from the billing department at ABC. Consider the different ways she could handle this phone call.

L1 CLASS ACTIVITY. Another possible role-play pertaining to this situation might be to have Janet talking with a friend about what to do. Have Janet's friend try to talk her into keeping the money for all the trouble ABC caused her.

L2 DISCUSSION. Debate whether or not it is proper to keep something that may not be rightfully yours even though you feel you were wronged by the rightful owner.

L1 CLASS ACTIVITY. Create a role-play where Todd and Joe are talking with the salesperson. Both Joe and the salesperson are trying to talk Todd into buying the stereo during this "special deal."

L1 DISCUSSION. Discuss the pros and cons of impulsive buying. Do you always get what you want? Do you always get the best price?

L2 DISCUSSION. Debate whether it is proper or not to use, without permission, someone else's credit card—even if you plan on paying the amount off promptly.

L1 CLASS ACTIVITY. Have students role-play different ways Joyce and Meg could handle the situation.

Discussing the Answers

Situation 1. Even though Janet may feel she is justified in keeping the money, it would be inappropriate for her to keep it. There is the possibility, however, if she were to call about the overpayment that ABC might let her keep it anyway as a good business practice.

Situation 2. Todd's use of his mother's account without her permission would not

be advised. Todd needs to step away from the situation to remove the emotional aspect and discuss the purchase with his mother before making a decision.

Situation 3. It would be appropriate for Joyce and Meg to address the smoking customer in an assertive manner or contact management to deal with the situation.

Answers to Chapter 32 Review

Using Health Terms

1. Testimonial
2. Consumer
3. Assertiveness
4. Unit price
5. Placebo
6. Quack
7. Documentation
8. Small-claims court
9. Better Business Bureau
10. Recall
11. Food and Drug Administration

Building Academic Skills

12. Answers will vary but should be supported logically.

Recalling the Facts

13. Whether or not the product is a brand name, the size of the product, the type of store in which the product is sold.
14. The right to safety, to be informed, to choose, and to be heard. Richard Nixon added the right to redress, and Gerald Ford added the right to consumer education.
15. They are usually expensive.
16. Testimonials; buy one, get one free; emotional pleas.
17. Misleading advertising.
18. By examining the ingredients of a product and the guarantee that accompanies it.
19. Hope.
20. Take in fewer calories, exercise to burn off more calories.
21. Be assertive and ask consumer-oriented questions or politely ask to be left alone.
22. A nonprofit organization sponsored by private business; general information on products and services, reliability reports, background information on local businesses and organizations, records of companies' complaint-handling performances. It also handles false advertising cases.
23. Food Safety and Quality Service of the Department of Agriculture.
24. The customer receives satisfaction or a reasonable adjustment or the company provides proof that the customer's

complaint is unreasonable or unwarranted.
25. The power of the media often encourages the merchant or business to take action.
26. Its procedures are simple, inexpensive, quick, and informal; usually a person can handle the process by oneself without an attorney's representation.
27. The Consumer Product Safety Commission.
28. Office of the Secretary, Federal Trade Commission, Washington, DC 20580.
29. It ensures that all food and food additives are safe, pure, and wholesome and honestly and correctly labeled; it ensures that cosmetics are safe and pure, truthfully labeled, and that

Using Health Terms

On a separate sheet of paper, write the term that best matches each definition given below.

LESSON 1

1. One's enthusiastic recommendation of a product.
2. Anyone who uses a product or a service.
3. The ability to state one's needs or wants in a positive, nonthreatening way.
4. The cost of a product per weight, volume, or content.

LESSON 2

5. Substance with no medical value but given for psychological effect.
6. One who dishonestly promotes medical products or treatments.

LESSON 3

7. Items such as sales receipts or canceled checks, which provide proof of a purchase or transaction.
8. A court that handles claims from $100 to $3,000.
9. A nonprofit organization that attempts to settle claims against local businesses.
10. The instruction to remove defective or harmful merchandise from store shelves.
11. A government agency that ensures the safety of foods and food additives other than meat and poultry.

Building Academic Skills

LESSON 3

12. **Reading.** A vital part of being a wise health consumer is deciding who to believe. Ralph Nader is a high-profile consumer advocate. Some people hold Nader in high esteem, others do not. Read an article about or by Ralph Nader. Decide if he is someone you would choose to regard highly. Support your opinion with statements from the information you have gathered.

Recalling the Facts

LESSON 1

13. What affects the price of a product?
14. What rights were given in President John Kennedy's Consumer Bill of Rights? How was it later amended and by whom?
15. What is one drawback of buying products for their convenience?
16. What are three common techniques used in advertising?
17. What does the right to be informed protect consumers from?
18. How might a consumer determine the quality of a product?

LESSON 2

19. What does quackery offer that consumers find difficult to resist?
20. What are some healthy ways to lose weight?

LESSON 3

21. What should a person do if a salesperson is pressuring him or her?
22. What is the Better Business Bureau and what services does it provide?
23. What federal agency ensures that meat and poultry and products made from them are safe?
24. What criteria must be satisfied before the Better Business Bureau considers a complaint settled?
25. How is unfavorable publicity helpful in getting a customer complaint resolved?
26. What are some advantages of going to small-claims court?
27. What federal agency protects consumers against the manufacture and sale of hazardous appliances and toys?
28. Where could you write to obtain more information about false advertising of consumer products?
29. How does the Food and Drug Administration protect the health of consumers?
30. Where should one go first when one is dissatisfied with a product or service?

REVIEW

Thinking Critically

LESSON 1

31. Evaluation. Which right under the Consumer Bill of Rights do you consider the most important? Explain your choice.

32. Synthesis. For two minutes, list all the advertising slogans and/or jingles you can think of. What conclusions can you draw from your list about the nature of advertising?

LESSON 2

33. Evaluation. Can education eliminate quackery? Support your answer.

34. Analysis. What emotions might a person experience if he or she spent money on a quack weight-loss remedy and lost weight but gained all of the weight back in a few months? Explain.

LESSON 3

35. Synthesis. BBBs are sponsored by private businesses. What advantages and disadvantages might there be to this sponsorship?

36. Evaluation. How would you distinguish between an effective complaint and an ineffective complaint?

37. Synthesis. Imagine that you have been cheated out of a large sum of money. Write a letter to a fictitious TV consumer reporter describing what happened. Predict how the problem might be solved "on the air."

Making the Connection

LESSON 1

38. Home Economics. Choose a health-care product and compare the price of that product in several different stores (convenience, specialty, supermarket). Summarize your findings in writing.

39. Math. Assume that all forms of promotion, including advertising, add 27 percent to the cost of the average grocery item. If a nationally advertised brand of paper towel sells for $1.03 a roll, how much should a generic brand sell for?

Applying Health Knowledge

LESSON 1

40. Which of the following is the best way to collect consumer information? Support your answer.
   a. Drive from store to store.
   b. Call various stores, requesting information.
   c. Write to various manufacturers.

41. Think of three purchases you have made recently. Which factors most influenced your decision? Do you feel these were good or bad?

42. Makers of name-brand products pay large sums of money to have their products used in movies. Do you feel this is fair advertising? Should it be permitted?

43. Write two ads about a product or service of your choice. In one, make misleading, faulty claims that attempt to entice the consumer. Write another that is honest and direct.

LESSON 2

44. An old expression is "Laughter is the best medicine." Some people claim to have actually been cured of diseases by watching movies that made them laugh. What do you think of this?

45. If a person became addicted to a placebo, would this be a physiological or psychological addiction? Explain.

46. It is the salesperson's job to ask if a customer needs help. What are some effective ways to decline? Explain.

Beyond the Classroom

LESSON 3

47. Community Involvement. See if your school or local libraries have a current copy of the Consumers Resource Handbook. If they do not, write to Consumer Information Center, Pueblo, Colorado 81009, requesting a copy of this free book or politely ask the librarians to do so.

ingredients are listed on each package; it ensures that drugs are properly labeled and safe and effective for their intended use.

30. Back to the store where the product or service was purchased and, if possible, the person who sold it.

Thinking Critically

31. Answers will vary but should be supported logically.
32. Answers will vary.
33. Answers will vary but should be supported logically.
34. Answers will vary. Possible answers: Anger/embarrassment at being gullible, frustration at being taken in, despair because of failure, pity because he or she tried hard and is still overweight.
35. Answers will vary. Possible answers: Advantages—it is a self-policing organization like the American Medical Association and the American Bar Association; since it is part of the business world it can get results quickly; no tax dollars are used to fund the BBB. Disadvantages—it may be susceptible to political pressure; if business declines, funds for the BBB would be withdrawn.
36. Answers will vary. Possible answer: An effective complaint will identify the problem and offer a solution, provide documentation, be directed to the store/person where product was purchased. An ineffective complaint would be poorly organized and emotional.
37. Letters will vary.

Making the Connection

38. Summaries will vary.
39. About 81¢.

Applying Health Knowledge

40. Answers will vary. Best answer: B—it is the least expensive, most efficient, and quickest way to gather information.
41. Answers will vary.
42. Answers will vary.
43. Ads will vary.
44. Answers will vary but should be supported.

45. Psychological addiction because the person would believe him- or herself unable to live without the placebo.
46. Answers will vary but should reflect assertive,

polite ways to decline, and examples should be supported.

Beyond the Classroom

47. Answers will vary.

Lesson Summaries

LESSON 1. Health services are concerned with the prevention of disease, the maintenance and promotion of health, and the treatment and cure of disease. Americans spend about $200 billion per year on health care, utilizing both inpatient and outpatient facilities and services. Government and private insurance programs can be purchased to protect individuals from the high cost of health-care services.

LESSON 2. There are three stages of health-care services available. Primary care is when an individual seeks a doctor. Secondary care occurs when the primary care doctor refers the patient to a specialist. Tertiary care is needed when the patient's condition requires advanced equipment or treatment. Doctors are generally in private practice or participating in a group practice, where several doctors unite to provide medical care. HMO doctors are paid by salary and not a fee for services, often stressing preventive medicine. Health-care outlets are also available for people who are not covered otherwise.

Introducing the Chapter

Help students develop a list of health-care facilities and services available in your community. The list should include hospitals and clinics (general and specialized), private doctors, dental offices and clinics, nursing homes, mental health facilities, neighborhood health centers, etc. In an urban area, the list will be extensive. In a rural area, discuss the availability of health care, travel required to reach specialty health-care facilities, and the availability of such transportation.

Performance Assessment ✓

Refer to pages T 23 to T 25 for a Performance Assessment strategy for this chapter. See the *Performance Assessment Activities* booklet for additional suggestions.

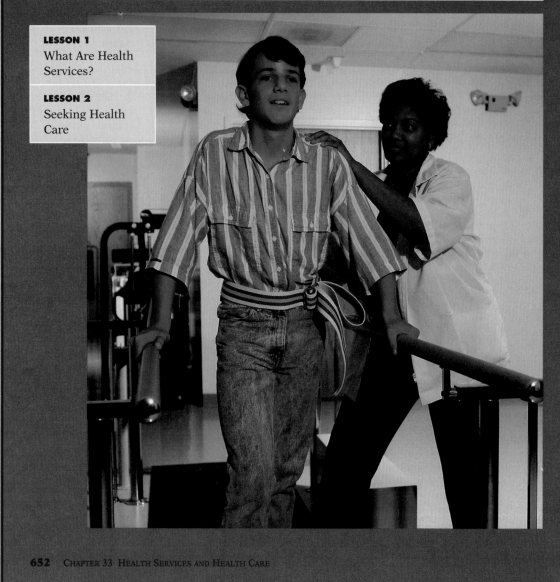

CHAPTER

33 HEALTH SERVICES AND HEALTH CARE

LESSON 1
What Are Health Services?

LESSON 2
Seeking Health Care

Key to Ability Levels

Teaching strategies have been coded for varying learning styles and abilities.

L1 Level 1 activities are basic activities and should be within the ability range of all students.

L2 Level 2 activities are average activities and should be within the ability range of average to above-average students.

L3 Level 3 activities are challenging activities designed for the ability range of above-average students.

LD LD activities should be within the ability range of learning-disabled students.

LEP LEP activities should be within the ability range of Limited English Proficiency students.

WHAT ARE HEALTH SERVICES?

A focus of health education is to provide health information in such a way that it influences people to take positive action about their health. Health services are another aspect of an overall health program. Health services involve prevention of disease, the maintenance and promotion of health, and the treatment and cure of disease.

The Range of Health Care

The American public spends about $756 billion per year on health care. About 7 million people are employed in some aspect of health-care delivery. The occupations and services range from very large hospitals to mobile vans, from air pollution controls in large cities to tuberculosis checks in small towns.

When a person is vaccinated against a disease that can spread, he or she is involved in preventive health services. People who are engaged in fitness programs are part of a health promotion program, while people who are being treated for cancer or obesity are in treatment or therapeutic types of programs. Health services can also be maintenance-oriented. Health maintenance includes the different types of assessments and examinations that are conducted periodically to make sure that individuals are free from disease.

Whatever the type of health service, it is a major part of the total health picture in the United States. Health service is more commonly referred to as **health-care delivery.**

Many different types of health resources exist in the United States. Health resources are places that people can go for various types of treatment. Think of some health resources in your community. Dentists' and doctors' offices, drugstores, nursing and retirement homes, hospitals, health maintenance organizations, poison-control centers, psychiatric outpatient clinics, public health clinics, mental health centers, suicide-prevention centers, and neighborhood health centers are all examples.

Types of Health Facilities

A **health facility** is a place a person goes to for health care. There are two basic types: facilities for inpatient care and facilities for outpatient care. The differences between inpatients and outpatients are as follows:

- **Inpatients** are people who require prolonged health care and are admitted to a facility and occupy a bed in it. Such people may need nursing service, extensive use of laboratory and X-ray services, or supervised rehabilitation.
- **Outpatients** receive various medical, dental, or other health services in a facility and return home the same day.

LESSON 1 FOCUS

TERMS TO USE
- Health-care delivery
- Health facility
- Inpatients
- Outpatients
- Medicare
- Medicaid

CONCEPTS TO LEARN
- Health care includes many different types of health services.
- Health facilities include hospitals and various kinds of nursing homes.
- Health insurance may be provided by government or private programs.

ATTITUDES AND BEHAVIORS TO EVALUATE
- Self-Inventory, page 666.
- Building Decision-Making Skills, page 667.

Focus

Lesson Objectives

After studying this lesson, students should be able to:
- name the major types of health-care facilities available in the United States and explain how they differ
- describe the types of health insurance currently available in the United States

Bellringer

Write the following on the chalkboard for students to work on while attendance is being taken: *If you had a sudden attack of appendicitis and needed surgery right away, to which hospital would you go? How long would you be likely to stay in the hospital? What would it cost? Who would pay for it?*

Introducing the Lesson

Refer to the Bellringer. Ask volunteers to share their responses, which may show considerable variation. Most teens have relatively limited experience with the health care system, so they are likely to be uncertain about such questions. Even adults may be shocked by the cost of a brief hospital stay and how little of the bill their health insurance will pay. Tell them that in this lesson they will learn how health facilities and health insurance policies differ. This will help them make the best choices for themselves when they are adult health-care consumers.

Resources for Lesson 1

- **Transparency** 30
- **Guided Reading** Activity 90
- **Workbook** Vocabulary Activity 90
- **Reteaching** Activity 90
- **Lesson 1 Quiz**
- **Performance Assessment** Activity 33

ABC News InterActive Videodiscs
AIDS, Side 1
Ch 22 The Cost of Care

DID YOU KNOW?

- In 1990, there were nearly 600,000 doctors in the U.S.
- Even some doctors do not have health insurance. It is estimated that 2.9 percent of U.S. doctors and 2.3 percent of registered nurses are uninsured.
- Family doctors are trained to diagnose and treat as many as 90 percent of the health problems most people face.

Building Vocabulary

- Copy each of the vocabulary terms on a 3-by-5 inch index card. Write each of the definitions of the terms as given in the lesson on additional cards. You may need several sets of cards in order to give one to each student. Mix up the cards and distribute them to the class. At your signal, have students find a match for their term or definition. After they have finished, have volunteers provide definitions for each term.
- Ask students to complete *Workbook Vocabulary Activity 90*.

Teach

Guided Practice

L1 EXPLANATION. Explain the new consumer role in health care. In the past, people relied on their doctors almost totally for health care. Today, consumers are more active in their own health promotion and more aware of preventive measures. This is partly due to the rising cost of health care.

L1 CLASS ACTIVITY. Have students brainstorm as many different specific hospitals and types of hospitals as they can think of. Then, have them categorize the hospitals they named according to length of stay, kind of services provided, and type of ownership.

L2 DISCUSSION. Have students discuss the responsibilities they think the individual should take in his or her own health care.

L1 SPEAKER. Invite a doctor to speak to the class about differences in outpatient and inpatient surgery. Have the speaker give some examples of the length of time patients are likely to be hospitalized for various illnesses and surgeries.

L1 DISCUSSION. Have students discuss the types of consumer problems that may occur with health services like hospitals and nursing homes, as opposed to health products, such as prescription and over-the-counter drugs. List the types of problems on the chalkboard.

FINDING HELP

An RMH, a Ronald McDonald House, is a temporary housing facility for parents and families of children being treated for serious medical problems. Families staying at the house contribute a small donation, except in cases of financial hardship. Community donations help support each house.

The first Ronald McDonald House opened its doors in 1974 in Philadelphia through the joint efforts of the Philadelphia Eagles and McDonald's® Restaurants. It was named the Ronald McDonald House partly because of McDonald's fund-raising support and because of the McDonald's clown, Ronald.

There are over 125 Ronald McDonald Houses in the U.S. For more information, contact McDonald's Corporation, McDonald's Plaza, Oak Brook, IL 60521

Hospitals

The hospital is perhaps the most familiar type of health facility in a community. Hospitals are used for both inpatient and outpatient care and are often centers for education and medical research. Hospitals are often classified according to the length of time patients must stay, the kinds of services provided, and the type of ownership.

- **Length of stay.** Hospitals can be long- or short-term care facilities. A long-term hospital is one in which patients stay more than 30 days. Having a spinal cord injury would involve a long-term hospital stay. A short-term hospital is one in which most patients stay less that 30 days. Having an appendectomy would involve a short-term stay.

- **Kinds of services provided.** General hospitals provide health care for most types of illnesses and injuries. Care given at a special hospital is for certain kinds of health needs. A children's hospital is an example of a special hospital. Treating tuberculosis could occur in a hospital that specializes in this disease. Special hospitals also may provide other types of services, such as at a research hospital, where facilities are available for medical research.

- **Type of ownership.** A nonprofit voluntary hospital may be owned by a church or other charitable group. A community hospital is owned by a community. Neither of these types of hospitals try to make a profit. These hospitals charge fees but also depend on donations to help cover costs of operation.

A private, or proprietary, hospital is operated like a business. This kind of hospital is expected to make a profit for the owners.

A government hospital is owned by federal, state, county, or local government. The staffs at these hospitals provide care for members of the armed forces and their dependents, veterans, and Native Americans. Many state hospitals care for patients who have tuberculosis or are mentally ill. Some county and local hospitals serve people who are economically disadvantaged and live near the hospital.

General hospitals provide health care for newborns and new mothers.

Additional Information

The Medical Hierarchy. The medical division of labor in the U.S. is very elaborate, with many practitioners filling roles other than that of physician. Nonetheless, physicians are the preeminent practitioners, and they are further subdivided into more than 20 specialties. These vary by the parts of the patient treated and the techniques used—as well as by the earnings, status, and power accorded to the practitioner. Doctors of internal medicine are at the top of the physician hierarchy, and within internal medicine higher status goes to cardiology than to urology or proctology, clearly reflecting the cultural symbolism we attach to the corresponding body parts.

At a skilled nursing facility, most residents require full-time medical care.

Other Health-Care Facilities

Other types of long-term health-care facilities are available. The following are the most common.

Nursing homes. Nursing homes are facilities in which care is provided for medical and nonmedical needs. Though most residents are 65 years of age or older, these facilities are used for people of all ages. A person with a serious, long-term illness or recovering from surgery may live at a nursing home. Some nursing homes are private and are run to make a profit. Others are nonprofit and may be owned by a church or other group.

There are basically three types of nursing home care. With personal residential care, the following is provided: assisted living in a sheltered environment, meals, and routine medical care and supervision, including use of medicines. A nursing home with intermediate care provides basic nursing care. Residents receive medical examinations more routinely. Programs for physical and speech therapy also may be provided. Social activities are planned for residents. At a skilled nursing facility, most of the residents have serious medical illnesses or disabilities. Consequently, medical care is needed more frequently. Twenty-four-hour nursing care is provided.

Health Insurance

Health insurance is a plan to pay for part or most costs of medical expenses and care associated with illness or disability. These costs can include medical tests, surgery, hospitalization, physician care, and medicines. Disability income insurance provides income for a period of time if a person is unable to continue working because of an illness or disability.

A person who is insured pays a premium, or fee, for insurance. This fee for the policy is paid either out-of-pocket, or through payroll deduction as part of a group plan with his or her place of employment. Health insurance plans vary widely, but there are two basic kinds of health insurance available—government programs and private programs.

L3 DISCUSSION. Have students consider reasons that outpatient surgery and second opinions are becoming more frequent in medical practice.

L3 DISCUSSION. Ask students to imagine that they need surgery in a few weeks. What steps would they take to select a hospital and prepare themselves for surgery?.

L1 SPEAKER. Invite a speaker from a local nursing home to talk about his or her health-care facility. Ask the speaker to describe a typical patient and why the patient is there. The speaker should address what the nursing home provides that is not available in the patient's own home.

L2 CLASS ACTIVITY. Ask each student to think about what kinds of design features should be included in an adolescent health-care facility that might not be as appropriate or necessary in a medical facility for another age-group. Have students list their ideas.

L1 SPEAKER. Invite a person from the health department to class to discuss the types of consumer needs and problems most often seen in the community. Have the speaker address what the consumer might do to ensure better health care and what plans are being developed to address voids in current health-care services

L1 EXPLANATION. Distinguish among the kinds of services and products that health insurance policies typically cover. Explain what a health insurance premium is and that monthly health insurance premiums can range from $50 to several thousands of dollars.

L1 COOPERATIVE LEARNING. Divide the class in half. Assign one half Medicare and the other half Medicaid. Have each group work to describe its type of medical insurance, including who is covered and who pays for it. A volunteer from each group should share their descriptions with the class.

L1 USING LIFE MANAGEMENT SKILLS TRANSPARENCY 30. Refer to the Teaching Transparencies Binder.

Across the Curriculum

Social Studies. Ask students to research federal agencies engaged in offering health-related services to individuals all over the world. Have them determine the original role of the World Health Organization in providing health services. Ask them to determine the original purpose of ACTION, which was a federal agency combining the Peace Corps, VISTA, and other voluntary agencies into a single organization, and explain how each of these forces dealt with poverty-related social, economic, and health problems in the United States and developing countries. Explain the types of health services these organizations are currently providing.

Government Health Insurance

Medicare is a health insurance program that is available to people who are 65 years of age and older and to people who receive social security disability benefits. Taxes help cover the two parts of Medicare—hospital and medical insurance. Medicare covers costs of hospital or nursing home care. Additional Medicare insurance can be bought to help pay physicians and other costs. The patient is responsible for any uncovered balance.

Some people who receive Medicare also are eligible for Medicaid. **Medicaid** is an assistance program of medical aid for people of all ages who are unable to financially afford medical care. This includes people with low incomes who have dependent children, people with high medical costs in relation to their income, or people who are disabled.

Medicaid benefits vary from state to state in the United States. Types of cases that may be paid for by Medicaid include crack babies, AIDS patients, and nursing home patients. Medicaid is paid for through federal and state taxes and covers both physician and hospital fees.

Worker's compensation is insurance to cover costs of injury or illness that is job-related. Compensation may be made to cover lost wages or to a family in case of death. Employers pay the cost of worker's compensation insurance.

Private Health Insurance

There are two basic kinds of private health insurance programs—individual and group. A person may choose an individual program if he or she does not qualify for a group program or has health needs that cannot be met in a group plan or if a group program is not available. In individual health insurance programs, the individual pays the premium himself or herself.

In group plans, employers offer an insurance plan as part of a job benefit. Group plans also may include the insured person's spouse and children. The employer usually pays a portion of the premium. The premiums for group plans are usually lower than for individual plans because more people are covered in the plan, and the charge per person can be less for administrative costs. To keep costs as low as possible, most insurance policies have a deductible that must be met and paid for each year by the insured before the insurance company will begin to pay the balance of medical charges. Usually, the higher the deductible, the lower the premium of the health insurance.

KEEPING FIT

Adolescent Health Centers

Traditionally teens have been left out of the health-care system. Usually until age 12, patients visited a pediatrician. After that, they would visit either a family doctor or a specialist to deal with specific problems. There is a critical need for teaching teens lifelong health strategies. Adolescent clinics are a new option that helps meet this need. At best, adolescent health centers help teens get health care in an atmosphere that treats them as individuals with dignity and a capacity for self-cure. Across the country adolescent health centers come in many varieties, ranging from experimental drop-in centers to programs that are an offshoot of established children's hospitals.

Additional Information

Health Services. According to the *Journal of the American Medical Association,* women and minorities are making up greater percentages of medical residency programs than in the past. The report states that women make up about 30 percent of these programs, up 7 percent from 1980 to a total of 82,902. Minorities are also up from 12,395 to 20,181 between 1980 and 1990. Asian and Pacific Islanders account for 9.5 percent of all medical residents, African Americans, 4.7 percent, and Hispanics, 5.6 percent.

Overcoming The Odds

D**r. Francisco Murphy-Rivera is a resident in family practice. He was graduated from the Universidad Central del Caribe, Cayey, Puerto Rico in 1991. He loves to spend the little free time he has with his wife and five-month-old twin daughters, Laura and Lourdes.

"All my life, I wanted to be a doctor," he begins. "I always told my mother I was going to be a doctor. All my games as a child had to do with this."

He continues, "Coming here was not easy. In Puerto Rico, there are good family practice residencies. My wife already had a good job. We had our own house, our families. When we decided to come to the U.S., we came alone by ourselves. We didn't know anyone. Then, twenty days after my residency started, my babies were born. But we have a very positive attitude. Having this positive attitude makes us remember that things could be worse. We have all the necessities."

Dr. Murphy-Rivera is committed to the idea of family practice. "Family practice is a specialty concerned with the continuous care of the patient from womb to tomb," he explains. "Family practice is concerned with how the patient is doing physically,

emotionally, and psychologically. It also means treating a patient as part of a total family system."

But being a family doctor is not always easy. Dr. Murphy-Rivera talks about the odds that many family practitioners today have to face. "There are too few family physicians in the U.S.," he says. "In some states there are a lot, but there is poor distribution. Some doctors don't want the 24-hour-a-day commitment. Others have amazing loans to repay for their medical educations and choose to go into specialties that pay more for this and other reasons."

With his busy schedule, Dr. Murphy-Rivera often gets only 5 or 6 hours of sleep each night. And he spends many hours, sometimes even days, away from his family. He says, "It can be 48 to 56 hours before I see them again. But when I arrive home, I try to be with them as much as possible."

Dr. Murphy-Rivera concludes, "So many people care only about knowledge. But knowledge alone isn't enough. There are basic abilities that I think are very important for a doctor to have. They are to establish a good doctor-patient rapport, to communicate effectively, and to be a good listener. I also think that people have to think that in a way they are the real doctors. There's no reason for me to take care of you if you don't take care of yourself. People have to be more involved with their own health care. We are not here just to heal conditions," he says. "We are here to prevent people from getting sick."

1. What are the personal odds that Dr. Murphy-Rivera has overcome?
2. What three basic abilities does he think every doctor should have?
3. How would you sum up Dr. Murphy-Rivera's philosophy of medicine? Is his approach to medicine and his patients one that appeals to you?

Overcoming Misconceptions

Chiropractic Medicine. In the late 1800s, the American Medical Association (AMA) denounced chiropractic medicine as quackery and forbade medical doctors from associating professionally with chiropractors. To do so was deemed unethical. As a consequence, for a long time chiropractors were ranked right alongside the sellers of snake oil.

Due to lawsuits brought against the AMA by chiropractors, the AMA officially rescinded its position. Since then, medical doctors increasingly refer patients to chiropractors, whom they recognize as better trained to deal with certain problems, particularly problems of body alignment.

Check for Understanding

- Assign and discuss the lesson review.

Evaluate

- Administer, grade, and discuss the *Lesson 1 Quiz.*

Reteach

- Ask students to work in small groups and to imagine that their job is answering an information hotline for foreigners settling in the United States. Ask each group to act out what they would say to the inquiring person about the types of health facilities available in the United States and the kinds of medical insurance available to pay for them.
- Ask students to complete *Reteaching Activity 90.*

Enrich

- Ask students to research the advantages and disadvantages of socialized medicine. Have them determine which countries have socialized medicine and how successful the system is in each country.
- Ask students to compare the health-care system in the United States with that of Canada. Have them identify the advantages and disadvantages of each system. Can they think of ways to combine the advantages of each into one improved health-care system?

Close

Ask students to summarize the most important points in this lesson. Have them identify different kinds of hospitals and nursing homes and describe the various kinds of health insurance programs.

Culturally Speaking

Fighting Tuberculosis

Annie Dodge Wauneka, a Navajo, grew up on a reservation where tuberculosis, TB, was a major cause of death. Annie was elected to the Tribal Council and appointed chairperson of the health committee. She wrote a Navajo-English medical dictionary, and convinced Navajo healers to work with nonNavajo doctors. Through her efforts, many Navajo began to get X rays and treatment. In 1963 she was awarded the Freedom Award by President Kennedy for her war against TB. She also received the name of "Warrior Who Scouts The Enemy" from the Navajo people.

Health insurance claim forms can be confusing to fill out.

Insurance policies can be difficult to read and understand. Many consumers are not sure exactly what their insurance covers. It may come as a surprise to many consumers to discover that the insurance policy covers only a small portion of the medical bill. Some plans provide only minimal coverage. Hospital coverage is likely to be for a limited number of days. Other plans are quite comprehensive and may include coverage of dental bills, prescription drugs, and various kinds of psychiatric counseling.

The important point to remember for you as a consumer is to treat health insurance like any other purchase. Use your consumer skills. Read everything carefully before signing any agreement. Ask questions if you do not understand. Compare several different companies' prices and coverage.

LESSON 1 REVIEW

Reviewing Facts and Vocabulary

1. What is the primary concern of health services?
2. Explain what health insurance is and what may be covered.
3. What are the two parts of Medicare?

Thinking Critically

4. **Analysis.** Compare and contrast the three different types of hospitals.
5. **Evaluation.** Read current articles concerning health-care delivery in the United States. Summarize in a short report what you think is good about the system and what are some of the problems.

Applying Health Knowledge

6. Interview several adults about their reasons for selecting the health insurance they have. Find out what their policy deductible is. Find out what their insurance provides for them.
7. Find out what Medicaid benefits are available in your state. Discover the criteria used in order to grant Medicaid benefits.

Answers to Lesson 1 Review

1. Prevention of disease, the maintenance and promotion of health, and the treatment and cure of disease.
2. Health insurance is a plan to pay for part or most costs of medical expenses and care associated with illness or disability.
3. Hospital and medical insurance.
4. See page 654.
5. Answers will vary.
6. Answers will vary.
7. Answers will vary.

SEEKING HEALTH CARE

Today we have many facilities and medical specialists to care for our needs and to help us live longer. Presently, we have three major stages of health care and hundreds of different specialists in the health-care field.

Stages of Health Care

Following are the three stages of health care:

- Primary care. If you get sick and call a doctor, most likely you call a general practitioner, a doctor who is in family practice. This kind of care, which the patient seeks on his or her own, is called primary care. It most often takes place in a doctor's office or a clinic.
- Secondary care. If a primary-care doctor refers a patient to a specialist, this is secondary care. Secondary care may involve a stay in a hospital for more extensive testing than could be received in a clinic or a doctor's office.
- Tertiary care. When a patient's condition requires specialized equipment or treatment, this is tertiary care. This type of care takes place at hospitals equipped with special technology. Examples of tertiary care include kidney dialysis treatment, heart or brain surgery, and cancer or burn treatment.

Forms of Medical Practice

Traditionally, the doctor has been the central figure in the delivery of health care in the United States. Most doctors are in **private practice;** that is, they are self-employed, functioning in individual practices, operating out of their own offices, and not sharing personnel, facilities, or income with any other doctor.

The Specialist

Doctors work generally in five major clinical areas: internal medicine, obstetrics and gynecology, pediatrics, psychiatry, and surgery. These primary-care areas are further broken down into secondary or specialty areas. For example, under internal medicine, there is a specialist who diagnoses and treats almost every organ or system of the body. Some of the most common specialists are as follows:

- Allergist. Diagnoses and treats patients for asthma, hay fever, hives, and other allergies.
- Anesthesiologist. Administers anesthetics (drugs that cause insensitivity to pain) during surgery; checks the patient's condition before, during, and after surgery.

SEEKING HEALTH CARE **659**

LESSON 2 FOCUS

TERMS TO USE
- Private practice
- Group practice
- Health maintenance organization (HMO)
- Hospice

CONCEPTS TO LEARN
- There are three stages of health care: primary, secondary, and tertiary.
- To choose a health care professional, you need to understand the various forms of medical practice.
- Many changes are occurring in the delivery of health care.

ATTITUDES AND BEHAVIORS TO EVALUATE
- Self-Inventory, page 666.
- Building Decision-Making Skills, page 667.

Lesson Objectives

After studying this lesson, students should be able to:
- give examples of primary, secondary, and tertiary health care
- describe trends in the delivery of health care

Bellringer

Write the following on the chalkboard for students to work on while attendance is being taken: *Write as many words as you can think of that relate to the terms* primary, secondary, *and* tertiary.

Introducing the Lesson

Introduce this lesson by shouting in a cheerleading style, "Give me a 1"-"1", "Give me a 2"-"2", "Give me a 3"-"3." Then hold up a blue first place ribbon. Ask students what the ribbon indicates. Repeat with red and white ribbons. (Students will indicate the ribbons represent first, second, and third places in a competitive event.) Referring to the Bellringer, ask students to give another set of terms that mean 1, 2, and 3. (Primary, secondary, and tertiary.) Relate these terms to the stages of health care. Indicate where each type of care might be obtained in your community.

DID YOU KNOW?

- A study found that doctors admit to lacking training in one or more of the areas most common to adolescent health problems, including drug addiction, eating disorders, and depression.
- One in seven U.S. teens has no health insurance.

Resources for Lesson 2

- **Transparency** 30
- **Guided Reading** Activity 91
- **Decision-Making** Activity 33
- **Workbook** Vocabulary Activity 91
- **Workbook** Application Activity 33
- **Reteaching** Activity 91

- **Enrichment** Activity 33
- **Health Labs** Activity 33
- **Cooperative Learning** Activity 33
- **Lesson 2 Quiz**
- **Chapter 33 Test**

Building Vocabulary

- Draw a horizontal line across the chalkboard. Ask students for the term that names a person who has a private practice in medicine. Write it above the line. Then ask for the name of a medical worker with a specific practice, and write it below the line. Have students pick the term for a general system of payments for medical expenses, and write it above the line. Below, as students name them, write the two specific programs for payment. Then ask volunteers to look up the meaning of any remaining vocabulary terms and read them aloud. Ask students to use each of the terms in a sentence that demonstrates its meaning.
- Ask students to complete *Workbook Vocabulary Activity 91.*

Teach

Guided Practice

L1 CLASS ACTIVITY. Ask students to write sentences that describe the ideal doctor or clinic. Have the students share their responses with the class. Explain that everyone should be careful in choosing the right doctor and clinic for specific health problems.

L1 DISCUSSION. Read the Hippocratic Oath that doctors take when receiving their medical licenses. Ask students why this is important. Discuss how this can be a conflict for doctors when they are involved in a case relating to euthanasia.

L1 DISCUSSION. Ask students to discuss why a person might choose to go to a family doctor with a specific problem rather than to a specialist. (Familiarity, doctor knows family history, etc.) Why might a person choose instead to go to a specialist? (Greater expertise about a specific ailment, more sophisticated equipment, etc.)

L1 USING LIFE MANAGEMENT SKILLS TRANSPARENCY 30. Refer to the Teaching Transparencies Binder.

DID YOU KNOW?

- Like some fast-food restaurants, an emergency room at Doctors Hospital in Detroit, Michigan, promises that if you aren't seen within 20 minutes, your treatment will be free.
- Many schools have a school nurse. But some high schools now also have health centers. Students can use these by applying and with written parental permission. The centers are staffed by social workers, nurse practitioners, part-time physicians, dieticians and mental health professionals.
- According to the Association of Independent Colleges and Schools, four of the five fastest-growing occupations in the '90s involve health care. These are medical assistant, physical therapist, physical therapy assistant, and home health aide.

- Cardiologist. Diagnoses and treats heart diseases.
- Dermatologist. Diagnoses and treats all forms of skin problems.
- Endocrinologist. Diagnoses and treats problems related to the endocrine glands.
- Gastroenterologist. Treats gastrointestinal (stomach and intestinal) disorders.
- Gynecologist. Diagnoses and treats problems related to female reproductive organs.
- Neurologist. Diagnoses and treats problems of the central and peripheral nervous systems.
- Obstetrician. Specializes in all aspects of childbirth—care of the mother before, during, and after delivery.
- Ophthalmologist. Diagnoses and corrects eye problems.
- Orthopedic surgeon. Performs surgery on bones and joints.
- Otolaryngologist. Treats ear, nose, and throat disorders.
- Otologist. Treats ear problems.
- Pathologist. Carries out laboratory tests of body tissues and fluids; studies the causes of death.
- Pediatrician. Specializes in the medical care of children.
- Plastic surgeon. Treats skin and soft tissue deformities; performs surgery to improve external features.
- Psychiatrist. Treats mental and emotional disorders.
- Radiologist. Examines and treats patients by using X rays and radium therapy.
- Thoracic surgeon. Performs surgery on the chest and the lungs.
- Vascular surgeon. Performs surgery on the heart and the blood vessels.
- Urologist. Treats disorders of the urinary tract (kidneys, ureters, urethra); also treats problems of the male reproductive organs.

Group Practice

While group practice has existed for many years, it has become more popular in recent years because of the rising costs involved in setting up

A dermatologist may be able to alleviate the problems associated with teenage acne.

660 CHAPTER 33 HEALTH SERVICES AND HEALTH CARE

Meeting Special Needs

Support Groups. There are over half a million support and self-help groups in the U.S. They deal with everything from drug abuse to divorce, from mental retardation to weight control. Groups are formed by individuals with similar concerns and are designed to provide information and resources and to give emotional support. Support groups are not meant to replace health-care professionals. Instead, they supplement and complement structured health-care services. For information about a group that deals with a specific concern, students can contact a local hospital, doctor, or social service agency. Have students make posters of names and phone numbers of these special groups in your area.

Radiologists are specially trained to interpret X rays.

CHOOSING A HEALTH-CARE PROFESSIONAL

As you begin to take a more active and responsible role in promoting your personal health and wellness, it is important that you choose a health-care professional who will work with you in your efforts. The best time to select a health-care professional is before you need one. Following are some guidelines for selecting a health-care professional:

- Ask a number of people for recommendations.
- Use the yellow pages of the phone directory, in which doctors are categorized by their specialties.
- Call your local medical society. Most medical societies will provide three names, chosen in rotation from the society's membership roster.
- Ask your local librarian or consumer protection agency if a directory of doctors has been compiled for your community. It will provide detailed information about doctors.
- When you have compiled a list of several possible health-care providers, prepare a list of questions you would like answered, and call the office of each person to get the information you need to make your decision.

and maintaining a medical practice. The rapid advances in medicine and the demand for specialization also make this option more attractive today than in former years.

Group practice is an arrangement in which two or more doctors join together to provide medical care. They diagnose through consultation and treat through the joint use of equipment, support staff, and funds for the maintenance and development of the practice.

Health Maintenance Organizations

When you go to doctors who are in private practice or in a group practice, you pay for their services each time you use them. Another option is now available to consumers—a **health maintenance organization (HMO).** HMOs stress preventive medicine in an attempt to reduce the high cost of medical care. Preventive medicine involves the consumer taking personal responsibility for his or her own health.

HELP WANTED

Surgical Technologist

Join our team! Become a surgical technologist in our surgery department. As a surgical technologist you will be an essential member of the medical team in the operating room. You will work with surgeons and nurses to provide patient care before, during, and after surgery. Job duties include preparing supplies for surgery, scrubbing patients, and assisting doctors with surgical procedures. Quick thinking and steady hands are definite pluses for this position. If you have completed a surgical technology program and passed the certification exam, we want you! For more information about this job opportunity, contact:
Association of Surgical Technologists
8307 Shaffer Parkway
Littleton, CO 80127

SEEKING HEALTH CARE **661**

Meeting Special Needs

Medical Treatment. If affordability is the issue and a teen can't afford to get medical treatment, suggest the following:

- Talk with a school nurse. Ask for a referral to a local clinic, a neighborhood health-care center or primary health-care center.
- Call a local health clinic.

- Call a local hospital or other medical facility. Ask what free services are available.
- Call the state welfare office.
- Call the local public health office.
- Call a local social service office.
- Call the state Medicaid office.
- In most states, people can apply for benefits at the local state welfare, public health, or social service agency.

DID YOU KNOW?

■ Pediatric emergency centers staffed by specialists and often open at night and on weekends are now being opened in many communities in the United States. This allows children to get specialized care without having long waits in traumatic and crowded emergency rooms. Such centers generally treat all ailments except for major head or spine trauma.

DISCUSSION. Ask students to talk about which factors seem to have the greatest influence on a person when choosing a doctor or health-care facility: word-of-mouth, media advertisements, Yellow Pages, recommendations from consumer organizations, referrals from doctors, or other sources.

SPEAKER. Ask an administrator or health-care provider from a holistic health center to speak to the class about the kinds of services offered in the center. With prepared questions, students should ask about what the center offers, endorses, or teaches in the areas of meditation and relaxation, biofeedback, visualization, acupuncture, nutrition, exercise, massage, hydrotherapy, etc.

COOPERATIVE LEARNING. Divide the class into small groups. Ask each group to work on one of the following projects to teach the public about the three stages of health care described in this lesson: chart, outline, mobile, diorama, jingle, bulletin board, billboard, or other visual, written, or musical form of display for the information.

CLASS ACTIVITY. Ask students to imagine that they work for the local health department and are assigned a restaurant to evaluate for health and sanitation standards. Have students brainstorm a list of criteria that could be used to judge the restaurant's cleanliness, safety, and overall concern for public health.

DISCUSSION. Ask students to discuss the advantages and disadvantages of living in a country that has so many treatment options.

Consumers pay regular fees and then are entitled to receive medical care for little or no additional cost. Consumers choose doctors who belong to the HMO. This may limit a person's choice of a doctor. However, within the HMO, a wide range of doctors and specialists is provided.

Members of HMOs are guaranteed treatment when they need it. HMOs save money by emphasizing preventive medicine and treatment for patients who do not need to be hospitalized—thus using expensive hospital care less often.

Trends in the Delivery of Health Care

In the last few years, other types of health-care outlets have developed. These outlets are designed to meet the needs of people who are not covered by other health-care supports. The people who receive service in these centers often make too much money to qualify for government medical benefits, but they do not make enough money to purchase their own private health insurance. Chief among these outlets are the following:

■ Adolescent health centers. Most of these centers are located in large cities. They are designed specifically to deal with problems relating to adolescence. These clinics address adolescents' physical, mental, and social health. The practitioners, for the most part, specialize in adolescent medicine.
■ Holistic health centers. These centers look at health in terms of the total person and put together a wellness plan for what an individual can do to improve personal health.
■ Neighborhood health centers. These centers are designed to meet local needs, particularly those of ethnic and social groups who have difficulty gaining access to existing health-care programs.
■ Alternative maternal-care birthing centers. Over 60 of these facilities exist throughout the United States. They are designed primarily to offer a homelike atmosphere, substantial savings on delivery costs, and opportunities to involve the entire family in the delivery of a baby.
■ Hospice care. Care for the terminally ill is becoming part of the mainstream of the health-care delivery system. The **hospice** provides a way of caring for the dying, not just a place where the dying are cared for. It unites the best techniques that have been devised for pain and symptom management with the provision of loving care.

KEEPING FIT

Questions to Ask About Your Doctor

■ Does he or she make you feel valued?
■ Does he or she listen to you carefully?
■ Do you feel comfortable with him or her?
■ Does he or she seem to give you adequate time and attention?
■ Does he or she give thorough exams?
■ Does he or she ask you for information relating to your health problem?
■ Does he or she respond to and even encourage your questions and comments?
■ Does he or she encourage you to take an active part in your own health care?
■ Does he or she encourage you to exercise preventive medicine?

DID YOU KNOW?

A stomachache requires medical attention if:

■ you also have vomiting and fever;
■ you have severe pain in the abdomen that doesn't go away;
■ your abdomen is very hard;
■ you have sudden pain and a bulging lump in your lower abdomen.

Across the Curriculum

Math. Have students find out the average salary for five different kinds of medical specialists. Find out, when it applies to the position, what the yearly cost of malpractice insurance is for each specialist and how these fees have risen in recent years. Then ask students to compute, using the figures in the annotation, the total estimated health-care expenditures the average person might incur during a 75-year life span. Help students compute the amount of money their own family has spent during the last year on medical expenses and health care. Make a graph of the class results.

Hospice care can be part of the health-care delivery system.

The following list describes characteristics of almost all hospice care outlets:

- They are open 24 hours a day.
- They provide a variety of services by health-care professionals.
- Hospice patients and their families are a central part of the care team.
- Volunteers are an integral part of the program.
- Emphasis is on optimal control of pain and other symptoms.
- A qualified doctor medically directs the programs.
- Programs provide inpatient and home care as needed.

ARE YOU IN CHARGE OF YOUR OWN HEALTH?

Throughout this book our discussions have centered on your taking an active role in preventing disease and in maintaining and promoting your own health. Each time you deal with a health concern, however, you need to know whose help, if any, you need. The list below will help you evaluate a given situation—but the key to successfully evaluating a health problem is being an informed consumer.

- Call an ambulance or rescue squad only if a situation is life-threatening or if the patient needs hospital care but cannot reach the hospital by car. Many communities as well as privately owned ambulance services charge for ambulance runs.
- Call your doctor's office when you need advice on whether to go to the hospital emergency room or when a condition for which you are being treated takes a bad turn. If you cannot reach your doctor, call a local emergency number and try to have an ambulance take you to the hospital with which your doctor is associated.
- Many large private clinics and HMOs staff their off-hour phones with nurses specially trained to give self-care information and to record questions and symptoms so that the doctor is well-informed when he or she returns your call.
- Call your doctor's office during regular hours when you need to ask if a problem requires an office visit or if you can get instructions for home treatment. You may be able to get assistance from a nurse practitioner, an office nurse, or a doctor's assistant.

Additional Information

HMOs. HMOs are the fastest-growing alternative to private doctors. In an HMO, the consumer makes a monthly membership payment for comprehensive health services. HMOs have been available for a long time, but until recently only a handful of people used them. Recent changes in laws and greater acceptance by the medical community have made HMOs an attractive option. HMOs can be—but are not necessarily—less expensive than other types of health insurance. One reason is that HMOs emphasize outpatient and preventive care whenever possible. The HMO Act of 1973 (Public Law 93-222) requires all employers with 25 or more employees to offer workers an opportunity to join a qualified HMO if one exists in the area.

Independent Practice

L1 PARENTAL INVOLVEMENT. Ask students to discuss the types of medical specialists that treat members of their family. Why and how did the family choose these particular specialists? Have students share their findings with the class.

L1 RESEARCH. Have students find out what the average daily cost (or the actual cost) at a particular facility is if you are a patient in each of the following types of facilities: private hospital, community hospital, alcoholism treatment center, psychiatric hospital, and nursing home. Have them present this information as a bar graph.

L1 READING. Have students read about the legal aspects of medical care for minors, including treatment with and without parental consent and doctor-patient confidentiality.

L2 RESEARCH. Divide the class into small groups. Assign each group one type of health-care facility to investigate. Such facilities could include an adolescent health-care center, a nursing home, a birthing center, a general hospital, etc. Each group should try to locate all of the health-care facilities of the type they have been assigned and show these with color-coded pins or colored and labeled stickers on a map of your area. Have all groups use the same map.

L2 RESEARCH. Ask the class to research fee-for-service medical care versus prepaid medical plans. Have them make a large bulletin board display which illustrates and explains the advantages and disadvantages of each. Some of this information may be gathered through interviews with people who see doctors in private practices and others who belong to health maintenance organizations (HMOs).

L2 COMMUNITY INVOLVE-MENT. Have students research the community for information regarding HMOs. Compare and contrast private and group practices with HMOs.

L2 WRITING. Ask students to read and write about Elizabeth Blackwell, the first woman American doctor, or David Hartman, the first blind American admitted to medical school in this century. Ask each student to translate this information into an original one-act play in which discrimination against the person reaches a climax and resolution quickly follows.

L3 RESEARCH. Have students research the two government-sponsored health insurance programs, Medicare and Medicaid. Have them determine the origin of each, how they are utilized by the population, and how they are frequently abused. Select several students to orally present their information. Have students discuss ways to prevent the abuse within the system.

L2 PERSONAL INVOLVEMENT. Present students with this dilemma, asking them to "think out loud" in writing: You have just been offered an extremely high-paying job as a nurse. The problem is that there is a serious health risk associated with the job, such as mental strain; long and exhausting hours; exposure to radiation, hazardous waste, or deadly infections; working with contaminated blood, etc. What would you do?

L1 PERSONAL INVOLVEMENT. Discuss how sound self-care can save money. Have students check the newspapers for announcements of self-care workshops. These might include CPR courses, first-aid courses, health fairs, etc. Students might receive credit for participating in a self-care workshop. The student should bring to class some proof of attendance and a brief summary on what he or she learned.

L1 USING THE LESSON RESOURCES. For additional student activities, refer to the lesson resources on page 659.

DID YOU KNOW?

■ Eighty-one percent of women see a doctor each year, and they average 6.2 visits annually. Only 67 percent of men see a doctor each year, and they average just 4.5 visits annually.

CONFLICT RESOLUTION

Last month, 16-year-old Raul spent the weekend home alone when his parents took a trip. While they were away, Raul developed severe stomach cramps, vomiting, and diarrhea. He wanted to call someone to stay with him or even take him to the hospital, but he was afraid his parents wouldn't allow him to stay home alone again. He also thought about how foolish he'd feel going to the emergency room just to find out he had a stomach virus. He wished he knew the difference between flu and food poisoning.

Where could Raul have called for information and to see if he needed medical attention?

HEALTH UPDATE

LOOKING AT TECHNOLOGY

What's Coming in Health Care?

There are many kinds of technology currently being considered, researched, or tested that may make great differences in Americans' health in the future. Among the new technologies are the following:

■ "Computerized patients" may be used within the next ten years as part of medical students' training. Computer-generated hypothetical, or made-up, patients will be presented to students, including complete medical histories and current symptoms. Using voice commands, the medical student will be able to order tests, get results, diagnose, and propose treatments. When the process is over, the computer will evaluate the student's performance and the outcome for the "patient."

■ Artificial organs will be developed using a combination of living cells and synthetic materials. This will decrease the need for organ donors and save the lives of the many people who need transplanted human organs but cannot get them.

■ Antibodies that prevent clogged arteries may undo the need for much surgery that now removes arterial blockages. A new study using rats shows that the use of an antibody that neutralizes the buildup of such blockages may keep their arteries clear.

■ Artificial blood is now being tested in clinical trials but does not yet have FDA approval. This "blood" will be especially useful for those people who refuse transfusions of human blood for religious reasons or because of fear of blood-transmitted infections.

Additional Information

Helping Yourself to Better Health Care. There are several ways you can help yourself get the best health care possible. If you have surgery planned, you should check to be sure that your surgeon is board certified. A reputable plastic surgeon, for example, should be certified by the American Board of Plastic Surgery. You also should call your surgeon's hospital to make sure he or she is allowed to do the planned procedure on the premises. And be sure to talk to your surgeon at least a month ahead of the scheduled operation about donating your own blood in the event you need a transfusion—that way, you avoid the risk of being infected with HIV, hepatitis, or other blood-borne diseases.

The Consumer and Health Care

The demand for health care far exceeds available services. As a consumer, what can you do to relieve some of this demand on the health-care system? The most important thing you can do is take greater responsibility in protecting and promoting your own health. You can take greater responsibility in preventing disease by examining your life-style. Many health problems are related to life-style factors, such as food choices and amount of exercise a person gets.

By supporting health education programs in your school and community, you can help people learn about their bodies and their health. Health education programs also teach people the skills to make good choices. This provides the basis for individual responsibility in the protection and promotion of health. Health education programs also provide new and current information on preventive health care.

Knowing is not enough; people must act on the information they have to reduce health risks. Consider these questions:

- What good does it do to know that seat belts save lives if people sit on their belts?
- What good does it do to know that cervical cancer can be detected through Pap smears if women fail to have such tests performed on a regular basis?
- What good does it do to be aware of the mounting evidence that smoking is a direct cause of cancer and heart disease if people continue to smoke?

The health-care delivery system cannot be expected to care for your health if you are not willing to invest in your own health care. You must see the relationship between yourself and the health-care system as a partnership, with both committed and motivated to care for and be responsible for your health.

LESSON 2 REVIEW

Reviewing Facts and Vocabulary

1. Name the differences between primary, secondary, and tertiary care.
2. What are the major clinical specialties?
3. What is meant by *HMO*? Describe the service.

Thinking Critically

4. **Synthesis.** Develop a set of criteria for selecting a doctor or a dentist. Compare your list with your classmates' lists.
5. **Analysis.** Consider the differences between a specialist and a general practitioner. Highlight the advantages and disadvantages of each type of doctor.

Applying Health Knowledge

6. Make a list of the health services and health facilities in your community. Using the public health department as a resource, try to determine whether the facilities are adequate. What are the most pressing health-care needs in your area?
7. During the 1800s scientists made many important discoveries in the field of medicine. Choose a scientific discovery from this time, and discuss its impact on your health today.

Answers to Lesson 2 Review

1. See "Stages of Health Care" on page 659.
2. Internal medicine, obstetrics and gynecology, pediatrics, psychiatry, surgery.
3. Health maintenance organization. For a description of the service, see "Health Maintenance Organizations" on pages 661 to 662.
4. Answers will vary but might reflect the information in "Choosing a Health Care Professional" on page 661. Comparisons will vary.
5. Answers will vary. Possible answer: A specialist can give the best care in his or her area of expertise, but can be costly.
6. Answers will vary.
7. Answers will vary.

Check for Understanding

- Assign and discuss the lesson review. Encourage LD students to focus on questions 1, 2, and 3.
- Assign and discuss the chapter review.

Evaluate

- Administer, grade, and discuss the *Lesson 2 Quiz.*
- Administer, grade, and discuss the *Chapter 33 Test.*
- Refer to the Performance Assessment strategy for this chapter. See pages T 23 to T 25.

Reteach

- Ask students to select a specific health problem and describe in writing how they would go about seeking health information and selecting a doctor. What questions would they ask a doctor about the problem?
- Ask students to complete *Reteaching Activity 91.*

Enrich

- Have students work in groups of three to write a script about a young married couple meeting with an insurance agent for the first time. Ask students to act out a scene where the agent explains the various health-insurance options, categories, prices, and needs. Have the couple discuss the options and choose from among them.
- Ask students to complete *Enrichment Activity 33.*

Close

Ask students to summarize the most important concepts in this lesson.

Helping Students Improve Their Health

Reinforcing Vocabulary

- **Stress-management techniques.** Strategies to deal with stresses of life in a healthful manner.
- **Hygiene.** The care one takes to ensure a clean and healthful appearance.
- **Immunized.** Protected against disease by vaccine.

Teaching Strategies

L1 DISCUSSION. Have students discuss their perception of how society views the elderly. Is adequate care provided in nursing homes, retirement villages, and other facilities that care for the health and well-being of the elderly?

L2 DISCUSSION. Have students debate the issue that some hospitals provide medical care for profit, denying medical attention to individuals who cannot pay. Should hospitals be permitted to refuse to treat a patient based upon a lack of income or a lack of medical insurance? If not, should the hospital financially suffer or should taxpayers be responsible for paying the bill?

L2 DISCUSSION. What role have malpractice lawsuits played in raising medical insurance premiums? What positive roles have malpractice lawsuits played? What negative roles have malpractice lawsuits played?

L2 CLASS ACTIVITY. A major political issue that has been debated in the past is whether medical insurance should be provided to all individuals by the government. Have students formulate a plan that could accomplish this goal on a small scale.

L2 SELF-ESTEEM. Identify which items in the Self-Inventory relate to self-esteem. Draw conclusions about the relationship between the level of self-esteem and how well a person takes care of his or her own health.

Self-Inventory

Are You an Advocate for Your Own Health?

HOW DO YOU RATE?

Number a sheet of paper from 1 through 20. Read each item below and respond with a *yes* or *no*. Total the number of *yes* responses. Then proceed to the next section.

1. I eat a healthy diet.
2. I get enough sleep and rest.
3. I get regular exercise.
4. I use stress-management techniques.
5. I share my feelings with others.
6. I wear a seat belt and exercise other kinds of safety consciousness.
7. I do not use alcohol or other drugs.
8. I read the instructions carefully before taking any medicine.
9. I practice regular and proper health care.
10. I avoid situations that put my health at risk.
11. I get regular medical checkups.
12. I have been immunized against the common communicable diseases.
13. If I feel myself getting sick, I take some immediate action.
14. I have a medical doctor or other source of medical care that I can call for help or advice.
15. I am honest and thorough in communicating with my doctor(s).
16. I consider myself to be an active partner along with my doctor(s) in my medical care.
17. I am not afraid to tell my doctor(s) what I think is wrong or that I disagree with him or her.
18. I have a good relationship with my doctor(s).
19. I make certain I understand what my doctor is saying and what kind of treatment plan I am to follow.
20. If my family had no family doctor, or I could not get in touch with the doctor, I would be able to contact an appropriate substitute.

HOW DID YOU SCORE?

Give yourself 1 point for each *yes* response. Find your total and read below to see how you scored. Then proceed to the next section.

18 to 20
Excellent. You are taking very good care of your health.

15 to 17
Good. You are taking good care of your health.

12 to 14
Fair. You are taking only fair care of your health.

Below 12
Look out! You are not taking an active role in your own health care.

WHAT ARE YOUR GOALS?

If you scored 15 or higher, complete the statements in Part A. If you scored 14 or below, complete the statements in Part B. Regardless of your score, complete Part C.

Part A

1. One way in which I can become more active in my own health care is ____.
2. The steps I will take to become more active include ____.
3. My time frame for taking these steps will be ____.
4. My reward for taking these steps will be ____.

Part B

5. The reason I do not get medical care is ____.
6. The steps that I will take to try to get adequate medical care include ____.
7. The people, organizations, or other resources I will use to try to get this medical care include ____.
8. My time frame for accomplishing this goal is ____.
9. My reward for taking these actions on behalf of my own health will be ____.

Part C

10. One area in which I want to improve my communication or relationship with my doctor(s) is ____.
11. The steps I will take to make this improvement are ____.
12. My time frame for taking these steps is ____.
13. My health rewards for doing so will be ____.

666 CHAPTER 33 HEALTH SERVICES AND HEALTH CARE

Meeting Students' Needs

For students who score *Excellent*. Suggest students write letters to local and state representatives to help correct the current problem that prohibits individuals from obtaining affordable medical insurance coverage.

For students who score *Good*. Suggest that students consider working a summer intern position in an allied medical field.

For students who score *Fair*. Encourage students to examine their current knowledge level in health services and health care. Allow students to interview a professional working in the health insurance industry.

For students who need to *Look Out!* Have students practice filling out medical insurance forms and/or visit a local hospital.

Building Decision-Making Skills

J eff made an appointment with his family doctor because he has had a cold and sore throat for several days. The doctor examined him, took a throat culture, and gave Jeff two prescriptions. Jeff doesn't know what the medicines are expected to do or if they are available as generic brands. What should Jeff do before he leaves the doctor's office?

WHAT DO YOU THINK?

1. **Situation.** Why does Jeff need to make a decision?
2. **Situation.** How much time does Jeff have to decide?
3. **Choices.** What choices does Jeff have?
4. **Consequences.** How might Jeff's health triangle be affected by his decision?
5. **Consequences.** What are the advantages and disadvantages of each choice?
6. **Decision.** What do you think Jeff should do? Explain your answer.
7. **Evaluation.** Have you ever been in a situation in which you did not want to show your ignorance by asking questions? What decision did you make? Would you make the same decision again? Why or why not?

A few years ago, Melissa's father was in a car accident and now wears an artificial leg, which is getting very worn. He needs a new one. The cost of a new artificial leg is very high. Her father is now old enough to receive Medicare, but payments from Medicare do not cover the full cost. Melissa's family has no supplemental insurance or savings to make up the cost difference. What might Melissa do to help?

WHAT DO YOU THINK?

8. **Situation.** Why does a decision need to be made?
9. **Choices.** What choices does Melissa have?
10. **Consequences.** What are the advantages of each choice?
11. **Consequences.** What are the disadvantages of each choice?
12. **Consequences** How might Melissa's future be affected with each choice?
13. **Decision.** What do you think Melissa should do?

J uan's grandmother is in a nursing home. Juan thinks one of the LPNs who is assigned to his grandmother treats her poorly. She does not give the same care to his grandmother as Juan sees her give other patients. Because of his concern, Juan is trying to spend more time with his grandmother to make up for the nurse's lack of care. He was really angry, though, when he came to see his grandmother one afternoon last week. She was feeling very weak. Juan discovered that the nurse had not given his grandmother her lunch until very late. Juan's grandmother is diabetic and needs to eat regular meals. What should Juan do?

WHAT DO YOU THINK?

14. **Situation.** Why does a decision need to be made?
15. **Choices.** What choices are there to consider?
16. **Consequences.** What are the advantages and disadvantages of each choice?
17. **Decision.** What do you think Juan should do?
18. **Evaluation.** Have you ever had to confront a person in authority? If so, describe the situation and the outcome. What did you learn from that situation?

SEEKING HEALTH CARE **667**

Discussing the Answers

Situation 1. Jeff has two possible solutions for this problem. Jeff could simply ask the doctor about his prescriptions; or, he could ask his pharmacist about the medications. Jeff needs to address his doctor about his medical concerns. The pharmacist at any pharmacy can provide valuable information about the medications.

Situation 2. Some individuals are eligible for supplemental insurance that will pay deductibles and co-payments. Perhaps Melissa can look into this possibility.

Situation 3. Juan can document instances of neglect or inadequate treatment and speak to the management about the improper treatment.

Answers to Chapter 33 Review

Using Health Terms

1. Health facility or health resource
2. Inpatients
3. Skilled nursing facility
4. Medicaid
5. Medicare
6. Primary care
7. Private practice
8. Cardiologist
9. Dermatologist
10. Group practice
11. Hospice

Building Academic Skills

12. One of the leading causes of bankruptcy in the United States is the cost of medical care.
13. A.

Recalling the Facts

14. A—outpatient; B—outpatient; C—inpatient.
15. Members of the armed forces and their dependents, veterans, and Native Americans.
16. Long-term is more than 30 days. Short-term is less than 30 days.
17. It may be owned by a church, other charitable group, or a community. Fees are charged for services, but donations also are needed to help cover costs.
18. Administers pain-killing drugs to patients during surgery and keeps track of their condition before, during, and after surgery.
19. Obstetrician.
20. Ophthalmologist.
21. Urologist.
22. By emphasizing preventive medicine and treatment for patients who do not need to be hospitalized.
23. A—4; B—1; C—2; D—3; E—5.

Thinking Critically

24. General hospitals provide health care for most types of illnesses and injuries. Special hospitals provide care for certain kinds of health needs.

Using Health Terms

On a separate sheet of paper, write the term that best matches each definition given below.

LESSON 1

1. A place a person goes to receive health care.
2. People who receive prolonged health care and who are admitted to a health-care facility and occupy a bed there.
3. A type of nursing home that houses residents with serious medical illnesses.
4. Assistance program of medical aid for people who are unable to afford medical care.
5. Government health insurance for people 65 and older and for people who receive social security disability benefits.

LESSON 2

6. Health care that patients seek on their own.
7. The medical practice of a doctor who is self-employed.
8. A doctor who treats heart diseases.
9. A doctor who treats skin problems.
10. A situation in which two or more doctors work together to provide medical care.
11. A place that promotes a special way of caring for people who are dying.

Building Academic Skills

LESSON 1

12. **Writing.** Rewrite the following sentence using appropriate spelling, capitalization, and punctuation.

    One of the leding cauzes of Bankrupcty in the united states is the cost, of medical kare.

LESSON 2

13. **Reading.** In which of the following sentences does *committed* mean devoted?
    a. Claire is committed to improving her health triangle.
    b. Two witnesses said that a man wearing a ski mask committed the crime.

Recalling the Facts

LESSON 1

14. Label each of the following patients *outpatient* or *inpatient*.
    a. Dr. Ibani performs arthroscopy on Leonard Seaton at 10:00 A.M. on Thursday. Len and his wife go out to dinner that evening.
    b. Juanita spends two hours in her dentist's office on Monday having her wisdom teeth removed.
    c. Mrs. Jackson's labor pains begin at 8:00 P.M. on Saturday. Mr. Jackson drives her to the hospital. The baby is born at 7:00 A.M. on Sunday. Mr. and Mrs. Jackson bring their new baby home on Tuesday.
15. Who receives care from the staffs at government hospitals?
16. Explain the difference between long- and short-term care hospitals.
17. Explain how a nonprofit voluntary hospital is operated.

LESSON 2

18. What does an anesthesiologist do?
19. What kind of specialist should a pregnant female see?
20. Mrs. Marcello requires cataract surgery. What kind of specialist is likely to perform the surgery?
21. Should a person with a bladder infection consult a urologist or a radiologist?
22. What are two ways in which health maintenance organizations try to keep down the costs of health care?
23. Number the following steps that describe actions you might take for an injury or illness. Number the least serious action 1 and the most serious 5.
    a. Go to the nearest emergency room.
    b. Take care of the problem yourself.
    c. Call a physician during office hours.
    d. Go to a 24-hour clinic or a nonhospital emergency facility.
    e. Call an ambulance.

Thinking Critically

LESSON 1

24. Analysis. How are general hospitals different from special hospitals? How are they the same?

25. Evaluation. What is the importance of health insurance?

LESSON 2

26. Analysis. Label each of the following types of health care *primary*, *secondary*, or *tertiary*.

  a. Sam has had what he believes is a bad cold. He calls his doctor, who tells him to take two aspirin and call him in the morning.

  b. In the morning, Sam feels no better. His doctor makes an appointment for him with an allergist. The allergist cannot find any substance to which Sam is allergic.

  c. Sam visits a psychiatrist. She decides his problems are not psychological.

  d. Sam makes an appointment with an otolaryngologist. Dr. Hillman finds that Sam has a tumor, which may be cancerous.

  e. Sam undergoes surgery to remove the tumor at a special cancer hospital in another state.

27. Analysis. What are the advantages and disadvantages of an HMO?

Making the Connection

LESSON 2

28. Social Studies. Health care in the United States is among the best in the world, but it is also the most expensive. In countries where health care is free or more reasonably priced, patients may not choose their own doctors and may have to wait for care. Some specialized care may not be available to everyone. Is it better to have good care at high cost for some or minimal care for everyone at low cost? Explain your answer.

Applying Health Knowledge

LESSON 1

29. Label each activity below as *health promotion*, *prevention*, *maintenance*, or *treatment*.

  a. eating properly every day

  b. not smoking

  c. getting a flu shot

  d. walking two miles three times a week

  e. taking an antibiotic for an infection

  f. having your teeth and gums examined by a dentist twice a year

  g. dieting to reduce being overweight

30. Your grandfather is basically healthy, but he is no longer strong enough for the physical labor of housekeeping and yard work. He does not take any medications. What kind of nursing home facility might best fit your grandfather's needs? Why did you choose the facility you did?

LESSON 2

31. Explain how prevention, maintenance, and treatment are related in a person's total health picture.

32. How would you interpret the following statement in relation to taking responsibility for your own health?

  The doctor cannot do what the patient will not do.

Beyond the Classroom

LESSON 2

33. Further Study. Interview someone who works in a health-care field. The person could be your family doctor, a nurse, or the pharmacist where you get your prescriptions filled. Find out what the person likes and dislikes about his or her work and what the requirements are for the particular job. Report to your class.

34. Community Involvement. Join the volunteer program at a health-service facility in your community.

25. Answers will vary but might include the idea that overwhelming medical costs can lead to bankruptcy for people who are not insured. In addition, people without health insurance may not be able to afford preventive or routine care, such as dental checkups.

26. A—primary; B—secondary; C—secondary; D—secondary; E—tertiary.

27. Answers will vary. Possible answers: Advantages—low cost per office visit, low or no fees for many services (which may include hospitalization), no forms to fill out. Disadvantages—relatively high membership fees, limited selection of health-care providers, limited geographical area covered.

Making the Connection

28. Answers will vary but should be supported logically.

Applying Health Knowledge

29. A—promotion; B—promotion; C—prevention; D—promotion or maintenance; E—treatment; F—maintenance; G—treatment.

30. Domiciliary care home. He cannot live independently but does not need nursing care or medication.

31. Answers will vary but should include the idea that prevention and maintenance may often make treatment unnecessary.

32. Answers will vary but should include the idea that individuals are responsible for protecting and promoting their own health by following good health practices.

Beyond the Classroom

33. Reports will vary.

34. No response is necessary, but you may wish to survey students to see how many have worked as volunteers in health-care facilities.

Lesson Summaries

LESSON 1. Each year, thousands of people are injured as a result of home accidents. One in every five accidental deaths occurs at home. Taking precautions to avoid falls, fire, electrical shock, and poisoning can be taken.

LESSON 2. The workplace can pose a threat to one's safety. When individuals participate in activities away from the home, they should be aware of possible hazards and follow basic safety rules.

LESSON 3. Most car accidents for young people do not involve a second vehicle, but instead result from the vehicle overturning, running off the road, or colliding with fixed objects. Ways to reduce risks of accidents and bicycle and skating safety are discussed in this lesson.

LESSON 4. Violence is on the rise. There are more rapes, thefts, shootings, and murders than ever before. Individuals should appraise the safety of situations and carry themselves in a way that may dissuade possible attackers.

Introducing the Chapter

Ask students to discuss safety practices on the school campus. List on the chalkboard the rules and practices that are brought out. The list may include:
- speed limit in parking lot
- no running in the halls
- wearing safety glasses in science lab
- shields over light bulbs
- protected storage of chemicals
- well-lighted hallways
- open fire lanes in parking lot

Ask why these rules and practices have been developed. (To protect us and to prevent accidents.)

Performance Assessment ✓

Refer to pages T 23 to T 25 for a Performance Assessment strategy for this chapter. See the *Performance Assessment Activities* booklet for additional suggestions.

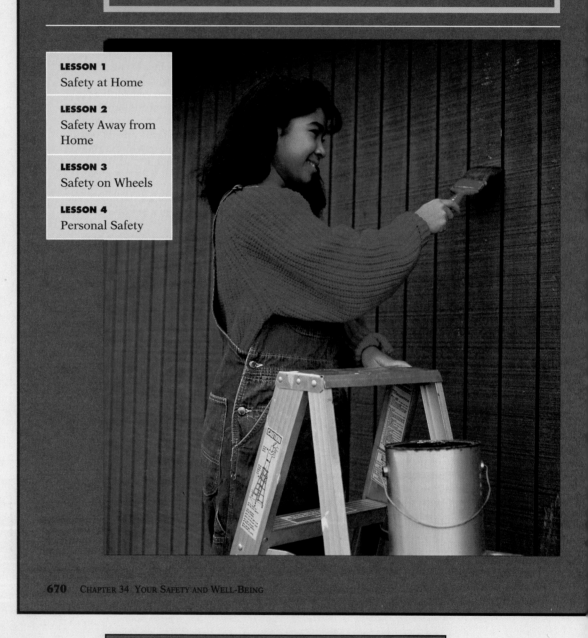

CHAPTER

34

YOUR SAFETY AND WELL-BEING

LESSON 1
Safety at Home

LESSON 2
Safety Away from Home

LESSON 3
Safety on Wheels

LESSON 4
Personal Safety

670 CHAPTER 34 YOUR SAFETY AND WELL-BEING

Key to Ability Levels

Teaching strategies have been coded for varying learning styles and abilities.

L1 Level 1 activities are basic activities and should be within the ability range of all students.

L2 Level 2 activities are average activities and should be within the ability range of average to above-average students.

L3 Level 3 activities are challenging activities designed for the ability range of above-average students.

LD LD activities should be within the ability range of learning-disabled students.

LEP LEP activities should be within the ability range of Limited English Proficiency students.

SAFETY AT HOME

Home should be the one place where you can feel safe and secure. Yet every year thousands of people are injured as a result of home accidents. These cause more disabling injuries than any other type of accident. Many are the result of hazards, such as objects carelessly placed or in poor condition.

Falls

Falls happen to people of all ages. They are the leading cause of accidental death and injury among the elderly. Small children, exploring on their own, are also at risk of injury. Although falls are not usually serious, in some instances they can be deadly.

Stairs are the most dangerous area in the home and the site of about one million injuries yearly in the United States. All stairways, indoors and out, should be well-lighted, in good repair, and equipped with sturdy handrails. Steps should have nonskid strips or well-fitting carpet.

Tripping hazards are a common cause of easily prevented falls. A loose rug is always a danger; if a room is not carpeted, area and throw rugs should be firmly fastened to the floor.

Bathtubs and showers also can be a source of falls. The use of safety rails and nonskid mats can help prevent these types of accidents.

People of all ages should avoid the temptation to use chairs, boxes, or other makeshift ladders to reach items on high shelves. Instead, a sturdy stepladder should be used.

Fire

What needs to be present in order for a fire to take place? That may seem like a simple question, but a very important set of elements must be present for a fire to start. By understanding that these three elements—fuel, heat, and air—must be present to make a fire burn, you have the basis of fire prevention.

Fuel for a fire can be carelessly stored rags, wood, coal, oil, gasoline, or paper. However, there still will not be a fire unless there is some heat to make the fuel burn. A heat source could be a match, an electrical wire, or a cigarette. Still there can be no fire unless air is present. The oxygen in the air feeds and fans the flames. If you remove any one of these elements, there can be no fire.

Fire Safety Devices

Because household fires kill thousands of people each year, it is essential that each home is equipped with two life-saving devices: a smoke detector and a fire extinguisher.

SAFETY AT HOME **671**

LESSON 1 FOCUS

TERMS TO USE
- Smoke detector
- Fire extinguisher

CONCEPTS TO LEARN
- A smoke alarm and fire extinguisher should be placed on every level of the home.
- Most fire deaths result from smoke inhalation rather than burns.

ATTITUDES AND BEHAVIORS TO EVALUATE
- Self-Inventory, page 688.
- Building Decision-Making Skills, page 689.

Lesson Objectives

After studying this lesson, students should be able to:
- identify the most important causes of home accidents and how they can best be prevented
- explain what is meant by *accident chain*

Bellringer

Write the following on the chalkboard for students to work on while attendance is being taken: *You are awakened at night in your bedroom by the clang of a smoke detector. Your room is smoky and you start to cough. You try to turn on the light, but the power is off. What should you do?*

Introducing the Lesson

Refer to the Bellringer. Ask students to share their responses. Tell them that if they do not already have a plan of action to follow in case of a home fire, they will learn how to make one in this lesson, as well as learn about other important causes of home accidents and injuries.

Building Vocabulary

- Ask students to look up and discuss the similarities and differences among the following terms: *flammable, inflammable, flame-resistant, flame-retardant,* and *fireproof.* Correct any misconceptions.
- Ask students to complete *Workbook Vocabulary Activity 92.*

DID YOU KNOW?

- Every year in the U.S., there are over 73 million accidental injuries, including 17.8 million wounds and lacerations, 11.5 million bruises, 6 million fractures, and 2.2 million skull injuries.

Resources for Lesson 1

- **Guided Reading** Activity 92
- **Workbook** Vocabulary Activity 92
- **Reteaching** Activity 92
- **Lesson 1 Quiz**
- **Performance Assessment** Activity 34

Teach

Guided Practice

L1 DISCUSSION. Ask students, outside of driving on the highway, where they are most likely to suffer a serious injury. (At home) Why is the home such a dangerous place?

L1 CLASS ACTIVITY. Ask students to identify the four basic types of accidents that are likely to occur in the home. Ask volunteers to describe one way in which each type of accident could occur.

L1 DISCUSSION. Which age-groups are most prone to injuries from falls? Where do most falls at home occur?

LEP DEMONSTRATION. To make the point that three elements (fuel, heat, and air) must be present for a fire to occur, make a drawing or model of a triangle, with each side of the triangle representing one of the elements. Show or explain to the class that if you remove any one of the sides of the triangle, the other two cannot be supported—and fire will not occur.

L1 CLASS ACTIVITY. Ask students to name several different sources of fuel that could start a home fire. (Rags, wood, coal, oil, gasoline, paper.) Have them describe the proper way to store each type of fuel to minimize the possibility of fire.

L1 DISCUSSION. What are some potential sources of heat that may start home fires? What precautions should be taken with these sources in order to lessen the risk of fire?

L1 DISCUSSION. What two fire safety devices are essential for the home? Which one is now required by law in new homes?

L1 CLASS ACTIVITY. Describe three specific types of home fires to the class and ask students what actions they should take in response to each.

L1 DISCUSSION. What causes most fire deaths? (Fumes) How can inhalation of toxic fumes from fire be reduced?

Smoke detectors save lives.

FIRE SAFETY PRECAUTIONS

The majority of home fires can be prevented if the following fire safety tips are observed.

Space Heaters
- Every gas or fuel-burning space heater must be properly vented, unless the unit is specifically designed to be unvented. In that case, make certain a window or door is opened slightly in the room in which the unit is operating.
- All space heaters should have tip-over shutoff switches and protective grilles around heating elements.
- Use only heavy-duty extension cords that match the electrical requirements of electric space heaters.

Matches and Lighters
- Keep matches and lighters where children cannot find them.
- Fill lighters in a well-ventilated area, away from flames. Try to avoid spills; if a spill occurs, wipe it up immediately.

Flammable Liquids
- Store gasoline outside the house and well away from ignition sources.
- Store gasoline only in containers designed specifically for this purpose.
- Never use gasoline for cleaning machine parts, clothing, or any other item.
- Use only fluids labeled as charcoal starters to light outdoor grills. Never throw any flammable liquid on a burning or smoldering fire.
- Use caution and observe good safety rules with other flammable liquids, such as nail polish remover, kerosene, rubbing alcohol, and paint thinner.

Upholstered Furniture
- Keep upholstered furniture away from stoves, ranges, space heaters, and fireplaces.
- Caution cigarette smokers against smoking when sitting on upholstered furniture, especially if the smoker is drowsy. A burning cigarette can be especially hazardous if the smoker is drinking alcohol or has been taking medication.

Clothing
- Do not wear loose-fitting long sleeves or full skirts around flames or a stove.
- Thin, lightweight fabrics ignite quicker than heavy, tightly woven fabrics like denim.
- By law, children's sleepwear (up to size 14) must be flame-resistant.

Smoke Detectors. The greatest danger from home fires occurs during the night when families are asleep. A **smoke detector** is an alarm used to awaken people and alert them in the event of smoke or flames. This device, mounted on a ceiling, sounds loudly if smoke passes into it. Smoke detectors are now recommended to be installed in new homes. They are economical to buy and easy to install. It is recommended that smoke detectors be placed on every level of the home, especially near sleeping areas. A smoke detector should be tested after it is installed and again at monthly intervals.

Fire Extinguishers. Each home should have a **fire extinguisher** on each floor. This is a portable device that puts out small fires by ejecting fire-extinguishing chemicals. If you are confident that you can control a fire quickly with an extinguisher, use it promptly and properly. Stand away from the flames, aim at the source of the fire, not at the flames,

Additional Information

Accidents. According to Tom Parker's book *In One Day*, each day in the United States numerous objects, many not usually thought to be dangerous, cause large numbers of emergency-room injuries. Here's a list of some of the offenders:

- stairs, steps, and ramps — 2,100
- bicycles and accessories — 1,420
- nails, screws, and tacks — 690
- drinking glasses — 300
- hammers — 150
- carpets and rugs — 140
- pencils, pens, desk supplies — 120
- toilets and sinks — 90
- television sets — 75
- paper bags and wrappers — 35
- ashtrays — 15
- aquariums and accessories — 15

and move the spray from side to side. If there is any doubt at all, forget the extinguisher, get out of the house, and call the fire department.

When selecting a fire extinguisher for the home, be certain that you and your family understand the manufacturer's specifications and directions. Check the dial on the equipment periodically to be certain that it still has sufficient pressure to be useful in an emergency.

Fire Safety Actions

Most deaths caused by fire result from smoke inhalation rather than burns. Inhaling toxic fumes is not what kills, but rather the lack of oxygen. The chemical by-products of combustion combine quickly with oxygen, preventing smoke-inhalation victims from getting oxygen from the air. Since smoke rises, stay low to the floor to escape. If you cannot escape your room, place towels and clothing in door cracks and vents.

Planning Escape from Fire. Most fatal home fires occur during the night. At this time, it is easy to become disoriented when smoke or fire is first detected. The best protection against injury or death from home fires is to establish escape plans and periodically conduct practice drills.

You and your family should draw a floor plan, including doors, hallways, and windows, of each story of your home. Use arrows to point to two ways of escape, if possible, from each room. Alternate escape routes are necessary in case one route is blocked. For example, if an upstairs door is blocked by fire, a ladder or a readily available rope coil is essential for escape through windows.

All escape plans should include the following steps:

- Turn on the bedroom lights.
- Use a predetermined signal to alert everyone to the fire. Smoke detectors, which should be in every household, will do this job. You also can use whistles, which could be kept in every nightstand.
- Before opening a closed door during a fire, test for warmth. If the door is warm, do not open it. Escape through a window instead.
- Always stay close to the floor in a smoke-filled room. Smoke rises, so there is more oxygen near the floor and visibility is better.
- After escaping, meet outside at a safe prearranged place. Do not go back into the house.
- Call the fire department from a neighbor's house.
- If a person is trapped inside a burning building, rescue is safer and usually faster if left to the fire department.

Although most fire departments cannot conduct routine inspections of individual homes, they can provide a variety of fire safety information if requested.

If you are caught near or in a fire, acting quickly and remaining calm could save your life and that of others. Remember the following:

- If a fire starts in a frying pan, put a lid on the fire.
- If a fire starts in the oven, turn off the oven, and smother the fire with baking soda. Never put water on a grease fire, because it will make the grease and the fire spread.

DID YOU KNOW?

- According to the U.S. Consumer Product Safety Commission, in one recent year, more than 180,000 children and adults had toy-related injuries.
- In 1990 alone, more than 12,000 Americans were injured by fireworks. Injuries included severe burns, blindness, and damage to the nerves of the face.
- Stair-related injuries sent as many as one million Americans to the hospital in 1990.
- Serious burns from hot food and hot water result in 37,000 injuries among U.S. children each year.
- Each year, about 27,000 house fires in the U.S. are caused by children playing with matches or fire.

L1 DISCUSSION. In addition to devising a floor plan showing alternate exits from each room, what steps should be included in all home fire-escape plans?

L1 DISCUSSION. What special precautions should be taken around upholstered furniture to lessen the risk of fire? How can clothing be a fire hazard?

LEP DEMONSTRATION. Bring into class several different potential fire hazards commonly found in the home, such as space heaters, lighters, matches, charcoal starters, and flammable liquids. Show students the correct way to use and store the devices and substances in order to minimize the risk of fire. Ask students to identify unsafe uses of the devices and substances.

L2 EXPLANATION. Explain how electrical shocks occur. How does one become part of the circuit that an electric current travels? What does being "grounded" mean? How is it related to shock?

L1 DISCUSSION. What are some of the most important ways to avoid electrical shocks in the home?

L1 DISCUSSION. What five elements are present in almost all accidents, combining to form an accident chain? How many elements must be changed in order to prevent the accident?

Independent Practice

L1 COMMUNITY INVOLVEMENT. Ask students to investigate the meaning and importance of child-proofing the home and yard. Then have them develop lists of child-proofing precautions for infants, toddlers, and preschoolers. Have them use the list to check their own homes, the homes of children they baby-sit, or the homes of neighbors with small children.

L1 PARENTAL INVOLVEMENT. Ask students, with the help of their parents, to make a list of all the potential poisons in their home environment. Most will be located in the kitchen, bathroom, utility area, basement, and garage, but all rooms should be inspected. Are any of the products stored in an unsafe way?

Additional Information

Fire Safety. Along with fireplaces, woodstoves have become popular sources of heat in some parts of the U.S. They're also dangerous. Like a fireplace, a woodstove's chimney may build up a lining of creosote—a gummy, highly flammable substance that is produced when wood is burned. Creosote is the most common cause of chimney fires.

To avoid a chimney fire with a woodstove or fireplace, one should keep the chimney free of creosote—and be prepared for emergencies. Once a year, the chimney should be cleaned by a trained chimney sweep who will use special brushes to remove the creosote. One should also keep a chimney fire extinguisher near the fireplace or woodstove and check it regularly.

L3 **RESEARCH.** Have students research and explain ways to put out fires. Is water the best way to put out all fires? What material is found in a fire extinguisher and how does it work? Have students write a brief report of their findings.

L2 **RESEARCH.** Ask students to research safety features and equipment used in fireplaces. What precautions should a home owner take to ensure family safety while enjoying a fireplace?

L1 **WRITING.** Ask volunteers to write a description of an accident, including a brief account of the situation, the unsafe habit or risk, the unsafe act, the accident, and the possible injuries—all the links in the accident chain.

L1 **COMMUNITY INVOLVEMENT.** Ask students who babysit to make up a list of questions to ask so that they can best protect themselves and the children they watch from injury in fire.

L1 **COMMUNITY INVOLVEMENT.** Divide the class into small groups. Have each group contact local hospitals, police departments, and fire departments to find out about the numbers and types of home accidents in your area over the past year.

L2 **RESEARCH.** Have students research materials that have low smoke points. What does the smoke point of a particular object have to do with its likelihood of causing a fire?

L1 **USING THE LESSON RESOURCES.** For additional student activities, refer to the lesson resources on page 671.

Unplug any appliance that does not seem to be working properly.

- If your clothes catch on fire, remember: stop, drop, and roll. Roll on the ground or roll up in a rug or blanket to smother the flames. If you remain upright or run, the flames will spread.

Electrical Shock

Shocks from electrical appliances can kill. Every year electrical shock kills more than 1,000 people. In addition, electrical shock starts almost 62,000 fires.

If you become part of the circuit that an electric current travels, you will be shocked. You become part of the circuit when you touch an exposed wire while you are grounded because the current can then pass through you to the ground.

Here are some precautions to take when using home electrical appliances and power tools:

- Any time anything seems to be wrong with an appliance or power tool, unplug it immediately.
- Never touch pipes or metal with an electrical appliance or tool that is turned on.
- Inspect cords occasionally for signs of cracked insulation. Have frayed cords replaced. Cords should not be placed under a carpet or rug because they can be damaged when walked on.
- To avoid electrical shock, disconnect appliances by pulling on the plug, not on the cord.
- Never use an electrical appliance or power tool if your body, clothing, or the floor is wet. This includes hair dryers, radios, and electric musical instruments.
- Call an electrician rather than try to make electrical repairs yourself.

Poisons

Everyday products, not just those marked with a skull and crossbones, can be poisonous. Most of these products are typically found in the kitchen, bathroom, utility area, basement, and garage. In families with children, household products and medicines should be kept in locked cabinets, or out of the reach of children. Never rebottle or repackage products, such as storing cleaning solutions in soft drink bottles.

K E E P I N G   F I T

What to Do If There's a Fire

- Crawl under the smoke.
- Close doors between you and the smoke.
- Don't open any door without feeling to see if it is hot. If it is, don't open the door.

- Don't try to fight a large fire.
- Don't stop to save anything except people.
- Never go back into a burning building.

- Call the fire department from outside your house unless the fire is very localized and small.
- If you should catch on fire, stop, drop, and roll.

674 CHAPTER 34 YOUR SAFETY AND WELL-BEING

Additional Information

Home Safety. Most homes built within the last 10 years have circuit breakers that automatically shut off the power to overloaded outlets. Only after the demand on the electric circuit has been reduced can the breaker switch be reset. This is an important safety feature.

In older homes, a fuse box controls the power flow. When an outlet is overloaded, its fuse wire melts, breaking the circuit. It's possible to continue to operate a fuse-controlled system, but this way may be hazardous. Never bridge a fuse or replace it with a penny—and never replace the blown fuse with a higher capacity fuse. The result is likely to be a blown circuit and an electrical fire.

Five Elements of Accidents

In studying accidents over the years, one important point has become clear: accidents do not just happen. In fact, most accidents follow a specific pattern.

Five elements are present in almost all accidents. They are the situation, the unsafe habit or risk, the unsafe act, the accident, and possible injuries—and they combine to form an accident chain.

- **The situation.** You and your friend Mary are listening to CDs in your room. You had just bought a new one by your favorite artist and you wanted to share it with her.
- **The unsafe habit.** As is your routine when you come home from school, you put your textbooks on the eighth step of the open stairway leading to the second floor. This step is shoulder height for you and is right beside your path to the kitchen.
- **The unsafe act.** When you came home from school today, as usual, you threw your textbooks on the stairway. After grabbing an apple from the kitchen, you hurried to your room to pick up your clothes before Mary came over.
- **The accident.** Mary enjoyed listening to your new CD and looking at your CD collection. Time passed quickly, and suddenly Mary realized if she did not hurry, she would be late getting home. She said good-bye and grabbed her jacket. As she ran down the stairs, she failed to see your books. Falling head first to the bottom of the stairs, she landed on her shoulder.
- **The injuries.** Mary broke her collarbone, and you felt terrible about her injury.

In the five elements that make up an accident, consider the first three as links in an accident chain and the last two as the result. If you break any one of the links,—or change the element—you will prevent the accident in all likelihood.

The safety-conscious person is always alert to the risk of a given situation. The safety-conscious person breaks the accident chain by changing the situation, changing unsafe habits or avoiding unnecessary risks, and acting in a safe manner.

Breaking the accident chain can prevent accidents from happening.

LESSON 1 REVIEW

Reviewing Facts and Vocabulary

1. Give some examples of hazards that cause falls in the home.
2. Explain the purpose of a smoke detector and a fire extinguisher.

Thinking Critically

3. **Analysis.** One safety expert has said, "Safety begins at home." What assumptions did the writer make?

4. **Synthesis.** Summarize the necessary conditions for any fire.

Applying Health Knowledge

5. Design a fire escape plan for your home. Include two escape routes from each room.

Answers to Lesson 1 Review

1. Poorly lighted or poorly maintained stairways, tripping hazards, loose rugs, bathtubs and showers, makeshift ladders.
2. Answers will vary but should reflect an understanding of the information in "Fire Safety Devices" on pages 671 to 673.
3. Answers will vary. Possible answers:

Accidents are preventable, most accidents occur in the home, people in the home are responsible for their own safety, safety education is the responsibility of parents/guardians.
4. Answers will vary but should include: fuel, heat, and air.
5. Fire escape plans will vary.

Check for Understanding

- Assign and discuss the lesson review.

Evaluate

- Administer, grade, and discuss the *Lesson 1 Quiz.*

Reteach

- Provide students with copies of floor plans of several different homes. Ask them to develop emergency exit routes from all rooms in the houses and indicate where smoke detectors and fire extinguishers should be placed. Have them justify their decisions.
- Ask students to complete *Reteaching Activity 92.*

Enrich

- Have students visit department stores, children's stores, or pharmacies to find examples of various child-safety devices. These might include safety door latches, door alarms, intercom systems (child monitors), and child-safety gates. For each device, have students answer the following questions: What is it called? Where is it available? How much does it cost? How does it work? What does it do, that is, what link in the accident chain is the device meant to break? Do the students think that using it would be an effective way to prevent accidents? Why or why not?

Close

Tell students that in this lesson they studied that the home is one of the most dangerous places to be. They also studied the causes of the most frequent home accidents and how to avoid them. If they apply what they learned to their own home life, they and their family will decrease the chances of being seriously injured in a home accident.

676 CHAPTER 34 YOUR SAFETY AND WELL-BEING

Focus

Lesson Objective

After studying this lesson, students should be able to:

■ identify basic safety rules that help prevent accidents at work and play

Bellringer

Write the following on the chalkboard for students to work on while attendance is being taken: *Recall an accident that occurred during a recreational activity. Write a brief description of the accident and the steps leading up to it.*

Introducing the Lesson

Refer to the Bellringer. Ask volunteers to share their responses. Have the class try to identify the cause of each accident and how it might have been prevented.

Building Vocabulary

■ Ask students to explain the term *drownproofing* in their own words.

■ Ask students to complete *Workbook Vocabulary Activity 93.*

DID YOU KNOW?

■ In the U.S., accidents are the leading cause of death for people under age 35, and the third leading cause of death for those over 35.

■ Death by firearms, or guns, accounted for 750 deaths among U.S. young people in 1990.

SAFETY AWAY FROM HOME

LESSON 2 FOCUS

TERM TO USE

■ Occupational Safety and Health Administration (OSHA)

CONCEPTS TO LEARN

■ Employers have a responsibility to provide a safe work environment.

■ Many accidents happen when people get overly confident, try to show off, or get talked into trying something they are not able to do well.

ATTITUDES AND BEHAVIORS TO EVALUATE

■ Self-Inventory, page 688.

■ Building Decision-Making Skills, page 689.

Safety and accidents can touch every aspect of daily living. Although many accidents occur at home, the workplace also can pose a threat to your safety. Additionally, if you participate in recreational activities, you will want to be aware of the possible hazards. Whether at home or away, you should always follow basic safety rules.

At Work

If you have a part-time job, you know the importance of safety at work. Whether you work in a fast-food restaurant, in a local grocery store, or around heavy equipment, it is essential that you are provided with a safe environment in which to work.

The United States **Occupational Safety and Health Administration (OSHA)** is an agency that promotes safe and healthy conditions at work. This organization develops and enforces health regulations and job safety. It also is involved in keeping employers and employees aware of industrial hazards. OSHA deals with fire prevention, protective clothing, and acceptable levels of exposure to asbestos and lead. OSHA workers inspect work sites to ensure compliance with their standards.

Employers can reduce your risk of injury at work by eliminating health hazards that are causing or may cause serious physical harm or death. It is the employer's responsibility to train you and make you aware of hazards and to inform you of any new safety rules.

You can promote a safe work environment by arriving at work well-rested and alert, learning the proper use of all equipment, and following established safety rules.

Outdoors

Sports and recreation can be fun. However, if people do not follow basic safety behaviors, sports and recreation can end in accidents, injury, and even death. Prevention requires planning ahead and taking necessary precautions.

Here are five important points to remember:

■ Know your abilities and skills as well as your limits, and stay within them. Many accidents happen when people become overly confident, try to show off in front of others, or get talked into trying something they are not able to do well.

■ Use the proper equipment and know how to use it in the way it was intended.

■ Take the time to warm up and stretch before you exercise or participate in a strenuous activity.

■ Cool down properly after you exercise or participate in a strenuous activity.

■ Learn the safety rules specific to your activity before getting started.

Resources for Lesson 2

■ **Guided Reading** Activity 93
■ **Workbook** Vocabulary Activity 93
■ **Reteaching** Activity 93
■ **Lesson 2 Quiz**

In and On the Water

Each year in the United States about 7,000 people die from drowning, and more than 1 million have close calls. Small children wander off and fall into unattended pools and ponds; boats overturn; swimmers panic when struck by a cramp, when caught in a current, or when they have swum out farther than they should.

Most of these drownings and near-drownings are avoidable. If people understand the risks of being around water and follow some basic rules of safety, the number of drownings would be greatly reduced.

Learning to swim increases your confidence in the water.

WATER SAFETY PRECAUTIONS

Swimming

Learn to swim well. Being able to swim gives a person confidence in the water and reduces the chance of panic during an accident or emergency. Swimming lessons are usually available in your community, at school, or at municipal pools. While swimming, heed the following precautions:

- Follow the posted swimming rules.
- Always swim with someone, preferably someone who knows lifesaving techniques.
- Avoid pushing and shoving. Never participate in horseplay or give fake cries for help.
- If you get a muscle cramp, do not panic. Relax, float, and press and squeeze the muscle until it relaxes.
- Swim only when a lifeguard is on duty.
- If you are pulled offshore by rapid currents or undertows, swim at a 45° angle toward shore until you are freed by the current.

Diving

Sporting accidents are second to car accidents as the cause of spinal injuries that result in paralysis. Water sports—diving in particular—pose the most serious threat. Stay safe following these guidelines.

- Always check the water depth before diving.
- Never dive into unfamiliar water or into shallow breaking waves.
- Be sure the area is clear of swimmers and floating objects before diving.
- Always dive straight ahead and not off the side of the diving board.
- Never go down a water slide headfirst.

Boating

Follow these safety rules when out in a boat:

- Learn how to handle a boat or canoe correctly.
- Use only boats that are in good condition.
- Observe the load limit of the boat.
- Always wear a life jacket when boating.

K E E P I N G   F I T

Safety in the Workplace

When working at a part- or full-time job, keep these safety guidelines in mind:

- Do not use any machine you have not been fully trained to operate.

- Do not work without required protective equipment, such as goggles, earplugs, or gloves.
- Do not work at a pace that is too fast to maintain safety standards.

- Do not work without breaks.
- Do not work for long stretches at a time.
- Remember, you have a right to expect safe work conditions and protection from injury.

Additional Information

Avoiding Water Accidents. Many drowning victims never intended going into the water in the first place—they fell in while fishing, walking, playing, boating, or cycling. Many of us can't swim well enough to save ourselves or others if we do fall into the water accidentally, so the best precaution is avoiding falling into the water in the first place.

Be cautious when alongside water—banks are often wet and slippery, or they may crumble underfoot. Never disregard danger notices and don't be overconfident because you can swim. Swimming in an icy lake is very different from swimming in a warm pool. Finally, don't go swimming or fishing by yourself.

Overcoming The Odds

Jyh-Hann ("John") Chang is in his twenties. He knows firsthand about the importance of safety. A few years ago, he had a body-surfing accident that changed his life.

When he was 19, John decided to go body surfing in dangerous conditions. "It was just a day or two after a hurricane," John says. "I knew that the waves would be a lot rougher. I remember wading in the water and thinking I'd just wait for a large wave to come in. When I chose one, it was the one that ended up breaking my neck. The next thing I knew, I was drowning. A passerby thought I was a log, and he was going to clear this log from the wave, but then he realized it was a body—my body. I was very fortunate that he was there. I'm very fortunate that I'm alive."

John continues. "The next thing I knew, I was being flown to a shock trauma unit. I was completely paralyzed from the neck down. That night the doctor told me I probably wouldn't walk again. It really didn't hit me until I went home. Everything around me reminded me of what I couldn't do anymore."

But John learned to cope, and he excelled. "I got myself back into college," he says.

"The college initially didn't want me back. They'd never had a person in a wheelchair there before. But my parents begged. My first goal was to do well academically. I did.

"After my sophomore year,"

John says, "I knew I needed to improve my social life. I gradually got involved in committees and clubs. In my junior year, I became vice president of the student body, and senior year, I became president of the student council and senior class president. I felt good about myself because I realized people were finally looking at me, at my qualities, not just at my wheelchair. I'd felt for the longest time that I had to be happy all the time. But it was when I acted like a real person—with good

times and bad times, with both depression and humor—that people started responding to me.

"I was commencement speaker at graduation," John goes on. "I spoke in front of seven thousand people. Then I began speaking at schools, camps, and universities about being disabled. Before my accident, my dream was to be a doctor, but no medical school will take me because I can't fulfill some of the physical requirements. I'm now working on a PhD in clinical psychology. I'm going to specialize in neuropsychology and help the physically challenged."

Despite obstacles, John hasn't stopped enjoying new challenges. "This year, I began to go back into sports," he says. "I do some sculling on the river and I've gone airplane gliding as well. It took me six years to find that I could enjoy the things I used to enjoy. So I guess I should never set a limit on how much I can grow."

1. What obstacles has John faced since his accident? What are some of the personal lessons he has learned along the way?
2. How might more attention to safety have prevented his accident?

Additional Information

Risk-Taking. Risk-taking is often in response to a dare from a peer. During the challenge to prove oneself, safety practices become unimportant and are disregarded. This type of behavior usually begins around age 10, and it may continue for some through adulthood.

Why are some people foolhardy while others are cautious? Some risk-taking may be done, whether consciously or unconsciously, to get attention. This may be especially true in troubled families. A child in the family may risk injury in the hope of drawing the family together. Adults who allow children to engage in risky behavior may be motivated at least in part by jealousy, anger, or even dislike for the child.

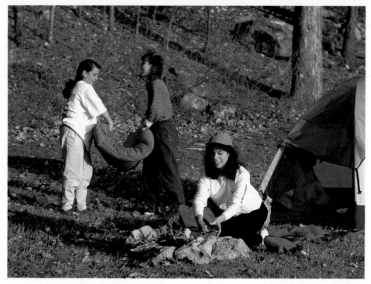

Camping is more fun when you follow safety precautions.

CONFLICT RESOLUTION

Ed was really happy when his uncle said he could borrow his tent to go camping with friends. Now out in the woods, his friend Larry has built a huge fire for them to cook their evening meal. Ed is concerned that wind will carry the fire to the trees. Larry says the fire will eventually die out overnight.

How should Ed handle this situation?

Camping

Unsafe behavior in and around campsites can lead to serious accidents. When camping, follow these guidelines:

- Stay in specified campsites.
- Never camp alone.
- Always let someone know where you are going and when you will return.
- Be knowledgeable about poisonous plants, insects, and snakes in the area.
- Carry plenty of fresh water.
- Never cook in a tent.
- Smother all fires with dirt and water.

LESSON 2 REVIEW

Reviewing Facts and Vocabulary

1. Describe the purpose of OSHA.
2. List basic rules of safety near water.

Thinking Critically

3. **Synthesis.** Develop a plan that would help reduce the number of drownings in your community.

4. **Analysis.** Compare safe and unsafe behavior when diving.

Applying Health Knowledge

5. Many communities offer swimming programs. Design a poster that advertises a swimming program in your area. Include information that would encourage someone to learn how to swim.

SAFETY AWAY FROM HOME **679**

Answers to Lesson 2 Review

1. OSHA promotes safe and healthy conditions at work.
2. See "Water Safety Precautions" on page 677.
3. Plans will vary but should reflect an understanding of water safety rules.
4. Answers will vary. Possible answers:

Safe behavior includes the diving tips on page 677. Unsafe diving would include diving into unfamiliar water, showing off, going off the side of the diving board, and going down a water slide headfirst.

5. Posters will vary.

Assess

Check for Understanding

- Assign and discuss the lesson review.

Evaluate

- Administer, grade, and discuss the *Lesson 2 Quiz.*

Reteach

- Ask the principal for copies of several old accident reports. Ask students to analyze them for the causes of the accidents and to identify ways they might have been prevented.
- Ask students to complete *Reteaching Activity 93.*

Enrich

- Have students investigate the myths and facts about when people are most accident-prone (for example, when their biorhythms are at an ebb or when there is a full moon). Ask them to organize their findings about these myths and facts in chart form. Then have each student show the chart to 10 people and ask them to describe their own "accident-proneness" in terms of the chart. Do their experiences fit better with the myth section or with the fact section of the chart?

Close

Tell students that in this lesson they studied some basic safety guidelines to help keep them safe at work and play. If they apply what they've learned at work and during leisure time, they'll decrease their risk of accident and injury.

SAFETY ON WHEELS

Lesson Objective

After studying this lesson, students should be able to:
- identify safety guidelines for travel on wheels

Bellringer

Write the following on the chalkboard for students to work on while attendance is being taken: *Do you wear seat belts? Why or why not? If you only wear seat belts sometimes, how often do you wear one?*

Introducing the Lesson

Refer to the Bellringer. Take a poll of the class and summarize their seat-belt habits on the chalkboard. Ask students who don't use seat belts to explain their reasons for not doing so.

Building Vocabulary

- Have students write a short paragraph describing a car accident in which they show clearly their understanding of the terms *car collision* and *human collision.*
- Ask students to complete *Workbook Vocabulary Activity 94.*

Guided Practice

L1 **DISCUSSION.** What is the leading cause of death for older teens and young adults? (Car accidents) What are the major contributing factors? (Speeding, alcohol)

L1 **SPEAKER.** Invite a driver-education teacher to class to explain what defensive driving means and to give students some examples of defensive driving techniques.

L1 **EXPLANATION.** Explain why children are at greater risk than adults in car accidents if they are not belted into a car seat.

L1 **DISCUSSION.** Should bicyclists and motorcyclists be required by law to wear helmets? Why or why not?

LESSON 3 FOCUS

TERM TO USE
- Human collision

CONCEPTS TO LEARN
- Most automobile accidents and deaths among young people do not involve a second vehicle.
- Many cyclists mistakenly ride on the wrong side of the road against traffic.

ATTITUDES AND BEHAVIORS TO EVALUATE
- Self-Inventory, page 688.
- Building Decision-Making Skills, page 689.

I t is frightening to realize that automobile accidents are the leading cause of death for people between the ages of 15 and 24 in the United States.

Auto Safety

Most automobile accidents and deaths among young people do not involve a second vehicle. Instead, they result from the young person's overturning the vehicle, running the vehicle off the road, or colliding with fixed objects, such as trees, light poles, and concrete walls. Such accidents often involve high rates of speed.

Taking a driver's education course can help you develop better driving skills and habits. Such a course can help you learn to anticipate problems before they occur.

Drive within the Speed Limit

Speed kills. This is a plain and simple fact, yet one that people often ignore. By driving within the legal limit, you lower your risk of accidents and reduce your risk of injury to yourself and others. You also save gasoline and wear and tear on your car and tires.

Use Seat Belts

There are two kinds of collisions within a single accident. The first is the car collision, in which the car hits something, buckles and bends, and then comes to a stop. The second collision is the **human collision,** which happens when a person hits some part of the car or is thrown from the vehicle. It is the human collision that causes injury.

To help understand just how severe the human collision can be, imagine a person's head striking a post at 30 miles (48 km) per hour. In a 30-mile-per-hour (48-km-per-hour) crash of a vehicle, an occupant strikes the interior of the car with a force of several thousand pounds, resulting in serious injury or death. Because the car's interior has very little give, the human body must absorb most of the force of the impact.

Infants or children are even more likely than adults to become like flying missiles during a crash. This is true whether they are in the front or rear seats. If adults hold children on their laps, the children become cushions that protect the adults from colliding with the dashboard or windshield. In this case, the children receive the brunt of the crash, often suffering severe or fatal head injuries. Thus, families need to use car restraints or car seats for children.

Many people wear seat belts only on long trips or when weather conditions seem particularly dangerous. Serious accidents, however, occur at all speeds, on all kinds of trips, and under all kinds of conditions.

680 CHAPTER 34 YOUR SAFETY AND WELL-BEING

Resources for Lesson 3

- **Transparency** 43
- **Guided Reading** Activity 94
- **Workbook** Vocabulary Activity 94
- **Reteaching** Activity 94
- **Lesson 3 Quiz**

However, the chances are greater of being in an accident close to home. The accident rate is low on expressways where much high-speed, long-distance travel takes place.

For every 100 young people killed in a motor vehicle accident in the United States last year, 80 would still be alive if they had been wearing a seat belt. When you use a seat belt, you are practicing accident and injury prevention. If your friends do not buckle up, ask them to do so. Though air bags are now installed in many cars, it is still important to use seat belts. Most states have laws requiring their use.

Do Not Drink and Drive

Over one-half of all automobile fatalities involve drivers who had been drinking. If people followed the law and did not drink while driving, millions of accidents and deaths could be prevented.

People who drink and drive risk not only their own health but also that of anyone else who may be on the road. Judgment and physical skills are impaired. Driving is risky when sober—the risk increases when one is or has been drinking.

Motorcycle Safety

Motorcyclists are seventeen times more likely to be killed in an accident than are people traveling in a car. There are several reasons for this.

- A two-wheeled vehicle slides more easily than one with four wheels.
- A motorcycle is more difficult to see than a car.
- Motorcycles accelerate faster than cars.
- Motorcycles weigh less than cars.
- Motorcyclists are virtually unprotected.

Regardless of whose fault an accident is, the cyclist loses. Besides following safety rules on the road, cyclists can increase their protection by wearing safety helmets and proper clothing. Cyclists need to be especially careful in wet weather because of poor tire traction on wet surfaces.

Bicycle Safety

Bicycling is a lot of fun, and it can provide good exercise for the whole family. Bicycles also are an excellent means of transportation.

KEEPING FIT

Helmets: Using Your Head

Three out of every four bike deaths and 70 percent of the bike-related hospitalizations involve head injuries. Therefore, one of the most important things you can do when riding on a bicycle or motorcycle is to wear a good helmet. It is estimated that bicycle helmets alone could cut head injuries by 85 percent.

When looking for a helmet, look for one with a seal of either the Snell Foundation or American National Standards Institute. Don't use helmets intended for other sports. Also be sure to replace any helmet that has been damaged.

SAFETY ON WHEELS **681**

---

682 CHAPTER 34 YOUR SAFETY AND WELL-BEING

Assess

Check for Understanding

- Assign and discuss the lesson review. Encourage LD students to focus on questions 1, 2, and 3.

Evaluate

- Administer, grade, and discuss the *Lesson 3 Quiz.*

Reteach

- Divide the class into four groups and assign each group one type of transportation on wheels. Ask each group to write a list of safety practices that should be followed when using that type of transportation.
- Ask students to complete *Reteaching Activity 94.*

Enrich

- Ask students to conduct a survey about seat-belt use. They should interview at least 20 to 30 adults and teenagers who drive. Have them design a brief questionnaire to get at patterns of seat-belt use and misconceptions about the role of seat belts in injury prevention.

Close

Tell students that in this lesson they studied important safety practices to follow when using cars, motorcycles, bicycles, skates, and skateboards. The practices most likely to prevent serious injury or death to teens are three safe-driving practices. They can be summed up as follows: don't speed; never drink and drive; and always wear a seat belt.

Wear protective equipment when skateboarding.

However, bicycles are involved in many injury accidents.

Four out of five collisions between bicycles and cars are caused by cyclists who disregard traffic rules. The most frequent mistake that cyclists make is riding on the wrong side of the road, against—rather than with—the flow of traffic.

Follow these guidelines for safe cycling:

- Ride on the right, keeping close to the side of the road. When riding with others, ride in a straight, single-file line.
- Always yield the right-of-way; you will not win against a car or truck.
- Watch for parked cars pulling into traffic and for car doors that swing open suddenly in your path.
- Obey the same rules as drivers, such as signaling before you turn and stopping for red lights and stop signs.
- Except when signaling, keep both hands on the handlebars at all times.

Three-fourths of all fatal bicycle accidents are due to head injuries. Wearing a hardshell helmet is a very important safety measure. Also, make sure your bike has a bright headlight and a red rear light and reflector for night riding. Wear reflective, or at least light-colored, clothing when riding at dawn, dusk, after dark, or in the rain. Be especially careful in wet weather. Bike tires have poor traction on wet surfaces.

Skating and Safety

Obey these safety rules when roller skating, skateboarding, or using in-line skates.

- Wear protective equipment—wrist guards, elbow and knee pads, hardshell helmet, and light gloves.
- If you fall, try to curl up into a ball and roll, staying loose. Tensing up will increase your chances of injury.
- Watch for and slow down around pedestrians.
- Keep your speed under control.

LESSON 3 REVIEW

Reviewing Facts and Vocabulary

1. What is a human collision?
2. List ways to prevent auto accidents.

Thinking Critically

3. **Evaluation.** Write a one-page paper that expresses your view on wearing a helmet when riding a motorcycle.
4. **Analysis.** The chances of being in an automobile accident are greater close to home. What support can you give to this statement?

Applying Health Knowledge

5. Collect several newspaper articles about accidents. Try to identify each of the links of the accident chain and ways the chain might have been broken.
6. A congressional representative has proposed that all cars have a device added to them so that no one can drive above the speed limit. Write a one-page response to this proposed legislation, based on what you have learned about accident prevention in this chapter.

---

682 CHAPTER 34 YOUR SAFETY AND WELL-BEING

Answers to Lesson 3 Review

1. It is the second collision in an automobile accident that takes place when a person hits some part of the car or is thrown from the vehicle.
2. Take a driver's education course, drive within the speed limit, use seat belts, do not drink and drive.
3. Answers will vary but answers should be supported.
4. Answers will vary. Possible answer: Most traveling is done close to home.
5. Answers will vary.
6. Responses will vary.

PERSONAL SAFETY

There are more cases of rape, thefts, shootings, murders, and gang violence than ever before. Because this violence is more widespread and more random than in the past, your chances of becoming a victim are very real.

Many causes for the increase in crime have been identified. For example, it is estimated that drugs and alcohol use are involved in two out of every three violent crimes. However, whatever the causes, we must all be concerned about not becoming victims.

Who are Victims?

Anyone can be a victim of a violent crime. No one is immune. That is the reason it is important to be prepared and know what to do not only to prevent but also to survive personal crimes. This is particularly necessary for teens because teens who are involved with or have friends who are involved with gangs, guns, alcohol, and/or drugs are more likely to be victims than other teens. However, everyone is at risk.

Consider these facts:

- According to the FBI, half of all rapes reported involve females under the age of 21.

- It is estimated that one out of three Americans will be the victim of a sexual attack or attempted attack sometime in his or her lifetime. Although this usually happens to females, males also are victims.

- Victims often know their attackers and may even be in ongoing relationships with them.

Preventing Becoming a Victim

It is wiser to give up jewelry, shoes, or a bike than to be shot. Other basic strategies are just common sense, such as always staying alert and aware of your surroundings.

Some Inner Tools of Self-Defense

When people talk about self-defense, they often mean learning physical strategies for stopping attacks. They imagine quick kicks and tricky tripping. However, mental or emotional strategies are also important. You may already have the following valuable self-defense tools within you.

- **Self-Esteem.** This includes the confidence you have in yourself. People with high self-esteem feel secure without being arrogant. They are not likely to be bullied or chosen as easy targets, particularly by people who know them.

PERSONAL SAFETY **683**

LESSON 4 FOCUS

TERMS TO USE
- Sexual assault
- Rape
- Date rape
- Acquaintance rape

CONCEPTS TO LEARN
- You have self-defense tools within you.
- Rape is an act of violence.

ATTITUDES AND BEHAVIORS TO EVALUATE
- Self-Inventory, page 688.
- Building Decision-Making Skills, page 689.

Focus

Lesson Objective

After studying this lesson, students should know how to:

- prevent, escape, and survive a violent personal attack

Bellringer

Write the following on the chalkboard for students to work on while attendance is being taken: *Write a list of places and/or situations that you would try to avoid because of the possibility of rape or other violent attack. If the place or situation were unavoidable, what else might you do to protect yourself from potential violence?*

Introducing the Lesson

Refer to the Bellringer. Ask volunteers to share their responses with the class. Did students focus on weapons or martial arts for protection? If so, steer discussion to the inner tools of self-defense described in this lesson. Did students consider the possibility of date or acquaintance rape? If not, ask specifically for ways to avoid it.

Building Vocabulary

- Students should demonstrate their understanding of the following terms by acting out situations in which individuals show these positive characteristics: *high self-esteem; assertiveness; self-protective attitude.*
- Ask students to find the legal definition of *rape* and then rewrite it in their own words. Does the definition apply equally to males and females?
- Ask students to complete *Workbook Vocabulary Activity 95.*

DID YOU KNOW?

- Homicide is the second leading cause of death for all teens and the first cause for black youth.

Resources for Lesson 4

- **Guided Reading** Activity 95
- **Decision-Making** Activity 34
- **Workbook** Vocabulary Activity 95
- **Workbook** Application Activity 34
- **Reteaching** Activity 95
- **Enrichment** Activity 34
- **Health Labs** Activity 34

- **Cooperative Learning** Activity 34
- **Lesson 4 Quiz**
- **Chapter 34 Test**
- **The Reality of Violence**
ABC News InterActive Videodiscs
Teenage Sexuality, Side 2
Ch 12 Acquaintance Rape

Guided Practice

L1 DISCUSSION. What are some of the factors behind the recent dramatic rise in violent crimes that affect teens?

L1 CLASS ACTIVITY. Ask students to make a list on the chalkboard of inner self-defense tools that will help them avoid being violently attacked. Have them explain each one.

LEP CLASS ACTIVITY. Ask students to demonstrate how they can use body language as a self-defense tactic.

L1 EXPLANATION. Explain why assertive, self-assured behavior is a good self-defense strategy.

L3 SELF-ESTEEM. How is a self-protective attitude related to self-esteem? Give examples. How would you describe the level of self-esteem of a person who is continually a victim or target of violence?

L2 COOPERATIVE LEARNING. Ask a group of students to write and act out a skit showing a potentially violent situation that is defused through verbal and body-language communication.

L1 DISCUSSION. What are several common-sense measures you should practice in order to avoid being trapped in your car by an attacker?

L1 EXPLANATION. Explain the best way to fight back if you are under attack. Consider a variety of situations.

L2 DISCUSSION. What is sexual harassment? Ask students to give examples of comments and behaviors they consider to be sexually harassing. Is there disagreement among class members? Why?

L1 COOPERATIVE LEARNING. Ask students to identify behaviors and situations they should avoid to reduce the risk of rape.

L1 SPEAKER. Invite a rape counselor (from a rape crisis center or hotline, for example) to class to discuss where, when, and why rapes occur, how best to avoid rape, and what one should do if raped.

Use your self-defense skills. Let your assertiveness and body language show your self-protective attitude.

- **Assertiveness.** Assertiveness is bold and confident behavior. Assertive people speak with definite conviction, leaving no doubt as to their feelings or intentions. Verbal assertiveness may prevent a physical attack. Phrases such as "Leave me alone" or "I'm not going with you" may throw an attacker off guard. Many attackers want easy victims they can overpower quickly.
- **Body language.** Actions often speak louder than words. Your body language can project your thoughts in a forceful way. Making direct eye contact, using a strong voice, keeping your body erect and chin held high, and using a deliberate stride can send the message that you are in charge of your safety.
- **Intuition.** Many people who have been raped report sensing that something was wrong just before the attack. Learn to trust your intuition. If you sense danger, get away.
- **A self-protective attitude.** Realize that you are worthy and have a right to be treated with respect and to be safe. Don't be afraid of insulting someone by walking away or by being overly cautious. Better to be safe than to be a victim.

Preventing Violence in Teen Relationships

Sometimes it is difficult for teens to tell if their relationships are safe. Although teens often play rough and tease one another, behavior can sometimes change and become harmful. No matter how close you are to someone, if his or her behavior changes or threatens your safety, you have a responsibility to speak up. Demand changed behavior, or get away. If anyone slaps, pushes, or threatens you, take it seriously. Verbal threats, put-downs, and yelling often are followed by physical abuse. Abusive behavior can be confusing because it is not always constant. It may be followed by apologies or statements of intention to do better. However, the cycle usually continues, and abusive behavior happens again.

How can you prevent being in a violent relationship? Don't allow another person to control you in any way. Don't allow anyone to isolate you from your friends or to physically assault you. Confront the person. Let him or her know that the behavior is unacceptable and even illegal. Talk to your parents, or a trusted friend. End the relationship, even if you like the person. Encourage the abuser to get help.

KEEPING FIT

How to Avoid Being a Victim

- Don't walk alone at night.
- Avoid wooded areas or dark alleys.
- At night, have your car keys ready when you are going to your car.
- Check the back seats to make sure no one is inside your car.
- After getting in the car, lock it.
- Park in well-lighted areas.
- Take down license plate numbers and descriptions of suspicious cars in your neighborhood and report them to the police.
- When walking at night, walk under lights and by the curb. Avoid doorways.
- Don't put your wallet or purse in an easy-to-grab place.
- Lock your car when you park it.

Additional Information

Violence. Violence is sometimes linked to brain tumors. It may also be caused by a deficiency in an important neurotransmitter, or brain chemical, called serotonin. Various drugs, such as alcohol, PCP (angel dust), and steroids (synthetic male hormones) may also induce violence.

Researchers at the Harvard Medical School recently studied a group of male and female athletes aged 17 to 51 who took steroids. The researchers concluded that the drugs caused serious mental side effects in about one-third of the athletes. Of those affected, 12 percent were diagnosed with psychoses and 22 percent with mood disorders. Such effects are usually, but not always, arrested when steroid use is stopped.

WHAT IS SEXUAL HARASSMENT

The term *sexual harassment* means different things to different people. It may take many forms, such as telling obscene jokes or stories, deliberate touching, pressure for dates, unwanted letters or calls, or rape.

Sexual harassment is a widespread problem. Its occurence is often controversial and open to debate because people hold different views of what it really is. Sexual harassment has become a major problem in the workplace and many companies now hold education and awareness programs for their employees. Sexual harassment is a form of abuse and should not be tolerated.

Preventing Sexual Assault and Rape

Sexual assault is attempted or actual physical attack with violent, sexual intent. **Rape** is sexual intercourse by force or threat. Rape is an act of violence and it is illegal. Frequently rapes occur when people are drunk or on drugs.

Victims of rape often know their attacker. When rape occurs between two people who are dating, it is called **date rape. Acquaintance rape** is rape by someone who is known casually by the victim or someone thought to be a friend.

There are preventive measures you can take.

- Have sexual limits and communicate them clearly.
- Do not drink or use drugs or date anyone who does.
- Do not go out alone or ride in a car with a person you do not know well.
- Do not put other's feelings ahead of your own safety.
- Take classes in karate or other forms of self-defense.
- Never open your door to anyone you do not know or trust.
- Use locks on doors and windows.
- Do not let strangers use your phone.
- Do not get into an elevator alone with a stranger.

Learn all you can to protect yourself.

Personal Space
Our idea of how much "personal space" we need is culturally influenced. Many Americans like to be about an arm's length from someone when they talk informally. People from some Middle Eastern cultures are comfortable standing inches apart. Test yourself: 1. Ask someone to walk toward you and tell them to stop when they are a comfortable distance away. 2. What factors make this distance change? Does the age or sex of the other person have an effect? Does it matter if the person is a friend?

L2 DISCUSSION. What is "date rape" or "acquaintance rape"? How common is it? Does it differ from rape by a stranger? Is it more or less devastating and why?

L1 DISCUSSION. What are some specific guidelines to follow to avoid being a victim of date or acquaintance rape?

L2 EXPLANATION. Explain how and why rape victims are often made to feel guilty or ashamed of what has happened to them. Elaborate on how this leads to underreporting of rapes and fewer convictions of rapists?

L2 CLASS ACTIVITY. Divide the class into two groups, one male and one female. Ask each group to share their fears of rape. How do fears of the two groups differ? Why? What are some specific ways that the fear of rape affects the daily lives of females in the class?

Independent Practice

L1 RESEARCH. Choose students to research the connection between the rise of violent crime in youth and the increase in the sale and use of illegal drugs like crack cocaine. Why do some experts argue that legalization of drugs would reduce violence and crime? For comparative purposes, have them investigate how alcohol prohibition was related to crime. Ask the students to take a stand for or against the legalization of drugs and to defend their views to the rest of the class.

L3 WRITING. Ask students to write an essay that conveys their idea of low self-esteem and how it is related to violent behavior. They should consider violent acts both directed against as well as perpetrated by individuals with low self-esteem.

L1 RESEARCH. Ask students to investigate stories (in newspapers or on television) about teens who have committed violent crimes. What was the crime and why was it committed? What might have prevented the crime? What happened to the offender? Was he or she treated differently than an adult might have been? Why or why not?

Overcoming Misconceptions

Cultural Studies. Tribal societies are dramatic proof that our expensive law and order machinery is not the only route to social order. Anthropologists have generally been impressed with the low levels of internal violence in tribal societies. But they don't attribute the low levels of violence to innate moral superiority of the "noble savage." Instead they believe that tribal cultures may be predisposed to lower crime rates because individual self-interest seldom conflicts with the interests of society as a whole. Theft, use of force, and similar behaviors are self-defeating in a society in which everyone's survival ultimately depends on mutual trust and cooperation.

L1 **COMMUNITY INVOLVE-MENT.** Have students talk to school staff members regarding weapons in their school. Are guns, knives, and other weapons a problem on the school campus? Has this changed through time? What rules and regulations are in place to prevent violence with weapons in school? How are they enforced? Do students feel that the rules and regulations violate their privacy? If so, is it a worthwhile trade-off?

L1 **COMMUNITY INVOLVE-MENT.** Arrange for students to observe or participate in a self-defense class and to interview the instructor. Have them ask under what circumstances such self-defense tactics should and should not be used. How advanced in training should one be in order to feel confident fending off an attacker who is bigger and stronger than oneself? What is the role, in general, of physical self-defense training in avoiding attack or injury?

L2 **RESEARCH.** Ask students to research the crime of rape. How has the legal definition of rape changed over the years? What penalties are there for rape? How often are rapists convicted and punished? How has this changed through time? Why? Have students present a report of their findings to the class.

L1 **COMMUNITY INVOLVE-MENT.** Have students collect newspaper articles on cases of rape or attempted rape that have occurred in their community. Ask them to identify in what if any ways the victims might have avoided attack.

L2 **RESEARCH.** Select students to research if a connection exists between violence on TV and violent acts committed by teens. What is the evidence? Ask them to summarize their findings and defend their conclusions.

L1 **USING THE LESSON RESOURCES.** For additional student activities, refer to the lesson resources on page 683.

DID YOU KNOW?

■ A mugger may watch you, get to know your schedule and route, and then ambush you. Deter muggers by varying your routine.

DID YOU KNOW?

■ According to the U.S. Bureau of Prisons, in 1991, there were over 65,000 prisoners in U.S. federal prisons. In 1995, that number is expected to be over 99,000.

■ Since 1983, the number of murders committed by juveniles has increased threefold, the number of rapes by juveniles has doubled, and the number of robberies has increased five times.

■ In 1989, Heath Wilkins and Kevin Stanford, then 16 and 17, were sentenced as adults and received the death penalty for the murder they committed. The Supreme Court upheld this death sentence in *Stanford* vs. *Kentucky*.

■ According to the F.B.I. Uniform Crime Reports, in this country there is a murder committed every 25 minutes, a rape every 6 minutes, a robbery every minute, a car theft every 22 seconds, and a burglary every 10 seconds.

■ The age group of 14 to 24 is responsible for the majority of violent crimes in our society.

■ Do not hitchhike or pick up hitchhikers.
■ Do not park your car, walk, or jog in remote areas.
■ If you are being followed, hurry to a place where there are other people, such as to a store.
■ Get to know your neighbors. Look out for each other.
■ If your car is rammed from behind or breaks down, stay in your car with doors locked and flasher lights on.
■ Keep a "Call Police" sign in your car and place it in the rear window in an emergency situation.

Escaping and Surviving an Attack

If you are attacked, try to run for help. If you cannot run, decide on another course of action. Scream, yell "fire," and/or physically disable or stun the person in some way. Watch for a moment when the attacker may be caught off guard so you can escape. Use your wits. Try different approaches. Don't assume you can't get away. You have a greater chance of escaping than you might think. If all else fails you may have to submit in order to survive.

HEALTH UPDATE

LOOKING AT TECHNOLOGY

DNA Banks: Genetic Information on File

DNA, or deoxyribonucleic acid, is a complex molecule found in all cells, mainly in their nuclei. It is the substance that makes up genes, the material that carries hereditary information that determines what characteristics a person will develop.

In the past, convicting criminals was often based on fingerprints, witness testimony, obvious physical evidence, and/or admissions of guilt, but often there was no absolute proof that a suspect committed a certain crime. With advancements in DNA testing, however, some criminals are now being located and convicted on the basis of a kind of genetic testing called DNA profiling. DNA profiling tests can be run on small amounts of blood or other body fluids such as semen. If the DNA from these samples matches body fluids left at the scene of the crime or on the victim, it is highly probable that the profiled suspect committed the crime.

Increasingly, DNA profiling information is being used in courtroom testimony. Now some states are taking steps to create extensive DNA computerized files known as DNA banks. Such information could be scanned and retrieved quickly when trying to identify suspects.

Many crime experts and law enforcement officials believe that DNA banks will take the guesswork out of much investigative work, get criminals identified and off the streets more quickly, and make the whole trial process more scientific. Others, however, believe that DNA profiling is a violation of the right to privacy as well as a violation of the Fourth Amendment to the United States Constitution, which states that citizens are protected against unreasonable searches.

Additional Information

What to Do If Attacked. Escape if you can. Negotiate if possible. Fight only if you have no choice. These are the key rules for dealing with an attacker. Precisely what you do depends on your strength, confidence, and willingness to fight back, and your assessment of the assailant.

An assailant who is drunk or using other drugs acts impulsively, so you can't predict what will happen if you try to defend yourself. In some cases, resisting violently may increase your chances of being killed. If you do fight, never give a warning. Strike as swiftly and as hard as you can and be ready to repeat the blow. And always scream for help as you fight.

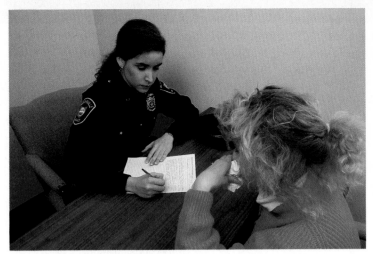

Always seek help in case of attack.

DID YOU KNOW?

■ Each year, the National Association of Town Watch sponsors an annual Night Out for crime prevention awareness. On this night, neighbors from thousands of communities turn on their porch lights, sit outside, talk, meet local police, and make it known to would-be criminals that they are looking out for trouble. When the program began in 1984, only 400 communities took part. In 1990, over 8,000 did.

■ According to the Children's Defense Fund, 40 percent of jailed juvenile offenders were under the influence of illegal drugs at the time they committed their most recent crimes.

What to Do After a Rape

If you or someone you know is raped, get help from your family or a friend after an attack and get it quickly. Do not take a shower or bath or discard any physical evidence. Get medical help right away. You may be hurt or infected and not know it. Have medical tests for pregnancy, STDs, and HIV infection. The male involved should also be tested for STDs and HIV. Report the rape to the police even if it is a date or acquaintance rape. You may want to request that someone of your sex take your report.

Call a rape crisis center and get counseling or join a support group. You will need help to recover from the emotional shock of being raped. Be patient. It takes time to recover from the trauma of an attack. Remember that you did not cause the rape and have no reason to be ashamed.

LESSON 4 REVIEW

Reviewing Facts and Vocabulary

1. What are three characteristics that are self-defense tools and may add to your chances of not becoming a victim?
2. What does it mean to be assertive?

Thinking Critically

3. **Evaluation.** Why do you think most incidences of rape are not reported?

4. **Synthesis.** Develop a plan that will help you reduce the chances of being physically assaulted or raped.

Applying Health Knowledge

5. Read an article about a rape situation. Identify three general concepts about rape that you learned from your reading.
6. Create a public service announcement about preventing date rape and acquaintence rape.

PERSONAL SAFETY **687**

Assess

Check for Understanding
■ Assign and discuss the lesson review.
■ Assign and discuss the chapter review.

Evaluate
■ Administer, grade, and discuss the *Lesson 4 Quiz*.
■ Administer, grade, and discuss the *Chapter 34 Test*.
■ Refer to the Performance Assessment strategy for this chapter. See pages T 23 to T 25.

Reteach
■ Have students apply what they learned in this lesson by describing hypothetical violent situations. For each situation, ask students to discuss ways the situation could have been avoided and otherwise, how the situation could best be handled.
■ Ask students to complete *Reteaching Activity 95*.

Enrich
■ Ask students to read a book or series of articles about body language and then give a talk on what they learned. They should demonstrate what various facial expressions, gestures, postures, and movements communicate in different cultures. Ask the class to discuss how misunderstandings could arise due to differences in body language among people of varying cultural backgrounds.
■ Ask students to complete *Enrichment Activity 34*.

Close

Review with the students ways to reduce their risk of being victims of violence, including rape.

Answers to Lesson 4 Review

1. Answers may include self-esteem, assertiveness, body language, and relying on intuition, or hunches.
2. Assertive people are bold and confident. They speak with conviction.
3. Answers will vary. Possible answers: Fear of not being taken seriously, fear of being accused of causing the rape, fear of humiliation or retaliation.

4. Plans will vary. See "Some Inner Tools of Self-Defense" on pages 683 to 684 and "Preventing Sexual Assault and Rape" on pages 685 to 686.
5. Answers will vary.
6. Answers will vary but may include information from pages 685 to 686.

Helping Students Improve Their Health

Reinforcing Vocabulary

- **Assertive.** Characterized as being confident and bold.
- **Aggressive.** Characterized as possessing a driving force or being full of combative energy.

Teaching Strategies

L1 EXPLANATION. Teenagers generally have a sense of immortality. Typically, adolescents do not believe that any harm may come to them because they are young and invincible. Unfortunately, it often takes a severe or fatal accident to show teenagers the dangers that exist from unsafe behaviors.

L1 EXPLANATION. Question 13 may be misinterpreted by parents and students. Frequently the term *limitation* or *limits* refers to preventing a student from reaching his or her potential, which has no limits. The term *limits* in this case refers to the physical or emotional limits that we all face due to age and lack of experience.

L2 DISCUSSION. Take a recent newspaper clipping from any newspaper that deals with an accident involving a teenager. Have students discuss how the accident occurred and what, if anything, could have been done by the teenager to have prevented the accident.

L1 DISCUSSION. Invite a police officer from the state highway patrol to discuss safety issues that may involve teenagers. Have the officer come prepared to show teenagers tasteful pictures or statistics that will reveal to teenagers how many of their peers lose their lives every year due to preventable accidents.

L1 CLASS ACTIVITY. Have students present a safety fair for students at a nearby elementary school. Have students demonstrate proper bicycle safety tips, explain how and why to avoid strangers, and discuss general home safety tips.

Self-Inventory

Staying Safe

HOW DO YOU RATE?

Number a sheet of paper from 1 through 22. Read each item below, and respond by writing *MT* if the statement describes you *all or most of the time*, *ST* if the statement describes you *some of the time*, and *N* if the statement *seldom or never* applies to you. Total the number of each type of response. Then proceed to the next section.

1. I avoid acting in an unsafe manner.
2. I avoid showing off.
3. I share personal safety concerns with trusted adults.
4. I am self-confident and sure of my self-worth.
5. I am assertive, especially when around aggressive individuals.
6. I use body language to send a message that I am in charge of my personal safety.
7. When I drive a vehicle or a motorcycle, I avoid tailgating. If I do not drive but ride a bicycle, I follow safety guidelines.
8. I follow posted speed limits when driving or cycling.
9. I use seat belts.
10. I do not drink and drive.
11. I avoid riding with drivers who speed or who drink and drive.
12. I allow myself sufficient time to get places without having to speed or be distracted.
13. I stay within my abilities and limits when taking part in sports and recreational activities.
14. I take the time to warm up before and cool down after physical activities.
15. I follow safety rules specific to my favorite activities.
16. I avoid touching plumbing or metal and an electrical appliance or tool at the same time.
17. I disconnect appliances by pulling on the plug, not on the cord.
18. I do not use an electrical appliance if my body, clothing, or the floor is wet.
19. I keep poisons out of the reach of children.
20. I do not rebottle or repackage products, which might cause harm to someone else.
21. I do not open the door of my home to anyone I do not know or trust.
22. When going out with someone I do not know well, I make sure we go with other friends of mine.

HOW DID YOU SCORE?

Give yourself 2 points for each statement that describes you *all or most of the time*, 1 point for each statement that describes you *some of the time*, and 0 points for each *seldom or never* response. Find your total and read below to see how you scored. Then proceed to the next section.

35 to 44
Excellent. Your safety-conscious attitude and behavior deserve high praise. Keep it up.

25 to 34
Good. You are doing a good job of practicing safe behavior, and it appears that you generally have a safe attitude.

15 to 24
Fair. You need to make safety attitudes and behavior more a part of your daily life.

Below 15
Poor. You are a serious threat to your own health and safety and that of others.

WHAT ARE YOUR GOALS?

If you received an *excellent* or *good* score, complete the statements in Part A. If your score was rated *fair* or *poor*, complete Parts A and B.

Part A

1. I plan to learn more about safety behavior in the following ways: ____.
2. My timetable for accomplishing this is ____.
3. I plan to share my information with others by ____.

Part B

4. The unsafe or risky behavior I would like to change most is ____.
5. The steps involved in making this change are ____.
6. My timetable for making this change is ____.
7. The people or groups I will ask for support and assistance are ____.
8. My rewards for making this change will be ____.

Meeting Students' Needs

For students who score *Excellent*. Encourage students to write and illustrate a booklet on safety issues that involve adolescents.

For students who score *Good*. Arrange for students to interview police officers, media reporters, or Children's Services workers on child and teenage safety issues.

For students who score *Fair*. Suggest that students begin to set goals that will help change student behaviors and that may improve a teenager's chances of avoiding an accident.

For students who score *Poor*. Ask students to examine their personal behavior choices to avoid potential accidents. Have students interview the parents of a child who has been injured through careless behavior.

Building Decision-Making Skills

A my has just started driving to school and has discovered that some of the students engage in driving games. These games include a driver trying to squeeze his or her car into the line of traffic as others try to squeeze the driver out. Quick starts, stops, and cuts are the rule, along with loud music, and passengers hanging out the window or the sun roof while yelling at people in other cars. Some drive faster than the posted limit, some tailgate, and some try to pass when they shouldn't. What should Amy do?

A. Tell her friends that she is not going to take part and insist that passengers in her car use seat belts.

B. Find a reason to be late leaving after school every day to miss the crowd and this game.

C. Learn the game so that she gets a reputation for risk-taking and others know she is not afraid.

WHAT DO YOU THINK?

1. **Situation.** Why does a decision need to be made?

2. **Choices.** What other solutions or choices could Amy try?

3. **Consequences.** How will people react to the direct approach? Will they respect her? Will they make fun of her?

4. **Consequences.** Is this an issue that the students should resolve on their own or do adults need to be involved? How will people react if they find out Amy brought adults into it?

5. **Consequences.** What are Amy's legal liabilities? What will happen if she gets a ticket or wrecks her car? What if someone gets badly hurt? How will this affect her driving privileges, her life-style, or her financial situation?

6. **Consequences.** How will Amy feel about herself in each situation? How will others feel about her, including her friends, other drivers, her parents, school officials, and so on?

7. **Consequences.** How would Amy's health triangle be affected by this decision?

8. **Decision.** What action do you think Amy should take and just how should she do it?

L ynn is walking home from school when a stranger drives up and asks if she is Lynn Andrews, daughter of Marcy Andrews. When she says yes, the man says her mother has been involved in a serious auto accident and has asked him to bring Lynn to the hospital. What should Lynn do?

A. Say no and get to a phone and call home, then call the hospital.

B. Go with him, since the man knew both Lynn's and her mother's name.

C. Call the police and report the license number and description of the car and the man.

WHAT DO YOU THINK?

9. **Situation.** What are the dangers here?

10. **Choices.** What other choices does Lynn have?

11. **Consequences.** What are the consequences of each choice?

12. **Decision.** Which choice do you think is best for Lynn?

13. **Decision.** What should Lynn do if the man becomes more insistent?

14. **Evaluation.** How do you think you would handle a similar situation?

Discussing the Answers

Situation 1. Amy should refuse to drive near those individuals who engage in unsafe driving practices. Also, she should not participate in these behaviors. Perhaps she could arrange to talk with the school principal and suggest solutions, such as charging for parking permits and hiring an off-duty police officer to monitor traffic.

Situation 2. Hopefully Lynn is aware that it is extremely dangerous to get into the car of a stranger. Lynn should immediately say no, begin screaming, and run to the nearest house, school, or phone. There, Lynn may call the police to inquire as to the validity of the stranger's story.

Helping Students Improve Their Health

Building Decision-Making Skills

Teaching Strategies

L1 CLASS ACTIVITY. Have students discuss the unsafe driving behaviors with which Amy is concerned. Have students develop a list of school driving rules to help in Amy's situation. Have students discuss any problems that may exist at their own school. What possible solutions to these problems may students propose? Have students interview the school principal on these issues, propose solutions to any existing problems, and recommend possible consequences for those students who choose to engage in unsafe driving practices in the school area.

L1 CLASS ACTIVITY. Have students role-play the part of Lynn as she is approached by a stranger who wants Lynn to get into his car. Have students practice various ways of dealing with this situation. Have students discuss the possible consequences that may result from getting into a car with a stranger.

L1 CLASS ACTIVITY. Another possible role-play situation pertaining to teenage safety and well-being is: You have just accepted a baby-sitting position and the mother is trusting you to take her child swimming at the local municipal swimming pool. You notice that the lifeguards frequently talk on duty and become careless in watching the children in the pool. You wonder if you should say anything to the pool manager.

DID YOU KNOW?

■ Unintentional injuries account for about half of all deaths among people aged 15 through 24, and three-quarters of these involve motor vehicles.

Answers to Chapter 34 Review

Using Health Terms

1. Smoke detector
2. Fire extinguisher
3. Occupational Safety and Health Administration (OSHA)
4. Human collision
5. Seat belts, air bags
6. Rape

Building Academic Skills

7. Paragraphs will vary but a safe camping trip should include bulleted items in "Camping" on page 679.
8. 468.
9. Articles will vary.
10. 141.

Recalling the Facts

11. Keep stairways well-lighted and in good repair. Equip them with sturdy handrails. Install nonskid strips or well-fitting carpet.
12. Stop, drop, and roll. Stop where you are, drop to the ground or floor, and roll on the ground or roll up in a rug to smother the flames.
13. Cover your face with a wet towel.
14. In locked cabinets out of the reach of children.
15. Eliminate health hazards, train employees and make them aware of hazards, inform employees of any new safety rules.
16. Arrive at work well-rested and alert, learn the proper use of all equipment, follow established safety rules, do not use alcohol or other drugs.
17. Knowing how to swim gives a person confidence in the water and reduces the chance of panic during an accident or emergency.
18. Auto accidents, sporting accidents.
19. Automobile accidents.
20. Lowers the risk of accident, reduces the risk of injury to self and others, saves gasoline and wear and tear on the car and tires.
21. See bulleted items in "Bicycle Safety" on pages 681 to 682.

22. Answers will vary. Possible answers: Wear a bicycle helmet, equip bicycle with a bright headlight and a red rear light and reflector for night riding, wear reflective or light-colored clothing, be careful during wet weather.
23. Wrist guards, elbow pads, knee pads, helmet, gloves.
24. Curl into a ball and roll, staying loose.
25. Helps one develop better driving skills and habits, helps one learn to anticipate problems.
26. Two-thirds.
27. Self-esteem, assertiveness, body language, intuition, a self-protective attitude.
28. Direct eye contact, a strong voice, an erect body with

chin held high, a deliberate stride.
29. See bulleted items in "Preventing Sexual Assault and Rape" on pages 685 to 686.
30. Try to run away and get help; scream; yell "fire"; disable or stun the person; look for a moment when the attacker may be caught off guard, allowing time to

---

Using Health Terms

On a separate sheet of paper, write the term that best matches each definition given below.

LESSON 1

1. A device that sounds an alarm if smoke passes into it.
2. A portable device that can be used to extinguish small fires by ejecting fire-extinguishing chemicals.

LESSON 2

3. An agency that promotes safe conditions in the workplace.

LESSON 3

4. When a person hits some part of the car or is thrown from the vehicle.
5. Devices installed in automobiles to protect people during collisions.

LESSON 4

6. An act of violence involving sexual intercourse by force or threat.

Building Academic Skills

LESSON 2

7. **Writing.** Write two paragraphs describing camping trips. In one paragraph, describe a safe camping trip. In the other paragraph, describe an unsafe camping trip.

LESSON 3

8. **Math.** According to statistics, if 585 young people have been killed in motor vehicle accidents, how many would have been alive if they had worn a seat belt?
9. **Writing.** Write a newspaper article convincing bicycle riders to wear helmets.

LESSON 4

10. **Math.** By September 15, 1991, 100 murders had been committed in Columbus, Ohio, during the year. If this rate continued for the remainder of the year, how many people would have been murdered in this city during 1991?

Recalling the Facts

LESSON 1

11. What can be done to reduce the number of falls that occur on stairways?
12. What safety phrase should you remember if your clothing catches fire? What does this phrase mean?
13. What is a good way to prevent smoke inhalation during a fire?
14. How should poisonous products in the home be stored to minimize their dangers?

LESSON 2

15. How can employers minimize the risk of work-related accidents?
16. How can employees minimize the risk of work-related accidents?
17. Why should everyone learn to swim?
18. What are the two major causes of spinal injuries that result in paralysis?

LESSON 3

19. What is the leading cause of death among people between the ages of 15 and 24?
20. List three advantages of driving within the speed limit.
21. List five guidelines for riding a bicycle safely.
22. How can bike riders minimize the risk of injury in case of an accident?
23. What five pieces of protective equipment should people wear when roller skating or skateboarding?
24. What should you do if you fall while using in-line skates?
25. What are the benefits of taking a course in driver's education?

LESSON 4

26. What fraction of violent crimes involve drugs and alcohol?
27. Name four self-defense tools you can use to help protect yourself from others.
28. Give examples of body language that can help protect someone from harm.
29. What measures can you take to help prevent rape?
30. What strategies can you use if you are attacked?

REVIEW

Thinking Critically

LESSON 1

31. Evaluation. Some argue that falls among the elderly would be eliminated if the elderly were put in nursing homes. Do you agree with this strategy? Explain your reasoning.

32. Synthesis. Name three flammable liquids that might be used in or around a home. Tell what precautions should be taken in using each.

33. Synthesis. What would you include in a home fire escape plan? Explain your answer.

34. Analysis. What parts of the accident chain are the easiest to break?

LESSON 2

35. Synthesis. Plan a project to illustrate the importance of bicycle safety in elementary school.

36. Evaluation. How would you measure the worth of seat belts as a safety measure?

LESSON 3

37. Evaluation. Some states have laws requiring a person to use a seat belt while driving or riding in a car and to wear a helmet while operating a motorcycle. What is your opinion of such laws and why?

38. Analysis. What are the health advantages and disadvantages of riding a bicycle?

LESSON 4

39. Evaluation. If someone is raped, that person should seek help. List, in order, the five most important things you think this person should do after an attack. Why did you rate each one as you did?

Making the Connection

LESSON 1

40. Math. Survey several classes in school to find out how many homes have smoke detectors. Compute the percentage of homes that have smoke detectors.

Applying Health Knowledge

LESSON 2

41. Mario wants to participate in the gymnastics program at Jefferson High. His parents must sign a paper giving him permission to do so. Before they sign the paper, they are required to watch a film showing the possible dangers of injury in all the sports programs offered at Jefferson. After viewing the film, they are reluctant to sign the paper. What arguments can Mario use to convince them his participation in gymnastics will be safe?

Beyond the Classroom

LESSON 1

42. Community Involvement. Find the telephone numbers for the fire department, the police department, and the poison control center in your community. Post these and other emergency numbers in your home by the phone. Interview a person from each of these agencies to find out what action they take when they receive a call.

LESSON 2

43. Parental Involvement. Talk to your parents about safety precautions that are necessary on their jobs. Ask them what they are required to do regarding safety in their work.

LESSON 3

44. Further Study. Several years ago the speed limit on interstate highways was 70 miles per hour. Then the federal government passed a law changing this limit to 55 miles per hour. Recently, states have been permitted to increase this limit to 65 miles per hour in certain areas. Do some research to find out what effect the reduction from 70 to 55 miles per hour had on highway accidents and injuries. Based on your research, what do you think will be the effect of increasing the speed limit from 55 to 65 miles per hour?

PERSONAL SAFETY **691**

you can't get away; use your wits.

Thinking Critically

31. Answers will vary but should be supported logically.

32. Answers will vary. Possible answers: Gasoline, kerosene, nail polish remover, rubbing alcohol, cleaning fluid, lighter fluid, paint thinner, propane fuel, engine oil. Gasoline and kerosene should be stored outside the home and kept away from any source of ignition. All flammable materials should be used according to manufacturer's directions and for the purposes for which they were specifically designed, should be kept out of the reach of children, should not be thrown on or near burning or smoldering fires.

33. Answers will vary but should include the numbered items in "Fire Safety Actions" on page 673.

34. The unsafe habit and the unsafe act.

35. Plans will vary but should reflect the elements of bicycle safety from "Bicycle Safety" on pages 681 to 682.

36. Answers will vary but should be supported logically.

37. Answers will vary but should be supported logically.

38. Answers will vary. Possible answers: Advantages—good exercise, inexpensive, environmentally sound; disadvantages—involves the risk of accident and injury, slower than a motor vehicle.

39. Answers will vary but might include some of the following actions: Contact a relative or friend for support; call a rape crisis center; report the rape to police; seek medical attention; be tested for pregnancy, sexually transmitted diseases, and HIV infection; get counseling or join a support group. Rating should be supported logically.

Making the Connection

40. Answers will vary. You may wish to compare class statistics to national statistics.

Applying Health Knowledge

41. Answers will vary. Possible answers: He could tell his parents he will stay within his abilities. He could point out the safety precautions used in the program and promise to follow them carefully.

Beyond the Classroom

42. Answers will vary.
43. Students' findings about their parents' jobs will vary.
44. Answers will vary.

LESSON 1. First aid is the immediate temporary care given to a person who has become sick or who has been injured. It continues until a proper medical authority arrives. During the first 5 minutes, one should check the surroundings for possible dangers, check the victim for breathing and pulse, control severe bleeding, and send for medical help.

LESSON 2. Between 1 and 2 million poisonings occur every year. Some poisons are swallowed or inhaled. Others enter the body through insect or animal bites. Even touching certain substances can cause poisoning. Each means of poisoning has specific guidelines for administering first aid.

LESSON 3. First aid for minor mishaps, such as nosebleeds, animal bites, bee stings, fractures, sprains, burns, fainting, objects in the eye, and an assortment of temperature- and weather-related emergencies, can be provided.

Introducing the Chapter

Remind students that first and foremost we want to prevent accidents from happening. When they do happen, however, we need to be prepared to reduce unnecessary suffering and to prevent further damage to people involved in those accidents. Tell students this chapter will help them learn to administer first aid for common emergencies. As they learn what to do in an emergency, they should also think in terms of how the injury could have been prevented.

Performance Assessment ✓

Refer to pages T 23 to T 25 for a Performance Assessment strategy for this chapter. See the *Performance Assessment Activities* booklet for additional suggestions.

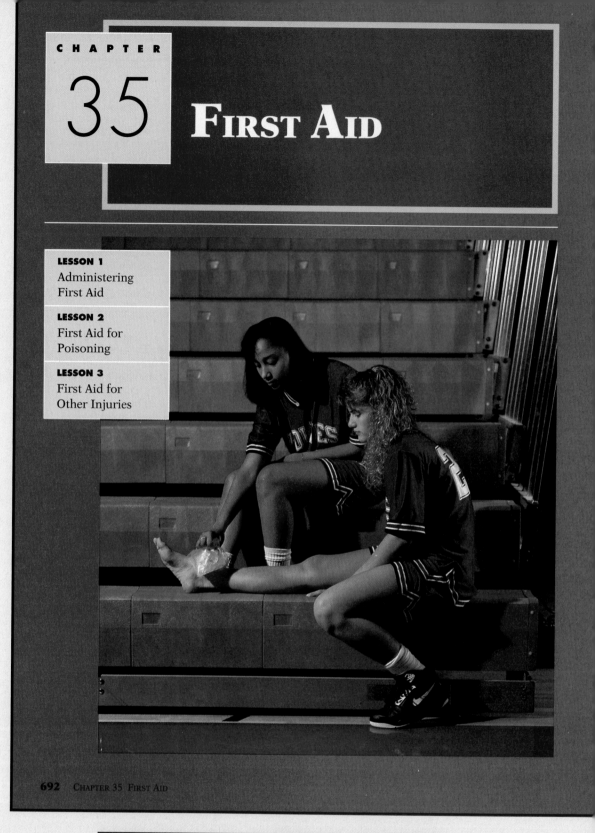

CHAPTER

35

FIRST AID

LESSON 1
Administering
First Aid

LESSON 2
First Aid for
Poisoning

LESSON 3
First Aid for
Other Injuries

Key to Ability Levels

Teaching strategies have been coded for varying learning styles and abilities.

L1 Level 1 activities are basic activities and should be within the ability range of all students.

L2 Level 2 activities are average activities and should be within the ability range of average to above-average students.

L3 Level 3 activities are challenging activities designed for the ability range of above-average students.

LD LD activities should be within the ability range of learning-disabled students.

LEP LEP activities should be within the ability range of Limited English Proficiency students.

ADMINISTERING FIRST AID

I magine you happened upon the scene of a traffic accident in which people had been hurt. Suppose you were on a bus and someone fainted. Would you know what to do in either of these emergency situations? **First aid,** or emergency care, is the immediate, temporary care given to a person who has become sick or who has been injured. First aid continues until a proper medical authority arrives at the scene of the emergency. Such authorities include persons on an emergency vehicle, a nurse, a physician, police officers, or firefighters.

Administering first aid is a serious job. It can mean the difference between life and death or between temporary and permanent disability. Because first aid can make life-changing differences, it is important to know—and know well—what you are doing when you give first aid.

Priorities in an Emergency

The first five minutes of an emergency situation are the most critical. During this crucial time it is important to remain calm and keep these six priorities in mind:

1. Check the immediate surroundings for possible dangers. Move the victim only if his or her life is threatened. Some life-threatening conditions include water deep enough for drowning to occur, a car that might catch on fire, or a room filled with smoke or poisonous fumes.
2. Check to see if the victim is conscious. If not, call for an ambulance at once.
3. Check breathing. Be sure the victim has an open airway. If he or she does not have an open airway, attempt to clear the airway; then administer rescue breathing if necessary. You will learn about this technique in Chapter 36.
4. Control severe bleeding. If blood is bright red and spurting, an artery has been damaged. You can control the bleeding by applying direct pressure to the wound. This lifesaving measure will be covered in depth later in this lesson.
5. Check the victim for poisoning. A **poison** is any substance—solid, liquid, or gas—that causes injury, illness, or death when introduced into the body. Treatment for poisoning is in the next lesson.
6. Send for medical help. Emergency Medical Services (EMS) can be summoned in many areas by dialing either 911 or 0. Learn the number for EMS in your area.

After the Priorities

Once you have taken steps to ensure the victim's safety and have administered life support procedures, you should attend to the following secondary measures:

LESSON 1 FOCUS

TERMS TO USE
- First aid
- Poison
- Pressure-point technique
- Shock

CONCEPTS TO LEARN
- Actions taken during the first five minutes of an emergency can save a person's life.
- The most important considerations in treating open wounds are stopping the bleeding, treating the victim for shock, and seeking medical care.

ATTITUDES AND BEHAVIORS TO EVALUATE
- Self-Inventory, page 710.
- Building Decision-Making Skills, page 711.

Lesson Objectives

After studying this lesson, students should be able to:
- define *first aid*
- identify the priorities in responding to an emergency
- differentiate between the types of wounds and know the first-aid treatment for each one
- describe shock and its treatment

Bellringer

Write the following on the chalkboard for students to work on while attendance is being taken: *Write your own definition of first aid.*

Introducing the Lesson

Introduce the lesson by reminding students of the responsibility that they take when they administer first aid. Emphasize the fact that they must know what they are doing or they risk doing more harm than good. Clarify the text definition of first aid by having students share their own definitions from the Bellringer. Place emphasis on the fact that first aid takes place until the proper medical authority arrives—it does not take the place of medical treatment. Tell students this lesson explains the basic rules of first aid.

Building Vocabulary

- Divide the class into two teams for a "Vocabulary Bee." Present a vocabulary term from this chapter and award a point to the team of the student who correctly defines the term.
- Ask students to complete *Workbook Vocabulary Activity 96.*

Resources for Lesson 1

- **Guided Reading** Activity 96
- **Workbook** Vocabulary Activity 96
- **Reteaching** Activity 96
- **Lesson 1 Quiz**
- **Performance Assessment** Activity 35

Guided Practice

L1 EXPLANATION. Bring a copy of the Good Samaritan Law for first aid, if your state has such a law. Explain to the class the requirements of this law which are to protect ordinary citizens who render aid to victims in need of assistance. This law does not require first-aid treatment to be administered if the person is unable to provide adequate treatment. Some states require that permission from the victim be given prior to administering first aid. This law does require that the person stay with the victim, call for help, or render basic first aid if possible. The law protects the citizen from being sued for administering basic first aid.

L1 DISCUSSION. Have students talk about accident situations in which the victim must be moved, such as fire, fallen wires, or nearby explosives. Then have them discuss when it would be unsafe to move the victim. (Broken bones, spinal injury.)

L1 CLASS ACTIVITY. Ask each student to fill out two index cards with information that might be important in case of emergency. On the first card, which is to be kept near a family phone, students should write their home phone number and address; the phone numbers of the police, ambulance, and fire department; the number of the poison control center; the pharmacist's number; family blood types; drug allergies; and phone numbers of neighbors to call in an emergency. The second card should be made for students' wallets or purses and should outline all of the above information plus any medical conditions that afflict the card carrier and the names and numbers of people to call in the event of an emergency.

L1 DEMONSTRATION. Invite a school nurse to visit the class to help you demonstrate basic first aid and treatment of wounds. Explain why direct pressure should not be used on a compound fracture.

Knowing how to administer first aid is a valuable skill for anyone.

HELP WANTED

Registered Nurse
Be at the center of the medical wheel. We need R.N.s who realize they are the connection between the patient and the medical profession. You must have the knowledge and personal skills to provide this link. You must be willing to accept responsibility, yet recognize your limitations. You will be the graduate of a two-, three-, or four-year program. Opportunities are virtually limitless for those who perform.
For more information contact:
American Nursing Association
2420 Pershing Road
Kansas City, MO 64108

- Learn as much as you can about what happened, and devise a plan of action. Give the victim a reason for each thing you do. This reassurance will provide much needed encouragement.
- See to the victim's continued safety and comfort. Keep the victim still and in the position most suited to his or her injury or condition. Add privacy if you can, sheltering the victim from disturbance and unnecessary handling.
- Make sure the victim maintains normal body temperature. Provide blankets or a coat for warmth; provide shade for cooling protection from a hot sun.
- Loosen tight or binding clothing, taking care not to jar the victim's neck or spine.

As you work, remember to reassure the victim. Part of your job is to keep him or her calm. Above all else, know your own limits and abilities. Do not try to do more than you have been trained to do.

READ MY WRIST

Another important procedure when treating an accident victim is to look for a piece of emergency medical identification on or near the victim. He or she may have a bracelet, necklace, or card carried in a wallet or purse advising of a medical condition that demands special attention.

People with diabetes or heart conditions and those subject to seizures or severe allergic reactions are among those who wear or carry emergency medical identification. The tag or card gives vital information to those who might be called upon to give the wearer first aid.

Treating Open Wounds

Open wounds are usually a result of external physical forces. Auto accidents, falls, and mishandled tools or other sharp objects are the most common causes of open wounds.

Types of Open Wounds

There are four basic types of open wounds:

- **Scrape.** (abrasion) This type of wound damages outer layers of skin. Abrasions are accompanied by little or no bleeding but may become infected. Abrasions are caused by scraping or rubbing.
- **Cut.** (incision or laceration) A cut can have jagged or smooth edges. Cuts are caused by sharp objects, such as knives or broken glass. A cut also can result when a hard blow from a blunt object opens the skin. Cuts result in bleeding. Deep cuts can damage nerves, large blood vessels, and other soft tissues. Heavy bleeding may result.
- **Puncture.** When a pin, splinter, or other pointed object pierces the skin, the resulting wound is a puncture. While external bleeding is usually limited, puncture wounds carry the potential for internal bleeding and damage to internal organs as well as an increased possibility of infection. The risk of infection increases when the object remains in the skin.

Additional Information

Medicine in History. Pioneer medical doctors worked on cadavers in hospitals and would deliver babies without changing clothing or using proper sterile procedures. When more women were found to be dying from infection from in-hospital deliveries than from in-home deliveries, doctors concluded it was because of the unsterile procedures used in hospitals.

After hearing Sir Joseph Lister, the famous British surgeon who established sanitary operating procedures, an American, Robert Johnson, set out to make dry, prepackaged antiseptic dressings, known today as Band-Aids®.

- **Avulsion.** This is a wound that results when tissue is separated partly or completely from the victim's body. Avulsions often occur in auto accidents and from animal bites. Since severed body parts can sometimes be reattached surgically, they should be sent along with the victim to the hospital.

First Aid for Open Wounds

There are four steps in applying first aid to open wounds. They include: stopping the bleeding, protecting the wound from infection, treating the victim for shock, and seeking medical care.

Stopping the Bleeding. Applying direct pressure to the wound is the best method for stopping bleeding, because this method prevents blood loss without interfering with circulation. Direct pressure involves applying force directly to the top of the wound. To protect yourself from communicable diseases, wear disposable latex gloves, and wash your hands as soon as possible after giving care.

To apply direct pressure, follow these steps:

1. Place a thick, clean cloth over the wound.
2. Place the palm of your hand over the cloth and press firmly. If blood soaks through, place added layers of cloth over the first. Never remove the original cloth; doing so might disturb blood clots that have formed.
3. Continue applying pressure to the wound until the bleeding stops.

Scrape

Cut

Puncture

Avulsion

WHEN THE PRESSURE IS ON

Sometimes the direct-pressure method is not enough to stop the bleeding. In such cases, the **pressure-point technique** can be a lifesaver. For this technique, apply pressure to the main artery supplying blood to the affected limb. The main arteries supplying the limbs are the brachial artery, which brings blood to the arms, and the femoral artery, which brings blood to the legs.

To apply pressure at a pressure point, use your fingers or the heel of your hand. Press the artery toward the bone. Remember to keep applying direct pressure while you use the pressure-point technique.

K E E P I N G   F I T

How to Stop a Nosebleed

The most effective procedure to stop a nosebleed is to pinch both nostrils shut with a thumb and index finger. The victim should sit down and lean slightly forward or stand up. Leaning backward or tipping the head back will cause the blood to run down the throat, causing nausea or choking. Pinching provides direct pressure to the wound, which is a broken surface capillary.

Sometimes people who have chronic nosebleeds have the problem area inside the nose cauterized. If a nosebleed is severe and cannot be stopped, medical help should be sought.

ADMINISTERING FIRST AID **695**

Additional Information

First Aid. When you teach first aid, it is important to stress two factors: do not put yourself in danger of becoming a victim yourself; do not do procedures you are not qualified or trained to do.

EMS, emergency medical services, refers to the local emergency resource in your area. Most areas have introduced the 911 telephone number, which will bring help. If students are not sure there is a 911 service in the area where an accident occurs, tell them to dial "0" and the operator will assist.

L1 DISCUSSION. Ask the class to discuss what might be used to apply pressure on a wound if a clean cloth is not available. If the cloth becomes soaked with blood, what procedure do you use to keep applying direct pressure to the wound?

L1 DISCUSSION. Which wounds are likely to produce severe bleeding? (Cut or avulsion. Also explain that facial injuries may not be serious, but do sometimes bleed very heavily.)

L1 DISCUSSION. Immediately following an accident, bystanders and onlookers often congregate around the injured people. Discuss how onlookers can help or hinder first-aid efforts. Should the person giving first aid rely on his or her own judgment or follow the advice of people "on the scene"? Explain that it is important that the person administering first aid always point to one person in the crowd to call for squads or ambulances. Often individuals assume that someone else will go, thus delaying help from arriving.

L1 DISCUSSION. What are the reasons for receiving a tetanus shot following a wound? What could happen to a person who received a wound from a dirty or rusty object and did not have a current tetanus shot?

L1 DISCUSSION. Talk about why the pressure-point technique applies pressure to arteries rather than veins. Review how students can determine whether blood vessels are arteries or veins.

L1 CLASS ACTIVITY. Ask students to list some shocking facts about shock. (It can kill. Its symptoms include shallow or uneven breathing; pale, cold, or moist skin; weak pulse; dull eyes; fully dilated pupils.) Have students practice what to do when a person is in shock in situations when there is a head injury and where there is not such an injury.

Independent Practice

L1 PARENTAL INVOLVEMENT. Ask students to look in their own homes for a first-aid kit or materials to make one. Have students discuss with their parents the necessary materials each home should have to treat first-aid emergencies. Have students share the actions of family members to provide first aid in their own home.

Overcoming The Odds

Todd Drake is 22. He is a senior at Texas A&M majoring in accounting. He loves to play baseball, basketball, golf, and racquetball. In fact, you might say he just plain loves life—especially since he almost lost his.

Todd tells about the accident that changed and almost claimed his life. "I was 11 years old when I got electrocuted. I was goofing around with a long aluminum pole when it touched a low-hanging wire. That's when 14,400 volts of electricity went through me and blew me about ten feet back onto the ground on my back."

The shock caused Todd to stop breathing. "My neighbor's uncle rushed out and gave me CPR. That saved my life. I remember nothing except being put in the ambulance and seeing my mom.

"The doctors assessed that I needed to go to Parkland Hospital Burn Unit in Dallas, Texas. I remember only that I was in the emergency room and had an incredible thirst and that they gave me a pain killer. Before I was through, I had 15 reconstructive surgeries and was in the hospital from April till July."

Todd's injuries were very severe. "They amputated my right arm below the elbow and all my toes except one. They took ligaments and tendons

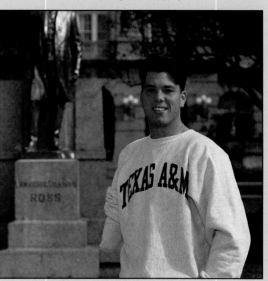

out of my right leg and my bicep muscle out of my left arm because they had been destroyed. My left hand had no movement because the nerves were burned. I had third-degree burns over 40 percent of my body. At one time, they didn't know if I was going to make it. Slowly, due to the surgeries, all the great care, and family love, I got better. I had incredible support from my family, my community, my church, and my friends—and that helped me a lot."

Despite the severity of his injuries, Todd wasn't about to be stopped. "In the hospital," he says, "all I could think of was getting out so I could play sports again." Playing baseball remains Todd's passion, and neither rejection by others nor

having just one hand have stopped him. "In high school, when I tried out for the baseball team, I got cut twice. But I was determined, and I made it my senior year. Today, when I play baseball, I do it all: I bat, play outfield, and catch."

Todd knows he is fortunate to be alive, and he is grateful that someone nearby knew CPR. "I've got a second chance on life. I'm trying to make the best of my education and do something for the world. I fully intend to go on to law school or graduate school, so I can be the most well-rounded person I can be."

Todd also advises teens to listen to warnings from adults about health and safety. "Listen to your parents and your teachers," he concludes, "because they are telling you what's good for you and safe for you."

1. How might you feel if someone you know was in a life-threatening situation, and you didn't know what to do? If you do not know basic first aid, what steps can you take to learn it as soon as possible?
2. What attitude has helped Todd through his ordeal? How might you apply this attitude to your life?

Additional Information

First Aid. The use of a tourniquet is not recommended by the American Red Cross as of 1988. The reasoning behind this decision is the misuse of the procedure and the subsequent loss of limbs. Direct pressure and artery pressure are the recommended procedure even in cases of a severed limb. When blood is spurting or flowing in a steady stream, it should be stopped imme- diately; otherwise the patient may lose enough blood to cause death.

When a limb has been severed, it is important to recover the lost body part, keep it on ice, and get to a hospital as fast as possible. Doctors are having encouraging success with reattachment of severed limbs.

Unless the injury involves a fracture, or broken bone, the bleeding body part should be elevated above the level of the victim's heart. The force of gravity helps slow the flow of blood.

Protecting the Wound. Normally, a clean cloth over an open wound will help protect it from infection. If a cloth is not available, a coat or any other clean covering will do.

Treating for Shock. *Shock* is the failure of the cardiovascular system to keep adequate blood circulating to the vital organs of the body. Shock can result from severe bleeding, heart attack, electrocution, poisoning, burns, or sudden changes of temperature.

You can recognize shock by these signs or symptoms: confused behavior, very fast or very slow pulse rate or breathing, trembling and weakness in the arms and legs, skin that is pale or clammy, pale or bluish lips and fingernails, and enlarged pupils.

When treating for shock, do the following:

- Keep the victim lying down.
- Make sure the victim maintains normal body temperature.
- Get medical help as soon as possible.

Unless you suspect a head injury, place the shock victim on his or her back with the feet elevated about 8 to 12 inches (20 to 30 cm) above the head. Elevating the feet in this manner helps return blood to the heart. A shock victim with a possible head injury should not be moved. Since emergency surgery may be required, shock victims should never be given food or drink.

Seeking Medical Care. See to it that the wounded victim gets immediate medical attention. Send someone for help, or if you are alone, shout for help. Leave the victim only after you have performed first aid and feel that you have lessened the risk of further injury or death.

Shock victims should be kept quiet and warm, with their feet elevated. Seek medical help immediately.

LESSON 1 REVIEW

Reviewing Facts and Vocabulary

1. Define *first aid, poison,* and *shock.*
2. List the six tasks that should be completed when one first encounters an emergency situation.
3. Name the four types of open wounds.

Thinking Critically

4. **Evaluation.** Tell some of the things you would include if you were assembling a first-aid kit. Explain your choices.

Applying Health Knowledge

5. Imagine you were asked to give a talk on first aid to a group of third graders. What points would you stress in your talk?
6. While cycling fast, your friend takes a bad spill. You rush to help and find that her skin is clammy and blood is spurting from her head. Describe the first aid you would administer.

Assess

Check for Understanding

- Assign and discuss the lesson review.

Evaluate

- Administer, grade, and discuss the *Lesson 1 Quiz.*

Reteach

- Have each student present a one-minute oral summary of the five priorities in an emergency. Ask volunteers to present additional information about general procedures to further assist the victim.
- Ask students to complete *Reteaching Activity 96.*

Enrich

- Ask students to interview a paramedic and write a job profile. Have them include the following information in the profile: job description, training, average education, average age, percentages of males and females, salary, job turnover rate, average length of service, etc. (Library research may be necessary.)

Close

Have students summarize the most important concepts studied in this lesson.

Answers to Lesson 1 Review

1. Definitions can be found on pages 693 and 697 or in the Glossary.
2. See numbered items in "Priorities in an Emergency" on page 693.
3. Scrape, cut, puncture, avulsion.
4. Answers will vary but might include: Clean cloths to cover wounds, phone numbers for EMS and the poison control center in your area to summon help.
5. Answers will vary. Along with first-aid procedures, students should emphasize that individuals should do only what they have been trained to do.
6. Check surroundings, check for consciousness, check her breathing, keep her lying down, apply direct pressure to the wound, check her body temperature, send for help.

Focus

Lesson Objectives

After studying this lesson, students should be able to:

- explain procedures for treating poisoning by swallowing, snakebite, or touching
- differentiate between poisonous and nonpoisonous snakes in the United States

Bellringer

Write the following on the chalkboard for students to work on while attendance is being taken: *List as many poisonous substances as you can.*

Introducing the Lesson

Check in the school or public library or call your state Extension Service for information listing many common household poisons and poisonous plants. To introduce this lesson, ask students to share their responses to the Bellringer. Ask them which of those poisonous substances are found in and around the home. If necessary, add to the list yourself. Ask students to continue this list by checking at home to see if they can find more examples. Remind them that these substances should be out of the reach of any younger siblings and to move them if necessary. Refer to this list when discussing first aid for poisons.

DID YOU KNOW?

- About 8,000 people are bitten annually by poisonous snakes, but only about a dozen die.
- Rattlesnakes account for about 60 percent of venomous snakebites and for almost all the deaths.
- Always get the snakebite victim away from the snake—snakes have been known to bite more than once.

FIRST AID FOR POISONING

LESSON 2 FOCUS

TERM TO USE

- Poison control center

CONCEPTS TO LEARN

- Poisons are hazardous to your health and can be life-threatening.
- Victims of poisoning need immediate treatment.

ATTITUDES AND BEHAVIORS TO EVALUATE

- Self-Inventory, page 710.
- Building Decision-Making Skills, page 711.

What do medicines, snakebites, auto exhaust, household cleaners, and many plants have in common? All are potentially poisonous to the human body. Do you remember from the last lesson what a poison is? A poison is any substance that causes injury, illness, or death when introduced into the body.

The American Red Cross estimates that between 1 and 2 million poisonings occur every year. Some poisons are swallowed or inhaled while others enter the body through insect or animal bites. Even touching certain substances, such as poison ivy, can cause poisoning. Most poisonings involve children under the age of 6.

Swallowing a Poison

Today most household cleaners, medications, and other potentially dangerous products come in containers with safety tops that are hard for children to remove. Yet in spite of these precautions, many poisonings still occur.

While the signs of oral poisoning are not as obvious as those in many other emergency situations, telltale symptoms do exist. These symptoms include sharp abdominal cramps, extreme drowsiness followed by a loss of consciousness, vomiting, chemical odor on the breath or chemical burns on the lips, and the presence of an open container of a potentially poisonous substance.

First Aid for Swallowing a Poison

When you suspect someone has swallowed a poison, do the following:

- Call the nearest **poison control center.** It is part of a nationwide network that has been set up in and around large cities. People can contact these centers 24 hours a day. The number of the poison control center nearest you should be posted in a highly visible place in your home.
- Be prepared to give information about the victim and the poison to the person on the phone. This information should include the age and weight of the victim, the name of the suspected poison, and the amount of poison swallowed, if known. The staff person at the control center will then offer assistance with the situation and tell you where to go for further help. Specific treatments for each type of poison are available.
- Treat the victim for shock. Use the same procedure you read about in the section on treating wounds in Lesson 1. It may also be necessary to help the victim maintain respiration and circulation through rescue breathing or CPR. You will learn about these techniques in the next chapter.

Resources for Lesson 2

- **Guided Reading** Activity 97
- **Workbook** Vocabulary Activity 97
- **Reteaching** Activity 97
- **Lesson 2 Quiz**

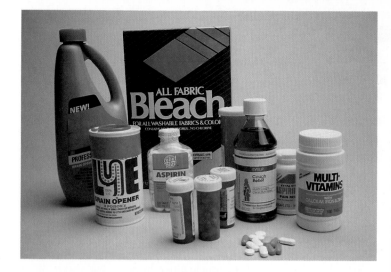

Dangerous substances should be kept out of the reach of small children.

A DO AND A DON'T

If you suspect someone has swallowed a poison, do look for and save the container of the suspected poison. You will need to give information about the poison to your telephone contact at the poison control center. Don't induce vomiting in the victim unless the poison control center advises you to do so. Some poisons, such as strong acids (bleach, toilet bowl cleaner) or strong alkalis (liquid drain cleaner), can do as much damage coming up as going down.

Poisoning by Snakebite

People who think of snakebites as hazards of life exclusively in rural areas are only partly right. Suburban environments and city parks can also be home to poisonous snakes.

Of the hundreds of varieties of snakes, only four poisonous types are found in the United States. These are the rattlesnake, the copperhead, the water moccasin (also called the cottonmouth), and the coral snake. More than half of all poisonous snakebites occur in Texas, North Carolina, Florida, Georgia, Louisiana, and Arkansas.

KEEPING FIT

To Prevent Accidental Poisoning of Children

- Keep all medicines out of their reach.
- Install childproof locks on cabinets and closets that contain anything that could poison a child.
- Buy medicines with child-

proof caps.
- Do not give children empty medicine bottles to use to play doctor. Next time they play, they might mistakenly use full ones.
- Don't remove labels from

medications. You may need to identify what a child has accidentally swallowed.
- Crawl around your house at the child's level. See what potentially hazardous substances children may see.

FIRST AID FOR POISONING   **699**

Culturally Speaking

Sandbox Trees

Sandbox trees, found in parts of Latin America, have poisonous bark with short spines. Their leaves also are poisonous. The sap of these trees is acidic and can burn skin and cause blindness. Exploding seed capsules from the tops of the trees have injured humans and animals. Nevertheless, sandbox trees are useful to humans. They are cut for wood, although people must wear masks and heavy gloves to protect themselves from the sap. The sap also is used to stun fish in streams so that they can be gathered for food. The poison does not affect the people who eat the fish.

Building Vocabulary

- Write each of the vocabulary terms for the chapter on a 3-by-5 inch index card. Write the definitions of these terms on additional index cards. Place the cards face down on a table and invite pairs of students to play "Match-Up." In this game, students take turns turning over a pair of cards in an effort to match a term with its definition.
- Ask students to complete *Workbook Vocabulary Activity 97.*

Teach

Guided Practice

L1 DISCUSSION. How can accidental poisonings occur? How could they be prevented? Why do people take such unnecessary risks?

L1 CLASS ACTIVITY. You are baby-sitting and suspect the 3-year-old child you are taking care of has swallowed some aspirin. You find the child sitting in his room playing with an aspirin bottle. Some pills remain in the bottle while some are found on the floor. Write out the first-aid steps you would take.

L2 CLASS ACTIVITY. Have students debate the following: *All baby-sitters should be required to take an emergency first-aid class before caring for children.*

L1 DISCUSSION. Discuss how to contact a poison control center in your area. What information should a caller be prepared to provide when calling a poison control center?

L1 CLASS ACTIVITY. Have students consider when they would call the following sources of assistance if they were baby-sitting during an emergency: When would it be most appropriate to contact a child's parents? When would it be most appropriate to call 911? When would it be most appropriate to call a poison control center? When would calling the child's doctor be the best response? Talk about how a person left in charge makes decisions in an emergency. What guidelines should sitters use in getting help?

Additional Information

Poisoning. You can suspect that a person has taken poison if any of the following are present: a poison container; observing or telling of poison ingestion; sudden illness or pain; lip or mouth burns; chemical smell on the breath; pupils of the eyes abnormal for the situation.

Calling the poison control center is more

advisable than following procedures noted on poison product labels. The directions for antidotes on many poison containers are not always the best practice to follow. Administering an incorrect procedure can cause more harm to the victim than the poison itself. After applying appropriate first aid, the poisoned victim should see a doctor.

L1 CLASS ACTIVITY. Bring in a selection of household cleaners for a classroom display. Point out the poison labels and instructions for counteracting the poisons. Your display should include poisons that, when swallowed, can be treated by inducing vomiting and those that cannot. Ask where products like these should be stored. (On high shelves or locked cupboards.) How do you teach young children not to get into these products if they find them? What responsibilities do the manufacturers have to protect children from accidental exposure to these poisonous products?

L1 DISCUSSION. Discuss childproof caps on medicines. Why are manufacturers required to put childproof caps on prescriptions and over-the-counter medicines?

L1 DISCUSSION. Discuss with the class why outdated medicines should not be taken and how to dispose of them properly so that no one could accidentally take them. (They should be flushed down the toilet.)

L1 DISCUSSION. Have students identify the types of snakes in your area. Review the indications as to whether or not a snake is poisonous.

L1 DISCUSSION. Discuss reasons why a person would carelessly or unnecessarily take a risk of being bitten. (Refer to the basic reasons accidents happen.)

L1 CLASS ACTIVITY. Have students outline the "dos and don'ts" for treating snakebites, giving a rationale for each.

L1 COOPERATIVE LEARNING. Divide the class into four groups. Assign each group one of the poisonous snakes found in the United States: rattlesnake, copperhead, water moccasin, and coral snake. Have each group prepare a two-page report about that particular snake. Have the groups present their reports to the class, and have students discuss the specific effects of a snakebite by each kind of reptile.

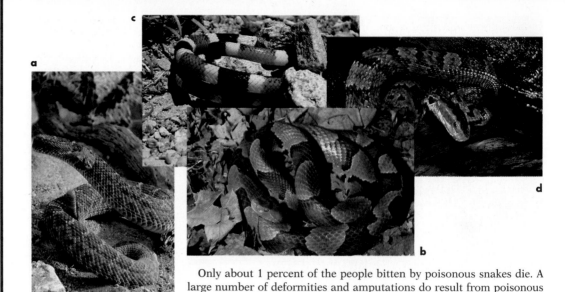

Know which snakes are poisonous: a. rattlesnake, b. copperhead, c. coral snake, d. water moccasin.

Only about 1 percent of the people bitten by poisonous snakes die. A large number of deformities and amputations do result from poisonous snakebites, so they should be treated immediately.

SNAKE SAVVY

A first line of defense against a poisonous snakebite is to know your enemy. A handy rule of thumb is summed up in the following rhyme: "Red and yellow mean a poisonous fellow; red and black, poison lack." In other words, if a snake's coloring includes consecutive bands of red and yellow, the snake is poisonous; a snake with consecutive red and black bands, on the other hand, will be nonpoisonous.

Once a victim has been bitten, a bite usually can be identified as one from a poisonous snake by the shape of the puncture wounds. A poisonous bite will also be accompanied by extreme pain and swelling, followed soon after by any or all of these symptoms: shortness of breath, nausea, dimness of vision, convulsions, a tingling sensation, or unconsciousness.

First Aid for Snakebite

If you are unsure about whether a snakebite came from a poisonous snake or not, treat the bite as though it were from a poisonous snake. You can administer first aid by following these steps:

1. Keep the victim calm. Your most important task is to get the victim to the hospital. Until you can complete this task, keep the victim as quiet as possible, preferably in a reclining position. The more the victim moves, the greater the risk that the venom will be circulated throughout the body.
2. Keep the bitten area at or below the level of the heart. If the bitten area is on a limb, keep the affected part immobile.
3. Call, or have someone call, EMS. Dialing 911 or 0 in many localities puts you in touch with EMS. Take careful note of any instructions you are given.

700 CHAPTER 35 FIRST AID

Additional Information

Snakebites. Inform students of the following considerations for the treatment of snakebites.

After first aid has been administered, the area around a snakebite may be cleaned using soap and water. Immobilize the affected part. You may need to observe the wound for symptoms.

Medicine to relieve pain should only be administered under medical advice. Aspirin or aspirin-containing products cause the blood to run thin and reduce the coagulation rate; this may cause the venom to spread more rapidly.

4. Delay the absorption of venom. Because snakes are coldblooded animals, their venom does the most damage in a cold environment. For this reason, avoid putting anything cold on the bite or giving the victim alcohol or sedatives. Aspirin, which can adversely affect blood coagulation, should also be avoided.
5. Maintain breathing, and prevent aggravation of the wound. If you are the victim of a snakebite and are alone, walk slowly and rest periodically. This will help keep blood circulation to a minimum.

Poisoning by Touching

Poisons that come into contact with the skin fall into two categories: those found on plants and those found in certain chemicals. The effects of touching these poisons are likewise twofold. In some cases the damage is limited to the area of the skin that touches the poison, whereas in others the whole body is affected.

First Aid for Touching a Poisonous Plant

The most common poisonous plants have the word *poison* in their names. These are poison ivy, poison oak, and poison sumac. A first defense against poisoning by any of these plants is to learn what they look like.

Interestingly, some people exhibit no reaction to poisonous plants. Those who do react develop a severe skin rash at the point of contact, followed later by various symptoms, which may include blistering, swelling, burning, and itching. In extreme cases, a fever occurs.

First aid for plant poisoning consists of three key steps:

1. Remove any clothing that may be contaminated.
2. Pour large quantities of water over the affected areas.
3. Wash the affected areas thoroughly with soap and water.

Calamine lotion can be used to relieve itching if a rash develops. If inflammation or pain is severe, seek medical attention.

First Aid for Touching a Poisonous Chemical

Pesticides, solvents, household cleaning agents, and highly abrasive cleaners are among the chemicals that can cause poisoning. A protec-

---

KEEPING FIT

Poison-Proofing Your Home

To poison-proof your home:
■ Check to see that any chemicals, cleaners, or other poisons are clearly marked and completely out of a child's reach.

■ Properly dispose of any old, unused poisonous substances.
■ Use the phone book and write the phone number of

the nearest poison-control center on a card. Place it next to the phone on the family's emergency number list.

Independent Practice

L1 **PARENTAL INVOLVEMENT.** Ask students to survey their homes for the placement of medicines and poisonous substances. Have them ask their parents to look for outdated medicines in the home and dispose of them properly. What precautions are taken in their home to avoid an accidental poisoning? Are medicines and poisonous substances put up or out of reach of small children? What methods are used?

L1 **RESEARCH.** Ask volunteers to visit hardware or department stores to determine devices that can be used in the home to secure poisonous substances away from small children. Have them share information with the class.

L1 **RESEARCH.** Have students find out where syrup of ipecac can be purchased. How much does it cost? What is the appropriate use of syrup of ipecac? Are there any suitable substitutes?

L2 **WRITING.** Ask volunteers to write the National Poison Center Network, Children's Hospital of Pittsburgh, 125 DeSoto Street, Pittsburgh, PA 15213, to obtain "Mr. Yuk" stickers to put on potentially dangerous substances in homes, especially where there are small children.

L2 **RESEARCH.** Have students research which common houseplants or yard plants are poisonous to small children. Are all parts of the plants poisonous? Are the plants poisonous to the touch or just if ingested? What is the appropriate first-aid response for a caretaker when a small child has tasted one of these plants? How can the need for first-aid procedures be reduced or eliminated?

L1 **RESEARCH.** Ask students to research the following: *Alcohol can be a poison.* Have the students explain to the class how this poison can lead to death and how an overdose from alcohol can affect the body. They should include information on drinking contests that result in alcohol poisoning.

L1 **USING THE LESSON RESOURCES.** For additional student activities, refer to the lesson resources on page 698.

Additional Information

Spider Bites. Just about all spiders are venomous, but very few have fangs long enough to endanger human health. The major exception is the black widow spider, whose venom is more deadly, by volume, than the rattlesnake's. Although most adults can survive the bite of a black widow spider, children and the elderly may not.

Black widow spiders live in all states but Alaska. Only the female bites, and she can be identified by a red spot on the abdomen of her otherwise coal-black body. Black widows hide in wood and brush piles, long grass, and under stones and logs.

If possible, the spider should be caught to confirm its identity, and antivenin administered as soon as possible.

Learn to recognize these poisonous plants: a. poison ivy, b. poison oak, c. poison sumac.

Assess

Check for Understanding

■ Assign and discuss the lesson review.

Evaluate

■ Administer, grade, and discuss the *Lesson 2 Quiz.*

Reteach

■ Ask students to make a large poster for the classroom of a chart relating to poisons. Have students provide the types of poisons, how poisonings can be prevented, and the first-aid procedure for each case. Display the poster in the classroom.
■ Ask students to complete *Reteaching Activity 97.*

Enrich

■ Have students research the beneficial use of venom in medicine. Why are rattlesnake hunts popular and beneficial to medicine? What is the cost of the venom and how is it processed into a serum?

Close

Have students summarize the most important concepts learned in this lesson.

DID YOU KNOW?

■ Of the 1 million poisonings in the U.S. each year, most occur in children under 5 years of age, and most of these occur in the home.

tion against such poisoning is to make sure safety caps on these products are securely in place when the products are not being used. They should also be stored out of the reach of small children.

Poisoning through direct contact with a chemical is usually characterized by a burning of the skin, which appears similar to a sunburn. Treatment, which should begin as soon after the contact as possible, parallels first aid for plant poisoning:

1. Remove any clothing that has come into contact with the chemical.
2. Remove as much of the chemical from the surface of the skin as you can by continuously flooding the area with water for 15 minutes.
3. Contact the nearest poison control center for information on how to treat the resulting burn. A toll-free number for the poison control center in your state may be listed in your local telephone directory. Otherwise, call the emergency room of your local hospital.

LESSON 2 REVIEW

Reviewing Facts and Vocabulary

1. Define *poison* and give three examples.
2. Name four ways poisoning occurs.

Thinking Critically

3. **Analysis.** In what ways are first aid for swallowing a poison and touching a poison similar? How are they different?
4. **Evaluation.** Which first-aid techniques would be especially important for a camper or a hiker to know? Explain your choices.

Applying Health Knowledge

5. Use an encyclopedia to learn more about other forms of poisoning, such as lead or mercury. In an oral report to your class, explain how to identify and avoid these types of poisons.

702   CHAPTER 35   FIRST AID

Answers to Lesson 2 Review

1. Any substance that causes injury, illness, or death when introduced into the body.
2. Swallowing, inhaling, insect or animal bites, touching certain substances.
3. See pages 698–702. Possible answers: Both require quick action and may require a call to the poison control center. When someone swallows a poison, the poison control center should be called right away to receive instructions. When someone touches a poison, the affected area should be treated first.
4. Answers will vary. Possible answers: For snakebite and for touching a poisonous plant because these are two situations campers or hikers might encounter.
5. Reports will vary.

FIRST AID FOR OTHER INJURIES

In addition to such life-threatening emergencies as severe bleeding and poisoning, life has its share of minor mishaps. You are baby-sitting and the child you are watching gets a nosebleed. You and your friend are going out the door when your friend slips and sprains an ankle. You are mowing the lawn when a piece of debris flies into your eye. You have been exercising in the heat and begin to get painful heat cramps.

As with major emergencies, knowing proper first aid in these and other common emergencies can help prevent further injury or complication.

Nosebleeds

Nosebleeds can happen when the nose is struck. Although people whose noses bleed often should see their health-care professional, infrequent, minor nosebleeds are not a cause for alarm.

To treat a nosebleed, do the following:

1. Keep the person quiet. Walking, talking, and blowing the nose may cause an increase in bleeding.
2. Place the person in a sitting position and have him or her lean forward. You do not want to tilt the head back, because doing so may cause the person to choke as the blood runs down the throat.
3. Apply direct pressure by pressing on the bleeding nostril.
4. Apply a cold towel to the person's nose and face.

If these measures fail to stop the bleeding, the person should seek medical help.

Animal Bites

A dog may be a person's best friend—but not when the dog bites. Dogs and other animals can transmit diseases to humans by biting them.

Any animal bite, and especially one in which the animal's teeth have pierced the skin, should be washed with soap and warm water, then covered with a clean dressing or bandage.

In addition to treating the wound, it is important to observe the victim for signs of illness. Many animals carry **rabies**—a viral disease of the nervous system that eventually causes madness and death. Dogs, squirrels, and rats are common carriers of this disease.

If you know the whereabouts of the animal that inflicted the wound, have the proper authorities capture that animal. Do not try to capture the animal yourself. Once the animal has been captured, call the local health center to learn where the animal has been taken for examination. Then call to find out if treatment for tetanus or rabies is needed.

LESSON 3 FOCUS

TERMS TO USE

- Rabies
- Sprain
- Frostbite
- Gangrene (GANG•green)
- Hurricane
- Tornado
- Earthquakes
- Blizzard

CONCEPTS TO LEARN

- Each type of injury has its own set of general and specific first-aid procedures.
- Natural disasters and severe weather activity are threats to health, safety, life, and property.
- Disaster preparedness can greatly reduce the potential negative effects of natural disasters and severe weather.

ATTITUDES AND BEHAVIORS TO EVALUATE

- Self-Inventory, page 710.
- Building Decision-Making Skills, page 711.

Focus

Lesson Objectives

After studying this lesson, students should be able to:

- describe proper first-aid techniques for common emergencies
- list various weather-related emergencies

Bellringer

Write the following on the chalkboard for students to work on while attendance is being taken: *Write down the first five words that cross your mind when you hear the word* emergency.

Introducing the Lesson

Have volunteers share their responses to the Bellringer. (Answers might include danger, panic, pain, injury, serious.) Point out that emergencies are not always life-threatening or serious. Some, such as minor burns and insect bites, are very common and happen to all of us. Ask volunteers who have suffered sprains or broken bones to share their experiences with the class. Tell students that in this lesson they will learn how to deal with these and other common injuries and emergencies.

FIRST AID FOR OTHER INJURIES **703**

Resources for Lesson 3

- **Guided Reading** Activity 98
- **Decision-Making** Activity 35
- **Workbook** Vocabulary Activity 98
- **Workbook** Application Activity 35
- **Reteaching** Activity 98
- **Enrichment** Activity 35
- **Health Labs** Activity 35
- **Cooperative Learning** Activity 35
- **Lesson 3 Quiz**
- **Chapter 35 Test**

- Divide the class into two groups. Write the terms *injury* and *emergency* on the chalkboard. Give one group the term *injury* and the other group the term *emergency*. Ask students to think of terms they associate with these terms, such as sprain, crutches, swelling.
- Ask students to complete *Workbook Vocabulary Activity 98.*

Teach

Guided Practice

L1 DISCUSSION. What causes nosebleeds? (Nosebleeds can result from injury or disease, after a cold or a period of strenuous activity, or high altitude.) Explain that a common misconception in treating nosebleeds is to tilt the head back. This risks blood running into the throat and windpipe, causing the victim to choke or vomit.

L1 DISCUSSION. What are suspicious signs to watch for in strange animals that might indicate rabies?

L1 EXPLANATION. Advise students about the danger of animal bites. Bites by any animal, especially if the skin is broken or pierced by its teeth, should be washed with soap and water, and covered with a clean dressing or bandage. If you do not know the animal, contact a police officer or an animal control warden so that the animal can be captured.

L1 EXPLANATION. Since animals can transmit diseases to humans, tell students to observe any animal that bites for unusual signs of illness, such as rabies. If the animal appears ill, call the local health department.

L1 CLASS ACTIVITY. Ask students to list animals that can carry rabies. Which animals have the highest incidence of rabies? Have students list ways to avoid animal bites.

Infrequent nosebleeds are not a cause for alarm, but should be treated properly.

DID YOU KNOW?

- A person who gets an animal bite needs to have had a tetanus shot within the previous five years or receive a new one.
- The rabies virus has a period of incubation of between three and seven weeks, though it can take longer to materialize.
- Treatment for rabies is an antibody given in five injections over a month's time.

Bee Stings

In most cases bee stings are minor emergencies and are easily treated. For people who are allergic to bee stings, however, stings can be serious and sometimes even fatal. To treat bee stings, do the following:

1. Using a piece of cardboard or other flat, sharp-edged object, scrape against the stinger until you pull out the venom sac. Do not use tweezers because they may rupture the venom sac, forcing painful venom into the skin.
2. Wash the area thoroughly with soap and water.

Once the stinger is out, watch for allergic reactions. An allergic person will usually carry a kit with adrenaline to open the airways.

Fractures

When a body part, such as a leg or an arm, is under stress and you hear a popping sound, it is usually a good indication that a bone has been fractured. Always treat such an injury as if the bone were broken.

In applying first aid to fractures, your main objective is to keep the bone end from moving. Never attempt to set the bone. Follow these guidelines for first aid for a fracture:

1. Keep the body part in the position it is in, and immobilize it with a splint. You can fashion a splint from everyday materials, such as rolled newspapers and heavy cardboard.
2. Seek medical care immediately.

Sprains

A **sprain** is a condition caused by a stretching or tearing of the soft tissue bands, or ligaments, that hold bones together at a joint. Wrists, knees, and ankles are among the areas most frequently sprained. To treat a sprain, follow these steps:

1. Immobilize the injured area. If the sprain is in the leg, make sure the victim stays off his or her feet.
2. Elevate the injured part to help reduce swelling.
3. Apply cold packs. This will also help keep swelling down. Never apply heat, which makes swelling worse.
4. Seek medical attention.

Burns

Critical burns need immediate care. Critical burns include those that involve breathing difficulties, burns covering more than one body part, and burns to the head, neck, hands, and feet. They also include chemical burns. There are three descriptions for burns:

- Superficial (first-degree) burns, like most sunburns, involve the top layer of skin. Healing takes five to six days.

704 CHAPTER 35 FIRST AID

Additional Information

Animal Bites. Animal bites and snakebites cause more alarm than the more common human bite. Infection is the guaranteed result of any bite unless it is cleaned thoroughly. Most bites are puncture wounds and should be treated accordingly.

A wild animal, such as a raccoon, that appears unusually friendly or domesticated may well be rabid. If the animal is sick, the result can be a bite that will infect an individual with rabies. A series of rather painful shots is the treatment.

Do not assume that a dog or cat that is young or especially friendly cannot be rabid. An animal should be tested for rabies if it has bitten anyone—even if it is your pet.

Is it a fracture or a sprain? How can you tell? What should you do for each?

- Partial-thickness (second-degree) burns involve the top layers of skin. The skin will have blisters and appear blotchy. Healing takes three to four weeks.
- Full-thickness (third-degree) burns destroy all layers of skin as well as nerves, muscles, fat, and bones. The burn looks black or brown.

First Aid for Burns

First aid for all burns includes the following:

1. Stop the burning by removing the victim from the source of the burn.
2. Cool the burn by soaking the burned area in cool water or using wet towels.
3. Cover the burn with dry, sterile dressings. This action helps prevent infection and reduces pain.

Protect a person with severe burns from drafts. Unless the victim is having trouble breathing, lay the person down. If possible, the burned area should be raised above the level of the heart.

Chemical burns should be flushed with large quantities of cool running water. Take off any clothing that has the chemical on it.

Fainting

Fainting is a temporary loss of consciousness brought on by a reduced supply of blood to the brain. People who faint usually recover within a few minutes. First aid for fainting includes the following steps:

1. Do not prop up the person. Leave him or her lying down on the back. If possible, elevate the legs 8 to 12 inches.
2. Loosen any tight or binding clothing.
3. Maintain an open airway. (Refer to Chapter 36.)
4. Sponge the person's face with water. Do not splash water over the face, because this may cause the person to choke.
5. If the person fails to revive promptly, seek medical help.

DID YOU KNOW?

- If a tick is attached to your skin, you can remove it by pulling slowly and firmly with tweezers.
- Some sea life, including some jellyfish and the Portuguese man-of-war, discharge venom on contact even after they are dead.
- One way to stop the pain from a jellyfish sting is to rub meat tenderizer, vinegar, salt, or sand on the area.

Additional Information

Insect Bites and Stings. Most insect bites and stings cause only minor discomfort, but some can cause serious complications and illness. For example, mosquitoes can transmit malaria and are also capable of spreading encephalitis (an inflammation of the brain) and yellow fever. The bite of a tick can cause Rocky Mountain spotted fever. Another tick, the deer tick, can infect people with Lyme disease, a disorder that begins with a red swelling and which, if left untreated, can lead to arthritis and neurologic or heart problems.

L1 DISCUSSION. How should stings be treated? (Stings from bees, wasps, or ants can cause death, but fatal stings are almost always a result of allergic reactions. Stings produce local pain and can cause swelling. Cold applications and soothing lotions, such as calamine lotion, can bring relief. A person allergic to bee stings should seek medical attention immediately.)

L1 EXPLANATION. Broken bones frequently occur among people playing unsupervised sports after school or during the summer. Taking some safety precautions, such as wearing padding during a game of tackle football, can help prevent broken bones.

L1 DISCUSSION. Why do contact sports require so much protection? Discuss the types of contact sports and the protection required to participate in each sport.

L2 DEMONSTRATION. Using an anatomical model of a skeleton, review the placement of bones. Explain how fractures occur in bones. Show the difference in a simple fracture and a compound fracture. Explain the difference between open and closed fractures. Explain that sprains occur in joints, not bones. Demonstrate for the class the difference between a separated shoulder and a broken collar bone.

L1 DEMONSTRATION. Bring some X rays of broken bones to class, and let students see how broken bones appear beneath the skin. Most doctors will have extra X rays.

L2 CLASS ACTIVITY. Give students the opportunity to try using crutches, arm slings, and finger splints. Then ask them to list some of the activities that would be difficult or impossible to do with sprains or broken bones. (Running with crutches, writing with a finger splint.)

L1 DISCUSSION. Ask the class what items in the classroom could be used as splints for a broken or injured wrist. (Hand and wrist could be immobilized by placing them on a large soft-covered book. They could then be wrapped with a scarf, belt, or undershirt.)

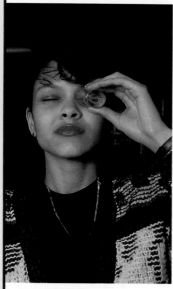

To remove a foreign object from the eye, gently flush with water.

Objects in the Eye

If a foreign object comes into contact with the surface of your eye, resist the impulse to rub the eye. Doing so may scratch the cornea. Instead, gently flush the eye with water, starting at the edge nearest the nose and working outward. If this measure fails to dislodge the object, cover both eyes and seek medical attention.

Heat Cramps

When a person is exposed to high temperatures over a prolonged period, the body loses essential water and salt. The resulting condition is known as heat cramps. Heat cramps are characterized by muscle cramps, heavy sweating, headache, and dizziness.

Here are some procedures to follow when heat cramps strike:

1. Move the victim, or help the victim move, out of the heat.
2. Using your hands, apply firm pressure to the cramped muscle. Gently massage the muscle to relieve the spasm.
3. Give the victim sips of a commercial sports drink, which will replace salt and water. The victim should consume about 4 ounces (118 ml) every 15 minutes. Be careful that the victim does not take in too much of the liquid at any one time. Excessive amounts of salt may induce vomiting. Do not give the victim salt tablets.

Frostbite

Have you ever noticed on bitter winter days that your fingers and toes are the first parts of your body to get cold? In extremely cold conditions, the body tries to conserve heat for its more vital internal organs. As a result, less blood is sent to the extremities.

If the temperature in body cells gets low enough, **frostbite** may occur. Frostbite is a condition in which ice crystals form in the spaces between the cells. This ice expands and kills tissue, and in the process, causes the skin to lose color and become insensitive to any feeling. Frostbite is common among those who spend long periods of time outdoors in temperatures at or below freezing. Several factors play a role in frostbite: the temperature, the length of time the person is exposed to the cold, the wind velocity, the humidity level, the amount of protective clothing worn, and the dampness of the clothing.

706 Chapter 35 First Aid

First Aid for Frostbite

Frostbitten skin is yellowish or gray in color and feels clammy or doughy. A frostbite victim will usually experience numbness in the frostbitten body part. Treat frostbite by doing the following:

1. Never rub the affected area. Rewarm the frozen body part by soaking it in water that is about 100° to 105°F (37.8° to 40.6°C).
2. Bandage the injured part, placing sheets of gauze between the warmed fingers and toes.
3. Seek professional medical attention as soon as possible.

If a frostbitten body part goes untreated, **gangrene** may set in. Gangrene is the death of tissue in a part of the body. Gangrene often requires amputation of the affected part.

COLD WEATHER ADVISORY

When you plan to spend prolonged periods outdoors during cold weather, it is vital that you dress properly. Wearing several layers of clothing will help retain body heat. Footgear and headgear are also important.

Be mindful, too, of the windchill. Any windchill of −25°F (−31.7°C) or colder presents a danger, with −72°F (−57.8°C) presenting a critical danger. Here are some temperature equivalents at different wind speeds. All are based on a thermometer reading of −10°F (−23.3°C).

When the wind blows at . . .	the windchill makes it feel like . . .
5 mph (8 km/h)	−15°F (−26.1°C)
10 mph (16 km/h)	−33°F (−36.1°C)
15 mph (23 km/h)	−45°F (−42.8°C)
20 mph (32 km/h)	−53°F (−47.3°C)

More Weather-Related Emergencies

Weather poses a threat not just to individuals but to entire communities. Hurricanes, tornadoes, and other natural disasters can cause widespread injury and death as well as property damage and loss.

Most communities have emergency sirens to warn of potentially dangerous situations. Some environmental conditions, however, occur without warning. Does your community have an emergency warning system? Do you know what to do in such an emergency?

Hurricanes and Tornadoes

A **hurricane** is a powerful rainstorm, characterized by driving winds. Hurricanes occur near coastal areas of the United States, mainly on the eastern and southern seaboards.

A **tornado** is a powerful, twisting windstorm that generally occurs in the central part of the United States. Tornadoes occasionally are associated with hurricanes. In recent times, tornadoes have been known to strike sporadically in all areas of the country. Knowing what to do in case of a hurricane or a tornado could save your life.

When severe weather conditions exist, the National Weather Service issues advisories called watches and warnings. A hurricane watch or a

DID YOU KNOW?

- Hypothermia is a condition that occurs when body temperature falls.
- This can result when experiencing extreme cold, windy, and wet weather conditions.
- Signs of hypothermia progress from shivering and loss of muscular control to a decrease in pulse and breathing rate. Death can also result.
- Treatment for hypothermia involves removing the affected person from the cold and slowly warming up the person's body. Medical attention should be sought.

L1 EXPLANATION. Explain to students that a muscle strain is a pulling or tearing of muscle fiber and a contusion is a bruise to the muscle fiber. A strain requires a longer rehabilitation period.

L1 DISCUSSION. What are the most common causes of burns? (Burns are caused most commonly by carelessness with matches and cigarettes; use of open fires; use of flammable liquids for starting fires or cleaning; immersion in bathwater that is too hot; and use of chemicals, such as lye and strong acids.)

L1 DISCUSSION. Do burns caused by different kinds of fires all have the same result? Are burns from a chemically-induced fire generally more severe than those from a wood-burning fire? What might account for the differences, if any, in the degree of injuries?

L1 EXPLANATION. Tell students that burns are described in terms of the extent of the body surface that is covered. An adult who has suffered burns on 15 percent of the body surface or a child, 10 percent—usually requires hospitalization. Burns on or around the face require prompt medical attention because swelling could obstruct breathing.

L1 DISCUSSION. What are smelling salts and how do they work? What kinds of other preparations have been used to help revive someone who has fainted? Are these beneficial or harmful? Why?

L1 EXPLANATION. Emphasize that in cases where chemicals enter the eyes, flush with water for at least 15 minutes and seek medical treatment immediately.

L2 COOPERATIVE LEARNING. Divide the class into groups. Assign each group one of the weather-related emergencies discussed. Have students research and develop a class presentation on their weather-related emergency. Presentations may include photos, drawings, past occurrences or disasters related to their weather emergency, what type of help is available, warnings, prevention, and first aid that might be necessary.

Additional Information

Heat-Related Illnesses. Heat exhaustion most often occurs when a person has worked or exercised for a long period in a warm, humid environment and has sweat heavily. This fluid loss results in reduced blood flow to the vital organs. A person with heat exhaustion experiences cool, pale, moist, or red skin. Headache, dizziness, and weakness are other symptoms. Often the victim feels better after cooling down and drinking water. However, without immediate care, heatstroke can result. During this more dangerous situation, the body's temperature control stops working. The victim no longer sweats because body fluid levels are low. Body temperature rises, and vital organs begin to fail. Death may result if emergency care is not given immediately.

L2 **RESEARCH.** Have volunteers contact the local health department to find out about the last reported case of rabies in your area. What animals in the area are most likely to carry rabies? What treatment is followed for rabies? Do health-care providers always wait to find out whether an animal that caused the bite was rabid before starting emergency treatment? What might guide their decision?

L1 **RESEARCH.** Ask volunteers to ask an athlete in the school who has experienced an injury in sports to describe the experience. What happened? What was the treatment? How long was the recovery? Share information with the class.

L2 **RESEARCH.** Ask students to choose one school sport and research what musculoskeletal injuries occur most frequently. The report should also mention measures that can be taken to reduce risk of injury.

L2 **RESEARCH.** Ask volunteers to contact a Shriner's burn hospital for children in the U.S. or the trauma center of a local hospital. Have them ask for brochures about treatment and care of children with severe burns. Share the brochures and information with the class.

L1 **PARENTAL INVOLVEMENT.** Ask students to make plans and procedures for their families to follow during weather-related emergencies. Have students provide a plan for each family member in case parents are not at home.

L2 **RESEARCH.** Have students research the natural disasters most likely to occur in your part of the country. They are to find out what to do in these emergencies, what preventive actions to take, and how to recognize possible dangers.

L1 **USING THE LESSON RESOURCES.** For additional student activities, refer to the lesson resources on page 703.

Hurricanes (top) and tornadoes (bottom) are dangerous weather storms.

tornado watch means that atmospheric conditions exist so that these events could develop. A warning means one has been sighted. Warnings are often accompanied by instructions. Do exactly as you are told without delay.

In general, preparation for a hurricane includes securing your property and then either going to a shelter or evacuating the area as the National Weather Service instructs. The farther inland you go, the safer you will be. Hurricanes have been known to build up enough momentum to carry their destructive winds inland for hundreds of miles.

A storm cellar or basement is the safest place to go for protection from a tornado. If neither option is available, a hallway or bathtub away from windows will suffice. If you are caught outside, get into a ditch and lie face down. Cover yourself, if possible, with a mattress, blanket, rug, or bulky winter clothing to protect yourself from flying objects.

Earthquakes

Heavy ground tremors from **earthquakes** occur often in some parts of the United States. California averages almost 5,000 weak but notice-

HEALTH UPDATE

LOOKING AT TECHNOLOGY

Skin Banks: New Hope for Burn Patients

A method of treating severe burns was developed at the University of Texas Medical Branch in Galveston. The technique is safer and less painful than the traditional method.

The entire burned area is surgically removed within a week of the accident and the area is temporarily covered with skin from a skin bank. Skin cells taken from other parts of the patient's body are then grown in a lab to make a new sheet of skin to replace portions of the temporary skin that was placed over the burn.

By placing the temporary skin over the area, the risk of infection is greatly reduced. In the traditional method, daily warm-water baths are used to loosen burned skin so that it can gradually be pulled or scraped off—a very painful procedure.

The temporary skin comes from skin banks. A skin bank is a tissue bank that gets and stores human skin, which comes from cadavers of people who consented to donate their skin upon their deaths. The skin is taken off at a thickness of between 15 to 18 thousandths of an inch. It is transported to the tissue bank in a solution, processed for transplant, cut into shapes for surgery, and preserved by freezing with liquid nitrogen. The skin is then placed in a bag in a quarantine freezer until tests on it come back showing that no diseases are present on the skin. It is then placed in a transplant freezer and is retrieved as needed by burn victims.

For information contact the American Burn Association at 4940 Eastern Avenue, Baltimore, MD 21224.

Overcoming Misconceptions

Myth. Seek help immediately upon arriving at a medical emergency. **Fact.** You are to assess the scene and check for breathing. If there is no breathing, administer rescue breathing and follow the steps outlined in this chapter. **Myth.** If someone is suffering from heat exhaustion, they should take salt tablets. **Fact.** To replace lost fluids, drink small sips of water. The rate is one pint per hour for every 70 pounds of body weight if you are exercising heavily at an air temperature of 92°F. **Myth.** For frostbite, submerge the body in hot water. **Fact.** This is not only wrong, but dangerous. The water temperature should be only 100° to 105°F.

able quakes per year. Knowing what to do during and after an earthquake is important to your safety.

Most casualties during an earthquake are not a direct result of the ground movement but result from falling objects or collapsing structures. If you are inside a building and begin to feel a tremor, follow these safety procedures:

1. Stay in the building.
2. Select a safety spot within a few steps of where you are standing, and go to it. Safety spots are areas that provide some measure of safety from falling matter. Try to find a heavy desk or table with enough space for you to fit underneath. Crawl under it and then hold on to this shelter to keep it from moving away from you.
3. If no such piece of furniture is handy, choose a corner of the room away from bookcases, tall shelves, sliding doors, chimneys, or anything else that may collapse.
4. If you live in an area prone to tremors, safeguard your home by bolting bookcases and other tall or heavy furniture to the wall. If you are outdoors when an earthquake hits, stay away from buildings, trees, and power lines.

Blizzards

A **blizzard** is a snowstorm with winds of 35 miles per hour (56 km per hour) or greater. Visibility is less than 500 feet (152 m), so it is easy for a person to get lost. The safest place to be during a blizzard is indoors. If you are caught outside, try to keep your mouth and nose covered, and keep moving so that you do not freeze. Try to follow a road or a fence to the closest safe place.

If you must go outside in a blizzard, wear protective clothing. All of the following will help protect you from freezing temperatures and frostbite: thermal, woolen undergarments; outer garments that will repel wind and moisture; head, face, and ear coverings; extra socks; warm boots; and wool-lined mittens.

Most earthquake injuries are caused by falling objects and collapsing buildings .

LESSON 3 REVIEW

Reviewing Facts and Vocabulary

1. Define *frostbite, gangrene, hurricane watch,* and *earthquake.*
2. What should you *not* do in treating a fracture? In treating a heat cramp?
3. Describe the three types of burns and the first aid for each.

Thinking Critically

4. **Evaluation.** Tell which of the first-aid measures you read about in this lesson you feel are most important to know. Give reasons.

5. **Analysis.** Compare and contrast hurricanes, tornadoes, and earthquakes.

Applying Health Knowledge

6. Research the kinds of natural disasters common to your area of the United States. Speak with someone at your local chapter of the American Red Cross about what action should be taken in disasters of this type. Summarize your findings, and share them with the class. If there is no chapter in your community, find out who is responsible for handling disasters or emergencies.

Check for Understanding

- Assign and discuss the lesson review.
- Assign and discuss the chapter review.

Evaluate

- Administer, grade, and discuss the *Lesson 3 Quiz.*
- Administer, grade, and discuss the *Chapter 35 Test.*
- Refer to the Performance Assessment strategy for this chapter. See pages T 23 to T 25.

Reteach

- Ask each student to make a collage showing the aftermath of one kind of weather-related emergency. Have students use pictures from newspapers and magazines in their collages. Then ask other students to guess what kind of natural event caused the damage pictured in each collage.
- Ask students to complete *Reteaching Activity 98.*

Enrich

- Most communities have civil defense shelters. Ask students to find out where the shelters are in your community. How do people know which one to go to? What qualifies a place to serve as a shelter? When have such shelters been used in the past? Ask students to summarize their findings in written reports.
- Ask students to complete *Enrichment Activity 35.*

Close

Have students summarize the most important concepts learned in this lesson.

Answers to Lesson 3 Review

1. Definitions can be found in the Glossary or on pages 706, 707, and 708.
2. Never attempt to set the bone. Do not give the victim salt tablets.
3. See pages 704 to 705 for first aid for burns.
4. Answers will vary but should be supported logically.
5. Answers will vary. Possible answers: All are natural disasters, can cause a great deal of damage, require certain conditions before they can occur, and in all cases knowing how to act is the best way to minimize one's risks. Each of them has a different area in which they most often occur. Hurricanes and tornadoes involve strong winds.
6. Findings will vary.

Helping Students Improve Their Health

Teaching Strategies

L1 EXPLANATION. Occasionally students may try to outthink the inventory items. Point out that the knowledge of first aid can be a valuable tool in an emergency situation. Also point out that it may be just as important to know what not to do. Ask students to answer the items as honestly as possible.

L1 DISCUSSION. Ask students if they have ever been in an emergency situation where first aid was needed. How did they or others react in this situation? Were they nervous or scared? Why? Did anyone there try to have a calming influence on others? If so, what did they do?

L1 CLASS ACTIVITY. Make up stickers with different symptoms written on them, such as severe bleeding, swelling, unconscious, pale, clammy skin, rapid pulse, etc. Have students pair up. Ask one student from each pair to be the victim and the other to be the administrator of first aid. Place combinations of stickers on victims to simulate a specific emergency circumstance. Have the student administering first aid describe and demonstrate appropriate procedures—including checking the surroundings for possible dangers and sending for help.

L2 SELF-ESTEEM. Discuss how developing first-aid skills might affect a person's level of self-esteem.

Self-Inventory

Emergency Behaviors and Attitudes

HOW DO YOU RATE?

A measure of the health of any community is the ability of its members to aid themselves and others in an emergency. Do you contribute to your personal health and to the health of your community? Number a sheet of paper from 1 through 15. Read each item below, and respond by writing *yes* or *no*. Total the number of *yes* and *no* responses. Then proceed to the next section.

1. I make a point of knowing the names of all my family's health-care professionals.
2. I keep a list of emergency phone numbers near a telephone in my home.
3. I know how to reach the police, the fire department, and emergency medical help from a public telephone.
4. I keep a fully stocked first-aid kit in my home.
5. I believe that first aid is everyone's responsibility.
6. I use only those first-aid skills for which I have had training.
7. I know how to treat different kinds of wounds.
8. I am aware of the five priorities related to an emergency situation.
9. I know what steps to take to stop heavy bleeding.
10. I have the ability to help someone who has swallowed a poison.

11. I can administer first aid for different types of bites and stings.
12. I know how to help a victim of nosebleed, fainting, heat cramps, and frostbite.
13. I am able to tell the difference between minor and serious burns and can treat each kind.
14. I know first aid for sprains and fractures.
15. I know what action to take in the event of hurricanes, tornadoes, and other natural disasters.

HOW DID YOU SCORE?

Give yourself 1 point for every *yes* answer and 0 points for every *no* answer. Find your total, and read below to see how you scored. Then proceed to the next section.

12 to 15
Excellent. You have the makings of a lifesaver in emergency situations.

8 to 11
Good. Many of your skills and attitudes are healthy; others need work.

4 to 7
Fair. You need to develop more emergency skills. By developing your first-aid skills, you could save a life.

Below 4
Poor. By your responses, you would be of little help in most emergency situations.

WHAT ARE YOUR GOALS?
Identify an area in which your score was low, and use the goal-setting process below to pave the way for a change.

1. The skill or attitude I would like to change is ____.
2. If this skill or attitude were changed, I would look, feel, or act differently in the following ways: ____.
3. The steps involved in making this change are ____.
4. My timetable for making this change is ____.
5. People I will ask for help or assistance are ____.
6. The benefits I will receive as a result of making this change are ____.

Meeting Students' Needs

For students who score *Excellent*. Suggest students contact the American Red Cross to inquire about an advanced first-aid class for certification.

For students who score *Good*. Suggest students consult your media specialist for extra information on first-aid skills.

For students who score *Fair*. Have students identify areas on the inventory where they were weakest. From these areas, have them pick three first-aid topics and write an extra-credit report on them.

For students who score *Poor*. (1) Have students make lists of their family's health-care providers, including phone numbers. (2) Have students select three first-aid topics to report on for extra credit.

Building Decision-Making Skills

S andy and some of her friends are playing volleyball on the beach after school. Sandy receives a volley from her brother Leo, and she successfully spikes the volleyball over the net. Unfortunately, on her way down from her jump, Sandy's left foot hits a rock that is hidden in the sand. A severe pain shoots through her ankle, and she screams in pain. She lies on the ground, clutching her ankle. Her brother runs to her. He can see that Sandy is in extreme pain. What should Leo do?

A. Tell Sandy to "shake it off" and get up and continue the game.

B. Ask Sandy if she heard a crack or a popping sound when she fell so that he can determine whether she has broken her ankle or only sprained it. Then administer the appropriate first-aid measures.

C. Tell Sandy to lie still while someone goes for help.

WHAT DO YOU THINK?

1. **Situation.** Why does a decision need to be made?

2. **Choices.** What other choices does Leo have?

3. **Consequences.** How might Leo's decision affect Sandy's health triangle?

4. **Consequences.** How might Leo's decision affect his own health triangle?

5. **Consequences.** What are the advantages of each choice?

6. **Consequences.** What are the disadvantages of each choice?

7. **Decision.** What decision do you think is best for Sandy?

8. **Evaluation.** Have you ever found yourself in a situation where a friend was injured and you had to decide what to do? What did you do? What would you do differently if you found yourself in a similar situation?

Building Decision-Making Skills

Teaching Strategies

L1 CLASS ACTIVITY. Create a role-play situation with Sandy injuring her ankle. Have a group gather and give suggestions as to what to do. Have one person take charge of the situation—reassuring Sandy and administering first aid.

L1 CLASS ACTIVITY. Role-play a situation where Carlos is talking with the poison control center. Try to incorporate both sides of the conversation.

L2 DISCUSSION. Debate the value of television shows showing people using first aid in emergency situations. Do these shows help or cause harm out in the "real world"? Do they cause people to do things that they may not be capable of doing safely?

L2 DISCUSSION. Tell students they all work in an office where their employer is requiring everyone to be certified in first aid. Divide the class into two groups and debate this issue.

L2 DISCUSSION. Tell students to imagine they are involved in an auto accident. One of the victims has numerous lacerations and is bleeding heavily. This victim is known to be HIV positive. Do you treat this victim? Why or why not? Are there any conditions where you would treat this victim?

C arlos is baby-sitting his twin cousins, Pedro and Pilar. He has put them to bed upstairs and is watching a video in the living room. Suddenly, he hears a crash. He races upstairs to find the twins in the bathroom with an open and half-empty bottle of pills on the floor. What should Carlos do?

A. Send the twins back to bed, and put the remaining pills back in the medicine chest.

B. Read the label on the bottle of pills to find out whether the pills could be harmful to children.

C. Call a poison control center, and describe the pills the twins may have taken.

WHAT DO YOU THINK?

9. **Situation.** Why does a decision need to be made?

10. **Situation.** Who will be affected by Carlos's decision?

11. **Situation.** Where can Carlos find the phone number for the poison control center?

12. **Choices.** What other choices does Carlos have?

13. **Consequences.** How might Carlos's decision affect the twins' health?

14. **Consequences.** What are the advantages of each choice?

15. **Consequences.** What are the disadvantages of each choice?

16. **Consequences.** What risks are involved in this situation?

17. **Consequences.** How will the twins' parents probably react to Carlos's decision?

18. **Decision.** What do you think Carlos should do?

19. **Evaluation.** Have you ever been in a situation similar to Carlos's? How did you handle it? What would you do differently if you encountered a similar situation in the future?

Discussing the Answers

Situation 1. This situation can have a couple of answers. Leo could use the aid of others to go for help while he administers first aid. He could also immobilize the injury, and without allowing Sandy to put weight on the ankle, take her to seek medical attention.

Situation 2. Carlos should assess the situation—clarifying if pills were taken, and if so, by whom. Regardless, he should call the poison control center for directions in dealing with the situation. It is important that Carlos remain calm—not only for himself, but to reassure his cousins.

DID YOU KNOW?

■ A sprained ankle should be taken seriously—some ankle sprains require surgical correction, while others lead to lifelong disability.

Answers to Chapter 35 Review

Using Health Terms

1. Cut
2. Puncture
3. Fracture
4. Shock
5. Poison control center
6. Poisonous
7. Nonpoisonous
8. Calamine lotion
9. Rabies
10. Sprain
11. Fainting
12. Heat cramps
13. Tornado
14. Blizzard

Building Academic Skills

15. Articles will vary.

Recalling the Facts

16. Wording will vary but should include: Gather information about what happened and figure out what to do, make sure the victim is as comfortable as possible, make sure the victim's body temperature remains close to normal, loosen restrictive clothing.
17. It is to alert medical personnel that a special medical condition exists; people who suffer from diabetes, seizures, heart conditions, or severe allergic reactions.
18. Stop the bleeding, protect the wound from infection, treat the victim for shock, seek medical care.
19. Injuries involving severe bleeding, heart attack, electrocution, poisoning, burns, sudden changes of temperature. Symptoms—confused behavior, extremes in pulse rate or breathing, trembling and weakness in extremities, pale or clammy skin, pale or bluish lips or fingernails, enlarged pupils.
20. Call the poison control center, be prepared to give the person at the center the information he or she will need, treat the victim for shock.
21. Age and weight of victim, the name of the suspected poison, the amount of poison swallowed.

22. Some substances will cause as much damage coming up as they did going down.
23. Poisonous snakebite.
24. Burning on the skin which appears similar to a sunburn.
25. No, the fractured area should be immobilized. Moving it may cause more damage.

26. B and D.
27. Keep the victim lying down on the back. Elevate the legs 8 to 12 inches, loosen tight clothing, maintain an open airway, sponge the victim's face with water, seek medical help if the victim does not revive quickly.
28. Temperature, wind velocity, humidity level, damp-

Using Health Terms

On a separate sheet of paper, write the term that best matches each definition given below.

LESSON 1

1. A jagged, irregular tear with heavy bleeding.
2. Type of wound in which the skin is pierced.
3. A broken bone.
4. A condition that occurs when vital organs are deprived of blood.

LESSON 2

5. Part of a nationwide network that provides information on treatment in cases of poisoning.
6. Snakes with bands of red and yellow.
7. Snakes with bands of red and black.
8. An over-the-counter medication that can be applied to relieve itching caused by exposure to poisonous plants.

LESSON 3

9. A viral disease of the nervous system that leads to madness and death.
10. A condition caused by a sudden stretching of soft tissues around a joint.
11. The temporary loss of consciousness due to a lack of blood to the brain.
12. Loss of essential water and salt from the body when it is exposed to high temperatures over a prolonged period of time.
13. A twisting windstorm.
14. A snowstorm during which visibility is less than 500 feet and wind speeds reach 35 miles per hour.

Building Academic Skills

LESSON 1

15. **Writing.** Emergency Medical Technician is a career that you or someone in your school may wish to pursue. Interview an Emergency Medical Technician in your community. Summarize your interview in an article for your school or local newspaper.

Recalling the Facts

LESSON 1

16. In your own words, describe four secondary measures one should attend to in an emergency situation.
17. Explain the function of emergency medical identification and who is likely to wear it.
18. Tell the four steps in treating an open wound.
19. What are possible situations in which shock might be an outcome? What are the symptoms of shock?

LESSON 2

20. What is the proper first aid for poisoning by swallowing?
21. What information should you give when you call a poison control center?
22. When treating a victim of poisoning by swallowing, why should one not induce vomiting unless directed to do so by someone at the poison control center?
23. Given the following symptoms, what would you conclude happened to the victim: puncture wounds, extreme pain and swelling, shortness of breath, nausea, dimness of vision, convulsions, a tingling sensation, and unconsciousness?
24. What is a characteristic of chemical poisoning by touch?

LESSON 3

25. If one suspects someone has suffered a fracture, should the victim be told to move the injured part to see if it works? Why or why not?
26. Which of the following should you *not* do in treating a burn victim?
    a. Submerge the burned area in cool water.
    b. Apply butter or oil to the burned area.
    c. Apply a clean, dry dressing.
    d. Pop any blisters that form and remove the burned skin.
27. What is the first-aid procedure for fainting?
28. What factors can play a role in frostbite? Which of these factors is within a person's control?

Thinking Critically

LESSON 1

29. Synthesis. Develop a series of principles that every good first aider should follow in an emergency.

30. Analysis. Methods of first aid sometimes change as new information becomes available. What implications does this have for anyone who has ever studied first aid?

LESSON 2

31. Synthesis. Why do you think over half of poisonous snakebites occur in Texas, North Carolina, Florida, Georgia, Louisiana, and Arkansas?

32. Analysis. How would treatment for poison ivy and treatment for battery acid on the skin differ?

LESSON 3

33. Evaluation. In some areas, emergency medical technicians decide whether to transport emergency victims to a hospital for further treatment. In other areas, anyone who calls for emergency help is transported to a hospital. Which procedure do you feel is better? Support your answer.

Making the Connection

LESSON 1

34. Dramatics. Work with several other students to prepare a skit dramatizing an accident involving an open wound and its treatment.

LESSON 3

35. Art. Make a poster illustrating the procedures to be followed in one of the following: hurricane, tornado, or earthquake.

36. Speech. Do some research to learn more about the American Red Cross. Prepare a speech describing its history and its involvement in weather-related disasters in your area if possible. Find out how the ARC recruits its workers and what you could do to become an ARC volunteer.

Applying Health Knowledge

LESSON 1

37. Discuss why it would be unwise to put one's own safety at risk when helping a victim.

38. Tell what type of wound would most likely result from each situation below.
   a. A dog bite.
   b. Wrestling on a carpet.
   c. Getting your hand too close to moving lawnmower blades.
   d. Being slashed with a knife.

LESSON 2

39. What is a highly visible place in your home where the phone number for the poison control center could be posted?

LESSON 3

40. Why do you suppose a cold towel applied to a person's nose or face is part of the first aid for a nosebleed?

41. For a sprain, first aid includes applying a cold pack. What is a cold pack? How can you make one? Should you put ice directly on a sprain? Explain.

Beyond the Classroom

LESSON 1

42. Parental Involvement. Share with your parents information you have learned in this chapter. Then, together, make your home more first-aid ready. Find and post the phone numbers for the nearest poison control center and other emergency numbers. Assemble or update a first-aid kit.

LESSON 3

43. Community Involvement. You have learned first aid for many different kinds of wounds in this chapter. Make a separate poster for each kind of first aid discussed in the chapter. Post each one where it is most appropriate. For example, a poster on how to treat chemical burns may be best suited for the chemistry lab.

ness of clothing, length of exposure, amount of protective clothing worn. The last two factors can be controlled.

Thinking Critically

29. Answers will vary but should stress the importance of first-aid training, remaining calm, being compassionate as well as reflect understanding of the priorities of an emergency situation and appropriate steps for different kinds of first aid.

30. Anyone who knows first aid should take refresher courses occasionally to become familiar with the latest techniques.

31. Answers will vary but might include the idea that these states have a higher number of poisonous snakes because of their warm climate; that people spend more time outdoors because of the climate; or that these states have more tourists who are not aware of the danger and are not cautious.

32. One needs to call a poison control center right away to find out how to treat a burn resulting from battery acid.

33. Answers will vary but should be supported logically.

Making the Connection

34. Skits will vary.
35. Posters will vary.
36. Speeches will vary.

Applying Health Knowledge

37. Answers will vary. Possible answer: If the rescuer got hurt, there might not be anyone else to help and the EMS would have two people to care for.

38. A—puncture; B—scrape; C—cut or avulsion; D—cut.

39. Answers will vary. Possible answers: Next to the telephone, on a message board, on the refrigerator.

40. The cold helps slow down the blood flow, thus helping the blood to clot.

41. A compress or a wrap with a cold temperature to be used on injuries. One can be made by wrapping ice in a sheet or towel, putting ice in a bag and wrapping it in a towel, or by wetting a towel, blanket, or sheet and refrigerating or

freezing it. No, ice directly on an injury would be uncomfortable.

Beyond the Classroom

42. No response is necessary, but you may wish to ask students what has been done to make their homes more first-aid ready.

43. Posters will vary.

Lesson Summaries

LESSON 1. The Heimlich maneuver can be used to dislodge substances obstructing the airway, though it should be administered only to conscious victims. Techniques differ slightly, depending on the age of the victim. Rescue breathing is necessary when a victim stops breathing. As with the Heimlich maneuver, rescue breathing techniques differ for young children and adults.

LESSON 2. Cardiopulmonary resuscitation (CPR) can be administered to victims of cardiovascular failure. It involves breathing for the victim and forcing the heart to pump blood by applying pressure to the victim's chest. Adjustments must be made in the technique when administering it to young children.

Introducing the Chapter

Tell students that more than half of all emergency victims die before they reach the hospital. In many cases, these victims would have had a good chance of surviving if someone at the scene of the accident had known a lifesaving technique. Remind students that they can never know when they might need this type of knowledge. Tell them that in this chapter they will learn how to aid a choking victim and administer CPR to assist a heart-attack victim.

Performance Assessment ✓

Refer to pages T 23 to T 25 for a Performance Assessment strategy for this chapter. See the *Performance Assessment Activities* booklet for additional suggestions.

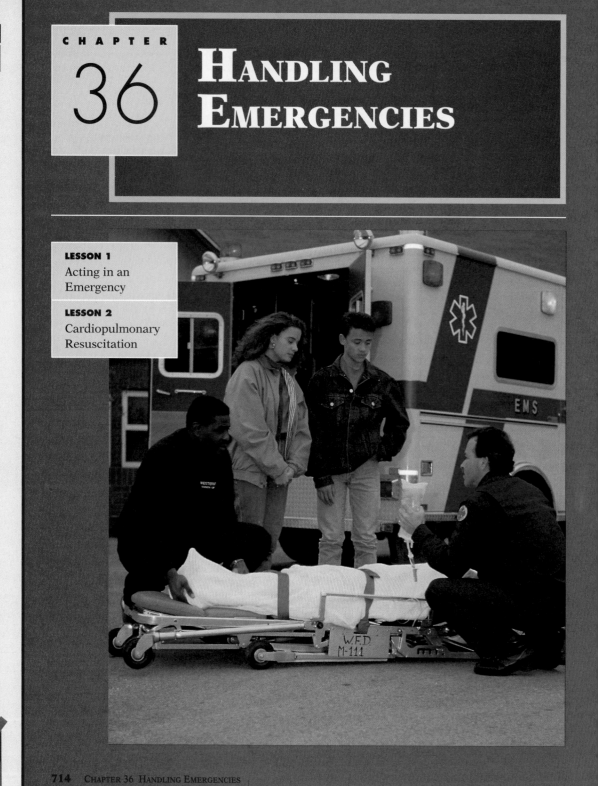

CHAPTER

36

HANDLING EMERGENCIES

LESSON 1
Acting in an Emergency

LESSON 2
Cardiopulmonary Resuscitation

714   CHAPTER 36 HANDLING EMERGENCIES

Key to Ability Levels

Teaching strategies have been coded for varying learning styles and abilities.

L1 Level 1 activities are basic activities and should be within the ability range of all students.

L2 Level 2 activities are average activities and should be within the ability range of average to above-average students.

L3 Level 3 activities are challenging activities designed for the ability range of above-average students.

LD LD activities should be within the ability range of learning-disabled students.

LEP LEP activities should be within the ability range of Limited English Proficiency students.

ACTING IN AN EMERGENCY

C onsider these life-threatening situations: A family is seated at dinner when someone at the table begins to choke. A group of people are standing on a busy city street corner when suddenly a middle-aged man among them clutches his chest and slumps to the ground. Scenes like these happen in the United States thousands of times each year, and thousands of times the victim dies—needlessly.

The most common cause of sudden death is heart attack. Drowning, electrical shock, drug overdose, stroke, smoke inhalation, and suffocation can also stop a person's breathing and circulation and result in sudden death. A knowledge of first aid in these cases is, literally, a matter of life and death.

First Aid for Choking

More than 3,000 Americans choke to death annually. Many of the deaths reported involve children under 4 years of age. Choking is the sixth leading cause of death in the overall population. It is a leading cause of accidental death in the home for children under 1 year of age.

These statistics are sobering. What is perhaps even more sobering is that a great many of these deaths could have been prevented.

In order for a choking victim to survive, immediate recognition and treatment are a must. A gasping for breath or a weak coughing noise, accompanied by an inability to talk, are indications that a person is choking. The victim may become pale, turn blue, or even lose consciousness. You can learn to recognize these signs and give aid.

The universal distress signal for choking is clutching the neck between the thumb and index finger. Learning this signal can help you save a choking victim. It can also help another person save you.

NO CHOKE

You can reduce your chances of becoming a choking victim by observing some simple safety tips:

- Take small bites of food when you eat.
- Eat slowly, chewing each mouthful of food thoroughly.
- Do not talk or laugh with food in your mouth.
- Do not go to sleep with chewing gum or food in your mouth.

Choking in Children and Adults

Hard as it may be to believe, many choking deaths result from mistaken identity. That is, people witnessing someone choking fail to administer first aid for choking because they wrongly believe that the victim is

ACTING IN AN EMERGENCY   **715**

LESSON 1 FOCUS

TERMS TO USE
- Abdominal thrusts
- Rescue breathing
- Carotid pulse

CONCEPTS TO LEARN
- The abdominal thrust should be administered only to conscious victims; it can also be self-administered.
- Maintaining an open airway and supplying a victim with oxygen are the main objectives for rescue breathing.

ATTITUDES AND BEHAVIORS TO EVALUATE
- Self Inventory, page 726.
- Building Decision-Making Skills, page 727.

Focus

Lesson Objectives
After studying this lesson, students should be able to:
- list the steps for aiding a choking victim
- demonstrate how to check for breathing and pulse
- demonstrate the process for administering rescue breathing

Bellringer
Write the following on the chalkboard for students to work on while attendance is being taken: *List as many causes of choking as you can.*

Introducing the Lesson
Introduce this lesson by clutching your neck between the thumb and index finger, showing the universal distress signal for choking. Ask the students if anyone recognized what you were doing. Explain the importance of their knowing this signal. Refer to the Bellringer. Ask volunteers to share their responses.

Building Vocabulary
- Have students write each of the lesson vocabulary terms as you pronounce them. Have students correct their papers as you read the correct spellings of the terms. Complete the activity by asking students to use each of the vocabulary terms in a sentence.
- Ask students to complete *Workbook Vocabulary Activity 99.*

DID YOU KNOW?
- The word *doctor* derives from the Latin verb *docere*, which means "to teach." When the word was first used, it was not specifically applied to people who practiced medicine. Rather, it was used in addressing any learned person who taught and was worthy of respect.
- Someone in the U.S. is injured in an accident every 4 seconds, and someone killed every 6 minutes.

Resources for Lesson 1

- **Transparency** 32
- **Guided Reading** Activity 99
- **Workbook** Vocabulary Activity 99
- **Reteaching** Activity 99
- **Lesson 1 Quiz**
- **Performance Assessment** Activity 36

Abdominal thrusts force out the substance blocking the airway.

L1 DISCUSSION. Why is it important to ensure that a person is really choking before you administer the abdominal thrust?

L1 DISCUSSION. How could you tell if a child or infant was choking? Would it be a good idea to proceed with the appropriate first aid even if you weren't sure? (No.) Why or why not? (You could cause the death of the child or infant.)

L1 EXPLANATION. Hand positioning is very important in administering thrusts for choking. Incorrect positioning of the hands could break ribs, causing internal problems.

LD CLASS ACTIVITY. To stress the importance of following written directions, have students first try using directions in the text for the various first-aid techniques before you assist them. Provide precautions when necessary.

L1 CLASS ACTIVITY. Bring a doll (several, if possible) to class. Have a volunteer read the procedure for helping a choking infant or small child. Have students take turns practicing the procedure on the doll(s).

L1 DISCUSSION. Discuss the reason for the term *café coronaries*. Why is it important for people to know, use, and recognize the universal distress signal for choking?

L1 CLASS ACTIVITY. Have students list foods which might cause choking in small children. (Whole grapes, nuts, popcorn, hard candies, large bites of food, or food that hasn't been cut up are some examples.) What else might cause a child to choke? (Eating too quickly, running or moving around while eating.)

L1 DEMONSTRATION. Using an anatomical model of the digestive system or a chart, review the function of the epiglottis as discussed in Chapter 13. Demonstrate what happens to the epiglottis when swallowing and how a person can choke by not allowing the epiglottis to function normally.

Learning the signal for choking can save another person's life and maybe your own.

suffering a heart attack. This is why fatal choking accidents in restaurants have been called "café coronaries."

If you suspect a child or adult is choking, ask the person, "Are you choking?" If the victim cannot breathe, cough, or speak, begin first aid immediately by administering **abdominal thrusts.** Also called the Heimlich maneuver, after the chest surgeon who developed the technique, these quick, upward thrusts force the diaphragm upward and force out the substance blocking the airway.

When administering abdominal thrusts to conscious victims, this is what to do:

1. Wrap your arms around the victim's waist, with the thumb side of your wrist against the victim's abdomen. Place your hand halfway between the lower tip of the victim's breastbone, or sternum, and the navel.
2. Grasp your fist with your other hand, and press into the abdomen with quick, upward thrusts until the blockage is dislodged. Abdominal thrusts on a conscious adult should be repeated until the object is coughed up or the person becomes unconscious.

Note that the abdominal thrust technique can be self-administered. If no other person is present, a choking victim can perform abdominal thrusts on himself or herself by leaning over the back of a chair or over the edge of a table.

Choking in Infants

Very young children often place buttons and other small objects in their mouths. Because of this, families with infants, children up to 1 year of age, should take a course in first aid for choking. Your local Emergency Medical Services (EMS) or local chapter of the American Heart Association or American Red Cross provides training in the use of effective techniques for infants who are choking. Use the following techniques only on conscious, choking infants:

1. Turn the infant to a downward angle over your arm.
2. Using the heel of your other hand, give four quick blows to the baby's back between the shoulder blades.

Overcoming Misconceptions

First Aid for Choking. The first instinct for most people is to hit a choking victim on the back and try to dislodge the object causing the obstruction. Actually this is the worst thing a first aider can do for the person. Hitting someone on the back can actually lodge the object deeper into the windpipe, making it more difficult or impossible to dislodge the object. Tell students to remember that if someone can cough, speak, or breathe, not to administer first aid, but to stay with the person and watch the person closely. If they determine a person is choking, they should direct someone to call 911 and proceed to administer the abdominal thrusts.

3. Turn the infant over, supporting its head, neck, and back between the shoulders. Press two fingers into the middle of the baby's sternum. This action is known as a chest thrust. Repeat the action four times.

4. Alternate administering back blows and chest thrusts until the object is dislodged.

Respiratory Failure

In some emergencies, such as choking, drowning, and electrical shock, a victim's breathing stops or becomes blocked. You can recognize breathing failure by a number of signs, including an absence of breathing movements, dilated pupils, and a bluish color to the lips, tongue, or fingernails.

When respiratory failure occurs, it is essential to give the victim oxygen immediately. Lack of oxygen to the brain can cause permanent brain damage within minutes after breathing stops. The most practical method in such an emergency is mouth-to-mouth or mouth-to-nose respiration. This technique, known variously as **rescue breathing,** artificial respiration, or resuscitation, has two main objectives:

Rescue Breathing for Adults

1. If the victim is unconscious, tilt the victim's head back while lifting the chin upward. Look, listen, and feel for signs of breathing.

2. If the victim is not breathing, close the victim's nostrils shut. Place your mouth over the person's mouth, forming a seal. Give two full breaths.

3. Look, listen, and feel again. Feel the carotid pulse. If there is a pulse but no breathing, give one breath every five seconds.

Rescue Breathing for Infants and Children

1. Position the head to clear the airway.

2. Cover and form a seal with your mouth over the victim's mouth and nose. Give one breath every three seconds for an infant. Give one breath every four seconds for a child.

DID YOU KNOW?

- Among Americans, choking is the sixth leading cause of accidental death.
- Many states have passed laws that require information about the Heimlich maneuver to be posted in restaurants. Some states also require that the information be posted in schools.
- About nine-tenths of all choking victims were eating when the choking incident occurred.

Culturally Speaking

SIDS and Co-Sleeping

Studies show that infants and adults interact even while they sleep. This interaction may help avoid sudden infant death syndrome (SIDS), a condition where an infant stops breathing while asleep. In cultures where infants sleep in contact with their parents, the infant and the parent respond to each other's breathing and movement. Scientists suggest that when the infant stops breathing, the co-sleeping adult will move and stimulate the infant to start breathing again, usually without even waking.

L1 **DISCUSSION.** What would you do if you were choking and no one was around? The abdominal thrust maneuver can be self-administered. That is, you could press your own fist into your upper abdomen by using a quick, upward thrust. What other objects might be available to administer the thrust? (Chair or sofa arm would work. Anything large and soft to not injure the ribs and heart.)

L1 **CLASS ACTIVITY.** Borrow mannequins from the American Red Cross or American Heart Association for students to practice rescue breathing. Demonstrate mouth-to-mouth breathing for the class. Emphasize that students should watch to see that the victim's chest rises when air is blown into the mouth. If the stomach rises, it is an indication of an obstructed airway and air is going into the esophagus, not the windpipe. If mannequins are not available, students can practice "look, listen, and feel" on partners without actually blowing into the mouth. Explain how this technique is different for babies, children, and adults. Explain the difference and demonstrate the procedure for each one.

L1 **EXPLANATION.** Tell students that the first steps in first aid are to determine if the victim is breathing. If rescue breathing is used on someone who is already breathing, a dangerous situation will occur.

L1 **EXPLANATION.** Tell students that when a person is unconscious and you do not know the extent or cause of injury to remember to always begin by doing a primary survey—checking the ABCs of first aid. A—open airway; B—check breathing; and C—check circulation.

L1 **CLASS ACTIVITY.** Have students practice the methods of opening the airway. Remind students of the importance of not moving the neck in case there is an injury to it.

L1 **USING LIFE MANAGEMENT SKILLS TRANSPARENCY 32.** Refer to the Teaching Transparencies Binder.

Additional Information

Choking. Dr. Henry J. Heimlich is the originator of the Heimlich maneuver or "Hug." About nine-tenths of all choking victims were eating when the choking incident occurred. Among Americans, choking is the sixth leading cause of accidental death. About one-tenth of all victims of choking are children. Many states have passed laws that require information about the Heimlich maneuver to be posted in restaurants. Some states also require that the information be posted in schools.

L1 EXPLANATION. Sometimes in rescue breathing, the victim's stomach may become bloated with air causing the victim to vomit. If this happens, make sure the victim's head is turned to the side so the vomit will not choke him or her.

L1 DISCUSSION. Since the procedures for rescue breathing are different for babies, children, and adults, what could happen to a child if you used the procedure for an adult? Discuss the effects of incorrectly using rescue breathing on anyone.

Independent Practice

L2 SELF-ESTEEM. Have students read accounts of people who were revived by rescue breathing. What emotional and psychological reactions did the victim have during and after this experience? How did the rescuer feel during and after this experience? (The "Drama in Real Life" segments of *Reader's Digest* or the "Young Mothers' Stories" in *Redbook* are good possibilities for such stories.) How might learning a skill like rescue breathing improve a person's level of self-esteem?

L1 PARENTAL INVOLVEMENT. Ask students to demonstrate and explain to their parents and family the procedures for administering first aid to choking victims and to persons that are not breathing.

L1 COMMUNITY INVOLVEMENT. Ask volunteers to contact the American Red Cross and the American Heart Association for pamphlets, posters, and materials available on choking and rescue breathing. Have students display the materials throughout the school and in their workplaces.

L3 RESEARCH. Have students research techniques to be used for administering first aid to someone who is drunk or unconscious from drugs. These individuals should be watched because they may stop breathing. In addition, they may begin to vomit and choke to death. Ask students to report their findings to the class.

L1 USING THE LESSON RESOURCES. For additional student activities, refer to the lesson resources on page 715.

If an infant is choking, alternate back blows and chest thrusts.

- to maintain an open airway
- to supply the victim with oxygen necessary for his or her survival

Additional measures are called for when a person is not breathing and has no pulse. You will learn about these measures in the next lesson.

Rescue Breathing for Adults

Rescue breathing for adults is different in some respects from rescue breathing for small children. The steps a person should follow when administering rescue breathing to adults are as follows:

1. Check to see whether the victim is conscious. Tap the person's shoulder and ask, "Are you all right?" If there is no response, direct someone to call EMS for help.
2. Place one hand on the bony part of the victim's chin and one on the forehead, and tilt the victim's head back while lifting the chin upward. This action moves the jaw and tongue forward, opening the airway.
3. Place your ear and cheek close to the victim's mouth and nose. Look, listen, and feel. Look at the chest to see whether it is rising and falling. Listen for air being exhaled from the lungs. Feel for exhaled air on your cheek.

K E E P I N G   F I T

How to Report an Emergency

If you have to report an emergency, keep these guidelines in mind:
- Give the emergency dispatcher the complete address and phone number where help is needed.
- Try to speak clearly and loudly.

- Try to stay as calm as possible.
- If the victim is unconscious or not breathing, tell the dispatcher. Many dispatchers are trained to tell people over the phone what to do until help can get there.

- If there are two or more of you who are uninjured, send one person to turn on the outside lights and another to the entrance or street to direct the ambulance to you.

Meeting Special Needs

Rescue Breathing. Explain to students that they may encounter difficult situations when trying to administer mouth-to-mouth resuscitation on individuals with special problems. For instance, if they have difficulty opening the airway of a person with dentures, they should remove the dentures. If a person has a mouth injury and teeth are broken in the mouth,

they should carefully remove any debris in the mouth before administering breathing. If a person has a trach tube in his or her throat, they should breathe through the tube and not worry about the nose or mouth. If the tube is clogged, they should remove it and breathe into the opening in the throat.

Overcoming The Odds

Tracey Maichle is 29. She has many hobbies and feels good about herself, partly because of her passion for her work. Tracey is a city firefighter.

Yet Tracey didn't always have as much confidence in herself, "Even though I had a terrific childhood," she begins, "I had a lot of problems as a child knowing that I was adopted. But when I was 18, I found my biological mother, then my biological father, and that helped me a great deal. It helped me find out and accept who I am."

Tracey had an early experience with fire that has stuck with her into adulthood. "My adoptive parents had a trailer down at the beach," she says. "One night, when I was about 13, my mother had put my little cousin down to sleep. I'd gone to bed. My mother had draped a towel over a light to make it dimmer for my cousin. I smelled smoke. At that point, there was no one else in the trailer but my cousin and me. I ran in and got my cousin, who was near the fire, and took him outside. It made me feel good, even though I was young. I'd always been taught the basics by my parents, like if you smell smoke, get out, get help, and stay calm. The basics worked."

Tracey's interest in rescuing

people in trouble continued. "I dated a volunteer firefighter for a number of years. I got tired of waiting in the car or waiting at the fire house. I began to want to help victims that were in car accidents or people whose houses were on fire." So Tracey went through fire school, got a certificate, then went through advanced training.

Tracey loves to talk about her experiences. "We had a 14- or 15-year-old male who had drowned. He had been under water for about 20 minutes. I did CPR until the paramedics got there and could use electric shock on him. They brought him back and took him to the hospital."

Having her own children has given Tracey new perspec-

tive on the importance of safety and safety training. She says, "My 14-year-old son went to get certified by the Red Cross for infant CPR because I have another son who is 18 months. Now the 14-year-old is really turned on to safety."

Tracey offers this advice. "If you are faced with an emergency, know who to call for help. In many areas that's 911. Try not to panic. Try to keep your wits about you. Most important, try to get training beforehand."

Tracey now feels very competent. "I have a lot of confidence in myself knowing that, when I come across an emergency, I can exhaust every possibility of trying to help that person, whether it be to save a life, get someone proper care, or save someone's property."

1. How do you react in emergencies? Do you think the way you react helps or hurts the situation? If you do not think you react in a calm or effective way, what steps can you take to change your reactions?
2. Do you feel trained to handle basic medical emergencies until professional help arrives? Do you know who to call to get help?

Additional Information

Rescue Breathing. Provide the following instructions to students. If a person loses consciousness while you are attempting to clear an obstructed airway, ease the person to the floor, protecting the head. Open the airway and attempt to give a breath. If you cannot ventilate, straddle the person's middle and give abdominal thrusts. Push forcefully inward and upward just above the navel. After the thrusts, do a finger sweep to remove any object inside the mouth. Retilt the head and try to give a breath. If still obstructed, continue this procedure until help arrives. If the object is removed, continue with mouth-to-mouth breathing and check pulse as recommended in CPR.

Check for Understanding

- Assign and discuss the lesson review. Encourage LD students to focus on questions 2, 3, 4, and 5.

Evaluate

- Administer, grade, and discuss the *Lesson 1 Quiz.*

Reteach

- Ask volunteers to demonstrate first aid for a choking victim. Ask them to role-play the adult choking victim and to use a doll to represent the infant choking victim.
- Ask students to complete *Reteaching Activity 99.*

Enrich

- Ask students to research one of the following topics and present their findings to the class: the growth, availability, and special benefits of trauma units; your state's laws requiring the posting of the Heimlich maneuver; your state's annual choking victim statistics.

Close

Have students summarize the most important concepts studied in this lesson.

---

4. If the victim is not breathing, pinch the victim's nostrils shut with your index finger and thumb. Place your mouth over the victim's mouth, forming a seal. Give the person two breaths with only enough air to make the chest rise (1 to 1½ seconds each). Check pulse and breathing together for 5 to 10 seconds.

5. Keeping the victim's head tilted, look, listen, and feel again. Determine whether the victim's heart is beating by feeling for the **carotid pulse.** This pulse is the heartbeat found on each side of the neck. You can locate the carotid pulse by placing your index and middle fingers on the Adam's apple and sliding them into the groove at the side of the neck. Do not use your thumb to feel for the pulse. You may feel your own pulse if you do.

6. If there is a pulse but still no breathing, begin giving the victim one breath every five seconds.

Periodically check the chest to see whether it is rising or falling. If it is moving, you know that air is getting into the lungs. Continue artificial respiration until the victim has started breathing again or medical help takes over.

Rescue Breathing for Infants and Children

Rescue breathing for infants and children parallels rescue breathing for adults, with these exceptions:

- When positioning the victim's head to clear the airway, do not tilt the head back as far as you would for an adult.
- For infants, cover and form a seal with your mouth over both the victim's mouth and nose rather than over the victim's mouth alone.
- Breathe in only enough air to make the chest gently rise. Breathe air into the infant's nose and mouth at the rate of one breath every three seconds. For a child, give one breath about every four seconds.

CONFLICT RESOLUTION

Ramon would really like to sign up for a CPR course being offered at school. His mom has had problems with her heart, and he knows he'd feel a lot less scared about it if he knew what to do in an emergency. However, Ramon just doesn't know if he could administer CPR in an emergency. Yet he knows he'd feel terrible if something happened to his mom when he might have been able to save her.

What do you think Ramon should do?

What might make it less difficult for him?

LESSON 1 REVIEW

Reviewing Facts and Vocabulary

1. Give another name for each of these terms: *abdominal thrust* and *artificial respiration.* Then use each term in an original sentence.
2. What are some signs of choking? Of respiratory failure?
3. What are the main objectives of rescue breathing?

Thinking Critically

4. **Evaluation.** Name two factors that might explain why two-thirds of all choking deaths involve small children.

5. **Analysis.** Compare first aid for choking in infants with first aid for choking in children and adults.

Applying Health Knowledge

6. Interview someone trained in emergency medical care. Write a report describing how he or she helps someone who is not breathing. In your report include equipment that is used to help perform rescue breathing.

Answers to Lesson 1 Review

1. Heimlich maneuver; rescue breathing or resuscitation. Sentences will vary.
2. See "First Aid for Choking" on page 715 and "Respiratory Failure" on page 717.
3. Maintain an open airway, supply the victim with oxygen necessary for his or her survival.
4. Answers will vary. Possible answers: Young children put lots of things in their mouths; or, Many people do not know the proper way to aid a choking child.
5. Answers will vary but should reflect an understanding of the information in "Choking in Children and Adults" and "Choking in Infants" on pages 715 to 717.
6. Reports will vary.

CARDIOPULMONARY RESUSCITATION

A mong the most serious life-threatening situations a person can encounter is failure of the cardiovascular system. Cardiovascular failure, as this condition is called, can be brought on by breathing failure, a drug overdose, a blockage in a blood vessel, electrical shock, or poisoning. Attempting to rescue a victim of cardiovascular failure is one of the most critical and weighty responsibilities a person can face.

Cardiopulmonary resuscitation (CPR), the lifesaving technique administered to victims of cardiovascular failure, requires no special tools, instruments, or equipment. It involves breathing for the victim and forcing the heart to pump blood through the body by applying pressure on the victim's sternum.

CPR for Adults

CPR consists of three steps. A good way of remembering these steps and the order in which they occur is to think of them as the ABCs of CPR: *A* stands for *airway*, *B* stands for *breathing*, and *C* stands for *circulation*.

Airway—Step A

When you witness a person collapsing or come upon a person who has collapsed, your first task is to determine if the victim is conscious. Tap the victim's shoulder and ask loudly, "Are you all right?" If the victim does not respond, and before beginning CPR, dial 911 for help or contact your local EMS. If someone is nearby, direct them to call.

If the victim is not lying flat on his or her back, you need to roll the victim to this position. Take care to roll the body as an entire unit. For example, do not turn the upper body first, followed by the lower body. Once the victim is flat on his or her back, open the airway by tilting the person's head back, and at the same time, lifting up on the chin.

Breathing—Step B

Check for breathing by looking, listening, and feeling.

- *Look* for the rise and fall of the chest.
- *Listen* for the sound of air being exhaled from the lungs.
- *Feel* for exhaled air on your cheek.

If the victim shows no sign of breathing, you must get air into his or her lungs at once by administering the steps outlined on pages 718 and 720 for rescue breathing.

CARDIOPULMONARY RESUSCITATION **721**

LESSON 2 FOCUS

TERMS TO USE

- Cardiopulmonary resuscitation (CPR) (CARD•ee•oh•PULL•muh•ner•ee ree•sus•uh•TAH•shun)
- Xiphoid (ZY•foyd) process

CONCEPTS TO LEARN

- CPR involves breathing for the victim while forcing the heart to pump blood to the body by applying pressure on the victim's sternum.
- Adjustments are made when administering CPR to infants and children.

ATTITUDES AND BEHAVIORS TO EVALUATE

- Self-Inventory, page 726.
- Building Decision-Making Skills, page 727.

Focus

Lesson Objectives

After studying this lesson, students should be able to:
- demonstrate the steps involved in administering CPR
- compare CPR for adults with CPR for small children

Bellringer

Write the following on the chalkboard for students to work on while attendance is being taken: *What is the purpose of CPR?*

Introducing the Lesson

Borrow a mannequin from your local American Red Cross, American Heart Association, or Emergency Medical Services. Before class begins, lay the mannequin on the floor. To introduce this lesson, tell students to imagine that you have just come into the room and found this "person" lying on the floor. Perform the entire CPR process, beginning by gently shaking the victim's shoulder and asking, "Are you all right?" Go through the entire process. After the demonstration, ask for responses to the Bellringer. Discuss what CPR is and who is qualified to perform it.

Building Vocabulary

- Have students write each of the lesson vocabulary terms as you pronounce them. Have students correct their papers as you read the correct spellings of the terms. Complete the activity by asking students to use each vocabulary term in a sentence.
- Ask students to complete *Workbook Vocabulary Activity 100.*

Resources for Lesson 2

- **Transparency** 31
- **Guided Reading** Activity 100
- **Decision-Making** Activity 36
- **Workbook** Vocabulary Activity 100
- **Workbook** Application Activity 36
- **Reteaching** Activity 100
- **Enrichment** Activity 36
- **Health Labs** Activity 36
- **Cooperative Learning** Activity 36
- **Lesson 2 Quiz**
- **Chapter 36 Test**

Guided Practice

L1 EXPLANATION. Tell students that CPR is to be carried out only by qualified persons. Persons not certified in CPR by an organization, such as the American Red Cross or the American Heart Association, should arrange to enroll in a class to learn the procedure. It is a skill you may never have to use, but if you are called upon to do it, you will be prepared. Persons not certified in CPR that try to perform the procedure can cause extreme harm and even death to another person.

L1 DISCUSSION. Review the ABCs of first aid and the proper techniques to carry them out.

L1 DISCUSSION. How is CPR similar to rescue breathing? How is it different? Are there times when both might be required?

L1 CLASS ACTIVITY. Ask students to look up and define *cardio-*, *pulmonary*, and *resuscitation*. Use materials from the American Heart Association to review the circulatory system studied in Chapter 13. Using a chart or model of the circulatory system, show students how compressions in CPR will do the work of the heart in moving the blood and oxygen throughout the body.

L1 COOPERATIVE LEARNING. Ask students to get a partner and practice finding the carotid artery and pulse. Is this pulse easier or more difficult to take than a wrist pulse? Why is a carotid pulse specified when performing CPR? Have students find their own xiphoid process by following their rib cage to the "notch" at the lower end of the breastbone or sternum. Emphasize the importance of hand placement so that ribs and the xiphoid process will not be broken and puncture a lung or the heart.

L1 USING LIFE MANAGEMENT SKILLS TRANSPARENCY 31. Refer to the Teaching Transparencies Binder.

Circulation—Step C

The third and most critical step in CPR is to move blood through the body to supply oxygen to the cells. The heart is located beneath the sternum. Compressions on the sternum force blood out of the heart and into the blood vessels. Remember that a person should be properly trained and certified before administering this procedure to anyone.

First, check the victim's carotid pulse for five to ten seconds. This is a very important step because chest compressions can harm the victim if his or her heart is beating. If you find no pulse, begin artificial circulation.

Finding the correct position to give effective compressions is essential. The pressure must be directly on the sternum to avoid injury to the ribs and above the xiphoid process so internal organs will not be damaged. The **xiphoid process** is located at the lower end of the sternum where the lower ribs meet the sternum. Refer to the illustrations and captions on this page.

After finding the correct position for hand placement, you should also position your body properly to administer compressions. Your shoulders should be directly over your hands and your elbows locked. When you push down, the weight of your body will compress the victim's chest. Push straight down. Each compression should push the sternum down 1½ to 2 inches (3.8 to 5.1 cm). Give compressions at a rate of 80 compressions per minute.

CPR is a combination of rescue breathing and chest compressions. You would alternate 2 full breaths and 15 chest compressions until the victim has recovered or until help arrives.

As you kneel facing the victim's chest, use your hand nearest the victim's feet. Find the xiphoid process, which is the lower end of the sternum that projects downward. Place two fingers at this point on the sternum.

Place the heel of your other hand on the victim's sternum just above your two fingers already positioned on the sternum.

Interlock the fingers of your two hands so that only the heel of the bottom hand is resting on the victim's sternum.

Additional Information

Legal Aspects of First Aid. Individuals who know first aid are legally required to give it only if they have a preexisting relationship with the victim, such as teacher-student, doctor-patient, parent-child, lifeguard-swimmer, driver-passenger. However, once individuals start to administer first aid, they must remain with the victim until others of equal or greater competence take over or until the victim refuses treatment and transportation.

On the other hand, first aiders should obtain the victim's consent, or they may risk incurring charges of technical assault and battery. Oral consent is valid. Consent is implied for emergency lifesaving first aid to the unconscious victim.

LOOKING AT TECHNOLOGY

Computerized Cardiac Defibrillators

A computerized cardiac defibrillator is a device used to evaluate and sometimes revive patients suffering from cardiac arrest by restoring their heart rhythms. Now available in many ambulances, these defibrillators help paramedics and emergency medical technicians avoid the need for guesswork in trying to determine what kind of immediate emergency care should be given.

When a person in the ambulance is not breathing and does not have a heartbeat, action has to be taken immediately. The paramedic or emergency medical technician attaches electrodes to the patient's body. The computer unit analyzes the patient's medical situation and determines whether an electric shock to jolt the heart is needed. If the computer decides that the patient does need such a shock, the paramedic or emergency medical technician pushes a button and the machine itself delivers the shock. If that isn't strong enough, the attendant pushes the button again. Another shock is administered. If after three tries the heart hasn't restarted, the attendant stops and does CPR, or cardiopulmonary resuscitation, until the patient gets to the hospital. Then doctors and other health-care workers take over.

The computerized cardiac defibrillator is one big step in emergency medicine. It means that many decisions once left up to paramedics or other emergency medical technicians, are now decided by the computer and based on careful, accurate scientific information. Ambulance attendants have a predetermined protocol to follow in dealing with cardiac patients that instructs them in exactly what steps to follow when using the computerized device and in what order. Despite the services provided by the computer, however, their training and input is still critical in helping cardiac arrest victims to get correct and lifesaving treatment.

KEEPING FIT

CPR in the Age of Hepatitis and AIDS

Many people who can perform CPR may be afraid to do so for fear of contracting hepatitis, HIV, or other communicable diseases.

A pocket mask makes performing CPR much safer. This device can be placed over the mouth or nose and mouth area. Some lay people carry these with them in the event an emergency may arise. Professional rescuers and others who feel they are likely to stop at the scene of an accident also use them.

The American Red Cross encourages the public to use something as a barrier between someone's blood and other body fluids and themselves when performing emergency lifesaving techniques.

CARDIOPULMONARY RESUSCITATION **723**

Additional Information

When to Stop CPR. First aiders should initiate CPR to the best of their knowledge and ability in cases they recognize as cardiac arrest. Resuscitation efforts should continue until one of the following occurs:

- Circulation and breathing have been restored;
- Resuscitation efforts have been transferred to another responsible person who continues the efforts;
- A doctor or doctor-directed person or team assumes responsibility;
- The victim is transferred to emergency medical services personnel;
- The rescuer is exhausted and unable to continue resuscitation.

L1 CLASS ACTIVITY. Ask someone certified in CPR, such as a trainer or nurse, to demonstrate CPR on a mannequin for the class. Allow students to practice on the mannequin, supervised by the trained professional. Emphasize that they should not practice this procedure on someone who has a heartbeat because it will put the heart into fibrillation and the person could die.

L1 DISCUSSION. CPR requires chest compressions at a rate of 80 to 100 per minute until help arrives. How could you time the compressions you were administering if you didn't have a clock or watch? Is there any way for two people to use a buddy system in administering CPR over a lengthy period of time until help can arrive?

L1 DISCUSSION. Can a person have a pulse but not be breathing? Can a person breathe without having a pulse? How does this relate to the procedures of first aid?

L1 DISCUSSION. How is CPR different for children and infants, and why? Emphasize that when giving breaths to an infant you only give puffs as if you were putting out a candle. An adult can blow out the lungs of an infant if not careful.

Independent Practice

L2 COMMUNITY INVOLVEMENT. Have students find out about CPR courses in your community. Where are they given? Who is eligible to take them? What is the cost, if any? How many sessions are there? Have students share this information with the class.

L3 RESEARCH. Have student volunteers look up more about emergency medical technicians. How are EMTs different from paramedics? What other careers deal with emergency care at the scene of the accident and during transport to a health-care facility? What training, experience, and personality traits would these jobs require?

1. Tip the infant's head back a little in order to open the airway.

2. Cover your mouth over the baby's mouth and nose and give puffs of air.

3. If there is no pulse, draw an imaginary line between infant's nipples. Place two or three fingers on sternum, one finger's width below the middle of the imaginary line. Compress downward ½ to 1 inch at a rate of 100 compressions per minute for an infant and 80 to 100 for a young child.

L1 COMMUNITY INVOLVE- MENT. Have students contact a local ambulance service or fire department to find out the cost of a normal run from the school to the nearest hospital. Are there any programs offered in your area for families to purchase memberships in an ambulance service? Some ambulance services offer a yearly family membership fee which would be the only cost to the family if the ambulance were actually used. Would this be a worthwhile expense for a family? Why or why not?

L2 WRITING. Ask volunteers to review Chapter 29 on Heart Disease. Have them summarize the most important concepts about heart disease and the symptoms of heart attacks in a written report. Have them share the report with the class.

L1 PERSONAL INVOLVEMENT. Ask volunteers to become qualified to use CPR.

L1 PARENTAL INVOLVEMENT. Ask students to talk to your parent-teacher organization about planning a workshop to teach CPR to parents.

L1 USING THE LESSON RESOURCES. For additional student activities, refer to the lesson resources on page 721.

CPR for Infants and Children

Because of differences in size, some adjustments need to be made when administering CPR to infants and children up to age 8.

Airway

Tip the child's head back only a little. Tilting the head back too far will close the airway.

Breathing

Cover your mouth over the child's nose and mouth rather than pinching the nose shut. For infants give small puffs of air.

Circulation

In infants, check the pulse at the inner arm just above the elbow. For a child, check the carotid pulse. If no pulse is detected, administer chest compressions as follows:

- **Infants.** Draw an imaginary line between the victim's nipples. Place two or three of your fingers on the sternum, one finger's width below the imaginary line. Compress ½ to 1 inch (1.3 to 2.5 cm) at a rate of 100 compressions per minute.
- **Children.** Place your middle and index fingers on the xiphoid process, and place the heel of your hand next to your index finger. With one hand, compress the sternum about 1 to 1½ inches (2.5 to 3.8 cm) at a rate of 80 to 100 compressions per minute.

For both infants and children, administer a breath after every five chest compressions.

DID YOU KNOW?

- Sudden death from heart attack is the most important medical emergency today. The only chance of survival for most people suffering cardiac arrest is CPR, which, when coupled with emergency medical treatment, increases the chances of survival to over 40 percent.

DID YOU KNOW?

- Access to your medical information might save your life in an emergency—especially if you are unconscious. One solution is Medic Alert, a worldwide nonprofit ID service that includes a bracelet or neckchain engraved with Medic Alert's 24-hour hot line and the person's critical medical facts. In an emergency, medical personnel can read the engraved information and call for medical details.

Across the Curriculum

Drama. Ask the drama teacher to help students develop scenarios related to emergencies to present in class. Have students determine the type of medical emergencies to be presented. An example could be: You and a friend go to a ball game with your dad. On the way out of the stadium, your dad clutches his chest as if he is in great pain. When you ask him what is the matter, he says that he is fine and has some indigestion or heartburn. You look closely and he is sweating and looks pale. What would you do?

First-aid training may help you save a life.

PROTECTING THE GOOD SAMARITAN

Even when first aid has been administered properly, complications sometimes arise. To protect rescuers from being sued in the event of such complications, Good Samaritan laws have been established in most states throughout the United States. According to these laws, no person who administers emergency care in good faith is liable for civil damages unless such acts are willfully or deliberately negligent.

This protection means that if you know first aid and are a layperson—that is, someone other than a medical professional who receives pay for services rendered—and you act in good faith, you cannot be held responsible for complications that might occur.

LESSON 2 REVIEW

Reviewing Facts and Vocabulary

1. Tell what *CPR* stands for. Then define the term and use it in an original sentence that also contains the term *xiphoid process*.
2. Who can administer CPR?
3. What are the ABCs of CPR?

Thinking Critically

4. **Analysis.** Compare the CPR given to an adult with that given to an infant or small child.
5. **Synthesis.** You are in the supermarket when a clerk suddenly slumps to the floor. Assuming you have been trained in CPR, what do you do first?

Applying Health Knowledge

6. Learn what you can about CPR and rescue breathing courses taught in your community. Prepare a directory of such courses, including the name of the organization, kind of instruction offered, and when and where classes are held.

CARDIOPULMONARY RESUSCITATION **725**

Answers to Lesson 2 Review

1. Cardiopulmonary resuscitation—the lifesaving technique administered to victims of cardiovascular failure. Sentences will vary. Xiphoid process—the lower part of the sternum that projects downward.
2. Only someone properly trained and certified in CPR.
3. Airway, breathing, circulation.
4. Both require one to be trained and certified and are based on ABCs of CPR. The tilt of the head, placement of compressions, and rate of compressions varies.
5. See "CPR for Adults" on pages 721 to 722.
6. Answers will vary.

Assess

Check for Understanding
- Assign and discuss the lesson review. Encourage LD students to focus on questions 1, 2, 3, 4, and 5.
- Assign and discuss the chapter review.

Evaluate
- Administer, grade, and discuss the *Lesson 2 Quiz.*
- Administer, grade, and discuss the *Chapter 36 Test.*
- Refer to the Performance Assessment strategy for this chapter. See pages T 23 to T 25.

Reteach
- Ask students to review the ABCs of CPR and then present this acronym in chart form. Have students translate this information into a catchy jingle which teaches what the *A* stands for, what the *B* stands for, and what the *C* stands for. For additional challenge, ask students to make up an acronym or other memory device to help people remember other critical information about first aid presented in this chapter.
- Ask students to complete *Reteaching Activity 100.*

Enrich
- Ask students to identify some of the possible psychological or medical concerns associated with rendering CPR, such as catching a communicable disease. Have students describe the ways rescuers may deal with these concerns in advance so that they do not hesitate in any emergency situation.
- Ask students to complete *Enrichment Activity 36.*

Close

Have students summarize the most important concepts learned in this lesson.

Self-Inventory

Are You a Lifesaver?

HOW DO YOU RATE?

There are many things you can do to save your own life and the lives of others. Number a sheet of paper from 1 through 12. Read each item below, and respond by writing *yes* or *no*. Total the number of *yes* and *no* responses. Then proceed to the next section.

1. I take small bites of food when eating.
2. I eat slowly, chewing each bite of food thoroughly before swallowing.
3. I try not to talk or laugh when I have food in my mouth.
4. I avoid taking sips of water or other beverages while there is food in my mouth.
5. I never eat or drink while in a reclining position.
6. I never go to sleep with chewing gum in my mouth.
7. I do not chew gum while playing sports.
8. I swim only in places where there is a trained lifeguard on duty.
9. I know what action needs to be taken to aid victims of choking, and I can perform that action.
10. I am trained in rescue breathing for adults and children.
11. I hold certification in CPR and know the procedure well.
12. I periodically review rescue breathing and CPR techniques.

HOW DID YOU SCORE?

Give yourself 1 point for every *yes* answer and 0 points for every *no* answer. Find your total, and read below to see how you scored. Then proceed to the next section.

10 to 12
Excellent. Your health choices show that you try to avoid risky situations and are prepared when emergencies arise.

7 to 9
Good. Your health choices are good, but you could be more cautious.

4 to 6
Fair. You are prone to health risks that could have serious consequences for yourself and others.

Below 4
Watch it! You are unprepared for life-threatening emergencies.

WHAT ARE YOUR GOALS?

Identify an area in which your score was low, and use the goal-setting process to pave the way for a change.

1. The behavior I would like to change is ____.
2. If this behavior were changed, I would look, feel, or act differently in the following ways: ____.
3. The steps involved in making this change are ____.
4. My timetable for making this change is ____.
5. People I will ask for help or assistance are ____.
6. The benefits I will receive as a result of making this change are ____.

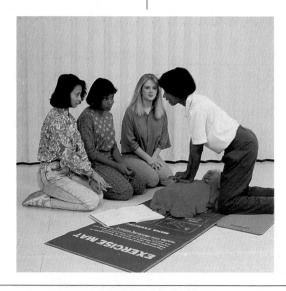

Using the Self-Inventory

Teaching Strategies

L1 EXPLANATION. Students frequently ask questions concerning liability when learning first-aid procedures. Assure students that the law will support all Good Samaritans that act in a manner consistent with a reasonably prudent individual. Individuals should do no more, and should do no less, than they have been trained to do.

L1 DISCUSSION. Invite an attorney to lead a discussion with your class on the Good Samaritan Law and its application to adolescents who may use first-aid procedures in an emergency.

L1 DISCUSSION. Have students discuss emergency situations that they have witnessed in their lives. Were people able to help because they had knowledge of first-aid procedures? How might the situation have turned out if people were or were not trained to handle an emergency situation?

L1 CLASS ACTIVITY. Invite members from your local fire department who are trained in emergency medical procedures to talk with students concerning home or school emergencies and the appropriate first-aid action to be taken.

L1 CLASS ACTIVITY. Have the class divide into groups. Assign various rescue procedures and scenarios to each group. Have students act out the scenario and rescue procedure in front of a video camera. Have students play the video rescue tape to the entire class as a graded project.

DID YOU KNOW?

■ Injuries kill more Americans ages 1 to 34 than all diseases combined, and they're the leading cause of death up to age 44.

Meeting Students' Needs

For students who score *Excellent*. Suggest that students look for summer employment that requires first-aid knowledge, such as being a lifeguard or camp counselor.

For students who score *Good*. Suggest that students enroll in first-aid courses offered by the American Red Cross.

For students who score *Fair*. Suggest that students examine their ability to handle emergency situations should they arise. Encourage students to involve their families in learning proper first-aid procedures.

For students who need to *Watch It*. Arrange for a guest speaker who experienced a life-threatening situation, but was aided by someone knowledgeable in first aid, to describe the incident.

Building Decision-Making Skills

Dan likes to play football. On Saturdays he and some friends from his neighborhood often meet in the park to play. Last week they met as usual, divided into teams, and were having a great time. Dan was really pumped. He loved being a receiver and had scored one touchdown that afternoon. He was hoping for another. On the next play, his team had possession of the ball. Gina was quarterback. Her pass was long, but Dan stretched and caught it in his fingertips. He went down holding the ball, but he did not get back up. His friends ran to where he lay. Dan was not breathing. Gina ran for help. What should his friends do?

A. Try to keep Dan warm and comfortable.
B. Raise his head with a pile of jackets.
C. Run for Dan's parents.
D. Check Dan's breathing and pulse. Begin rescue breathing if necessary.

WHAT DO YOU THINK?

1. **Situation.** Why does a decision need to be made? How much time is there to decide?
2. **Choices.** What other choices do Dan's friends have?
3. **Consequences.** What are the advantages of each choice?
4. **Consequences.** What are the disadvantages of each choice?
5. **Consequences.** What risks are involved in this decision?
6. **Decision.** What is the best solution for Dan? Explain your answer.
7. **Evaluation.** How would you handle a similar situation? What steps need to be taken in order to be prepared to help someone? What would be your concerns about helping someone?

Greta's brother Dave was driving her and a carload of her friends home from a concert. Suddenly, a car passed Dave at a high speed. Unfortunately the driver's speed did not allow time to maneuver a right curve in the road, and an accident occurred. Dave pulled over and ran to the wrecked car. A family was trapped inside. Two of the people in the car were unresponsive. What should Greta and her friends do?

A. Stay quietly in Dave's car and wait for Dave to tell them what to do.
B. Follow Dave to see what they can do to help.
C. Leave Dave and take the car to find a phone to call for emergency help.
D. Try to flag down a passing motorist to send for help.

WHAT DO YOU THINK?

8. **Situation.** What decisions need to be made? What are the dangers involved?
9. **Consequences.** What are the advantages and disadvantages of each choice listed above?
10. **Choices.** What other possibilities exist for Greta and her friends?
11. **Consequences.** What are the probable consequences of each of these choices?
12. **Choices.** What choices will Dave have to make? Who will be affected by his choices?
13. **Consequences.** How will others feel about Dave in each of his choices?
14. **Decision.** What is the best choice for Greta and her friends to make?
15. **Evaluation.** How would you respond if you were Dave or Greta in this situation? What factors should you consider?
16. **Evaluation.** Have you ever been in a similar situation? If so, how did you handle it? What did you learn from it?

Discussing the Answers

Situation 1. It is important that students react immediately. Because it is possible that Dan has suffered a neck or back injury, he should not be moved unless absolutely necessary, and only then as a single unit. It is imperative that someone qualified administer rescue breathing. If no student is qualified, one student should stay with Dan while others seek someone knowledgeable of first aid.

Situation 2. One person should drive to seek help. Qualified individuals should administer first aid if the situation is safe.

Building Decision-Making Skills

Teaching Strategies

L1 CLASS ACTIVITY. Have students participate in a role-play situation in which Gina and the other students playing football respond to Dan's injuries. Have students practice responding to different emergency situations.

L1 CLASS ACTIVITY. Have students participate in a role-play situation in which Dave, Greta, and Greta's friends witness a car accident. Have students act out their responses to this emergency situation. Have students practice responding to different variations of this scenario. Different scenarios may include: (1) The wrecked car is leaking gas. (2) One member of the family has a severe wound that is bleeding profusely. (3) One member of the family is not breathing, while another member of the family is in full cardiac arrest.

L1 CLASS ACTIVITY. Other possible role-plays pertaining to handling emergencies include: (1) You and a friend are listening to music in the backyard when the mother of the little girl that lives next door begins screaming. You and your friend run over to the neighbor's yard just in time to see the little girl floating face down in the neighbor's swimming pool. (2) You and several of your friends have found an old deserted warehouse. One of your friends accidently comes into contact with some live, exposed electrical wires. There is a flash of light and your friend collapses on the floor and is not responding.

L1 DISCUSSION. Have students discuss concerns that they may have about helping someone who has been a victim of an accident or a sudden illness. Would students be able to help in an emergency? Would students be willing to help in an emergency?

Answers to Chapter 36 Review

Using Health Terms

1. Emergency Medical Services, the American Heart Association, or American Red Cross
2. Absence of breathing movements
3. Café coronaries
4. One breath every 4 seconds
5. Diaphragm
6. Abdominal thrust
7. Carotid
8. Resuscitation
9. Sternum
10. Cardiovascular failure
11. Xiphoid process

Building Academic Skills

12. Speeches will vary but main points should be supported logically.
13. About 1.3 per second. Answers will vary. For 19 minutes—about 1,383 compressions; for 52 minutes—about 3,785 compressions.

Recalling the Facts

14. Permanent brain damage can occur within minutes.
15. Place the index and middle fingers on the victim's carotid artery.
16. It sometimes takes 8 to 10 thrusts.
17. The rescuer should look to see if the victim's chest is rising and falling (thus taking in air), listen for air being exhaled, feel for exhaled air on one's cheek.
18. Use your hand or the back of a chair to perform abdominal thrusts on yourself.
19. Ask, "Are you choking?"; administer abdominal thrusts.
20. Turn the infant over one arm with his or her face down, administer quick blows between the baby's shoulder blades, turn the infant over and press two fingers into the baby's sternum four times, alternate back blows and chest thrusts until the object is dislodged.
21. See numbered items in "Rescue Breathing for Adults" on pages 718 and 720.

22. Wording will vary but should include: Take small bites of food, chew food well, do not talk or laugh with food in your mouth, do not go to bed with gum or food in your mouth.
23. See numbered items in "Choking in Children and Adults" on page 716.
24. Maintain an open airway; supply the victim with

oxygen for his or her survival.
25. Breathing failure, drug overdose, a blockage in a blood vessel, electrical shock, poisoning.
26. When the victim has no pulse.
27. To breathe for the victim and force his or her heart to pump blood through the body.

28. The area to compress, the depth of compressions, and the rate of compressions are different. A person uses only two or three fingers on an infant to make the compressions; on a child one uses the heel of one's hand.
29. Ask, "Are you all right?", have victim lying flat on his or her back, administer res-

---

REVIEW

Using Health Terms

On a separate sheet of paper, write the term that best matches each definition given below.

LESSON 1

1. Organization that provides training in the use of effective techniques for choking.
2. Signs of breathing failure.
3. Choking accidents in restaurants have been called this.
4. Rate of rescue breathing for a child under 8 years old.
5. Muscle located right below the lungs.
6. A quick upward movement used on an adult choking victim.
7. Major artery located in a person's neck.
8. The act or process of reviving.

LESSON 2

9. Breastbone.
10. Condition in which the heart and/or cardiovascular system do not function properly.
11. The posterior part of the sternum.

Building Academic Skills

LESSON 2

12. **Writing.** Imagine that you have become a spokesperson for the American Red Cross. Write a speech to be given to area high schools, persuading your peers of everyone's need to know procedures for choking, artificial respiration, and CPR. Make sure your speech is clear and concise and supports your ideas.
13. **Math.** For cardiopulmonary resuscitation on an adult, one should administer 80 compressions per minute. Estimate and then calculate how many this would be per second. Now record the time it takes to do 2 full breaths. Allowing for the breaths, estimate and then calculate how many compressions one would need to do if one had to perform CPR for 19 minutes; for 52 minutes.

Recalling the Facts

LESSON 1

14. When respiratory failure occurs, why is it important that the victim receive oxygen quickly?
15. Explain how one should feel for a victim's pulse.
16. When performing the Heimlich maneuver, why is it important not to give up after one or two tries?
17. What is the significance of look, listen, and feel when administering rescue breathing?
18. If one is alone and choking, what is the best thing to do?
19. What are the steps for aiding an adult choking victim?
20. What is the procedure for aiding a choking infant?
21. Outline the steps to follow in giving artificial respiration to adults.
22. In your own words, tell four ways a person might avoid becoming a choking victim.
23. What is the proper technique for performing an abdominal thrust?
24. What are the two main objectives for rescue breathing?

LESSON 2

25. What are some situations that can bring on cardiovascular failure?
26. When should cardiopulmonary resuscitation be administered?
27. What is the purpose of cardiopulmonary resuscitation?
28. How does administering cardiopulmonary resuscitation to young children differ from that for infants?
29. Briefly explain the steps in administering cardiopulmonary resuscitation to an adult.
30. Outline the steps for administering artificial circulation to an adult.
31. Why must one be careful not to press on the xiphoid process?
32. What are the measurements for compression when performing cardiopulmonary resuscitation on an infant, child, and adult?

REVIEW

Thinking Critically

LESSON 1

33. Analysis. What is the importance of knowing any universal distress symbol, such as the one for choking?

34. Analysis. Why do you suppose abdominal thrusts cannot be performed on an infant?

LESSON 2

35. Evaluation. What are some reasons one might be hesitant to become involved in an emergency situation?

36. Evaluation. Of all the reasons given for why people choose not to get involved in emergency situations, which do you feel are valid? Explain your answer.

37. Analysis. When administering CPR, two people can be better than one. What do you think is the reason for this?

38. Evaluation. It is part of some religious beliefs that any kind of medical intervention should not be conducted. Imagine that a physician in an emergency room administered first aid to a person whose faith forbids it, and that victim sues the rescuer. The rescuer is protected by the Good Samaritan laws. In your opinion, is it a good law? Explain your answer.

Making the Connection

LESSON 1

39. Science. Draw the respiratory system showing how the abdominal thrust forces the diaphragm upward and dislodges a foreign object.

40. Language Arts. Research the universality of body language. Make a notebook of eight words and their interpretation in body language. Learn these words and share them with the class.

41. Home Economics. Make a list of items that need to be kept away from small children to prevent choking. Make a poster to display this information. Share your poster with your class.

Applying Health Knowledge

LESSON 1

42. Make a list of at least five items that may cause choking in small children.

43. A person should not use his or her thumb to take a pulse. Find out why.

44. When one is administering artificial respiration to an infant, why is it important not to breathe full breaths into the baby?

LESSON 2

45. Now that you have studied artificial respiration and cardiopulmonary resuscitation, identify three places where emergency situations that require these techniques might take place. Check to see whether the people at these locations are trained and certified to administer these procedures.

46. When administering CPR to an adult, it is important to kneel over the victim so that the rescuer's shoulders are directly over the victim's chest. Why is this necessary?

47. List reasons you can think of that no one should give CPR without proper training and certification.

Beyond the Classroom

LESSON 2

48. Parental Involvement. Describe to your parents the importance of learning cardiopulmonary resuscitation. Take a basic first aid course or a CPR class with your parents.

49. Community Involvement. Check to see who is the closest person to your home, school, and/or workplace who knows CPR. Ask the person if you could call on her or him for assistance if the need arises. Get the person's phone number and keep it in a place close to the phone.

50. Further Study. Research and write a short report on the beginnings of the American Red Cross or the American Heart Association. Find out what role the organization plays today in your community.

---

cue breathing, provide artificial circulation.

30. Check for pulse, put the heel of the hand over the sternum, compress the sternum, administer rescue breathing, alternate between sets of compressions and pairs of breaths until help arrives.

31. It could break and harm the liver.

32. Infant—1/2 to 1 inch; child—1 to 1 1/2 inches; adult—1 1/2 to 2 inches.

Thinking Critically

33. Universal distress signals can cut across verbal language barriers.

34. Because of their smaller size, injury may result.

35. Answers will vary. Possible answers: Personal liability, fear of contracting a communicable disease, lack of knowledge or expertise, inability to perform under pressure, apathy.

36. Answers will vary but should be supported logically.

37. Answers will vary. Possible answers: It is sometimes necessary to administer CPR for long periods of time and one person could become overly tired and ineffective, but two people can take turns. One person might be more knowledgeable than the other and have a calming influence.

38. Answers will vary but should be supported logically.

Making the Connection

39. Drawings will vary.
40. Answers will vary.
41. Posters will vary.

Applying Health Knowledge

42. Answers will vary. Possible answers: Large marshmallows, peanut butter, hot dogs, parts of toys, buttons, coins, pebbles, acorns.

43. People have a pulse in their thumbs so one may not be able to determine whether it is his or her own pulse or the victim's.

44. A full adult breath could damage a baby's smaller lungs.

45. Answers will vary. Possible answers: Restaurants, athletic events, homes, movie theaters, on the street, at work.

---

46. This helps the rescuer put his or her weight into the chest compressions, which require a lot of strength.

47. Answers will vary. Possible answer: Without proper training or certification, one could actually do more harm than good.

Beyond the Classroom

48. No response is necessary.
49. No response is necessary.
50. Reports will vary.

Glossary

A

Abdominal thrusts. Quick, upward thrusts that force the diaphragm upward and force out the substance blocking the airway; Heimlich maneuver.

Absorption. The passage of digested food from the digestive tract into the circulatory system.

Abstinence. Choosing not to be sexually active; choosing not to use alcohol or other drugs.

Acquaintance rape. Rape by someone known casually by the victim or someone thought to be a friend.

Acquired immune deficiency syndrome (AIDS). A fatal communicable disease caused by HIV, with no known effective treatment or cure.

Active immunity. Immunity developed by one's body to protect one from disease.

Addiction. A physiological or psychological dependence on a substance or activity.

Additive interaction. An interaction that occurs when medicines work together in a positive way.

Adolescence. The stage between childhood and adulthood.

Adoption. The act of taking a child into one's family and legally assuming responsibility for that child, agreeing to raise him or her to adulthood.

Adrenal glands. Glands responsible for secreting hormones that help maintain the body's sodium and water balance, affect metabolism, and cope with stressors.

Adrenaline. A hormone secreted by the adrenal glands to prepare the body to respond to a stressor; the emergency hormone.

Advertising. The way by which a manufacturer gains one's attention for its product.

Advocate. Someone who speaks out for a position or product.

Aerobic exercise. Vigorous activity that uses continuous oxygen; activity that increases the lung's capacity to hold air.

Aesthetic. Artistic; responding to or appreciating that which one perceives as beautiful.

Age norm. Things a person is expected to be doing at a particular chronological age.

Aggravated assault. Unlawful attack often with a weapon, and having the intent to hurt or kill.

Aggressive. Being overly forceful, pushy, or hostile.

AIDS dementia complex. A progressive disorder that destroys the brain tissue of a person with AIDS.

Al-Anon. A worldwide self-help organization for family members and friends of alcoholics.

Alateen. An offshoot of Al-Anon specifically for teens and preteens between the ages of 12 and 20, whose parents or other family members or friends have drinking problems.

Alcoholics. People with alcoholism; people addicted to alcohol.

Alcoholics Anonymous (AA). A worldwide organization or support group that has played a major role in helping people to get and stay alcohol- and drug-free.

Alcohol-impaired driving. Driving under the influence of alcohol.

Alcoholism. Addiction to alcohol; a physical and psychological dependence on alcohol.

Allergens. Substances to which the body's immune system overreacts.

Alveoli. A cluster of thin-walled air sacs found at the end of each bronchiole.

Alzheimer's disease. A progressive, degenerative disorder that causes general mental deterioration.

Amino acids. Chemical substances that make up proteins.

Amphetamines. Stimulants that speed up the heart and breathing and cause anxiety, sleeplessness, and loss of appetite.

Anabolic steroids. Synthetic derivatives of testosterone.

Anaerobic exercise. Intense physical activity in which the body's supply of oxygen to produce energy does not meet the demand; activity that improves muscular strength, muscular endurance, and flexibility.

Analgesics. Medicines that relieve pain without loss of consciousness.

Angina pectoris. A condition in which one experiences pain and tightness or pressure in the chest as a result of the heart's not getting enough oxygen.

Anorexia nervosa. A psychological disorder that involves the irrational fear of becoming obese and results in severe weight loss from self-induced starvation.

Antagonistic interaction. An interaction that occurs when the effect of a medicine is canceled or reduced when taken with other medicine.

Antibiotics. Medicines that kill or reduce harmful bacteria in the body.

Antibodies. Proteins that destroy or neutralize pathogens in your body.

Antidiuretic hormone. One of two hormones secreted by the posterior lobe of the pituitary gland.

Antisocial personality disorder. A condition characterized by a person's constant conflict with society.

Antivenins. Blood fluids that contain antibodies and act more quickly than vaccines.

Anxiety disorders. Disorders in which real or imagined fears prevent a person from enjoying life.

Appendicitis. The inflammation of the appendix.

Appendicular skeleton. The bones of the shoulders, arms, hands, hips, legs, and feet.

Aqueous humor. In the eyeball, watery fluid that fills the cavity between the cornea and the lens.

Arteries. The largest of the blood vessels and those that carry blood away from the heart.

Arteriosclerosis. A condition in which the walls of arteries become thick and lose their elasticity.

Arthritis. Inflammation of a joint; conditions that cause aching, pain, and swelling in joints and connective tissue throughout the body.

Artificial respiration. See *rescue breathing*.

Assertive. Standing up for one's own rights in a firm, but positive, way.

Atherosclerosis. A condition in which the artery wall thickens due to fatty deposits that restrict blood flow.

Athlete's foot. An infection of the skin between the toes caused by the ringworm fungus.

Autonomy. The confidence that one can control one's own body, impulses, and environment.

Axial skeleton. The bones of the skull, sternum, ribs, and vertebrae.

Axon. The part of the neuron that carries impulses away from the cell body.

B

Balloon angioplasty. A procedure that involves threading a balloon-tipped catheter through the body to the site of a blockage, inflating the balloon, and opening a path for the blood to flow through; officially known as percutaneous transluminal coronary angioplasty.

Basal metabolism. The absolute minimum amount of energy required to maintain the life processes in one's body.

Battery. The use of physical force to control someone through the use of power.

B cells. Lymphocytes that are produced and that mature in bone marrow; stimulated by T helper cells to make antibodies.

Benign. Noncancerous.

Better Business Bureau (BBB). A nonprofit organization sponsored by private businesses.

Bile. A bitter fluid produced in the liver that is important to the breakdown of fats.

Binaural hearing. The ability to determine the direction a sound comes from by being able to hear it with both ears.

Biodegradable. Able to be broken down by microorganisms.

Biofeedback. Biological feedback about one's body; the process of becoming aware of physical events in one's body that one is normally not aware of, with the intent of gaining voluntary control of such events.

Biological age. One's age as determined by how well different parts of one's body are functioning.

Biopsy. A procedure in which a small amount of tissue is removed and examined for the presence of abnormal or cancerous cells.

Biosphere. The thin layer of soil, water, and air near the earth's surface.

Birth defects. Genetic conditions and many other types of diseases and disorders that are caused by a variety of other factors.

Bladder. A muscular organ that stores urine.

Blastocyst. A cluster of cells that has a hollow space in the center; the stage following the zygote stage.

Blended family. A type of nuclear family in which one or both parents have been married before and in which each may have a child or children from a previous marriage.

Blizzard. A snowstorm with winds of 35 miles per hour (56 km per hour) or greater.

Blood alcohol concentration (BAC). The amount of alcohol in a person's blood expressed by a percentage.

Blood pressure. The force of blood against the

walls of blood vessels as blood flows through the cardiovascular system.

Body composition. The percent of fat, lean muscle, bone, connective tissue, water, and so forth in the body.

Body system. A group of organs that work together to perform a common function.

Brain death. The loss of function of the entire brain, including the brain stem.

Brain stem. The division of the brain that connects the spinal cord to the brain.

Bronchi. Bronchial tubes that lead into the lungs.

Bronchioles. Divisions of the bronchial tubes within the lungs.

Bruise. An injury to tissue under the skin.

Bulimia. An eating disorder in which the victim follows a very restrictive diet, then binges in response to hunger, followed by self-induced vomiting, purging through laxative abuse, or following severely restrictive diets.

C

Calorie. A unit to measure the energy in food and the energy one's body burns.

Cancer. Abnormal, uncontrolled cell growth.

Capillaries. The smallest blood vessels.

Carbohydrate loading. Storing extra glycogen in the muscles before strenuous exercise.

Carbohydrates. Sugars, starches, and fiber that are the body's preferred source of energy.

Carbon monoxide. A colorless, odorless, poisonous gas that can be found in cigarette smoke and automobile exhaust fumes.

Carcinogenic. Cancer-causing or poisonous.

Carcinogens. Cancer-causing agents.

Carcinomas. Cancers that develop in epithelial tissue—tissue that forms the skin and linings of body organs.

Cardiac arrest. A condition in which the heart stops completely.

Cardiac muscle. Striated tissue that forms the walls of the heart.

Cardiopulmonary resuscitation (CPR). The lifesaving technique that involves breathing for the victim of cardiovascular failure and forcing his or her heart to pump blood by applying pressure on the victim's sternum.

Cardiorespiratory endurance. The ability of the heart, lungs, and blood vessels to send fuel and oxygen to the body's tissues during long periods of vigorous activity.

Cardiovascular diseases. Diseases of the heart and blood vessels.

Carjacking. The hijacking or stealing of a car by force with a weapon.

Carotid pulse. The heartbeat that can be felt on each side of the neck.

Cartilage. A strong, flexible material that allows for smooth movement in joints, supports the nose and ears, connects the ribs to the sternum, and acts as a cushion between adjoining vertebrae.

Catheter. A thin, flexible plastic tube that can be guided through blood vessels to certain body organs.

Cell. The basic unit of structure of all living things.

Cell body. The part of a neuron that has a nucleus and is the center for receiving and sending nerve impulses.

Cerebellum. The part of the brain that functions as a center for the coordination of skeletal muscle movement.

Cerebral palsy. A group of nonprogressive neurological disorders that are the result of damage to the developing brain either before or during birth.

Cerebrum. The largest, most complex part of the brain, consisting of the right and left hemispheres, that controls muscular activity and receives sensory input.

Cervix. The round, muscular neck, or bottom part, of the uterus.

Chancre. A reddish sore at the place where a pathogen enters the body.

Chemotherapy. The use of anticancer medications in the treatment of cancer.

Child abuse. Physical harm, including sexual abuse, and/or emotional harm to children.

Chlamydia. A sexually transmitted disease that attacks the reproductive organs.

Chlorofluorocarbons (CFCs). Compounds of chlorine, fluorine, and carbon believed to be a major factor in ozone reduction.

Cholesterol. Fatlike substance.

Choroid. The middle layer of the eyeball wall, containing the iris, the suspensory ligaments, and the ciliary muscles.

Chromosomes. Tiny structures within the nuclei of cells, which carry genetic information.

Chronic bronchitis. A condition in which the bronchi are irritated.

Chronic fatigue syndrome (CFS). A type of fatigue that is long-term and for which the cause is unknown.

Chronological age. One's age as determined by the number of birthdays one has had.

Chyme. A substance formed when food and gastric juices mix together.

Circumcision. A procedure in which the foreskin is surgically removed.

Cirrhosis. Scarring; a condition of the liver in which scarring reduces blood flow in the liver.

Clinical death. The cessation of a person's body functions.

Clinical depression. A condition in which feelings of sadness and hopelessness last for more than a few weeks and interfere with one's daily activities and interests.

Clinical psychologist. A psychologist who diagnoses and treats emotional and behavioral disorders.

Cliques. Exclusive friendship groups that usually share common interests and backgrounds.

Cluttered-nest syndrome. A phenomenon in which grown children return home to live with their parents.

Codependency. Being overly concerned with other people's behavior and problems and feeling driven to fix and control those problems.

Communicable diseases. Diseases caused by the direct or indirect spread of pathogens from one person to another.

Communication. A process through which messages are sent and received; openness among family members, including displays of tenderness, warmth, and humor.

Compromise. A way of solving a problem in which each person gives up something in order to find a solution that satisfies everyone.

Compulsion. An urgent, repeated behavior.

Congenital. Existing at or dating from birth.

Congenital syphilis. A condition in which a pregnant female who had syphilis transferred the infection to her unborn child.

Conjunctiva. A protective mucous membrane attached to the inner surface of the eyelids that continues over the outer surface of the eyeball.

Consequence. The result of an action.

Conservation. Preserving the environment.

Consumer. Anyone who uses a product or service.

Consumer health. The process of helping one select health products and services wisely, and letting one know where to go or what to do if one has been treated unfairly or needs help.

Cooling down. Gradually decreasing activity after exercise in order to allow one's pulse rate to slow down.

Cornea. A colorless, transparent part of the sclera in the front part of the eye.

Coronary angiography. Procedure used to help evaluate the extent of coronary artery disease.

Coronary bypass surgery. A procedure to create detours around obstructed or narrowed coronary arteries so that blood can reach the heart.

Crisis. An extreme change in a person's life.

Cross-contamination. Spreading bacteria from one food to another.

D

Daily Food Guide. A publication that offers an easy way to choose a varied, balanced, and moderate diet.

Date rape. Rape that occurs between two people who are dating.

Deafness. The loss of the ability to hear.

Decision. The act of making a choice or coming to a solution.

Defense mechanisms. Strategies used to deal with stressful situations.

Deforestation. The destruction of forests.

Dendrites. The part of the neuron that receives and carries impulses toward the cell body.

Dentin. Material that surrounds the pulp.

Depressants. Sedatives; drugs that tend to slow down the central nervous system.

Dermis. The inner, thicker layer of skin.

Desertification. The conversion of grasslands, rain-fed cropland, or irrigated cropland to desertlike conditions.

Designer drugs. Drugs made with synthetic substances by street chemists.

Detoxification. The process of removing drugs from one's body.

Developmental task. Something that needs to occur during a particular stage for a human being to continue his or her growth toward becoming a healthy, mature adult.

Diabetes. A chronic disease that affects the way body cells convert food into energy.

Diaphragm. A muscle that separates the chest and abdominal cavity.

Diet. Everything a person eats and drinks.

Digestion. The physical and chemical breakdown of foods into smaller pieces.

Digestive enzymes. Proteins that speed up the breakdown of food.

Discrimination. A form of prejudice in which people are singled out and treated negatively as a result of one factor, such as age, sex, race, ethnicity, or some physical trait.

Distress. Negative stress.

Divorce. The legal dissolution, or ending, of the marriage contract.

Dormant. Inactive.

Down syndrome. A condition, characterized by mild to serious mental retardation, that is the result of a chromosomal abnormality.

Drug. Dangerous and often illegal substance, including alcohol and tobacco.

Drug dependence. Drug addiction.

E

Earthquakes. Heavy ground tremors.

Electrocardiogram (EKG or ECG). A test that produces a graph of the electric activity of the heart.

Elimination. The expulsion of undigested food or body wastes.

ELISA. Enzyme-linked immunosorbent assay; a test to detect the presence of HIV infection.

Embolus. A blood clot that moves from the point where it was formed.

Embryo. A cluster of cells, or blastocyst, that has implanted itself in the uterus.

Emotions. Feelings that influence everything one does.

Empty-calorie foods. Foods that have little or no nutritional value.

Empty-nest syndrome. The phenomenon of children entering adulthood and leaving home.

Enabling. Trying to protect the person having trouble with alcohol or drugs from facing the consequences of his or her drug-related problems.

Enamel. The hardest material in the body; material that covers the crown of the tooth.

Encephalitis. An inflammation of the brain caused by a virus and sometimes by a bacteria.

Endocrine glands. Ductless glands that secrete hormones into the bloodstream.

Endocrine system. The body system consisting of ductless glands and the hormones they produce.

Enriched. A product that has had nutrients lost in processing added back.

Environment. All of one's surroundings, including family, location, and experiences.

Epidermis. The outer, thinner layer of skin.

Epilepsy. A disorder of the nervous system characterized by a sudden burst of nerve impulses in the brain that results in a seizure.

Esophagus. A muscular tube that extends from the pharynx to the stomach and is situated behind the trachea and heart.

Estrogen. A female hormone first released during puberty.

Estuaries. Ecosystems where seawater mixes with fresh water.

Eustress. Positive stress.

Exploited. Used for someone else's benefit.

Extended family. A family with one or more relatives in addition to the nuclear or single-parent family.

Extensors. Muscles that straighten a limb.

External auditory canal. A passageway about 1 inch long that leads to the eardrum and protects the ear by keeping out foreign substances.

External respiration. The exchange of oxygen and carbon dioxide between the blood and the air in the lungs.

F

Fallopian tubes. A pair of tubes through which a mature ovum travels.

Family. A group of people related by blood, marriage, or adoption.

Fatigue. A tired feeling that lowers one's level of activity.

Fatty liver. A condition in which fats have built up in the liver, preventing normal functions of liver cells.

Federal Trade Commission (FTC). A federal agency that prevents the unfair, false, or deceptive advertising of consumer products and services.

Feedback. Messages from others that tell how others feel about a person or idea.

Fertilization. The union of an egg cell and a sperm cell that can occur only if sperm cells are present when the ovum is in the Fallopian tube; conception.

Fetal alcohol syndrome (FAS). A condition in which a fetus has been adversely affected by its mother's heavy alcohol use during pregnancy.

Fetus. An embryo from the eighth week after conception to birth.

Fibrillation. A rhythmic disturbance that occurs when the muscle fibers of the heart contract in an uncoordinated manner.

Fire extinguisher. A portable device that puts out small fires by ejecting fire-extinguishing chemicals.

First aid. Emergency care; the immediate, temporary care given to a person who has become sick or who has been injured.

Fitness. Readiness. Fit people are better equipped than nonfit people to handle day-to-day situations.

Flexibility. The ability to move a body part through a full range of motions.

Flexors. Muscles that bend a limb.

Fluoroscope. A machine that provides a live picture, often used by doctors to look directly at the heart shadow.

Follicle. A small pocket that holds the hair root in the dermis.

Food additives. Substances added to food intentionally to produce a desired effect.

Food allergy. A condition in which the body's immune system overreacts to allergens in some foods.

Food and Drug Administration (FDA). A federal agency that ensures all food and food additives, other than meat and poultry, are safe, pure, wholesome, and honestly and correctly labeled.

Foodborne illness. A condition caused by eating food contaminated with bacteria; food poisoning.

Fortification. The process of adding nutrients not naturally present.

Fraternal twins. Two embryos with different genetic makeup.

Friendship. A significant relationship between two people, based on caring, consideration, and trust.

Frostbite. A condition in which ice crystals form in the spaces between the cells.

Functional disorder. A mental disorder that occurs as a result of psychological causes in which no brain damage is involved.

G

Gallbladder. An organ that stores bile.

Gallstones. Small crystals formed from bile that can block the bile duct between the gallbladder and the duodenum.

Gangrene. The death of tissue in a part of the body.

Gastric juices. Liquids that contain hydrochloric acid, digestive enzymes, and mucus and that start the digestion of proteins.

Gastritis. A disorder in which the mucous membrane that lines the stomach becomes inflamed.

Genes. Small sections of chromosomes that control hereditary characteristics.

Genetic condition. Disease or disorder, illness, or other condition of malfunction with which one is born.

Gerontologist. People who study the process of aging.

Glucose. A sugar formed in the body during digestion.

Glycogen. The form in which carbohydrates are stored in the body.

Goal. An aim that requires planning and work to attain; definite plan one has in one's life.

Gonorrhea. A sexually transmitted disease caused by bacteria that live in warm, moist areas of the body.

Group practice. A situation in which two or more physicians unite to provide medical care.

H

Halitosis. Bad breath.

Hallucinogens. Psychedelics; drugs that alter mood, thought, and the senses.

Hashish. Dark brown resin collected from the tops of the cannabis plant.

Health. The state of total physical, mental, and social well-being.

Health care delivery. Health service.

Health education. The providing of health information so as to influence people to change attitudes so that they take positive action about their health.

Health facility. A place a person goes for health care.

Health maintenance organization (HMO). A health plan in which one pays regular fees and then receives medical care for little or no additional cost.

Health resources. Places that people can go for various types of treatment.

Health services. The aspect of an overall health program concerned with the prevention of disease, the maintenance and promotion of health, and the treatment and cure of disease.

Heart attack. A common way to refer to a number of disorders that involve the heart and blood vessels, but in general occurs because the heart muscle cells are not getting the oxygen and nutrients they need.

Hemodialysis. A technique in which a person is connected to an artificial kidney machine.

Hemoglobin. The oxygen-carrying substance in red blood cells.

Hepatitis. A serious inflammation of the liver that is most often caused by viral infection.

Heredity. The passing of characteristics from parents to offspring.

Hernias. Weak areas in the muscle supporting various organs; ruptures.

Herpes simplex type 2 virus. An STD in which a virus causes blisterlike sores, called genital herpes, in the genital area.

Hiatal hernia. A condition in which the upper part of the stomach pushes through the diaphragm.

Hierarchy of needs. A ranked list of things human beings must have to survive and thrive.

High blood pressure. Hypertension.

Histamine. A substance released when a cold-causing virus invades one's respiratory system.

Holistic. Whole; considering physical, mental, and social influences on the whole person and his or her health.

Homicide. The willful killing of one human being by another.

Hormones. Body chemical produced by ductless glands that regulate the activity of different body cells; the cause of physical and emotional changes.

Hospice. A place that promotes a special way of caring for the dying.

Host. The plant or animal on which a parasite feeds.

Human collision. In an accident, the act of a person hitting some part of the car or being thrown from the vehicle.

Human immunodeficiency virus (HIV). The virus that attacks the body's immune system and leads to AIDS.

Hurricane. A powerful rainstorm characterized by driving winds.

Hurricane watch. A National Weather Service advisory that means atmospheric conditions exist so that a hurricane could develop.

Hypertension. High blood pressure.

Hypochondria. A somatoform disorder in which one experiences a preoccupation with the body and fear of presumed diseases.

I

Identical twins. Two embryos with the same genetic makeup.

Implantation. The process by which cells attach to the lining of the uterus.

Indigestion. A condition in which one's body does not properly break down foods.

Inhalants. Substances with fumes that are sniffed and inhaled to give a hallucinogenic high.

Inpatients. People who require prolonged health care and are admitted to a facility and occupy a bed in it.

Insulin. A hormone produced in the pancreas that aids the body in converting glucose into energy to be used by the cells.

Integumentary system. The system that includes the skin, hair, nails, and sweat glands.

Internal respiration. The exchange of gases between the blood and the body cells.

Interneurons. Nerve cells within the brain and spinal cord that relay impulses from sensory neurons to motor neurons.

Intervention. The act of interrupting the addiction continuum before the alcoholic or addict hits bottom.

Involuntary. Not within a person's conscious control.

K

Kidneys. Organs that filter blood to remove harmful substances from the substances one's body can use.

L

Labyrinth. The inner ear; consists of the vestibule, semicircular canals, and cochlea.

Lacrimal gland. A gland located above the eye that is responsible for producing tears.

Lactose intolerance. A condition in which the body is unable to digest milk sugar.

Larynx. The voice box.

Leukoplakia. Thickened, white, leathery-appearing spots on the inside of a smokeless tobacco user's mouth.

Life expectancy. The average number of years a group of people is expected to live.

Life-style factors. Repeated behaviors related to the way a person lives, which affect one's level of health.

Ligaments. Strong bands or cords of tissue that connect bones to bones at a joint.

Lipids. Fatty substances that do not dissolve in water.

Look-alike drugs. Drugs made from legal substances to look like illegal drugs.

Lymph. A clear, yellow fluid that flows through lymphatic vessels.

Lymph nodes. Masses of tissues that filter lymph.

Lymphocytes. A type of white blood cell that multiplies in lymph nodes and lymph tissue to destroy invading pathogens.

Lymphomas. Cancers that develop in blood-forming tissues and the lymphatic system.

M

Mainstream smoke. Smoke that a smoker blows off.

Malignant. Cancerous.

Manic-depressive disorder. A condition in which a person's moods shift dramatically from one emotional extreme to another for no apparent reason.

Manipulation. An indirect, and often sneaky or dishonest, means of trying to control another's attitudes or behaviors.

Marijuana. A hemp plant that is smoked, eaten, or drunk for intoxicating effects.

Marital adjustment. How well people within a marriage adjust and adapt to the marriage and to each other.

Marriage. The joining of a man and a woman according to custom or law.

Mastication. The process of chewing.

Medicaid. An assistance program of medical aid for people of all ages who are unable to financially afford medical care.

Medicare. A health insurance program available to people who are 65 years of age and older and to people who receive social security disability benefits.

Medicine. A substance that, when taken into or applied to the body, helps prevent or cure some disease, injury, or medical problem.

Medicine misuse. Using medicine in a way that is not intended.

Megadoses. Very large amounts of nutrient supplements.

Melanoma. Skin cancer.

Meningitis. An inflammation of the meninges.

Menstrual cycle. The time from the beginning of one menstrual period to the onset of the next.

Menstruation. The process of shedding the lining of the uterus.

Mental disorders. Mental and emotional problems.

Mental health. The process of accepting and liking oneself and adapting to and coping with the emotions, challenges, and changes that are part of life.

Mental illness. Medical disease or disorder that affects one's mind and prevents a person from enjoying life.

Metabolism. The sum total of all chemical reactions within a cell.

Metastasis. The process of cancer cells spreading.

Mobile. Likely to move from place to place.

Motor neurons. Nerve cells that carry impulses from interneurons within the brain and spinal cord to muscles and glands.

Multiple sclerosis. A progressive disorder in which the myelin sheath that surrounds nerve fibers is destroyed.

Multiplier effect. The act of taking drugs or medicines with alcohol.

Muscular endurance. The ability of muscles to keep working over a period of time without causing fatigue.

Muscular strength. The ability to exert force against resistance.

Mycobacterium avium intracellulare (MAI). An opportunistic infection that is the leading cause of wasting syndrome, a gradual deterioration of all body functions; associated with AIDS.

N

Narcotics. Drugs made from the opium poppy flower and medicines used to relieve pain and induce sleep.

Nephrons. The functional units of the kidneys.

Neurologist. A doctor who specializes in organic disorders of the brain and nervous system.

Neurons. Nerve cells that are the functional and structural parts of the nervous system.

Neutrophils. One type of phagocyte that is most actively involved in the process of phagocytosis.

Nicotine. The addictive drug in cigarettes that raises blood pressure and increases heart rate.

Noncommunicable diseases. Diseases that are not caused by pathogens and not transmitted through contact.

Nongonococcal urethritis (NGU). A sexually transmitted disease caused by several different kinds of bacterialike organisms that infect the urethra in males and the cervix in females.

Nontoxic. Not harmful or poisonous to humans.

Nonverbal communication. The act of sending messages through facial expressions and body movements.

Nuclear family. Parents and one or more children sharing a household.

Nutrient-dense. High in nutrients relative to caloric content.

Nutrients. Substances in food that the body needs to function properly.

Nutrient supplements. Pills, powders, and liquids that contain nutrients.

Nutrition. The science of looking at how the body uses nutrients and at how and why people eat.

O

Obesity. Excess body fat.

Obsession. A very damaging emotional and social preoccupation.

Occupational Safety and Health Administration (OSHA). A federal agency that promotes safe and healthy conditions at work.

Open-dating. The practice of putting dates on food packages to indicate expiration, freshness, packing, or last sale date of product.

Organ. Two or more tissue types that perform a specific job.

Organic. Derived from living organisms without the use of chemicals.

Organic disorder. A mental disorder caused by a physical illness or an injury that affects the brain.

Ossicles. Three small bones that are linked together and located behind the eardrum that connect the eardrum with the inner ear.

Ossification. A process by which cartilage cells are replaced by bone cells and minerals.

Osteoarthritis. A condition in which the mechanical parts of a joint suffer from wear and tear.

Osteomyelitis. An inflammation of the soft inner surface of the bones.

Osteoporosis. A condition that results from a lack of calcium in the bone.

Otosclerosis. A hereditary disease that is a common cause of partial deafness.

Outpatients. People who receive medical, dental, or other health services in a facility and return home the same day.

Ovaries. Female sex glands that house the ova and produce female sex hormones.

Overweight. Weighing more than 10 percent over the standard weight for height.

Ovulation. The process in which the ovaries release one mature ovum each month.

Ovum. An egg cell.

Oxytocin. One of two hormones secreted by the posterior lobe of the pituitary gland.

P

Pancreas. A gland that serves the digestive and endocrine systems.

Papillae. Small projections that cover the tongue's surface.

Parasite. Microorganism that uses a living plant or animal as a food supply.

Parathyroid glands. The glands located on the lobes of the thyroid gland and that regulate the body's calcium and phosphorous balance.

Parkinson's disease. A progressive disorder that interferes with the transmission of nerve impulses from the motor areas of the brain.

Passive. Giving up, giving in, or backing down without standing up for one's own rights and needs.

Passive-aggressive personality disorder. A condition in which one is often uncooperative with others and displays anger indirectly.

Passive immunity. The temporary immunity an infant acquires from its mother.

Passive smoke. Cigarette, cigar, or pipe smoke inhaled by nonsmokers.

Pathogens. Tiny microorganisms that invade the body and attack its cells and tissues, causing many common diseases.

Peer pressure. The control and influence people of the same age or social group have over one another.

Peers. People one's own age.

Pelvic inflammatory disease (PID). A painful infection of the Fallopian tubes, ovaries, and/or the uterus as a result of untreated gonorrhea or chlamydia.

Penis. The male external reproductive organ composed of spongy tissue that contains many blood vessels.

Peptic ulcers. Ulcers that develop in the digestive system.

Percent body fat. The amount of fat in the body in relation to total body weight.

Percutaneous transluminal coronary angioplasty (PTCA). See *balloon angioplasty*.

Periodontal disease. An inflammation of the periodontal structures.

Periodontium. The area immediately around the teeth; the gums, periodontal ligament, and the jawbone.

Peripheral. Located away from the center.

Peristalsis. A series of involuntary muscle contractions that moves food through the esophagus and the entire digestive tract.

Personal identity. Factors that one believes make one unique ordifferent from everyone else.

Personality. A complex set of characteristics that makes each person unique and distinctive from everyone else.

Phagocytosis. The process in which certain white blood cells surround and eat up invading bacteria.

Pharmacist. A person concerned with the preparation, distribution, and sale of medicine.

Pharynx. The throat.

Phobia. An extreme fear that causes a person to limit normal functioning to avoid the fear.

Phonocardiograph. A test that involves placing a microphone on a person's chest to record heart sounds and signals, transferring them through photography to graph paper.

Photochemical smog. Pollution that occurs when vehicle exhausts, activated by sunlight, combine with other hydrocarbons in the atmosphere.

Physical fitness. The ability to carry out daily tasks easily and have enough reserve energy to respond to unexpected demands.

Physiological dependence. A chemical need of the body for a drug.

Phytoplankton. Microscopic organisms found in open, sunlit waters that are the basis of food webs in freshwater and marine life and are a factor in maintaining the composition of the atmosphere.

Pituitary gland. The gland that is situated at the base of the brain and that regulates other endocrine glands; the master gland.

Placebo. A substance that has no medicinal value, which is given for its psychological effect.

Placenta. A blood-rich tissue developed from an outer layer of cells from the embryo and tissue from the mother.

Planned pregnancy. A pregnancy in which a decision is made to get pregnant before the baby is conceived.

Plaque. Fatty deposits that can build up along the inner lining of the arteries; on teeth–a sticky, colorless film that acts on sugar to form acids that destroy tooth enamel and irritate gums.

Plasma. The liquid part of blood.

Platelets. The smallest parts of the blood; crucial to clotting of the blood.

Platonic relationship. A friendship in which there is affection but not romance.

Pneumocystis carinii pneumonia (PCP). An opportunistic infection associated with AIDS.

Poison. Any substance that causes injury, illness, or death when introduced into the body.

Poison control center. A center that one can call for information about what to do when someone has ingested a poison.

Poliomyelitis. A viral infection that affects motor neurons in the spinal cord and brain stem.

Post-traumatic stress disorder. A condition in which a person who has experienced a traumatic event feels severe and long-lasting aftereffects.

Precaution. A planned, preventive action taken before an event to increase the chances of a safe outcome.

Precycling. Reducing waste before it occurs by making environmentally sound decisions about purchases.

Prejudice. A negative feeling toward someone or something that is based on stereotypes, not experience.

Pressure-point technique. Method used to stop bleeding by applying pressure to the main artery supplying blood to the affected limb.

Prevention. The act of practicing healthy habits to keep oneself well and free from disease and other ailments.

Primary care. The care one seeks on one's own, usually administered by one's family doctor.

Private practice. The medical practice of a doctor who is self-employed.

Progesterone. A female hormone first released during puberty.

Proteins. A vital part of every body cell.

Psychiatrist. A medical doctor who deals with mental, emotional, and behavioral disorders.

Psychoactive drugs. Drugs that affect the central nervous system and alter normal functioning of the brain.

Psychological dependence. The belief that one needs a drug in order to feel good or function normally.

Psychosomatic. Involving both the body and the mind.

Puberty. The beginning of adolescence; the period of time when males and females become physically able to reproduce.

Pulmonary circulation. The flow of blood from the heart to the lungs and back to the heart.

Pulmonary emphysema. A condition in which the tiny air sacs in the lungs through which oxygen is absorbed into the body are destroyed.

Pulp. Very sensitive, living tissue inside the tooth.

Pulse recovery rate. The rate at which one's heart beats following activity.

Q

Quack. A dishonest promoter of useless medicinal products or treatments.

Quackery. The act of dishonestly promoting useless medicinal products.

Quality of life. The level of health and satisfaction that a person has in being alive.

R

Rabies. A viral infection of the brain and spinal cord transmitted to humans through the bite of an infected animal.

Random violence. Violence committed for no particular reason and/or against anyone who happens to be around at the time.

Rape. Sexual intercourse by force or threat.

Recall. The process of instructing a manufacturer to take its product that is already on the market, but considered to be unsafe, off the shelves.

Recommended Dietary Allowances (RDA). Guidelines for the amounts of 19 essential nutrients that most people need daily and for calories and estimated intake for seven other vitamins and minerals.

Recovery. The process of getting well again; the process of learning to live an alcohol- or drug-free life.

Recycling. Treating or changing waste so that it can be reused.

Reflex. A spontaneous response of the body to a stimulus.

Refusal skills. Techniques and strategies that help one say no effectively.

Relapses. For people in recovery, periodic returns to drinking and drug use.

Relationship. A bond or connection between people.

Rescue breathing. The process of providing oxygen for a victim who has stopped breathing.

Resident bacteria. Bacteria that live in one's mouth and intestines and on one's skin and help protect one from harmful bacteria.

Resting heart rate. One's heart rate while one is not active.

Retina. The layer of the eyeball wall that contains the nerve cells and the processes responsible for vision.

Rheumatoid arthritis. A destructive and disabling inflammation of the joints.

Risk. A behavior with an element of danger that may cause injury or harm.

Risk factor. A characteristic that has been shown to increase the chances of getting heart disease.

Role. A part that one plays, especially in a relationship.

S

Saliva. A secretion that starts the digestion of carbohydrates.

Saprophytes. Bacteria that digest nonliving food materials, such as milk and meat.

Sarcomas. Cancers that develop in connective and supportive tissues, such as bones, muscles, and tendons.

Saturated. In the case of fatty acids, having hydrogen linked to all the carbon atoms on the chain.

Schizophrenia. A severe mental disorder in which one exhibits abnormal emotional responses or no emotional responses.

Sclera. A white, tough membrane that helps the eye keep its spherical shape and helps protect the eye's delicate inner structure.

Scoliosis. A side-to-side curvature of the spine.

Scrotum. A sac outside the male's body that contains the testes and protects sperm by regulating the temperature of the testes.

Sebaceous glands. Glands that produce an oily secretion called sebum and that are connected to hair follicles.

Secondary care. The care one receives when one is referred by a primary-care doctor to a specialist.

Secondary sex characteristics. Body hair and the development of breasts in the female and muscles in the male.

Self-actualization. The continuing process of striving to develop one's capabilities to their fullest.

Self-esteem. The confidence and worth one feels about oneself; influences everything you do, think, feel, and are.

Semen. A mixture of fluids from the seminal vesicles, the prostrate gland, and Cowper's glands combined with sperm; seminal fluid.

Sensory deafness. Hearing loss caused by excessive noise over a long period of time.

Sensory neurons. Nerve cells located in the skin and other sensory organs that have specialized receptor ends.

Sexual assault. Attempted or actual physical attack with violent, sexual intent.

Sexually transmitted disease (STD). A communicable disease that is spread from person to person through sexual contact.

Shock. The failure of the cardiovascular system to keep adequate blood circulating to the vital organs of the body.

Sidestream smoke. Smoke that comes from burning tobacco.

Single-parent family. A family in which children live with one parent at a time.

Skeletal muscles. Voluntary muscles attached to bones that cause body movement.

Small-claims courts. Courts that deal with consumer complaint claims that range from $100 to $3,000.

Small intestine. An organ in which a major part of digestion and absorption occurs.

Smoke detector. An alarm used to awaken people and alert them in the event of smoke or flames.

Smooth muscles. Involuntary muscles located in such places as intestines and blood vessels.

Social age. One's age as determined by a person's life-style.

Sprain. An injury to soft tissues surrounding a joint.

Stereotype. An exaggerated and oversimplified belief about an entire group, such as an ethnic group, a religious group, or a certain sex.

Sterility. A condition in which a person is unable to reproduce.

Stigma. A mark of shame.

Stimulant. A drug that increases the action of the central nervous system, the heart, respiratory rates, and blood pressure, and causes the pupils to dilate and appetite to decrease.

Strain. A condition in which muscles have been overworked.

Stress. The body's and mind's reactions to everyday demands.

Stressor. A stimulus that produces a stress response.

Stroke. A condition in which the blood supply to a part of the brain is cut off, and as a result, the nerve cells in that part of the brain cannot function.

Sweat glands. Glands that secrete perspiration through ducts to pores on the surface.

Synapse. A narrow gap between the axon end on one neuron and the dendrite of another over which an impulse must cross.

Synergistic effect. The interaction of two or more medicines that results in a greater effect than when the medicines are taken independently.

Synthetic. Made from laboratory chemicals.

Syphilis. A sexually transmitted disease that attacks many parts of the body.

Systemic circulation. The flow of blood to all body tissues except the lungs.

T

Tar. A thick, sticky, dark fluid produced when tobacco burns.

Target heart rate. Seventy to 85 percent of one's maximum heart rate.

Tartar. A very hard substance that irritates the underlying bone as well as the surrounding gums of one's teeth; calculus.

T cells. Lymphocytes produced in the bone marrow that travel to the thymus gland where they mature, then fight specific pathogens.

Tendinitis. A condition when a tendon—the connective tissue of the muscles and bones—is stretched or torn.

Tendons. Bands of fiber that connect muscles to bones.

Tertiary care. The care one receives when one's condition requires specialized equipment or treatment.

Testes. Two small glands that produce sperm; testicles.

Testimonial. A person's enthusiastic recommendation of a product.

Testosterone. A male hormone that causes the testes to produce sperm and is responsible for physical changes during puberty.

Thanatology. The study of death and adjustments that need to be made in association with the death of a loved one.

Therapy. Treatment technique.

Thrombosis. The presence or formation of a blood clot that forms in a blood vessel and usually remains attached to its point of origin.

Thyroid gland. The largest gland in the endocrine system that regulates the metabolism of carbohydrates, fats, and proteins in body cells.

Time-management skills. The ability to effectively arrange one's time.

Tinnitus. A condition characterized by a ringing noise in one's ears.

Tissue. Cells with similar structure that do similar work.

Tolerance. A condition in which the body becomes used to the effects of a medicine or drug.

Tooth decay. A disease of the digestive tract that weakens the tooth and affects the way one can bite and chew food.

Toxins. Poisons produced by some bacteria.

Trachea. The windpipe.

Tranquilizers. Depressants that reduce muscular activity, coordination, and attention span.

Transition. Change.

Tumor. A mass of tissue caused by the uncontrolled division of abnormal cells.

Type I diabetes. Diabetes that usually occurs in people under 15 years of age and that requires daily injections of insulin to sustain life.

Type II diabetes. Diabetes that usually occurs in adults over 40 years of age and can often be controlled by diet and exercise.

U

Ulcer. An open sore on the skin or in the mucous membrane.

Umbilical cord. Cord that connects the embryo to the placenta and through which nutrients and oxygen from the mother are carried through blood vessels to the embryo, and waste products from the embryo are carried to the mother.

Undernutrition. Not consuming enough essential nutrients or calories for normal body functions.

Underweight. Being 10 percent or more below normal weight.

Unit price. The amount that a unit of a product costs.

Unit pricing. The practice of showing the cost per unit of different-sized packages of a product.

Unplanned pregnancy. A pregnancy in which a baby is conceived accidentally.

Uremia. A series of symptoms caused by the kidneys' inability to rid wastes from the body.

Ureters. Tubes that lead from the two kidneys to the bladder.

Urethra. A small tube that extends from the bladder to the outside of the body.

Urine. Liquid waste material that collects in the bladder until it is ready to be passed out of the body.

Uterus. A small, muscular, pear-shaped organ in a female body.

V

Vaccination. The process by which a vaccine is injected into the body.

Vaccine. A preparation containing weakened or dead pathogens of a particular disease given to prevent one from contracting that disease.

Vagina. A muscular, very elastic tube in the female that is a passageway from the uterus to the outside of the body; the birth canal.

Values. Principles that one considers important and that guide one's life.

Veins. The vessels that carry the blood back to the heart.

Verbal communication. Sending messages using words.

Violence. The use of physical force to injure or abuse another person or persons.

Viruses. Small, simple life-like forms.

Vitreous humor. A fluid found behind the lens that keeps the eyeball firm.

Voluntary. Within a person's conscious control.

W

Warming up. Engaging in activity that prepares the muscles for the work that is to come.

Weight cycling. The cycle of losing, regaining, losing, and regaining weight; seesaw or yo-yo dieting.

Wellness. An overall state of well-being; total health.

Western blot. A test that is very specific in identifying HIV antibodies.

Withdrawal. A physical reaction that occurs when a person stops taking a drug or medicine on which he or she is physiologically dependent.

X

Xiphoid process. The lower part of the sternum that projects downward.

Z

Zygote. A fertilized egg cell.

Glossary/Glosario

A

Abdominal thrusts/empujones abdominales: empujones rápidos hacia arriba que hacen subir el diafragma y hacen que salga la sustancia que esté bloqueando la tráquea; maniobra de Heimlich.

Absorption/absorción: paso del alimento digerido desde el sistema digestivo hasta el sistema circulatorio.

Abstinence/abstinencia: la opción de no tener relaciones sexuales; la opción de no usar alcohol ni otras drogas.

Acquaintance rape/violación por un conocido: violación por algún conocido de la víctima o por alguien a quién se considera como amigo.

Acquired inmune deficiency syndrome (AIDS)/Síndrome de inmunodeficiencia adquirida (SIDA): enfermedad letal contagiosa, causada por el VIH, para la cual aún no hay cura o tratamiento eficaz.

Active immunity/inmunidad activa: inmunidad que desarrolla el cuerpo para protegerse de las enfermedades.

Addiction/adicción: dependencia psicológica o fisiológica en una sustancia o actividad.

Additive interaction/ interacción aditiva: una reacción que ocurre cuando las medicinas obran juntas de modo positivo.

Adolescence/adolescencia: etapa entre la niñez y la vida de adulto.

Adoption/adopción: acoger en la familia a un(a) niño(a) y asumir su responsabilidad de forma legal, comprometiéndose a criarlo(a) hasta la edad de adulto.

Adrenal glands/glándulas suprarrenales: las glándulas responsables de secretar hormonas que ayudan a mantener el equilibrio entre el sodio y el agua del cuerpo; afectan el metabolismo y ayudan a hacer frente al estrés.

Adrenaline/adrenalina: hormona que secretan las glándulas adrenales para preparar al cuerpo a responder a algo que cause estrés; la hormona de la emergencia.

Advertising/publicidad: el modo por el cual un fabricante logra que nos fijemos en su producto.

Advocate/defensor: alguien que apoya o defiende una posición o un producto.

Aerobic exercise/ejercicio aeróbico: actividad vigorosa que consume oxígeno continuamente; actividad que aumenta la capacidad de los pulmones para contener oxígeno.

Aesthetic/estético: artístico; que responde o aprecia aquello que uno percibe como hermoso.

Age norm/edad cronológica típica: lo que se espera que una persona sea capaz de desarrollar a cierta edad cronológica.

Aggravated assault/agresión grave: ataque ilegal cometido, a menudo, con un arma y en el cual la intención del agresor es causar daño o matar a la víctima.

Aggressive/agresividad: conducirse con contundencia, insistencia u hostilidad.

AIDS dementia complex/complejo de demencia ocasionado por el SIDA: trastorno progresivo que destruye los tejidos del encéfalo de una persona con el SIDA.

Al-Anon/Al-Anon: organización mundial de ayuda para los familiares y amigos de los alcohólicos.

Alateen/Alateen: una rama de Al-Anon específicamente para los adolescentes y pre-adolescentes, entre las edades de 12 y 20 años, cuyos padres u otros familiares, o amigos tienen problemas con el alcohol.

Alcoholics/alcohólicos: las personas que padecen de alcoholismo; las personas adictas al alcohol.

Alcoholics Anonymous(AA)/Alcohólicos Anónimos (AA): una organización mundial o grupo de apoyo que ha jugado un gran papel en ayudar a la gente a dejar el alcohol y las drogas y no volverlos a usar.

Alcohol-impaired driving/conducir impedido por el alcohol: conducir bajo la influencia del alcohol.

Alcoholism/alcoholismo: adicción al alcohol; la dependencia física y psicológica del alcohol.

Allergens/alergenos: sustancias en las comidas contra las cuales reacciona el sistema inmune del cuerpo.

Alveoli/alvéolos: conjunto de sacos con paredes delgadas para el aire ubicados en la punta de cada bronquiolo.

Alzheimer's disease/trastorno de Alzheimer: un trastorno progresivo, degenerativo que causa deterioro mental por completo.

Amino acids/aminoácidos: sustancias químicas que componen las proteínas.

Amphetamines/anfetaminas: estimulantes que aceleran el corazón y la respiración y causan ansiedad, insomnio y la pérdida del apetito.

Anabolic steroids/esteroides anabólicos: derivados sintéticos de la testosterona.

Anaerobic exercise/ejercicio anaeróbico: actividad física intensa en la cual el abastecimiento de oxígeno del cuerpo para producir energía no cumple con la demanda; actividad que mejora la fuerza muscular, la resistencia muscular y la flexibilidad.

Analgesics/analgésicos: medicinas que alivian el dolor sin la pérdida del conocimiento.

Angina pectoris/angina de pecho: una condición en la cual uno experimenta un dolor y tirantez o presión en el pecho cuando el corazón no recibe suficiente oxígeno.

Anorexia nervosa/anorexia nerviosa: un trastorno psicológico que incluye el miedo irracional a estar gordo y que resulta en la pérdida excesiva de peso debido a la autoinanición.

Antagonistic interaction/interacción antagónica: una reacción que ocurre cuando los efectos de una medicina se cancelan o se reducen al tomarse con otra medicina.

Antibiotics/antibióticos: medicinas que matan o reducen las bacterias perjudiciales en el cuerpo.

Antibodies/anticuerpos: proteínas que destruyen o neutralizan los patógenos en el cuerpo.

Antidiuretic hormone/hormona antidiurética: una de dos hormonas que secreta el lóbulo posterior de la glándula pituitaria.

Antisocial personality disorder/trastorno de personalidad antisocial: una condición caracterizada por el constante conflicto de una persona con la sociedad.

Antivenins/antitoxina: fluidos sanguíneos que contienen anticuerpos y que actúan más rápidamente que las vacunas.

Anxiety disorders/trastornos de ansiedad: trastornos en el que las fobias, sean imaginadas o reales, impiden que la persona disfrute la vida.

Appendicitis/apendicitis: la inflamación de la apéndice.

Appendicular skeleton/esqueleto apendicular: los huesos de los hombros, los brazos, las manos, las caderas, las piernas y los pies.

Aqueous humor/humor acuoso: en el ojo, sustancia acuosa que llena la cavidad entre la córnea y el cristalino.

Arteries/arterias: los más grandes de los vasos sanguíneos que parten del corazón.

Arteriosclerosis/arteriosclerosis: una condición en la cual las paredes de las arterias se endurecen y pierden su elasticidad.

Arthritis/artritis: inflamación de una articulación; condición que causa molestia, dolor e hinchazón en las articulaciones y los tejidos conjuntivos del cuerpo.

Artificial respiration/respiración artificial: ver *respiración de rescate.*

Assertive/afirmativo: defender sus propios derechos de una forma firme, pero positiva.

Atherosclerosis/aterosclerosis: una condición en la cual la pared de la arteria se ensancha debido a depósitos de grasa que impiden la circulación de la sangre.

Athlete's foot/pie de atleta o tiña podal: una infección de la piel entre los dedos de los pies causada por el hongo de la tiña.

Autonomy/autonomía: la certidumbre de que uno puede controlar su propio cuerpo, sus impulsos y el ambiente.

Axial skeleton/esqueleto axil: los huesos del cráneo, del esternón, las costillas y las vértebras.

Axon/axón: la parte de una neurona que lleva los impulsos desde las células del cuerpo.

B

Balloon angioplasty/angioplastia con globo: un procedimiento que incluye ensartar un catéter con un globo en la punta, a través del cuerpo hasta donde está el bloqueo, y luego inflar el globo para abrir el camino para que la sangre fluya; conocido oficialmente como angioplastia coronaria transluminal y percutánea.

Basal metabolism/metabolismo basal: la cantidad mínima absoluta que se requiere para mantener los procesos vitales del cuerpo.

Battery/acometimiento: el uso de fuerza física para controlar a alguien.

B cells/células B: los linfocitos que se producen y maduran en la médula ósea; estimulados por las células T ayudantes para producir anticuerpos.

Benign/benigno: no canceroso.

Better Business Bureau (BBB)/Oficina de Mejoramiento de los Negocios: una organización sin fines de lucro patronizada por negocios privados.

Bile/bilis: un fluido amargo producido por el hígado cuya función es esencial para la descomposición de las grasas.

Binaural hearing/audición binaural: la habilidad para determinar la procedencia de un sonido al poderlo oír con ambos oídos.

Biodegradable/biodegradable: capaz de ser descompuesto por microorganismos.

Biofeedback/retroalimentación biológica: retroalimentación biológica acerca de tu propio cuerpo; el proceso de enterarse de los acontecimientos de tu propio cuerpo que, por lo general, desconoces con el fin de lograr control voluntario de ellos.

Biological age/edad biológica: la determinación de nuestra edad basándose en cuán bien funcionan las distintas partes del cuerpo.

Biopsy/biopsia: un procedimiento por el cual se extirpa un poco de tejido para analizarlo y ver si contiene células anormales o cancerosas.

Biosphere/biosfera: la fina capa de tierra, agua y aire cerca de la superficie de la tierra.

Birth defects/defectos de nacimiento: condiciones genéticas y muchos otros tipos de enfermedades y trastornos que son causados por una variedad de distintos factores.

Bladder/vejiga: un órgano muscular que contiene la orina.

Blastocyst/blástula: un conjunto de células que tienen una cavidad en el centro; la etapa que sigue a la del cigoto.

Blended family/familia mixta: un tipo de familia nuclear en la que uno o ambos padres han estado casados anteriormente y en la que cada uno tiene hijos del matrimonio anterior.

Blizzard/ventisca: una tormenta de nieve con vientos de 35 millas (56 km) o más por hora.

Blood alcohol concentration (BAC)/ concentración de alcohol en la sangre (CAS): la cantidad de alcohol en la sangre de una persona según se expresa en porcentajes.

Blood pressure/presión sanguínea: la fuerza de la sangre contra las paredes de los vasos sanguíneos al fluir la sangre por el sistema cardiovascular.

Body composition/composición corporal: el porcentaje de grasa, músculo magro, hueso, tejido conjuntivo y agua en el cuerpo.

Body system/sistema corporal: un grupo de órganos que obran conjuntamente para lograr una función común.

Brain death/muerte encefálica: la pérdida de la función del encéfalo entero, incluyendo el bulbo raquídeo.

Brain stem/bulbo raquídeo: la división del encéfalo que conecta la espina dorsal al encéfalo.

Bronchi/bronquios: tubos bronquiales que conducen a los pulmones.

Bronchioles/bronquiolos: divisiones de los tubos bronquiales dentro de los pulmones.

Bruise/magulladura: una lesión al tejido subcutáneo.

Bulimia/bulimia: un trastorno de la alimentación en el cual la víctima sigue una dieta muy estricta, luego come en exceso como reacción al hambre, y procede a provocar el vómito, darse purgantes y a seguir dietas exageradamente rigurosas.

C

Calorie/caloría: una unidad para medir la energía en los alimentos y la energía que quema el cuerpo.

Cancer/cáncer: crecimiento anormal y descontrolado de las células.

Capillaries/capilares: los vasos sanguíneos más pequeños.

Carbohydrate loading/almacenamiento de carbohidratos: almacenar glicógeno extra en los músculos antes de hacer ejercicio extenuoso.

Carbohydrates/carbohidratos: azúcares, almidones y fibra que son la fuente de energía preferida del cuerpo.

Carbon monoxide/monóxido de carbono: un gas venenoso, incoloro e inodoro, que se encuentra en el humo de cigarrillo y en el humo de escape de los automóviles.

Carcinogenic/carcinogénico: que causa cáncer o envenena.

Carcinogens/carcinógenos: agentes que causan cáncer.

Carcinomas/carcinomas: cáncer que se desarrolla en el tejido epitelial—tejido que compone la piel y las membranas que cubren los órganos del cuerpo.

Cardiac arrest/paro cardíaco: una condición en la cual el corazón se para por completo.

Cardiac muscle/músculo cardíaco: tejido estriado que forma la pared del corazón.

Cardiopulmonary resuscitation (CPR)/ resucitación cardiopulmonar (RCP): la técnica salvavidas que incluye respirar por la víctima de un fallo cardiovascular y, mediante la aplicación de presión sobre el esternón de la víctima, forzarle a que el corazón bombée sangre.

Cardiorespiratory endurance/resistencia cardiovascular: la habilidad del corazón, los pulmones y los vasos sanguíneos de enviar energía y oxígeno a los tejidos del cuerpo durante largos períodos de actividad vigorosa.

Cardiovascular diseases/enfermedades cardiovasculares: enfermedades del corazón y los vasos sanguíneos.

Carjacking/robo de un auto: hurtar un auto por la fuerza, utilizando un arma.

Carotid pulse/pulso de la carótida: el latido cardíaco que se puede sentir a cada lado del cuello.

Cartilage/cartílago: un material fuerte y flexible que permite el suave movimiento de las articulaciones, sostiene la nariz y las orejas, conecta las costillas al esternón y actúa como un cojín entre las vértebras contiguas.

Catheter/catéter: tubo de plástico, delgado y flexible, que se puede conducir a través de los vasos sanguíneos hasta ciertos órganos del cuerpo.

Cell/célula: la unidad básica de estructura de todo ser viviente.

Cell body/cuerpo celular: la parte de una neurona que tiene un núcleo y es el centro para recibir y enviar impulsos nerviosos.

Cerebellum/cerebelo: la parte del encéfalo que funciona como centro para la coordinación del movimiento esqueletomuscular.

Cerebral palsy/parálisis cerebral: un grupo de trastornos neurológicos no progresivos que son el resultado del daño sufrido por el encéfalo durante su desarrollo antes o en el momento del nacimiento.

Cerebrum/cerebro: la parte mayor y más compleja del encéfalo, que consiste de los hemisferios derecho e izquierdo, que controla la actividad muscular y recibe información sensorial.

Cervix/cérvix: el cuello redondo y muscular, la parte inferior, del útero.

Chancre/chancro: una llaga rojiza en el sitio donde los patógenos invaden el cuerpo.

Chemotherapy/quimioterapia: el uso de medicamentos anticancerosos en el tratamiento del cáncer.

Child abuse/abuso de los niños: daño físico, incluyendo el abuso sexual, y/o el daño emocional que se le haga a los niños.

Chlamydia/clamidia: una enfermedad transmitida sexualmente que ataca los órganos reproductores.

Chlorofluorocarbons(CFCs)/clorofluorcarbonos: compuestos de cloro, flúor y carbono, los que se piensa que son un factor principal en la reducción del ozono.

Cholesterol/colesterol: sustancia semejante a la grasa.

Choroid/coroides: la capa intermedia de la pared del ojo, la cual contiene el iris, los ligamentos suspensorios y los músculos ciliares.

Chromosomes/cromosomas: pequeñas estructuras dentro de los núcleos de las células, las cuales contienen información genética.

Chronic bronchitis/bronquitis crónica: una condición en la cual los bronquios están irritados.

Chronic fatigue syndrome (CFS)/síndrome de fatiga crónica: un tipo de fatiga que es de largo plazo y para la cual se desconoce la causa.

Chronological age/edad cronológica: la edad de una persona basada en la cantidad de años que haya cumplido.

Chyme/quimo: la sustancia que se forma cuando se mezclan los alimentos y los jugos gástricos.

Circumcision/circuncisión: el procedimiento por el cual se extirpa quirúrgicamente el prepucio de los varones.

Cirrhosis/cirrosis: cicatrización, una condición del hígado en la cual las cicatrices reducen el flujo de sangre en el hígado.

Clinical death/muerte clínica: el paro de las funciones del cuerpo de una persona.

Clinical depression/depresión clínica: una condición en la cual los sentimientos de tristeza y de desesperanza duran por más de unas semanas e interfieren con los intereses y actividades diarias de la persona.

Clinical psychologist/psicólogo clínico: persona que diagnostica y trata trastornos del ánimo y de conducta.

Cliques/grupos exclusivos o pandillas: grupos de amistades exclusivas que por lo general comparten intereses y orígenes.

Cluttered-nest syndrome/síndrome del nido revuelto: el fenómeno en el cual los hijos adultos regresan a vivir en el hogar de los padres.

Codependency/codependencia: preocuparse excesivamente de la conducta y problemas de otras personas; las ansias agudas de arreglar y controlar esos problemas.

Communicable diseases/enfermedades contagiosas: enfermedades causadas por la transmisión, directa o indirecta, de patógenos de una persona a otra.

Communication/comunicación: un proceso a través del cual se envían y se reciben mensajes; la franqueza entre los miembros de la familia, lo que incluye la demostración de ternura, afecto y simpatía. También significa ser capaz de expresar sentimientos negativos.

Compromise/concesión: un modo de resolver un

problema en el cual cada persona rinde algo de modo que se halle una solución que satisfaga a todos.

Compulsion/compulsión: una conducta urgente que se repite.

Congenital/congénito: que existe o que se inicia al nacer.

Congenital syphilis/sífilis congénita: una condición en la cual una mujer embarazada que tiene sífilis transmite la infección al feto.

Conjunctiva/conjuntiva: una membrana mucosa protectiva pegada a la superficie interior de los párpados que continúa sobre la superficie exterior del ojo.

Consequence/consecuencia: el resultado de una acción.

Conservation/preservación: la conservación del medio ambiente.

Consumer/consumidor: cualquier persona que usa un servicio o un producto.

Consumer health/salud del consumidor: el proceso de ayudar a uno a elegir con juicio los productos y servicios de salubridad; y el permitirle a uno saber dónde ir o qué hacer si a uno lo han tratado injustamente o si uno necesita ayuda.

Cooling down/enfriamiento: la reducción gradual de actividad tras hacer ejercicio de modo que se permita que el pulso disminuya.

Cornea/córnea: la parte incolora y trasparente de la esclera en la parte delantera del ojo.

Coronary angiography/angiografía coronaria: procedimiento que se usa para evaluar cuan extensa es la enfermedad de la arteria coronaria.

Coronary bypass surgery/cirugía del puente coronario: un procedimiento para crear una desviación alrededor de las arterias coronarias obstruidas, de modo que la sangre pueda llegar al corazón.

Crisis/crisis: un cambio extremo en la vida de una persona.

Cross-contamination/contaminación cruzada: la propagación de bacterias de un alimento a otro.

D

Daily Food Guide/Guía Diaria de Alimentos: una publicación que ofrece una forma fácil de escoger una dieta variada, balanceada y moderada.

Date rape/violación durante una cita: la violación que ocurre entre dos personas que están saliendo juntas.

Deafness/sordera: la pérdida de la habilidad de oír.

Decision/decisión: el acto de hacer una elección o llegar a una solución.

Defense mechanisms/mecanismos de defensa: estrategias que se usan para hacer frente a situaciones de mucho estrés.

Deforestation/tala: la destrucción de los bosques.

Dendrites/dendritas: la parte de una neurona que recibe y lleva impulsos hacia las células del cuerpo.

Dentin/dentina: el material que rodea la pulpa.

Depressants/depresivos: sedantes; drogas que tienden a retardar el sistema nervioso central.

Dermis/dermis: la capa más gruesa y profunda de la piel.

Desertification/desertificación: la conversión de prados o tierras de regadío, a condiciones desérticas.

Designer drugs/drogas diseñadas: drogas hechas con sustancias sintéticas por químicos clandestinos.

Detoxification/desintoxicación: el proceso de sacar las drogas del cuerpo.

Developmental task/tarea de desarrollo: algo que necesita ocurrir durante una etapa en particular para que un ser humano continúe su desarrollo, hasta convertirse en un adulto saludable y maduro.

Diabetes/diabetes: una enfermedad crónica que afecta la forma en que las células del cuerpo convierten los alimentos en energía.

Diaphragm/diafragma: un músculo que separa el pecho de la cavidad abdominal.

Diet/dieta: todo lo que una persona come y bebe.

Digestion/digestión: la descomposición física y química de los alimentos a pedazos más pequeños.

Digestive enzymes/enzimas digestivas: proteínas que aceleran la descomposición de los alimentos.

Discrimination/discriminación: una forma de prejuicio por el cual se elige a ciertas personas y se les trata mal como resultado de un factor, como la edad, el sexo, la raza, la etnia o algún rasgo físico.

Distress/estrés negativo: estrés que causa angustia.

Divorce/divorcio: la disolución legal o la terminación del contrato matrimonial.

Dormant/latente: inactivo.

Down syndrome/síndrome de Down: una condición caracterizada por un retraso mental de ligero a agudo que resulta de anormalidades de los cromosomas.

Drugs/drogas: sustancias peligrosas y a menudo ilegales, que incluyen el alcohol y el tabaco.

Drug dependence/dependencia de las drogas: la drogadicción.

E

Earthquake/terremoto: temblores de tierra severos.

Electrocardiogram(EKG)/electrocardiograma (ECG): una prueba que produce una gráfica de la actividad eléctrica del corazón.

Elimination/eliminación: la expulsión de alimentos no digeridos o desperdicios del cuerpo.

ELISA/ELISA: muestra inmuno-sorbente relacionada a la enzima; una prueba para detectar la presencia de la infección del VIH.

Embolus/émbolo: un coágulo de sangre que se mueve del lugar donde se formó.

Embryo/embrión: un conjunto de células o blástula que se ha implantado en el útero.

Emotions/emociones: sentimientos que influyen en todo lo que uno hace.

Empty-calorie foods/comidas sin valor nutritivo: comidas que tienen escaso valor nutritivo.

Empty-nest syndrome/síndrome del nido vacío: el fenómeno en el cual los hijos al hacerse adultos se van de la casa.

Enabling/responsabilizarse: tratar de proteger a la persona que tiene problemas con el alcohol o las drogas, de las consecuencias de su problema de adicción.

Enamel/esmalte: el material más duro del cuerpo; el material que cubre la corona de los dientes.

Encephalitis/encefalitis: una inflamación de encéfalo causada por un virus y a veces por una bacteria.

Endocrine glands/glándulas endocrinas: glándulas de secreción interna que secretan hormonas en el torrente sanguíneo.

Endocrine system/sistema endocrino: el sistema del cuerpo que consiste de glándulas de secreción interna y las hormonas que producen.

Enriched/enriquecido: un producto al cual se le agregan los nutrimentos que ha perdido durante el procesamiento.

Environment/ambiente: todo nuestro entorno, incluyendo la familia, la ubicación y las experiencias.

Epidermis/epidermis: la capa exterior de la piel la cual es la más delgada.

Epilepsy/epilepsia: un trastorno del sistema nervioso caracterizado por un arrebato de impulsos nerviosos en el encéfalo como resultado de un ataque.

Esophagus/esófago: un tubo muscular que se extiende desde la faringe hasta el estómago y el cual está situado detrás de la tráquea y el corazón.

Estrogen/estrógeno: una hormona femenina que se libera por primera vez durante la pubertad.

Estuaries/estuarios: ecosistemas donde el agua de mar se mezcla con el agua dulce.

Eustress/estrés positivo: estrés benéfico.

Exploited/explotado: usado para el beneficio de otro.

Extended family/parentela: una familia con más de un pariente además de la familia nuclear o la consistente de un solo padre.

Extensors/extensores: músculos que enderezan las extremidades.

External auditory canal/canal auditivo externo: una vía, de más o menos, una pulgada de largo que conduce al tímpano y la cual protege el oído al mantener fuera los cuerpos extraños.

External respiration/respiración externa: el intercambio de oxígeno y dióxido de carbono entre la sangre y el aire en los pulmones.

F

Fallopian tubes/trompas de Falopio: un par de tubos a través de los cuales viaja el huevo maduro.

Family/familia: un grupo de gente relacionada por sangre, matrimonio o adopción.

Fatigue/fatiga: una sensación de cansancio que le reduce a uno el nivel de actividad.

Fatty liver/hígado grasoso: una condición en la cual las grasas se han acumulado en el hígado, evitando el funcionamiento normal de las células del mismo.

Federal Trade Commission (FTC)/Comisión Federal de Comercio (CFC): una agencia federal que impide que se anuncien de forma injusta y fraudulenta los productos y servicios de consumo.

Feedback/retroalimentación: mensajes de otras personas que nos indican cómo se sienten acerca de una persona o una idea.

Fertilization/fecundación: la unión de una célula de huevo y una célula de esperma que solo puede ocurrir si las células de esperma están presentes cuando el óvulo está en la trompa de falopio; concepción.

Fetal alcohol syndrome(FAS)/síndrome de alcoholismo fetal: una condición en la cual un feto ha sido adversamente afectado debido a que su madre hizo uso excesivo del alcohol durante el embarazo.

Fetus/feto: un embrión a partir de las ocho semanas de concepción hasta el nacimiento.

Fibrillation/fibrilación: una perturbación rítmica que ocurre cuando las fibras musculares del corazón se contraen de una manera no coordinada.

Fire extinguisher/extinguidor de fuego: un aparato portátil que apaga pequeños fuegos al disparar sustancias químicas para ese fin.

First aid/primeros auxilios: cuidados de emergencia; los cuidados inmediatos y momentáneos que se le da a una persona que ha caído enferma o que se ha lesionado.

Fitness/estar en forma: soltura física. Las personas que están en buena forma física se encuentran en mejores condiciones de sobrellevar las situaciones cotidianas, que las personas que no están en buena forma.

Flexibility/flexibilidad: la habilidad de mover cualquier parte del cuerpo por todo un campo de movimiento.

Flexors/flexores: músculos que doblan una extremidad.

Fluoroscope/fluoroscopio: una máquina que provee un retrato en vivo, con frecuencia empleada por los médicos para ver directamente la sombra del corazón.

Follicle/folículo: una pequeña bolsa que sujeta la raíz del pelo a la dermis.

Food additives/aditivos: sustancias que se le agregan a los alimentos con el propósito de producir un efecto deseado.

Food allergy/alergia por alimento: una condición en la cual el sistema inmune del cuerpo reacciona a los alergenos en algunos alimentos.

Food and Drug Administration (FDA)/Administración de Alimentos y Drogas: una agencia federal que asegura que todas las comidas y los aditivos, a no ser las carnes y las aves, son fiables, puros, íntegros y que han sido etiquetados con precisión y honradez.

Foodborne illness/enfermedad transmitida por alimentos: una condición causada por ingerir comida contaminada por bacteria; envenenamiento por comida contaminada.

Fortification/fortificación: el proceso de agregar nutrimentos donde no suelen ocurrir por naturaleza.

Fraternal twins/mellizos fraternales: dos embriones con composición genética distinta.

Friendship/amistad: una relación significativa entre dos personas basada en el cariño, la consideración y la confianza.

Frostbite/congelación: una condición en la cual se forman cristales de hielo en los espacios entre las células.

Functional disorder/trastorno funcional: un trastorno mental que ocurre como resultado de causas sociológicas sin que exista lesión encefálica.

G

Gallbladder/vesícula biliar: el órgano que aloja la bilis.

Gallstones/cálculo biliar: pequeños cristales que se forman de la bilis y que pueden bloquear el conducto biliar entre la vesícula y el duodeno.

Gangrene/gangrena: la muerte del tejido en una parte del cuerpo.

Gastric juices/jugos gástricos: líquidos que contienen ácido clorhídrico, enzimas digestivas y mucosa y que comienzan la digestión de las proteínas.

Gastritis/gastritis: un trastorno en el cual la membrana mucosa que cubre el estómago se inflama.

Genes/genes: pequeñas secciones de cromosomas que controlan las características hereditarias.

Genetic condition/condición genética: una enfermedad, trastorno, quebranto o estado de mal funcionamiento con el que se nace.

Gerontologist/gerontólogo: persona que estudia el proceso de envejecimiento.

Glucose/glucosa: un azúcar formado en el cuerpo durante la digestión.

Glycogen/glucógeno: la forma en la cual los carbohidratos se almacenan en el cuerpo.

Goal/meta: algo que requiere planificación y trabajo para poder lograrlo; plan definitivo que uno tiene para su propia vida.

Gonorrhea/gonorrea: una enfermedad transmitida sexualmente causada por bacterias que viven en áreas calientes y húmedas del cuerpo.

Group practice/grupo de médicos: una situación en la cual dos o más doctores se unen para proveer cuidado médico.

H

Halitosis/halitosis: mal aliento.

Hallucinogens/alucinógenos: psicodélicos; drogas que alteran el humor, el pensamiento y los sentidos.

Hashish/hashís: resina marrón oscura que se recoge de la parte del cáñamo (cannabis).

Health/salud: estado de pleno bienestar físico, mental y social.

Health care delivery/rendimiento de cuidados de salud: servicio de salud.

Health education/educación de la salud: proveer información sobre la salud para lograr influir a la gente para que cambien su actitud y tomen pasos positivos respecto a su salud.

Health facility/ambulatorio: un lugar a donde va una persona para recibir atención médica.

Health maintenance organization (HMO)/organización para el mantenimiento de la salud: un plan de salud en el cual uno paga una cuota regularmente y luego recibe cuidados médicos por poco o ningún costo adicional.

Health resources/recursos de salud: lugares a los que la gente puede ir para obtener varios tipos de tratamiento.

Health services/servicios de salud: los aspectos de un programa general de la salud que incluye la prevención, tratamiento y cura de las enfermedades, y el mantenimiento y promoción de la salud.

Heart attack/ataque al corazón: nombre común para referirse a varios trastornos que tienen que ver con el corazón y los vasos sanguíneos, pero que generalmente ocurre porque las células del músculo cardíaco no están recibiendo el oxígeno y nutrimentos que necesitan.

Hemodialysis/hemodiálisis: una técnica en la cual a una persona la conectan a una máquina de riñón artificial.

Hemoglobin/hemoglobina: la sustancia que porta oxígeno en los glóbulos rojos.

Hepatitis/hepatitis: una inflamación grave del hígado que por lo general la causa una infección viral.

Heredity/herencia: el paso de características de los progenitores a los descendientes.

Hernias/hernias: áreas débiles en el músculo que sostiene a varios órganos; ruptura.

Herpes simplex type 2 virus/virus tipo 2 de herpes simplex: una ETS en la cual un virus causa llagas como especie de ampollas en el área genital, las cuales se denominan herpes genital.

Hiatal hernia/hernia hiatal: condición en la cual la parte superior del estómago se empuja sobre el diafragma.

Hierarchy of needs/jerarquía de necesidades: una lista que anota, por orden de importancia, las cosas que los seres humanos necesitan para sobrevivir y tener bienestar.

High blood pressure/tensión arterial alta: la hipertensión.

Histamine/histamina: una sustancia liberada cuando un virus que causa resfriado le invade a uno el sistema respiratorio.

Holistic/integral: que toma en consideración la influencia física, mental y social sobre la persona por completo y su salud.

Homicide/homicidio: el acto premeditado en que un ser humano mata a otro ser humano.

Hormones/hormonas: sustancias químicas que se producen en el cuerpo por las glándulas endocrinas las cuales regulan la actividad de distintas células del cuerpo; la causa de cambios físicos y emocionales.

Hospice/hospicio: un lugar que promueve un modo especial de cuidar a los moribundos.

Host/huésped: la planta o animal del cual se alimenta un parásito.

Human collision/choque humano: durante un accidente, el hecho de una persona darse contra cualquier parte del auto o ser arrojada del mismo.

Human immunodeficiency virus (HIV)/virus de inmunodeficiencia humana (VIH): el virus que ataca el sistema de inmunidad del cuerpo y conduce al SIDA.

Hurricane/huracán: una tormenta potente con lluvias caracterizada por ráfagas.

Hurricane watch/vigilancia de huracán: un pronóstico del Servicio Meteorológico Nacional que significa que existen las condiciones atmosféricas para que se desate un huracán.

Hypertension/hipertensión: tensión arterial alta.

Hypochondria/hipocondría: un trastorno somatoforme en que uno experimenta una preocupación con el cuerpo y un temor a supuestas enfermedades.

I

Identical twins/gemelos idénticos: dos embriones con la misma composición genética.

Implantation/implantación: el proceso por el cual las células se adhieren al forro del útero.

Indigestion/indigestión: una condición en la cual el cuerpo no descompone bien los alimentos.

Inhalants/inhalantes: sustancias con vapores que al olerlos e inhalarlos producen un estado de alucinación.

Inpatients/pacientes internos: pacientes que requieren cuidado médico prolongado y que se admiten en un hospital y ocupan una cama.

Insulin/insulina: una hormona producida por el páncreas que ayuda al cuerpo a convertir la glucosa en energía para que las células la usen.

Integumentary system/sistema integumentario: sistema que incluye la piel, el pelo, las uñas y las glándulas sudoríparas.

Internal respiration/respiración interna: el intercambio de gases entre la sangre y las células del cuerpo.

Interneurons/interneuronas: células nerviosas en el encéfalo y el bulbo raquídeo que transmiten impulsos desde las neuronas sensoriales a las neuronas motoras.

Intervention/intervención: el hecho de interrumpir la continua adicción antes que el alcohólico o el narcómano empeore.

Involuntary/involuntario: fuera del control consciente de la persona.

K

Kidney/riñón: órgano que filtra la sangre para quitarle las sustancias dañinas de aquellas que el cuerpo puede usar.

L

Labyrinth/laberinto: el oído interno; consiste del vestíbulo, los canales semicirculares y la cóclea.

Lacrimal gland/glándula lagrimal: una glándula situada encima del ojo cuya función es producir lágrimas.

Lactose intolerance/intolerancia láctica: una condición en la cual el cuerpo no puede digerir el azúcar de la leche.

Larynx/laringe: órgano productor de la voz.

Leukoplakia/leucoplasia: lesión caracterizada por manchas blanquecinas, ligeramente elevadas dentro de la boca de los que mascan tabaco.

Life expectancy/expectación de vida: el promedio de años que se espera que un grupo de personas viva.

Life-style factors/factores del estilo de vida: conductas repetidas relacionadas al modo de vivir de una persona que afectan el nivel de su salud.

Ligaments/ligamentos: bandas fuertes o cordones de tejidos que conectan los huesos en una articulación.

Lipids/lípidos: sustancias grasas que no se disuelven en agua.

Look-alike drugs/drogas parecidas: drogas hechas de sustancias legales con el propósito de parecerse a las ilegales.

Lymph/linfa: un líquido transparente y amarillo que fluye por los vasos linfáticos.

Lymph nodes/nódulos linfáticos: masas de tejidos que filtran las linfas.

Lymphocytes/linfocitos: tipo de glóbulos blancos que combaten los patógenos.

Lymphomas/linfomas: cánceres que se desarrollan en los tejidos que forman la sangre y el sistema linfático.

M

Mainstream smoke/humo directo: humo que el fumador exhala.

Malignant/maligno: canceroso.

Manic-depressive disorder/trastorno maníaco depresivo: una condición en la cual el humor de una persona cambia dramáticamente de un extremo emocional a otro sin ninguna razón aparente.

Manipulation/manipulación: un medio indirecto, y a veces solapado o bajo, de tratar de controlar la conducta o la actitud de otra persona.

Marijuana/mariguana: la planta del cáñamo (cannabis) que se fuma, se come, o se bebe por sus efectos de intoxicación.

Marital adjustment/ajuste matrimonial: lo bien que las personas dentro del matrimonio se ajustan y se adaptan al matrimonio y mutuamente.

Marriage/matrimonio: la unión de un hombre y una mujer de acuerdo con las tradiciones y la ley.

Mastication/masticación: el proceso de masticar.

Medicaid/Medicaid: programa de asistencia médica para personas de todas las edades que no pueden pagar por el cuidado médico.

Medicare/Medicare: programa de seguro de salud accesible a personas mayores de 65 años de edad y a personas que reciben beneficios para lisiados a través del seguro social.

Medicine/medicina: una sustancia que, cuando se ingiere o se aplica al cuerpo, ayuda a prevenir o a curar una enfermedad, lesión, o problema médico.

Medicine misuse/mal uso de medicinas: el uso de un medicamento contrario a su propósito.

Megadose/megadosis: grandes cantidades de suplementos nutricionales.

Melanoma/melanoma: cáncer de la piel.

Meningitis/meningitis: la inflamación de las meninges.

Menstrual cycle/ciclo menstrual: el tiempo desde el inicio del período menstrual al inicio del próximo período.

Menstruation/menstruación: el proceso de despojar el forro del útero.

Mental disorders/trastornos mentales: problemas mentales y emocionales.

Mental health/salud mental: el proceso de aceptarse y gustarse uno mismo y adaptarse y hacer frente a las emociones, los retos y los cambios que forman parte de la vida.

Mental illness/enfermedad mental: enfermedad o trastorno médico que afecta la mente e impide que la persona disfrute la vida.

Metabolism/metabolismo: la suma total de todas las reacciones químicas dentro de una célula.

Metastasis/metástasis: el proceso de propagación de las células cancerosas.

Mobile/móvil: capaz de moverse de un sitio a otro.

Motor neurons/neuronas motoras: células nerviosas que llevan impulsos desde las interneuronas dentro del encéfalo y la espina dorsal a los músculos y glándulas.

Multiple sclerosis/esclerosis múltiple: un trastorno progresivo en el cual la membrana de mielina que rodea las fibras nerviosas se va destruyendo.

Multiplier effect/efecto multiplicador: el hecho de tomar drogas o medicinas con alcohol.

Muscular endurance/resistencia muscular: la habilidad de los músculos para seguir trabajando a lo largo de un período de tiempo sin fatigarse.

Muscular strength/fortaleza muscular: la habilidad de ejercer fuerza contra la resistencia.

Mycobacterium avium intracellulare (MAI)/micobacteria avium intracelular: una enfermedad oportunista que es la causa principal del síndrome de debilitación, del deterioro gradual de todas la funciones del cuerpo y que está asociada con el SIDA.

N

Narcotics/narcóticos: drogas hechas de la flor de la amapola del opio y las medicinas que se emplean para aliviar el dolor e inducir el sueño.

Nephrons/nefrones: las unidades funcionales de los riñones.

Neurologist/neurólogo: un médico que se especializa en trastornos orgánicos del encéfalo y del sistema nervioso.

Neurons/neuronas: células nerviosas que forman la parte funcional y estructural del sistema nervioso.

Neutrophils/neutrófilos: un tipo de fagocito; los cuales están más activamente involucrados en el proceso de fagocitosis.

Nicotine/nicotina: la droga adictiva en los cigarrillos que hace subir la presión y aumenta la palpitación cardíaca.

Noncommunicable diseases/enfermedades no transmisibles: enfermedades no causadas por patógenos y que no se transmiten por contacto.

Nongonococcal urethritis (NGU)/uretritis no gonococa: una enfermedad transmitida sexualmente causada por varios tipos de organismos parecidos a las bacterias que infectan la uretra en los hombres y el cuello de la matriz en la mujer.

Nontoxic/no tóxico: no dañino o venenoso para los humanos.

Nonverbal communication/comunicación no verbal: el hecho de enviar mensajes por medio de expresiones faciales y movimientos corporales.

Nuclear family/familia nuclear: los padres y uno o más hijos que comparten el hogar.

Nutrient-dense/denso en nutrimentos: rico en nutrimento respecto al contenido calórico.

Nutrients/nutrimentos: sustancias en los alimentos que el cuerpo necesita para funcionar adecuadamente.

Nutrient supplements/suplementos nutritivos: píldoras, polvos y líquidos que contienen nutrimentos.

Nutrition/nutrición: la ciencia de ver cómo el cuerpo usa los nutrimentos y cómo y por qué la gente come.

O

Obesity/obesidad: exceso de grasa en el cuerpo.

Obsession/obsesión: una preocupación emocional y social muy perjudicial.

Occupational Safety and Health Administration (OSHA)/Departamento de Seguridad y Salud Ocupacional: una agencia federal que promueve condiciones seguras y saludables en el lugar de trabajo.

Open-dating/fechado abierto: la práctica de poner la fecha en los paquetes de alimentos para indicar la fecha de caducidad, la frescura, la fecha de envase o el último día para la venta del producto.

Organ/órgano: dos o más tipos de tejido que realizan una tarea específica.

Organic/orgánico: derivado de organismos vivientes sin el uso de sustancias químicas.

Organic disorder/trastorno orgánico: un trastorno mental causado por un quebranto físico o una lesión que afecta el encéfalo.

Ossicles/osículos: tres huesillos que se unen, situados detrás del tímpano y que lo conectan con el oído interno.

Ossification/osificación: el proceso por el cual las células cartílagas se reemplazan por células óseas minerales.

Osteoarthritis/osteoartritis: una condición en la cual las partes mecánicas de una articulación sufren deterioro cotidiano.

Osteomyelitis/osteomielitis: la inflamación de la superficie blanda del interior de los huesos.

Osteoporosis/osteoporosis: la condición que resulta de la falta de calcio en los huesos.

Otosclerosis/otosclerosis: una enfermedad hereditaria que es la causa común de la sordera parcial.

Outpatient/pacientes ambulatorios: gente que recibe servicios médicos, dentales o de otro tipo en un local médico y luego se van a su casa el mismo día.

Ovaries/ovarios: glándulas sexuales femeninas que contienen los óvulos y producen las hormonas sexuales femeninas.

Overweight/sobrepeso: pesar más del 10 por ciento sobre el estándar de peso para la estatura.

Ovulation/ovulación: el proceso por el cual los ovarios liberan un óvulo maduro todos los meses.

Ovum/óvulo: una célula de huevo.

Oxytocin/oxitocina: una de dos hormonas formadas por el lóbulo posterior de la glándula pituitaria.

P

Pancreas/páncreas: una glándula que sirve al sistema digestivo y al endocrino.

Papillae/papilas: pequeñas proyecciones que cubren la superficie de la lengua.

Parasite/parásito: microorganismo que se alimenta de una planta o animal vivo.

Parathyroid glands/glándulas paratiroides: las glándulas situadas en los lóbulos de la glándula tiroides que regulan el equilibro de calcio y fósforo en el cuerpo.

Parkinson's disease/enfermedad de Parkinson: un trastorno progresivo que interfiere con la transmisión de impulsos nerviosos desde las áreas motoras al encéfalo.

Passive/pasivo: darse por vencido, acceder o retroceder sin defender los derechos y necesidades.

Passive-aggressive personality disorder/trastorno de la personalidad pasivo-agresiva: una condición en la cual uno a menudo no coopera con los demás y demuestra la ira indirectamente.

Passive immunity/inmunidad pasiva: la inmunidad temporal que un bebé obtiene de su madre.

Passive smoke/humo indirecto: humo de cigarrillo, de cigarro o de pipa que inhala la persona que no fuma.

Pathogens/patógenos: microorganismos que invaden el cuerpo y atacan sus células y tejidos, causando muchas enfermedades comunes.

Peer pressure/presión paritaria: el control e influencia que la gente de la misma edad o grupo social se ejercen mutuamente.

Peers/compañeros o contemporáneos: personas de la misma edad.

Pelvic Inflammatory Disease (PID)/Enfermedad Pélvica Inflamatoria: una infección dolorosa de las trompas de falopio, los ovarios y/o del útero como resultado de la gonorrea o la clamidia sin tratamiento.

Penis/pene: el órgano externo del macho para la reproducción compuesto de tejido esponjoso que contiene muchos vasos sanguíneos.

Peptic ulcers/úlceras pépticas: úlceras que se forman en el sistema digestivo.

Percent body fat/por ciento de grasa corporal: la cantidad de grasa en el cuerpo con relación al peso total del cuerpo.

Percutaneous transluminal coronary angioplasty (PTCA)/angioplastia coronaria transluminal percutánea: ver *angioplastia con globo*.

Periodontal disease/enfermedad periodontal: una inflamación de las estructuras periodontales.

Periodontium/periodontio: el área que rodea los dientes; las encías, los ligamentos periodontios y la quijada.

Peripheral/periférico: alejado del centro.

Peristalsis/peristalsis: una serie de contracciones de los músculos involuntarios que mueve los alimentos a través del esófago y por todo el sistema digestivo.

Personal identity/identidad personal: factores que creemos que nos hacen singulares o distintos de todo el mundo.

Personality/personalidad: un conjunto complejo de características que hacen que cada persona sea única y distinta de los demás.

Phagocytosis/fagocitosis: el proceso en el cual ciertos glóbulos blancos rodean y se comen las bacterias invasoras.

Pharmacist/farmacéutico: una persona que tiene que ver con la preparación, distribución y venta de medicina.

Pharynx/faringe: la garganta.

Phobia/fobia: un temor extremo que hace que una persona limite sus funciones normales para evitar el miedo.

Phonocardiography/fonocardiografía: una prueba que incluye colocar un micrófono en el pecho de una persona para anotar los sonidos y señales del corazón, transmitiéndolos a través de fotografía a un papel de gráfica.

Photochemical smog/smog fotoquímico: la contaminación que ocurre cuando el escape de los autos, activados por el sol, se combinan con otros hidrocarbonos en la atmósfera.

Physical fitness/bienestar físico: la habilidad de desempeñar las tareas cotidianas con facilidad y tener energía suficiente para responder a demandas inesperadas.

Physiological dependence/dependencia fisiológica: la necesidad química que siente el cuerpo por una droga.

Phytoplankton/fitoplancton: organismos microscópicos que se hallan en aguas abiertas y soleadas y que son la base de las redes de alimento de la vida marina y de agua dulce y que son un factor en el mantenimiento de la composición de la atmósfera.

Pituitary gland/glándula pituitaria: la glándula situada en la base del encéfalo que regula las otras glándulas endocrinas; la glándula maestra.

Placebo/placebo: una sustancia que no tiene valor medicinal, la cual se administra por su efecto psicológico.

Placenta/placenta: tejido rico en sangre, que se desarrolla de la capa exterior de las células del embrión y de los tejidos de la madre.

Planned pregnancy/embarazo planificado: un embarazo en el cual antes de concebir, se toma la decisión de estar embarazada y de tener un bebé.

Plaque/placa: depósitos de grasa que se acumulan a lo largo del forro interior de las arterias; en los dientes—una película pegajosa e incolora que actúa sobre el azúcar para formar ácidos que destruyen el esmalte de los dientes e irrita las encías; sarro.

Plasma/plasma: la parte líquida de la sangre.

Platelets/plaquetas: las partes más pequeñas de la sangre; de suma importancia para la coagulación.

Platonic relationship/relación platónica: una amistad en la cual hay afecto pero no romance.

Pneumocystis carinii pneumonia (PCP)/pulmonía neumocística de carinii: una infección oportunista asociada con el SIDA.

Poison/veneno: cualquier sustancia que causa daño, quebranto o muerte cuando se introduce en el cuerpo.

Poison control center/centro de control de envenenamientos: un centro al cual se puede llamar para pedir información acerca de qué se debe hacer cuando alguien ha ingerido un veneno.

Poliomyelitis/poliomielitis: una infección viral que afecta las neuronas motoras en la espina dorsal y la corteza encefálica.

Post-traumatic stress disorder/trastorno de estrés postraumático: una condición en la cual la persona que ha experimentado un suceso traumático sufre los efectos posteriores durante un largo tiempo.

Precaution/precaución: una acción preventiva planificada que se toma antes de un acontecimiento para aumentar las posibilidades de que todo salga sin percances.

Precycling/preciclaje: la reducción de desperdicios previo a que ocurran al tomar decisiones beneficiosas para el medio ambiente respecto a compras.

Prejudice/prejuicio: un sentimiento negativo hacia alguien o algo basado en estereotipos y no en la experiencia.

Pressure-point technique/técnica del punto de presión: método empleado para parar una hemorragia al aplicar presión a la arteria principal que suple sangre a la extremidad afectada.

Prevention/prevención: el hecho de practicar hábitos saludables para mantenerse bien y libre de enfermedades y quebrantos.

Primary care/cuidado primario: cuidado que uno busca de su cuenta, generalmente administrado por el médico de cabecera.

Private practice/práctica privada: la práctica médica de un doctor que tiene su propia consulta.

Progesterone/progesterona: una hormona femenina que se libera inicialmente durante la pubertad.

Proteins/proteínas: una parte vital de todas las células del cuerpo.

Psychiatrist/psiquiatra: un doctor en medicina que trata los trastornos mentales, emocionales y de la conducta.

Psychoactive drugs/drogas psicoactivas: drogas que afectan el sistema nervioso central y alteran el funcionamiento del encéfalo.

Psychological dependence/dependencia psicológica: la creencia de que uno necesita una droga para sentirse bien y funcionar con normalidad.

Psychosomatic/psicosomático: que concierne tanto al cuerpo como a la mente.

Puberty/pubertad: el comienzo de la adolescencia; el período de tiempo cuando el varón y la hembra son capaces de reproducirse físicamente.

Pulmonary circulation/circulación pulmonaria: el flujo de sangre desde el corazón a los pulmones y de vuelta al corazón.

Pulmonary emphysema/enfisema pulmonar: una condición en la cual se destruyen los sacos de aire diminutos en los pulmones, por los cuales el oxígeno se absorbe en el cuerpo.

Pulp/pulpa: tejido viviente dentro del diente muy sensitivo.

Pulse recovery rate/razón a la cual el pulso se repone: la razón a la cual el corazón late tras alguna actividad.

Q

Quack/curandero: un promovedor deshonrado de productos y tratamientos médicos.

Quackery/curanderismo: el hecho deshonrado de promover productos médicos inútiles.

Quality of life/calidad de vida: el nivel de salud y satisfacción que una persona tiene al estar viva.

R

Rabies/rabia: una infección viral del encéfalo y la espina dorsal trasmitida a los humanos por la mordida de un animal infectado.

Random violence/violencia al azar: violencia cometida sin ninguna razón en particular y/o en contra de cualquiera que se encuentre en el lugar equivocado.

Rape/violación: coito por la fuerza o bajo amenaza.

Recall/devolver al fabricante: el proceso de instruir a un fabricante a que retire de la venta un producto que ya lanzó al mercado debido a que se le considera perjudicial.

Recommended Dietary Allowance (RDA)/Ración Dietética Recomendada: pautas para las cantidades de los 19 nutrimentos esenciales, para las calorías y la cantidad estimada de otras siete vitaminas y minerales que la mayoría de la gente necesita a diario para mantenerse saludables desde la infancia hasta la adultez.

Recovery/recuperación: el proceso de volver a estar bien; el proceso de aprender a vivir una vida libre de alcohol y drogas.

Recycling/reciclaje: tratar o cambiar los deshechos de modo que se puedan volver a usar.

Reflex/reflejo: la reacción espontánea del cuerpo a un estímulo.

Refusal skills/destrezas de rechazo: técnicas y estrategias que nos ayudan a decir que no eficazmente.

Relapses/recaídas: para las personas en recuperación, es la vuelta periódica al uso del alcohol o las drogas.

Relationship/relación: un vínculo o conexión entre las personas.

Rescue breathing/respiración de rescate: el proceso de proveerle oxígeno a una víctima que ha dejado de respirar.

Resident bacteria/bacteria residente: bacterias que viven en la boca, los intestinos y en la piel y que nos protegen de las bacterias dañinas.

Resting heart rate/frecuencia de los latidos del corazón en reposo: latidos del corazón cuando no está activo.

Retina/retina: la capa de la pared del ojo que contiene las células nerviosas y los procesos responsable de la visión.

Rheumatoid arthritis/artritis reumatoide: una inflamación destructiva de las articulaciones que incapacita.

Risk/riesgo: una conducta con un elemento de peligro que puede causar lesión o daño.

Risk factor/factor de riesgo: una característica que se ha demostrado que aumenta los chances de que ocurra un ataque al corazón.

Role/papel: la parte que uno desempeña, especialmente en una relación.

S

Saliva/saliva: una secreción que da comienzo a la digestión de carbohidratos.

Saprophytes/saprofitos: bacteria que digiere materiales comestibles no vivos, tales como la leche y la carne.

Sarcomas/sarcomas: cánceres que se desarrollan en los tejidos conjuntivos y en los de soporte, tales como los huesos, los músculos y los tendones.

Saturated/saturado: en el caso de ácidos grasos, que tiene hidrógeno enlazado a todos los átomos de carbono en la cadena.

Schizophrenia/esquizofrenia: trastorno mental severo en el cual uno exhibe reacciones emocionales anormales o no exhibe ninguna reacción emocional.

Sclera/esclera: una membrana blanca y fuerte que contribuye a mantener la forma esférica del ojo y protege su delicada estructura interna.

Scoliosis/escoliosis: una curvatura de lado a lado de la espina dorsal.

Scrotum/escroto: una bolsa en el exterior del

cuerpo del varón que contiene los testículos y protege los espermatozoides al regular la temperatura de los testículos.

Sebaceous glands/glándulas sebáceas: glándulas que producen una secreción oleaginosa llamada sebo y que están conectadas a los folículos del pelo.

Secondary care/cuidado secundario: el cuidado que uno recibe cuando la doctora de cuidado primario lo refiere a uno a un especialista.

Secondary sex characteristics/características sexuales secundarias: vello corporal y el desarrollo de senos en la hembra y de músculos en el varón.

Self-actualization/autorrealización: el proceso continuo de luchar por alcanzar el máximo de la capacidad propia.

Self-esteem/autoestima: la confianza y sentimiento de valer que uno tiene acerca de sí mismo; influye en todo lo que hacemos, pensamos, sentimos y somos.

Semen/semen: una mezcla de fluidos de las vesículas seminales, la glándula próstata, las glándulas de Cowper combinada con la esperma; fluido seminal.

Sensory deafness/sordera sensorial: la pérdida de la audición causada por el ruido excesivo a través de largo período de tiempo.

Sensory neurons/neuronas sensoriales: células nerviosas situadas en la piel y en otros órganos sensoriales que tienen puntas receptoras especializadas.

Sexual assault/agresión sexual: atentado de ataque sexual o acto en sí con intención de violencia sexual.

Sexually transmitted disease (STD)/enfermedad transmitida sexualmente: una enfermedad contagiosa que se propaga de una persona a otra a través del contacto sexual.

Shock/choque: el fallo del sistema cardiovascular para mantener suficiente sangre circulando a los órganos vitales del cuerpo.

Sidestream smoke/corriente de humo secundaria: el humo que proviene de quemar tabaco.

Single-parent family/familia con solo la madre o el padre: familia en la cual los hijos solo viven con uno de los padres a la vez.

Skeletal muscles/músculos del esqueleto: músculos voluntarios pegados a los huesos que causan los movimientos del cuerpo.

Small-claims courts/cortes de litigios pequeños: cortes que tratan las demandas sobre las quejas de los consumidores que van desde $100 hasta los $3,000.

Small intestine/intestino delgado: un órgano donde toma lugar la mayor parte de la digestión y la absorción.

Smoke detector/detector de humo: una alarma que se usa para despertar a la gente y alertarlos en el caso de incendio.

Smooth muscles/músculos lisos: músculos involuntarios situados en tales lugares como los intestinos y los vasos sanguíneos.

Social age/edad social: la edad de una persona según lo determina su estilo de vida.

Sprain/esguince: una lesión de los tejidos suaves que rodean una articulación.

Stereotype/estereotipo: una creencia exagerada y simplificada acerca de un grupo entero, como un grupo étnico, religioso, o cierto sexo.

Sterility/esterilidad: una condición en la cual una persona no puede reproducirse.

Stigma/estigma: una marca de vergüenza.

Stimulant/estimulante: una droga que aumenta la acción del sistema nervioso central, el corazón, la respiración y la presión arterial y que causa que las pupilas se dilaten y que disminuya el apetito.

Strain/tensión: una condición en la cual los músculos han trabajado demasiado.

Stress/estrés: la reacción física o mental del cuerpo hacia situaciones diarias.

Stressor/causante de estrés: un estímulo que produce una reacción de estrés.

Stroke/ataque de apoplejía: una condición en la cual la sangre que va al encéfalo se ve interceptada, y como resultado, las células nerviosas en esa parte del encéfalo no pueden funcionar.

Sweat glands/glándulas sudoríparas: glándulas que secretan sudor a través de conductos hasta los poros en la superficie de la piel.

Synapse/sinapsis: un espacio estrecho entre la punta del axón de una neurona y la dendrita de otra neurona a través de la cual tiene que cruzar un impulso.

Synergistic effect/efecto sinergístico: la reacción de dos o más medicinas que resulta en un efecto más fuerte que cuando se toman por separado.

Synthetic/sintético: hecho de sustancias químicas de laboratorio.

Syphilis/sífilis: una enfermedad transmitida sexualmente que ataca muchas partes del cuerpo.

Systemic circulation/circulación sistémica: el flujo de sangre a todos los tejidos del cuerpo con excepción de los pulmones.

T

Tar/alquitrán: un fluido grueso, pegajoso y oscuro que se produce al quemar tabaco.

Target heart rate/meta de frecuencia cardíaca: de 70 a 80 por ciento de la frecuencia cardíaca de una persona.

Tartar/sarro: una sustancia muy dura que irrita los huesos subyacentes tanto como las encías que rodean los dientes: cálculo.

T cells/células T: linfocitos producidos en la médula ósea que van a la glándula del timo donde maduran y luego combaten patógenos específicos.

Tendinitis/tendonitis: una condición en la cual el tejido conjuntivo de los músculos y los huesos o los tendones se estira o se desgarra.

Tendons/tendones: bandas de fibra que conectan los músculos a los huesos.

Tertiary care/cuidado terciario: el cuidado que se recibe cuando uno tiene una condición que requiere tratamiento o equipo especializado.

Testes/testículos: dos glándulas pequeñas que producen esperma.

Testimonial/testimonio: la recomendación entusiasta de una persona que endosa un producto.

Testosterone/testosterona: una hormona masculina que hace que los testículos produzcan esperma y la responsable de los cambios físicos durante la pubertad.

Thanatology/tanatología: el estudio de la muerte y los ajustes necesarios en conexión con la muerte de un ser querido.

Therapy/terapia: técnica de tratamiento.

Thrombosis/trombosis: presencia o formación de un coágulo de sangre que se forma en un vaso sanguíneo y que, por lo general, no se mueve del lugar de origen.

Thyroid gland/glándula tiroides: la glándula más grande del sistema endocrino la cual regula el metabolismo de carbohidratos, grasas y proteínas en las células del cuerpo.

Time-management skills/destrezas para el manejo del tiempo: la habilidad para aprovechar con eficacia el tiempo que uno tenga.

Tinnitus/tintineo: una condición caracterizada por un retintín en los oídos.

Tissue/tejido: células con las mismas estructuras y que hacen la misma función.

Tolerance/tolerancia: una condición en la cual el cuerpo se acostumbra a los efectos de una medicina o droga.

Tooth decay/caries dentales: una enfermedad de las vías digestivas que debilita los dientes y afecta el modo en que uno puede morder y masticar la comida.

Toxins/toxinas: venenos producidos por algunas bacterias.

Trachea/tráquea: conducto que transporta aire a los pulmones.

Tranquilizers/tranquilizantes: depresivos que reducen la actividad muscular, la coordinación y el lapso de atención.

Transition/transición: cambio.

Tumor/tumor: una masa de tejido causada por la división incontrolada de células anormales.

Type I diabetes/diabetes tipo I: diabetes que por lo general le ocurre a personas menores de 15 años de edad y que requiere inyecciones diarias de insulina para poder sobrevivir.

Type II diabetes/diabetes tipo II: diabetes que por lo general le ocurre a las personas de más de 40 años de edad y que se puede, con frecuencia, controlar con dieta y ejercicio.

U

Ulcer/úlcera: una llaga abierta en la piel o en la membrana mucosa.

Umbilical cord/cordón umbilical: cordón que conecta el embrión a la placenta y a través del cual los nutrimientos y el oxígeno fluyen desde la madre hasta el embrión, a través de los vasos sanguíneos; y los desechos del embrión son transportados hasta la madre.

Undernutrition/subnutrición: el no consumir los suficientes nutrimentos esenciales o calorías para el buen funcionamiento del cuerpo.

Underweight/bajo peso: estar 10 por ciento o más por debajo del peso normal.

Unit price/precio por unidad: la cantidad que una unidad de un producto cuesta.

Unit pricing/indicación del precio por unidad: la práctica de mostrar el precio por unidad de los distintos tamaños de envases de un producto.

Unplanned pregnancy/embarazo no planificado: un embarazo en el cual un bebé se concibe por accidente.

Uremia/uremia: una serie de síntomas causados por la inhabilidad de los riñones para deshacerse de los desperdicios del cuerpo.

Ureters/uréteres: tubos que conducen desde los dos riñones hacia la vejiga.

Urethra/uretra: un pequeño tubo que se extiende desde la vejiga al exterior del cuerpo.

Urine/orina: desecho líquido que se recoge en la vejiga hasta que está lista para salir del cuerpo.

Uterus/útero: órgano pequeño y muscular en forma de pera en el cuerpo de la hembra.

V

Vaccination/vacunación: el proceso por el cual se inyecta una vacuna en el cuerpo.

Vaccine/vacuna: una preparación que contiene patógenos debilitados o muertos de una enfermedad en particular y que se da para evitar que se contraiga esa enfermedad.

Vagina/vagina: tubo muscular y muy elástico en la hembra que sirve como conducto desde el útero hacia el exterior del cuerpo; el canal de nacimiento.

Values/valores: principios que uno considera importantes y que nos sirven de guía en la vida.

Veins/venas: los vasos que portan la sangre de regreso al corazón.

Verbal communication/comunicación verbal: el envío de mensajes por medio de la palabra.

Violence/violencia: el uso de la fuerza física para causar daño o abusar de otra persona o personas.

Virus/virus: una forma de vida muy pequeña y simple.

Vitreous humor/humor vítreo: un fluido que se encuentra detrás del cristalino del ojo que lo mantienen firme.

Voluntary/voluntario: dentro del control consciente de una persona.

W

Warming up/calentamiento: participar en actividad que prepara los músculos para el trabajo venidero.

Weight cycling/ciclo de peso: bajar, aumentar, volver a bajar y volver a aumentar de peso.

Wellness/bienestar: un estado de bienestar general; plena salud.

Western blot/prueba Western blot: una prueba que es muy específica para identificar los anticuerpos del VIH.

Withdrawal/síndrome de abstinencia: una reacción física que ocurre cuando una persona cesa de tomar una droga o medicamento del cual ha llegado a depender.

Xiphoid process/proceso xifoides: la parte baja del esternón que se proyecta hacia abajo.

Z

Zygote/cigoto: una célula de huevo fertilizada.

Index

A

AA. *See* Alcoholics Anonymous
Abscess (tooth), 316
Abdominal hernia, 282
Abdominal thrust, 716
Abrasion, 694
Absorption, 275
Abstinence
  from alcohol, 464-467, 510, 558
  from drugs, 558
  from sexual intercourse, 166, 543, 549,
  557, 559
  from tobacco, 445
Abuse, 89-91
  and parenting, 129
Acceptance stage, and death, 190, 191
Accident chain, 675
Accident prevention, 671-82. *See also*
  Safety
Accidents, and alcohol, 18, 464-65, 681
Acetaminophen, 426, 427, 432
Acetylsalicylic acid, 426
Acid rain, 598
Acne, 161, 199-200
Acquaintance rape, 683, 685-687
Acquired immune deficiency syndrome.
  See AIDS
Acromegaly, 242
Actin, 210
Active immunity, 527
Acupuncture, 224
Addiction, 482
  alcohol, 473
  definition, 497-500
  recovery, 501-505
  See also Alcohol; Drugs; Tobacco;
  Withdrawal
Addison's disease, 243
Addictive interaction of medicines, 429
Additives, 394, 395, 396, 416
Adenoids, 263
Adipose tissue, *See* Body fat; Fat
Adolescence, 159-69
  and nutrition, 375
  See also Teens
Adolescent health centers, 656, 662
Adopt-a-Grandparent, 186
Adoption, 87, 127-28
Adoptive family, 84
Adrenal glands, 66, 67, 240-41, 243
Adrenaline, 66, 221
Adrenocorticotropic hormone (ACTH),
  240
Adulthood, 169, 178-86
  developmental tasks in, 175-77
Advertising, 635-37
  alcohol, 465, 467, 472
  food, 372
  medicine, 430
Advocate, consumer, 644
Aerobic exercise, 344, 345, 347, 353
Aerosols, 599, 603, 626
Aesthetic needs, 34
Affective disorders, 50-53
Afterbirth, *See* Placenta

African sleeping sickness, 521
Age
  and developmental norms, 182
  and marriage, 119
  measuring, 182, 185
  and pregnancy, 308
Aggravated assault, 107
Aggressiveness, in communication, 112-
  13
Aging, 177, 182-190
  and skin, 202
Agriculture Research Center, 647
AIDS (Acquired immune deficiency
  syndrome), 188, 264, 544, 555-63. *See
  also* HIV
AIDS dementia complex, 563
Air
  and environmental issues, 625
  and pollution-related ailments, 597-99,
  602
Air conditioners, 599, 616
Airway, 721, 724
Al-Anon, 499, 510-511
Alateen, 499, 511
Alcohol, 459-73
  and accidents, 18, 464-65, 469, 681
  and advertising, 467
  as drug, 500
  and families, 498, 508
  insurance for treatment, 489
  in medicines, 427
  mental and social aspects, 463-67
  and other drugs, 485
  physical effects, 459-62
  and pregnancy, 140-41
  prohibition, 464
  and teenagers, 21, 462
Alcohol dehydrogenase, 462
Alcoholics Anonymous World Service,
  Inc., (AA), 74, 461, 503, 511
Alcoholism, 471-73, 497, 499. *See also*
  Addiction; Codependency
ALD, 434
Aldosterone, 241
Allergies, 266, 396, 419, 450, 659
Allergist, 659
Aluminum, recycling of, 618
Alveoli, 266, 267
Alzheimer's Association, 233
Alzheimer's disease, 233-34
Amblyopia, 324
Amoebic dysentery, 521
American Academy of Orthotists and
  Prosthetists, 207
American Association for Respiratory
  Care, 447
American Association of Pastoral
  Counselors, 58
American Athletic Union (AAU), 520
American Burn Association, 708
American Cancer Society, 305, 306, 309,
  583, 636
American College of Obstetricians and
  Gynecologists (ACOG), 305

American Dental Hygienists Association,
  318
American Dietetic Association, 390,
  410
American Heart Association, 255
American Hospital Association, 234
American Institute of Stress, 70
American Medical Association, 140, 185,
  304, 576
American Mental Health Fund, 28
American Nephrology Nurses'
  Association, 289
American Nursing Association, 694
American Occupational Therapy
  Association, 504
American Optometric Association, 320
American Paper Institute, 618
American Parkinson Disease Association,
  233
American Physical Therapy Association,
  355
American Physiological Society, 363
American Red Cross, 257, 693, 716, 719,
  723
American Society for Medical
  Technology, 518
American Society of Radiologic
  Technologists, 279
American Speech-Language-Hearing
  Association, 327
Americans With Disabilities Act, 235
American Veterinary Medical
  Association, 87
Amino acids, 379, 380
Ammonia, 280
Amniocentesis, 148
Amniotic sac, 138
Amphetamines, 481, 483
Amygdala, 35
Amylase, 281
Anabolic steroids, *See* Steroids
Anaerobic exercise, 345, 346, 353
Analgesics, 426
Anemia, 258
Anesthesiologist, 659
Angel dust, *See* Phencyclidine
Anger, 40-41
  and death, 189, 191
Angina pectoris, 572
Angioplasty, 260, 576
Animal bites, 703
Animals
  and communicable diseases, 523
  and Lyme disease, 529
  and medical research, 525
  and parasites, 519
  and vaccines, 425
Anorexia nervosa, 411, 412
Antacids, 432
Antagonistic interaction of medicines,
  429
Antiarrhythmics, 427
Antibiotics, 426, 428
  pathogen resistance to, 538

Antibodies, 262, 379, 526, 555, 664,
  and HIV, 560
Antidiuretic hormone (ADH), 240
Antihistamines, 432
Antiseptics, 524
Antisocial personality disorder, 53
Antivenins, 425
Anus, 276, 279, 286
Anxiety disorders, 49-50
Aorta, 250, 254, 257
Apathy, 21
Apgar test, 143
Appendicitis, 285-86, 654
Appendicular skeleton, 204
Appetite, 281, 408
Aqueous humor, 321
Arachnophobia, 50
Arguing. *See* Fighting
Arterial blockage, 664
Arteries, 254-55
  and pressure points, 695
Arteriosclerosis, 446, 570
Arthritis, 209, 426, 589-91
  and quack remedies, 640
Arthritis Foundation, 209, 590, 640
Arthroscopic surgery, 208
Artificial organs, 664
  blood, 664
  blood vessels, 578
  heart, 260, 577
Asbestos, 580, 676
Ascorbic acid (Vitamin C), 380, 381
Aspartame, 396
Aspirin, 426, 432, 433, 645
Assertiveness, in communication, 113,
  684
Association Football, 340
Association of Independent Colleges and
  Schools, 660
Association of Surgical Technologists,
  661
Asthma, 266
  bronchial, 268
Astigmatism, 324
Atherectomy, 260
Atherosclerosis, 570
Athlete's foot, 200, 521
Athletic trainer, 346
Atmosphere, and environmental issues,
  625
Atrium, atria, 249, 250, 257, 573
Attitudes, 7, 8, 19, 42, 43
  childhood development of, 153
  and safety, 684
  toward achievement, 33, 67
  toward others, 30
  toward stress, 66
  See also final sections of each chapter:
  Self-Inventory;
  Building Decision-Making Skills
Audiologist, 327
Auditory. *See* Ears; Hearing impaired
Audubon Society, 615
Auricle, 326, 327
Australia, 451
Autonomic nervous system (ANS), 228,
  229
  saliva secretion, 276
Autonomy, in early childhood, 152
Auto safety, 680
Avulsion, 695

Axial skeleton, 204, 205
Axons, 223

B

Babies, intelligence in, 141
Babysitting, 142, *See also* Child care
Bacteria, 417, 517-18, 519, 537
Bad breath, 282, 442, 446, 447
Balance, sense of, 329
Ball-and-socket joints, 206
Balloon angioplasty, 576
Barbiturates, 481, 485
Bargaining stage, and death, 189
Barnard, Christiaan (Dr.), 250, 576-77
Barriers, to pathogens, 523
Bases, *See* DNA
Battered spouses, 89
Batteries, and recycling, 618-19
Battery, 107
B cells, 262, 263, 264, 525-26, 555
Beauty aids, 638
Beer, 459, 460
Bee stings, 704
Behavior, 36
  and adolescent development, 161
  models for, 152
  and parenting, 129
Behavioral therapist, 59
Benign tumor, 579
Beta blockers, 427
Better Business Bureau (BBB), 642-43
Bicycle safety, 681-82
Bile, 280, 281, 283
Binaural hearing, 328-29
Bingeing, 412, 414
Biodegradable products, 622
Biofeedback, 77
  and disease prevention, 530-531
Biological age, 182
Biological defenses, 523-24
Biological diversity, and environmental
  issues, 624
Biomechanics, 346
Biopsy, 579
Biosphere, 604
Birth, 143
Birth canal, 303
Birthing centers, 662
Birth defects, 147-48
  alcohol and, 468
  drugs and, 140
Births, multiple, 306
Bites, 699, 703
Blackhead, 200
Bladder, 288
Blastocyst, 137, 139
Blended families, 84, 130
Blindness, 321-24
  diabetes and, 586
  from gonorrhea, 542
  and STDs, 547. *See also* Eyes
Blisters, 200-201
Blizzards, 709
Blood
  artificial, 664
  cells, 250-51, 525
  clot, 258

donating, 251, 252, 558
effects of alcohol in, 460
in exercise, 354
transfusions, 556
types, 252
vessels, 255. *See also* Cardiovascular
  system
Blood alcohol concentration (BAC), 470
Blood bank, 252
Blood pressure, 254, 258
  and medicines, 427
  and nicotine, 442. *See also*
  Hypertension
Blues, 35, 51. *See also* Attitude; Mood
Boating safety, 677
Body
  acceptance and use of, 161
  care of, 201-203
  composition of, 342-43
  fat, vs body weight, 342, 358, 404
  fluids, 556
  frame, 405, 406
Body language, 111-12, 685
  and self-defense, 684
  See also Communication
Body-mind connection, 42
Boils, 200
Bone marrow, 251, 258, 577
  transplant, 584, 585
Bones, 204
  aging and, 183
  fractures in, 207
  types of, 205-206
Booster shots, 529
Boredom, 37
Botulism, 416, 518
Bowman's capsule, 288
Braces
  body, 206
  leg, 232
  teeth, 317
Brain, 35, 159-60, 222, 225-28
  death, 187
  dominant hemisphere of, 228
  dysfunction, 148
  effects of alcohol on, 459, 462
  stem, 224, 226-28, 231
  surgery, 229
  weight of, 223
Bread, 386, 391
Breakfast, 390
Breastbone, 204
Breast cancer, 306, 581
Breast-feeding
  and AIDS, 141, 558
  and smoking, 449
Breasts
  and adolescent development, 159
  self-examination of, 309
Breathing, 721
  and aging, 183
  and high altitudes, 356
  in infant CPR, 724
  and posture, 268
Bronchi, 266, 267
Bronchioles, 266
Bronchitis, 267
Bronchodilator, 268
Bruise, 361
Bulimia, 412, 414
Bunion, 208

Bureau of Consumer Protection
(Aeronautics), 647
Burn-out, 354
Burns, 704, 705, 708
Bursitis, 208

C

Caffeine, 387, 415, 432, 531
Calamine lotion, 701
Calcium, 204, 209, 243, 383, 385, 418
and aging, 179, 183
Calculus, 316
Calipers, 342, 405
Calluses, 201
Calories, 340, 389, 403-404
empty, 386, 459
insufficient, 407, 410, 411
Calorimeter, 409
Camping, safety, 679
Canada, 286, 451, 646
Cancer, 579-85
breast, 306
cross-cultural, 286
and exercise, 338
Hodgkin's disease, 264, 579
leukemia, 259-260
lung, 443, 444, 446, 449, 599
quackery and, 585
of reproductive organs, 299-300, 306
skin, 198, 202-203, 580
treatment, 427, 581-82
warning signs, 580
Canine Partners for Life, 214
Cannabis, 481, 488-89
Capillaries, 254-55, 266
Carbohydrate loading, 413
Carbohydrates, 241, 376, 388-89, 403, 517
and digestion, 275
and mood, 38
Carbon dioxide, 249-50, 251, 599-600, 606
Carbon monoxide, 443, 599
Carcinogenic substances, 442, 580, 602
Carcinoma, 579
Cardiac arrest, 573
Cardiac muscle, 212
Cardiologist, 660
Cardiology technician, 260
Cardiopulmonary resuscitation (CPR), 187, 573, 696, 720, 721
Cardiorespiratory endurance, 342, 345
Cardiovascular diseases, 569-74
prevention, 578
treatment, 575-78
Cardiovascular system, 249-61, 444, 697
and exercise, 340
and medicines, 427
See also Blood
Career
adolescent preparation for, 161
and adult choices, 175-76
and marriage, 120
mid-life changes in, 179, 180
Careers, in health care, 659-60. See also
individual names
Carjacking, 108
Carotid pulse, 720, 722

Carriers, 146, 150
Cartilage, 204, 208
CAT (computerized axial tomography)
scan, 580
Cataract, 324
Catheter, 575-76
Cauterization, 695
Cavities, 315, 317
Celiac sprue disease, 374
Cells, 137, 183, 187, 204, 222
and viral infections, 519, 523
See also individual types
Cementum, 315
Center for Interaction of Animals and
Society, 43
Center for Marine Conservation, 618
Center to Prevent Handgun Violence, 107
Centers for Disease Control and
Prevention (CDC), 70, 441, 544, 558
Central nervous system (CNS), 222, 224
Cereals, 386, 391
Cerebellum, 224, 226, 231
Cerebral
cortex, 187
embolism, 574
hemorrhage, 574
Cerebral palsy, 222, 236-37
Cerebrum, 224, 225
Cervical cancer, 306
Cervix, 143, 303
Chancre, 540
Chemical defenses, 523-24
Chemical pollutants, 601
Chemicals, poisonous, 701-702
Chemotherapy, 582, 584
Chernobyl, 607
Chest compressions, 722
Chicken pox, 519
Child abuse, 89-90, 94
Child Abuse Prevention Council, 91
Child care, cost of, 131
Childcare assistant, 127
Children, development of, 152-53. See
also Development; Parenting
Children, and poisoning prevention, 699, 701
Children's Defense Fund, 86, 131, 687
Child's Play Touring Theater, 149
China, 286
Chlamydia, 547
Chloride, 383
Chlorine, 382
Chlorofluorocarbons (CFCs), 599, 617
Choices
and food, 375
of health care professional, 661, 662
identifying, 19
important for adolescent, 164
and parenting, 129
See also final section of
chapters:Building Decision-Making
Skills
Choking, 715-17
Cholera, 601
Cholesterol, 252-53, 258, 378-79, 387, 571, 572, 578
label definition, 395
and medicine, 427
and tobacco, 446
Chorionic villi sampling (CVS), 150
Choroid, 320

Chromosomes, 144
Chronic diseases, 497, 590
bronchitis, 267, 444
Chronic fatigue syndrome (CFS), 70-71
Chronic obstructive pulmonary disease
(COPD), 444
Chronological age, 182
Chyme, 277-78, 280
Cigarettes, 442-43. See also Smoking;
Tobacco
and substance abuse, 484
Cigars, 443. See also Smoking; Tobacco
Cilia, 443, 523
Circulation, cardiovascular, 722
in infants and children, 724
Circulatory system, 446. See also
Cardiovascular system
Circumcision, 299
Cirrhosis, 462
Claustrophobia, 50
Cleanliness, 202, 308
and disease prevention, 527-30
Cleft lip, 147
Cleft palate, 147
Climate, 605
and environmental issues, 625
See also Weather
Clinical death, 187
Clinical depression, 50-51
Clinical psychologist, 56-58
Cliques, 103
Clostridium
botulinum, 416
perfringens, 416
Clotbusters, 260
Clothing, 354, 365
recycling, 619
Clots, 258, 427
Clotting, 251, 261. See also Hemophilia
Clove cigarettes, 443
Clubfoot, 147
Cluttered-nest syndrome, 181
Coach, 112
Cobalt, 383
Cocaine, 481, 484
Cocaine Anonymous (Coc-Anon), 503, 511
Cochlea, 327, 328, 330
Codeine, 427, 432, 481
Code of silence, 95
Codependency, 506-511
Colas, 387, 415, 635
Cold, and weather emergencies, 706-707
Colds, 263, 264, 267, 432, 518, 528,
remedies for, 432
Coliform bacilli, 517
College Board, 131
Colon, cancer of, 286, 581
Color blindness, 150, 322
Coma, 187, 231
Communicable diseases, 234, 517-31
causes, 517-523
defenses against, 522-526
preventing, 527-31
Communication, 91, 111-12
about death, 191
and decisions, 166
and relationships, 111
Compensation, 74
Competition nutrition, 413
Composting, 620

Compromise, 92
Computer eyestrain, 324
Computerized axial tomography (CAT) scan, 580
Computerized cardiac defibrillator, 723
Computerized medical training, 664
Conception. *See* Fertilization
Concussions, 231
Cones, 322
Conflicts, 180
  and decisions, 17
  and friendship, 102
  in marriage, 123
Congenital heart disease, 256
Congenital syphilis, 543
Conjunctiva, 319, 321
Conjunctivitis, 324
Conscience, childhood development of, 153
Consequences, identifying and evaluating, 19-21
Conservation, of energy fuels, 615. *See also* Energy and Environmental issues
Consistency, and parenting, 129
Constipation, 283
Consumer advocate, 644
Consumer Affairs Offices, 644
Consumer Bill of Rights, 633
Consumer Product Safety Commission (CPSC), 645
Consumer services, government, 645-47
Consumer skills, 641-47
  and food, 393
  and health insurance, 658
Consumers
  and health, 633-37
  and health care, 665
Contact, and contagious diseases, 522-23
Continuing-care facilities, 505
Contraction, muscular, 210
Controlled Substances Act, 431
Contusions, 231
Convenience, and consumer products, 634
Cooking, and energy saving, 616
Coolants, 599
Cooling, and energy saving, 616
Cool down, 354, 356
Cooper, Kenneth (Dr.), 344
Copper, 383
Corn, 201
Cornea, 320, 321
Coronary angiography, 575
Coronary bypass surgery, 576
Corti, organ of, 328
Cosmetics, and consumer safety, 645
Costs
  AIDS treatment, 563
  alcohol-related accidents and conditions, 464
  arthritis, 589
  cancer research and treatment, 583
  cold remedies, 518
  consumer products, 634
  coronary bypass, 578
  digestive medication, 280
  drug use, 490
  drunk driving, 471
  food, 372
  health care, 653

health insurance, 636
illegal drugs, 479
medicine, 431
quack remedies, 639, 640
smoking, 452
unit pricing and, 396
  See also Finances
Coughing, 228, 522
Counseling, 91, 502, 510. *See also* Therapy
Counselor, 58
Couples. *See* Family
Couvade, 303
Cowper's glands, 298, 300
Cowpox, 528
CPR *See* Cardiopulmonary resuscitation
Crack, 481, 484
Cramps
  abdominal, 285
  heat, 362, 706
  menstrual, 304
  muscle, 213, 361-62
Cranial meninges, 225
Cranial nerves, 222, 228
Crank (methamphetamine), 483
Craving, for drugs, 503
Cretinism, 242
Crime, 683-87
  and safety, 683
Crisis, 93
Crista, 329
Crohn's disease, 286
Cross-contamination, of food, 417
Crossed eyes, 324
Crying, 39
Cults, 108
Culture shock, 58
Curare, 701
Custody, 84
Cuticle, 198
Cuts, 694
Cyanocobalamin (Vitamin B$_{12}$), 380
Cystic fibrosis, 145, 148
Cystitis, 289-90
Cysts, 306

D

Daily Food Guide, 385
Dairy products in diet, 386
Dandruff, 201
Date rape, 685-87
Dating, 103
Deafness. *See* Ears; Hearing impaired
Dealers, drug, 486
Death, 187-91
  from abuse, 90
  acceptance of, 177
  alcohol-related, 464-65, 469
  from asthma, 266
  from bypass surgery, 578
  from cancer, 583
  divorce comparable to, 123
  and family, 95
  infantile, 139, 141
  leading causes of, 8
  stages of acceptance, 187-90

sudden, 715
  teen suicide, 167
  tobacco-related, 441-444
Decision making, 16-21, 165
  and alcohol, 466, 467
  and health care, 661
  and health insurance, 646
  model, 18
  See also final section of each chapter: Building Decision-Making Skills
Defense mechanisms, 73-74
  against pathogens, 522-24
Defibrillators, 260, 723
Deforestation, 604-605, 625
Degenerative diseases, 233
Dehydration, 283, 413, 415
Delirium tremens, (DTs), 473
Delta-9-tetrahydrocannabinol (THC), 488
Dendrites, 223
Denial, 74
  stage, in death, 189, 191
Dental hygiene. *See* Teeth
Dental hygienist, 318
Dental surgery, 317
Dentin, 315
Deoxyribonucleic acid (DNA), 145, 203, 686
Dependence, physiological, 429, 461, 482. *See also* Addiction; Codependency
Depressants, 481, 484-85
Depression, 50-51, 167
  stage, in death, 189, 191
Dermatologist, 660
Dermis, 198-99
Desertification, 605
Designer drugs, 489
Detoxification, 501, 504
Development
  adolescent, 160-161
  childhood, 151-53
Development, industrial, and environmental issues, 624
Developmental tasks, 151-153
Diabetes, 284, 586-88
  insipidus, 242
  mellitus, 243
Diabetic emergencies, 588
Dialysis, 290-91
Dialysis technician, 289
Diaphragm, 266
Diaphyses, 205
Diarrhea, 283
Diary. *See* Journal
Diastolic pressure, 254
Didanosine (ddI), 563
Dideoxycitidine (ddC), 563
Diet, 374, 406
  and aging, 179
  and cancer, 580, 583
  and cardiovascular disease, 571, 578
  and cardiovascular system, 261
  choices, 385-92, 634
  and digestive system, 287
  and disease, 286, 426
  liquid protein, 410
  pills, 410
  in PMS, 305
  during pregnancy, 140
  and teeth, 318
  and training, 412

See also Food; Nutrients; Nutrition; Recommended Dietary Allowances
Dietary Guidelines, 385
Dietetic Technician, 410
Dietician, 390
Dieting
  fads, gimmicks, and aids, 408-409, 640
  yo-yo, 409
Digestion, 275
Digestive juices, 524
Digestive system, 275-87
  alcohol in, 459-60
  and cancer, 581
  organs of, 276, 279-81
Dilation, in eye, 320
Diphtheria, 529
Disabilities, 148, 233, 235. *See also* Handicapped
Discipline, and parenting, 129
Disease prevention. *See* Health services
Diseases
  spread of, 522-23, 525
  tobacco-related, 441-450
Disks, 232
Dislocation, 208, 360
Disorders. *See* Functional disorders; Mental disorders; individual names of diseases and conditions
Displacement, 74
Distress, 65
Diuretics, 427
Diving safety, 361, 677
Divorce, 84, 87, 93, 123
  in mid-life, 179
  and teenagers, 122
DNA (Deoxyribonucleic acid), 145, 203
  banks, 686
Doctors, 659-61
Dominant traits. *See* Genes
Doppler ultrasound, 260
Dormant stage, in disease, 545
Doublespeak, 112
Doubt, in early childhood, 152
Down syndrome, 148, 235, 236
Drinking. *See* Alcohol
Drip irrigation, 607
Driver's education, 680
Driving and alcohol, 464-71
  and accidents, 696
  costs, 470-71
Drowning, prevention, 677
Drug dealers, 486, 490
Drug enforcement officer, 491
Drug testing, 490
Drug treatment, insurance for, 489
Drugs, 21, 104, 425
Drugs, illegal, 479-91, 503
  addiction, 482, 497-500
  costs, 479
  and family, 95
  illegal transport, 486
  and pregnancy, 140
  psychoactive, 483-87
  in tobacco, 442
  types, 481
  See also Addiction
DUI (driving under the influence), 464-71
Duodenal ulcers, 285
Duodenum, 278, 280, 281

Dwarfism, 147
DWI (driving while intoxicated), 464-71
Dysentery, amoebic, 521

E

Ears, 326-31
  drum, 326, 327
  wax, 331
Earthquakes, 708-709
Eating
  disorders, 411-12
  habits, 373
Ecosystems, 598
Ecstasy, 489
Educational counselor, 58
EEG (electroencephalogram), 35
  technician, 234
Egg cell. *See* Ovum
Ejaculatory duct, 298
EKG (ECG) (electrocardiogram), 575
Elder abuse, 89
Elderly, 180, 185
Electrical shock, 674
Electrocardiogram (EKG, ECG), 575
Electroconvulsive therapy, 56
Electrodermal response (EDR), 531
Electroencephalogram (EEG), 35
  and biofeedback, 530
Electrolytes, 382
Electromagnetic fields (EMFs), 582
Electromyogram (EMG), 530
Electron microscope, 519
Elimination, 275
ELISA, 560
Embolus, 258, 570
Embryo, 137-139. *See also* Fetal development
Emergencies, 663, 715-25
  when and where to report, 718, 719
Emergency Medical Services (EMS), 693, 716
Emergency medical technician (EMT), 723
Emotional needs, 33-34
Emotions, 35, 37-43, 95
  in adolescence, 160
  and advertising, 637
  expression of, 38-39
  independence of, 161
  and food, 373
  and stress, 71
Emphysema, pulmonary, 269, 444, 445
Empty-calorie foods, 386, 459
Empty-nest syndrome, 181
Enabling. *See* Codependency
Enamel, 315, 316
Encephalitis, 234
Endocrine system, 238-43
  and aging, 183
Endocrinologist, 660
Endometriosis, 306
Endurance, 342-45
Energy, and environmental issues, 625
  conservation of, 606, 615-16, 625
  and recycling, 618, 621

Energy, human, 415
  and aging, 183
  and nutrition, 376
  rechanneling, 76
Enriched foods, 394-95
Environment, human, and behavior, 35-36
Environmental issues, 597-609, 615-27
  and consumer products, 621, 622
  and education, 623
  involvement in, 622-27
Environmentalist, 606, 626
Environmental Protection Agency (EPA), 603, 622, 626
Enzyme-linked immunosorbent assay (ELISA), 560
Enzymes, 379
  digestive, 278, 280
Epidemiologist, 563
Epidermis, 197-98
Epididymis, 297-98, 300
Epiglottis, 265, 266, 277
Epilepsy, 235, 236
Epilepsy Foundation of America, 233
Epinephrine, 241
Epiphyses, 205
Equilibrium. *See* Balance
Equipment, 365
Erikson, and stages of development, 152, 159, 178, 180, 182
Escape, as stress defense, 74
Esophagus, 277
  and heartburn, 282
Estrogen, 159, 242, 303
Estuaries, 598
Ethics, medical, 190
Ethyl alcohol, 459
Europe, 73, 150, 598
Eustachian tube, 327
Eustress, 65
Evaluation of fitness, 357
Exercise
  and diabetes, 587
  and elderly, 184, 186
  and fitness, 180, 337-47
  and high altitudes, 356
  lack of, 261
  and menstruation, 304-305
  for muscular development, 215
  and pregnancy, 140-41
  program for, 343, 344, 353-59
  and weight, 404, 406, 408
Exercise physiologist, 363
Extensors, 212
External auditory canal, 326, 327
Eyebrows, 319, 324
Eye drops, in newborns, 539
Eyelashes, 319
Eyelids, 319
Eyes, 319-25
  objects in, 706
  problems of, 324
Eyestrain, 324

F

Fainting, 705
Fallopian tubes, 137, 138, 302-303, 305

Falls, prevention of, 671
Families
    and addiction, 507
    and alcoholism, 473
Family
    adoptive, 84
    blended, 84, 130
    and counseling, 91
    doctor, 656
    extended, 84
    foster, 84-85
    multigenerational, 84
    size, 86
    systems, 83-89, 91
    therapy, 510
Farsightedness, 324
Fast foods, 392, 634
Fasting, 410, 413
Fat
    and calories, 179, 404
    content of body, 358
    in diet, 387-88
    tissue, in aging, 183
Fathers. *See* Parenting
Fatigue, 69-71
Fats, 377-78, 403
Fat-soluble vitamins, 382
Fatty liver, 461
FDA. *See* Food and Drug Administration
Fear, 39-40
Fecal occult blood test, 580
Feces, 279, 283
Federal Aviation Administration (FAA), 647
Federal Trade Commission (FTC), 647
Feedback, 30-31
Feelings, 43. *See also* Emotions
Femur, 205
Fermentation, 459
Fertilization, 137, 302-303
Fetal alcohol syndrome (FAS), 140, 468, 498
Fetal development, 138-42, 148, 150 *See also* Prenatal development
Fetus, 139
Fever, 524, 531
Fiber, 179, 276, 277, 279, 377, 388, 419
Fibrillation, 572-73
Fibrin, 251
Fighting, 90, 108
Filters, 450
Filtrate, 289
Finances
    and adolescents, 165
    and family problems, 93
    and parenting, 126, 128, 131
    See also Costs
Fingerprints, 198
Fire
    and emergency action, 673-74
    prevention, 671-74
Firefighter, 719
Fireworks, 18, 673
First aid, 693-709, 715-18
    electrical shock, 696
    emergencies, 693
    open wounds, 694-97
    poisoning, 698-99
Fish in diet, 386
Fitness, 176, 337-47
    evaluation, 357

journal, 357
    See also Exercise
Flexibility, 342-43
Flexible fiberoptic endoscope, 580
Flexors, 212
Fluid intake, 291, 412. *See also* Dehydration; Urinary system
Fluorine, 383
Fluorocarbon gases, 601
Fluoroscope, 575
Folacin (folic acid), 380
Follicles, 198, 199
Follicle stimulating hormone (FSH), 240
Food, 371-97
    additives, 394
    allergy, 419
    avoiding problems with, 403-419
    and consumer safety, 417, 645-47
    diary, 419
    and environmental issues, 624
    fortification, 395
    groups, 385-86
    and headaches, 228
    irradiation, 417
    labeling, 393-97
    and mood, 38
    pyramid, 386
    and quackery, 638
    and safety, 416-19
    See also Diet; Nutrients; Nutrition
Food and Drug Administration (FDA), 393, 395, 416, 430, 432, 645
Foodborne illness (food poisoning), 416-417, 518
Food Safety and Inspection Service (FSIS), 647
Footprints, 198
Forests, and environmental issues, 624
Fortified foods, 395
Fossil fuels, 599-600, 625
Foster family, 84-85
Fractures, 207
    first aid for, 704
Fragile X syndrome, 146
Fraud, and consumer products, 638
Fraud, and U.S. Postal Service, 644
Freckles, 198
Freon
    as inhalant, 482
    in environment, 603
Friendships, 102-103
    in adolescence, 163
    intergenerational, 183
    See also Relationships
Frostbite, 363, 706-707
Fructose, 396
Fruit, 388, 391
Functional disorders, 49-54
Fungi, 521
Fungus infections, 200, 521

G

Gallbladder, 280, 281, 283
Gallstones, 283
Gamma rays, 417
Gangrene, 707
Gangs, 104, 107, 108, 115, 683
Gas, and digestion, 282-83

Gasoline, as inhalant, 482
Gastric juices, 278
    and resistance to disease, 524
Gastritis, 285
Gastroenterologist, 660
Gastrointestinal disorders, and biofeedback, 530
General anxiety disorder, 50
Generally recognized as safe (GRAS), 395
Generativity, 180
Generic medicines, 428
Genes, 144-46
    and research, 498
Genetic code (DNA), 145
Genetic disorders, 146-50, 235
Genetic research, and twins, 147
Genital
    herpes, 544-45
    warts, 546
Germicides, 524
Gerontologists, 182, 185
Giantism, 242
Gingivitis, 317
Glands, 198, 238-43, 298
Glass, and recycling, 619
Glasses, 324. *See also* Lenses
Glaucoma, 324
Glomerulus, 288
Glucagon, 241
Glucose, 241, 281, 586
Gluten, intolerance for, 374
Gluteous maximus, 211, 215
Glycogen, 241, 280, 413
Goals, 9, 12, 14-15
    for adolescents, 164
    setting, 353
Goiter, 242
Gonadotropic hormones, 240
Gonorrhea, 537-39, 542
Good Samaritan laws, 725
Government consumer services, 645-47
Grain products, 386, 388, 391
Grand mal seizures, 236
Graves' disease, 240
Greenhouse effect, 599-600
Grief, 95, 188, 191
Groin, 300-301
Group medical practice, 660-61
Group therapy, 56
GROW, 40
Growth, 150. *See also* Adolescence; Childhood; Infancy; Prenatal development; Teenagers
Growth hormone, 239-40, 242
Guidance counselor, 76
Gum disease, 317-18
Guns, and violent death, 107
Gynecologist, 304, 660

H

Hair, 203
    and aging, 183
    body, 159
    cells, in ear, 327, 328, 329
    follicles, 198, 199
    problems, 201
Halfway houses, 505

Halitosis, 282, 317
Hallucinogens, 481, 486-87
Handicapped, 14, 233, 235
Hangnails, 201
Hardening of the arteries, 259. *See also* Arteriosclerosis
Harvard Medical School, 578
Hashish, 481, 488
Havighurst, Robert, 161
Hazardous substances, 625
HDL, 446
Headaches, 70, 226, 229
  and biofeedback, 530
  and food, 228
Head lice, 201
Head of household, 86-87
Health
  centers, for adolescents, 656, 660
  clubs, 345
  continuum, 6
  definitions of, 3-5
  education, 4
  facilities, 653-55
  of family and society, 83, 89
  and fitness, 337
  foods, 416-17
  habits, 7
  insurance, 636, 646, 655-56
  and marriage, 124
  and parenting, 128-29
  physical, 5, 371
  and relationships, 101
  self-management of, 663
  and stress, 71
  teacher, 5
  triangle, 6
Health care resources, 653-56, 659-65
  for adolescents, 656
  for infants, 128
Health Maintenance Organizations (HMOs), 661-62
Health-risk appraisal, 5
Hearing impaired, 329, 330
Hearing loss, 148
  problems, 183
  See also Ears
Heart, 249-50
  and aging, 183
  strengthening, 357
Heart attack, 571-72
Heartburn, 282
Heart disease, 8, 255, 261, 378, 446
  congenital, 256
  and technology, 260
  See also Cardiovascular disease
Heart-lung machine, 576
Heart murmurs, 256
Heart rate, 355, 358
Heart valve surgery, 577
Heat, risks to health from, 362-63
Heat cramps, 706
Heating, and energy conservation, 616
Height, 150, 239, 241
Heimlich maneuver, 716
Help, and families, 93. *See also* Family counseling; Parents Anonymous
Help, when to seek, 28, 697
Hemodialysis, *See* Dialysis
Hemoglobin, 251, 259, 379
Hemophilia, 150, 261, 557
Hemophiliac, 562

Hemorrhoids, 286
Hepatitis, 286, 519, 531
  and CPR, 723
Heredity, 35, 144-50
  and alcoholism, 498
  and cancer, 585
  and disease, 497
  and hypertension, 569
  and obesity, 404
  See also Genetics
Heritage, 31
Hernia, 362
  abdominal, 282
  hiatal, 282
Herpes, 544-45
Heroin, 481, 486. *See also* Drugs
Hiccups, 228, 267
Hierarchy of needs, 32
Hinge joints, 206
Histamine, 432
HIV, Human immunodeficiency virus, 264, 555-63
  origin, 555-56
  and pregnancy, 141
  prevention, 559
  and rape, 687
  testing, 560-61, 562
  transmittal, 556-59
  See also AIDS
Hodgkin's disease, 264, 579
Holistic approach, 6
Holistic health centers, 662
Homeless, 29, 41, 77, 93
Homicide, 107
Hormones, 37, 159, 238-43, 302, 379
  and aging, 183
Hospice care, 662-63
  and death, 190
Hospital administrator, 663
Hospital records, 646
Hospitals, 654
Hospital stay, 584, 654
Host organisms, 517
Househusbands, 127. *See also* Parenting
Human collision, 680
Human immunodeficiency virus. *See* HIV
Humor, as attitude, 7. *See also* Laughter
Hunger, 281
Hurricanes, 707-708
Hydrochloric acid, 278, 285
Hygiene, personal, 301, 308
  and disease prevention, 528
Hyperopia, 324
Hypertension, 569-70. *See also* Blood pressure
Hyperventilation, 267
Hypochondria, 50
Hypodermis, 199
Hypothalamus, 66, 228, 281
Hypothermia, 707

I

Ice, 481, 483
Identification, 74
  emergency medical tag, 694, 724
I Have a Dream Foundation (IHAD), 12
Ileum, 278

Illness, and elderly, 180. *See also* Diseases
Illustrator, medical, 539
Immune deficiency, 264
Immune system, 524
  and aging, 183
Immunity, 527
Immunization, 425, 426, 527-31
Incision, 694, 695
Incontinence, 289
Incus, 326, 327
Independence, in adults, 175-76
  and aging, 186
Indigestion, 282
Industry, in childhood, 153
Infancy, 152
Infant care, 128
Infection. *See* Pathogens; Symptoms; names of individual diseases
Inferiority, in childhood, 153
Inflammatory response, 524
Ingredient listing, 394-96
Ingrown toenail, 201
Inhalants, 482, 489
Initiative, in childhood, 153
Injuries
  avoiding, 360-65
  head, 231
  prevention of, 237
  spinal cord, 231-32
  toy-related, 673
Inner ear, 327-28
Inpatient, 653
Insecticides, as inhalant, 482
Institute of Scrap Recycling, 618
Insulin, 238, 241, 243, 427, 586
Insurance, health, 636, 655-656, 658
Integumentary system, 197-203. *See also* Skin
Intelligence, in babies, 141
Interbrain, 228
International Special Olympics, 625
Interneurons, 221
Intervention, 500
Intestinal viruses, 416
Intestines, 278-79. *See also* Digestive system
Intoxication, 459, 460. *See also* Alcohol; Driving
Involuntary muscles, 212
Iodine, 240, 242, 383
Iris, 320, 321
Iron, 251, 258, 280, 379, 383, 385, 418
Islets of Langerhans, 241
Isokinetic, 346
Isometric exercise, 346
Isotonic exercise, 346

J

Jaundice, 286
Jejunum, 278-79
Jellyfish sting, 705
Jenner, Edward (Dr.), 528
Job, 30. *See also* Career
Jock itch, 200
Joints, 206
  and aging, 183
  and arthritis, 589-91
  injuries to, 207-08

Journal, 42
  and weight control, 407
Journal of the American Medical Association, 66
Journey from Darkness, 323

K

Kennedy, John (President), and
  consumer rights, 633
Kidney disease, and diabetes, 586
Kidneys, 288-91
  and aging, 183
  artificial, 284
  effects of alcohol on, 460
  stones, 290-91
Kids Against Pollution, 623
Killed-Virus Vaccine, 529
Knee-jerk reflex, 230
Knee surgery, 208
Kübler-Ross, Elisabeth, 188-90

L

Labeling
  definitions, 395-97
  food and, 393-97
Labeling of Hazardous Art Materials Act,
  626
Labyrinth, 327
Laceration, 694, 695
Lacrimal glands, 319
Lactic acid, 517
Lactobacilli, 517
Lactose intolerance, 282, 285, 409
Laetrile, 585
Landfill, and recycling, 617-18
Land use, and environmental issues, 604-
  09
Lang, Eugene, 12
Langerhans, Paul, 241
Laparoscopy, 308
Large intestine, 279
Larynx, 265
Laser surgery, 317
Laughter, 67
Laws
  and drugs, 504
  and immunizations, 529
  and marriage, 119, 543
  and tobacco, 451-53
Lawsuits, and STDs, 541
Laxative abuse, 412
LDL, 446
Lead exposure, 676
Lead poisoning, 598
Lean, label definition, 395
Left-handedness, 228
Legumes, 380
Leigh's disease, 149
Lens, 321
Lenses, corrective, 322
Leukemia, 259-61, 584
Leukoplakia, 447
Leuteinizing hormone (LH), 240
Lewis, F. John (Dr.), 576
Lice, 519
  head, 201
  pubic, 546
Licensed Practical Nurse (LPN), 672
Licensing Boards, 643-44
Life cycle, 137-50, 175-91
Life expectancy, 7-8, 182
  and AIDS, 560
Life-style, 7, 183
  and cancer, 286
  sedentary, 286, 337
Ligaments, 206
Lighting, and energy conservation, 616
Limitations, in physical activities, 364
Lipase, 281
Lipids, 377
Liquor, 459
Listening, 111-112. *See also*
  Communication
Lithotripsy, 291
Litter, 625
Little People of America, 147
Liver, 279-80
  conditions, 286
  effects of alcohol on, 459-60, 461-62
  transplant, 280
  and viruses, 519
Live-virus vaccine, 528
Lobes
  cerebral, 225
  of lung, 266
  of pituitary gland, 239-240
Lockjaw, 518
Longevity, and relationships, 101
Look-alike drugs, 490
Love
  loss of, and suicide, 168
  and marriage, 121
  and parenting, 131
Lumps, 580
  and cancer detection, 300, 306, 309
Lung cancer, 444, 445, 581, 583
Lungs, 266-67
  and high altitudes, 356
  strengthening, 357
Lyme disease, 529
Lymphatic system, 262-64, 526
  and cancer, 581
Lymphocytes, 262, 263, 526, 555
Lymphoma, 579
Lysergic acid diethylamide (LSD), 481,
  487

M

Magnesium, 383
Magnetic resonance imaging (MRI), 358,
  580
Mainstream smoke, 448
Malaria, 259, 521
Malignant tumor, 579
Malleus, 326, 327
Malocclusion, 317
Mammogram, 309
Manganese, 383
Manic-depressive disorder, 51
Manipulation, 105
Marijuana, 469, 481, 484, 488-89
Marine biologist, 600
Marital adjustment, 121
Markers, felt-tip, as inhalant, 482
Marriage, 119-24
  adolescent preparation for, 161
  blood test prior to, 543
  and health, 124
  in midlife, 179
Marrow, 204-206
Maslow, Abraham, 32-34, 101
Massage, 362
  foot, 213
Mastication, 275
Mastoid process, 327
Maternal care, 662
Maturity, and marriage, 122
MDMA, 489
Meals, 390-92. *See also* Food; Nutrition
Measles, 519
Measles, vaccine, 528
Meat, 386, 391
  and consumer safety, 647
  in diet, 386
Meatborne Hazard Control Center, 647
Mechanical mechanisms, 523
Medicaid, 656
Medic Alert, 724
Medical
  ethics, 190
  history, 646
  identification bracelet, 694
  illustrator, 539
  laboratory technician, 518
  therapy, and mental disorders, 56-59
Medical Group Management
  Association, 663
Medical quackery. *See* Quackery
Medicare, 656
Medicines, 425-35
  absorption of, 427-28
  and consumer safety, 645
  misuse, 430
  reaction to, 428-29
Medulla oblongata, 226, 228
Megadose, 419
Melanin, 198
Melanoma, 580-581
Memories, 14
Memory skills, in adolescence, 160
Meninges, cranial 225
Meningitis, 234
Menopause, and calcium deficiency,
  418
Menstruation, 303-304
  and iron loss, 418
Mental disorders, 49-59
Mental health, 5, 27-43
  connection to physical, 42
  and exercise, 338, 341
  facilities, 655
  professionals, 55-59
Mental Health Association, 53
Mental illness, 49
Mentally ill, residence of, 59
Mental retardation, 140, 148, 498
Mentor, 185
Mercury poisoning, 601
Metabolism, 240
  and aging, 183
  basal, 340
  and calorie requirements, 403
  and exercise, 340
  and fat, 409
Metastasis, 579

Methadone, 481, 486
Methamphetamine, 483-84
Michael and Charles Barnett Center, 149
Micronutrients. *See* Vitamins
Midbrain, 187, 228
Middle age, mid-life. *See* Adulthood
Middle ear, 326-27
Middle East, 277
Minerals, 204, 209, 240, 280, 382-83
  and environmental issues, 624
Miscarriage, 141, 307
  and STDs, 543
Mites, 519, 546
Moles, 200, 580
Molybdenum, 383
Money, and adolescents, 165
Moniliasis, 546
Mononucleosis, 519, 526
Monosodium glutamate (MSG), 228
Mood, 53, 228
  as attitude, 7
  and food, 38
  See also Blues; Emotions
Morphine, 427, 481, 486
Mothers. *See* Parenting
Motorcycles, and accidents, 18
Motorcycle safety, 681
Motor neurons, 221
Mourning, 191
Mouth, 275, 315-18
Mucous membranes, 278, 523
Mucus
  in tears, 319
Multiple sclerosis (MS), 232, 233
Multiplier effect, 462
Mumps, 519
Murder, 107, 683
Muscle
  mass, 413, 415
  tension, and biofeedback, 530
  tissue, 211, 359
  tone, 210
  types, 211-12
Muscles
  and adolescent development, 159
  and aging, 183
  and exercise, 353-59
Muscular dystrophy, 150, 212, 214, 215
Muscular Dystrophy Association, 212
Muscular strength and endurance, 342-44
Muscular system, 210-15
  injuries to, 361-62
Myasthenia gravis, 213-15
Mycobacterium avium intracellulare (MAI), 562
Myelin, 223, 233
Myofibrils, 210
Myopia, 324
Myosin, 210
Myxedema, 242

N

Nails, 183, 198, 201-203
Naming a baby, 138
Narcolepsy, 483
Narcotics, 427, 481, 485-86. *See also* Drugs
Narcotics Anonymous (Nar-Anon), 503, 511

Nasal cavity, 265
National Academy of Sciences, 602
National Adolescent Student Health Survey, 547
National Aeronautics and Space Administration (NASA), 337
National Association of Cardiovascular Pulmonary Technology, 260
National Association of Emergency Medical Technicians, 723
National Association of Social Workers, 36
National Association of Student Councils, 21
National Association of Town Watch, 687
National Cancer Act, 583
National Cancer Institute, 388, 583
National Captioning Institute, 328
National Center for Health Statistics, 589
National Childcare Association, 127
National Clearinghouse for Alcohol and Drug Information, 74
National Consumers League, 644
National Council on Alcoholism and Drug Dependence, 74, 461
National Diabetes Data Group, 586
National Education Association, 5, 76, 112
National Institute on Drug Abuse, 490
National Institutes of Health (NIH), 146, 647
National Marrow Donor Program, 577
National Mental Health Association, 28, 53, 128
National Multiple Sclerosis Society, 233
National Office of the Consumer Federation of America, 644
National Recreation Association of Japan, 75
National Rehabilitation Hospital, 233
National Society to Prevent Blindness, 325
National Weather Service, 707
Natural, label definition, 395
Natural catastrophes, 609
Natural products, 622, 624
Nausea, 282, 283
Nearsightedness, 324
Need, for drugs. *See* Addiction
Needles, 556
Needs, 32-34
Neighborhood health centers, 662
Nephritis, 290
Nephrons, 288
Nerve deafness, 330
Nerve impulse, 223-24
Nervous system, 221-37
  and exercise, 338
  problems and care, 231-37
Nest. *See* Empty-nest syndrome; Cluttered-nest syndrome
Neurologist, 56, 660
Neurons, 210, 221-24
Neurosyphilis, 542
Neutrophils, 524
Niacin, 380
Nicotine, 442, 449, 450
Night blindness, 321

Nixon, Richard (President), 583
  and consumer rights, 634
Nocturnal emission, 299
Noise, 329
Noncommunicable diseases, 569-91
Nongonococcal urethritis (NGU), 545-47
Nonsmokers' rights, 450, 453
Nonspecific resistance, 523
Nontoxic products, 622
Nosebleeds, 695, 703
Nuclear energy, 606-607
  and waste from, 607
Nuclear family, 83
Nursing homes, 655
Nutrient-dense foods, 407, 413
Nutrients, 376-84
  definition, 371
  food sources of, 380, 381, 383
  and mood, 38
  supplements, 418
  See also Vitamins
Nutrition, 371, 375
  and sports, 415
Nutrition Information Label, 393-94, 395, 397
  on shelves, 397

O

Obesity, 389, 404-406, 578, 588. *See also* Overweight
Obsession, 506
Obsessive-compulsive disorder, 50
Obstetrician, 140, 660
Occupation. *See* Career
Occupational Safety and Health Administration (OSHA), 676
Occupational therapist, 504
Oceanic Society, 618
Oceans, and environmental issues, 624
Oil, in skin, 198-99
Oil
  recycling, 619
  spills, 602
Oils, 377-78. *See also* Fats
Old age. *See* Elderly; Aging
Ombudsman, 643
Open-dating label, definition, 396
Ophthalmologist, 660
Opium, 481, 485-86
Opportunistic infection, 561
Optic nerve, 321, 322
Optometric technician, 320
Oral hygiene. *See* Mouth; teeth
Organ of Corti, 328
Organic
  disorders, 49
  foods, 417
  products, 622
Organs, artificial, 664
Orthodontics, 317
Orthopedic surgeon, 660
Ossicles, 326
Ossification, 204
Osteoarthritis, 591
Osteoblasts, 204
Osteomyelitis, 207
Osteoporosis, 207, 418
Otolaryngologist, 660

Otologist, 660
Otosclerosis, 330
Ouabain, 701
Outdoor recreation and safety, 676
Outer ear, 326, 327
Outpatients, 653
Oval window, 326
Ovarian cysts, 306
Ovaries, 238, 239, 240, 242, 302, 303, 305
Overeaters Anonymous, 415
Over-the-counter (OTC) medicines, 425, 431-32
Overweight, 404, 483
 and diabetes, 588
 and heart disease, 578
 See also Obesity
Ovulation, 240, 302, 304
Ovum (ova), 137-39, 144, 145, 240, 242, 308
Oxidation, in liver, 459
Oxygen, 66, 187, 354
 in brain, 225
 and brain death, 187
 in cardiovascular system, 249-51
Oxytocin, 240
Ozone layer, 599, 601, 603

P

Pacemakers, 260, 577
Packaging, and waste, 617
Pancreas, 238, 239, 241, 243, 280, 281, 586. *See also* Endocrine system
Pantothenic acid, 380
Paper products, 605
 and conservation, 618
 and recycling, 619
Papillae, 276-77
Pap smear, 306, 545, 579
Parahormone, 240
Paralysis, 232
Paranoid schizophrenic disorder, 53-54
Paraplegic, 232
Parasites, 517, 519
 and foodborne illness, 416
Parasympathetic ANS, 229
Parasympathetic nervous system, 229
Parathyroid glands, 240, 243
Parents Anonymous, 91
Parenting, 125-31, 169
 adolescent preparation for, 161
Parkinson's disease, 233, 483
Partnership for a Drug-Free America, 503
Passive-aggressive personality, 53
Passive immunity, 528
Passive smoke, 442, 448, 450
Passivity, in communication, 113
Pastoral counselor, 58
Pathogens, 517-528, 538
 and medicines, 426
 and spread of, 522-23
Pathologist, 660
Pectin, 277
Pediatric emergency centers, 662
Pediatrician, 660
Peer counselors, 167

Peer pressure, 103-105, 163, 165-67, 463
 See also final sections of chapters:
  Building Decision-Making Skills; Self-
  Inventory
Pelvic inflammatory disease (PID), 539, 547
Pelvis, 140, 205, 305. *See also* Uterus
Penicillin, 426, 542-43
 and syphilis, 540
Penis, 297-99
Pen Pals, 102
Peptic ulcers, 285
Pericardium, 249
Periodontal disease, 316
Periodontitis, 318
Periodontium, 315
Periosteum, 204
Peripheral nervous system (PNS), 222, 228
Peristalsis, 277-279
 reverse, 283
Personal identity, 161-62
Personal safety, 683-87
Personality, 34
 disorders, 53-54
 types, 72-73
Perspiration, 67, 382
Pesticides, 417, 603
 and environmental issues, 606, 625
Petit mal seizures, 236
Phagocytosis, 524
Pharmaceutical companies, 433
Pharmaceutical sales representative, 435
Pharmacist, 435
Pharynx, 265, 266, 277
Phencyclidine (PCP), 481, 486
Phenylketonuria (PKU), 148, 235, 426
Phobia, 40, 49
Phonocardiography, 575
Phosphorus, 204, 209, 240, 383
Photochemical smog, 597-98
Physical fitness, and exercise, 342-47
Physical health, 5
 connection to mental, 42
Physical needs, 33
Physical therapist, 660
Physical therapist assistant, 355, 660
Physicians. *See* Doctors
Physiological dependence, 482, 497
Physiologist, 363
Phytoplankton, 599
Piles. *See* Hemorrhoids
Pimple, 200
Pinched nerve, 232
Pipes, 443
Pituitary gland, 66, 239, 242, 297
 and alcohol, 460
Placebo, 639
Placenta, 138, 143
Plants, poisonous, 700, 701
Plaque, 316, 318
Plasma, 250
Plastics
 and recycling, 620, 625
 and waste, 617-18
Plastic surgeon, 660
Platelets, 251
Platonic relationship, 103
Pleura, 266

Pleurisy, 268
Pneumocystis carinii pneumonia (PCP), 561
Pneumonia, 268, 428
Poison control center, 698
Poisons, 674, 698-702, 705. *See also* Venom
Polio (poliomyelitis), 235, 428, 519, 520
 oral vaccines, 528
Pollutants, 597-603
 and environmentalism, 627
Pollution, 597
 and conservation, 622-27
 effect on lungs, 269
 and recycling, 618
Polyunsaturated fats, 377
Pons, 228
Pooling, blood, 356
Population, 604
Population growth, and environmental issues, 624
Postal service, and fraud, 644
Post-traumatic stress disorder, 50
Posture, 268
Potassium, 382, 383
Poultry, 386
 and consumer safety, 647
Poverty, 129
 and violence, 108
 effects on pregnancy, 139
Precautions, 17
Precycling, 617
Preejaculatory fluid, 298
Pregnancy, 127, 137-42, 303, 307
 and alcohol, 468
 and drugs, 489, 504
 and HIV, 558
 and smoking, 449
 and STDs, 539, 543, 545, 547
 teenage, 122, 139
 See also Prenatal care; Reproductive cycle
Prejudice, 103, 105
Premenstrual syndrome (PMS), 304-305
Prenatal care, 140-41, 148-50
Prenatal development, 142
 and drugs, 504
 and smoking, 449
Prenuptial agreement, 120
Prescriptions, 54, 431, 433, 435
Preservatives, 396
Pressure-point technique, 695
Prevention
 of communicable diseases, 527-31
 as health goal, 9
 of STDs, 549
 See also Accident prevention; Health services; Safety
Preventive medicine and HMOs, 661
Price. *See* Costs
Pricing, unit, 396
Primary care, 659
Problem-solving skills, and adolescent development, 28, 161
Processed foods, and labeling, 393-97
Progesterone, 159, 240, 242
Programs, for addiction counseling, 505
Progressive disease, 497
Projection, 74

Prolactin, 39
Prostate gland, 300
Prosthetics technician, 207
Proteins, 145, 241, 379, 380, 403
  in dermis, 198
  and mood, 38
Protozoans, 521
Psoriasis, 200
Psychiatrists, 54, 56, 660
Psychoactive drugs, 483-87
Psychoanalysis, 56
Psychological dependence, 482, 497
Psychosomatic illness, 71
Psychotherapy, 56
Puberty, 159. *See also* Adolescence;
    Reproductive system; Teenagers
Pubic lice, 546
Public safety, 639, 645
Public speaking, 39
Pulmonary circulation, 249
Pulmonary embolism, 258
Pulmonary emphysema, 444
Pulp, 315
Pulse
  and biofeedback, 530
  recovery rate, 345
Puncture, 694, 695
Pupil, 320, 321
Purging, 412

Q

Quackery, 433, 638-40
  and cancer, 585
Quadriplegic, 232
Quality, and consumer products, 635
Quality of life, 8
  and families, 85-86
Quitting smoking, 445, 449-52

R

Rabies, 519, 523, 703, 704
Radiation sickness, 607
Radiation therapy, 582, 584
Radioactive wastes, and environmental
    issues, 625
Radioactivity, 606-07
Radiofrequency current catheter
    ablation, 260
Radiologic technologist, 279
Radiologist, 660
Rainfall distribution patterns, 600, 605
Ralph Nader's Public Citizen, 644
Random violence, 106
Rape, 106, 107, 683, 685-87
  and alcohol, 465
  prevention, 685-686
Rationalization, 74
RDA (Recommended Dietary
    Allowances), 384, 393, 394
Reactions, to vaccines, 529
Recall, of consumer products, 645
Recessive traits. *See* Genes
Rechanneling energy, 76
Recommended Dietary Allowances, 384

Recovery
  from addiction, 501-505
  from codependency, 509-511
Rectum, 286
Recycling, 617-20, 625
Red blood cells, 250-51
Reflex action, 229-30
Reflex arc, 230
Reforestation, 625
Refusal skills, 73, 112-13, 167, 464-65
  and tobacco, 450-52
Registered nurse (RN), 694
Regression, 74
Regulation, of pollutants, 598, 599
Rehabilitation counselor, 471
Relapses
  and drugs, 502
  and tobacco, 451
Relationship, loss of, and suicide, 168.
    See also Marriage
Relationships, 101-13
  and adolescents, 161
  and adults, 175-77
  building healthy, 111-13
Relaxing, 76
Remarriage, 84, 124, 179
  and parenting, 130
Repression, 74
Reproduction, 137-50
Reproductive system, 297-309
  cancer in, 581
  female, 302-309
  male, 297-301
Rescue breathing, 717-20
Resident bacteria, 517, 522-526
Respiration, 228, 266
Respiratory system, 265-69
  cancer in, 581
  and exercise, 340
  failure in 717
  and smoking, 444
Respiratory therapist, 447
Responsibility, 21
  for health, 3
  and parenting, 125
Retina, 321-22
  detached, 325
Reye's syndrome, 426
Rheumatic fever, and strep throat, 519
Rheumatoid arthritis, 589-90
Rh factor, 252
Riboflavin (Vitamin B_2), 380
Ribs, 204, 205
Rickets, 198
Rickettsias, 519
Right-handedness, 228
Ringworm, 200, 521
Riots, 70
Risks, evaluating, 17
Rights of passage, 160
Rocky Mountain spotted fever, 519
Rods, 321
Role, 101
Roles, and codependency, 507
Ronald McDonald House, 654
Roosevelt, Theodore (President), 615
Root, 315-16
Rosch, Paul (Dr.), 70
Roundworms, 521
Rubella, vaccine for, 528

Runaways, 29, 90
Ryan White Comprehensive AIDS
    Resources Act, 562

S

Sabin vaccine, 235, 520
Saccharin, 396
Safety, 671-87
  at home, 671-75
  away from home, 676-79
  on wheels, 680-82
  personal, 683-87
Salivary glands, 238, 275-76, 447
Salk vaccine, 235, 520
Salmonella, 416
Salt, 389, 415
  and hypertension, 569-70
  loss of, 706
  See also Sodium
Salt-free, label definition, 395
Saprophytes, 517
Sarcoma, 579
Sarcomeres, 210
Saturated fats, 377
Saving energy, 616. *See also*
    Conservation; Environmental issues
Saying no, 167. *See also* Refusal skills
Scabies, 546
Scalp, infections, 521. *See also* Hair
Schizophrenia, 52, 53-54
Sclera, 320
Scoliosis, 206, 207, 214
Scrotum, 297-98
Seat belts, and injury prevention, 680-
    81
Sebaceous glands, 198
Sebum, 198-99
Secondary care, 659
Secondary sex characteristics, 159, 242,
    297, 302
Sedative-hypnotics, 485
Sedentary life-style, and calorie needs,
    403
Self-actualization, 34, 176
Self-definition
  in adolescence, 164-69
  in adulthood, 175-77
Self-esteem, 10-15, 28, 30, 683, 696
  and friendships, 102
  goals for improving, 13
  and violence, 107-109, 683
Self-evaluation, 20, 357
Self-examination, 299, 301, 309, 580
Self-Inventory. *See* final section of each
    chapter
Semen, 298
Semicircular canals, 327, 329
Senses. *See* Ear; Eye; Integumentary
    system; Nervous system
Sensory deafness, 329
Sensory neurons, 221
Septum, 249, 257
Set point theory, 405, 407
Sewage, 601. *See also* Waste
Sex
  genetic determination of, 144, 145
  and role in society, 161

Sexual assault, 685
Sexual harassment, 685
Sexually Transmitted Diseases (STDs) 21, 537-49, 555
Shingles, 519
Shock, 697, 698, 705
Shopping, and conservation, 620. *See also* Consumer skills
Shyness, 33
Sibling rivalry, 86
Sickle-cell anemia, 148, 258-59
Side-effects, of medicine, 428
Sidestream smoke, 448
Single-parent family, 84, 86-88, 126-27, 129
Sinus infection, 316
Size, 241
Skating, safety, 682
Skeletal system, 204-09
    injuries to, 360
Skin, 197-203
    and aging, 183
    banks, 708
    cancer, 580, 581
    conditions, 161
    and poisons, 701
    problems of, 199-201
    and viral infections, 519, 524
Skin Cancer Foundation, 200
Skinfold test, 342, 405
Skull, 204, 205
Sleep, and mental health, 33
    and SIDS, 717
Small-claims Court, 643
Small intestine, 278-79
    partial removal of, 287
Smallpox, 519, 528
Smog, 597-98
Smoke detector, 672
Smokeless tobacco, 443, 446-47
Smokestacks, and environmental issues, 598
Smoking
    avoiding effects on lungs, 269
    and cardiovascular system, 261, 571
    dangers of, 446
    and drugs, 488-89
    and heart disease, 578
    and lung cancer, 583
    and mainstream smoke, 448
    passive, 448
    and pregnancy, 141, 449
    quitting, 449-53
    and sidestream smoke, 448
    teenagers and, 441-42, 446
Smooth muscle, 212, 228
Snacks, 391
Snakebite, 699-701
Sneezing, 263, 522
Social behavior, and relationships, 176-77
Social development, in adolescents, 160, 161
Social worker, 36, 59
Society of Illustrators, 539
Sodium, 382, 383, 389-90, 394, 415, 569-70, 578. *See also* Salt
Sodium-free label definition, 395
Solid waste management, 625
Solvents, as inhalant, 482

Somatic nervous system, 228
Somatoform disorders, 50
Somatotropic hormone, 239
Sound waves, 328
Spasms
    and medicine, 427
    muscular, 243
Specialists, 659-60
Specific resistance, 525
Speculum, 305
Speech, 111. *See also* Communication
Speed, 483
Sphincter, 277, 280, 289
Sphygmomanometer, 254
Spinal column, 225
Spinal cord, 210, 222
Spinal fluid, 225
Spine, 204
Spirochetes, 540
Spleen, 262, 263
Sports
    and high altitudes, 356
    and nutrition, 412-15
    and safety, 676
Spousal abuse, 89
    and alcohol, 465
Sprains, 207-208, 360, 704
Stair-related injuries, 671, 673
Stapedius, 215
Stapes, 204, 208, 326, 327
Staphylococcus aureus, 416
Starches, 376, 389. *See also* Carbohydrates
State licensing boards, 643-44
STDs. *See* Sexually transmitted diseases
Stereotypes, 105, 510
Sterility, 300, 305, 539, 547. *See also* Reproductive system
Stepparents, 84
Sternum, 204, 205
Steroids, 480, 482, 491
    risks from, 363
Stillbirth, 539, 543
Stimulants, 442, 481, 483
Stomach, 277-78
    and effects of alcohol, 460-61
Stop Teenage Addiction to Tobacco (STAT), 453
Strabismus, 324
Strain, 212-13, 361
Strength, 342-44
Strengthening the family, 91-93
Strep throat, 519
Streptococcal bacteria, 519
Stress, 65-77, 241
    and biofeedback, 530
    disorder, 50
    factor scale, 69
    management, 72-77
    physical responses to, 66-67
    reduction through exercise, 354
    and STDs, 548
Stressor, 65-67
Stretching, 355, 356
Stroke, 258, 573-74
Structure, in family, 92
Sty, 324
Styrofoam, 603, 617, 623, 625
Sublimation, 74
Substance abuse. *See* Drugs

Substitutes, food, 395-96
Sudden infant death syndrome, 717
Sugar, 376, 387
    in alcohol, 459
Sugar, low, label definition, 395
Sugars, 388-89. *See also* Carbohydrates
Suicide, 51-53, 68, 167-69
Sulfa drugs, 426, 428
Sulfites, 396
Sulfur, 383
Sulfur dioxide, 597
Sullivan, Louis (Dr.), 9
Sun, effect on skin, 198, 202-03
Sunburn, 202
Sunlight, and smog, 597-98
Suntanning, 200
Support groups, 76, 503, 511
Surgeon, 576. *See also* Doctor
Surgeon General, 468
Surgery
    arthroscopic, 208
    and cancer, 581
    dental, 317
    fetal, 140
    laser, 208, 317
    open-heart, 576
Surgical technologist, 661
Surroundings. *See* Environment
Swallowing, 228, 277
Sweat glands, 199, 238
Swimming, safety, 677
Sympathetic ANS, 229
Sympathetic nervous system, 39, 229
Synapse, 223, 224
Synergistic effect of medicine, 429
Syphilis, 540-43
Systemic circulation, 250
Systolic pressure, 254

T

Tampons, 305
Tanning, and cancer, 202-03, 580
Tanning parlors, 200
Tar, 442, 444
Target heart rate, 355
Target weight, 406
Tartar, 316
Taste buds, 276-77
Tay-Sachs disease, 148
T cells, 262, 264, 526, 555
Teacher, 168
Tears, 39, 319, 523
Teens, teenagers
    and alcohol, 463
    definition, 164
    and disease transmittal, 558
    marriage and, 122
    pregnancy, 139, 169
    and STDs, 547
    suicide among, 51-53, 167-69
    and tobacco, 441-42, 446
    See also Adolescence
Teeth, 275, 315-18
    and decay, 286
    and tobacco, 444, 447
TeleCaption decoder, 328

Telecommunications Device for the Deaf (TDD), 328
Television, 35, 86, 106, 109-110
Tel-Med Tape Library, 637
Temperature, 197, 228, 297, 524, 531
Temporal bone, 326
Tendinitis, 361
Tendons, 206
Tennis elbow, 361
Terminal illness, and hospices, 662
Tertiary care, 659
Testes, 297
Testicular cancer, 299
Testimonials, and consumer products, 637
Testosterone, 159, 240, 242, 297, 489
Tests, and stress, 76
Tetanus, 518, 529
Tetany, 243
Tetracycline, 426
Thalamus, 228
Thanatology, 188
THC (Delta-9-tetrahydrocannabinol), 488
Therapy, 56
  physical, 355
Thermal trainer, and biofeedback, 531
Thiamine (Vitamin B$_1$), 380
Thighbone, 205, 208
Thoracic surgeon, 660
Throat, 265, 267, 519
Thrombosis, 258
Thrombus, 570
Thymus gland, 262, 263
Thyroid gland, 240, 242
Thyroid-stimulating hormone (TSH), 240
Thyroxine, 240
Ticks, 519, 705
Time
  and choices, 179
  management, 73
Tin cans, and recycling, 620. See also Aluminum
Tinnitus, 331
Tires, and recycling, 620
Tobacco, 441-53
  and alcohol, 460
  See also Smoking
Tobacco leaf, 452
Toenail, ingrown, 201
Tolerance, 429, 497
  for alcohol, 461
  for drugs, 482
Toluene, 626
Tongue, 276-77
Tonsillitis, 264
Tonsils, 262, 263-64
Tornadoes, 707
Toxic products, 626
Toxic right-to-know law, 395
Toxic shock syndrome (TSS), 305
Toxin, 518, 626. See also Hazardous substances
Toxoids, 529
Trachea, 265-66, 277
Tradition, and consumer products, 635
Tranquilizers, 481, 485
Transfer addictions, 502
Transfusions, 252, 556
Transitions, 180
Transmittal of STDs, 549

Transplants, 290
  heart, 576-77
  liver, 280
  skin, 708
  tissue, 581, 584
Transportation, and consumer protection, 647
Trichinosis, 521
Trichomoniasis, 305, 546
Tropical forests, and environmental issues, 604-05, 624-25
Trust, in infancy, 152
Trypsin, 281
Tuberculosis, 268-69, 654, 658
Tumor, 579
Turpentine, 626
Twins, 147, 406
Typhoid, 601
Typhus fever, 519
Tyramine, 228

U

Ulcers, 285
Ultrasound, 150, 260
  and gallstones, 283
Ultraviolet rays and radiation, 202-203, 580, 599, 603
Umbilical cord, 138
Undernutrition, 405
Underweight, 405
United Cerebral Palsy Associations, Inc., 222
United Nations Environmental Program, 603
U.S. Bureau of Justice, 107
U.S. Consumer Product Safety Commission, 673
U.S. Department of Agriculture (USDA), 179, 393, 395
U.S. Department of Health and Human Services, 9, 432
U.S. Drug Enforcement Agency, 491
Unit Price, 396, 634
Urea, 280
Uremia, 290
Ureters, 288, 289
Urethra, 289-90, 298, 299
Urinary system, 288-91
Urine, 288-89, 298
Urologist, 660
Uterine cancer, 306
Uterus, 137, 138, 143, 303-06. See also Placenta; Ovum
Utricle, 328
Uvula, 277

V

Vaccines, 235, 425, 527-29
  measles, 528
  polio, 428, 520
Vaccination, 528
Vagina, 303
Vaginal discharge, 308, 547
Vaginitis, 305, 546
Valium, 481

Values, 36, 163, 166-67
  in adolescence, 164
  See also Behavior
Valves, 255, 577
Varicose veins, 257
Vas deferens, 298, 300
Vascular surgeon, 660
Vasodilators, 427
Vegetables, in diet, 386, 388
Vehicle exhaust, 597-98
Vehicles, 598
  and safety, 680-82
Veins, 254-55
  varicose, 257
Vena cava, 250
Ventricles, 249, 254
Ventricular assist device, 260
Venules, 254
Vertebrae, 204
Vestibule, 327
Veterans Affairs Medical Center, 276
Veterinarian, 87
Victim, avoiding becoming, 684
Villus (villi), 279
Violence, 106-10, 168, 683
  alcohol-related, 107-109, 464-65
  and family, 95, 106
  and guns, 107-109, 683
  prevention, 109
  and safety, 683-87
  in school, 106-107, 168
  and teens, 106-107, 686
  on television, 106, 109-110
Viral hepatitis, 519
Viruses, 518-19
  and immunity, 527
  intestinal, 416
  and warts, 200-01, 519
Vision, problems of, 183, 322-24. See a
  Eyes
Vitamins, 179, 202, 209, 280, 378, 380-81, 583
  fat-soluble, 419
  and skin color, 198
Vitiligo, 200
Vitreous humor, 321
Vocal chords, 265
Voice box, 265
Volcanic eruptions, 609
Volunteering, 130
Vomiting, 228, 283
  and poisoning, 699

W

Walking, 180
War, 607, 609
Warm lines, for parents, 126
Warm-up, 355
Warts, 200, 519, 546
Waste, body, and urinary system, 275, 279, 288
Waste, and environmental issues, 601, 618
  disposal, 605
  hazardous, 605
  nuclear, 607
  reduction, 615-20

Water, as nutrient, 382
Water-borne diseases, 601
Water, and environmental issues,
   624
  pollution, 600-602
  supply, 600-602
Water, safety around, 677
Weapons, and violence in schools, 168
Weather-related emergencies, 706-09
Weather, risks to health due to, 362-63,
   706-07
Weight, 359, 403-10
  and biofeedback, 530
  cycling, 409
  and exercise, 340
  management, 410
  and quack control techniques, 640
  and smoking, 452
  training, 353, 356
Wellness, 6, 22

Western blot, 560
Wet dream, 299
Wheelchairs, 232
White blood cells, 251
Whitehead, 200
Windchill, 707
Windpipe, 265. *See also* Airway
Wisdom teeth, 316
Withdrawal, following addiction, 429,
   450, 482, 497
Worden, J.W., 191
Work, 30
  and families, 86
  and marriage, 120
  and parenting, 125-27
  and safety, 676
Workout, 355-56
World Pen Pals, 102
Wounds, open, 694-97
Wrinkles, 183, 198, 199

X

Xiphoid process, 722, 724
X-linked condition, 150
X rays, 269, 309, 580, 660

Y

Yard waste, and recycling, 620
Yawning, 73
Yeast infection, 305
Youth at Risk, 29
Yo-yo dieting, 409

Z

Zidovudine (AZT), 563
Zinc, 383
Zygote, 137, 144, 303. *See also* Ovum

Cover, © David Madison 1992;
Back Cover, Steve Whalen-Viesti Associates

2, Terence Turner/FPG International;
4, 8, Rod Joslin;
9, Custom Medical Stock Photo;
11, file photo;
13, Mak-I Photo Design;
14, 15, Gabe Palmer/The Stock Market;
17, Mak-I Photo Design;
18, Aaron Haupt;
20, Mak-I Photo Design;
26, Matt Meadows;
29, Mak-I Photo Design;
30, Gabe Palmer/The Stock Market;
34, (t) Rod Joslin, (b) Doug Martin;
38, Mak-I Photo Design;
41, 42, Crown Studios;
45, Ed Wheeler/The Stock Market;
48, 50, Mak-I Photo Design;
51, file photo;
57, Dr. Warren Rhodes;
58, 61, Mak-I Photo Design;
64, Doug Martin;
66, Mak-I Photo Design;
68, Doug Martin;
71, Crown Studios;
72, Bob Mullenix;
73, Crown Studios;
75, Mak-I Photo Design;
78, Crown Studios;
82, Aaron Haupt;
84, 85, 88, Bob Mullenix;
90, Gail Meese/Meese Photo Research;
91, Bob Mullenix/Photographic Illustrators,Inc.;
92, Doug Martin;
94, Mak-I Photo Design;
95, First Image;
96, Gabe Palmer/The Stock Market;
100, Bob Mullenix;
103, Photographic Design Group;
104, Kenji Kerins;
109, Bob Mullenix;
110, Matt Meadows;
114, Bob Mullenix;
118, Doug Martin;
120, Sandy Roessler/The Stock Market;
121, 122, Mak-I Photo Design;
127, Aaron Haupt;
129, Rod Joslin;
130, Mak-I Photo Design;
132, 136, file photo;
139, © Vladimir Lange/The Image Bank;

141, Mak-I Photo Design;
142, Lennart Nilsson/The Incredible Machine/National Geographic Society;
147, Doug Martin;
149, Robin Laskey Chipman;
151, 152, 153, Gale Zucker;
154, 158, Doug Martin;
161, Mary Lou Uttermohlen;
162, Doug Martin;
163, Aaron Haupt
166, David Frazier;
168, Bryan Peterson/The Stock Market;
169, 171, Mak-I Photo Design;
174, Bob Mullenix;
176, Rod Joslin;
179, Matt Meadows;
181, Ronnie Kaufman/The Stock Market;
184, The Presidential Sports/Fitness Festivals;
185, Roy Morsch/The Stock Market;
186, Catherine Ursillo/Photo Researchers, Inc.;
189, (t) Matt Meadows, (b) Gale Zucker;
190, George Disario/The Stock Market;
191, Matt Meadows;
193, Rod Joslin;
196, Doug Martin;
199, David Stoecklein/The Stock Market;
200, Biophoto Associates/Science Source/Photo Researchers, Inc.;
201, Custom Medical Stock;
203, Bob Mullenix/Photographic Illustrators,Inc.;
206, Aaron Haupt;
212, First Image;
214, Darlene Sullivan/Canine Partners for Life;
216, Margaret Kois/The Stock Market;
220, Aaron Haupt;
227, Paul Facenda Photography;
230, 232, Bob Mullenix;
234, Will & Deni McIntyre/Photo Researchers, Inc.;
236, Gail Meese/Meese Photo Research;
237, Bob Mullenix;
243, Hattie Youne/Science Photo Library/Photo Researchers, Inc.;
244, Joe Sohm/The Stock Market;
248, Aaron Haupt;
251, Matt Meadows;
253, Mak-I Photo Design;

254, Matt Meadows;
258, Science Source/Photo Researchers, Inc.;
259, file photo;
268, Crown Studios;
270, Rod Joslin;
274, Bob Mullenix;
283, file photo;
284, Ted Bartoshesky;
287, Elaine Shay;
291, Werner H. Muller/Peter Arnold, Inc.;
296, Bob Mullenix;
299, John Walsh/Science Photo Library/Photo Researchers, Inc.;
301, Michael Keller/The Stock Market;
306, Matt Meadows;
307, Thibeault:Design,Inc.;309, American Cancer Society/Ken Frick;
310, Spandorfer & Jordan/Photo Researchers, Inc.;
314, Doug Martin, courtesy Dr. Clayton N. Hicks;
317, (t) Michael Philip Manheim/The Stock Market, (b) Van Bucher/Photo Researchers, Inc.;
323, Muncy & Muncy Inc.;
325, 329, Crown Studios;
330, Bob Mullenix;
331, Crown Studios;
332, Doug Martin;
336, Bob Mullenix;
337, Mak-I Photo Design;
339, 341, 344-345, Bob Mullenix;
347, Kenji Kerins;
349, Rod Joslin;
352, Bob Mullenix;
354, Doug Martin;
356, 359, Bob Mullenix;
361, (l) David Madison,(r) File photo;
362, Mak-I Photo Design;
363, Bob Mullenix;
364, First Image;
366, David Madison;
370, Bob Mullenix;
373, (tl-tr) Aaron Haupt, (bl) file photo, (br) Gabe Palmer/The Stock Market;
374, Doug Martin;
377, 379, Platinum Productions;
381, Mak-I Photo Design;
384, Bob Mullenix;
386, USDA;

388, Bob Mullenix;
389, 394-397 Platinum Productions;
402, Hickson & Associates;
404, Mak-I Photo Design;
405, Craig Hammell/The Stock Market;
407, Bob Mullenix;
408, Aaron Haupt;
412, Mak-I Photo Design;
413, Aaron Haupt;
414, Anthony Edgeworth/The Stock Market;
417, Henley & Savage/The Stock Market;
418, Elaine Shay;
419, 424, Bob Mullenix;
426, Matt Meadows;
427, Aaron Haupt;
429, 431, 433, Matt Meadows;
434, Elizabeth Zeschin;
435, Rod Joslin;
436, Mak-I Photo Design;
437, Rod Joslin;
440, Mak-I Photo Design;
443, (t) Martin Rotker/Phototake, (b) Camera M.D. Studios;
445, Doug Martin;
446, Mak-I Photo Design;
448, Bob Mullenix;449, Mak-I Photo Design;
450, (t) Jules T. Allen, (b) Bob Mullenix;
453, Bob Mullenix;
458, Hickson & Associates;
460, Matt Meadows;
463, 465, Kenji Kerins;
466, Doug Martin;
469, Mak-I Photo Design;
471, Gabe Palmer/The Stock Market;
472, Bob Mullenix;
473, Wes Thompson/The Stock Market;
478, Aaron Haupt;
480, Mak-I Photo Design;
484, Focus on Sports;
485, Doug Martin;
487, Biomedical Communications/Photo Researchers, Inc.;
489, Alon Reininger/Woodfin Camp & Associates, Inc.;
490, Jerry Wachter/Focus On Sports;
496, Aaron Haupt;
499-501, 503 Doug Martin;
505, Mak-I Photo Design;
507-508, 511, Doug Martin;
512, Mak-I Photo Design;
516, Doug Martin;
518, Bob Mullenix;
519, file photo;

520, Harry Smith;
521, Elaine Shay;
522, Aaron Haupt;
523, (t) Elaine Shay, (b) Alan Carey;
524, 528, Bob Mullenix;
529, file photo;
530, 532, Bob Mullenix;
536, Doug Martin;
538, James Westwater;
542, 543, Custom Medical Stock Photo;
545, Matt Meadows;
548, Doug Martin;
549, Mak-I Photo Design;
550, 554, 556, Matt Meadows;
557, Jennifer Nicols;
558, Sharon Remmer;
561, (l) AP/Wide World Photos, (r) Rick Rickman/Duomo Photography, Inc.;
564, Bob Mullenix;
568, Doug Martin;
570, Bob Mullenix;
572, Larry Mulvehill/Photo Researchers, Inc.;
575, Superstock;
577, Custom Medical Stock Photo;
580, American Cancer Society/Ken Frick;
582, Philippe Plally/Science Photo Library/Photo Researchers, Inc.;
583, William Roy/The Stock Market;
584, William's Photography;
587, 589, Custom Medical Stock Photo;
590, Hickson & Associates;
591, (l) Allen Lee Page/The Stock Market, (r) CNRI/Science Photo Library/Photo Researchers, Inc.;
592, Ken Frick;
596, Bob Winsett/Tom Stack & Associates;
598, Superstock;
602, Joe Sohm/Chromosohm 1990/The Stock Market;
605, Rafael Macia/Photo Researchers, Inc.;
607, Jerry Irwin/Photo Researchers, Inc.;
608, Jeffre J. Dean;
609, Ken Frick;
610, Bob Mullenix;
611, Joe Sohm/Chromosohm 1990/The Stock Market;
614, 617, Mak-I Photo Design;
620, Matt Meadows;
623, Kids Against Pollution;
624, Matt Meadows;
625, Nigel Dickinson/Tony Stone Worldwide;
626, 627, E. R. Degginger;

628, Jon Riley/Tony Stone Worldwide;
632, Doug Martin;
634, Elaine Shay;
635, (tl) Bob Mullenix, (tr) Harry Haralambou/Peter Arnold, Inc., (cl) Aaron Haupt, (cr, br, bc, bl) Bob Mullenix;
636, David J. James/Texas Inprint;
639, Mak-I Photo Design;
640, Aaron Haupt;
642, Mak-I Photo Design;
643, Bob Mullenix/Photographic Illustrators, Inc.;
644, 645, Elaine Shay;
648, Bob Mullenix;
652, Doug Martin;
654, Tom Stewart/The Stock Market;
655, Matt Meadows;
657, Jim Dallas Studio;
658, 660, Bob Mullenix;
661, Matt Meadows;
663, Jeff Bates;
664, Bob Mullenix;
670, Mak-I Photo Design;
672, Bob Mullenix;
674, Crown Studios;
675, Mak-I Photo Design;
677, Bob Daemmrich;
678, Juh-Hann Chang;
679, Bob Daemmrich;
682, Kenji Kerins;
684, Mak-I Photo Design;
685, Matt Meadows;
687, Rod Joslin;
692, Doug Martin;
694, Blair Seitz/Photo Researchers, Inc.;
696, Photo by Chandler Arden, Texas A & M Photo Services;
696, Tim Thorp;
697, Mak-I Photo Design;
699, Rod Joslin;
700, 702, E. R. Degginger;
704, 705, Rod Joslin;
706, Bob Mullenix;
708, E. R. Degginger;
709, David Weintraub/Photo Researchers, Inc.;
710, Aaron Haupt;
714, Bob Mullenix;
716, Matt Meadows;
718, Aaron Haupt;
719, First Image;
725, Rod Joslin;
726, Matt Meadows.